Ancient Marbles in Great Britain

Adolf Michaelis

Alpha Editions

This edition published in 2020

ISBN : 9789354041532

Design and Setting By
Alpha Editions
www.alphaedis.com
email - alphaedis@gmail.com

ANCIENT MARBLES

IN GREAT BRITAIN

DESCRIBED BY

ADOLF MICHAELIS,

PH. D., PROFESSOR OF CLASSICAL ARCHAEOLOGY IN THE UNIVERSITY
OF STRASSBURG,

TRANSLATED FROM THE GERMAN

BY

C. A. M. FENNELL, M.A.,

LATE FELLOW OF JESUS COLLEGE, CAMBRIDGE.

EDITED FOR THE SYNDICS OF THE UNIVERSITY PRESS.

Cambridge:
AT THE UNIVERSITY PRESS
1882

TO MY BELOVED FRIEND

GEORGE SCHARF, Esq., F.R.S.L., F.S.A.

MEMBER OF THE GERMAN ARCHAEOLOGICAL INSTITUTE,
DIRECTOR OF THE NATIONAL PORTRAIT GALLERY

THIS WORK IS INSCRIBED

IN GRATEFUL REMEMBRANCE OF MANY HAPPY DAYS

SPENT UNDER HIS HOSPITABLE ROOF

1861, 1873, 1877.

M. C.

THE AUTHOR'S PREFACE.

The object of the present work is to supply archæologists and those interested in archæology with more complete and accurate information than has hitherto been provided concerning the treasures of ancient sculpture, stored up in the galleries of Great Britain, the abundance and excellence of which appear to be but little known in detail, notwithstanding that they are admitted in general terms.

In order to guard against erroneous expectations, it should be borne in mind that the title "Ancient Marbles" does not imply antique sculptures of every description, but only the relics of Greek and Roman origin which have been imported into Great Britain from classical soil. I have accordingly excluded Egyptian and Oriental art as well as the Anglo-Roman remains found in Great Britain. Whatever the book may contain not included within the limits of the above definition, must be looked at as an accessory which, I venture to hope, will at least not be troublesome to the reader.

For obvious reasons no catalogue is given of the Sculptures preserved in the British Museum. With the exception of the few Museums of a public character, such as those in Cambridge and Oxford, private galleries therefore have supplied the main part of

this catalogue. Everybody knows, how widely spread
they are over the country, though perhaps few are
aware how difficult it is to get information about
them, much more to obtain such access to them as
shall enable a visitor thoroughly to examine the works
of art, without being at every moment disturbed by the
impatient noise of the housekeeper's keys. But the
greatest of all hindrances is the want of good catalogues or other literary means of general, as well as
special, preparation and instruction. Up to the present
day the Student had to depend chiefly on JAMES
DALLAWAY's *Anecdotes of the Arts in England* (1800),
however superficial and antiquated the book may be.
The French translation published under A. L. MILLIN's
authority, *Les Beaux-arts en Angleterre* (1807), added
nothing of consequence, the editor not having himself
visited the collections. Nor did Dallaway's own revised edition, which appeared in 1816 with the title
Of Statuary and Sculpture among the Ancients, though
it was enriched by useful additions, materially alter the
unsatisfactory character of the book. A selection only of
particularly remarkable monuments is contained in the
splendid volumes published by the SOCIETY OF DILET-
TANTI, the *Specimens of Antient Sculpture, selected from
several collections in Great Britain* (1809 and 1835).
If we add a few special publications, some of them
scarcely accessible to persons most interested in their
contents, such as the works on the Oxford Marbles
(1763), on the Museum Worsleyanum (1794), on the
Ince collection (1809), on the Marbles of Woburn
Abbey (1822), on the Museum Disneianum (1849), and,
last not least, Prof. NEWTON's valuable *Notes on the
Sculptures at Wilton House* (1849), we should exhaust
nearly all that has been done in England itself to-

wards our special knowledge of those treasures. The greater are the thanks due to the late Count CLARAC, who, after a personal inspection in 1833, employed Mr Brotherton to make drawings of the Statues in the most important private galleries, which he incorporated in his copious *Musée de Sculpture* (vols. III.—V., 1832—1841). Unsatisfactory as these sketches in outline may be with regard to style, they still suffice to give an approximate idea of the subjects represented. Hence CLARAC's work is still one of the most important books to be consulted on English private collections, as far as Statues are concerned ; Busts and Reliefs not being included within its scope.

Of more modest pretensions, though scarcely less meritorious, are the observations scattered through the writings of various travellers in Great Britain. Older works, like those by VOLKMANN[1], GOEDE[2], SPIKER[3], may be left out of consideration, as they afford very little valuable information. The notes published from C. O. MÜLLER's journals of 1822, in Böttiger's *Amalthea*, Vol. III. (1825), deal only with the collections in Lansdowne House and at Petworth. Richer in observations and notices is the well-known book of Dr WAAGEN, which was first published in German with the title *Kunstwerke und Künstler in England* (1837, 1838), and afterwards, in English, with the results of several subsequent visits incorporated, as *Treasures of Art in Great Britain* (3 vols., 1854), supplementary to

---

[1] *Neueste Reisen durch England. Aus den besten Nachrichten und neueren Schriften zusammengetragen von* J. J. VOLKMANN. 4 vols. Leipzig, 1781-1782. (Compiled chiefly from English sources.)

[2] *England, Wales, Irland und Schottland. Erinnerungen von einer Reise in den Jahren* 1802 *und* 1803. 2nd edition. 5 vols. Dresden, 1806.

[3] *Reise durch England, Wales, und Schottland im Jahre* 1816. 2 vols. Leipzig, 1818.

which is the volume styled *Galleries and Cabinets of Art in Great Britain* (1857). Waagen, however, was chiefly attracted by works of modern art, especially of painting; as to antique sculpture his eye was less sure, his studies less extensive and thorough. The chief value of his book, therefore, to classical archæologists, consists in pointing out a great number of dispersed marbles, which he had the opportunity of observing in the course of his various journeys. Still, it may easily be understood that his notes should have appeared sufficiently new and interesting to be extracted, for the use of the French public, by G. BRUNET in the *Revue archéologique*, vol. x. (1853). The first archæologist, however, after Count Clarac, who, with a full mastery of the different parts of archæological science, made private galleries of ancient art in England the object of a special examination, was ALEXANDER CONZE, then Professor of Archæology in the University of Halle. In the *Archäologischer Anzeiger* of 1864, a supplement of the *Archäologische Zeitung* of Berlin, he communicated, in the most concise form, many valuable notices extracted from his journals. More recently a supplement to them was contributed by the late Professor F. MATZ, to the *Archäologische Zeitung* of 1873, in which also some collections, hitherto unknown, were first presented to the notice of the learned public.

The author of this work first visited England in 1861. But the immense riches of the British Museum then left me little leisure to go in quest of private collections, with the exception of the gallery of Lansdowne House, a few notices of which I published in the *Archäologischer Anzeiger* of 1862. In the autumn of 1873, accompanied by my friend Professor Matz, I undertook a tour through different parts of England. My

attention was at that time mainly directed to Greek
Sepulchral Reliefs, that of my companion to Roman
Sarcophagi, the collection and publication of these
classes of monuments having been undertaken by
the Academy of Vienna, and by the German Archæological Institute, respectively; but whatever time
could be spared was devoted to the examination
of antique monuments of other descriptions. The
results of these inquiries, together with such notices
as were supplied by the books of reference then accessible to me, were published in an article "On the
private collections of ancient art in England," in the
Archäologische Zeitung of 1874, pp. 1—70. This rather
detailed sketch forms the foundation of the present
work, to undertake which I have been led, partly
by my own interest in the subject, partly by the re-
quests of friends and colleagues, especially in England.
Favourable circumstances having enabled me to become acquainted with those galleries to a greater extent
than perhaps any other living archæologist, I thought
it my duty, putting aside for some years other tasks of
a more inviting nature, to undertake the irksome,
mosaic-like work of drawing up a descriptive catalogue of the marbles they contain. In doing this,
I hoped also to pay a small tribute of affection and
gratitude to a country in which I have seen and learnt
much, and have formed many valuable and pleasant
personal connexions, and experienced much kindness
and hospitality. Another visit to England in 1877
helped me to complete my former inquiries.

With the exception of Castle Howard, which I
was accidentally prevented from visiting, I have
personally inspected nearly all the principal galleries.
As to the minor collections, of which often scarcely

more than the name is known, it would not be reasonable
to expect that a foreigner, without any other assistance
than that afforded by his limited private means, should
be able to discover and examine them. I must hope
that the publication of this necessarily incomplete work
will stimulate others to supply its deficiencies, and I
shall be very thankful for any information which may
be communicated to me. But even of the larger collections, it would have been impossible to give a full
and satisfactory account from my individual unaided resources. To my friend Dr CONZE I am indebted for
the free use of all his original notes. The papers left
by the late Professor MATZ, now the property of the
German Archæological Institute, supplied a considerable number of drawings and descriptions, particularly
of Sarcophagi. Prof. BERNOULLI of Basel, liberally
complying with my request, placed also at my command
all the notes he had made during a visit to England
in 1875, which, as they chiefly concerned busts and
other portrait sculptures, formed a most valuable supplement to Conze's, Matz's and my own notes. In the
case of articles which are not founded upon notices
made by myself or by my friends (indicated by *B, C, M*,
see p. 210), the notice is borrowed from the special
catalogue or from one of the other books quoted at the
top of each collection ; in these instances, of course,
I should not be made responsible for blunders which
may occur. The measures are throughout given in
metres and centimetres. Full accuracy, however, can
be warranted only where either I or one of my friends
have taken them, experience having more than once
shewn that measures taken by others in English feet
and afterwards converted into metres (a foot being
equal to 0·305 m.) prove to be not quite exact.

The catalogue itself is naturally an unconnected
series of articles, which can hardly be what is called
"pleasant reading."   General readers, however, will I
hope be interested by the Introduction, in which I have
attempted to give a synopsis of the whole subject, and
to shew, from original sources and in connexion with
other historical incidents, in what manner and to what
extent Peacham's saying about the transplanting of
old Greece into England has been realized.

It should be added that the manuscript of my book
was finished in October 1878, and the delays incident
to the processes of translation, printing, and revision
will explain why in the later portions of the work books
have been consulted and other additions made, which
refer to the last year or two, and which could not find
place in the former parts.

There remains the agreeable task of acknowledging
the assistance I have experienced in the course of this
work.   My thanks are due, in the first place, to the
possessors of many of the collections here described.
Though nearly unprovided with introductions, and
generally obliged to risk a bare personal application,
I feel bound to state that with a very few exceptions
my applications to visit galleries met with a courteous
permission.   I must deprive myself of the satisfaction
of naming individuals who have shewn me special
kindness, lest I might seem ungrateful towards others.
For much aid and many hints I have to thank the
officers of the British Museum, Prof. NEWTON, Mr
FRANKS, Mr POOLE, and Mr MURRAY; and also Mr
DOYNE C. BELL, in London, Mr HOLMES, at Windsor
Castle, and Dr ACLAND, of Oxford.   To the Rev.
ALEXANDER NAPIER, of Holkham, I am indebted for
his effective advocacy of the publication of this work

by the Syndics of the Cambridge University Press; to Mr C. A. M. FENNELL for undertaking the heavy and irksome task of translating a volume of such a size and nature; to Prof. SIDNEY COLVIN for the pains he has bestowed on the revision of the translated text and on the superintendence of the illustrations. In the revision of the text I have had the further advantage of the skilled assistance of Prof. NEWTON and Mr MURRAY. To all these gentlemen I gladly proffer my sincere thanks. Lastly I desire to express my cordial gratitude to my dear friend Mr GEORGE SCHARF, whose richly furnished library, extensive knowledge, unremitting goodness, and kind interest in my plans and pursuits, have been to me of invaluable assistance. It is my earnest desire that my friend may accept the dedication of this dry, but, I hope, not useless work, as a token of my true and sincere affection and a memorial of some of my most precious associations with England.

STRASSBURG, *June*, 1882.

TABLE OF CONTENTS.

LIST OF PLATES AND WOODCUTS.

GEOGRAPHICAL DIRECTORY.

BEDFORDSHIRE : Battlesden, Woburn Abbey.

BERKSHIRE : Windsor Castle.

CAMBRIDGESHIRE : Cambridge.

CHESHIRE : Marbury Hall.

DERBYSHIRE : Chatsworth.

DORSETSHIRE : Kingston Lacy.

ESSEX : Colchester, The Hyde.

GLAMORGANSHIRE : Margam, Penrice Castle.

HAMPSHIRE : Broadlands, Stratfield Saye.

HEREFORDSHIRE : Shobden.

KENT : Canterbury, Knole, Penshurst, Ramsgate, Tunbridge Wells.

LANCASHIRE : Ince Blundell Hall, Liverpool.

LINCOLNSHIRE : Brocklesby Park.

MIDDLESEX : Hillingdon Court, London, Osterley Park, Stanmore Hill.

NORFOLK : Holkham Hall, Houghton Hall, Ketteringham Hall, Narford Hall.

NORTHAMPTONSHIRE : Castle Ashby, Easton Neston.

NORTHUMBERLAND : Denton Hall.

NOTTINGHAMSHIRE : Clumber Park.

OXFORDSHIRE : Blenheim Palace, Ditchley, Oxford.

SCOTLAND : Broom Hall, Dalkeith Palace, Dunrobin Castle, Edinburgh, Hamilton Palace, Rossie Priory, Winton Castle.

STAFFORDSHIRE : Trentham Hall.

SUFFOLK : Ickworth.

SURREY : St Ann's Hill, Deepdene, Pippbrook House, Richmond, Wimbledon.

SUSSEX : Bignor Park, Chichester, Petworth House.

WARWICKSHIRE : Birmingham, Warwick Castle.

WESTMORELAND : Lowther Castle.

WIGHT, ISLE OF : Osborne.

WILTSHIRE : Salisbury, Stourhead House, Wilton House.

YORKSHIRE : Boynton, Duncombe Park, Hovingham, Castle Howard, Newby Hall, Rokeby Hall, Wentworth Castle, Wentworth House.

ADDENDA AND CORRIGENDA.

P. 5. The earliest instance of an English collector of ancient sculpture at Rome is afforded by Henry of Blois, Bishop of Winchester, brother of King Stephen, who lived at Rome about A.D. 1150; *see Monum. Germ. Histor., Script.*, vol. xx., p. 542. Cf. R. Pauli in the *Academy* 1880, Nov. 6, p. 330.

P. 34, l. 13 : discovered] *read:* copied
P. 45, l. 25 : fifty-two] *read:* eighty-three
P. 60, l. 8 *dele :* that
P. 70, n. 177, l. 7 : 1783] *read:* 1753
P. 75, l. 5 *dele:* Hon.
P. 81, n. 205 *add:* Academy, 1878, p. 142, note ‡.
P. 89, n. 229 : nos. 38, 66] *read:* nos. 40, 46
P. 104, l. 1 : decade] *read:* decades
P. 105, l. 4 : 1778] *read:* 1777
P. 108, n. 275 *add:* Guattani, *Mon. Ined.*, 1805, p. LXXXVII.
P. 118, l. 15 : Kistophors] *read:* Kistophoros
P. 126, l. 16 : Mr Anson] *read:* Lord Anson
P. 157, l. 420 at the end, *add:* Arch. Zeit., 1880, pp. 83f.
P. 160, n. 430 *add:* Edm. Oldfield, *Trans. R. Soc. Lit.*, vol. VI., New Series, pp. 130 ff.
P. 161, l. 3: 23] *read:* 24
P. 162, n. 436 *add:* Vaux, *Trans. R. Soc. Lit.*, vol. VIII., New Series, p. 590.
P. 166, l. 3 from end: found] *read:* founded
P. 171. For the matters treated in §§ 94 and 95 cf. Vaux, *Trans. R. Soc. Lit.*, vol. VIII., New Series, pp. 559 ff.
P. 176, l. 17. The seats of Lady Charlotte Glamis, widow of Thomas George Lord Glamis (*d.* 1834), are Strathmore, Glamis-Castle, Forfarshire, and Paul's Warden, Hertfordshire.

P. 211. In ALNWICK CASTLE (Northumberland), the seat of the DUKE OF NORTHUMBERLAND, is preserved, besides some Roman cinerary urns of great beauty (Waagen, *Treas.*, IV., p. 473), the famous Beverley collection of gems.

P. 211, St Ann's Hill, no. 5, *add:* Clarac, IV. 755, 1844.—In Piranesi's *Vasi*, I. Pl. 52 there is an engraving of a large marble vase (*krater*), in the possession of Lord Holland, with reliefs said to represent the *suovetaurilia*. It is evident from the engraving that at least the upper part of the vase is entirely modern ; but also the reliefs which show a scene of sacrifice (*camillus*, priest near tripod, flute player, *popa* slaying a hog, servant bringing a bull, etc.) convey a rather modern impression.

P. 211. The vases preserved at Castle Ashby have lately been examined by Dr Furtwangler, see *Arch. Zeit.*, 1881, pp. 301 ff.

P. 212, Battlesden, l. 3. The right spelling of the owner's name, as kindly communicated by him, is BROMILOW.

P. 213. Bignor no. 2 *add:* Clarac, IV. 666 B, 1508 A.

P. 215, no. 3, l. 9: surrounded] *read:* flanked.

P. 216, Boynton, no. 2, *add:* Probably identical with Cavaceppi, *Racc.*, III. 52, cf. Bernoulli, *Röm. Ikonogr.*, I. p. 194.

P. 220, no. 11, l. 8 after "*vannus*" *add:* on his head.—The altar seems to have come from the Barberini collection, cf. *Documenti ined. per serv. alla storia dei Musei d'Italia*, IV. p. 39 "*Una piccola base triangolare di ara con tre bassi rilievi, uno rappresentante una Sacerdotessa in atto di sagrificare, l'altro una Baccante, et il terzo un Sileno con canestro di frutti in testa e patera in mano.*"

P. 225, no. 32 *add:* Piranesi, *Vasi*, I. Pl. 49.

P. 226, no. 33 *add:* Piranesi, *Vasi*, I. Pl. 49. A third similar vase in the possession of Lord Palmerston is given in Piranesi, Pl. 28.

P. 229, l. 19 *dele:* even

P. 229, no. 17, l. 3: charm of] *read:* charm nor of

P. 231, no. 26 *add:* Clarac, IV. 772, 1924.—In the verses, l. 5, *read:* Νικηφορίδος

P. 235, no. 62 *add:* Clarac, III. 476, 904.

P. 236, no. 82 *add:* Clarac, V. 784, 1962.

P. 238, no. 91. Apparently identical with Piranesi, *Vasi*, II. Pl. 105.

P. 242, no. 1, l. 8: II. 892] *read:* II. 8, 92.

P. 243, l. 17: πλημοχοή] *read:* πλημοχόη

P. 246, no. 4, l. 1: Pan; τροπαιοφόρος figured] *read:* Pan; figured as τροπαιοφόρος

P. 248, no. 15 *add:* C. I. Gr. 3635.

P. 251, l. 9: Ἀπολλόδωρου] *read:* Ἀπολλοδώρου

P. 251, l. 11: the style of] *read:* the style and

P. 253, l. 2 *add:* Lacroix, *Iles de la Grèce*, Pl. 6.

P. 262, no. 76 *add:* Benndorf, *Vorlegeblätter*, C, Pl. 9, 3. 4.

P. 263, no. 88 *add:* Muratori 1327, 11 (in Ficoroni's possession).

P. 266, no. 89 *add:* Muratori 1316, 11 (in Ficoroni's possession).

P. 266, no. 93 *add:* Bernoulli, *Röm. Ikonogr.*, I. p. 163, and the quotations given there in note 4.

P. 268, l. 5 *read:* aufgestützen Fusses

P. 270, no. 111, l. 1: column] *read:* stele

P. 274, no. 45. On the representation of Seirens with fish tails, which is not antique, cf. the learned disquisition of J. Bolte, *de monumentis ad Odysseam pertinentibus*, Berlin 1882, pp. 33. 59 ff.

P. 278 *dele:* CORFE CASTLE.

P. 289, no. 35, l. 8: as a vase] *read:* it is a vase.

P. 290, no. 39, l. 3: Pl. 69] *read:* Pl. 68.

P. 306, no. 19, l. 1: Pl. 7] *read:* Pl. 27.—A replica of this fine statue is at Tersatto Castle, near Fiume, cf. Schneider in *Archaeologisch-epigraphische Mittheilungen aus Oesterreich*, V., p. 159, no. 2. In this statue Seilenos has a tail.

P. 307, l. 6, p. 308, l. 16, and p. 313, no. 34, l. 17: Amadei] *read:* Amidei

P. 308, no. 24 *add:* Clarac IV. 574, 1251 A.

P. 310, no. 26. A short abstract of my memoir, accompanied by a poor
woodcut, is given in *The Antiquary*, 1882, January, pp. 6–8. I need
scarcely say that the attempt to ascribe the Holkham bust to Phidias
or to Kresilas (p. 8) is exclusively due to the author of that article.

P. 311, no. 29 *add:* Bernoulli, *Röm. Ikonogr.*, I. p. 92, where a slight sketch of
the fine head is given.

P. 313, no. 36 *add:* Montfaucon, *Ant. Expl.*, III. Pl. 6, 3.

P. 316, no. 46: Meade] *read:* Mead, and *add:* [*]

P. 317, no. 48. Perhaps identical with F. Ursinus, *Imagines*, Pl. 75. *C. I. Gr.*
6079?

P. 317, no. 49 *add:* Gruter 988, 4.

P. 317, no. 50, l. 9: no. 110] *read:* no. 66

P. 318, no. 52. The last passage refers not to no. 52, but to no. 51.

P. 318, no. 53. The identity of the Holkham bust and the bust found at
Tivoli has been doubted by Bernoulli, *Röm. Ikonogr.*, I. p. 290 (cf.
pp. 70 ff.) on account of the latter being mentioned as still existing in
the Capitol in the *Beschreibung der Stadt Rom*, III. 1, p. 124. In
matter of fact, the Tivoli bust, in compliance with Ursinus' will, came
into the Capitol, and is described as being there in Rossini's *Mercurio
errante*, 1693 (p. 13 of the 6th edition, 1739), and in the *Descrizione
delle statue...ne Palazzi di Campidoglio* (p. 130 of the 3rd edition,
1775). On the other hand, neither Ridolfino Venuti in his rather
detailed account (*Roma moderna*, 1741, p. 9) mentions the bust, nor
does E. Q. Visconti know that the bust ever was in the Capitol
(*Iconogr. Rom.*, I. p. 130 Mil.), nor has it found a place in the careful
Vasi's *Itinerario istruttivo di Roma*, I. p. 81 of the edition of 1804.
The bust reappears on its old place first in Platner's *Beschreibung*,
l. cit. (1837) as a head placed on a modern bust of coloured stucco,
with a modern inscription "Lucius Cornelius Praetor"; short notices
of it are also to be found in Nibby, *Roma nell' anno 1838. Parte
moderna*, II. p. 627, and in Tofanelli, *Indicazione delle sculture...
nel Museo Capitolino*, 1846, p. 130. Now, however, neither Dr
Dressel nor Dr Schwartz, requested by Prof. Bernoulli and by myself
respectively to make inquiry, is able to find any trace of that bust
in the Capitol. To me it appears more than probable, that the
Holkham bust, which is not a head but a complete bust, as is the
engraving in Gallaeus, and which by the grove on the nape of the
neck bears witness of its being the very bust found at Tivoli, was
abstracted from the Capitol in some way at the beginning of the
18th century and found its way into the hands of Kent; that for more
than a century its loss had been forgotten in Rome; that in our
century the vacant place of the old inventories has been filled up by
some head put on a modern bust of stucco and christened with the
old name; and that finally this head has disappeared in the recent
rearrangement of the Capitoline collections.

P. 321, l. 10. Cf. especially the statue of Zeus in the eastern pediment of the temple of Zeus at Olympia (Overbeck, *Plastik*, 3. ed., I. p. 420, fig. 90, no. 1 H).

P. 327, no. 16. Bernoulli, *Röm. Ikonogr.*, I. p. 119, note 1 says that the globe on the l. hand is possibly antique.

P. 330, no. 50 *add:* Muratori 884, 8 (Mancini collection in Rome). The inscription runs thus : *D. M.* | *P. Aelius Aug. lib.* | *Taurus proc.*

P. 331, no. 52 *add:* Muratori 1549, 8 (in Ficoroni's possession).

P. 332, no. 66 *add:* Engelmann, *Beiträge zu Euripides*, I. *Alkmene*, Berlin 1882; a sketch of the vase is given on p. 5.

P. 338, l. 1 *dele:* Cavaceppi, *Racc.*, II. 36.

P. 338, no. 6, l. 3 : no. 8] *read:* no. 9

P. 343, no. 24 *add:* *Mon. Matth.*, I. 70 " Bacchans."

P. 348, no. 34, l. 1 : 1696 B] *read:* 1646 B.

P. 364, no. 128, l. 2 : Pl. 22] *read:* Pl. 2, 2.

P. 369, no. 176. Cf. Bernoulli, *Röm. Ikonogr.*, I. p. 122.

P. 373, no. 215, l. 4 : kitchen] *read:* Temple

P. 377, no. 226 *add:* Muratori 1539, 6 (in the Giustiniani Villa outside the Porta del Popolo).

P. 378, no. 231 *add:* Muratori 1745, 15.

P. 379, no. 233, l. 8 : autumn] *read:* summer

P. 379, no. 236, l. 1 : *Engr.* 84, 3] *read:* *Engr.* 84, 4.

P. 380, no. 239 *add:* Muratori 1224, 3 (Marchese Capponi).

P. 380, no. 240 *add:* Muratori 996, 9 ; he gives *Claudio* and *hic situs est.*

P. 391, no. 274 : barrel] *read:* belly

P. 403, no. 312 *add:* Muratori 1695, 3.

P. 403, no. 313 *add:* Muratori 1476, 10.

P. 404, no. 316 *add:* Muratori 1198, 10 (Villa Montalto).

P. 404, no. 317 *add:* Muratori 1665, 4.

P. 404. no. 318 *add:* Muratori 1524, 1 gives the inscription, then in the Cesarini Villa, as follows "*e schedis Ptolomei*" (a good authority) : *Dis Manibus sacrum* | *M. Burrio Felici patron.* | *benemerenti fecer.* *M. Burrius Hermes* | *M. Burrius Pulpus* | *et Burria Philumene* | *M. Burrius Puncilus* | *M. Burrius Atticus* | *M. Burrius Abascantus.*

P. 404, no. 319 *add:* Muratori 1545, 9.

P. 404, no. 320 *add:* Muratori 1698, 9.

P. 405, no. 322 *add:* Muratori 1273, 11.

P. 406, no. 330 *add:* Muratori 1252, 10.

P. 407, no. 341. The same inscription is to be found on a different cippus in Piranesi, *Vasi*, I. Pl. 52.

P. 408, no. 350 *add:* Cf. Muratori 1598, 11 = 1738, 9.

P. 409, no. 354 *add:* Muratori 1634, 10.

P. 409, no. 356 *add:* Muratori 1153, 5.

P. 409, no. 362 *add:* Muratori 1164, 8 (Villa Montalto).

P. 410, no. 364 *add:* Cf. Muratori 1705, 11 (Villa Giustiniani).

P. 410, no. 373. Identical with Piranesi, *Vasi*, II. 112 ?

P. 413, no. 399, l. 3 : *Engr.* 110, 3] *read:* *Engr.* 110, 1.

P. 426, no. 11 *add:* Muratori 1206, 7 (in the vigna of Seb. Lazzarini, near Rome).

P. 428, no. 28. A vase of similar shape is engraved in Piranesi, *Vasi*, I. Pl. 9, F.

P. 429, no. 1 *add:* Bernoulli, *Röm. Ikonogr.,* I. p. 136, and the authorities quoted by him. Henzen (*C. I. L.,* VI. 1, 1326) doubts the genuineness of the inscription.

P. 430, no. 3 *add:* Bernoulli, *Röm. Ikonogr.,* I. pp. 280 ff.

P. 434, no. 2. Helbig's interpretation has become uncertain since the discovery of the monument of Manius Cordius Thalamus (*Bullet. comun.,* IX. Pl. 19, 20), on which an indisputable head of Minerva is covered with the mask of Medusa.

P. 441, no. 16 *add:* Gruter 613, 9 (in the church of SS. Cosma e Damiano, at Rome), who gives *Antoniniano.*

P. 442, l. 6: as it seems] *read:* as it were

P. 442, no. 24 *add:* Gruter 675, 1 (in the possession of the Mattei family, in Trastevere, near the Ponte S. Bartolommeo).

P. 444, no. 29. Cf. Bernoulli, *Röm. Ikonogr.,* I. p. 91.

P. 445, no. 33, l. 11: in drapery carving] *read:* of drapery

P. 455, no. 67. As to the epoch of the original of this statue, cf. K. Lange, *Arch. Zeit.,* 1881, p. 197 note 2.

P. 457, no. 71 *add:* Gruter 676, 13 (Cardinal Cesi).

P. 462, no. 81, l. 1: Terminal bust] *read:* Terminal figure

P. 464, l. 9. "Mr Grenville" is no doubt a member of the family of the Marquis of Buckingham, who was at that time in Italy collecting marbles for Stowe, cf. Piranesi, *Vasi,* I. Pl. 15.

P. 473, no. 1, l. 2: statues] *read:* statue

P. 499, no. 94. This is probably the fragment of marble discovered in the Casali Villa, on the alleged site of the *campus Martialis* (Ovid, *Fast.* 3, 521. Paulus Festi epit. p. 131), which was thought to be a *meta,* though its shape showed very little similarity to a real *meta.* It was for some time preserved in the garden of the said villa, and afterwards bought by an Englishman for a large sum. Cf. *Beschr. d. Stadt Rom,* III. 1, pp. 477. 502.

P. 502, no. 3 *add:* Clarac, III. 476 C, 906 E.

P. 504, no. 8, l. 24. In the Berlin group certain details are such as to leave it uncertain whether Dionysos or Priapos is meant.

P. 517, no. 3, l. 19. It is probably the "*statua alta pal. 6, rappresentante un Fauno colla siringa e bastone,*" described in the inventory of the Barberini collection made in 1738 (*Docum. ined.* etc., IV. p. 50).

P. 544, no. 10, l. 17: freely] *read:* fully

P. 552, no. 42, l. 2: 970] *read:* 970 D

P. 566, no. 111 *add:* Benndorf, *Vorlegeblätter,* C, Pl. 11, 3.

P. 576, l. 2. The principal name may be *Nicherōs.*

P. 600, no. 6 *add:* C. I. Gr. 6138.

P. 624, l. 6: statue identical] *read:* statue is identical

P. 635, l. 20: version] *read:* copy

P. 642, l. 13: over] *read:* beyond

P. 642, no. 80. Cf. Muratori 1319, 8.

P. 655, no. 91 *add:* Muratori 999, 6 (Ang. Borioni).

P. 669, l. 30 *dele:* 46, this bust being not modern.

P. 684, no. 55, l. 4 *add:* [*]

P. 684, no. 60, l. 1 : *Collib.*] *read: Monum. lib.*

P. 712, no. 198 *add:* Muratori 1296, 10 (Montalto Villa).

P. 721. Two drawings by Miss Agnes C. Imlach communicated to Mr Conze enable me to give a more detailed description of the two stelae at Winton Castle.

1. **Attic sepulchral stelè**, very tall, flanked by two pilasters, and crowned with a rounded top, on which a graceful anthemion is developing itself. In the field stands a maiden, facing l., in slight movement. She is draped with a chiton and a wide cloak which entirely envelops her l. arm. The hair which falls down on to the nape of the neck shews a simple arrangement. The head is bent, looking at a small doll which she holds in her raised r. hand. Beautiful Attic style of the 4th century. On the architrave is the name Ἀριστομάχη, written in the characters of that period. H. 1·63. L. 0·45.

2. **Attic sepulchral stelè**. Between two pilasters is a female figure, seated on a chair, facing l. She is draped and wears a high head-dress. She shakes hands with another female, draped, who stands opposite to her. Relief of good character, which would suggest a better time than that of the inscription written in the pediment and on the architrave in large characters of the somewhat ornamented style of Roman times : (in the pediment) Κλαυδία, (on the architrave) Ἄφφιον ἐκ Μελιτέων. As to the second name of the lady, cf. *C. I. Gr.*, nos. 3167. 3278. H. 0·99. L. 0·50.

P. 735, no. 117 *add:* Benndorf, *Vorlegeblatter*, C, Pl. 10, 2.

P. 745, no. 186, *A add:* Muratori 1144, 7 (Marchese Lovatelli at Rome).

P. 748, no. 219 *add:* Benndorf, *Vorlegeblatter*, C, Pl. 10, 1.

P. 768. ROME, COLLECTIONS, *add:*

    Borioni *R.* Rossie 91

    Capponi *R.* Ince 239

    Casali Lowther 94

    Cesarini *R.* Ince 318

    Cesi *R.* London, Lansdowne 71

    SS. Cosma e Damiano *R.* London, Lansdowne 16

    Ficoroni *R.* Cambridge 88. 89. C. Howard 52

    Giustiniani *R.* Ince 226. 364?

    Lazzarini *R.* Liverpool 11

    Lovatelli *R.* Woburn 186, *A*

    Mancini *R.* C. Howard 50

    Mattei in Trastevere *R.* London, Lansdowne 24

    Montalto *R.* Ince 316. 362. Wilton 198

INTRODUCTION.

ON THE INFLUX OF ANTIQUE SCULPTURES INTO GREAT BRITAIN.

INTRODUCTION.

ON THE INFLUX OF ANTIQUE SCULPTURES INTO GREAT BRITAIN.

PRELIMINARY.

NO other country in Europe can at this day boast of such a wealth of Private Collections of antique works of art as England, which in this particular recalls the Rome of the sixteenth and seventeenth centuries. Great is the number of town-houses and palaces, still greater the number of country-seats, in which the noble and the rich treasure up, by the side of incomparable masterpieces of modern painting, considerable collections of antique works of art, especially of sculpture. So numerous are they, that few have any notion of this abundance of treasures, and perhaps no one individual enjoys a really comprehensive knowledge of them. Whatever has once reached the region of this Enchanted Island has remained there as it were spell-bound. These collections have in frequent instances experienced great vicissitudes. Many have more than once changed owners, many have come to the hammer in public auction ; they have been moved from one place to another, and in consequence have often found their way into remote and inaccessible hiding-places ; indeed a certain number of specimens have been utterly lost sight of, so that only a happy chance can bring them back to light. Very few however, and those under quite peculiar circumstances, have made their way back across the Channel. "England," says a gifted writer on art, "is to works of art what the grave is to the dead ; her gates do not open again to let them out[1]."

[1] Bürger, W., *Les Trésors d'Art en Angleterre*, Brussels and Ostend, 1862, p. 1.

The works of ancient Greek and Roman art in England alone constitute the subject of the present volume. The student who attempts to trace the introduction of such works into the country, will soon notice that there are three clearly defined periods in the development of this branch of dilettantism. In the first, which embraces the time of the Stuarts and their immediate successors, it is individual collectors who strike into the path indicated. Only a few undertook to collect the larger works in marble. There is consequently a preponderance over these of the smaller objects of art, bronzes, coins, gems, which, being more easily attainable and more easy to transport, have at all times formed a favourite object of the antiquarian collector's enthusiasm. The destinies of these old collections are for the most part, like the whole circumstances of the time, variable and frequently violent. At the end of the period only a few had entirely or even partially preserved their old condition. At this day the collection at Wilton House is the solitary unimpaired representative of that epoch; besides which, of the treasures of the illustrious Earl of Arundel the greater part is still to be found at Oxford, in the secure possession, not of a private person, but of the University.

Then comes the heyday of dilettantism in England, the last century, especially in its latter half. In an unintermitting stream the ancient marbles of Rome poured into the palaces of the aristocracy of Britain, whose wealth in some cases afforded the means of gratifying a real artistic taste by these rare possessions, and in others enabled them at any rate to fall into the new fashion of dilettantism, the *furore* for antique art. The older Roman collections were bought up; fresh excavations were instituted. Englishmen settled in Rome and dealt in the acquisitions without which *milord* on his travels could not well return home from the 'grand tour.' Of course other countries tried to secure their share, but England stood foremost. During this period of fifty or sixty years there came into being most of the private collections of antiques in which the island abounds, and those the largest and most valuable. Their general character depends upon the fact that their origin has been almost exclusively in the soil of Rome and its immediate vicinity.

At the beginning of this century the possession of a gallery of sculpture ceased to be indispensable to *bon ton*. The importation of antiques came to a stop, owing to the interruption of commercial intercourse entailed by the protracted war against Napoleon. Other fashionable tastes sprang into existence or were revived. Once again the interest, or at any rate the active enthusiasm, for collections of antique works of art, became the privilege of a few real lovers of such things. While however this abatement of zeal took place in private circles, the State stepped into the place of individual amateurs with abundant energy. Since the opening of this century the British Museum has advanced with rapid strides to the supreme position of having the finest collection of antiques in the world. It was no longer Rome, or Italy generally, which filled the rooms of this institution with late copies or imitations of Greek originals; but Greek art itself, represented by a stately series of its most beautiful creations, entered the museum in triumph, and asserted a might of simple grandeur before unknown. The British Museum must in this respect remain altogether beyond the reach of rivalry. The sum of its priceless treasures has been completed by means of excavations specially undertaken, and successful acquisitions made with unremittent zeal at the sites of discoveries. They have often been increased by donations or purchases of private collections. In fact, the British Museum has gradually thrown all private collections far into the background. It seems therefore only natural and desirable that in the future also the several brooklets should discharge themselves into this mighty stream.

The object of the ensuing sketch is to follow this development more closely into detail, and at the same time to draw attention to such general considerations as must necessarily escape notice during the study of the collections taken severally. If in these preliminary remarks the older collections are found to be treated more fully than the newer, and those which have been dispersed than those still existing, no apology is needed.

I cannot help lamenting the general inadequacy of the aids at my disposal. Only occasionally have I been enabled to give more than a mere outline of my subject. However, I have at any rate aimed at accuracy and certainty in its delineation. Much will undoubtedly have escaped me, notwithstanding the assistance of friends quite qualified to offer criticism and advice, as I was able to devote but a short time to the use of a mass of literary aids only available in England. But in the case of the great majority of these collections, there is an absolute dearth of accounts of their origination and of the sources of their component elements. There is undoubtedly much information on such matters, either in the form of short memoranda or complete correspondence, still preserved among the archives of those families whose ancestors in bygone times acquired the collections. I have had access to only a small proportion of such unprinted papers. It is to be hoped that my book will call forth communications of such records. Of previous labourers in a more general style in the same field, it is only necessary to mention the occasional paragraphs in Horace Walpole's *Anecdotes of Painting*, and Dallaway's useful though too superficial and uncritical books. Should these drawbacks not seem sufficient to secure indulgence for the shortcomings of the following sketch, the reader may earn the gratitude of the public and of the author by pointing out or laying open new sources of inquiry.

I.

THE ARUNDEL MARBLES AND OTHER
EARLY COLLECTIONS.

1. It was late before England joined the competition *No antiquities in
England
in the 16th
century.* of the nations which desired to possess a share of the abundance of antique sculptures which since the fifteenth century have come to light in unheard-of numbers from the soil of Italy. In the course of the sixteenth century we see Francis I. of France, Philip II. of Spain, Rudolf II. of Germany, taking pains to raise their residences in Paris, Madrid, and Prague to equal rank with the palaces of the Roman nobles by decorating them with works of antique art. Princes of lesser rank, such as the Electors of Bavaria, follow their example ; and even private persons of wealth are loth to be left behind. I may instance the Welser family of Augsburg, between which city and Italy there were intimate connections. In England during the Tudor period no trace yet showed itself of a similar interest ; although the influence of Italy in other fields of culture was scarcely so deeply impressed on England at any other time as in the sixteenth century. The long dis-tance from Italy, the insular position of the country, the keenness of political and religious oppositions and dissensions, a puritanical aversion from images of heathen deities, might constitute the main reasons why in this particular England lagged behind the continental states throughout the whole of the sixteenth century.

Henry,
Prince of
Wales.
2. It was under the Kings of the house of Stuart that
a change first began. It appears that the first to aim at the
possession of antique works of art was the eldest son of
James I., PRINCE HENRY, "that hopeful cherisher of great
and noble things," who died young A.D. 1612. He laid
the foundation of a collection of coins which, his brother
Charles subsequently enlarged, and acquired the collection
of gems made by Abraham Gorlaeus of the Netherlands
(*d.* A.D. 1609)[2]. He further left his brother eighteen small
statues, but as they are designated in the catalogue of
works of art in the possession of King Charles the First,
as "Florentine brazen statues," and as their description
contains several strange particulars[3], it is doubtful whether
genuine antique statues are meant or whether they were
not rather modern imitations, like many specimens in the
possession of Charles I. Prince Henry had not yet reached
his eighteenth year when he died. Had he lived longer, to
his lot there would probably have fallen a share of the
glory, which now belongs to another, of being prover-
bially styled the "father of *vertù*" in this country. We
pass now to the individual thus designated, from whom
a distinguished Society of friends and promoters of genuine
art has been able with propriety to take its name.

Lord
Arundel's
tours in
Italy.
3. THOMAS HOWARD, EARL OF ARUNDEL AND
SURREY (*b.* A.D. 1585), reinstated by A.D. 1621 in the
dignity hereditary in his family of Earl Marshal of
England, stands indisputably at the head of English art
collectors[4]. His delicate health had early taken him
to Italy for a comparatively long visit, from which he

[2] Evelyn, *Letter to Pepys*, 1689,
Aug. 12. Walpole, *Anecdotes of Painting*, ch. VIII. (Sad. de Caus). IX.
(Charles I.). Chamberlain to Carleton
in Birch's *Court and Times of James I.*
I. p. 227.
[3] *A Catalogue of King Charles the
First's Capital Collection*, transcribed
by Vertue. London, 1757, p. 21, "the

eighteen little Statues which came to
his Majesty by the decease of Prince
Henry." Cf. Carleton to Chamberlain (Birch, *James I.* I. p. 212).
[4] Walpole, *Anecd.* ch. IX. Dallaway, *Anecdotes*, p. 229. Ellis, H.,
The Townley Gallery, I. p. 57. Edwards, *Lives of the Founders of the
British Museum.* I. p. 183. Cf.

first returned home at the end of the year 1612. The
direction of his taste was finally determined by a renewed
sojourn of twelve months, A.D. 1613, 1614. By the King's
order the young lord, accompanied by his wife Alathea
Talbot, daughter of the Earl of Shrewsbury, had conducted
the Princess Elizabeth as bride to her betrothed husband,
Frederick, the Elector Palatine. "Thence he went into
Italy, where he very much pleased himself, and either took
up or improved his natural disposition of being the great
master and favourer of arts, especially of sculpture, design,
painting and architecture, which rendered him famous and
acceptable to all ingenious spirits both at home and
abroad[5]." Thus we are told by Sir Edward Walker, who had
stood in close relations to him and his house. Peacham's
often-quoted words refer to the same juncture as the beginning of the Earl's activity as a collector. They will be
found in their proper place further on. It deserves notice
that Arundel had in his suite no less a person than Inigo
Jones, whose artistic taste developed itself for the first
time during this journey in the direction of that classical
style which characterized his later designs[6]. We may fairly
conjecture that the Earl's natural taste for art must have
been much stimulated by the influence of the practical
knowledge and mature judgment of his elder companion.
Relations were in various forms kept up between the two
men afterwards.

4. We cannot now prove in detail how much Lord *Michaelian*
Arundel got together at that time in person, how much *Marbles.*
gradually by his agents, several of whom he employed
in Italy and "generally in any part of Europe where
rarities were to be had[7]." He is said to have himself

Michaelis in *Im neuen Reich*, 1878, I.
pp. 921, 964. I have taken pains to refer
on all occasions as far as possible to
the original authorities, and I hope
that the account has consequently been
made both more complete and more
accurate.

[5] *Historical Discourses*, London,
1705, p. 212.
[6] Sir Dudley Carleton to John
Chamberlain, 1613, July 9 (Birch,
James I. p. 255).
[7] Walker, *Hist. Disc.* p. 222.

obtained leave to institute excavations on the sites of
ruins about Rome, and it is also related that he discovered
in subterraneous chambers a whole number at a time of
splendid Roman portrait-statues. These were soon restored in the usual manner, and furnished with the high-
sounding names of Cicero, Marius, and so forth. They
still at this day adorn the collection at Oxford[8]. Others
were obtained by purchase. "He made a wonderful
and costly purchase of excellent statues, whilst he was in
Italy and Rome, some whereof he could never obtain permission to remove from Rome, though he had paid for
them[9]." That Arundel's aims were pitched high we learn
from two instances accidentally recorded[10]. In the Circus
of Maxentius (usually called of Caracalla) not far from the
Via Appia, there lay an obelisk of about sixteen metres in
length broken into four pieces. It was only the difficulty
of transport to the sea which deterred the Earl from purchasing the fragments and putting them together in London;
which city might otherwise have been able to boast an
obelisk long before the bringing over of Cleopatra's needle.
What happened instead was that Bernini (A.D. 1651) crowned his fantastic fountain in the Piazza Navona with the
obelisk in question. The purchase of the Meleager (then
called Adonis) of the Pighini palace, which now constitutes
one of the chief ornaments of the Belvedere, was likewise one
of Arundel's schemes, but it miscarried upon the refusal
of the owner to part with his treasure even for a high price.
For the element of cost never came into consideration with
respect to the Earl's passion for collecting. "His expenses,"
says his embittered opponent Lord Clarendon[11], "were
without any measure, and always exceeded very much his
revenue." If we measure those aspirations by the results,
certainly most of the sculptures of Italian origin, which

[8] Dallaway, *Anecd.* p. 236.
[9] Clarendon, *Hist. of the Rebellion,*
Oxf. 1849, I p. 78.
[10] Evelyn, *Diary,* 1645, Feb. 16.
1644, Nov. 6.
[11] *Hist. of the Reb.* l. cit.

are still to be found among the remains of the Arundel
collection at Oxford, seem rather insignificant. For there
are only a few specimens which rise above the level of
mediocrity; the best portion of that collection being undoubtedly or probably derived not from Italy but from
Greece.

5. In the first period of the reawakening of classical *The*
culture, Poggio Bracciolini, the great pioneer of the Re- *country of*
naissance, had already made use of his connection with *Greece.*
some friends in Chios to get a few antiques from Greece
to grace his villa near Florence, the Valdarniana [12]. Again,
about the middle of the fifteenth century, the enthusiastic
traveller Ciriaco de' Pizzicolli of Ancona, during his repeated wanderings through the islands of the Archipelago,
had turned his attention to the relics of Greek art [13].
These districts were then under the rule of Italian princes.
But since the Turks had established themselves in absolute
dominion over them, it had become more and more difficult to pursue such interests. At best the nobles and merchants of Venice could place themselves in possession of
one or two specimens, and there was a general impression
that " all above ground was gone to Venice [14]." Or else
the ambassador of a Western power to the Sublime Porte
would use his residence as an opportunity for collecting
what presented itself to him. So it was with the French
ambassador, Des Hayes [15]. We hear too of similar efforts
of the Provençal scholar Claude Peiresc, who most zealously
turned to account his wide-spread connections for his
scientific works [16]. But the merit of having caused these
classic shores to be ransacked for the express purpose of
collecting antiques belongs to the Earl of Arundel, and

[12] Shepherd, *Life of Poggio Bracciolini*, Liverp. 1802, p. 291. G.
Voigt, *Die Wiederbelebung des class.
Alterthums*, Berlin, 1859, p. 173.
[13] Jahn, O., *Aus der Alterthums-
wissenschaft*, Bonn, 1868. p. 333.

[14] Roe, T., *Negotiations*, London,
1740, p. 647.
[15] Roe, p. 154. Laborde, *Athènes*,
1. p. 62.
[16] Gassendi, *Fabr. de Peiresc vita*,
Par. 1641, p. 227.

the energy with which he followed up this task in the midst of so many others, quite answers to one of the characteristic qualities of his nation.

6. The first opportunity was presented by the mission of Sir Thomas Roe to Constantinople, as ambassador from James I., in the year 1621 [17]. The Earl Marshal, by birth and position one of the foremost among the dignitaries of the English nobility, might well count on meeting with no refusal if he earnestly requested the ambassador at his departure to pay regard in his interest to the treasures of antiquity, works of art, and manuscripts, and to collect them for him. In fact, Sir Thomas was quite willing to be of service, and declared himself ready "to look back upon antiquity" besides pursuing his own vocation, which was "to attend new things," all the more so as he was himself "a lover of such vertues," though no great connoisseur. Had he had an idea to what troubles and unpleasantnesses he was about to expose himself by undertaking this commission, he would probably have been less ready and willing to enter upon this "quarry and stone business." For some time indeed the affair went on tolerably smoothly. Immediately upon his arrival at Constantinople Roe collected information about the localities which gave the best promise of a return. In particular the Bishop of Andros pointed out the places of sepulture in Rheneia (great Delos) as a rich mine of treasures. This spot has been ransacked again and again up to the present day, and is not yet exhausted. He set the British consul to work to institute inquiries within his district. Here was the commencement of a system which has since been employed with such important results. Sir Thomas was indefatigable in asking the necessary permis-

[17] *The Negotiations of Sir Th. Roe in his Embassy to the Ottoman Porte,* London, 1740. These letters have been often used since the time of Horace Walpole, but never thoroughly used up. So far as they refer to our present subject, they will be found arranged in order in the Appendix to this Introduction. I have looked though some other correspondence of Sir Thomas', which is preserved in the British Museum, for notices of this kind, but to no purpose.

sion from the Turkish authorities, though not always with
the desired effect. The very first letters tell of a "maid of
Smyrna," which Arundel seems to have mentioned to Roe,
and of a fragment of a lion holding a bull's head in its claws
at Lampsacus. The two specimens were not however secured. Yet Sir Thomas, though barely arrived at the Bos-
phorus, was already on the high road towards anticipating
the fame of Dr Schliemann, since he was able to offer the
Earl "a stone taken out of the old palace of Priam in Troy,
cut in horned shape." It is a pity that this stone, as indeed
many other Trojan antiquities, had no recommendations
except the high-sounding name of its alleged place of
discovery.

7. Unfortunately there are only a few letters remaining *William Petty.*
of the correspondence between Roe and Arundel. Consequently we cannot say what induced the Earl, Roe's efforts
notwithstanding, to send out a special agent to the Levant,
—whether, for instance, the practical fruit of the exertions
of the much-occupied diplomatist seemed too trifling, or
whether he perhaps had knowledge that a dangerous rival
would likewise lay claim to Sir Thomas' services. However
this might be, in the last months of the year 1624 there first
appeared at Smyrna, and at the beginning of the ensuing
year actually at Constantinople, William Petty, charged with
commissions from Lord Arundel, and warmly recommended
to the ambassador. This gentleman had been educated at
Cambridge [18], and had entered Lord Arundel's service. In
all probability his value had already been proved by lucky
purchases in Italy before he was sent out to the East with
the new commission [19]. At all events he forthwith impressed
Sir Thomas Roe with his superior practical knowledge,

---

[18] Dallaway, *Of Statuary*, p. 277,
quoting Cole's *Athenæ Cantabri-
gienses* (MS.). The often-repeated
assertion that this Petty is an ancestor
of the Marquis of Lansdowne rests on
a confusion with the famous Sir
William Petty, whose daughter, Anne
Petty, married to Thomas Fitzmaurice,
Earl of Kerry, was the grandmother
of the first Marquis of Lansdowne.
The two William Pettys were not, so
far as I know, related to one another.
[19] Chandler, R., *Marmora Oxoniensia*, Oxf. 1763, p. 1.

which the latter recognised without reservation. With this Petty combined an unflinching energy, a power of endurance proof against all exertions and privations, and lastly a regardlessness in gaining every advantage which Roe was destined soon to learn to his cost. The latter writes to Lord Arundel, " There was never man so fitted to an employment, that encounters all accident with so unwearied patience, eates with Greeks on their worst days, lies with fishermen on planks at the best, is all things to all men, that he may obtain his ends, which are your lordship's service." And on another occasion, not without bitterness, " Your lordship had good experience in a man for such an employment, that spares no pains nor arts to effect his services."

The Duke of Buckingham.   8. It was certainly high time for Lord Arundel to transfer his interests to such active hands. Not long before Petty arrived at Constantinople, GEORGE VILLIERS, DUKE OF BUCKINGHAM, had preferred to Sir Thomas Roe a similar request to that which Lord Arundel had made earlier. The uncontrolled favourite of King James and his son had entered into competition with Arundel in more than one order of connoisseurship. In Antwerp he had purchased the collection of the great Peter Paul Rubens, which comprised, besides pictures, antique vases, statues and medals[20]. ".At Yorke House[21]," says an eye-witness, "the Galleries and Roomes are ennobled with the possession of these Romane Heads and Statues, which lately belonged to Sir Peter Paul Rubens." In Venice Buckingham had purchases of pictures effected through the ambassador Sir Henry Wotton, just as he now laid claim to Sir Thomas Roe's services for the

[20] Walpole, *Anecd.*ch.x.(Rubens).
[21] Peacham, H., *The Compleat Gentleman*, 3rd Impression, London, 1634, p. 108. York House in the Strand is meant, not the Palace of Whitehall, which at that time was still often called York House in addition to its other names. In the *Catalogue of the Curious Collection of*

Pictures of George Villiers, Duke of Buckingham, London, W. Bathoe, 1758, there are indeed no antiques, only a few copies of antiques in bronze (pp. 22, 23); but this catalogue comprises merely the portion of the old collection which was rescued from the storms of the revolution for the young duke.

acquisition of antique sculptures. Not, to be sure, all specimens whatsoever without discrimination. For instance, he cautioned Sir Thomas against the purchase of works in alabaster, as being seldom genuine. "Neither am I so fond of antiquity as to court it in a deformed or mishapen stone; but where you shall meet beauty with antiquity together in a statue, I shall not stand upon any cost your judgment shall value it at." It is a matter of course that the ambassador did not neglect the wishes of the all-powerful minister, but willingly agreed to execute his directions (Jan. A.D. 1625). At the same time he did not forget his obligations to Lord Arundel, who had been beforehand in enlisting his services.

9. Not long afterwards Petty presented himself to Sir *Roe's and Petty's joint plans.* Thomas, and soon found out how on the one hand to prove himself serviceable to him by his practical knowledge, and on the other hand to inform himself as to the ambassador's plans, and to provide himself plentifully with permits and letters of authorization such as could only be procured through the intervention of the ambassador. At first all went on in perfect harmony, and the two men launched out together into high-flown and quite romantic plans. When in our own generation Ponsonby first conceived the idea of removing the reliefs from the Mausoleum out of the walls of the Turkish fortress of Budrum, and acquiring them for England, some regarded this as "an unreasonable request" to the Porte[22]. Yet how modest this wish was compared with the designs of Roe and Petty! They proposed nothing less than to get into their power six out of the twelve large reliefs which adorned the so-called "Golden Gate," the finest of the gates of Constantinople. This gate was erected by Theodosios the Great. Through it the Byzantine Emperors used to make their solemn entry into the city. But since the conquest by the Turks it had not been opened, but built up and enclosed with

---

[22] Fellows, *The Xanthian Marbles*, p. 9.

new strong works of defence, the so-called "Seven Towers."
Though it had become consequently quite inaccessible, yet
it was still regarded as the principal gate. For about a
year this Quixotic plan cuts a grand figure in the correspondence. To get the consent of the Sultan to the
demolition soon proved to be just as impracticable as the
idea of reaching their object by corrupting the highest
functionaries of State. A clandestine removal with the
help of the soldiers stationed on the spot was impossible
on account of the weight of the marble slabs and the height
at which they were built in. So they had recourse to
stratagem. It was agreed that a Turkish priest should
denounce the figure sculptures, as opposed to the religion
of Mohammed, and so bring about their removal from their
conspicuous position. If once they were transferred to
another place it would not be difficult to get them out of
the way. In fact a priest was engaged for this purpose,
and a sum of 600 crowns proffered in case of success ; a
temporary deposit of 500 dollars being actually made by
way of preliminary. But even this hope proved delusive.
At last the Grand Treasurer, whose coffers could in times
of war take advantage of every extra source of supply,
promised to take the matter in hand and to contrive a
clandestine removal. Now however the garrison began to
get uneasy. A superstitious feeling gained ground that in
connection with the removal of the enchanted sculptures a
great mischief threatened the city. There was nothing left,
unless they would expose themselves to serious danger, but
to give up the whole plan. We cannot but regret this, as
the reliefs soon afterwards disappeared altogether. Only a
few of the many visitors to Constantinople ever saw them
again[23]; no one has drawn or described them more closely,
so that Roe's tolerably full description consequently retains
some value.

[23] E. g. Wheler, *Journey into* — *Voyage d'Italie* &c., Lyons, 1678, I.
Greece, London, 1682, p. 194.   Spon,   p. 262.

10. Sir Thomas, who had undertaken engagements in *Arundel and Buckingham.* two quarters, considered that he should be keeping faith with both parties if he were to divide the fruit of the joint labours of Petty and himself between Lord Arundel and the Duke of Buckingham (this indeed was his plan with reference to the sculptures just mentioned); while he reserved exclusively for Buckingham what he should acquire by himself without Petty's cooperation. To this effect he entered into agreements with Petty, in which the latter apparently acquiesced, and submitted like proposals to Arundel. But the illustrious Earl Marshal, full of pride in his noble ancestry, was not disposed to entertain the idea of any such compromise with the detested upstart of whom he had just begun to find himself the antagonist in the field of politics. The notion of taking shares with the new-created Duke was not at all to the taste of the twenty-first representative of the long line of Earls of Arundel, who according to the testimony of an adversary "lived towards all favourites, and great officers, without any kind of condescension[1]." The impassioned collector could not make up his mind thus to share the spoil for which he had at first instituted the chase with the rival who had come later upon the scene. He roundly refused the proposal, to the great embarrassment of Sir Thomas, who now found himself saddled with the difficult task of serving two masters.

11. Petty meanwhile, after a stay of some months in *Petty's actively.* Constantinople, had set off on his travels. His nominal purpose was energetic action for their common interests. The needful firmans and permits had been got by means of Roe. But as a matter of fact Petty evinced little inclination for partnership with the ambassador, and was probably confirmed in this disinclination by Lord Arundel. It could not possibly escape him how much more favourable the prospects were for himself than for the diplomatist,

[1] Clarendon, *Hist. of the Rebellion.* I. p. 78.

tied by his office to the Court and obliged to depend on the
zeal and acumen of his agents. For Petty the road to his
special undertakings lay open. His conduct with respect
to the Golden Gate was in the highest degree characteristic.
The reliefs had originally appeared to Roe too much
mutilated to be of value. Petty however formed a far
more favourable judgment of them, and persuaded Roe to
offer for them the sum above-mentioned. Now, while on
his travels, Petty suddenly advised the ambassador not to
apply more than two hundred dollars to that purpose.
The latter, who had in the meantime become suspicious
of Petty's designs, got an inkling of his desire to place
himself in sole possession of the reliefs at a convenient
season. So he gave Petty free leave to withdraw from
their common transactions, but at the same time explained
that he would himself in any case pursue the undertaking
further and at his convenience divide the spoil between
Buckingham and Arundel. When Petty found the ambassador so resolute, he without more ado gave up his objection
and actually went back to the original agreement. His
route took him at first to Pergamon and Samos. According
to his letters to Roe he found only a trifling spoil, fragments of no considerable value. But the ambassador
learnt through other channels that the harvest had been
very rich and highly valuable, and so found himself over-
reached by the "close and subtle borderer." He openly
expressed his chagrin to Lord Arundel (Oct. 20, A.D. 1625).
However he none the less bestirred himself, when Petty
on his voyage from Samos to Ephesos suffered shipwreck
in the narrow strait, and lost not merely his collections but
also his papers, to replace the latter by fresh ones, such
precarious work it was to apply so often for such orders
and permits. Petty himself was not discouraged by his
mischance, but at once resumed his activity. At first he
was put into prison by the Turks as a spy, but soon
managed to satisfy them as to his status and to get

free. He promptly set to work in Chios and made preparations for fishing the submerged treasures up again from the bottom of the sea. In this he seems to have actually succeeded. Then he betook himself to Ephesos and Smyrna. Here he was lucky enough to make a valuable haul[25]. One Samson, commissioned by the Provençal scholar Peiresc, had not long before acquired a number of stones bearing inscriptions at the price of fifty gold pieces. Among these was the extremely valuable chronological table destined to be known to all the world as the *Marmor Parium*. Through some intrigues on the part of the sellers Samson had been cast into prison and the collection had been dispersed. Petty now arrived, and had the good fortune to bring the specimens together again and to secure them, though at a high price, for Lord Arundel. Thence he went to Athens, where he spent the summer of the year 1626. He there met with an emissary of Roe's. Through him Sir Thomas probably learnt what Petty had achieved. He writes to Buckingham in November of that year: "Mr Petty has raked together two hundred pieces, all broken, or few entire; what they will prove, I cannot judge." Apparently Petty left the Levant soon after this, but not before he had despatched the result of his labours to England, where the marbles arrived at Arundel House in the year 1627. Here they forthwith excited the greatest interest, especially the inscriptions; and among these again principally the two large fragments of the chronological table. The renowned John Selden, the *magnus dictator doctrinae nationis Anglicae*, undertook the deciphering and interpretation, assisted by Patrick Young and Richard James. By the following year, A.D. 1628, appeared Selden's *Marmora Arundelliana*, which spread abroad the fame of the inscriptions and of their collector over all the world[26]. (In the same year was born

[25] Gassendi, *N. Cl. Fabricii de Peiresc vita*, Par. 1641, p. 227, ad annum 1629. Prideaux, *Marm. Oxon.*

Oxf. 1676, praef. fol. 5.

[26] Selden's book unfortunately includes only 29 Greek and 10 Latin

the Earl's grandson, Henry Howard, through whom the
collection was subsequently scattered to the winds.) Peiresc
too now learnt what had become of his former property;
but so far from being envious, he expressed delight that
both the stones themselves and the task of appreciating
them had fallen into such good hands. About the sculptures there was at first less talk.

Roe's
efforts. 12. In the meantime Sir Thomas Roe most zealously
endeavoured, even independently of Petty, to minister fairly
to the desires of his noble employers. At first he even yet
purposed to let the Earl Marshal as well as the Duke of
Buckingham have his share. But the former, as we can
easily understand, fell gradually more and more into the
background. His and Petty's conduct had after all annoyed
Roe not a little, and moreover Buckingham, as the con-
fidential adviser of the king and leading statesman of the
hour, could throw quite another weight into the scale:—
through his mediation, that is to say, Sir Thomas might well
hope to be recalled as soon as possible from his difficult
and unpleasant post. So we find no letter of Roe's to
Arundel in the collection later than March A.D. 1626;
on the other hand there is an unbroken series of reports
to Buckingham as to the progress of the researches. For
a long time the result was extremely small, although no
pains were spared. These researches extended as far as
Alexandria and Sinope. Some of the chief towns of Asia
Minor, such as Ankyra and Brussa, again Troy and Pergamon, the south coast of Roumelia, and the principal
islands of the Archipelago, were searched thoroughly by
the British consuls, by native speculators, by agents specially
sent out. But yet little or no success presented itself;
stones entirely defaced or modern works were purchased
for high prices, or the difficulty of transport frustrated the

inscriptions. This is all the more to
be regretted, because in the following
period a large portion of the inscriptions were utterly lost before copies of
them had been taken.

hopes of bringing away the heavier specimens from the
interior to the sea. A few fragments of statues, some
heads and reliefs, composed the entire produce, until at
last, at the beginning of the year 1627, a more competent
agent travelled through the Morea. For almost a year
he collected in the different districts of the peninsula and
on the islands, and contrived to inflame the zeal of the
poorer inhabitants :—"Our search has begotten a diligence
and care in all the inhabitants of the Arches and Morea."
Now at length there came to light whole statues, beautiful
and well-preserved specimens, and part at least of these were
successfully conveyed to accessible harbours, such as Patras.
Some, to be sure, had to wait for a better opportunity.
So the efforts of Sir Thomas then seemed after all to be
receiving their reward, but only just in time, as in the
meanwhile his hopes of a speedy recall were realised. He
reported with pride on the handsome acknowledgments
which competent judges paid to his collection ; moreover,
his excellent new agent expressed himself willing and
ready to go on collecting for Buckingham even after Roe's
departure. Suddenly, at the beginning of the year 1628,
the news came that this agent had died at Patras. Fresh
difficulties as a matter of course presented themselves ; the
treasures, which were still scattered far and wide, had to be
secured and collected. Roe must have been glad to be able
to hand the business over for completion to his successor,
who had meanwhile arrived (April, A.D. 1628). On the
27th of June, A.D. 1628, being already in Smyrna, he announces to the Duke that he is now having the fruit of
the labours of many years put on board ship.

13. Buckingham was destined not to enjoy the ac- *Buckingham's
marbles.*
tual possession of these treasures. When they arrived in
London he had already fallen by the hand of an assassin *Other collectors at
Court.*
(Aug. 23, A.D. 1628). What became of the antiques seems
to be indicated by an undated letter of Lord Arundel to his
Countess, which, it would seem, can only be assigned to the

beginning of the year 1629[27]. Scarcely had the Earl, who was engaged at Court at the royal palace of Theobald's, heard of Sir Thomas Roe's return, when he instructed his Countess to look well after whatever he might have brought with him in the way of "antiquities, goddes, vases, inscriptions, medals, or such like," and with this view to get the assistance of the learned Sir Robert Cotton, or at any rate of a fit and proper person, and that too with all speed, so that the Lord Chamberlain might not anticipate her. This dreaded rival was PHILIP HERBERT, EARL OF MONTGOMERY, later fourth Earl of Pembroke, destined afterwards to secure himself a place in the history of art as Vandyck's principal patron. Vandyck's portrait-group of the Earl and his family at Wilton House, one of the most celebrated works of the master, is an appropriate commemoration of his fame. This Lord Pembroke is, however, otherwise scarcely known as a collector of antiques. For the rest we do not know whether Lord Arundel's pains were crowned with success. If they were, Sir Thomas's exertions turned out after all to be exclusively for his benefit. We learn, at all events, from these lines that there were already other connoisseurs of antiques at Court[28]. Two

[27] See Appendix No. 19. The careful Tierney (*Hist. of Arundel*, II. p. 435) conjecturally places the undated letter in the year 1619, after Roe's return from his ambassadorship to the Great Mogul (Sept. 1619, see Thomas Birch, *Court and Times of James I.* II. p. 190); yet the antiquities are little in accordance with such an occasion. The return from Constantinople occurred after many perils at the beginning of the year 1629 (Birch, *Charles II.* I. pp. 409, 415, II. pp. 5, 8); the ship Samson, of London, in which he had embarked, had in November A.D. 1628 already arrived in London (Birch, I. p. 434). That the Court in those years frequently resided at Theobald's, is to be inferred from several letters in Birch (I. p. 452, II. pp. 23, 24). In July, A.D. 1628, Arundel had, after a long period of disgrace, again

gained admission to Court and was enjoying the royal favour (Birch, I. pp. 382, 419, 441, 449). Nothing consequently stands in the way of my proposed date. Thus the Lord Chamberlain was not William, 3rd Earl of Pembroke, as Tierney thinks, but his younger brother Philip, Earl of Montgomery, who succeeded his brother in that office A.D. 1626 (Birch, I. p. 123 and *passim*, II. p. 74, *Simonds d'Ewes' Autobiogr.* London, 1845, II. p. 189).

[28] From a letter of Lord De L'Isle and Dudley, the present owner of Penshurst, to Mr G. Scharf, I extract the note that there "of antique sculpture a great collection once existed belonging to the second Earl, but with many other things has long since passed away." The SECOND EARL OF LEICESTER, Robert Sidney (A.D. 1595–1616), was the father of

other notices confirm this evidence. The accomplished
LUCY, COUNTESS OF BEDFORD, of whom Ben Jonson
sang, one of the most distinguished ladies of the Court
of the first Stuarts, had likewise laid claim to Roe's
services, that he might enrich her collection of coins
during his stay at Constantinople; and in the year 1626
the sorely pestered diplomatist was able to send her tid-
ings that her wishes had been fulfilled[29]. Nay, so early
as the year 1617 mention is made of antique heads in
the possession of SIR MICHAEL DORMER. These were
coveted after the owner's death by other connoisseurs[30],
and when in the autumn of A.D. 1616 LORD ROOS quitted
England for ever, "he gave the Earl of Arundel all the
statues he brought out of Italy, at one clap[31]"—so much
better than any one else did the Earl seem entitled to the
possession of such treasures. It is presumably also to be
attributed to the example of Lord Arundel that KING
CHARLES I. likewise collected antiques, besides forming
his wonderful picture-gallery. Before his accession he had
added to the modest beginnings made by Prince Henry, by
purchases of his own, and as a matter of course he had no
lack of presents[32]. Now, however, in the year 1628, we see
the king likewise turning his eyes to Greece. He had let Roe
go unmolested, but now turned to account the presence in
the Archipelago of his admiral Sir Kenelm Digby, in order
to get antiques collected for himself in those regions.

Algernon Sidney and of Waller's
Sacharissa. I find neither in Collin
and Blencowe, Sidney Papers, nor
in Ewald, Life of Algernon Sidney,
any mention of those antiques.

[29] Appendix No. 12. The Countess was already dead in the following
year. With respect to her cf. L. Aikin,
Memoirs of the Court of James I. 1.
p.211. Wiffen, Memoirs of the House
of Russell, London, 1833, 11. p. 106,
117.

[30] Chamberlain to Carleton, 1617,
Apr. 19 (Birch, James I. 11. p. 6).

[31] Chamberlain to Carleton, 1616,
Oct. 12 (Birch, 1. p. 428).

[32] In the Catalogue of Charles I.'s
Collection, p. 17 No. 69, p. 181 No.
8, antiques are mentioned, which the
King had bought when prince. He
had brought with him from Spain a
statue of Faustina (p. 181 No. 9) which
he had obtained on the well-known
journey for a bride. Others he had
bought when King (p. 25 No. 25, p.
26 No. 27) or had received as presents
"of the young Heriott's widow, at his
decease" (p. 12 No. 10, p. 23 No. 14)
or from Lord Cottington (p. 23 No. 12,
pp. 28, &c.),probably modern throughout.

*Peacham's
"Compleat
Gentle-
man."*

14. Very characteristic of the contrast between these beginnings of English collections and those of the continent is the distinction laid down by Henry Peacham, a scholar of Trinity College, Cambridge, in the second edition of his *Compleat Gentleman* (A.D. 1634), a survey of all that is best worth knowing for a gentleman[33]. In Italy, he observes, the antiques are certainly the most beautiful, but owing to the strict ordinances against their exportation very difficult to secure. "But in Greece and other parts of the Grand Signiors Dominions (where sometime there were more Statues standing than men living, so much had Art out-stripped Nature in those dayes) they may be had for digging and carrying. For by reason of the barbarous religion of the Turks, which alloweth not the likenesse or representation of any living thing, they haue been for the most part buryed in ruines or broken to peeces; so that it is a hard matter to light upon any there, that are not headlesse and lame, yet most of them venerable for antiquitye and elegancy. And here I cannot but with much reverence, mention the every way Right honourable Thomas Howard Lord high Marshall of England, as great for his noble Patronage of Arts and ancient learning, as for his birth and place. To whose liberall charges and magnificence this angle of the world oweth the first sight of Greeke and Romane Statues, with whose admired presence he began to honour the Gardens and Galleries of Arundel-House about twentie yeeres agoe, and hath ever since continued to transplant old Greece into England. King Charles also ever since his comming to the Crowne, hath amply testified a Royall liking of ancient statues, by causing a whole army of old forraine Emperours, Captaines, and Senators all at once to land on his coasts, to come and doe him homage, and attend him in his palaces of Saint James, and Sommerset house. A great part of

---

[33] The passage, which is in chapter XII. *Of Antiquities*, pp. 107, 108, is wanting in the first edition of A.D. 1622. Peacham was tutor to the Earl of Arundel's children, whom he attended into the Low Countries (Walpole, *Anecd., Catal. of Engravers* under the year 1637).

these belonged to the late Duke of Mantua : and some
of the Old Greeke marble-bases, columnes, and altars were
brought from the ruines of Apollo's Temple at Delos, by
that noble and absolutely compleat Gentleman, Sir Ken-
helme Digby, Knight [34]."

15. Peacham's remark about the Greek statues in ques- *Lord*
tion, that they are generally headless and lame, is confirmed *Arundel's*
by the condition of the remains of the Arundel collection *Greek Sculptures.*
at Oxford. Perhaps not a single statue of undoubted Greek
origin among them is preserved with its original head,—
but neither, in truth, can so very many statues discovered
in Italy boast of this distinction. They include, however,
a number of very fair draped statues, which do not, it is
true, belong to the dazzling prime of Greek sculpture, yet
in comparison with Roman draped figures from Italy exhibit the superiority of a fresher and more *naïf* treatment,
and certainly deserve to be allowed the opportunity of
making the most of this superiority by being better placed
for exhibition. They remind the student strongly of sculptures known to be derived from Asia Minor[35], and are
therefore likely to belong to the collection of specimens
which Petty made there. In order that he might be the
better able to apply these statues to the decoration of his
house, Lord Arundel had them restored, by a fairly qualified artist, to the completeness which they lacked[36]. At
this day manifest restorations are here and there to be
recognised, which are as different from Guelfi's later abominable botchings as day is from night. All the full-length
statues, however, are far surpassed in value by one female

---

[34] In the year 1639 the French
ambassador de la Haye saw in Delos
a statue of Apollo, "*que les Anglais
ont scié en deux, de haut en bas, pour
en emporter une partie*" (*Les Voyages
du Sieur Du Loir*, Paris, 1654, p. 8).
Thus so early as that time the English
were made answerable for all the
injuries which befell antiques.

[35] See below, Cat., art. London,
South Kensington Museum, Nos. 1, 2.

[36] This is vouched for by Kennedy,
who is, to be sure, anything but trustworthy (*Descr. of Wilton House*, p. 14).
It is, however, also confirmed by the
statues themselves. Lord Arundel
employed, amongst others, the sculptors Hubert le Soeur and Francesco
Fanelli (Dallaway, *Anecd.* p. 230), yet
they were both mainly, if not exclusively, bronze-founders.

bust, though even this is not entirely uninjured. This was the only one of the antiques belonging to Lord Arundel which the engraver Wenzel Hollar, when brought by the Earl to England and variously employed by him, found worthy of his burin[37]. Besides this a few Greek reliefs, especially of the sepulchral class, call for attention; these, though not of the very first rank, are nevertheless fine examples of this attractive class of sculpture.

Increase of the collection. Its rising fame.

16. The formation of the Arundel collection was by no means brought to a close on the arrival of Petty's Greek marbles in the above-named year 1628. We even learn that immediately before the outbreak of the civil war a fresh batch of antiquities arrived[38]. Petty continued to be actively engaged on behalf of the Earl even after his return from the Levant. Some years later he tried hard, though in vain, to win over the mathematician John Greaves to Lord Arundel's service. This gentleman had travelled with Petty in Italy, and was then contemplating travels in the East. Petty offered him on behalf of the Earl a fixed salary of £200 a year and "such fortunes as that Lord could heap upon him," if he would accompany him (Petty) to Greece[39]. Notwithstanding Greaves' refusal, the idea of farther researches in Greece was not given up. The chief augmentations to the collection came, however, still from Italy, where in addition to Petty the younger Henry Vanderborcht collected for Lord Arundel. By this artist, too, the Earl caused many specimens in his collections to be drawn or engraved[40]; as indeed at that time access to these treasures was to all appearance made easy for artists in

---

[37] Oxford, Univ. Gall. No. 59. G. Parthey, *Wenzel Hollar*, Berlin, 1853, p. 126 No. 590; the engraving is dated A.D. 1645.

[38] Chandler, *Marm. Oxon.* p. 2.

[39] Ward, John, *The Lives of the Professors of Gresham College*, London, 1760, p. 337. Greaves was in Italy probably from A.D. 1633 to 1636; in

the year after that he was Pococke's travelling companion.

[40] Walpole, *Anecd.* ch. IX. (Arundel). He also states in the *Catalogue of Engravers* to the year 1631 that there was in Paris a collection of 367 engravings from objects in the Arundel collection, prepared between A.D. 1631 and 1638.

general[41]. Arundel House became in this way a sort of
gathering-place for scholars and friends of art. The
guests at Lord Arundel's house made up for any deficiency
in learned culture on the part of their host[42]. Francis
Junius, who had stayed in his service from A.D. 1620 as
librarian and tutor, first to his youngest son (the ill-fated
Lord Stafford) and subsequently to his grandsons[43], wrote
at Arundel's instance his learned work *de Pictura Veterum*
(1637),—in which, singularly enough, we find no allusion to
the antiques of the house. Other scholars, Cotton, Selden,
Young, James, have been already mentioned. There was
also no lack of distinguished visitors. In December A.D. 1628
King Charles and his Queen honoured Arundel House with
a visit, on which occasion all the rooms were inspected[44].
Foreigners who came to London were welcome guests at
Arundel House, and in their presence the Earl, who had
himself lived a long time abroad, if he showed them his
treasures, laid aside some of that unbending punctilious
dignity which he never threw off in the presence of his
own countrymen[45]. The latter took their revenge in all
manner of sarcasms. One observed that "he was only
able to buy the antiquities, never to understand them[46]."
Another thought it ridiculous in Lord Arundel "to give so
many hundred crowns for an urn a mason would not have
valued at a penny[47]." "Sir Francis Bacon coming into the
Earl of Arundel's garden, where there were a great number
of ancient statues of naked men and women, made a stand,

[41] Jan de Bisschop (Episcopius) has engraved several Arundel statues in his *Signorum veterum Icones, semi-centuria altera* (about A.D. 1670), after drawings of the younger Jaques de Geyn, who had travelled in England.
[42] This at any rate is the view of Clarendon, *Hist. of the Rebellion*, Oxf. 1849, i. p. 78.
[43] Tierney, *Hist. of Arundel*, ii. p. 507.
[44] Pory to Joseph Mead, 1628, Dec.

19 (Birch, *Charles I.* i. p. 451).
[45] Clarendon, *Hist. of the Reb.*, l. cit. R. Symonds in Walpole's *Anecd.* ch. IX. (Arundel). The fame of the collection naturally extended even in foreign countries. See J. Sandrart, *Teutsche Akademie*, Nurnberg, 1675, i. p. 41.
[46] Clarendon, *l. cit.*
[47] Osborn, F., *Historical Memoirs*, in his Works, 7th ed., London, 1673, p. 497.

and as astonished cried out: The resurrection[48]!" Strange
that on Easter Sunday A.D. 1626 it was the great philosopher's own fate to close his eyes in this very house[49]!

*General
view of the
Arundel
collection.*
17. The marbles, which are always brought forward as
the most popular division of the Arundelian antiques, are
said according to old catalogues to have amounted to
thirty-seven statues, one hundred and twenty-eight busts,
and two hundred and fifty inscribed stones, exclusive of
sarcophagi, altars and fragments[50]. A portrait painted by
Paul Vansomer in A.D. 1618 shows the Earl in the act of
pointing with a stick to various statues near him[51]. In a
much later picture by Vandyck, which represents the Earl
and his Countess, there is introduced as a subsidiary figure
the beautiful bronze head of the so-called Homer (more
correctly of the aged Sophokles). This was one of the
choicest pieces of the collection, and has since then found
the place which it merits in the British Museum[52]. The
statues were distributed over the house and garden. The
busts were chiefly used for the decoration of the gallery.
The inscriptions were for the most part let into the garden
walls. To the sculptures are to be added two other valuable
classes of objects, namely, the gems and the coins. Arundel
bought Daniel Nice's cabinet, comprising examples in both
these classes, for £10,000[53]. His collection of coins was
considered quite admirable[54], but the fame of the Arundel
gems stood still higher. This collection comprised not less
than one hundred and thirty cameos and one hundred and

[48] *Works of Bacon,* ed. Spedding,
VII. p. 177, from Tenison's *Baconiana,*
1679.
[49] Spedding, *Letters and Life of
Bacon,* VII. p. 550.
[50] Kennedy, *Descr. of Wilton House,*
pp. 13—15, drawn up from papers belonging to Thomas Earl of Pembroke;
after whom Dallaway, *Anecd.* p. 233.
Sundry errors in their representations
are corrected according to superior
authorities in the following pages.
[51] Dallaway (*Anecd.* p. 238 note)

was acquainted with the picture in
Worksop Manor. Another portrait of
the Earl and Countess by the same
master is in Arundel Castle (Waagen,
Treas. III. p. 30).
[52] Walpole, *Anecd.* ch. IX. *ad fin.*
The picture is in Arundel Castle
(Waagen, *Treas.* III. p. 30).
[53] Evelyn to Pepys, 1689, Aug.
12.
[54] Clarendon, *Hist. of the Rebellion,*
I. p. 78, ed. Oxon.

thirty-three intaglios. To be sure, far from all the contents
of the cabinet were really antique; yet of not less artistic
value, at least, than real antiques, were such master-pieces
of the glyptic art of the Cinquecento as the world-renowned
gem with the marriage of Cupid and Psyche, bearing the
supposititious signature of an engraver, Tryphon[55].

18. With respect to the antiques of KING CHARLES,
which Peacham couples with Arundel's, we possess only
imperfect information from the catalogue which Abr. Vanderdoort, keeper of the royal collection in Whitehall, made
about the year 1639[56]. At Whitehall was kept the most
unimportant portion of the sculptures, chiefly statuettes
and busts. The catalogue never states whence they were
derived ; nor is it always clear whether they were antique
or modern. This document is supplemented by some
statistical statements in the inventories subsequently made
at the instance of Parliament with a view to the sale of
the collections[57]. According to these, there were in the
residences named by Peacham (A.D. 1634), St James's and
Somerset House to wit, and in their gardens, one hundred
and sixty-nine statues altogether, and as many as two
hundred and thirty more in the Palace of Greenwich.
It is obvious that this large number of nearly four
hundred statues did not consist merely of antiques. Many
were undoubtedly modern works manufactured by Nicholas
Stone and others for the adornment of the gardens and
galleries. To some extent we can still realise the nature
of the collection to our mind's eye by means of a resource
hitherto overlooked. In the Royal Library at Windsor there

King Charles I's collection of Antiquities.

---

[55] Brunn, *Geschichte der griech. Künstler*, II. p. 635.

[56] *A Catalogue and Description of King Charles the First's Capital Collection of pictures, limnings, statues, bronzes, medals, and other curiosities ; now first published from an Original Manuscript in the Ashmolean Museum at Oxford. The whole transcribed and prepared for the press, and a good* part of it printed, by the late ingenious Mr Vertue, and now finished from his papers. London, printed for W. Bathoe, 1787, 4. There are several copies (Brit. Mus. Harl. 7352); a portion of the original MS., with King Charles's notes in his own handwriting, is in the Royal Library at Windsor.

[57] Vertue has given extracts therefrom in his *Catalogue*.

is a book with drawings in red chalk of statues and busts
which were lost in the burning of Whitehall A.D. 1698[58]. The
great majority of these are presumably derived from Charles
I.'s collection. There are drawings of sixty-four statues,
of which the greater number appear to be antique, though
much restored. Others are certainly modern. None of them
are of the first class, but several specimens are not without
interest. The genuineness of the busts, nearly two hundred
in number, is far more open to suspicion. High-sounding
names have been arbitrarily given to them, considerable
ingenuity having been expended in their selection. All the
specimens in this book maintain throughout the character
of antiques or imitations of Italian origin. It may be
that, as Peacham intimates, part of them were derived from
the Gonzaga collection at Mantua, whence Charles, about
A.D. 1629, had obtained the most valuable portion of his
picture gallery[59]. Nothing in these drawings suggests Greek
extraction. Among all the vestiges of the royal collection, I can recognise the signs of Greek origin only in
a single modest monument, which is probably to be traced
to Sir Kenelm's exertions on behalf of the King in the
Archipelago. This is a round pedestal with a Greek inscription, from Delos, which at first stood in St James's
Park, later in the gardens of Whitehall[60].

*Vicissi-
tudes of the
Royal Col-
lection
after 1649.*   19.   The zeal both of the King and his Earl Marshal
for the collection of antiquities was brought to an un-
welcome end by the outbreak of the civil war. As early
as A.D. 1645 Parliament attached the Buckingham collec-

---

[58] Cf. *Archaeol. Zeitung*, 1874,
p. 68. The folio volume bears the
title: Drawings of Statues and Busts
that were in the Palace at Whitehall
before it was burnt. Preserved by Sir
John Stanley, Bart., who belonged to
the Lord Chamberlayne's office at the
time the Palace was burnt down. (He
was deputy Chamberlain.) The letterpress is Italian. Eighteen specimens
are mentioned specially by name on
a prefatory sheet. I shall give a

fuller account of the contents of this
volume in another place.
    [59] As to the determination of the
date see Waagen, *Treasures of Art*, I.
p. 7. The acquisition thus occurred
during the confusion of the Mantuan
War of Succession.
    [60] *C. I. G.* 2286. Patrick Young
had seen the marble in the Garden
of St James's (A.D. 1633), Prideaux
at Whitehall (A.D. 1676).

tion at York House. The paintings and statues were dispersed[61]. A similar fate presently befell the royal collection[62]. Only a few months after the monarch's death Parliament decreed the sale of his property, of which the works of art constituted not the least valuable part (March, A.D. 1649). Inventories were taken by a special commission. From these are taken the numerical estimates above cited. A reserve price was fixed for each work of art, and in many cases this reserve was tolerably high. A "Commodus in the habit of Hercules," a Muse, and a terminal figure, were valued at £200 apiece; a "Tiberius Caesar in the habit of a priest" at £500, a Silenus even at £600; and, as it seems, these pieces were actually sold.[63] The valuation of the grand total of three hundred and ninety-nine statues reached the sum of £17,989. 10s. 6d[64]. A large number were unfortunately dispersed. Cardinal Mazarin is reported to have bought many statues. All that is certain is that Queen Christina of Sweden purchased the choice of all the medals and jewels[65]. The auctions dragged on till the year 1653. It is certain however that far from all the antique sculptures were sold. Parliament itself had already from the very beginning of the sale reserved such works "as should be thought fit to be reserved for the use of the state," and delegated their

[61] Walpole, *Anecd.* ch. IX. (Charles I.) according to the *Journal of the Commons. Catalogue of the Collection of the Duke of Buckingham*, Lond. 1758, preface.

[62] For the subject generally cf. the account given in Walpole's *Anecd.* ch. IX. Cf. also *Calendar of State Papers* (Domestic), 1649, pp. 10, 70, 170.

[63] I borrow these values from a prefatory sheet of the book of drawings at Windsor, cited in note 58. Walpole, too, mentions the Tiberius; Dallaway, *Anecd.* p. 232, mentions others.

[64] *Catalogue of King Charles I.'s Collection*, p. 7. Waagen, *Treasures*, II. p. 467.

[65] Lord Clarendon is the principal authority, *Hist. of the Rebellion*, book XI. § 251 (IV. p. 547, Oxf.). He makes the above statement about Queen Christina; of Mazarin's purchases he only mentions "all the rich beds and hangings and carpets," of those of Don Alonzo de Cardenas, the Spanish Ambassador, "many pictures and other precious goods." Dallaway (*Anecd.* p. 232) reports that they both bought statues also; with reference to Mazarin, he probably borrowed this from the untrustworthy Kennedy, *Description of Wilton House*, p. 18. At that time no such antique sculptures seem to have gone to Spain. Cf. Hübner, *Die ant. Bildwerke in Madrid*, Berlin, 1862, p. 8.

selection to the Council of State. Cromwell exerted himself
more than any one, though not always with success, to
restrain a barbarous squandering of art-treasures. Thus for
instance, on the 13th of February, A.D. 1651, the surveyor
of the works, Mr Carter, was directed "to take care to bring
twelve statues from James House to bee placed in the garden
of Whitehall, which are to bee such as hee shall find to bee
most proper for that use." This direction was carried out,
and on the 16th of April the twelve statues "worthy to be
kept for their antiquity and rarity" were definitively excluded from the sale. The above-mentioned sculptures
from St James's Palace also followed soon, when that
building was fitted up as barracks. They were to be
brought "to some other place more convenient"; "the
heads with the pedestalls belonging unto them may be sent
into the gallerie in Whitehall to stand there untill the
Trustees [for sale of the late King's goods] shall make sale
of them[66]." In fact they underwent such a sale in the same
year 1651; but Cromwell prevented their delivery to the
purchasers, who after his death laid a complaint before
the Council of State; we do not know with what result[67].
At any rate an important part of the sculptures remained
in Whitehall, which was, as is well known, the usual
residence of the Protector in his last years. These sculptures formed, we can tell, the nucleus of the royal collection of antiques after the Restoration; for some of the
statues included in the inventories for the sale of King
Charles's property reappear among the drawings of the
above-mentioned book in the Library at Windsor[68]. It is
however evident from this latter that the collection also

[66] The documents concerning the transaction in the Record Office have been published by W. Noel Sainsbury, in The Fine Arts Quarterly Review, I. 1863, p. 166; cf. now too Calendar of State Papers (Domestic), 1651, pp. 45, 78, 151, 207, 218, 243, 252, 257.
[67] Walpole, l. cit.

[68] The Catalogue of King Charles I.'s Collection, p. 7 (Waagen, Treasures, II. p. 467), brings nine statues into special prominence; three of which (Nos. 3, 6, 8) recur amongst the draw-ings, two (Nos. 1, 7) were modern copies in bronze.

received sundry additions under Charles II., through the
agency of the painter Sir Peter Lely[69]. On the other hand,
it is not clear how it comes about that those drawings
comprise almost twice as many specimens as the "list of
the Statues in Marble and Figures in Brass, in Whitehall,"
which Will. Chiffinch, of the King's bedchamber, had
drawn up for James II.[70] This list is, at least apparently,
official. While it enumerates only twenty-eight groups
and statues, one hundred and six busts and one relief, the
book contains sixty-four groups and statues and one hundred and ninety-six busts; moreover the numbers attached
to the several drawings seem to indicate that the collection
altogether contained more specimens than are shown in the
extant drawings. Since, as is well known, a very considerable part of the picture gallery of Charles I. was also
brought together again after the Restoration, it is clear that
the halls and galleries of Whitehall will have contained a
very fine collection of art-treasures so long as it continued
to be the luxurious residence of the court of the two last
Stuarts. Yet it fell out as though this creation of the
dynasty of the Stuarts had been destined not to outlive
their fall. All that grandeur perished on the disastrous
night of the 4th of January, A.D. 1698, when a fearful fire
destroyed the whole palace except Inigo Jones's Banquet-
ing Hall[71]. Sundry sculptures were rescued and stolen in
the general confusion. This was the case with a crouching
Venus which had been purchased by Lely; four years later
however it was found and recovered by the Crown[72]. But

---

[69] On fol. 26 there is a lead-pencil
note to No. 88, a crouching Venus,
"bought by Lilly the Painter, with
several other his Ma[jes]tie rarities." Note
72, 121.

[70] A Catalogue of the Collection of
Pictures, &c., belonging to King
James the Second. London, W.
Bathoe, 1758, p. 101. The print has
been made from a copy of Vertue's: the
original manuscript is in the British
Museum, Cod. Harl. 1890.

[71] Evelyn, Diary, 1698, Jan. 5.
Macaulay, History of England, ch.
XXIII. The equanimity with which
King William took the loss is shown
by a letter to Heinsius of the 7/17 Jan.
(old and new style) 1698 in Ranke's
Englische Geschichte. IX. p. 212, 2nd ed.
[72] Walpole, l. cit. She is to be
found in Chiffinch, p. 108 No. 1336;
among the drawings at Windsor on
fol. 26 No. 88 (see above, note 69) as
"Elena di Troia." A very beautiful

the collection of Charles I. as a whole was utterly and irretrievably lost.

20.   The Arundel collection fared somewhat better. The Earl Marshal had quitted England for ever A.D. 1641, and died soon afterwards (A.D. 1646) at Padua. A valuable portion of his collections, the gems and jewels, had previously been taken to Holland for safety [73]. By the Earl's will all his goods were left to his Countess Alathea to be at her own disposal absolutely, the greatest part of them having been purchased with her money [74]. Most uncomfortable relations subsisting between the mother and her eldest son Henry Frederick, the new Earl, are said to have brought about a partial breaking-up of the collections, yet this is by no means certain [75]. Again, it is not clear whether the antiques were divided at once or rather after the death of the old Countess [76]. One share fell to the mother's favourite, her younger son, William Howard, Viscount Stafford, and was removed to Tart Hall, a house situated in the neighbourhood of Buckingham Gate, which the Countess had had built for her A.D. 1638 by Nich. Stone [77]. This part of the collection remained there until A.D. 1720, when after the death of Henry, Earl of Stafford, eldest son of the hapless Viscount, all the contents were sold by auction. On this occasion Dr Mead purchased the above-mentioned bronze head of "Homer." Works in marble appear by the sale-catalogues not to have been included in this portion of the property [78]. In any case the majority of the sculp-

relic of King Charles's collection is the magnificent cameo with the portrait of the Emperor Claudius in Windsor (Fortnum in the *Archaeologia* XLV. pl. 1).

[73] Evelyn, *Letter to S. Pepys*, 1689, Aug. 12, mentions Amsterdam; Walpole, *Anecd.* ch. IX. (Arundel), Antwerp. Pictures also were sent there. See Causton, *The Howard Papers*, p. 56.

[74] Tierney, *Hist. of Arundel*, II. p. 503. The will is published in Howard, Ch., *Historical Anecdotes*, London, 1769.

[75] Evelyn, *l. cit.*, but Tierney, *l. cit.*, contradicts him.

[76] Walpole, *l. cit.* Dallaway, *Anecd.* p. 234.

[77] Walpole, *Anecd.* ch. VIII. (Stone).

[78] Walpole, *Anecd.* ch. IX. (Arundel), had seen a printed catalogue, which was miserably drawn up, with the prices, in the possession of Mr West ; he states the amount of the proceeds at £6,535; Dallaway, *Anecd.* p. 239, *Of Statuary*, p. 284, mentions, after Howard's *Historical Anecdotes*, £8,852. 11s., and gives the several

tures, as indeed of the antiques generally, remained in
Arundel House as the heritage of the eldest son. There
fresh dangers threatened them. For by order of Parliament
the entire property of the Arundel family was laid under
attachment, A.D. 1651, and, just as in the case of the king's
collections, an inventory of the " severall goodes, picktures,
and statues at Arundell House in the Strand" was prepared. Indeed, owing to "the recusancy of Alathea, late
Countesse Dowager of Arundell and Surrey," the proposal
of sale was again raised two years after her death (A.D. 1656),
and to some extent at least was carried out [79]. However,
to all appearance only pictures were dealt with by this
measure; the antiques most likely suffered damage through
insufficient supervision on the part of the owner and negligence on that of his personal attendants rather than by
direct measures of the government [80].

21. By the time that the Restoration had put an end
to the insecurity of personal property, the Earl Henry
Frederick had died (A.D. 1652). His eldest son, Thomas
Howard, who was reinstated by Charles II. in the old family
dignity of the Duchy of Norfolk (A.D. 1662), resided as a
lunatic at Padua, where he died (A.D. 1677). The care of the
family property consequently devolved upon the second
son, Henry Howard, whom his father had already regarded
as his future heir and successor [81]. To his charge then
Arundel House with its costly collections was entrusted.
But he had nothing in common with the artistic interests
of his grandfather. The derangement of the property and
family circumstances explain his paying no heed to a proposal [82], which came from a thoroughly friendly quarter, to
make the statues known to the world by an illustrated

classes; for example, Jewels and
Curiosities £2,467. 7s. 10d., Medals
£30. 10s. 6d.
   [79] See Sainsbury, W. Noel, in The
Fine Arts Quarterly Review, I. 1863,
p. 168, " Extracts from the Documents
of the Record Office."
   [80] Cf. Edw. Browne's Journal,

1664, March 1, in Brit. Mus. Sloane
MS. 1906 (Causton, The Howard
Papers, p. 143).
   [81] Causton, The Howard Papers,
p. 63.
   [82] Evelyn, in letter to Henry
Howard, of Norfolk, 1667, Aug. 4.

publication. The carelessness with which the venerable
relics were allowed to perish was inexcusable, nay absolutely criminal. The inscriptions, which Selden's book
had made especially famous, were "miserably neglected
and scattered up and down about the garden and other
parts of Arundel House, exceedingly impaired by the
corrosive air of London[43]". Many were destroyed, others
stolen; indeed they were so little regarded that on the
repair of the house they were used as building material!
In this way the upper half of the very valuable *Marmor
Parium* disappeared in a chimney of the palace, and it
would have been utterly lost to the learned world had not
the diligence of Selden and his friends discovered it betimes[44]. The heir behaved with equal carelessness with respect to the famous library of his ancestors, "suffering the
priests and everybody to carry away and dispose of what
they pleas'd, so that abundance of rare things were irre-
vocably gone[45]." Under such circumstances it was a veri-
table deliverance that an old friend of the family, John
Evelyn, used his influence with the owner to such purpose
that he assigned his treasures to safe hands, more, it is
true, in indifference to their value than from high-minded
liberality. In the year 1667 the library was at Evelyn's
instance presented to the Royal Society[46], which had not
long before been founded. The presentation of the marbles to the University of Oxford followed. They comprised
"all those stones, coins, altars, &c., and whatever had inscriptions on them, that were not statues," inclusive of the
slabs let into the garden walls[47]. This collection had once
consisted of two hundred and fifty inscribed stones. But of
these only one hundred and thirty-six arrived at Oxford[48].
The remainder had been lost in those few decades! The

[43] Evelyn, *Diary*, 1667, Sept. 19,
and in the letter quoted.
[44] Prideaux, *Marmora Oxoniensia*,
Oxf. 1676, preface.
[45] Evelyn, *Diary*, 1678, Aug.
29.

[46] Evelyn, *Diary*, 1667, Jan. 9,
Mar. 4, 1678. Aug. 29.
[47] Evelyn, in letter to H. Howard,
1667, Aug. 4; *Diary*, 1667, Sept. 19,
Oct. 8, 17, 25.
[48] Prideaux, *l. cit.*

University did not fail to bestow academic honours on the
giver of the donation as well as on Evelyn who had suggested it. The marbles themselves retained the honourable
name of *Marmora Arundeliana*. Yet even there they
at first found only partial protection, "inserted in the walls
that compass the area of the [Sheldonian] theatre[69]." It
was no sufficient amends for this treatment that the University had them edited afresh by one of her scholars in a
folio volume, which was dedicated to Lord Henry Howard[90].
It was not until a much later period that the stones were
brought out of the open air into a room in the neighbouring
Schools, where they lay for a long time promiscuously in
utter disorder, until at last most of them were built into
the walls ; others, quite separated from their old companions, must to this day be sought in a damp basement room
of the Ashmolean Museum, which lies near the Schools.
The various collections which especially belong to this
Museum were presented to the University ten years later
than the Arundelian marbles.

22.　The donation of the inscriptions was only the be- *Dispersion
ginning of the dispersion of the collections of Arundel of the whole
collection.*
House[91]. In the year 1678 Lord Henry, now 6th Duke of
Norfolk and Earl Marshal, resolved to pull down the old
family seat with a view to the laying out of streets (Arundel Street, Norfolk Street, Surrey Street and the erection
of dwelling-houses on the land. A part only of the garden
next the river was reserved for the site of the new ducal
palace (Norfolk House). The antiques were now got rid

[89] Evelyn, *Diary*, 1669, July 7—
15. H. Howard had already received
the degree of D.C.L. on June 5, A.D.
1668 (Wood, *Fasti*, II. p. 303).
[90] *Marmora Oxoniensia, ex
Arundellianis, Seldenianis aliisque
conflata. Rec. et expl. Humphridus
Prideaux.* Oxf. 1676, fol. The book
comprises besides 14 inscriptions bequeathed by J. Selden or presented by
sundry benefactors. A gift also of the
well-known Oriental traveller George
Wheler was soon added (A.D. 1683).

[91] Most of the details of the follow-
ing account are taken from a letter
from James Theobald to Lord
Willoughby de Parham, P.S.A., 1757,
May 10, which is copied in Howard,
*Ch. Historical Anecdotes of some
of the Howard family*, London, 1769,
pp. 91—110. On this point cf. Walpole,
Anecd. ch. IX. (Arundel). Kennedy,
Description of Wilton House, p. xv.
Dallaway, *Anecd.* p. 236. Causton,
Howard Papers, pp. 176, 189.

of, probably all the more recklessly that by the following
year the Duke went to reside for a long time out of
England, in consequence of the measures taken by Parliament after the Popish Plot [92]. As no purchaser came
forward for the whole quantity, a partition began. The
majority of the busts, together with a number of statues
and bas-reliefs, which had adorned the gallery, were bought
by Thomas, Earl of Pembroke. We do not know accurately when this purchase was made. A few of the statues
were appropriated after the Duke's death (A.D. 1684) by his
widow, whose second husband, Col. Maxwell, wanted four
years later to have them sold by auction; but the new
Duke protested against this [93]. The remainder were at
first brought over into the reserved part of the garden,
partly under a colonnade which was situated there. Yet
the emptying of the house was carried on with such remiss-
ness, that broken statues and sarcophagi, remnants of the
Arundel collection, were found ten years later in the cellars
of the newly-built houses in Norfolk Street. The statues
under the colonnade fared ill indeed. "When the workmen
began to build next the Strand, in order to prevent in-
croachments, a cross wall was built to separate the ground
let to building from that reserved for the family mansion;
and many of the workmen, to save the expense of carrying
away the rubbish, threw it over this cross wall, where it fell
upon the colonnade, and at last by its weight broke it
down, and falling on the statues, &c. placed there broke
several of them." In spite of this sad mishap a purchaser
was found for the greater part in the year 1691 [94], in the
person of Sir William Fermor, afterwards Lord Lempster.
He had them brought to his country seat, Easton Neston,
near Towcester, Northamptonshire. The purchase money

[92] Causton, *l. cit.* p. 202, quotes
Pennant as follows: "During the
madness of the popish plot, the statues
were buried: the mob would have
mistaken them for popish saints."
May not there be some confusion

h ie with the facts to be next mentioned?
[93] Causton, *l. cit.* p. 269, quotes
to this effect the *Journals of the
House of Lords*, XIV. pp. 105, 106.
[94] Evelyn, *Diary*, 1691, Mar. 21.

was extremely small, being only £300; but the Duke's
want of cash was so pressing, that he did not hesitate to
close the bargain[86]. Of the remainder a few broken statues
were given by the Duke to a servant of the family named
Boyder Cuper, who used them for the decoration of a
pleasure-ground which he kept, called Cuper's or Cupid's
Gardens, in Lambeth, opposite Somerset House[90]. Here
they subsequently (A.D. 1717) attracted the attention of
two lovers of art, John Freeman Cook, of Fawley Court,
Henley on Thames, and Edmond Waller (of the poet's
family), of Beaconsfield. These gentlemen bought the
specimens for £75, divided them between themselves, and
conveyed them to the two places mentioned. Lastly,
whatever statues and fragments remained in the gardens
of Arundel House after these repeated dispersals, the Duke
of Norfolk had removed across the Thames to a piece of
ground at Kennington which he held on lease. In this
situation the marbles were gradually buried under deep
layers of rubbish intended to protect the ground from the
inundations of the neighbouring river. After a considerable lapse of time, when houses were being built on that
site, several of these specimens were again brought into
the light of day. This was their second disinterment, their
first having been from the soil of Greece. They then passed
into the possession of that famous lover of art, Lord

[86] With respect to the Duke's want
of cash, see Causton, *l. cit.* pp. 238, 246.
Walpole, Horace, *Anecd.* ch. IX.
(Arundel), and Howard, Henry,
Family Memorials, 1836, p. 41,
ascribe the sale to the Duchess, who
was in need of money. She was,
according to their own testimony
(Causton, p. 238), not in England at
all till the autumn of A.D. 1691; still
the matter is not free from doubt (see
ibidem, p. 260).

[90] Cunningham, *Handbook of
London*, 1850, p. 150. The garden
no longer exists; see Horace Walpole's
letter to Montague, 1746, June 24
(*Letters*, ed. Cunningham, II. p. 32).

According to Dallaway, *Of Statuary*,
p. 282 note *n*, "the marbles placed in
Cuper's Garden were drawn and engraved for the last edition of Aubrey's
Antiquities of Surrey." I am only
acquainted with the edition of 1719,
which contains no such engravings.
Smith (*Vollebens*, II. p. 201) mentions
etchings of several of the Arundelian
fragments given in Nichols, *History of
Lambeth*. Cf. also Ince, No. 64. In
the year 1854 W. P. Williams Freeman, Esq., presented to the British
Museum a statue (Graeco-Roman
Sculp. No. 9) said to have been
formerly in the Arundel collection
(*Synopsis*, 63rd ed., 1856, p. 88).

Burlington, who had them brought to Chiswick. Indeed
at Lord Petre's suggestion a regular excavation was made,
in the course of which there were "discovered six statues,
without heads or arms, lying close to each other, some of
colossal size, the drapery of which was thought to be
exceeding fine." These torsi were removed to Worksop
Manor, the seat of the Duke of Norfolk, where they
probably perished in the great fire of A.D. 1761[97]. Other
specimens were dispersed at other times. One fragment
of a pillar actually came to be used as a roller for Mr
Theobald's bowling-green at Waltham Place, Berkshire.
Sic transit gloria mundi.

23. Thus the marbles of the first collection of antiques
in England were scattered to the winds—an example and
a warning of the insecurity which attaches to such property
when in private hands. It fared no better with the other
departments of the collection. "The coins and medals
came into the possession of Thomas Earl of Winchelsea,
and in A.D. 1696 were sold by his executors to Mr Thomas
Hall[98]." It is not known what became of them subsequently.
The fortunes of the celebrated collection of gems were particularly strange. It had with the exception of a few pieces
remained in its original condition[99]. When the Duke of
Norfolk, after scandalous litigation which extended over
many years, obtained in A.D. 1700 a divorce from his wife
Lady Mary Mordaunt, she kept as security for her claims
on the Duke, according to the terms agreed to between the
parties, "a box of jewels of great value which had belonged
to the old Duke[100]," that is to say about two hundred and

[97] Langston, *Howard Papers*, p.
324, where it is also said "The statues
of the Arundel collection have been
preserved to memory by the etchings
of Dr Ducarel."

[98] Walpole, *Anecd.* ch. IX.
(Arundel). Earl Thomas is not meant,
for he was dead by A.D. 1639, but his
son, John Howard, 3rd Earl, who
died A.D. 1689. Besides this another

collection of coins belonging in A.D.
1719 to the Earl of Winchelsea, at
that time Heneage, the 8th Earl, is
mentioned by Haym, *Tesoro Britannico*, 1719, I. p. xi.

[99] Walpole, *l. cit.*, Story-Maskelyne, *The Marlborough Gems*, 1870,
pref.

[100] Luttrell, *Diary*, IV. p. 622.

fifty cameos and intaglios of either antique or Renaissance
workmanship. As the Duke died in the following year
without having yet discharged his obligations, Lady Mary
treated the gems as her own property and bequeathed
them A.D. 1705 to her second husband Sir John Germain.
He in turn left them to his second wife Lady Elizabeth
Berkeley, who in A.D. 1762 presented them as a wedding
gift to her great-niece Lady Mary Beauclerk, on the occasion of her marriage with Lord Charles Spencer. Lastly
this lady made over the costly collection to her brother-in-
law George Spencer, 3rd Duke of Marlborough, in accordance with a family arrangement. Thus the old Arundel
collection, after having passed in the course of time through
so many hands, formed the nucleus of the famous Marlborough gems. These were transferred, so recently as
the year 1875, into the possession of Mr Broomielow, of
Manchester, and are now kept at his country seat of
Battlesden in the neighbourhood of Woburn.

24. We must however return to the marbles. The *The*
portion which Lord Lempster had bought and taken to *Pomfret marbles.*
Easton Neston was here visited by a melancholy fate. The
purchaser's son Lord Thomas, afterwards first EARL OF
POMFRET, having been in Rome, conceived the unhappy
idea of having the statues, which in truth had suffered
severely, restored in the Italian manner. He therefore
engaged a scholar of Camillo Rusconi, one Guelfi, whom
Lord Burlington had brought over to England about A.D.
1714, to do the work. It could not easily have been entrusted to more unfortunate hands Great as has been the
blundering perpetrated in all quarters in the shape of
so-called "restorations," yet hardly ever have any antiques
been so shamefully tampered with as in the tasteless additions made by this shallow botcher. Even subsequently
the protection afforded to the marbles was very insufficient,
as we learn from a description by George Vertue, who paid
the house a visit probably in A.D. 1734. The small statues

and busts fared best. These, as for instance the so-called
"Marius," were employed for the adornment of the hall
and staircase of the house. A large number of the sculptures were set out along the garden front of the house, or
in the various parts of the garden itself, and so once more
exposed to all the decaying influence of the damp climate[101].
No wonder if the traces of such gross negligence are but
too manifest at the present day. Special attention was here
aroused by the "Tomb of Germanicus," that is to say, a
very ordinary Roman sarcophagus, on which had once
stood in Arundel House a genuine or supposed bust of
that Prince found in Ankyra[102], and which now retained its
silly name though a small statue of Jupiter had succeeded
to the place of the bust in question. The majority, however,
were contained in a conservatory "full of statues, busts,
bassorilievos, urns, altars, crammed full, and lying con-
fusedly as if it was the shop of a statuary!" Here stood
in one corner the supposed Cicero "with his handkerchief
in his right hand," in another the colossal Minerva, against
the walls a number of other statues, with fragments of bas-
reliefs scattered about over the floor, &c. &c. The impression conveyed is effectively described by the young Horace
Walpole: "in an old green-house is a wonderful fine statue
of Tully haranguing a numerous assembly of decayed emperors, vestal virgins with new noses, Colossus's, Venus's,
headless carcases and carcaseless heads, pieces of tombs, and
hieroglyphics[103]." The gardener and housekeeper, the usual

[101] A Description of Easton Neston
in Northamptonshire, the seat of the
Right Hon. the Earl of Pomfret,
printed as an appendix to the Catalogue of the Collection of the Duke
of Buckingham, London, Bathoe, 1738,
pp. 53—59. The time of the visit seems
to follow from the enumeration of
Vertue's travels in Horace Walpole's
Anecdotes (Vertue).

[102] Chandler, R., Marmora Oxoniensia, p. vii. No. 11.

[103] Walpole to G. Montagne, 1736,
May 20. Cf. the same to H. Mann,
1753, July 21: "The Cicero is fine
and celebrated; the Marius I think
still finer. The rest are Scipios, Cin-
cinnatuses, and the Lord knows who,
which have lost more of their little
value than of their false pretensions
by living out of doors; and there is
a green-house full of colossal fragments."

ciceroni for English art-collections, were able to tell Vertue
the high prices which would be asked for some of the figures.
No wonder, if such a curious kind of sculpture-gallery had
really been taken for a shop! But at least the fate of dis-
persal was spared to this portion of the Arundel collection.
For when after the death of the Earl of Pomfret his son
and successor, being deeply in debt, was obliged to sell the
furniture of Easton Neston, the Countess dowager Hen-
rietta-Louisa bought the statues and presented them to the
University of Oxford (A.D. 1755). The chief portion of
the Arundel sculptures were thus once more brought together with the inscribed stones of the same collection[104].
The University did honour to the donor in a solemn *actus*,
of which Horace Walpole has again given us an ironical
description[105]; and made provision for a handsome publication by the learned Hellenist, Richard Chandler[106], of its
collection of antiques as thus enriched. The sculptures
themselves, however, remained in the Schools for more than
a century in a confusion similar to that at Easton Neston.
Now at least they are disencumbered from Guelfi's restorations, and for the most part arranged. Only, however, by
far the smallest number of specimens are in the well-lighted
ground-floor rooms of the magnificent University galleries;
most can only be found after wearisome search in the
gloomy cellars of this palatial building, even into their
darkest recesses. We hope that this is the last stage of
ill-treatment which the famous Arundel marbles have had
to suffer, and that for them there may even yet be at
some time a day of final resurrection.

[104] Walpole to H. Mann, 1755,
March 10. In Easton Neston there
remains a memorial of the sculptures
in the wall-paintings of the staircase
by Sir James Thornhill, who has introduced a number of the antiques of
the Pomfret collection in his series of
pictures illustrating the history of
Diocletian.
[105] Walpole to H. Mann, 1756, July

24. Cf. 1762, Jan. 4, on the wish of
the Countess to be buried in Oxford:
—"I dare say she has treasured up
some idea of the Countess Matilda,
that gave St Peter his patrimony."
[106] *Marmora Oxoniensia*, Oxford,
1763, fol. Here Guelfi's abominable
restorations have been immortalised.
It is only quite lately that they have
been done away with.

25. In this respect it fared best with that section of the Arundel marbles which had come into the possession of Lord Pembroke. To the love of art, by which more than one member of the Herbert family has distinguished himself, Wilton House bears conspicuous testimony. William, the first Earl, had Holbein for his adviser with respect to the building of his mansion in place of the ancient abbey. Philip, the fourth Earl, likewise employed Inigo Jones as architect, and was the most distinguished patron of Vandyck. He laid the foundation of the noble picture-gallery. We have before observed (p. 20) from a casual remark of Lord Arundel's that he also turned his attention to antiques. The Grand Duke of Tuscany, who had been his guest for three weeks at Wilton House, is said to have made him a present of some statues[107]. But THOMAS HERBERT, EIGHTH EARL OF PEMBROKE (*succ.* A.D. 1683), was the real founder of the collection of sculptures, which equally with the picture-gallery constitutes at this day the fame of Wilton House; he also spared no pains or expense to form a very rich cabinet of medals[108]. He can in this respect be designated as the most distinguished imitator of Lord Arundel in this early period.   He too, like Lord Arundel, knew Italy from personal observation. He seems to have acquired the basis of his collection of antiques by the purchase of the sculptures in the gallery of Arundel House. It consisted chiefly though not exclusively of busts. For these Lord Pembroke, like many collectors of that time, had a particular enthusiasm. He found a great satisfaction in seeing himself surrounded by the great men of old in effigy, in the same manner as his walls were crowded with

---

[107] I find this notice in Volkmann, *Neueste Reisen durch England,* Leipzig, 1781, t. p. 482, without being able to trace its origin. Of the two works named therein one (Wilton No. 70) is certainly derived from the Mazarin collection; about the other, a Flora, I cannot ascertain anything. The whole account is very suspicious.

Evelyn, who was in 1654 at Wilton, only mentions "the court and fountaine of the stables adorn'd with the [antique?] Cæsar's heads" (*Diary,* 1654, July 20).
[108] *Ædes Pembrockianæ,* London, 1774, p. 93. *Numismata Pembrokiana,* 1746. 4.

the portraits of illustrious members of the family and other
contemporaries. To satisfy that predilection, he was, it is
true, liberal in bestowing great names upon busts impossible really to identify. This characteristic of the Earl is
found also in the most celebrated bust-collector of Rome,
Cardinal Alessandro Albani, who could not bear a bust
to be nameless, and on account of his eagerness in christening unknown heads was occasionally designated by
Winckelmann as "the audacious priest" (*kecker Pfarr-
herr*)[109]. "An ancient virtuoso," remarks Horace Walpole[110],
"indeed would be a little surprised to find so many
of his acquaintances new baptized. Earl Thomas did not,
like the Popes, convert Pagan chiefs into Christian ; but
many an emperor acts the part at Wilton of scarcer Caesars." And yet even this is not the worst. A great part
of these high-sounding names are bestowed upon works
manifestly of the sixteenth or seventeenth centuries; for
perhaps no other collection in England is so well supplied
with false antiques as that in Wilton House.

26. The eighteenth century was destined to bring *The
Mazarin
collection.* important accessions to the collection, above all by the
purchase of a great part of the Mazarin cabinet. Strange
to say, Lord Arundel's name was connected with these
sculptures too. He had once, that is to say, helped Cardinal Richelieu with advice and practical aid in the collection, in Italy and especially in Rome, of his much-
admired gallery of sculptures. The Earl Marshal had,
it is said, given the Cardinal the opportunity of buying a
whole palace in Rome, the antiques from which the latter
forthwith had conveyed to Paris, and had moreover
given him information as to about eighty busts in different parts of Italy[111]. After Richelieu's death (A.D.
1642) the sculptures out of the *Palais Cardinal,* which
was subsequently, as is well known, the *Palais Royal,* came

109 Winckelmann, letter to Muzel-
Stosch, 1760, Jan. 5.
110 *Anecdotes* (Vertue).
111 Kennedy. *Description of Wilton
House,* p. xvii.

into the possession of his successor Cardinal Mazarin. He
made additions to them by further important purchases in
Rome, and employed them all for the adornment of the
neighbouring *Palais Mazarin* newly built by him[112]. Nearly
four hundred sculptures were here altogether. Among
these were about one hundred and sixty statues and more
than two hundred busts, the latter mostly provided with
modern drapery of costly variegated kinds of marble, and
placed on correspondingly rich pedestals. Among the heads
themselves there were indeed very many modern works.
The lower gallery of the palace as well as the adjoining
rooms were filled exclusively with sculptures, while the
gallery on the first floor was furnished with statues only
in the niches, but for the rest was chiefly adorned with
pictures and other works of art. The whole was regarded
as one of the greatest sights of Paris, as the *merveille de
la France*. Yet the fortunes of the collection were hardly
less varied than those of the contemporary English collections. During the war of the Fronde, when Mazarin was
obliged to leave Paris and even France for a time, a part
of the sculptures was sold and dispersed (A.D. 1652); but
so great was the dread inspired by the all-powerful minister,
that after his return all his scattered property was delivered
up to him again. When the Cardinal died in A.D. 1661 the
antiques were valued at 150,000 livres. They fell in equal
shares, as did the whole palace, to the Duc de Mazarin
with his wife, a niece of the Cardinal's, and her brother the
Duc de Nevers. The former, a rough and half-crazy man
who lived in a perpetual state of quarrel with his wife, took
advantage of the absence of the co-heiress to enter the
gallery one fine morning armed with a large hammer, and
to belabour the undressed statues in a fit of pretended

[112] For the Mazarin collection cf.
*Inventaire de tous les meubles du Car-
dinal Mazarin. Dressé en 1653* [by
J. Bapt. Colbert] *et publié d'après
l'original conservé dans les archives
de Condé* [by Henri d'Orléans, duc

d'Aumale]. London 1861. H. Sauval, *Histoire et Recherches des Antiquités de la ville de Paris,* Paris
1724, II. pp. 175–177 (written about
1654). Laborde, *le Palais Mazarin,*
Paris 1846, p. 185, note 68.

prudery; not content with this, and regardless of all remonstrance, he returned in the evening with five or six
attendants all armed in like fashion, and carried on his
crack-brained work of destruction till midnight. Whatever
was naked, male or female, fell a victim to his mad fury,
and he only allowed the draped figures and busts to remain.
This happened in the year 1670[113]. The scandalous event
made the greatest sensation in Paris. However, the mis-
fortune had occurred and could not be undone. It was not
in the least lessened, but only relegated to the region of
the comic, by the nude statues being "frocked" in a sort of
drapery of plaster of Paris, just as the Pope's sense of
decency a hundred years later enveloped the Aphrodite of
Knidos in a cloak of tin. For a long time the antiques
in the Palais Mazarin continued to stand in that ridiculous
disguise. In this state the well-known naturalist, Dr Martin
Lister, saw them in A.D. 1698, and the sight elicited from
him some ironical remarks[114]. Subsequently, perhaps when
the palace was purchased by the *Compagnie des Indes* and
became the show place of John Law's bubble company,
Lord Pembroke secured a large portion of the sculptures,
while the rest remained in the palace up to the time of
the French Revolution[115]. The Earl had here too made
the busts his chief object, purchasing them to the number
of fifty-two with their costly variegated marble pedestals.
But his predilection furnished most of them with new
names. Even at the present day busts of this origin at
Wilton House can for the most part be recognised with
tolerable certainty, but still more unmistakeable evidence
of their source is borne by the statues derived from the
Mazarin collection, some of them still furnished with the
numbers they originally bore there, in the hammer-marks

[113] *Mélange curieux des meilleures
pièces attribuées à Mr. de Saint-Évre-
mond*, 3rd edition, Amsterdam 1726,
II. pp. 272, 307.
[114] *A Journey to Paris in the year
1698*, London 1699, p. 29.

[115] Blondel, *Architecture française*,
Paris 1754, III. p. 71. It appears to
have given a *catalogue raisonné*. cf.
Kennedy, *Description of Wilton House*,
p. xii.

with which their nude parts are disfigured. Some reliefs
also were bought by Lord Pembroke at the same time.

27. Lastly the Earl completed his gallery by the purchase of single pieces. When the Giustiniani family of
Rome began to sell the antiques of their superabundantly
rich collection, which was estimated at thirteen hundred
pieces, Pembroke was among the buyers, along with the
most distinguished of the antiquaries of Rome, Cardinal
Alessandro Albani. Some few busts were contributed by
the collection of sculptures belonging to the honourable
but then lately impoverished family of Valetta in Naples,
which was sold A.D. 1720, it is said, for 1100 ducats[116]. One
of these acquisitions was the very effective bust bearing the
arbitrary name of Apollonios of Tyana (Wilton No. 94), for
which was paid the high price of £270. Sir Andrew
Fountaine, a friend of Lord Pembroke, brought with him
from Italy a rare specimen, a mosaic relief (No. 27), clearly
a modern counterfeit, but in any case a great curiosity,
worthy to shine amongst the other treasures of Wilton
House[117]. All these works were distributed over the halls,
galleries, saloons and rooms of the spacious mansion, and
provided the favourite amusement of the owner. Unfortunately the Earl was not satisfied with christening and
re-christening the statues and busts on labels placed on the
pedestals, or in catalogues, but often the newly forged
names were chiselled into the monuments themselves, sometimes in Latin, sometimes in extremely questionable Greek.
This has even been done in the case of a cinerary urn, which
its inscription would authenticate as that of Horace! It
was another ingenuous development of this taste to ascribe
pieces of middling decorative sculpture to artists of high renown, as for instance Kleomenes[118], or to assign to a work

[116] There seems to have been a
catalogue of the collection by Fabretti, v. Kennedy, *l. cit.* p. xviii., cf.
Justi, *Winckelmann,* II. 2 p. 392.
[117] Winckelmann, *Werke,* III. p.
xxiii.,Dresden ed. Fernbhann,*Rhein.*

Museum, XXIX. 1874. p. 561 &c.
In Wilton House there are two busts
of Sir Andrew, by Roubiliac and by
Hoare.
[118] Wilton Nos. 10. 124. 151. 170.
The popularity of this name was

the most fabulous origin without having found any palpable
support for it [18]. Earl Thomas himself left notices of this
kind, and the year before he died at the age of seventy-eight
(A.D. 1732), there appeared the first printed catalogue, which
has been followed by a whole series of works of a similar
description [19]. Thus the fame won by the Pembroke collection soon extended far beyond the boundaries of England,
and was maintained undiminished even when other collections had in truth outstripped it, not only in the artistic
value of their contents but in comparative freedom from the
intermixture of spurious antiques. Even at this day the
collection of Wilton House exercises a peculiar charm.
Recently it has been arranged with great taste after the
design of the late Westmacott in the cloister-like galleries
round the square court of the mansion. Though this favourable impression fades a little on a closer examination of
the numerous antiques, yet there is amongst them a small
number of works which are of unusual interest and which
will always hold their own.

28. The Royal collection, the Arundel collection, and *P. Lely.*
the beginnings of the Pembroke collection were the chief *Lord Win-chelsea,*
evidences of English interest in antiques during the time of *Lord Carteret,*
the Stuarts. The first was annihilated by fire before the *J. Kemp.*
century came to its close. The second passed out of the
possession of the family into many strange hands. The
third alone has been preserved by a more propitious fortune uninjured to this day. Besides these, but meagre
records of similar efforts have been handed down from the
seventeenth century. SIR PETER LELY, for instance, in
addition to his celebrated collection of pictures, many of

due to the Venus de' Medici. To il-
lustrate the *naïveté* of such christen-
ings, Kennedy's effusion (p. xxx.) is
peculiarly apposite: "Among the best
pieces of sculpture relating to the
Romans may be reckoned that by
Cleomenes, of Curtius leaping into
the fiery gulph" [No. 87, a modern
relief]. "This sculptor was one of
the most eminent of his time, and

was sent from Corinth to Rome by
Polybius, the celebrated Historian, to
execute this work" ! Winckelmann
was quite right to ask why Polybius
might not rather have sent Kleomenes straight to Wilton (*Werke*, III.
p. vi.).

[119] Wilton No. 144.

[120] For a list, see below, *Cat.*, art.
Wilton House (introduction).

which came from the Buckingham and Arundel collections,
possessed a few antiques which were sold with the above-
mentioned objects of art in A.D. 1682[121]. Another collector
was JOHN HENEAGE, THIRD EARL OF WINCHELSEA, who,
as we saw above (p. 38), secured the coins and medals of the
Arundel collection. When ambassador to the Porte, he
took advantage of a stay at Athens (A.D. 1675) to purchase
a few sculptures[122]. Soon after his death (A.D. 1689), his
collections, either in whole or part, were sold (A.D. 1696)[123].
Interest in art was also kept up in other members
of his family. His second son Heneage, later fifth Earl,
visited the cabinet of one Jean Gailhard, at Angers, A.D.
1676. This he saw again at Paris seven years afterwards,
then considerably increased. Indeed this collection came
to England, not however into the possession of the nobleman just mentioned, but into that of GEORGE, FIRST BARON
CARTERET, who in consideration thereof settled an annuity
of £200 on its collector, his former governor. Lord Carteret
died A.D. 1695, and during the minority of his son John,
afterwards Earl of Granville, JOHN KEMP, F.R.S., bought
a considerable portion of the collection, and enlarged it by
other purchases[124]. Kemp's cabinet, at that time one of the
curiosities of London, comprised a number of marbles, to wit
eleven statues, but almost all of them under two feet in
height, besides twenty busts, sixteen reliefs and a remarkable
number of inscriptions. These specimens were with few
exceptions derived from Italy. The principal portion of the
antiques, however, consisted of the small bronzes, among
which were sixty-three statuettes, which at that time gained

[121] *A Catalogue of Sir Peter Lely's
capital Collection of Pictures, Statues,
Bronzes, &c.*, as an appendix of the
*Collection of the Duke of Bucking-
ham*, London, Bathoe, 1758. Of antiques only a statue of Apollo and two
heads are specified (p. 53), a crouching
Venus of which Episcopius knew as
existing in his house (*Signorum Veterum
Icones* Plate 77) passed into the royal
collection, see above, note 69. The

auction took place 1682, see Walpole
Anecd. ch. xii. (Lely).
[122] Spon, *Voyage d'Italie* &c.,
Lyons, 1678, II. p. 187.
[123] See above, note 98.
[124] MS. note of the learned Thomas
Birch (d. A.D. 1766) in his copy of the
Monumenta Kempiana, now in the
British Museum. In reference to Lord
Winchelsea, cf. Dallaway, *Of Statuary*,
p. 194, note *m*.

for the collection considerable fame. A year after Lord
Stafford's share of the Arundel collection at Tart Hall had
been sold, the Kemp collection too came under the hammer (March, A.D. 1721). It was described by R. Ainsworth
in an extraordinary catalogue. The sum realised by it
was one thousand and ninety pounds eight shillings and
sixpence[125].

29. Among the purchasers at these sales we come Dr Mead.
across DR RICHARD MEAD, the most celebrated physician
of his time, already at that period Vice-President of the
Royal Society, and afterwards physician in ordinary to
George II. He was born A.D. 1673, and received his early
training from the renowned Graevius of Utrecht. He made
a journey to Italy in the years 1695 and 1696, which took
him to Florence, Rome, and Naples. This tour was not
merely turned to account for the benefit of his medical
studies, but was also utilized for laying the foundation of a
collection of antiques[126]. Of this, the most extensive part
consisted of coins and gems. There were, however, nine
especially valuable fragments of antique mural paintings,
six of which most probably came from the Baths of Titus[127].
Antique works of this class are, it need not be said, very
rare, and it is consequently only natural that Mead should
have set a high value on this acquisition ; for his credit's
sake we will hope that it was not he who authorized the
wretched re-painting which so sorely disfigures the extant

[125] Monumenta Vetustatis Kempiana et vetustis scriptoribus illustrata
eosque vicissim illustrantia. London,
1720. The sum is stated by Birch,
l. cit.
[126] Museum Meadianum, London
(1754). The first part, the coins, was
sold by auction in February ; the
second, the antique and modern works
of art together with natural curiosities,
in March, 1755. There is a copy in
the British Museum with a list of the
buyers and the prices, from which I
have taken a portion of the above
account. Cf. also Walpole to R.
Bentley, 1755, March 27.

[127] Mus. Mead. pp. 241—243. Seven
of them can be traced, viz. in Bartoli,
Picturae antiquae cryptarum Roma-
narum, &c. delin. a Petro Sancti Bar-
tholi, illustr. a Bellorio et Caussco,
Rome, 1750, pl. 3, 5, 6, and Turnbull, Curious Collection of Ancient
Paintings, London, 1744, pl. 3, 26,
29, 30. The two last are now in
the British Museum; of the others
two passed to Mr White (still in the
possession of Sir M. White Ridley in
London), two to Mr Stewart, one to
Mr Hollis, one to Mr Mussell, the ninth
(Turnbull 3) was in the first instance
excluded from the sale.

M. C.   4

remains. Especially numerous again in Mead's collection were the small bronzes, which are proportionally less costly and more easily moveable than larger specimens, and at the same time present the advantage of offering opportunity for the display of much erudition. Still there was no lack of works in marble, to wit, three statues, various reliefs, many of which were decidedly spurious, and a fair quantity of busts. The crown of the collection was without question the Arundel bronze head of 'Homer' (Sophokles), which Mead had purchased at the auction in Tart Hall. Lastly there were, as an excellent supplement of the highest value to the above-mentioned fragments of painting, one hundred and sixty copies of antique pictures which had been discovered at Rome, executed by the artistic hand of Pietro Sante Bartoli. They had originally belonged to Cardinal Massimi. Mead set such a peculiarly high value on these drawings, that he bequeathed them in his will, together with one of the original antique paintings, to be preserved as heirlooms in the family. His intentions, it is true, produced no lasting effect, for the drawings at least appear to have been soon afterward purchased by George III., and are to this day in the Royal Library at Windsor[128].

Soon after Mead's death (A.D. 1753), the remainder of his collection was sold by public auction (A.D. 1755). The Earl of Exeter secured the bronze head for one hundred and thirty guineas, and a few years afterwards bequeathed it to the British Museum, thus at last placing it in safe hands. Subsequently a few of the antique paintings found their way to the same destination. Sir Philip Methuen

[128] The volume at Windsor, furnished with George I.'s stamp and the arms of the Vittoria family (*Arch. Zeitung*, 1871, p. 67, XXII.), belonged originally to "Don Vincenzo Vittoria, Canonico di Xativa nel regno di Valenza," yet the painted title-page proceeds jointly from Cardinal Massimi, who had been nuncio in Spain for some time, and from P. Sante Bartoli. The contents are in agreement with the accounts in *Mus. Mead.* p. 213 and in Turnbull. *Coll. of Anc. Paintings*, p. 3, note 3, p. 9. There are now indeed only somewhere over one hundred and forty drawings remaining, but a few sheets are wanting.

purchased a bronze head of Silenus. By a singular chance, two remarkable terminal busts with inscriptions, one the portrait of Theophrastos, and one purporting to be that of Xenokrates —were bought for Cardinal Albani, and after a brief interval made the return journey to Rome, where they had once adorned[129] the Palazzo Massimi alle colonne. The majority of purchasers however were English. Their number affords clear evidence how widely spread was the taste for collecting antiques about the middle of the last century, especially for collecting small works of art. We shall come across many of the names again (Lord Leicester, Lord Carlisle, Marquis of Rockingham, Lord Egremont, Lord Cavendish, Horace Walpole, Hollis and Brand, Lyde Browne); others I have not again met with in connection with these researches. This may be said of some of the most eager bidders, such as General Campbell, Captain Bootle, Mr Mussell, Mr Stewart, &c. It is only the first-named whom I find again; namely at the sale (A.D. 1742) of the Earl of Oxford's collection, which is of little import-ance as to antiques. Here he figures as the purchaser of a marble bust of Alexander the Great[130]. Might not this possibly be the beautiful bust at Blenheim?

30. Small bronzes also made up the principal portion of the collection of CONYERS MIDDLETON, which this scholar, who is especially known as the biographer of Cicero, had formed during his residence in Italy about A.D. 1724. Besides statuettes, there were in particular all sorts of utensils, lamps, sacrificial and culinary implements, to which his attention was chiefly turned. He devoted to their ex-planation a special volume furnished with illustrations (A.D. 1745). Shortly before, he had sold the whole collection to Horace Walpole, who subsequently exhibited them at

Conyers Middleton.
Collectors of coins.
Courten.
Hans Sloane.

[129] Visconti, *Iconogr. grecque*, i. pp. 259, 307, Mil. Cf. Spon, *Voyage d'Italie*, i.p. 396. Winckelmann, *Mon. Ined.* i. p. 77. The "Xenokrates" is now in Munich (Glypt. no. 133). [130] *A Catalogue of the Collection of the Rt. Hon. Edward, Earl of Oxford.* Sold by auction, March, 1741-42. 4to.

4—2

Strawberry Hill[131]. But the most widely-spread form of
the passion for antiques was that for ancient coins. Haym,
the meritorious editor of the *Tesoro Britannico*, enumerated
about A.D. 1720 seventeen considerable collections of coins
in England[132]. A larger or smaller collection of coins was
also rarely wanting in that very favourite kind of 'museum'
which mixed up in motley confusion all possible curiosities
from the realms of nature and art. The Ashmolean Museum in Oxford affords an example of this to the present
day. The germ of this institution was the oldest cabinet
of the kind, formed by the two Tradescants, father and
son. Of a similar character was WILLIAM COURTEN'S
museum (Charleton's)[133], "perhaps the most noble collection
of natural and artificial curiosities, of ancient [especially
Roman] and modern coins and medals that any private
person in the world enjoys[134]." " It consisted of minatures,
drawings, shells, insects, medailes, natural things, animals,
minerals, precious stones, vessels, curiosities in amber,
christal, achat, &c.[135]." The bare enumeration of all 'these
glories dazes one.' And yet the collection has every claim
to our respect. For after it had been made over by the
founder (A.D. 1702) to DR HANS SLOANE, the later physician
in ordinary to George I., and more and more materially
increased by him (so that the "antiquities of Egypt, Greece,
Etruria, Rome, Britain and even America" filled several
ground-floor rooms of his house in Chelsea), it passed
immediately after Sloane's death (A.D. 1753) into the possession of the State for the sum of twenty thousand pounds,
and constituted, with the Harleian Manuscripts and the
Cottonian Library, one of the foundation stones of the

[131] Middleton, Conyers, *Germana
quaedam antiquitatis eruditae monumenta, quibus Romanorum veterum
varii ritus illustrantur,* London,
1745. 4to. Walpole to Mann, 1744,
June 18. Cf. below, note 172.
[132] *Tesoro Brit.* I. p. xi., II. p. v.
On coin-collectors of the 17th century,
see Evelyn, in letter to S. Pepys,

1689, Aug. 12.
[133] Edwards, *Lives of the Founders
of the British Museum,* I. p. 264.
[134] Thoresby, *Diary,* 1695, May
24. Cf. Evelyn, *Diary,* 1690, March
11.
[135] Evelyn, *Diary,* 1686, Dec. 16.
Cf. also his letter to Pepys, quoted in
note 132.

British Museum[136]. At that time the number of medals
and coins amounted to thirty-two thousand, of "antiquities"
to one thousand one hundred and twenty-five, of cameos
and intaglios to about seven hundred. Two apartments
in Montagu House, the first home of the Museum, sufficed
for the accommodation of this portion of the newly-formed
national collection. Nowadays the Sloane antiques are
utterly overwhelmed by the immense riches of the department of antiquities; but it must never be forgotten that
the wish expressed by Sir Hans in his will, gave occasion
for the founding of the grandest museum in the world, and
that his example pointed out the right way of rescuing
costly collections, brought together with trouble and expense, from the vicissitudes of private possession.

31. The last-named collectors belonged principally to *The Duke*
the rank of commoners, and had for the most part them- *of Devon-*
selves formed their cabinets when travelling in foreign *shire.*
countries. There was however in the first decades of the last
century no lack of nobles to follow, although in relatively
modest guise, the example of Arundel and Pembroke.
Horace Walpole[137] mentions by the side of the latter, as a
collector of coins and statues in the time of Queen Anne, the
DUKE OF DEVONSHIRE. He probably means William, the
first Duke, who died A.D. 1707. He was much engaged in
travel, and enjoyed the reputation of a connoisseur in art
and poet; he too it was who raised the splendid mansion
of Chatsworth. Love for art indeed was at one time quite
domiciled in his family. A grandson of the said Duke,
Lord Charles Cavendish, was one of the original trustees
of the British Museum[138], and his great-grandson William,
fourth Duke, a son-in-law of Lord Burlington, the oracle
on art in the time of George I., joined the Society of
Dilettanti soon after its foundation[139]. Meantime the

---

[136] Edwards, *l. cit.*, I. p. 273.   *ad init.*
Gentl. Mag. XVIII. (1743) p. 302.   [138] Edwards, *l. cit.* I. p. 321.
[137] *Anecd. of Painting*, ch. XVI.   [139] 1740, Febr. 1.   *Historical*

passion for collecting seems to have turned in the main
more towards modern art, and in the sphere of antiques,
more towards engraved gems than sculptures[119]. It has
already been mentioned that EDWARD HARLEY, SECOND
EARL OF OXFORD, possessed several sculptures; they
were however quite subordinate to the treasures of the
well-known Harleian library, which he zealously increased.
Of more importance for our study is another group of
noblemen who travelled and collected for themselves in
Italy. These find their more appropriate place in the
next section.

Notices of the Society of Dilettanti,
London, 1855, p. 117. Winckelmann,
Gesch. d. Kunst, VII. 2. 17, mentions
a bronze head of Plato which it seems
likely that the Duke of Devonshire
had got over from Greece about thirty
years before (that is to say about
1730); this would refer to the second

or third Duke, who died respectively
A.D. 1729 and A.D. 1755, unless
Winckelmann was thinking (A. D.
1762) of the then living Duke, the
fourth.
    [120] See below, Cat., arts. Chats-
worth, and London, Devonshire
House.

II.

THE GOLDEN AGE OF CLASSIC DILETTANTISM.

ROME AND ENGLAND.

32. As early as the sixteenth century it was quite *Travels to the South in the time of the Stuarts.* usual for Englishmen to go to Italy in pursuit of the higher culture. The flourishing universities of Bologna and Padua were regarded by the British lovers of learning as the proper high school, particularly for the students of Law and Medicine; and the youth of the nobility was not slow to improve its manners in the chief towns of Italy— or to corrupt them according to the opinion of the stricter sort, who were never tired of descanting upon the ruinous influence of Hesperian licentiousness, or of quoting the proverb *'Inglese italianato è un diavolo incarnato'*[141]. English language and poetry were, like English music, under the special influence of Italy. It is therefore all the more remarkable that neither in the works of the poets nor of the moralists, to whom the subject would have been so appropriate, do we find even the smallest allusions to the master-pieces of antique art, which were scattered in such profuse abundance throughout the whole of the peninsula and concentrated in particular at Rome. We can only

[141] My friend and colleague, Prof. B. ten Brink, refers me to Roger Ascham's *Schoolmaster*, written A.D. 1563 (*The English Works of R. A.*, London, 1761, p. 245—261), and to William Harrison's *Description of England*, 2d ed. 1587, book 2, ch. 3 and 5 (pp. 81, 129, ed. Furnivall). Ascham betrays in another place (*Works*, p. 394) an interest in antique coins.

suppose that the eyes of the young Briton of that day
were not yet open to them; that to his Northern nature
the peculiar excellences of ancient sculpture were still a
sealed book.

In the seventeenth century it was different. Lord
Arundel gave the lead, in the sense of being the first
who visited Italy for nothing so much as for her art
treasures. From the diary of John Evelyn, whom Lord
Arundel himself when on his death-bed provided with the
necessary hints, we are introduced in a lively manner to
the pursuits of a well-educated gentleman, who lets slip no
opportunity of gaining that personal knowledge of the
remains of ancient beauty, which Peacham had already
reckoned among the essentials of his complete gentleman.
George Wheler's description of the journey to Greece and
the Levant which he took in company with Jacob Spon
of Lyons (A.D. 1675—1676), has, together with the work
of his then travelling companion, the charm and the value
of a first journey of exploration in a land at that time
almost unknown. Towards the close of the century the
number rose greatly of those who visited the south for the
sake of art, and brought home some memento or other of
their travels. Lord Pembroke, Lord Lempster, the Duke of
Devonshire, and Dr Mead may be mentioned here once
more as instances of this growing habit.

The fashion of the 'grand tour.' Sir A. Fountaine. Lord Burlington.   33. The idea, however, that 'the grand tour,' through
the continental countries, particularly France and Italy,
was the necessary complement to a refined training and
gave it a final polish, and that art was an essential element
in this higher culture, does not appear to have been very
generally realised before the beginning of the eighteenth
century. The travellers naturally found Rome the most
agreeable rendezvous, and the English soon formed the
chief contingent in that international society, which there
took part in the *conversazioni* of native learned men and
friends of art, and which allowed itself to be initiated into the

wonders of the Eternal City in a shorter or longer time, by
obliging *ciceroni*, like Francesco de' Ficoroni (*d.* A.D. 1747)[142].
Purchases of pictures and antiquities were perpetually made,
extravagant or modest according to the means and inclination of individuals. The result was that the English
gradually attained the first rank among purchasers of art-
treasures. The conviction of their inexhaustible wealth thus
gained by practical experience overcame in the natives all
prejudices aroused by the heresy and habits of life of their
northern guests. The treasures they had collected were
used by the English gentlemen to adorn the beautiful
country-houses scattered over the country, and more
than one traveller after his return enjoyed on the strength
of the information picked up in Italy the reputation
of a distinguished connoisseur, or even of an infallible
oracle in matters of good taste and art. The advice of SIR
ANDREW FOUNTAINE (A.D. 1675—1753), who travelled in
Italy at the beginning of the century and who interested
himself particularly in ancient coins, was eagerly sought
by collectors at home[143]; thus we have already found him
concerned in the formation of the Pembroke Collection.
The position which RICHARD BOYLE, EARL OF BURLING-
TON (A.D. 1695—1753), the patron of Will. Kent, Geo.
Vertue, and other artists, occupied after his return from
Italy as an authority on architectural matters is well known,
though every one does not agree to the almost unqualified
encomium of Horace Walpole[144]. In the garden of his villa
at Chiswick, which he built himself, and which eventually
became the property of his son-in-law, the Duke of Devon-

<hr>

[142] Ficoroni himself mentions some
of his English acquaintances, *Le Vestigia e Rarità di Roma Antica*, Rom.
1744, preface. With respect to
Ficoroni, whose name is inseparably
connected with the noblest creation of
antique draughtsmanship, the bronze
cista of the Collegio Romano, cf.
Justi, C., in Lützow's *Zeitschrift für
bildende Kunst*, VII. (1872) p. 302. I

have to thank this scholar for the
communication of several extracts from
Ficoroni's unpublished correspondence.

[143] Ficoroni, *Vestigia*, p.98, Haym,
Tesoro Britannico, I. p. xi., Justi in the
Neues rhein. Museum, XXIX. (1874)
p. 582.

[144] Walpole, *Anecd.* ch. XXII. (Burlington, Kent).

shire, stood several ancient statues, which had been found
in the villa of Hadrian at Tivoli[146]. In his town mansion,
the stately Burlington House, the Elgin marbles were later
to find a temporary home. The present use of the site
for the head-quarters of the most prominent societies who
have devoted themselves to the nurture of art and antiquities in England, ensures the perpetuation of Lord Burlington's name in a manner most appropriate to the interests
he had at heart.

Th. Coke (Lord Leicester.) 34. A younger contemporary of Lord Burlington was
MR THOMAS COKE (A.D. 1728 LORD LOVEL, A.D. 1744
EARL OF LEICESTER), who spent a long period in Italy,
and of whose travels a number of interesting details
are to be gathered from an account-book kept by one
of his servants, which is now preserved in the library at
Holkham[146]. In this we find in the broadest contrast items
for kitchen purposes, tailor, &c. side by side with *pour-
boires* for seeing collections, travelling expenses, payments
for art purchases, &c. Mr Coke was absent from England
from A.D. 1714 to A.D. 1718, travelling in France and
Germany as well as Italy. He was at Rome in the year
1716, and again the following year after an excursion to
Florence and Pisa. He had dealings with the above-mentioned antiquary Ficoroni, a needy fellow, of whom drawings from antique gems could be occasionally bought for a
few crowns. There occurs even more frequently the name of
Francesco Sante Bartoli, son of the celebrated engraver
Pietro: and no inconsiderable number of copies from
ancient paintings, which form a conspicuous feature in
the library at Holkham, may be traced to the artistic
hands of the two Bartoli. The 'Cavaliere' Coke, as he
was called in Italy, was diligent in having sketches made

[145] Volkmann, *Neueste Reisen
durch England*, Leipz. 1781, II. p.
440. Cf. above, § 22.
[146] For the opportunity of examin-
ing this volume I have to thank the

Reverend Alexander Napier of Holkham, who had discovered this very
interesting document in the library
(of Holkham) entrusted to his care.

of other antiques, statues, busts, &c. ; and he was so fortunate as to obtain for fifty crowns a book of drawings, which are partly executed by no less a person than the great Raphael himself. Lastly, however, Mr Coke obtained possession of a small number of original works in marble of more remarkable artistic character than anything that had hitherto been brought from Italy to England. In some of these transactions he employed as agent William Kent, who afterwards designed for him the plan of Holkham Hall. Among these works are : The Artemis from the Casa Consiglieri, which cost nine hundred crowns[147]; the so-called Lucius Antonius, which was restored in a masterly manner by Bernini; and the so-called Zeus, to which Kent intended to give a place of honour on the staircase of the new mansion[148]. All these are objects which would suffice to adorn any museum, and which must have aroused double admiration before the still brighter splendour of Lord Leicester's later acquisitions put them somewhat in the shade.

The warm interest for antiquity, which Mr Coke brought home with him from Italy, was however in the mean time to be splendidly illustrated in another way. Among the autographical treasures that he obtained was an exhaustive work, in manuscript, by Thomas Dempster, a Scotchman who had died almost one hundred years before (A.D. 1625) while working as a professor at Bologna. It was an extraordinarily industrious and learned compilation of every sort of information about Etruria and the Etruscans. Coke not only had this work printed in Florence in two large folio volumes, but further had sketches made of all the Etruscan works of art that were within his reach, and then had them engraved on ninety-three copper plates.

[147] See below. Cat., art. Holkham, no. 24. "Purchased and sent out of Rome by the Earl of Leicester; for which offence his Lordship was put under arrest, but released soon after at the instances of the Grand Duke of Tuscany." So Mr Brettingham tells us in his work on Holkham; to the same effect Dallaway, *Anecd.* p. 276; the statements in the account-book contain no confirmation of the story.
[148] Holkham, no. 36, 51.

He further induced a friend from Florence, the excellent
and learned senator Filippo Buonarroti, to add to the
work an appendix containing observations of solid value[149].
The book thus produced (through Coke's liberality) has
acquired a heightened interest inasmuch as it has been the
innocent cause of that foolish Etruscomania which pre-
vailed for many years in Italy—a startling example of the
length to which that people can be led by misdirected local
patriotism in conjunction with confused, uncritical learning.

*Lord Car-
lile, Lord
Boss-
borough,
Duke of
Beaufort.* 35. At the same time that Mr Coke was in Italy,
Ficoroni had the opportunity of making the acquaintance
of HENRY HOWARD, afterwards FOURTH EARL OF CAR-
LISLE (A.D. 1694—1758), a connection of the Howards of
Arundel and Norfolk, and of making him familiar with the
antiquities of Rome (A.D. 1717). Later (A.D. 1739) he
looked with pride on this pupil of his, who then surpassed
his former teacher in knowledge[150]. The vast Castle Howard,
one of Vanbrugh's ponderous creations, which the third
Earl had begun, and Earl Henry finished, still contains a
very heterogeneous collection, the foundation of which was
laid in Italy by Earl Henry at the time of which we speak.
This collection includes few objects of real consequence,
and illustrates by the number of its portrait-busts, particularly those of imperial Roman times, the prevailing
tendency of antiquarian interest in that period. It will however always possess a certain importance on account of the
number and variety of its antiques, a number afterwards
increased by art-loving successors of the first collector.

The fate of the collection founded by WILLIAM
PONSONBY, VISCOUNT DUNCANNON, later SECOND EARL

---

[149] *Thomae Dempteri de Etruria
Regali libri VII., nunc primum editi
curante Thoma Coke Magnae Britan-
niae armigero*, II. fol. Flor. 1723,
1724. The text was ready for the
press as early as A.D. 1719, but Buonarroti's supplement delayed the appearance of the second volume until
the year 1726. For the *Etruscheria*,
cf. Justi, *Winkelmann*, II. 1, pp. 245
—249, 267—270.
[150] According to a letter of Ficoroni; cf. his *Vestigia*, p. 132. A
characteristic anecdote relating to the
year 1739 is told by Walpole in a letter
to R. West, 1740, May 7.

OF BESSBOROUGH (*d.* A.D. 1793), was less fortunate. He lived a great deal on the continent till A.D. 1739, and in Italy laid the foundation of his collection, which he afterwards enlarged by considerable purchases in England and other countries. He however sold his beautiful assortment of gems, composing about two hundred specimens, catalogued in the year 1761 by L. Natter, to the Duke of Marlborough. There remained then in his villa at Roehampton only the marbles, a collection of some repute, which was sold by auction not long after the owner's death[151]. The collection of HENRY SOMERSET, THIRD DUKE OF BEAUFORT (A.D. 1745), appears to have fared no better. He bought a considerable number of sarcophagi, which were brought to light A.D. 1726 in a tomb near Rome, and which were supposed to have been the coffins of the personal attendants of the Empress Livia. The Duke was probably present at Rome at the time of the discovery[152]. A number of these sarcophagi may be seen at the present day at Wilton House; we may therefore presume that Lord Pembroke, that ardent collector, purchased them, or else received them as a present from the Duke of Beaufort[153].

36. We have only space briefly to mention here a few *Other travelling collectors. The Richardsons.* other travellers, who, like Lord Carlisle, had dealings with Ficoroni in Rome, and who as well as the Earl have made themselves known, to some extent at least, as lovers and collectors of works of art[154]. SIR JOHN and SIR CHARLES FREDERICK[155], Mr LETHIEULLIER (perhaps one of those Lethieulliers who were among the first benefactors of the

---

[151] April, 1801. *Account of the Statues, &c., at Ince,* Appendix. Dallaway, *Of Statuary,* page 349. One of the finest specimens was the torso of Venus, once belonging to Baron Stosch, Ince, no. 63. See below, Cat., art. Petworth, no. 12. A second sale took place in July, A.D. 1850.

[152] Gori, *Monumentum libertorum Liviae Augustae det.* 1726, Flor. 1727, pref. p. xx.

[153] Wilton, no. 60, 111, 129, 143, 155.

[154] Ficoroni's Correspondence; cf. his *Vestigia.* p. 130.

[155] Sir Charles Frederick's collection was sold A.D. 1786; one of the purchasers was Townley, v. *Anc. Marb. Brit. Mus.* v. Pl. 4, 3 and 4, Pl. 10, 1. Sir Charles had offered Ficoroni a considerable sum for his bronze cista, but in vain. See Ficoroni, *Memorie di Labico,* p. 74.

British Museum[124]), EYRES, CONVERS (MIDDLETON?), are similar names. Were the papers of Ficoroni, Gori, or Baron Stosch at our disposal, the number could easily be considerably increased. A fact characteristic of the time is that now (A.D. 1722) appeared the first English guide to works of art in Italy, a book by the RICHARDSONS, father and son, compiled from materials collected by the latter, which for a long time was looked upon as an indispensable companion. Forty years later Winckelmann decided that, in spite of its faults and omissions, and of the fact that the author described the works of art as one who had beheld them but in a dream, it was yet the best book that was to be had[127].

Founda-
tion of the
Society of
Dilettanti.

37. Who, that has passed some time in Italy, but must have discovered by experience that the deep artistic impressions there received form an invisible but firm bond by which he feels himself united to all those who have enjoyed a similar happiness and brought home similar recollections? Nay, the whole band of those who in successive ages have made for art's sake the pilgrimage to Rome, form in some sort a spiritual community, tacitly knit together by a common devotion to the beautiful. Participation in such feelings more easily draws together people who are personally unknown to each other. Sentiments of this kind gave rise to the SOCIETY OF DILETTANTI[128]. "In the year

[124] Edwards, *Lives of the Founders of the British Museum*, I. p. 347. Gordon, A., *An Essay towards explaining the hieroglyphical figures on the coffin belonging to Captain Lethieullier*, London, 1707.

[126] *An Account of some of the Statues, Bas-reliefs, Drawings, and Pictures in Italy, &c.*, London, 1722, 2nd ed. 1754. Walpole, *Anecd.* ch. XVII. ("Jonathan Richardson"). Winckelmann, *Gesch. d. Kunst*, pref. p. xiv. (*Werke*, III. p. vi).

[128] Hamilton, W. R., *Historical Notices of the Society of Dilettanti*. Printed for private circulation only. London, 1855, 4°. An extract from

this is to be found in the *Edinburgh Review*, CV. 1857, pp. 493 – 517 [Lord Houghton]. For the use of the original I am indebted to the kindness of Professor Sidney Colvin, Cambridge. From this and other sources I have drawn up a fuller sketch of the history of the Society, published in Lützow's *Zeitschrift für bildende Kunst*, XIV. pp. 65 – 71, 104 – 113, 133 – 145. Judging by the official chronology in the statement of accounts, the foundation of the Society did not take place, according to the received opinion, A.D. 1734, but towards the end of the preceding year, probably in December, A.D. 1733.

1734" (more probably 1733), "some gentlemen who had
travelled in Italy, desirous of encouraging at home a taste
for those objects which had contributed so much to their
entertainment abroad, formed themselves into a Society
under the name of *The Dilettanti*, and agreed upon such
resolutions as they thought necessary to keep up the spirit
of the scheme." This description is taken from the preface
of the *Antiquities of Ionia*, published by the Society in
the year 1769. While friendly and social intercourse stood
confessedly among the primary objects of the Society[159],
the more intellectual aims were by no means neglected ;
and the learned and art-loving world is indebted to the
liberality of this distinguished body for that splendid succession of publications on the subject of Greek and Roman
Antiquities, from Stuart's and Revett's classical *Antiquities
of Athens*, down to the not less important works of
Cockerell, Penrose, and Pullan, which laid the foundation
and form the model of all such productions[160]. All these
volumes command similar respect on the score of irre-
fragable trustworthiness in reporting facts and in pursuit
of truth. Excellent as is their outward form, yet no sacrifice
has ever been made to external display, to the detriment
of unconditional material reliability. In this respect the
publications of the Society are unequalled.

38. Englishmen may well experience satisfaction and *Activity*
pride, as they review the long list of distinguished and *of its members.*

---

[159] " In this respect no set of men
ever kept up more religiously to their
original Institution." So say the
Dilettanti themselves, while Horace
Walpole writes (to Mann, 1743, April
14): "the *Dilettanti*, a club, for
which the nominal qualification is
having been in Italy, and the real one,
being drunk ; the two chiefs are Lord
Middlesex [afterwards Duke of Dorset]
and Sir Francis Dashwood, who were
seldom sober the whole time they were
in Italy." Compare with this the description of the young Englishman in
Rome in a letter of Lady Mary Wortley

Montagu, 1753, June 3, in her *Letters
and Works*, edited by Lord Wharncliffe, III. p. 61.

[160] *Antiquities of Athens*, IV. 1762
—1816; *Ionian Antiquities*, III. 1769
—1840; Chandler, *Inscriptiones Antiquae*, 1774; *Travels*, II. 1775, 1776;
Specimens of Antient Sculpture, II.
1809, 1835; *Unedited Antiquities of
Attica*, 1817; Gell, W., *Rome and its
Vicinity*, 1834; Bröndsted, *Bronzes
of Siris*, 1836; Penrose, *Principles
of Athenian Architecture*, 1851 ;
Cockerell, *Temples of Aegina and
Bassae*, 1860.

respected names of men who have devoted their ample
means or their personal co-operation, for nearly a century
and a half, to the noble purposes of this Society. As a
matter of course the names of the most important collectors
are not missing from the list. Among the members for the
first ten years, we find the Hon. W. Ponsonby (Earl of
Bessborough), Mr R. Grenville (Earl Temple), Mr Wellbore
Ellis (Lord Mendip), the Marquis of Hartington (Duke of
Devonshire), Lord Lovel (Earl of Leicester), Mr (afterwards
Sir John) Frederick, Mr Thomas Brand, and Sir Charles
Wyndham (Earl of Egremont); also Spence, the celebrated author of *Polymetis*. It would carry us too far to
enumerate in this place even the most important names of
the succeeding period[161]; few only are missing of those
with whom we shall afterwards have to occupy ourselves.
At times we see distinctly how admission into the Society
was the immediate result of a journey to Italy. Thus Lord
Charlemont returned in the year 1755 from the South
after an absence of nine years, and became a member of
the Society in the following year. The Duke of Roxburghe
was in Italy in the year 1762 and Viscount Palmerston in
the year 1764: both joined the Dilettanti A.D. 1765, and so
did Mr W. Weddell in the following year, soon after his

[161] I extract only the following
names of amateurs and men of learning,
appending the year of their admission:
Mr Duncombe, 1747; Edw. Wortley
Montagu, 1749; Lord Anson, 1750;
J. Stuart, Nich. Revett, 1751; Marquis of Rockingham, J. Dawkins,
1755; Lord Charlemont, 1756; Rob.
Wood, 1763; Lord Montagu (Marq.
of Montheriner), 1764; Duke of Marlborough, Viscount Palmerston, 1765;
W Weddell, 1766; Duke of Buccleuch,
1767; Steph. Fox (Lord Holland),
1769; (Sir) Jos. Banks, 1774; Duke
of Dorset, 1776; Sir Will. Hamilton,
1777; Sir Rich. Worsley, 1778; Lyde
Browne, 1780; R. Payne Knight, Sir
Henry C. Englefield, 1781; Ch.
Townley, 1786; James Smith Barry,
1788; Hon. Frederick North (Earl
of Guilford), 1790; John Hawkins,
J. B. S. Merritt, 1799; Tho. Hope,

1800; Lord Northwick, 1802; Alex.
Marquis of Douglas (Duke of Hamil-
ton), 1803; Sam. Rogers, 1803; Lord
Aberdeen, 1806; (Sir) W. Gell, 1807;
Fred. Foster, W. Wilkins, 1809;
W. R. Hamilton, 1811; W. M. Leake,
1814; R. Westmacott, 1817; Duke
of Bedford, 1819; Marquis of Chandos
(Duke of Buckingham), 1823; Mar-
quis of Northampton, 1832; Mar-
quis of Douglas (Duke of Hamilton),
1833; Sir Stratford Canning (Lord
Stratford de Redcliffe), Alex. Baring
(Lord Ashburton), 1834; Charles
Fox, 1837; Sir J. C. Hobhouse (Lord
Broughton), 1839; F. C. Penrose,
1852; Lord Houghton, 1852; W.
Watkiss Lloyd, 1854; C. T. Newton,
1863; Sidney Colvin, 1871; C. Knight
Watson, 1871; Lord Acton, 1872;
J. Fergusson, 1875.

return from Italy. The ten years from A.D. 1760 to 1770 are on the whole distinguished by a peculiarly lively interest in the objects of the Society, due partly perhaps to the fact that in the year 1762 the first volume of Stuart's and Revett's great work appeared under its auspices. Next, in the year 1764, Chandler, Revett and Pars were sent to the Levant, which mission was the first independent undertaking of the Society. Other members, such as Lord Anson, Lord Charlemont, James Dawkins, and Robert Wood, and afterwards Sir William Hamilton, added a fresh lustre to the Society by the distinction of their own travels and discoveries or the value of their publications. Many of the Dilettanti also gave private support to learned enterprises, even independently of the undertakings which were under the patronage of the whole Society. But for the liberality of J. Dawkins, who was supported by Lord Malton (afterwards Marquis of Rockingham) and Lord Charlemont, Stuart and Revett could never have had the leisure to complete their Athenian labours[162]. As these two authors had opportunities of executing buildings in London and in the country for members of the Society[163], they were able to offer proof that the efforts of the Dilettanti were not merely directed to theoretical inquiry into dead matters of history, but that living and contemporary art was meant, and was able, to derive benefit from their work.

39. In the meantime very favourable opportunities *State of things at Rome.* were offered in Italy for the purchase of antique sculptures. Great collections had been made in Rome in the seventeenth century by the princes and Cardinal-nephews, the *Foundation of the Capitoline Museum.* Barberini, Borghese, Giustiniani, Ludovisi, Odescalchi, Pamfili, Rospigliosi, and others. This high tide in the native love of art was however followed at the beginning of the eighteenth century by an equally significant ebb,

---

[162] *Antiq. of Athens*, IV. p. xxiii. Lord Anson got for Stuart also the lucrative sinecure of a surveyor to Greenwich Hospital. As to Stuart's later habits of life cf. J. Th. Smith, *Nollekens*, I. p. 38.   [163] *Antiq. of Athens*, IV. pp. xxviii. xxxi.

caused by the increasing pecuniary embarrassments of the
noble families of Rome. The Giustiniani family led off,
and we have seen how Lord Pembroke availed himself of
the opportunity. In the year 1724 the sculptures of the
Odescalchi Museum, originally collected by Queen Christina
of Sweden, were sold to Spain for the sum of twelve thousand doubloons (about £9400), and placed in the Palace
of San Ildefonso[164]. Four years later Ficoroni negociated
the sale of the Chigi collection for thirty-four thousand
scudi (about £7600), to the King of Poland at Dresden;
and even Cardinal Alessandro Albani, who was a most
enthusiastic collector, was obliged on account of straitened
means to part with thirty statues to the same monarch for
twenty thousand scudi (about £4500)[165]. These events
caused great excitement in Rome. It was said, as in
ancient times, *Romae omnia venalia*, and an effort was
made to save as much as possible for the Eternal City.
Cardinal Albani's incomparable collection of portrait-busts
was bought, not by a foreign amateur, but by the Pope, in
the year 1734, and the founding of the Capitoline Museum
seemed to provide the most effectual means of obviating
the dispersion of antique sculptures. Remarkable specimens were purchased from various palaces and villas; others
were presented to the Pope; others again were acquired by
means of excavations expressly set on foot. During the
pontificates of two Popes, Clement XII. and Benedict XIV.,
of the houses of Corsini and Lambertini respectively (A.D.
1730—1758), the Capitoline Museum received its essential
form; only few additions having been made to it, and those
in the times immediately succeeding[166].

[164] Hübner, *Antike Bildwerke in
Madrid*, Berlin, 1862, p. 14. Winckelmann in letter to Mengs, 1761, Nov.
18 (*Opere di R. Mengs*, Rome. 1787, p.
420), states the price of 12,000 scudi
(about £11,500), Fea, *Storia delle Arti
del Dis.*, II. p. 38, of 25,000 doppi, or

nearly 75,000 scudi (c. £16,800).
[165] Hettner, *Die Bildwerke der kgl.
Antikensammlung zu Dresden*, 3 ed.
Dresden, 1875, p. iii.—vi.
[166] Justi, C., in *Im neuen Reich*,
Leipzig, 1871, II. p. 121.

40. The result was that a splendid treasure was secured *Dealers*
to Rome. But the movement which had once set in among *and restor-*
private collections was not checked. On the contrary it *ceppi.* *ers. Cava-*
received a stronger impulse. Private purchasers, among
whom the apothecary Borioni and above all the crafty
Belisario Amidei deserve to be mentioned, vied with each
other and with the government. Trade in antiques, and
excavations in search of them, were carried on with great
vigour. The fabrication of spurious antiques was not
omitted, but was in fact a general custom. In mutual
emulation Flavio Sirleti, Anton Pichler, the Costanzo
family, and other less skillful hands cut "antique" gems
or provided stones of genuine antiquity with modern inscriptions. So with marbles. Sometimes an old appearance
was given to new works by an artificial roughening of the
surface, or by the use of chemicals. Sometimes insignificant
old fragments were restored with more or less skill, that is
to say trimmed into apparent completeness by arbitrary
additions; and in this way otherwise worthless specimens
were made saleable. The most celebrated virtuoso in this
branch was BARTOLOMMEO CAVACEPPI, who had invented
a regular system of methodical restoration, which in theory
was excellent and almost incontrovertible, but in practice was
only in so far to be commended as Cavaceppi surpassed most
of his contemporaries in taste and execution. Through
several decades all the most important finds and purchases
of antique sculptures passed through Cavaceppi's hands
and were made to submit to his rejuvenating arts. He
and his fellow-workers must not be blamed for this. No
one, or at least very few, would have bought the broken
torsi and limbs as they were taken out of the ground. Besides, from the days of the Renaissance restorations had
been considered a matter of course. Here and there an
individual might object to this or that particular example
of the process: yet no one doubted the principle that restorations *must* be made; and even so fine a connoisseur as

Cardinal Albani carried on the business with such enthusiasm that he gained the title of *réparateur en chef de l'antiquité*[167]. The Elgin Marbles were the first to break the spell. Canova pronounced that it would be sacrilege for a modern hand to complete these fragments; and the British Museum has been the first and unluckily the only institution to abide by the principle thus laid down, and check the unwarrantable introduction of arbitrary interpolations into ancient work.

Perry, the Walpoles, Hollis and Brand, and smaller collectors.

41. This was the state of affairs in Rome at the time the Society of Dilettanti was founded. "There are now selling," writes Horace Walpole in the summer of A.D. 1740, "no less than three of the principal collections, the Barberini, the Sacchetti, and Ottoboni[168]." The fact that MR PERRY in the year 1740 contented himself with purchasing only a small number of busts, must be attributed to moderation on his part, or the particular direction of his taste; with his purchases he adorned his house at Penshurst[169], which is so venerable and rich in memories. Similarly SIR ROBERT WALPOLE (afterwards LORD ORFORD, A.D. 1745) had a dozen busts purchased in Rome for the adornment of his country seat of Houghton Hall; these were catalogued by his son Horatio in the *Aedes Walpolianae*[170]. HORACE WALPOLE himself, during his stay in Rome (A.D. 1740) "made but small collections, and bought only some bronzes and medals, and a few busts," among them the famous Vespasian in touchstone from the auction of the Cardinal Ottoboni[171]. Some later purchases in England were added from the effects of Mead, Middleton and others, and so was formed the cabinet which remained at Straw-

167 Cf. Justi, C., *Winckelmann*, II. 1, pp. 317—324. Cavaceppi, *Raccolta d' antiche statue, &c. restaurate da B. C.*, III. Rome 1768—1772. There are forcible remarks on the hazardous nature of restoration in Casanova's *Discorso sopra gl' antichi*, Leipzig, 1770.

168 To R. West, 1740, May 7.

169 See under Penshurst.

170 See under Houghton Hall. The catalogue was already drawn up in the year 1743, but was first published only A.D. 1747, v. Walpole's *Letters*, ed. Cunningham, I. p. lxv.

171 Walpole to R. West, 1740, Oct. 2. Cf. the letter to H. S. Conway, 1740, April 23.

berry Hill for nearly a century. The possessor himself
esteemed, as of the highest value after the Vespasian,
an eagle from the baths of Caracalla; a small bronze
bust of Caligula, which was found among the first excavations of Prince d'Elbœuf at Herculaneum (A.D. 1711),
and was a present from Sir Horace Mann; and a small
head of Serapis in basalt from the Barberini palace, of
which he had at last (A.D. 1786) become the possessor after
it had passed through the hands of Sir William Hamilton
and the Duchess of Portland[172]. The sculptures obtained
by the pair of intimate friends THOMAS HOLLIS (A.D.
1720—1774) and THOMAS BRAND (who afterwards called
himself Brand-Hollis) were more numerous. These were
picked up by the two collectors, especially by the first, on
various journeys to Italy beginning with the year 1748,
and the number was completed by purchases in England.
After A.D. 1761 they were all placed in the Hyde, the
country seat of Hollis, in the hall constructed expressly for
the purpose[173]. At a later date, after additions by John
Disney, the collection was brought to Cambridge, where it
forms an important part of the University Museum. We
can only regret that its quality is, with few exceptions,
below the average; moreover there are not a few spurious
imitations side by side with the genuine antiques. The
blame must rest upon the purchaser, whether this was Hollis
himself or his Roman friend, Jenkins. Finally we come to

[172] *A Description of the Villa of
Mr Horace Walpole, at Strawberry-
hill, near Twickenham, Middlesex*
(*Works of H. Walpole*, II. pp. 393.—
516). Add to this the catalogue of the
sale: *A Catalogue of the Classic Contents of Strawberry-Hill collected by
Hor. Walpole*, April 25, May 21, 1842.
(A copy with notes of the buyers and
prices is in the possession of G. Scharf.)
Dallaway, *Anecd.* pp. 293, 384. The
Vespasian was sold for £220. 10s. See
Hamilton Palace. For the eagle, see
below,Cat.,art.London.Lord Wemyss
(sold for £210); for the Caligula, Walpole to H. Mann, 1767, May 30 (sold

for £48. 6s.); for the Serapis, Walpole
to Conway, 1786, June 18 (bought
by Walpole for £173. 5s., sold A.D.
1842 for £78. 15s.). Besides this
mention should be made of the sitting
Ceres with a cow in her lap (*Spec. Ant.
Sculpt.* II. Pl. 58; Clarac, 438 E, 786;
F. Müller-Wieseler, *Denkmäler* II. 8,
91), which was sold to Mr Cope for
£73. 10s.
[173] *Museum Disneianum*, preface.
For the origins of the collection, see
below,Cat.,arts.Cambridge and Hyde.
The *Memoirs of Th. Hollis, Esq.*,
London, 1780, 4to, tell us nothing
about the origin of the collection.

LORD ANSON and LORD MALTON, SIR RICHARD HOARE, MR WELLBORE ELLIS (afterwards Lord Mendip), and MR FOX (afterwards Lord Holland), who obtained a small number of statues and busts for their villas at Shugborough[174], Wentworth House, Stourhead, Twickenham[175], and Kingsgate (Isle of Thanet[176]); though their purchases did not give a distinctive stamp to the character of those country seats. Nevertheless the young Roman Prince Bartolommeo Corsini, who was travelling in England as early as A.D. 1753, expressed his surprise at the number of fine statues which he often found collected in country houses, even in those which were situated quite far from the high road and buried in the wilderness; he spoke of them as "dragged together out of all countries with vast pains and cost[177]."
But it was not these bargains that could have brought to the British their reputation in Rome as leading purchasers of antiques, nor to their native island that character as a strongbox of works of ancient sculpture which she was soon to enjoy.

---

[174] In Shugborough, Staffordshire, were several chambers adorned with a great number of statues, v. Pennant, *Journey from Chester to London,* Lond. 1782, p. 68 (Adonis, Thalia, Trajan in the attitude of haranguing his army, a number of rude Etruscan figures). Volkmann, *Reisen,* III. p. 294. Cf. Cavaceppi, *Raccolta,* I. 36 (Venus), 37 (Bacchus), 54 (Pedestal), II. 60 (crouching Venus), III. 54 (Pedestal). The collection has been sold, see Birmingham, Lowther, nos. 64, 65; Richmond, no. 40.

[175] Lord Mewlip's collection was sold by auction A. D. 1802. One of the principal buyers was H. Blundell. See under Ince.

[176] The Fox collection was subsequently brought to St Ann's Hill; see Cat. *sub voce.*

[177] This interesting letter, of which Justi informed me and which Dr Knapp has copied for me, is in the Corsini Library at Rome, Cod. 1568. It is addressed to the celebrated antiquary Bottari from London, dated Oct. 9, 1783. "*L'Inglesi da un certo tempo in qua si sono un poco più umanizzati:*

è vero che si ha da sostenere da essi un primo abbordo un poco freddo, e che prima di trattare una persona, la vogliono conoscere; conosciuta però che l'hanno, le cortesie che le praticano sono cordialissime, non essendo fondate che su l' amicizia, e non avendo altro fine che la medesima. Questo costume sarebbe desiderabile che fosse adottato da tutte le nazioni, la maggior parte delle quali fanno consistere la politezza del vivere in un vano e fallace esteriore....Abbiamo fatto un giro nella campagna ed abbiamo veduto le delizie et le fabbriche veramente magnifiche di questi signori. Tutto quello che v' è di più bello e di più grande, altrove nelle città, qui è in campagna; un superbo palazzo cavato da Vitruvio o da Palladio o copia delle opere de' più famosi architetti, ornato di bellissime statue e pitture astratte con gran fatica e spesa da tutte le parti del mondo, è situato non solamente in campagna, ma in luogo totalmente fuori di strada e deserto." Cf. also Winckelmann *Geschichte der Kunst,* pref. p. xxiii. (*Werke,* III. p. xv.)

42. Thomas Coke, by this time EARL OF LEICESTER, *Lord Leicester.* who had been a member of the Society of Dilettanti since A.D. 1740, was the first to strike another chord. He had had a magnificent palace built for him by the elder Brettingham on the north coast of Norfolk, at that time still desolate,—mainly after the designs of his former travelling companion Kent. Its whole west front was occupied by a beautiful gallery with two dome-roofed rooms adjoining. Here, as well as in the staircase hall, were niches provided for statues; but the specimens brought at an earlier date from Italy by the Earl himself were not sufficient to fill them, and it was necessary to make fresh purchases (about A.D. 1755). The commission was entrusted to the younger Matthew Brettingham, who had already bought busts for Lord Orford to adorn his neighbouring seat of Houghton Hall, and he now had an opportunity of proving, as he did not fail to do, that he was competent to execute a still more important commission. Eleven statues, eight busts, a relief, and some mosaic slabs were obtained through his agency, including a few modern and some insignificant specimens, but at the same time a considerable number of good and a few excellent works[17a]. The Silenus (no. 19) is one of the most remarkable statues which are to be found in any private collection in England; the Poseidon and the Venus Genetrix (nos. 18, 23), as well as the two colossal female statues (nos. 33, 34), are also of the highest interest. Among the busts the Thukydides and the so-called 'Sulla' (nos. 26, 29) are highly interesting; and finally the colossal head of the Aphrodite (no. 37) is a work of truly sublime beauty which would be an ornament to the richest museum. Not a few of the statues were purchased by Brettingham from Cardinal Albani, who at that time was making a fresh collection to adorn the villa which he was building, and who sold much that appeared to him of

[17a] For the information in detail see under Holkham.

secondary value with the view of obtaining something better in its place. That the first-rate Silenus, still incrusted with its earthy coating, was among them, may suffice to show that even such a practised connoisseur as Albani was to some extent liable to errors of judgment. Cardinal Furietti, the sculptor Carlo Monaldi, the dealer Belisario Amidei, and Cavaceppi were the men with whom Brettingham had most to do ; the last mentioned was employed by him especially upon the redintegration of the injured specimens. On the whole, Lord Leicester, who soon afterwards (A.D. 1759) died, had every reason to be contented with the execution of his commission.

Lord Egremont.
43. Still more extensive was the activity displayed by the same Brettingham for Charles Wyndham, second EARL OF EGREMONT. The grand collection of sculptures, which still in our day adorns the princely castle at Petworth, is almost entirely the fruit of Brettingham's exertions[179]. It includes at present no fewer than twenty-four statues, among them several of high value, while others are in an unusual state of preservation, and also nearly twice as many busts. Not a few of the latter are of interest ; a colossal female head of heroic character deserves, on the score of its grand expression and elevated style, a place of honour equal to that of the Holkham Aphrodite. Though Lord Egremont was lavish of the means for procuring these treasures, his agent no less deserves also that full recognition for his zeal and skill which was accorded to him later on by the Dilettanti[180]. Unfortunately we have hardly any information of the sources from which the specimens were derived. The celebrated Apollo (no. 5) had long before stood in the Vettori palace at Rome. A number of statues had passed through Cavaceppi's hands ; others were obtained secretly from private collections. Gavin

[179] For particulars see Cat., art. Petworth.
[180] *Specimens of Antient Sculpture*, I. on Pl. 72. As to the Duke of Somerset (Algernon Seymour 1st Earl of Egremont) being there named as the person who gave the commission, there is perhaps a mistake for his nephew, the second Earl, who succeeded him A. D. 1750.

Hamilton's name is also among those mentioned in connection with the forming of the collection. Be that as it may, the Egremont collection when it reached England was at any rate—perhaps with the exception of the Arundel Marbles at Oxford—the most extensive aggregate of antique sculptures in the whole country, and could bear comparison with any of them in point of value. Hence they received, even long afterwards, a special preference in the choice of plates for the *Specimens of Antient Sculpture*. First of all indeed, it was their lot to remain for a long time packed up in their cases. Meanwhile the collector died (A.D. 1763), and his son and heir was then still a child. This may account for the sale of certain specimens; but at the same time fresh purchases were occasionally made. The partially mutilated statues, which had often had to submit to sad restorations, gave rise to much shaking of the head in the neighbourhood; it being considered an excellent joke to describe the castle at Petworth as a "hospital for decayed statues." Appreciation of the beauty of ancient sculpture was at that time only just beginning to be felt ; and those who objected to the broken torsi did not bethink them how few statues have come down to us through the long succession of centuries in good and perfect preservation. As a matter of fact Petworth is comparatively rich in complete specimens.

44. Matthew Brettingham belonged to a band of *British Artists in Rome.—Gavin Hamilton.* young British artists at Rome, who had been pursuing their professional studies there since about A.D. 1740, and each of whom lived to render good service in more than one department. Among his friends were the two painters Gavin Hamilton, a Scotchman, and James Stuart, as well as the architect Nicholas Revett. In the year 1748 these four planned a journey together on foot to Naples[1]. The two latter have won for themselves a world-wide renown by their labours at Athens (A.D. 1750—1755). Of

[1] *Antiq. of Athens*, IV, p. xxviii.

the assistance which they received from several rich patrons
in the circle of the Dilettanti, mention has been made
above. The idea of making this expedition, which may
be said to mark an epoch, had in reality emanated from
HAMILTON, who was only hindered from taking part in it
personally by some circumstance unknown to us[182]. Instead
of doing this he was soon to display another kind of activity
along the same line as Brettingham, but on a far larger
scale. The preference which Hamilton as a painter showed
for Homeric and other classical subjects—every visitor to
the Villa Borghese knows his paintings from the Trojan
legends—stood in close connection with his enthusiasm for
ancient sculpture. At the same time he was not without
an eye to the main chance. While he hoped for scientific
advantages from the Athenian undertaking, he also had in
view the possibility of commercial profit, so that his love
for old sculpture was not purely platonic. He did not
allow the numerous opportunities of obtaining antique
marbles, which presented themselves in that age at Rome,
to escape him; and who can reproach him if he chose
to part with his purchases, to his fellow-countrymen on
their travels and to other amateurs, with advantage to
himself? It must be distinctly borne in mind that not the
least suspicion of any unfair or even questionable transaction has ever fallen upon Hamilton in connection with
his dealings in antiques. This is the more estimable,
seeing that lax principles in the art-trade of Rome were
quite a matter of course[183]. Hamilton had always been
known as a trustworthy and honourable gentleman, to
whom fortune was on that account so favourable as
generally to reward his spirit of enterprise with the richest
results[184].

[182] *Ibidem*, p. xxii.
[183] Justi, *Winckelmann*, II. 1, p.
318. Paciaudi, *Lettres au Comte de
Caylus*, Paris 1802, pp. 89, 264.
[184] Visconti repeatedly speaks of
Hamilton in terms of the highest

praise; in *Mon. Gabini*, pref., he calls
him "*zolertissimo ed indefesso cercatore
d'antichità.*" Cf. Fea, *Relazione di
un Viaggio ad Ostia*, Rome 1802,
p. 43.

45. Most intimately connected with the name of *Thomas Hamilton* is that of the Englishman, THOMAS JENKINS[185]. *Jenkins.* He too was originally a painter, though of far less talent than Hamilton, and was fortunate enough to be high in the favour of such a rich patron as Hon. Thomas Hollis, to whom he himself attributed his entire career and fortune. He had at his disposal considerable means, which he knew how to turn to advantage in two ways; partly as a banker, in which capacity he came into relation with the majority of his rich travelling fellow-countrymen; partly as a dealer in antiquities, whereby he understood how to use the said relation in the most profitable manner. In former days he enjoyed an unimpeached reputation. He was much looked up to on account of his artistic and historic knowledge, and was frequently consulted by Cardinal Albani, Winckelmann, and Raphael Mengs. On coins and gems he was especially an authority. He was courteous to scholars, and raised no difficulty about permitting them to make known any of the antiques in his possession. In this he showed himself to have more knowledge of the world than those who selfishly hid their treasures: for the money-value of a good work of art is increased rather than lessened by publicity[186]. He was generally looked upon as an honest and disinterested person; and was as such recommended by Winckelmann to be agent for the sale of the celebrated collection of gems, the property of the late Baron Stosch, which was afterwards purchased by Frederick the Great for Berlin[187]. This account of Jenkins' character is borne out by the following anecdote. It appears that a poor *valet de place* had purchased a cameo cheap and asked Jenkins' opinion as to its value. The latter paid him the high price of nine hundred pounds, with the words: "You are a poor fellow; I can

[185] Justi, *Winckelmann*, II. 1, p. 319—321. See especially Gorani, *Mémoires Secrets et Critiques...de l'Italie*, Paris, II. p. 25—28. Gorani was in 1779 and 1790 in Italy.

[186] Guattani, *Monum. Ined.* 1786, p. xxxii.
[187] Winckelmann to Muzel-Stosch, 1763, Dec. 7.

make your fortune without loss to myself; there are four thousand scudi." The lucky man, so the story continues, had a house built for himself with the money, and the following inscription introduced over the door :—" *Questa casa è fatta d'una sola pietra*[188]." But Jenkins did not keep himself free, as Hamilton did, from the noxious influences of certain Roman colleagues, men " for whom conscientiousness and scruple were incomprehensible ideas." He soon assumed something of that theatrical bearing, those affected raptures, by means of which the Italians understand so thoroughly how to impose and force hard bargains upon strangers. No one was a greater master than Jenkins of the art of making the best bargain out of his wares; as a rule it was only with great trouble that he could be induced to allow himself to name a price, naturally a very high one ; when the purchaser agreed to his figure, Jenkins did not tear himself from his darling gem without gestures of extreme emotion, and displays of extreme grief at parting from it. He would weep, and could even manage to draw tears from the sympathising purchaser. In fact to such an extent did he carry his acting that he declared himself ready at any time to take back the work of art he had sold, and this he has actually been known to do. " He would," observes our authority, Jos. Gorani, "furnish material for an excellent comedy. Perhaps his emotion is genuine, perhaps he is really attached to his stock-in-trade. In any case, if this affectation is part and parcel of his business, we must acknowledge that he has brought it to the highest possible degree of perfection."

His practices.   46. But Jenkins did not confine himself to acting ; he was unfortunately guilty of more evil practices. Let us hear the original testimony of Nollekens, who lived at Rome for nearly ten years, from A.D. 1760, and who was

[188] *Souvenirs de Charles-Henri Baron de Gleichen*, Paris 1868, p. 201. Gleichen was in 1755 and 1756—58 in Rome. Visconti, who drew up a catalogue for Jenkins of his inscriptions, calls him a " *mercante di ragione che fa onore alla sua patria*" (*Mus. Pio-Clem.* I. on Pl. 45).

himself actively engaged, now in renovating a small fragment of a terra-cotta relief by extensive additions, now in
lending an antique 'patina' to a marble figure, which had
been very much mended, by steeping it in tobacco juice[189].
J. T. Smith puts the following words into his mouth[190] : " I
got all the first and the best of my money, by putting
antiques together. Hamilton, and I, and Jenkins, generally used to go shares in what we bought; and as I had to
match the pieces as well as I could, and clean 'em, I had
the best part of the profits. Gavin Hamilton was a good
fellow, but as for Jenkins, he followed the trade of supply-
ing the foreign visitors with intaglios and cameos made by
his own people, that he kept in a part of the ruins of the
Coliseum, fitted up for 'em to work in slyly by themselves.
I saw 'em at work though, and Jenkins gave a whole handful of 'em to me to say nothing about the matter to any-
body else but myself. Bless your heart! he sold 'em as
fast as they made 'em." The history of the Minerva of
Newby Hall is an illustration of the enormous percentage
which Jenkins made[191], and what is related about the statue
of Venus in the same collection will serve to exemplify his
general mode of procedure in such matters. After he had
purchased the beautiful torso of Hamilton for a moderate
price, and had it furnished by Cavaceppi with a head
that did not belong to it, the statue was advertised as uninjured ; its origin was shrouded in mystery ; an extraordinarily high price, about which buyers and sellers were
bound to keep silence, was demanded, and then increased
on the score of the difficulty of obtaining permission for
exportation. By a false announcement that the King of
England was the purchaser the papal government was
cajoled into giving the permission[192], and finally an exact

[189] (Combe) *Ancient Terracottas in
the British Museum*, London, 1810.
Smith, *Nollekens*, I. p. 11, II. p. 62.
[190] *Nollekens*, I. p. 250.
[191] See Newby Hall, no. 23.

[192] Newby, no. 20. Dallaway in
Nichols' *Illustrations Liter. Hist.* III
p. 728. Winckelmann to Fuessly,
June 19, 1765, to Schlabbrendorf, June
22, 1765.

statement of every restoration was given to the custom-
house authorities in order to reduce the fees. In fact even
so brilliant a customer as Charles Townley, with whom
Jenkins carried out many joint undertakings, was not secure
against his tricks; and the former found it necessary to take
particular measures of precaution to protect himself from
imposition. This is shown by an often-repeated anecdote of
Dallaway's, if indeed it be authentic. The purport is that
Townley thought it advisable to appear suddenly incognito
at Rome on the occasion of one such joint excavation, and
was actually witness of the fact that Jenkins secretly put
out of the way the most valuable fragment that was found[193].

His pur-
chases of
antiques.

47. In spite of this the name of Jenkins appears in
connection with that of Hamilton on all occasions on which
Englishmen were collecting antiques in Rome at that
time. The reason of this must lie in the extraordinary
promptness with which Jenkins contrived to put himself
in possession of the coveted objects. Jenkins and Hamilton not only found out and bought up single specimens,
which were then, far more numerously than at the present
day, scattered through the halls, galleries, cellars and court-
yards of the palaces and private houses of the Eternal City;
but they also, the former especially, turned to account the
straitened circumstances of their possessors, so as to acquire
whole collections at one stroke. It was a favourable circumstance for Jenkins that about A.D. 1766 the Cardinal
Albani, in those days the most important and in fact almost
the only Roman collector, brought his purchases to a close,
his villa being just then finished after about ten years' work.
The formation of the Capitoline Museum had already been
completed. Accordingly the Villa Montalto or Negroni,
originally founded by that powerful Pope, Sixtus V., dis-

193 Dallaway *l. cit.* p. 727, repeated by Ellis, *Townley Gallery*, I. p.
4, who however already refers to the
somewhat different version, probably
emanating from Townley himself,
which is given in *Specimens of Antient
Sculpture*, I. on Pl. 40.

gorged all its treasures into Jenkins' depôt (A.D. 1786)[194].
The Duke of Modena, at that time the owner of the Villa
d'Este at Tivoli, the most fanciful creation of the Renaissance,
suffered from chronic shortness of funds, and so pretty
nearly about the same time the last remnants of its treasures,
still amounting to about sixty-five specimens, went the same
way, after the Capitol and the Villa Albani had had the
first and second choice among them[195]. The Villa Mattei,
an unusually rich museum, had a little before this undergone
a strange vicissitude, inasmuch as at the very moment when
its collection of sculptures was published in three folio
volumes (A.D. 1778), the originals were scattered to the four
winds, and no inconsiderable share of them fell into Jenkins'
hands[196]. The Altieri, Barberini, Capponi, Lante palaces,
etc.; the house of the late apothecary and art-collector,
Borioni; and many similar treasuries of antique art, whether
filled in more remote or more recent times, kept yielding up
to Jenkins rich material; he even extended his undertakings beyond Roman territory, purchasing, for instance, the
sculptures of the Caraffa-Colombrano palace at Naples[197].
Much was saleable without more ado. Other specimens
had first to be renovated, or if an earlier restoration had
not been successful, to undergo the treatment a second
time. A lively traffic therefore went on between Hamilton
and Jenkins on the one side, and, on the other, the sculptors and restorers, Cavaceppi first and foremost, then Albaccini, Antonio d'Este, Nollekens, Pacetti, Piranesi, etc.
All these moreover carried on their private business in antiques, so that there was no lack of competition. One of
the most dangerous competitors in the earlier part of this
period was Belisario Amidei, "our tyrant—all the more so

[194] Visconti, *Mus. Pio-Clem.*, III.
on Pl. 14. Guattani, *Monumenti Inediti*, 1787, p. xlvi. (Arsoli, Prince)
Notizie istor. della Villa Massimo,
Rome, 1836.
[195] Justi, *Winckelmann*, II. 1, p. 25.
See below, Cat., arts. Ince, Marbury.

[196] Amaduzzi in the preface to
the *Monumenta Matthaeiana*, 1778,
vol. I.
[197] The documents are to be found
in the descriptions of the particular
collections; see especially Ince, Marbury, &c.

because he is well-to-do and has no need to deal[198]." Jenkins however came out winner from this contest as from others.

48. In addition to the vast number of antiques which had long been known, and some of which had already often changed possessors and now were brought once more into the market, resources yet untouched revealed themselves to the spirit of enterprise that distinguished this band. The soil of Rome and of its environs has at all times been ready to yield up hidden treasures to the explorer, even though every one did not possess the divining rod of Cardinal Albani. As early as A.D. 1761 we hear of excavations which Jenkins set going in Corneto[199]; and amongst the sculptures obtained by Brettingham, for Lord Egremont, was a Satyr, which Hamilton had dug up in the Campagna[200]. But it is not till about the year 1770 that the succession of grand undertakings begins, in respect of which the Scotch architect, JAMES BYRES (A.D. 1733—1817), is occasionally mentioned in conjunction with Hamilton and Jenkins[201]. Such excavations were for the most part started at the risk of those who undertook them, and on the condition that the owner of the ground, the papal government, and the Pope himself, should all have a share in the find. Thus great hazard was involved in every enterprise, and many an attempt, undertaken at great cost, remained quite fruitless. Hamilton's practical instinct and luck in making discoveries displayed themselves in this connection. In the year 1769 he began this branch of work with an excavation in Hadrian's Villa, below Tivoli, that inexhaustible mine, which, worked at intervals ever

[198] Paciaudi, *Lettres à Caylus*, p. 133 (1760, March 22). Cf. Casanova, *Discorso sopra gl' antichi*, Leipz., 1770, p. iii.

[199] Paciaudi, *l. cit.*, p. 248 (July 10, 1761).

[200] Petworth, no. 6.

[201] Dallaway, *Anecd.*, p. 273. The Extracts of Letters from Gavin Hamilton to Ch. Townley in the same volume, pp. 364—381, are of great value, yet it would be desirable to make a fresh comparison of them with the originals, as the reasonable suspicion suggests itself that Dallaway has in this instance too proceeded with his usual carelessness, especially as to the dates. Cf. *The Academy*, 1878, p. 141, 142. An attempt on my part to get a sight of the originals has unfortunately come to nothing. Townley also carried on a correspondence with Byres for many years. See Ellis, *Townley Gallery*, p. 5.

since the sixteenth century, had yielded for the Farnese
and Este collections, and more recently for the Capitol and
the Villa Albani, an extensive series of their most precious
contents. Hamilton might have every confidence that he
would surely not dig here in vain. As a first step, it was
necessary to divert a lake, the so-called Pantanello, in order
to come at the desired point. The trouble was richly re-
warded by more than sixty marbles, chiefly busts, including
some of the first rank, which were buried in deep slime,
and, partly on that account, excellently preserved. Two
years later (A.D. 1771), followed an excavation which was
richer in statues, though otherwise perhaps less productive;
this was on the Via Appia, in the so-called *tenuta del Colombaro*[202]. The following years were full of fresh undertakings, attended, it is true, by varying results. Repeated
excavations, besides those on the Via Appia (at Roma
Vecchia), and at Prima Porta, were set on foot in the
country round the Alban Mountains (Albano, Grotta ferrata,
Genzano, Nemi); among these that undertaken at Monte
Cagnuolo, between Genzano and Civita Lavigna, was particularly distinguished for its yield of fine specimens[203].
In the year 1775 followed Castel di Guido, the ancient
Lorium, situated on the road to Civita Vecchia. This
revealed some good sculptures, such as the little Cupid
drawing a bow of the Townley collection[204]. In many
parts of the extensive circuit of the ancient town of Ostia
Hamilton repeatedly broke ground[205], sometimes with considerable results, although the limekilns which he discovered
bore witness to the former destruction of valuable marbles.
At last the malaria of the marshes compelled him to aban-
don his labours. A brilliant close to this prolonged activity
in exploration was made in the year 1792 by an excavation

202 Or Palombaro, see the map of
the Via Appia, by P. Rosa, in the
Monumenti dell' Instituto, v. Pl. 47.
203 *Brit. Mus.* II. on Pl. 45, X.
frontisp. and Pl. 25, 26.
204 *Museum Marbles*, II. Pl. 33,

35, 43. Petersburg, Hermitage, no. 5
(Lyde Browne, Cat. 1779, no. 36).
205 1775: *Mus. Marbles*, II. 22.
1776: *ibid.* I. 8, III. 5. 1788: Fea,
Viaggio ad Ostia, Rome, 1802, p. 43.
1792: Dallaway, *Anecd.* p. 376.

on the territory of the ancient Gabii (*Pantan de' Griffi*), which Hamilton carried out in conjunction with the owner of the ground, Prince Marco Antonio Borghese. These "*Monumenti Gabini*" did not however come into the art market, but were procured in their entirety for the Villa Borghese, and are at the present day to be found in the Louvre[206]. Private friends of art derived just as little advantage from the excavations which the Papal government instituted in different parts of their territory for the benefit of the Vatican Museum[207]. On the other hand, Hamilton and his comrades were by no means the only men who dug on speculation. For examples we may mention the group of Muses and the terminal portraits of men of letters, now forming the chief contents of the Hall of Muses in the Vatican, which were discovered by Domenico de Angelis in the *Pianella di Cassio*, not far from Tivoli (1772); a similar small find in the Villa Fonseca, on the Caelian (1773); an excavation by Niccolò la Piccola on the road from Tivoli to Palestrina (1775—76); the discovery of the splendid Massimi Diskobolos in the Villa Palombara on the Esquiline (1781); and the excavations of Count Fede in Hadrian's Villa, which brought to light, among other things, two fresh copies of the Diskobolos of Myron and the Lansdowne Herakles (A.D. 1791)[208]. After the year 1794 the most distinguished excavator was an English painter, ROBERT FAGAN, who dug with great success, and in particular obtained rich gains by repeated researches in the soil of Ostia[209].

49.   Thus during several decades the soil of Rome and a wide extent of surrounding country was most zealously

[206] E. Q. Visconti, *Monumenti Gabini della Villa Pinciana*, Rome, 1797.
[207] Visconti, *Museo Pio Clementino*, I.—VII. Guattani, *Monumenti Inediti*, 1784—1789, 1805.
[208] Tivoli: *Mus. Pio Clem.*, I. on Pl. 8. *Museum Marbles*, II. 32.—Villa Fonseca: *Mus. Pio Clem.*, VI. Pl. 20, 24, 31. *Museum Marbles*, X. Pl. 43, I.

—La Piccola: *Museum Marbles*, I. 10, 11, 37. (For another excavation made by the same person see Ince, no. 30.)—Villa Palombara: Cancellieri, *dissertaz. epistol. sopra la statua del discobolo*, Rome, 1806. —Count Fede: Welcker, *alte Denkmaler*, I. pp. 421—424.
[209] Fea, *Viaggio ad Ostia*, pp. 45—57. See § 62, and Cat., art. Deepdene.

turned up, and there resulted an abundance of treasures
which might more than content even the most eager purchasers. Naturally these were not exclusively works of either
the first or second rank. Those who undertook the task
might well be content if, amid much chaff, they found a
respectable quantity of good grain, and here and there, once
in a way, a pearl. To single these out a peculiarly refined
taste and practised eye were needed; to obtain them
when so selected, a heavy purse. For the most part the
newly discovered marbles came out of the earth in a
wretched plight, broken, mutilated, corroded, or encrusted
with the dirt of centuries. It was therefore always made a
great point that they should be properly cleaned—often
to the great detriment of their freshness—and vamped
up with old, or new, additions. Only after such treatment
could they be regarded as fit for a *salon*. Jenkins, who
knew men so well, made it a reproach to the conscientious
Hamilton, that "he did not understand the taste of English
virtuosi, who had no value for statues without heads; and
that Lord Tavistock would not give him a guinea for the
finest torso ever discovered[210]." Many purchasers flattered
themselves with the belief that they were in possession of a
genuine, well-preserved antique, when in reality only the
smallest part of it was ancient, and perhaps a peculiar
charm, something quite out of the common and worthy of
mark, had been attached to it by arbitrary additions. Such
additions gave opportunity for marvellous feats in the art
of mystic or other fashionable interpretation. "At Rome,"
says an eye-witness, "you may often see broken statues
made into busts or heads. I myself have looked on while
statues were sawn in half and attached to marble slabs as
reliefs, or conversely, while figures in good condition were
sawn off a relief, and a principal figure thus frequently
made out of a subordinate one. From this we can see

---

[210] Dallaway in Nichols' *Illustr.
Lit. Hist.* III. p. 728. For Hamilton's
opinion as to Jenkins, see his letter to
Lord Shelburne, Aug. 6, 1772 (*The
Academy*, 1878, p. 168).

what traps are laid for the learned...I only say this to
call attention to the fact of the difficulties which, in a few
centuries time, antiquaries will have with the antiquities of
our manufacture[211]." But who cared for this? *Mundus
vult decipi, ergo decipiatur* was the motto of those Roman
art-dealers. So long as their purchasers were contented
with these cobbled wares, they might leave it to professed
archæologists to discriminate between the genuine and the
spurious, and seek after the truth with pedantic conscientiousness; for themselves the only question was, what would
by the taste of those times be considered beautiful and paid
for as such. It is essential that we should bear in mind
this predicament of almost all the antiques brought to
England in the second half of the last century, if we would
form a just estimate of their value and make them available
for scientific purposes.

*King
George III.
The Duke
of Marl-
borough.* 50. In the year 1760, the young GEORGE III. ascended
the throne. He enjoyed the reputation of taking interest in
art, especially ancient art[212]; and even though he did not
collect marbles, yet he had shown this interest in two ways.
Through the agency of James Adam, a younger brother of
the royal architect, Robert Adam, celebrated for his work
on Diocletian's Palace at Spalatro, the King (A.D. 1762)
purchased from Cardinal Albani his grand collection of
drawings and prints at the price of fourteen thousand scudi
(about three thousand guineas). This collection had been
started in the seventeenth century by the Commendatore
Cassiano dal Pozzo, and was particularly valuable as preserving, at least in the form of copies, works of classic art
which have been since destroyed or lost to sight. The illustrious Winckelmann, who was librarian to the Cardinal, might
protest; but he found his master's need of gold more potent
than his own representations[213]. In the Royal Library, dal

[211] Casanova, *Discorso sopra gl'
antichi,* pp. xli., xlii., l.
[212] H. Walpole to H. Mann, 1760,
Nov. 1. Doran, "*Mann*" *and manners,* II. p. 98.

[213] Winckelmann to Mengs. 1762,
Juli 28 (*Opere di A. R. Mengs,* Rome,
1787, p. 424); to Usteri, 1763, Jan. 1.
For the collection itself see under
Windsor. A small but valuable por-

Pozzo's drawings found themselves side by side with those brought by Mead from Rome, and the latter may perhaps have suggested the purchase from the Cardinal[214]. In this manner was formed a collection which is perhaps unsurpassed in its way as a source of archæological knowledge. The second acquisition included the collection of gems belonging to Smith, consul at Venice, who had become bankrupt ; this, though far inferior to its fame, yet contained a few fine specimens[215]. From the same source came some drawings, probably at the same time with the consul's select library, which was purchased for the King as early as A.D. 1762[216]. With regard to gems, we may mention that the royal cabinet was far outdone by the precious collection formed by GEORGE SPENCER, THIRD DUKE OF MARLBOROUGH (succ. A.D. 1758, died A.D. 1817 . To the Arundel gems, which he obtained from his sister-in-law, he added the collection of Lord Bessborough, and a selection of excellent specimens out of the cabinet of the Venetian Count Antonio Maria Zanetti, together with other occasional purchases. Thus arose a cabinet of gems of unusual importance, rich alike in ancient jewels and in magnificent specimens of the art of the Renaissance; the Duke had the choicest of these engraved in costly style and published in a sumptuous *ouvrage de luxe*[217]. The

tion of the dal Pozzo collection has passed through the hands of Dalton, Macgowan, and Townley into the possession of A. W. Franks, Esq., of the British Museum.

[214] See note 118.

[215] Gori, *Dactyliotheca Smithiana*, II., Venice, 1767, edited under the King's patronage. C. D. Forinum, *Notes on some of the Gems and Jewels of Her Majesty's Collection at Windsor Castle* (*Archæologia*, XLV.), p. 3. According to Mariette (Letter to Paciaudi, Feb. 26, 1767, in Nisard's *Corresp. de Caylus* II. p. 346), Smith understood nothing about gems, and only collected so as not to be outdone by Zanetti (note 217). Cf. also Lady Mary Wortley Montagu's *Letters and Works*, III. p. 89. In the year 1758

the King, then Prince of Wales, had thought about buying the cabinet of the deceased Baron Stosch ; see Winckelmann to Franke, 1759, Jan. 1.

[216] Ashpitel, A., *On the Italian Architectural Drawings in the R. Library at Windsor*. Read at the Ordinary General Meeting at the Royal Institute of British Architects, June 16, 1862. Edwards, *Lives of the Founders of the Brit. Mus.* II. p. 469. Doran, "*Mann*" *and manners*, II. p. 99.

[217] Cf. §§ 23, 35. Story Maskelyne, *The Marlborough Gems*, 1870, p. VI. *Choix de pierres gravées du cab. du Duc de Marlborough*. II. 1780, 1791, 2nd ed., London, 1845. For Zanetti see Gori, *Gemme antiche di A. M. Zanetti*, Ven. 1750, fol.

King's love of collecting, which soon became known in
Italy, was used by the Roman dealers, such as Jenkins,
as a means of procuring under this flag unfettered transport to England for works purchased by private individuals,
their exportation out of the Papal States being in ordinary
cases forbidden[218]. Thus the King's interest, even though
illegitimately employed, stood his art-loving subjects in
good stead.

British
travellers.
51. The number of Englishmen who visited Rome
was meanwhile continually on the increase. The longing
to visit that wonderful city was not a little awakened or
stimulated by the magnificent engravings in which the
Venetian GIAMBATTISTA PIRANESI (A.D. 1721—1784), who
was afterwards assisted by his son Francesco, represented
the ruins of the Eternal City with wonderful poetic feeling
and artistic skill. The four folio volumes of his *Roman
Antiquities*, dedicated originally to Lord Charlemont, appeared A.D. 1756; the *Views of Rome* about a quarter of a
century later. Piranesi's name was soon in everybody's
mouth, his works in the libraries of all dilettanti. Men made
pilgrimages to Rome to acquaint themselves with these
astonishing monuments; whether their exalted expectations
were fulfilled or disappointed, depended on the degree of
enthusiasm and poetic feeling which they brought with
them. We become acquainted with many of the English
travellers of this day from Winckelmann's letters[219]. They
included some very original characters, such as Lord Bal-
timore, who under Winckelmann's guidance ran through
the Villa Borghese in less than ten minutes, and cared for
none of the ancient statues except the Apollo Belvedere[220].
The Duke of Gordon "shewed scarcely a trace of animation
as he sat in his carriage, while Winckelmann described to

Cf. Walpole to Mann, 1762, Jan. 4.
Mariette to Paciaudi, 1762, July 10,
1765, Febr. 1, March 28 (in Nisard's
Corresp. de Caylus, II. pp. 329, 353,
359). The Duke paid £480 for four
specimens.

[218] Cf. note 192.
[219] Justi, *Winckelmann,* II. 2, pp.
34—40. Winckelmann to Genzmar,
1764, Dec. 22.
[220] Winckelmann to Usteri, 1763,
Jan. 1; to Franke, 1763, Jan. 15.

him, with the choicest expressions and grandest illustrations,
the beauties of the ancient works of art[221]." With regard to
one or two others Winckelmann says: "They walk into
your house like very sticks, in a glamour of hypochrondria,
and like men who understand nothing of the spring-time of
life; for to joy they are strangers. How can any host take
pleasure in such charcoal souls[222]?" However they were not
all like this. Many evinced the liveliest interest in nature and
art, and Cavaceppi and Jenkins could relate stories of the
way in which this interest proved its activity in hard cash.
We have only to turn over the leaves of the three volumes
of Cavaceppi's *Raccolta d' antiche Statue*, published in the
years 1768—1772, if we would learn how great a part of
the sculptures that had passed through the hands of that
restorer have found their way to England; at the same
time the great number of those which are merely described
as "to be found in England," but are no longer traceable
at the present day, shows how many may still lurk here
and there in unknown hiding-places[223]. No price was too
high for the British purchasers; thirty thousand scudi
(about six thousand guineas) were offered to Cardinal
Furietti for the two black marble Centaurs which now
stand in the Capitol; and Locke had already advanced one
thousand zecchini (£600) for the Barberini candelabra, but
could not get permission to take them out of the country[224].
They afterwards (A.D. 1770) found their way into the Vatican.
"Perhaps it will occur to some mad Englishman to have
even Trajan's column transported to London,"—this indig-
nant utterance of Winckelmann describes the British passion
for costly undertakings, against which as " President of

[221] Winckelmann to Usteri, 1763,
March 18.
[222] Winckelmann to Fuessly, 1767,
June 3; to Riedesel, 1767. June 2.
[223] *Raccolta*, 1. 15—21, 35, 38, 39,
41, 43; II. 6; III. 2, 7, 12, 18, 19,
26, 29, 30, 32, 34, 37, 39, 42—44,
47, 49, 51, 52. On Pl. 16 of the

third volume there is a Venus represented, which went to the bottom of
the sea on the voyage from Italy to
England.
[224] Winckelmann to Riedesel,
1763. April; to Muzel-Stosch, 1763,
Dec. 7; 1766, Oct. 4.

Antiquities" he had in the interests of Rome to con-
tend[223].

*Lyde
Browne.*

52.   Certain collectors, almost exclusively members of
the Society of Dilettanti, stand out conspicuously among
this great crowd.   One of the most persevering was LYDE
BROWNE, who had been active ever since about the middle
of the century in forming the collection of sculptures which
adorned his house at Wimbledon.   He continued these
efforts during thirty years, availing himself in great measure of the assistance of Jenkins.   When he first issued a
catalogue in the year 1768[226], the collection already included a considerable number of sculptures, chiefly busts,
which had been obtained, partly from contemporaneous
excavations, partly from various Roman palaces and villas
(Barberini, Giustiniani, Massimi, Spada, Verospi, etc.).
Like Lord Leicester's agent Brettingham, and like Townley at a later date, Browne also obtained not a few specimens from Cardinal Albani.   But the most important
additions were made in the following decade, when Hamilton and his associates developed that activity which has
been described above ; a new catalogue dated A.D. 1779[227]
shows a very marked increase, including numerous specimens due to the excavations conducted by Hamilton.   It
almost appears as if Browne had contemplated the publication of some of his finest pieces; at any rate two statues,
twenty busts, and a relief were drawn by Cipriani on sheets
of large-sized paper, which quite give us the impression
that they were meant to serve as materials towards a publication[228].   Two of these drawings represent busts which

[223] To Muzel-Stosch, 1768, Febr.
26.

[226] *Catalogus veteris aevi varii
generis monumentorum, quae Cime-
liarchio Lyde Browne Arm. apud
Wimbledon asservantur.* 1768. (In
the Brit. Museum.)

[227] *Catalogo dei più scelti e preziosi
marmi, che si conservano nella Galleria del Sigr. Lyde Browne, Cava-*

*liere Inglese, a Wimbledon, nella Con-
tea di Surry, raccolti con gran spesa
nel corso di trent' anni, molti dei quali
si ammiravano prima nelle più celebri
Gallerie di Roma.*   London, 1779.
(In the Brit. Museum.) This is probably the catalogue which Dallaway,
Anecd. p. 389, got printed in the year
1787.

[228] These hitherto unused draw-

are to be found in the Egremont Collection at Petworth[229]; and some remarkable specimens of the Browne collection have reached the British Museum through Townley's hands, such as the beautiful head of a barbarian ("Decebalus") and an excellent head of an Amazon of the type ascribed to Polykleitos[230]. The final fate of the collection is also worthy of remark, as it is one of the few which have found their way out of England again. The Empress Catherine II. of Russia had engaged in the purchase of all kinds of antiques at Rome through the agency of Cavaceppi[231]. In the year 1780 her purchase of Lord Orford's valuable picture gallery at Houghton Hall, at the price of thirty thousand pounds, showed that such undertakings might succeed in England as well as elsewhere; and in A.D. 1785 an agreement was concluded with Lyde Browne by which his collection as it then stood passed for the sum of twenty-three thousand pounds into the possession of the Empress[232]. The affair, to be sure, was not brought to a conclusion without a hitch. Either the imperial agent became bankrupt after Mr Browne had received his first instalment, and the rest of the sum could not be recovered from the Empress[233]; or else, as another account goes, "the imperial Catherine failed in performing the whole agreement, to the satisfaction of the representatives of that gentleman[234]." We may therefore infer that the entire

ings have been in the British Museum since A.D. 1855, MS. Add. 21118. They must have been made between A.D. 1768 and 1779, as the numbers written on some of them refer to the older catalogue of 1768. The specimens which are not specified in this are not numbered at all. Sundry more extensive notices about Browne's purchases may be extracted from Townley's Memoranda in the Bodleian Library, Oxford.

[229] Nos. 11 and 15 of those drawings = Petworth nos. 38, 66.

[230] *Ancient Marbles Brit. Mus.* II. Pl. 27, III. 6, X. 3, 5, XI. 37.

[231] See Cavaceppi, *Raccolta*, and

Guédéonow, *Ermitage Impérial, Musée de Sculpture antique*, 2nd ed., Petersburg 1865, pref.

[232] The date according to Dallaway, *Of Statuary and Sculpture*, London, 1816, p. 274; in the *Anecdotes* he had said "about the year 1787." The sum he states in both places at the same figure; in the book of drawings (note 228) only £20,000 is mentioned.

[233] So according to Dallaway, *Anecdotes* (1800) p. 389.

[234] So in Dallaway's later version: *Of Statuary* (1816) p. 274. Or should we read "dissatisfaction"?

collection had not yet been removed to St Petersburg, a
conclusion which seems to be confirmed by the actual contents of the collections in that city[235]. And in this case the
acquisitions of Lord Egremont and of Townley, already
mentioned, may have been made from that part of the
collection which remained in England.

*Lord Pal-
merston,
Weddell,
Wal-
modon.*   53. In the year 1764 the young HENRY TEMPLE,
SECOND VISCOUNT PALMERSTON, made his Italian tour,
and brought back to Broadlands a small collection of
paintings and marbles. He had entered into business
relations with Hamilton and Cavaceppi; whether he had to
do with Jenkins as well is not apparent. Conspicuous
among the ancient marbles is a colossal head of Aphrodite,
which has unfortunately undergone rather serious injury.
Though of good Greek work, the Viscount bought it for
the insignificant price of five pounds, perhaps because the
head had remained without any renovation. It is this
very fact which in our eyes raises its value[236]. Far more
important were the purchases made in the following year
by WILLIAM WEDDELL, ESQ., one of the first on whom
Jenkins tried his skill in dealing; Weddell also had
transactions with Nollekens and Cavaceppi. He had to
pay high, and sometimes enormous, prices, but the selection
with which he adorned his country seat of Newby Hall
was undeniably valuable and tasteful. The Aphrodite and
the Athene are comparable with any statues in private
English collections; among the colossal busts there are
some of unusual interest and exalted beauty, and among

---

[235] The sculptures, formerly all
together in the Castle Zarskoje-Sselo,
are now some of them in the Castle
at Pawlowsk (Stephani, *Mm. de
l'Acad. Imp. de St. Pétersbourg*, 7th
series, vol. XVIII.), and some in the
Hermitage (Stephani, *Bulletin de
l'Acad.* XVII. p. 500—513). Several
of the principal specimens are not
forthcoming in St Petersburg.

[236] See below, Catalogue, art.
Broadlands. The date is settled by
Lord Palmerston's autograph memorandum concerning his purchases, for
acquaintance with which I am indebted to the kindness of the Rt.
Hon. W. Cowper Temple. Lord Palmerston travelled in the company of
Garrick and others; cf. Doran, "*Mann*
and manners, II. p. 114. In the
year 1770 Lord Palmerston had the
interesting monument of the Secun-
dinii at Igel near Trier drawn by W.
Pars, who accompanied him on a
renewed tour, see Schorn, *Abhandl. d.
Bayr. Akad.* XII. p. 272.

the sarcophagi two of great interest. For the most part
these sculptures had only come to light quite recently, but
among them seem to have been a few which had held a place
among the known antiquities of Rome as early as the sixteenth century. Weddell showed a refined taste in the sort
of sculpture gallery which he built in immediate connection
with his dwelling rooms ; it consisted of three comfortable
chambers of moderate dimensions, greatly conducive to quiet
enjoyment of the marbles. The piety of his successors
has maintained the original character of this gallery
quite intact[27]. In the same years HANS LUDWIG VON
WALMODEN, Minister Plenipotentiary for Hanover at
Vienna, was forming his collection, one of some importance, combining original antiques with excellent copies of
the most famous ancient statues ; the latter were executed
by Cavaceppi, Albaccini and others. Cavaceppi and Hamilton, with Nollekens, were the chief agents in these purchases. As son of the Countess of Yarmouth, Walmoden
stood in close relations to the Court of George II.; but
his collection gained a heightened interest in the eyes of
English connoisseurs from the fact that the possessor was
compelled to part with a large portion of it at a later time.
Lyde Browne was one of the purchasers. What is now to
be seen in the palace of Herrenhausen near Hanover is therefore only a remnant of the original Walmoden collection[28].

54. Among the Englishmen who at that time visited *Locke,*
Rome, but contented themselves with a smaller number of *Richmond,*
ancient sculptures, there are still a few who deserve *Duncombe,*
Jennings,

Duke of

---

[27] See Catalogue, art. Newby
Hall.

[28] *Verzeichniss der Bildhauer-
werke &c. in d n kgl. hannoverschen
Schlössern,* Hann. 1844, pp. 2—42.
Cf. Gori, *Archivio Storico di Roma,*
II. p. 214 (May 27, 1761). Winckel-
mann to Schlabbrendorf, 1762, Jan. 1.
Justi, *Winckelmann,* II. 2, p. 315.
Several interesting notices in reference
to that collection occur amongst Town-
ley's Memoranda in the Bodleian

Library, Oxford ; thus for instance we
find that the nymph with the shell
in Pawlowsk (No. 11 Stephani) had
passed from the Walmoden collection
and been purchased by Lyde Browne.
This was after the year 1779, as at
that date it is not to be found in the
Catalogue (note 227). The *Asteaga-
lizusa* of the Townley collection
(*Mus. Marbles,* II. Pl. 48) also belonged formerly to Walmoden (Winckelmann, *Gesch. d. Kunst,* XI. 3, 16).

Lord Exeter, Lord Yarborough, Lord Cawdor, &c. mention. WILLIAM LOCKE, ESQ., a descendant of the famous philosopher, had as early as the middle of the century, while staying at Rome, where he habitually associated with Wilton and Cipriani, acquired a lively interest in ancient and modern art; and had from time to time exerted himself to adorn his mansions in Norbury Park, Surrey, and Portman Square, London, with a few select specimens. We have already mentioned how he meditated, but did not effect, the acquisition of the Barberini candelabra[239]. The gems of his collection were a Diskobolos, and a beautiful torso of a Venus, which has become famous by its eventful fortunes. When Locke sold his antiquities in subsequent years, the torso, for which the Empress of Russia had sanctioned the offer of eight hundred pounds, passed for the same sum into the possession of CHARLES LENNOX, THIRD DUKE OF RICHMOND. This Duke of Richmond was a great lover of art, who, as early as the year 1758, had arranged in his house in Privy Gardens, Westminster, a gallery of plaster casts for the benefit of art students. Here the torso happened to be when a fire broke out in the house, A.D. 1791. The marble was much injured by the flames, and afterwards, at the sale of the Duke of Richmond's works of art, A.D. 1820, it was purchased for a guinea by a dealer in casts, who sold it again six weeks later to the painter Devis for fifteen pounds, soon after which it was transferred to the British Museum for the same price[240]. The Diskobolos was obtained by a member of the Dilettanti society, CHARLES DUNCOMBE, ESQ., who already possessed at his country seat of Duncombe Park a small number of statues and busts; to this he afterwards added a celebrated specimen, a dog, which Horace Walpole reckoned among the best representations of animals in classical art[241]. This dog

---

239 Note 224.
240 Nochden in Böttiger's *Amalthea* III. Leipz. 1825, pp. 3—18. Smith, *Nollekens* II. pp. 168—173.

180. *Anc. Marbles Brit. Mus.* XI. Pl. 35.
241 See Cat., art. Duncombe Park.

came from the collection of H. CONSTANTINE JENNINGS,
of Shiplake, once an ardent customer of Cavaceppi's, whose
art treasures were afterwards put up to auction[242]. Among
the customers of Nollekens was the EARL OF EXETER,
who behaved in the most generous manner in the disposal
of his antiques. He not only presented to the British
Museum the Arundel bronze head of 'Homer,' which he
had bought at Mead's auction, but also gave an excellent
head of Niobe, purchased from Nollekens, to the EARL
OF YARBOROUGH, who independently of this gift possessed one or two good marbles[243]. MR HOPE obtained
in the year 1763 a few antiques, notably a group of two
boys, playing with knuckle-bones[244]. Many of the collectors who have been already mentioned were probably also
active at this period ; the EARL OF BESSBOROUGH, for
instance, does not seem to have formed his collection at
a single purchase ; and more than one of the DUKES OF
DEVONSHIRE assisted the efforts of the Dilettanti. The
MARQUIS OF MONTHERMER, whose antiquities passed
into the possession of the DUKE OF BUCCLEUCH[245], LORD
CAMELFORD[246], SIR JOHN MACPHERSON[247], and LORD
CAWDOR may also have made collections at this time,
but it is impossible for me to speak more exactly on
the subject. The same Lord Cawdor was one of the

242 Cavaceppi, *Raccolta*, I. Pl.
6–9. The Athlete came into Lord
Cadogan's possession (Dallaway, *A-
need.* p. 390).

243 See Cat., art. Brocklesby, nos. 5,
15. Lord Exeter also possessed a Bacchus (Dallaway, *Anecd.* p. 390). If I
am not mistaken a sale of objects of art
once took place at Burleigh House.

244 Winckelmann *Monum. Ined.*
1. p. 41, and in a letter to Bianconi
1763 March 26(Fea, *Storia* III. p. 236).
See Heydemann, *Knöchelspielerin im
Palast Colonna*, Halle, 1877, p. 17.
Cavaceppi, *Raccolta* I. 22 (Venus). I
do not know where these marbles are
kept, certainly not at Deepdene, although Hope belonged to the Scoto-
Dutch family, so that the title of

'Lord' was only conferred on him by
Cavaceppi and Winckelmann owing
to Italian misuse thereof.

245 Both were members of the Dilettanti Society. Dallaway, *Anecdotes*,
pp. 337—339, enumerates three statues,
fourteen busts and four miscellaneous
specimens at that time set out in
Privy Gardens, Westminster. So far
as I know the collection was not
conveyed over to Montagu House,
but is dispersed. Cf. moreover Waagen. *Treas.* I. p. 37.

246 Dallaway, *Anecd.* p. 386: a
fountain Nymph and several other
good statues.

247 Dallaway, *Anecd.* p.386: about
twenty mutilated heads, and two small
figures, imperfect.

first men in England to start a collection of painted vases[248].

55. These English collectors of the seventh decade of the last century had in their purchases at least the advantage of a scarcity of rivals. The French appear to have taken no part in the competition[249], with the exception of Count Caylus, who however collected no marbles and who died as early as A.D. 1765. The Russian Empress and the King of Prussia, the Prince of Dessau and General Walmoden, were the only competitors besides a few private individuals, and their purchases seldom exceeded moderate limits. Of Romans themselves, hardly any made a collection except Cardinal Albani, and he had in essentials already completed his purchases. This state of things was suddenly and completely changed by the death of Clement XIII. (whose interest in art had limited itself to providing the naked angels in his pictures with clothes, and the antique statues in the Belvedere with tin fig-leaves), and by the accession of the cultured Cardinal Ganganelli to the papal throne, under the name of Clement XIV. (A.D. 1769). At this time it seemed once more, as at the beginning of the century, as though the enormous export of antiques, particularly to the "galleries of the Scauri and Luculli of Great Britain[250]," were threatening Rome with the loss of her choicest treasures, and all the more so from the richness of the yield just then in course of being gathered in from the excavations newly undertaken by Gavin Hamilton and others. The Pope therefore decided to follow the

---

[248] The collection enjoyed a high reputation, see Dallaway, *Anecd.* pp. 388, 391. *Of Statuary*, p. 350. In the sale in the year 1800 such men as the following interested themselves as purchasers: Townley (*Anc. Marbl. Brit. Mus.* III. Pl. 4, x. Pl. 27), Blundell (see Ince, pref.), the Duke of Bedford (see Woburn, nos. 61, 101, &c.). For the vases see Dallaway, p. 387.

[249] Paciaudi to Caylus 1760 Jan. 23 (*Lettres*, p. 118), "*je suis bien étonné*

qu'à Paris il n'y ait point d'amateurs ...je crois que c'est comme chez nous, personne ne fait plus de cabinet... Je suis vraiment fâché que ces diables d'Anglais emportent dans leur pays ces belles antiquités." Caylus confirms this, see Nisard, *Correspondance inédite du Comte de Caylus*, Paris, 1877, I. p. 144.

[250] Guattani, *Mon. Ined.* 1784. p. 9.

example of Clement XII. and Benedict XIV. by starting
as a collector himself, and he received the most ardent
co-operation from his treasurer, Monsignore Braschi; who
in the year 1775 succeeded Clement in the chair of Saint
Peter as Pius VI., and carried out on a much extended
scale the plans of his predecessor. Instead of enlarging
the Capitoline Museum, it was soon thought more expedient to append a new museum, the MUSEUM PIO-
CLEMENTINUM, to the already long-illustrious Belvedere
statues in the VATICAN PALACE. The superintendence
and publication of this collection were entrusted to Giambattista Visconti, and after his death, to his son, the great
Ennio-Quirino. The right of the government to forbid the
export of valuable specimens, which now resembled a right
of pre-emption, was more stringently exercised, and a
severe rivalry maintained against foreign amateurs for the
acquisition of high-class marbles. On the other hand, enterprising spirits were encouraged to begin fresh excavations,
the government waiving certain onerous preliminary rights.
Moreover the government itself, in emulation of private individuals, undertook, for the benefit of the new Museum,
several excavations that proved highly productive. The
rooms of the Museum increased yearly in space and magnificence, and when about ten years had passed, although
by no means completed, it was considered the first Museum
in Rome and even in the world[201]. In truth it was high time
for the Eternal City to bestir itself. In the year 1775 one
of the most famous collections, that of the Villa Medici,
was removed to Florence, whither some of the principal
specimens had already been taken a century before. The
imminent extinction of the house of Farnese in Parma
threatened with the same fate the collections of the Farnese Palace and the Farnesina. These were actually transported to Naples in the year 1787, after the King of Naples

[201] A detailed history of the Vati-   The works mentioned in note 207
can Museum has not yet been written.   furnish the principal data.

had succeeded to the inheritance, and were there combined, in the Museo Borbonico, with the splendid results of the Herculaneum excavations.

*Competi-
tors from
other
quarters.
Charles
Townley.*

56. This new enterprise on the part of the papal government made it harder for private individuals to compete. All the more credit therefore is due to those who entered the field in spite of obstacles. They sometimes met with brilliant success, a success which, to be sure, was only rendered possible by the spirit of enterprise displayed as above narrated by Hamilton, Jenkins and others. The Pope's example and the activity of the foreigner seemed to have their effect even on the Italians themselves. Monsignore Chigi and the Prince Borghese engaged in excavations on their estates which proved highly productive, while Monsignore Borgia struck out other ways of forming for himself a remarkable collection. The Spanish Ambassador, Azára, developed in this direction great eagerness and activity, the fruits of which at a later date were turned to the advantage of the Royal Museum at Madrid; just as the similar exertions of Cardinal Despuig served to embellish a distant country house on the Island of Majorca. The Spanish Cardinal Zelada, again, formed a collection of coins. Gustavus III. King of Sweden, and the Landgrave Frederick II. of Hesse, employed a brief sojourn at Rome in founding or enriching the Museums at Stockholm and Cassel. Polish emigrants such as Poniatowsky and Potocki were among the followers of the fashion. The front rank however was still occupied by the English, notably by CHARLES TOWNLEY (A.D. 1737—1805)[182]. This gentleman sprang from an old family in Lancashire, and was

[182] The principal authority on Townley is the memoir by Dallaway, which first appeared A.D. 1811 in *The General Chronicle and Literary Magazine*, vol. V., and was afterwards republished in John Nichols' *Illustrations of the Literary History of the Eighteenth Century*, III., London, 1818, pp. 721—746, and in the extract in Dallaway's *Of Statuary*,

p. 324. From this source Ellis' account, *The Townley Gallery*, I. pp. 1—13, is almost exclusively derived; cf. Edwards' *Lives of the Founders of the British Museum*, pp. 369—380. There are shorter articles in Chalmers and in the *Biographie Universelle*, and several interesting details in Smith's *Nollekens*, I. pp. 257—266.

on his mother's side a descendant in the sixth degree of
the old Earl of Arundel. He was brought up in France,
and his first visit to Italy was paid in the year 1765. As
an ardent Jacobite he found all doors open to him at
Rome, where he lived for a good many years; he also
visited the South of Italy and Sicily. At Naples he struck
up a friendship with William Hamilton, the British Envoy,
and it was in this city that he formed that acquaintance
with the adventurer Pierre François Hugues, which proved
so perversive of his scientific views. Hugues, a native of
Lorraine, is best known to us under the pseudonym which
he had then adopted, Hancarville[251]. It must have been
this companionship which awakened in Townley that interest in antiques which he soon displayed with such spirit
and munificence that he may be designated the successor,
not merely in time but in spirit, of Cardinal Albani. He
entered into close connection with Gavin Hamilton and
Jenkins, and had a considerable share in their undertakings, which he promoted with his gold, sharing with
them their risks and their successes. His first acquisition
was that remarkable fragment, the group of two street
boys who have fallen out over their game at knuckle-
bones. This he purchased, A.D. 1768, from the widowed
Princess Barberini. In spite of the competition set on foot
in the mean time by the Vatican Museum—Townley being
in Italy A.D. 1765—1772, and Clement XIV. having begun
to collect A.D. 1769—in spite of this, the Roman collections
and the new excavations afforded sufficient opportunity to
Townley for the formation of a rich collection, which he by
no means restricted to marbles. Bronzes, coins, gems, vases
were obtained at great expense, while a look-out was also
kept for drawings. To a collector of such means and such
zeal, four years' residence at Rome must have been sufficient
to put into shape a museum such as might well challenge
comparison with any of the collections of his countrymen.

[251] Justi, *Winckelmann*. II. 2, p. 381.

M. C.

57. In the year 1772 Townley quitted Rome and moved his quarters to London, where he bought himself a house in Westminster (7, Park Street) and fitted it up according to his tastes. Here the sculptures he had up to this time acquired found a suitable resting-place. Neither his relations with Rome, however, nor his purchases, by any means came to an end; on the contrary, he remained in constant communication with Hamilton and Jenkins, and re-visited Rome himself from time to time. Thus for about twenty years his collection still kept continually receiving rich additions from Italy; being farther increased by all kinds of purchases in England (*e.g.* from Lyde Browne) and by presents, as from Lord Cawdor. It was not till within the last ten years of the century that it could be regarded as on the whole completed, though even then, until a short time before Townley's death, single specimens were occasionally introduced. By this time it formed one of the greatest sights in London, and might in fact have taken a high place among the collections of antiques of the day, not only in England but in all Europe. The sculptures were distributed with rare taste in the various rooms of the house, so that the visitor found his impressions being constantly deepened. Hall, staircase, and parlour were adorned by preference with sepulchral monuments, inscriptions, and terra cotta reliefs. The drawing-room contained a selection of the most beautiful busts, including Townley's favourite, that exquisite portrait of a Roman lady, which is best known under the name of the Clytie; other heads, such as that of Homer, with its pictorial mode of execution, served as appropriate adornments for the library. But the most brilliant room was the dining-hall, against the walls of which stood the finest statues of the collection, while outside the windows the glance swept over the pleasant verdure of St James's Park. In this room Townley delighted to give on Sundays dinners worthy of their surroundings. His guests were partly artists, partly his friends

among the Dilettanti Society (which Townley joined in the
year 1786), partly foreigners of distinction. An event of
importance occurred in the year 1784, when, in company
with Sir William Hamilton, Hancarville came to pay a
long visit at Townley's hospitable mansion, and there
finished his great work[254], a fantastic farrago of mystico-
symbolical revelations and groundless hypotheses which
utterly captivated both Townley and Payne Knight. This
was the wisdom which Townley delighted to dish up for
the visitors to his collection, towards whom he always displayed the greatest amiability and liberality—a genuine
mystagogue of the most genial type. A painting by
Zoffany, a regular guest at the house, represents Townley
in his library, surrounded by his beloved books and a few
chosen antiques, in conversation with Hancarville, near
whose chair stand Charles Greville and Thomas Astle :
it affords a lively illustration of the animated intercourse
which we may suppose to have been occasioned, at the
focus of antiquarian science and antiquarian interests, by
Hancarville's presence in London[255].

58. Another Lancashire man, a friend of Townley, *H. Blun-*
though considerably older, was HENRY BLUNDELL (A.D. *dell.*
1723—1810), resident at Ince[256]. It is said that he accompanied Townley on one of his journeys to Rome, and was
there seized with the rage for collecting ; according to
another account, he already possessed his best specimens
before he became acquainted with Townley. At any rate
it is certain that his first purchases were made from
Jenkins in the year 1777[257]. At that time Blundell was
already fifty-four years of age. But, as if eager to make
up for lost time, he pursued the undertaking he had

---

[254] *Recherches sur l'Origine, l'Es-*
prit et les Progrès des Arts de la Grèce.
London, 1785, II. 4to.
[255] The original is in Townley
Hall, and has been engraved.
[256] Dallaway in Nichols' *Illustra-*
tions, III. p. 739 (repeated : *Of*
Statuary, p. 352). Spiker, *Reise durch*
England im J. 1816, Leipz., 1818,
I. pp. 396—403. For the rest see
under Ince.
[257] See on Ince, no. 44.

begun with zeal and energy. Visconti, who knew him
personally, calls him a man of fine taste[208]. Blundell himself bore the expressive motto *age quod agis*. His chief
agent was a Mr Thorpe, once a member of the now extinct
order of Jesuits. Jenkins remained the principal purveyor,
and from his stores numerous specimens, which had once
stood in the Villa Mattei, found their way to Ince, whither
they were afterwards followed by the most important
specimens of the Villa d'Este and a few from the Villa
Negroni. There are many among this number which do
not serve to raise our opinion of Jenkins' business principles; for instance, not a few sepulchral monuments,
which had hitherto stood in the Villa Mattei without inscriptions, were in the interval made more valuable by the
addition of 'antique' inscriptions. Many other collections
were ransacked besides the depôt of Jenkins, and the most
various dealers in art were laid under contribution. Importation in this quarter continued till after the year 1790,
and many piquant particulars are related in connection
with it; as, for instance, that on one occasion Blundell
recognised and bought among some French war plunder in
London a relief (Ince, No. 221), which he had himself on a
previous occasion purchased in Rome and presented to the
Pope. At the beginning of our own century sales in London
still yielded rich and precious objects. An example full
of comic naïveté of the manner in which people at Ince
thought they might deal with remarkable monuments to fit
them for modern inspection is furnished by the marble
numbered 25 in that collection. The Ince marbles could in
no wise be compared as to quality with those of Townley,
which they perhaps even surpassed in number; but still
they do not deserve the contemptuous verdict which has
been passed upon them in many quarters. The worst feature
of the collection is that its really good and in several
instances exquisite specimens are thrown into the shade

[208] Visconti, *Museo Pio Clem.*, III. on Pl. A, 9.

by so many that are unimportant or quite worthless, or
badly disfigured by restorations, or spurious. No collection in the world had need to be ashamed of the Theseus
(No. 43). Among the heads, as among the reliefs, there are
many of distinguished merit; but sight and mind become
stupefied if they have to toil through hundreds of inferior
marbles. A rigorous weeding-out could only have heightened the value of the collection, and the praise expended
by Visconti on the collector is misleading. It is still worse
if we read the commentaries of the collector himself, which
he partly set forth in a printed catalogue (A.D. 1803),
partly dictated on his death-bed, as the text for a great
illustrated publication (A.D. 1809). Side by side with most
homely trivialities we here once more encounter that insipid
mystic symbolism of Hancarville, which seems to be inspired by Townley, but is not seldom criticised in a re-
freshing manner by a rationalistic doubt of Blundell's
own. The collector's love for his treasures gave further
proof of its sincerity in the stately buildings which he
had erected for their reception. The dome-room of the
so-called Pantheon is in fact a very imposing chamber,
which may well remind us, *si parva licet componere magnis*,
of the Rotunda of the Vatican Museum. The museum at
Ince accordingly became a favourite resort for lovers of
art and curiosity from the neighbouring Liverpool, to such
an extent that the comfort of the inmates was occasionally disturbed thereby, and in consequence obstacles
were placed in the way of visitors.

59. It was chiefly from the same sources and about
the same time that JAMES SMITH-BARRY formed the collection with which he adorned the gallery and a hall of
his country seat, Marbury Hall in Cheshire[269]. The names
of Hamilton and Jenkins, of the Villas Mattei and Este,
once more come before our notice, so that the collector
appears to have been a direct rival to Blundell. The &c.

Smith-Barry, Mansed-Talbot, Sir Thomas Robinson, Duke of Dorset, Sir G. Strick-land, Duke of St Albans, &c.

[269] See Cat., art. Marbury.

limitation in number to a comparatively few specimens can
scarcely be regarded as a disadvantage; for the more valuable statues are more easily appreciated among them. We
must regard as its brightest ornament the *ara* from Naples,
transformed by the restorations of Jenkins into a vase,
representing Paris captivated by the beauty of Helen, the
Roman imitation of a Greek original. Besides this we
must not pass over one or two small but genuine Greek
fragments in this collection, as such treasures were at that
time seldom met with in English galleries.—The activity
of THOMAS MANSEL-TALBOT, who also amassed his sculptures through the help of Hamilton and Jenkins[260], dates
perhaps from a somewhat earlier period, apparently not
later than the eighth decade of the century. His little
collection included two or three specimens of considerable
merit, quite undeserving of the fate, which they shared with
the Petworth marbles, of lying packed up for a long time
in their cases until a place was cleared for them in the
conservatory. To the remoteness of Margam Abbey (it is
probably the only place in Wales which can boast of a
collection of ancient marbles) we must ascribe the fact that
the antiques in the conservatory and afterwards in the hall
have remained scarcely less unknown to the learned world
than at the time when they were still shut up in their
cases.—Among the collections of still smaller extent which
were, like these, formed by Jenkins' assistance at that
period, the following deserve mention. SIR THOMAS
ROBINSON founded the collection, consisting especially
of busts and statuettes, which is to this day to be found
at Rokeby Hall[261]. Its chief attraction was a large relief of
the children of Niobe, found at Naples; this was to have
been sent by the King of Naples as a present to the King
of Spain, but fell into the hands of English men-of-war.
—Busts again form the majority of the sculptures with

[260] See Cat., art. Margam.
[261] See Cat., art. Rokeby Hall. Dallaway, *Anecd.*, p. 388.

which JOHN FREDERICK, THIRD DUKE OF DORSET (died
A.D. 1799), decorated the venerable rooms at Knole ; but
they are far exceeded in value by the remarkably well-
preserved statue of Demosthenes, which found a worthy
resting-place in the ancient hall of that mansion[262].—SIR G.
STRICKLAND set up about a dozen marbles in Boynton
Hall. The taste displayed in their selection was spoken
of in high terms. Especial admiration was bestowed on
one statue of a so-called Juno, remarkable equally for its
workmanship and for its preservation[263].—GEORGE, LORD
TEMPLE, afterwards MARQUIS OF BUCKINGHAM (A.D.
1753—1813) adorned the spacious gardens of Stowe with
a few marbles, especially vases artistically enriched, which
he had brought with him from Italy in the year 1774[264].—
GEORGE, THIRD DUKE OF ST ALBAN'S (d. A.D. 1786)
brought home about A.D. 1780 a number of marbles from
Rome of less importance. The finest of these were purchased by Townley at the Duke's sale[265]. A near relation of his, LORD VERE, possessed a few sculptures at
Hanworth[266], and LORD BATEMAN had a Hermes at
Shobden on which a particularly high value was set by
Townley[267]. BROWNLOW NORTH, Bishop of Winchester,
decorated the episcopal residence at Chelsea with all kinds
of antiquities, which he had collected in the year 1791 in
Italy[268]. Finally DR ADAIR was at Baiae in A.D. 1771 just
when a couple of bearded heads of Dionysos were found ;
these he bought, and parted with at a later date to Townley[269].

60. High above all these collections of the second and
third rank stands the magnificent museum formed in the

*Lord
Shel-
burne.*

---

[262] See Cat., art. Knole.
[263] See Cat., art. Boynton.
[264] Stowe, A Description of the
House and Gardens of George-Grenville-
Nugent-Temple, Marquis of Buckingham. Buckingham, 1797, 4to.
H. R. Forster, The Stowe Catalogue,
London, 1848, p. 47, nos. 726, 728,
739, 745. Dallaway, Aneed., p. 383.
[265] Anc. Marbles Brit. Mus., V.

Pl. 2, 5; 9, 3; X. 1. Ellis, Townley
Gallery, II. p. 64; Spec. Ant. Sculpt.,
I. Pl. 31.
[266] Dallaway, Aneed., p. 390: "a
few marbles, sold in 1798."
[267] See Shobden.
[268] Faulkener, History of Chelsea,
I. p. 293.
[269] Anc. Marbles Brit. Mus., II.
Pl. 29, 30.

last decade of the century by WILLIAM, SECOND EARL OF
SHELBURNE, afterwards FIRST MARQUIS OF LANSDOWNE
(A.D. 1737—1805)[20]. Though deeply involved in the
politics of his time, Lord Shelburne showed the liveliest
interest in nature, art, and science. He gave proofs of
this by his gardens at Bowood, the building of Shelburne House, his art collections, and the founding of his
library. In the year 1771, after the death of his first
wife, and in a breathing-space in his public activity, he
visited Italy. The fact of his not afterwards joining the
Dilettanti Society is fully explained by the preponderance
of other political parties in that body. At Rome, Lord
Shelburne, who at that time was planning the building
of his new palace, entered into close relations with Gavin
Hamilton, by whom he had a plan sketched for the arrangement and decoration of a sculpture gallery. A small
number of antiques were purchased by him personally,
others were procured for him by Hamilton in the following years; these were partly the choicest specimens from
Hamilton's own excavations, partly the result of purchases
elsewhere. Shelburne had done well to turn to a man of
honour like Hamilton, instead of to Jenkins. Considering
the number of competitors, among whom the Vatican
Museum stood in the first rank, it is surprising to see how
fine a selection of excellent works was brought together.
It is true that the purchases were continued for a long
time, into the last decade of the century, but the majority
of the most remarkable marbles are the result of Hamilton's earlier excavations in the years 1770—1780; e.g. the
so-called Jason, the Hermes, the Amazon, and the Discobolus, which last has been badly disfigured by mistaken
restoration. The Herakles, however, did not come to light
till later. Among the heads there are not a few of con-

[20] Fitzmaurice, Lord Edmond,
Life of W. Earl of Shelburne, London,
1875—76, particularly II. p. 226, III.
p. 445. The Academy, 1878, Aug. 10,
17, 24, 31, Sept. 7. Cf. Cat., art.
London, Lansdowne House.

spicuous merit ; the Hermes, with the petasus, has become
a general favourite.   Finally, we have a few excellent
reliefs.   It is instructive to compare this collection with
that of Blundell, which was begun a little later (A.D. 1778).
While at Ince the crowd of worthless specimens hinders
and impairs the enjoyment of what is really good, the
collection at Lansdowne House bears a truly aristocratic
character.   The value of the collection, however, is appre-
ciably raised by the tasteful manner in which Lord Lansdowne applied it to the decoration of his new-built palace.
No bare sculpture gallery was erected for them, in which
the chilliness of the marbles one beside the other is often
apt to have a chilling effect on the visitor ; but, as is also
the case at Holkham Hall, the stately reception rooms
were throughout prepared to accommodate them, and the
works produced for decoration were once more introduced
into the midst of life.   On his first entry, the hall and the
staircase gave the right tone of feeling to the visitor.   In
the dining-hall and breakfast-room a number of niches
were adorned with smaller but by no means insignificant
statues.   The library, at that time still the shelter of those
manuscript treasures which later found their way to the
British Museum, added to these possessions the appropriate decoration of a row of portraits and other busts ;
and received its crowning ornament in the ' Jason.'
Finally, there is true magnificence in the impression produced by the great ball-room, with its two semi-circular
ends, in which there are spacious niches containing the
finest treasures of the collection ; between the niches, as in
the Rotunda of the Vatican, either a lovely head, or a
statuette, on pillar-pedestals.   Smaller groups, reliefs, an
excellent bust of Athene, etc. are distributed in the middle
of the room.   With perfect right we may designate the
whole arrangement, the rooms and their decorations, as
one of the most distinguished and tasteful creations of
the kind, which in England at any rate can scarcely find

its peer. One likes to imagine moving about these rooms
that choice society which the refined owner well knew how
to collect about him, finding in their animated discussions
some compensation for the numerous annoyances of his
political career.

Thomas
Hope.

61. A similar fine taste for art regulated the activity
in collecting displayed by THOMAS HOPE, a member of the
rich family of bankers, who had returned to his English
home and people from Amsterdam. He made a collection
in the last ten years of the eighteenth century; two of the
principal specimens of his collection, the great Athena, for
a long time wrongly considered a copy of the Parthenos of
Phidias, and the beautiful Hygieia were only dug up in
A.D. 1797 at Ostia by Fagan[271]. The collection of Greek
vases, which came from Sir William Hamilton, formed a
very distinctive part of his art treasures. Though Hamilton
had some time before sold a first collection to the British
Museum, excavations undertaken in A.D. 1789 and 1790
and other purchases had supplied him afresh with abundance of material for a second. In the year 1798 he sent
the whole to England, with a view of selling it there, after
an attempt to dispose of it at Berlin for seven thousand
pounds had fallen through. Eight chests, a third part of
the freight, were lost by shipwreck; the rest was purchased in the year 1801 by Hope, and served him as
the foundation of his collection, which he still further
increased from various other sources[272]. The owner, with
his fine taste for art, now brought his entire mansion in
London (Duchess Street) into the most correct accord
with his collections which he could devise. All the rooms
and all their contents, down to the humblest utensil or

[271] See Deepdene. Cf. *Gentl.*
Mag., 1831, Apr.
[272] W. Tischbein, *Collection of*
Engravings from Ancient Vases dis-
covered 1789 and 1790, now in the
possession of Sir W. Hamilton, Naples,
1791—180?, IV. The letterpress is

by Hamilton, Prince Italinsky,
the Russian ambassador, and Fon-
tanini. Cf. J. H. W. Tischbein, *Aus*
meinem Leben, Brunswick, 1861,
II. pp. 169—180. Edwards, *Lives of*
the Founders of the British Museum,
I. p. 357.

piece of furniture, were made after Hope's own drawings
and designs, not uninfluenced by the Pompeian discoveries,
and at the same time in full harmony with the antiquarian tendencies of art in the Napoleonic era[273]. The
statue-gallery was bordered on both sides with statues,
the picture-galleries derived an air of life from a few
marbles, and the vases served as the main adornment of
three rooms. In this condition the Hope collection remained during many years in London, much visited and
admired by strangers; at last it was taken to the magnificent country seat of Deepdene, once the property of the
Howard family. The classical sculptures, intermingled
with masterpieces of Thorwaldsen and Canova, and with
copies of celebrated antiques, there form a magnificent
adornment to the galleried hall and to some other apartments. Of the collection of vases, only a remnant is preserved.

62. Throughout almost the entire century, and to a *The Revo-*
constantly increasing extent during its last decennium, *lution in Rome and*
the importation into England of antique sculptures from *its conse-*
Italy, especially from Rome, was carried on. We cannot *quences. Earl of*
but marvel at the inexhaustible wealth of the Eternal *Bristol.*
City and her Campagna, when we recollect that besides
the collections formed at Rome itself, Florence, Madrid,
Paris, St Petersburg, Stockholm, England and Germany
have derived thence almost all their antiquities, while
Naples alone, in addition to the Farnese marbles, possessed a mine of discoveries apart in the buried cities of
her vicinity. Now, in consequence of events of world-wide
interest, a pause occurred in the commerce in antiques at
Rome. Byres had left Rome as early as A.D. 1790; Gavin
Hamilton died there in the year 1797, his death being
ascribed to excitement and anxiety caused by the advance
of the French; Jenkins was actually driven out of Rome

[273] *Household Furniture and in-* *by* Thomas Hope. London, 1807,
terior decoration executed from designs fol.

by these invaders and died in 1798, just as he landed in
his native country at Yarmouth after a violent storm. He
had concealed a collection of engraved gems on his person,
but all the property he had left behind at Rome was con-
fiscated by the French[274]. Very curious were the fortunes
of FREDERICK, FOURTH EARL OF BRISTOL, Bishop of
Derry (A.D. 1730—1803). Having been settled at Rome
for a long time, he had eagerly collected statues and paintings, chiefly modern, but also including several antiques, in
the hope of adorning therewith the castle which he intended
to have built at Ickworth. "In 1798 he was arrested by
the French, and confined for a time in the Castle of Milan;
and his valuable collection fell into the hands of the Repub-
licans. On this occasion a remonstrance was presented to
Citizen Haller, administrator of the finances of the army
of Italy, signed by three hundred and forty-three artists of
various nations, in favour of the restoration of the collection
to their munificent patron. It was redeemed for the sum
of ten thousand pounds, under an arrangement with the
Directory—and within a week after the payment of the
money, the collection was again plundered, and the whole
dispersed[275]!" To what purpose could the British Earl-
Bishop complain of such treatment, when even the Villa
Albani and the papal collections fared hardly better; when
churches and palaces were plundered without mercy; and
when an undisciplined soldiery despoiled the private apartments of the Pope himself after he had been led off to
France? Even these events resulted in profit to English
collectors. On one occasion, for instance, the Roman agent
of an English merchant purchased from a Frenchman not
fewer than forty-five chests full of marbles, tables, and so
on, the product of such booty. On its voyage to England
the vessel was four times captured and four times rescued

[274] Ellis, *Townley Gallery*, i. p. 5.
[275] J. Gage, *History and Antiquities of Suffolk. Thingoe Hundred*,
London, 1838. p. 301. *Gentleman's
Magazine*, May, 1798, vol. LXVIII. i,
p. 434.

again before safely reaching Liverpool. Thence its freight
had first of all to be reshipped to London in order to find
purchasers. It has already been mentioned that on this
occasion Blundell bought again, for two hundred and sixty
guineas, a relief which he had purchased at Rome for less
than ten pounds and then presented to the Pope[276], and
which is one of the most remarkable of his collection. We
may well feel surprised that in such restless times Fagan
still had courage to undertake excavations at Ostia, and
that Hope and another customer of Fagan's, Prince Augustus Frederick, found means to secure the safety of his
acquisitions[277]. This state of things was not to last long;
in the year 1801, to repeat the expression employed
at Rome, "an end was put to the abuse and disorder
of commercial profit in such excavations, and a new papal
epoch set in[278]." In other words there set in an epoch
of complete stagnation, which lasted as long as the wars of
Napoleon held all Europe in suspense. In regard to the
antiquarian relations between England and Rome, a pause
like this, when the former agents for the trade in antiques
disappeared from the scene, and Rome could be no comfortable residence for the travelling Englishman, served as
a complete break with tradition.—

63. The same was the case at Naples. Ever since *William*
A.D. 1764 the post of English ambassador had been filled *Hamilton and his*
by Mr, afterwards Sir WILLIAM HAMILTON (1730—1803), *first collection.*
who formed the centre of an unusually eager intellectual
society, in which Hancarville, who like Hamilton has been
already mentioned, played an important part[279]. Hamilton
had two governing passions, the collection of antiques and
the study of natural science. The gratification of the first
was attended with no small difficulty owing to the jealousy

276 Ince, no. 221.
277 He bought a statue of Venus
which King William IV., A.D. 1834,
presented to the British Museum
(*Anc. Marbles Brit. Mus.*, XI. Pl.
34); see Urlichs, *Glyptothek*, p. 30.

278 C. Fea, *Viaggio ad Ostia*, Rome,
1802, p. 57.
279 Justi, *Winckelmann*, II. 2 pp.
381—397. Edwards, *Lives of the
Founders of the British Museum*, I.
pp. 347—361.

of the Bourbon Government. Luckily for him, however, the interest of the King was so fully engrossed by the excavations at Herculaneum, that he looked with disdain on all other varieties of antique art, except paintings and bronzes. A large field was therefore left open to the energies of Hamilton, who bought collections small and great, and privately instituted excavations on his own account. He was particularly interested in the painted vases that were then still commonly called Etruscan, although their Greek origin was getting to be more and more recognised, and was distinctly proclaimed by Mazocchi, Winckelmann, and Hancarville. Hamilton was not the first nor the only Briton who collected vases ; some time earlier we find the names of FREDERICK and THOMS mentioned as those of possessors of vases, and LORD CAWDOR collected as well as Hamilton[280]. But to Hamilton belongs the merit of being the first to appreciate with warmth the severe beauty of their shapes, colouring and drawing, the mingled simplicity and feeling of the designs figured upon them ; and it was he who recognised the value of these unpretentious vessels for forming and ennobling modern art-taste. The magnificent *édition de luxe*, for which Hamilton paid no less than forty thousand ducats (six thousand pounds), was particularly calculated to exhibit the importance of the vases in this respect. Hancarville's abstruse text at any rate rightly emphasized the worth of these simple materials for the history of the forgotten art of Greek painting ; nor did it at that time exercise a prejudicial effect, since it fell in with prevalent views on mythology[281]. However, Hamilton did not limit himself to vases. Of these he had brought together seven hundred and thirty ; but his collection further contained one hundred and seventy-five terra cottas, three hundred pieces

[280] Passeri, *Picturæ Etruscorum in vasculis*, 1767, Pl. 44, 45, 47, 128. Cf. above, note 248.
[281] *Antiquités Etrusques Grecques* et Romaines tirées du cabinet de Mr Hamilton à Naples, Naples, 1766, 1767, IV. fol.

of glass, six hundred and twenty-seven bronzes, chiefly
armour, one hundred and fifty objects in ivory, one hundred and fifty gems, as many gold articles of jewellery,
more than six thousand coins, particularly of Magna
Græcia, and lastly miscellaneous articles of various kinds
including some few marbles. All these treasures Hamilton
brought to England A.D. 1772, after a residence of eight
years in Naples, and sold to the British Museum for
£8,400. This event was noteworthy for its result in two
directions. The purchase was the first considerable addition made by public money to the Museum since its
foundation, and formed the groundwork of a Department
of Antiquities. At the same time it is well known how
great an influence Hamilton's publication, and especially
the originals, exercised on Josiah Wedgewood's manufacture. In an incredibly short time his imitations met with
wide-spread favour, and contributed very materially to
making the 'Greek,' 'Etruscan' or as they were sometimes even called 'Pompeian' vases popular.

64. In the year 1777 Sir William Hamilton joined the *Sir W.
Hamilton's*
Dilettanti Society. On the occasion of a second visit home *second
collection.*
(A.D. 1785) he resigned the celebrated glass vase from the
Barberini Palace, with white reliefs on a blue ground, to
the widowed DUCHESS OF PORTLAND, daughter of the
Earl of Oxford, mentioned above. This lady died soon
after. Her possessions were sold by auction (A.D. 1786) and
the vase, numbered 4155 in the complete cabinet, was
bought in by the family after the bidding had gone up to
one thousand and twenty-nine pounds; since A.D. 1810 it
has been deposited in the British Museum under the name
of the 'Portland vase' and has there been accessible to
the public, not, as is well known, without serious detriment to its integrity[282]. Yet another specimen, the most

[282] Walpole to Lady Ossory, 1785,
Aug. 10. *A Catalogue of the Portland Museum, lately the property of
the Duchess Dowager of Portland,*
*deceased; which will be sold by Mr
Skinner and Co. on the 24th of April,
1786, and the 37 following days.* The
antiques come last on the list (June 7);

important of its kind, came to England through the agency
of Sir William Hamilton, viz. the huge marble vase,
discovered in the year 1769 by Gavin Hamilton and presented by the purchaser to the Earl of Warwick, from
whom it took its usual name[283]. Sir William had in the
main renounced further collecting. It was therefore unwise
of him to return to Naples, for how could so enthusiastic a
collector resist the numerous opportunities of returning to
his ancient passion? It is a fact that in the year 1787
Goethe found Hamilton's private art-vaults, to which it
was difficult to get access, quite filled with busts, torsos,
vases and bronzes; there were also two splendid bronze
candelabra, which "might have perhaps strayed from the
Pompeian excavation, and have lost themselves here[284]."
Tischbein tells us that engraved gems were also not wanting, and he describes vividly how new discoveries of vases
completely overcame Hamilton's resolutions and soon made
him once more an eager purchaser. Tischbein once saw
him coming from Court, in full court dress, with stars and
orders, carrying a basket full of vases; a ragged lazarone
held one handle of the basket and the English Minister the
other.—(A similar story is told of Cardinal Albani[285].)
Thus a second collection was formed, which was engraved
by Tischbein and of which we have already recorded the
fate above[286]. Though larger and more important than
the first, it was less fortunate, as it had not the protection
of a public museum, but was exposed to the vicissitudes
of private ownership. At the present day we know the
whereabouts of but very few of these vases. When they
were sent to England (A.D. 1798), the Republic was already
knocking at the door of the decayed Bourbon Kingdom.
At the close of the year Hamilton fled with the royal

the purchase of the vase was alleged to
have been made for the Duke of Marlborough.
    [283] See Cat., art. Warwick Castle.
    [284] Goethe, *Italienische Reise*, 1787,

May 27.
    [285] J. H. W. Tischbein, *Aus
meinem Leben*, Brunswick, 1861, II.
pp. 100—107, 169—180.
    [286] Cf. above, § 61.

family to Palermo. He returned once more to his beloved
Naples to leave her again for ever in A.D. 1800, a sick,
broken-down old man. The commerce in antiquities between England and Naples was interrupted for a long
time after this; French rule at Naples making such relations quite impossible.

65. In comparison with Italy in the last century, *Relations with Greece.*
Greece, at least with regard to the trade in antiques, hung
far behind. There are however many scattered traces
to show that the English who lived in Greece—merchants,
ecclesiastics, physicians—had genuine feeling for the past
history of their adopted home, and neglected no opportunity for collecting antiquities. The first successful undertaking, the search for the desert city of Palmyra, was
entered on by English merchants from Aleppo in the year
1691. Collections of coins were made at the beginning of
the eighteenth century by British merchants and clergy in
the same place, with such zeal that the prices within a few
years rose to exorbitant amounts[257]. A physician and a
clergyman of the British merchant colony in Constantinople provided Dr Mead with antiquities about A.D. 1730[258],
and in A.D. 1779 DR SWINNEY, the resident clergyman in
that city, sent to England the splendid bronze statuette of
Herakles found in Syria, which soon afterwards came into
Townley's possession[259]. Smyrna in particular appears
once more, as in Petty's time, to have been a fruitful mine
of discoveries. Winckelmann mentions an English physician who in A.D. 1763 obtained permission to make
excavations there, and another Englishman who received
two ships full of statues, eight of which were in perfect
condition and which he sent home together with some

[257] *Relation of a Voyage to Tadmor,*
Sept. 29, 1691. Seller, *Antiquities
of Palmyra,* London, 1696. For the
trade in coins see the letters for the
years A.D. 1696—1708 in the MS.
Cuper., no. 1 fol. 19, 64, 77, 81, 82,
97, 99, 114 (Archives at the Hague);

cf. Michaelis in *Im neuen Reich,* 1876,
I. pp. 990—994.
[258] Ellis, *Townley Gallery,* II. p.
303; *Corp. Inscr. Graec.* 3797.
[259] *Anc. Marbles Brit. Mus.,* III.
Pl. 2.

busts[290]. From Smyrna also were the reliefs which Matthew
Duane and Thomas Tyrwhitt bought at a sale in London
A.D. 1772, and presented to the British Museum[291]. Our
interest is, however, less warmly awakened by the isolated
British residents in the East than by the travellers.
These could no longer rest contented with Italy, but
sought also the Levant. In A.D. 1725 MR TOPHAM
brought to London a relief from Attica, which reached the
British Museum more than half a century later[292]; and
towards the middle of the century the learned Greek
scholar and physician, DR ANTHONY ASKEW, brought
some marbles home with him from Athens, for example
the beautiful sepulchral monument of Xanthippos, which
was acquired by Townley at his sale in A.D. 1775[293]. About
the same time Lady Bute, daughter of the well-known Lady
Mary Wortley Montagu, handed over to Trinity College,
Cambridge, a small number of Greek marbles, which her
father, the Honourable Edward Wortley Montagu, had
brought home in A.D. 1718 from his embassy at the Porte[294].
As early as A.D. 1744 the Dilettanti were in possession of a
fragment of the Parthenon frieze, probably presented by
one of the members, just as one subsequently came to
Smith-Barry; another was in the possession of the Duke
of Devonshire. How many similar *souvenirs de voyage*
may still be scattered here and there[295]! The Dilettanti
soon appear in the foreground among the travellers to
Greece and to the East. One of the first was JAMES,
VISCOUNT, afterwards EARL OF CHARLEMONT, who since
A.D. 1749 had visited Sicily, Greece, Asia Minor, and

[290] Winckelmann to Bianconi, 1763,
Apr. 30 (Fea, *Storia*, III. p. 259).

[291] Ellis, *Townley Gallery*, II. p.
160—165.

[292] *Anc. Marbles Brit. Mus.* II.
Pl. 41.

[293] Ellis, *Townley Gallery*, II. p.
29, 107, 300. Askew was in Greece
about the year 1748.

[294] See Cat., art. Cambridge, Trinity
College.

[295] The fragments belonged to the
north friezes, slabs XXXV. and XXXII.,
and to the south metopes, no. XVI. See
Michaelis, *Der Parthenon*, Leipzig,
1871, pp. 249, 250. Newton, in *The
Academy*, 1875, Oct. 2, p. 363. A
fragment in the Hope collection does
not belong to the Parthenon. See
Cat., art. Deepdene, no. 14.

Egypt in company with Mr Francis Pierpont Burton (afterwards Lord Conyngham), Mr Scott, Mr Murphy, and the
artist Richard Dalton, who has perpetuated some of the
knowledge gained during this journey in several instructive
engravings; here, for example, we find the first serviceable
views of the Parthenon and the Erechtheion[296]. In the
following year two pairs of travellers met in Athens; on
the one hand James Stuart and Nicholas Revett, who had
just begun there that undertaking by which they opened a
new epoch in antiquarian studies, and on the other James
Dawkins and Robert Wood, who were starting thence on
their hardly less celebrated expedition to Palmyra. This
is not the place to speak of the scientific results of these
two undertakings; what they brought back in the way of
antiques does not appear to have been of great importance.
DAWKINS' small collection was presented after his death
(A.D. 1759) by his brother Henry to the Oxford University[297]. From the journey of Chandler, Revett and Pars
(A.D. 1764—1766), undertaken at the cost of the Dilettanti
Society, and in accordance with Wood's instructions, resulted as the most valuable fruit the *Ionian Antiquities*.
These travellers apparently brought no originals to England
except inscriptions, which the Society consigned in the
year 1785 to the British Museum[298].

66. The first British traveller who brought home rich *Sir*
booty from Greece itself was SIR RICHARD WORSLEY *Richard Worsley.*
(A.D. 1751—1805)[299]. For some time British resident at
Venice he started A.D. 1785 for Greece, where he remained till A.D. 1787, part of the time at Athens and
part on the islands and coasts of Asia Minor. He spared
no expense in making a splendid collection. In it the

[296] Hardy, *Memoirs of the Earl
of Charlemont*, p. 11, 19 ff. Dalton,
A series of Engravings, &c., London.
1751—52. *Antiquities and Views,
&c.*, London, 1791.
[297] Chandler, *Marmora Oxonien-*

sia, p. v.
[298] [W. R. Hamilton], *Historical
Notices of the Society of Dilettanti*,
London, 1855, p. 41.
[299] See Brocklesby. Dallaway, *Of
Statuary*, p. 350.

Greek reliefs, or fragments of reliefs, take the first place.
Such a work as the Girl with the Doves from Paros[300], by
dint of its charming *naïveté*, constitutes one of the most
attractive creations of Greek art which remain to us; this
single specimen is worth a whole museum-full of Roman
works turned out by the gross. When Worsley proceeded
from Greece to Rome, he availed himself here also of the
opportunity of enriching his collection; we may name as
a work of peculiar charm a group of Dionysos with Eros.
The busts and gems which he acquired were less important.
The last he bought of Sir William Hamilton[301]. At the
same time Worsley caused to be engraved at Rome some
of the plates which he intended for the magnificent publication of his museum. For the most valuable portion of
the explanations that were to go with the plates he was
indebted to the friendship and kindness of Ennio Quirino
Visconti. When he had returned to his home in the Isle
of Wight, Sir Richard arranged his beloved specimens at
his beautifully-situated country house of Appuldurcombe,
and then devoted his leisure to the publication of the work
in question[302]. Its production did not cost less than three
thousand pounds. The result was a work which, in outward
splendour, can vie with any hitherto published. One cannot,
however, help feeling that, as in the *Marlborough Gems*,
the engraved fragments are occasionally, as it were, lost
in the wide surface of the white paper. As containing
works chiefly of Greek art, the *Museum Worsleianum* must
take a place of honour, among the publications of the

---

[300] Brocklesby, no. 17.
[301] Visconti, *Mus. Pio Clem.* VI.
Pl. 7, n. 2.
[302] *Museum Worsleianum*, II. fol.
Both volumes exhibit the date 1794.
It is however to be gathered from the
preface to the second volume that
the first was not published before the
year 1798, the second several years
later. This explains Dallaway's statement that upon Worsley's death, A.D.
1805, not more than 27 out of the

250 copies were distributed. In the
year 1824 a new edition of 250 copies
was prepared from the original copper-
plates. The subsequent destruction
of these was stipulated for by Lord
Yarborough with the publisher. See
Böttiger's *Amalthea*, III. p. 393,
where the sums given above are
stated. Dibdin, *Bibliomania*, p. 712,
and Savage, *Librarian* I., are cited as
putting the figure at £27,000.

last century, beside the *Antiquities of Athens* and the *Ionian
Antiquities;* though it cannot be denied that at the present
day, when so many other remains of genuine Greek sculpture have become known to us, these fragments, with the
exception of a few specimens, have lost some of their importance: but even in the British Museum the above-mentioned Girl with Doves would hold its own. At any rate
the Worsley marbles do not deserve to be left to ruin in a
damp summer-house: a fate which now threatens them
since they have been removed from Appuldurcombe to
Brocklesby Park and there incorporated with Lord Yarborough's sculptures.

67. Amongst the number, by no means small, of British
travellers who visited the Greek coasts during the last
twenty years of the eighteenth and in the first few of the
present century, the following names also deserve special
mention in this place. J. B. S. MORRITT, who travelled
there in the years A.D. 1795 and 1796. Besides keeping
his eyes open for the solution of difficult questions (such
as the position of Troy), he indulged an interest in trans-
portable remains of antiquity. His booty certainly does
not appear to have been great, if we may draw any inference from the present contents of the collection in Rokeby
Hall. One of the principal specimens, a bronze helmet from
Olympia, with an archaic inscription, was given up by Morritt to Payne Knight. Morritt's efforts were frequently
thwarted by the opposition of the Turkish magistrates,
both in Athens, where he wished to get one or two slabs
of the friezes and a metope from the Parthenon, and in
Ephesus and Amyklae[503]. At the latter place a better
fortune attended the efforts of the highly-cultivated young

*Morritt,
Lord
Aberdeen,
Clarke,
R. Wal-
pole,
Hawkins.*

[503] See Rokeby. Morritt, *Observations on a Dissertation by J. Bryant,*
1795; *a vindication of Homer, &c.*
1798. Walpole's *Memoirs relating to
Turkey.* London, 1818, p. 33, 567.
Corp. Inscr. Graec. 29 (Walpole,

Travels in the East, London, 1820,
p. 588). *Report from the Elgin Committee,* London, 1816, p. 130. Morritt
belonged to the Dilettanti Society
from the year 1799.

GEORGE, FOURTH EARL OF ABERDEEN (*d.* A.D. 1860), who
was travelling in Greece in the year 1803. He there succeeded in obtaining a few very remarkable reliefs, which
place before our eyes in the minutest detail the parapher-
nalia of a feminine toilet. To these were added sepulchral
reliefs from Attica and perhaps some other specimens.
Since A.D. 1861 the collection has been in the British
Museum as a present from the son and heir of the collector[304]. Only two bronzes, which came from Paramythia,
were given by Lord Aberdeen to Payne Knight[305]. Of
more importance were the marbles which DR E. D. CLARKE
(A.D. 1769—1822), Fellow of Jesus College, Cambridge,
brought home from his extensive travels in the Levant
(A.D. 1801—2), although all the rest stand far behind the
colossal fragment of the Kistophors from Eleusis, in which
the owner, with pardonable enthusiasm, was willing to recognise the goddess of the mystic sanctuary herself. The
embarkation of the enormous block caused difficulties
enough; next, the ship containing it sank in the neighbourhood of Beachy Head; but a successful effort was
made to recover the precious freight. The whole collection
was presented by Clarke to Cambridge University, and for
many years formed the ornament of the vestibule of
the Public Library[306]. This example of liberality immediately found an imitator in ROBERT WALPOLE, an alumnus
of Trinity College, who on his return in the year 1808 from
his long travels in Greece and Asia Minor, presented the
few specimens he had brought with him to the University.
Other Cambridge scholars followed suit[307]. The most fortunate among these travellers was the naturalist JOHN
HAWKINS, resident for a long time at Zante, whence he

---

[304] Walpole's *Memoirs*, p. 452.
[305] *Spec. Ant. Sculpt.* II. p. lxvi.
[306] Clarke, *Travels in various
countries of Europe, Asia and Africa*,
II. sect. i.—iii. London, 1812—1816.
Greek marbles, &c. in Cambridge,

Cambr. 1809. Otter, *Life and Remains of E. D. Clarke*, London, 1824,
ch. VI.
[307] See Cat., art. Cambridge, Fitzwilliam Museum.

undertook several journeys of various extent through Greece, without being an actual collector of antiquities. He paid two visits to Jánnina, at that time the residence of the dreaded Ali Pasha; on the first occasion (A.D. 1795) an excellent bronze statuette of Hermes was presented to him; on the second (A.D. 1798) he bought a bronze relief of singular beauty, representing the visit of Aphrodite to Anchises. Both specimens came from a place in the neighbourhood named Paramythía[308].

68. The small Hermes in question, like Lord Aberdeen's two bronzes, was only the remains of a larger find which had been made in Paramythía about two years before, and the greater part of which, if we except those specimens that had been put in the smelting furnaces of a bronze-founder at Jánnina, had found its way to Russia and thence afterwards to England. The fortunate purchaser was RICHARD PAYNE KNIGHT (A.D. 1749—1824), one of the most influential connoisseurs of the time[309]. When he was only a youth of seventeen, he had visited Italy and spent many years there; he was there again in the year 1777, and with Charles Gore and the landscape painter Philip Hackert made a journey to Sicily. He kept a diary of this visit, which has been made public by Goethe[310]. In the year 1781 he joined the Dilettanti Society and met Hancarville when on his visit to Townley (A.D. 1784); on which occasion that ingenious professor of the fantastic seems to have bewitched him. The following year again found him travelling southwards, and in A.D. 1785 he laid the foundation of his collection with a bronze head which he bought of Jenkins[311]. In opposition to Aristotle, who reckons magnitude an essential characteristic of beauty, Payne Knight

Payne Knight as a collector.

Lord Northwick.

[308] Hawkins in Walpole's *Travels*, pp. 481, 482. *Spec. Ant. Sculpt.* II. Pl. 20, 21. See Bignor. He was a fellow of the Society of Dilettanti from the year 1799.

[309] Böttiger, *Amalthea*, III. Leipzig, 1825, pp. 408—418. Edwards, *Lives of the Founders of the British Museum*, I. p. 401—412.

[310] Goethe, *Philipp Hackert (Werke,* XXXVII. 1830, pp. 146—218, where he is erroneously called Henry, cf. pp. 320—324).

[311] *Spec. Ant. Sculpt.* I. Pl. 20, 21.

held that magnitude and beauty cannot be united, and
he only took delight in the smaller productions of antique
art. Hence his preference for bronzes and coins, which
he was able to indulge during a long stay at Naples in
company with Sir William Hamilton. It is well known
that the coins of Magna Graecia and Sicily surpass all other
antique coins in the beauty of the dies from which they
have been struck. Here therefore Payne Knight found a
wide field for his particular taste, and he succeeded in
forming a cabinet of Greek coins that was quite unequalled. In this field he soon found a rival in SIR
JOHN RUSHOUT, afterwards second LORD NORTHWICK.
During the last ten years of the century the latter
made his wonderful collection of silver coins, to which only
the choicest specimens, true gems of their kind, gained ad-
mittance[312]. In Payne Knight's collection the eye is particularly attracted by the small bronzes, even more than by the
coins, and these the possessor liked to designate his "jewels
in bronze." In this respect his cabinet far surpassed any
other; his friend Townley, for instance, had only a very
few bronzes. This superiority was due to Payne Knight's
refined taste in combination with good luck in collecting.
One specimen of the bronze treasure from Paramythia had
come to England through the hands of a Greek dragoman,
and knowledge of this reached Payne Knight. Not content with buying this specimen, he sent an agent to Russia
to hunt up the rest, and the agent succeeded in finding
nine or ten pieces which had come into the hands of a
Herr von Wiessiolowski and the Count Golovkin; two
more of the scattered specimens were presented to him, as
we have said, by Lord Aberdeen[313]. His plans were moreover furthered by the circumstances of the time. The

[312] Noehden, G. H., *Select ancient
coins, chiefly from Magna Graecia and
Sicily, from the cabinet of Lord Northwick.* London, 1824. (250 *copies
only.*)

[313] Heyne, in *Goettinger gelehrte
Anzeigen,* 1800, pp. 1801 — 1805.
Kochler, *Gesammelte Schriften,* VI. p.
31—38. *Specimens Ant. Sculpt.* II.
p. lxv. Cf. Stephani, *Apollon Boë-*

Hermes with the golden necklace, which had been discovered sixty years before not far from Lyons, passed through
the hands of three French owners in succession, and at
last came into the possession of Payne Knight in the year
of terror A.D. 1792[314]. For another specimen, a Bacchic
mask, he was indebted to the dissolution of the Jesuit
College in Lyons[315]. A considerable part of the collection came from the Duc de Chaulnes, who died at the
commencement of the Revolution, and who is known by his
Egyptian travels (A.D. 1765), and his researches in natural
history[316]. Thus many specimens in Knight's cabinet
had their own pedigree. Auctions and dealers, friends
and correspondents on the continent, were eagerly laid
under contribution. In comparison with the statuettes,
bronze heads and masks, and coins and medals, the
gems and the few marble heads of this collection received
little consideration. At Payne Knight's death the value
of the whole was estimated at from £50,000 to £60,000.
That it was all bequeathed to the British Museum is well
known.

69. The more unreservedly we recognise Payne Knight's *Payne*
skill and taste in collecting, without necessarily sharing his *Knight as a littéra-*
indifference to larger marble works,—the higher we are *teur. The*
bound to estimate the result of his zeal, inasmuch as it ran *"Speci-mens of*
in a line far removed from the path chosen by the majority *Antient Sculpture."*
of contemporary dilettanti,—the more unconditionally we
praise his liberality,—the greater all the while must be our
reserves in connection with his literary activity. He made
his *début* as an author with an article on the God of
Lampsakos[317], which deserves blame far less on account of

---

dromios, Petersb. 1860, pp. 6, 44.—
Bronzes of Paramythia in *Spec. Ant.
Sculpt.* I. Pl. 32, 43, 44, 52, 53, 63.
II. Pl. 22, 23, 24.
[314] *Spec. Ant. Sculpt.* I. Pl. 33,
34. Caylus, *Recueil* VII. p. 268.
[315] *Spec. Ant. Sculpt.* II. Pl. 35.
[316] Dallaway, *Of Statuary*, p. 326.
Spec. Ant. Sculpt. I. Pl. 18, 19.

[317] *An account of the remains of
the worship of Priapus lately existing
in Isernia; to which is added a dis-
course on the worship of Priapus and
its connexion with the mystic theology
of the ancients*, 1786, 4to. The copies
of this work in the market were afterwards bought in by the author.

the offensiveness of its subject than for its unsound, un-
methodical, mythological fantasies after the manner of
Hancarville. But at that time, when treatment such as
this was in vogue, it was the first-named characteristic
that called forth especial reprobation. A further publication[318] introduced Payne Knight to the public as a didactic
poet of considerable tediousness. The work which followed
this[319] showed him to be a despiser of Christianity and an
enthusiastic follower of the doctrines of Lucretius. One
would have thought that a treatise held to be indecent, an
anti-Christian book, and a tedious poem, would have sufficed to banish the author from good society in England.
By no means! As a connoisseur Payne Knight enjoyed
a respect so immoveably firm, as an oracle in matters of art
he was considered altogether so infallible, that all his literary sins were forgotten. His treatise on taste[320] was regarded as laying down the canon, and he who would have
ventured to raise a doubt about him would have had to
atone bitterly for such sacrilege. His influence extended
particularly over the Society of Dilettanti, in which he and
Townley gave the tone in all questions of antique art. It
was these two who, immediately after the completion of
the second volume of *Ionian Antiquities* (A.D. 1797), proposed to the Society to publish in a magnificent volume the
most interesting and most beautiful specimens of ancient
sculpture to be found in English collections. The Society
accepted the proposal, and the *duumviri* were entrusted
with the selection; Townley having the decision in the
matter of marbles. That the collections of the editors themselves received the most notice, twenty-three specimens
being selected for publication from each, was not only
natural, but justified by the intrinsic importance of the
selected pieces. Among other collections that of Petworth

[318] *Landscape, a didactic poem,*
1794.
[319] *The progress of civil society,*
1796, 4to.
[320] *Analytical enquiry into the
Principles of Taste,* 1805.

had the honour of contributing nine examples; that of the
Marquis of Lansdowne four; that of Mr Hope two; those
of Lord Yarborough and the Earl of Upper Ossory one
each. Many collections were nót represented at all, because a plan was speedily formed of producing a second
volume. The sixty-three monuments published in the
first volume were engraved on seventy-five plates at a
cost of £2,300; they are most of them executed in a
masterly way, so that the book is really a model publication, and quite worthy of the Society[321]. The text
was written by Payne Knight. In his description of the
statues and judgment of their style, in his information as
to their origin, restorations, &c., he observes throughout
an appropriate precision and brevity; digressions into
critical territory occur seldom, although there are many
explanations which read both singular and entertaining at
the present day. The exhaustive introduction gives us,
like Winckelmann's introduction to his *Monumenti Inediti*,
a glance over the development of ancient art. Though
much in it is questionable, or even quite wrong, this introduction belongs nevertheless to the best of Payne Knight's
writing. All things considered, the first volume of *Specimens of Antient Sculpture in Great Britain*, which appeared
in the year 1809, and had been ten years in preparation,
forms a brilliant conclusion to the century of antique dilettantism in England.

70. There is yet one memorial, of a more modest kind, *J. Dalla-
which dates from this time. As at the commencement of *way.*
the epoch of dilettantism the book of the two Richardsons
had served to introduce Englishmen on their travels to the
art treasures of Italy, so at the close of the epoch the same
service with regard to English collections might naturally

---

[321] *Specimens of Antient Sculpture,
selected from several collections in Great
Britain, by the Society of Dilettanti,*
Vol. I. London, 1809, fol. Cf. [W.
R. Hamilton] *Historical Notices of the
Society of Dilettanti,* pp. 53—56. The
engraving of the plates occupied from
A.D. 1799 to 1807; as they were sold
to the publishers Thomas Payne and
White and Cochrane, the actual pub-
lication only cost £1222, for which
the Society secured 60 copies.

be welcomed both by natives and foreigners. This task was undertaken by JAMES DALLAWAY, a man who, having been educated at Oxford and then resided for a long period in Italy and Constantinople, finally became secretary to the Earl Marshal, and in that capacity devoted his leisure to literary pursuits. His connection with the Earl Marshal Charles Duke of Norfolk, a descendant of the great Earl of Arundel, drew him towards the history of the services rendered by Arundel to art collecting in England; and his old attachment to the University of Oxford, where the remains of the Arundel collection were preserved, kept this interest alive. In the year 1800 Dallaway published his *Anecdotes of the Arts in England*, the middle portion of which treats of sculpture[322]. His purpose was merely to provide a *"cicerone* book" for travellers, *quem tollere rheda possis*, and the book does not in fact offer much more. The notes of the individual collections are generally nothing more than a bare reprint of the haphazard nomenclatures which are usually given in collections for the information of visitors. These have been for the most part mechanically copied by Dallaway without personal inspection, without intimate knowledge, and without criticism. The different collections receive extremely unequal consideration. In the small Palmerston cabinet more specimens are mentioned by name than in the whole throng of marbles at Ince; the Lansdowne gallery is disposed of with striking indifference; Dallaway even says in the year 1816, though he was then living in London, that "this collection consists principally of torsos and mutilated statues." The only collections that he treats with any comprehensiveness are Townley's and that at Oxford; here extensive previous work was at his disposal, in the shape partly of printed books, partly of Townley's own notes. The informa-

---

[322] *Anecdotes of the Arts in England, or comparative remarks on Architecture, Sculpture, and Painting, chiefly illustrated by specimens at* Oxford. London, 1800. For our object. pp. 228–391 are important. Cf. Kraft and Böttiger, *A. L. Millin,* Leipzig, 1819, pp. 81–84.

tion to be gleaned from Gavin Hamilton's letters to Townley
was particularly valuable. Dallaway was throughout entirely dependent on the previous works at his disposal. He
follows them without any criticism; for which reason it is
essential to analyse his compilation almost into its primitive elements, and it is well never to follow Dallaway
implicitly without satisfying ourselves about his authorities,
or at least about the possibility of authentic information
being in his possession. Dallaway however deserves our
thanks in two particulars. He at least makes an effort to
sketch the history of the introduction of antique statuary into England in chronological order, and thus gives many a
hint how to find the way through the entanglement of
scattered notices; although for a great part of his notes,
particularly those which refer to the seventeenth century,
it is better to turn for ourselves to his chief authority, Hor.
Walpole's *Anecdotes of Painting*. Dallaway's second merit
consists in giving us information about many collections
which have since been lost sight of or dispersed. In the
latter respect the new edition of the section referring to
sculpture, which Dallaway undertook sixteen years later,
is valuable. Some points are here corrected, and not a
little is added[523]. After all until quite modern times
Dallaway's book has been the only means of obtaining
information about the private collections of antiques in
England. The interest which it aroused as a guide-book
was sufficient to cause a French version of it to be made;
and to this A. L. Millin supplied some unimportant foot-
notes, written without any independent knowledge of the
collections themselves or of the specimens they contained[524].

71. But a time approached when many of these valua- *Sales. Increase of*

---

[523] *Of Statuary and Sculpture
among the Antients. With some account of specimens preserved in England*, London, 1816. Many of the circumstances here given are taken from
the memoir of Townley (note 252).

[524] *Les beaux-arts en Angleterre.*

*ouvrage traduit de l'Anglois de M.
Dallaway par M***, publié et augmenté
de notes par A. L. Millin.* Paris,
1807, 2 vols. Millin also proposed to
have the second work translated, see
Böttiger, loc. cit. p. 84.

the British Museum. ble antiques were to pass into other hands than those of their first collectors, a time marked by many auctions. Of some we have already heard. In A.D. 1775 Dr Askew's collection, in A.D. 1786 those of the Duchess of Portland and Sir Charles Frederick, and shortly afterwards that of the Duke of S. Albans, had been put under the hammer[325]. About the same time Lyde Browne had sold his marbles to St Petersburg; and Locke and Jennings had voluntarily parted with theirs[326]. We first hear of the collections of Mr Chace Price and Mr Beaumont when the fact of their sale is announced to us[327]. At the close of the last century and the opening of the present, sales, often of great importance, followed one another in rapid succession, Lord Vere's (A.D. 1798), Lord Cawdor's (A.D. 1800), Lord Bessborough's (A.D. 1801), Lord Mendip's (A.D. 1802), and as far as I know the collections of the Duke of Buccleuch and Mr Anson were sold not long after[328]. The same fate seemed to threaten the splendid collection of the Marquis of Lansdowne, for the second Marquis had taken them over from his father's executors for the sum of eight thousand pounds and had then settled them on his widow. However the third Marquis, half-brother to the second, was fortunately able to buy them from her and so to preserve them from the fate of the Arundel gems (A.D. 1809)[329]. The excavators and the dealers, the Hamiltons and Jenkinses, had now passed away; the ranks of the collectors began to thin visibly in their turn. Lord Palmerston died A.D. 1802, Sir Will. Hamilton in the next year, and in the single year A.D. 1805 Lord Lansdowne, Sir Richard Worsley and Mr Townley. Sometimes there were no direct heirs to inherit

---

[325] Notes 293, 282, 155, 265.
[326] § 52, notes 240, 242.
[327] Of the former Dallaway, *Anecd.*, p. 389, mentions a Venus Salutifera, and several vases of considerable value, of the latter a Cupid and an eagle, which both passed into Townley's possession (*Anc. Marbl. Brit. Mus.* XI, 37, X. 58, 1), and further a

colossal Venus, and one of a small size.
[328] Notes 266, 248, 151, 175, 245, 174. Henry, third Duke of Buccleuch, died A.D. 1812.
[329] Mrs Jameson, *Companion to the private galleries of art in London*, London, 1844, p. 334, XI.

the collections, sometimes the heirs did not share the interests of their predecessors, or again pecuniary circumstances might oblige the family to sell its treasures:—in any case there was but too often cause for the melancholy reflection "how insecure is the permanency of heirlooms[330]!" The old race passed away, new times had dawned—who could foretell whither the tastes of the new generation might lead? It was therefore natural enough that ardent collectors, very unwilling to entertain the probability that the results of all their trouble would soon be scattered to the four winds, should seek some means of preserving their collections from such a fate. The way had long since been indicated; it had been struck out by the Popes in Rome under the eyes of Townley and Payne Knight. The Arundel collection was under the protection of the Oxford University, and Clarke had just presented his sculptures to Cambridge. Another public institution was yet nearer at hand. The BRITISH MUSEUM, founded on the legacy of Hans Sloane, had been already several times enriched by presents, from Thomas Hollis, the Lethieullier family and Sir William Hamilton[331]. The nucleus of a Department of Antiquities had been formed by the purchase (A.D. 1772) of the first Hamilton collection, and a most valuable addition had been made to this nucleus by the booty won from the French in the Egyptian expedition (A.D. 1802)[332]. To enlarge the rooms, and to make available a more free and thorough use of the collections, were part of the plan of the excellent director, Joseph Planta. Since A.D. 1791 Townley had been a trustee of the Museum, and although he had occasionally projected the removal of his collection at some opportune moment to Townley Hall, the thought now struck him to bequeath his marbles to this national institution, on

[330] H. Walpole to Lady Ossory, 1785, Aug. 10.

[331] Edwards, *Lives of the Founders of the Brit. Mus.*, I. pp. 347, 360. One of Hamilton's donations, for example,

is the beautiful head of Herakles, found at the foot of Vesuvius (*Anc. Marbl. Brit. Mus.*, I. Pl. 11).

[332] Edwards, *l. cit.*, I. pp. 361—368.

one condition only, that within two years special rooms
should be erected for their reception (A.D. 1802). His idea
was not carried out precisely in this way, but after his death
his sculptures were bought from his heirs for the nation at
the price of £20,000, and the collection was made complete
by the purchase of his bronzes, gems, coins and drawings in
A.D. 1814[333]. In the same year 1805 the British Museum
was opened free to the British public, many troublesome
formalities having up to that time been required in order
to obtain admission. Three years later (A.D. 1808) the
new Townley Gallery was completed and there appeared
for the first time a *Synopsis of the Contents of the
British Museum*[334]. Sixteen years later (A.D. 1824) Payne
Knight's liberal legacy was added. Thus the three men who
may be considered chief representatives of the Dilettanti
Society at the time of its most brilliant season of activity,
namely Hamilton, Townley and Knight, were yet again
so far united after their death that the results of their
favourite pursuits all passed into the safe keeping of the
public Museum of the British nation.

[333] Dallaway in Nichols' *Illustr.
Liter. Hist.* III. p. 741. Ellis, *Townley
Gall.*, I. pp. 10—12. Edwards, *l.
cit.*, I. pp. 368, 400. The price
amounted to £8200. A portion of
Townley's drawings are in the possession of A. W. Franks, Esq., Brit.
Mus. (note 213).
[334] Edwards, *l. cit.*, I. pp. 336—
341.

III.

THE BRITISH MUSEUM AND THE PRIVATE COLLECTIONS.

GREECE AND ENGLAND.

72. "To transplant old Greece into England." This *Travellers in Greece: Dodwell, Gell, Leake.* was what old Peacham had once commended as a merit in Lord Arundel. The idea of which the Earl had merely set the initiative, and which had then for a long time received little attention, now at length began to be more and more realised. The expeditions of Stuart and Revett and those of the Dilettanti, the travels of Worsley, Clarke, and their companions, showed plainly that the archæological magnet was veering strongly in the direction of Greece. When the French domination in Italy made it, if not impossible, yet difficult and disagreeable for the English to travel there, the attraction of Greece became all the stronger, especially taken in connection with the unlimited predominance of English influence in all quarters of the Turkish empire after the overthrow of the French arms in Egypt. It may not be inappropriate here to remember that just at the opening of this century a great impulse was given to the study of Greek throughout Europe, while the study of Latin, which had so long occupied the foreground, was for a time pushed aside. The interests for which F. A. Wolf and Immanuel Bekker, Gottfried Hermann and August Bœckh, Boissonade and Koraïs and many others were working and striving on the Continent, were represented in England by the brilliant constellation of Richard Porson

and his school. It might be said that all concerns relating
to antiquity received a Greek colour. Nor must it be
forgotten that the disclosure of the wonderland of Egypt,
effected by the French expedition, opened a new perspec-
tive, and to a certain extent invited our own countrymen to
similar discoveries. Accordingly from the beginning of this
century a stream of enterprising travellers poured into
Greece: and first in the list stood the English. Out of a very
large number there can be mentioned here only those three
to whom we are most indebted for topographical and archæological researches: EDWARD DODWELL (A.D. 1767—
1832)[335], WILLIAM GELL (A.D. 1777—1836)[336], and MARTIN
LEAKE (A.D. 1777—1860)[337]. They are, however, less remarkable as collectors of antiquities than on account of
their other merits. Dodwell formed a small collection in
which a few choice specimens were to be found among a
good many insignificant pieces (though all had a certain
value because of the accurate accounts given of their places
of discovery)[338]. Leake brought home from his repeated
and extensive travels not only a considerable number of
marble sculptures, which he presented for the most part to
the British Museum[339], but also a very fine collection of
Greek coins[340], which, together with sundry bronzes and

---

[335] Dodwell was in Greece A.D.
1801, and again A.D. 1805, 1806.
Basarilievi della Grecia, 1812. *Classical Tour*, II. 1819. *Cyclopian or
Pelasgic Remains*, 1834.
[336] Gell visited Greece at the same
time as Dodwell, and again A.D.
1811—1813 (note 343). *Ithaca*, 1807.
Argolis, 1810. *Itinerary of the Morea*,
1817. *Itinerary of Greece*, 1819.
Journey in the Morea, 1823. *Probe-
stücke von Städtemauern*, 1831. See
also the works on Pompeii and Rome.
His drawings were bequeathed (A.D.
1853) by the Hon. Keppel Craven to
the British Museum.
[337] Leake was four times in Greece
from A.D. 1802. *Athens*, 1821. *Asia
Minor*, 1824. *Demi of Attica*, 1829.
Morea, III. 1830. *Northern Greece*,
IV. 1835. *Peloponnesiaca*, 1846.

[338] [Braun, E.] *Notice sur le musée
Dodwell*, Rome, 1837. Amongst
the Graeco-Roman antiquities the 115
bronzes constitute an important section. All or most of the 143 vases
went to Munich (Jahn, *Vasensamm-
lung K. Ludwigs in München*, Munich, 1854, p. vi.), among them the
celebrated 'Dodwell vase.' A head
once in Dodwell's possession from the
west pediment of the Parthenon, belonging to the second figure from the
north end, has disappeared (*Class.
Tour*, I. p. 325). See below, note
420.
[339] E. g. *Mus. Marbles*, XI. Pl. 17,
18. Millingen, *Uned. Mon.* II. Pl.
9, 10, 16.
[340] *Numismata Hellenica*, 1856—
59. *Arch. Zeitung*, 1846, p. 206—210.
See Cat., art. Cambridge.

vases, were purchased after his death by the University
of Cambridge.

73. The activity of a second and, so to speak, inter- *Cockerell*
national party of travellers, belongs to the second decade *and other architects*
of our century, A.D. 1810—1815. This circle of intimate *—Bassae.*
companions were so fortunate as to discover the pediment
groups of the temple of Athene at Aegina (A.D. 1811),
and the frieze of the Temple of the Apollo Epikurios at
Bassae near Phigalia (A.D. 1812). With the Dane Broendsted, the Livonian Baron Stackelberg, the Germans Linkh
and Baron Haller of Hallerstein, there were associated as
representatives of England J. FOSTER, and above all the
excellent C. R. COCKERELL. The four last-named explorers
were in the summer of A.D. 1811 guided to the discovery of
one of the slabs of the frieze by a fox, which crawled under
the confused ruins of the temple of Apollo. After some difficult negotiations with Veli Pasha, then governor of the
Morea, they at last obtained permission to make excavations,
and in the summer months of A.D. 1812 that magic scene of
mountain grandeur was witness to the development of a busy
and various activity among its silent rocks and mighty oaks.
The discoverers and their friends—Cockerell was not among
those present—lived in huts of boughs round the temple,
and had the satisfaction of seeing the numberless sculptured fragments gradually piece themselves together into
the perfect whole. The whole undertaking was finished
in August, and soon after, new difficulties having arisen
and been overcome, the complete and costly result of the
excavation was securely stowed away at Zante. Two years
later it was there put up to auction[341]. Though the discovery
of these two series of sculptures at Aegina and Bassae was
undoubtedly the most important, still it was not the sole

[341] Combe, T., *Mus. Marbles*, vol.
IV., 1820. Stackelberg, *der Apollo-
tempel in Bassæ*, Rome, 1826.
Cockerell, *The Temples of Jupiter
Panhellenius* [more correctly, *of
Minerva*] *at Aegina and of Apollo*
Epicurius at Bassae. London, 1860.
A beautiful specimen of the vases in
Foster's possession is represented in
Stackelberg's *Gräber der Hellenen*,
Pl. 21, 1.

fruit of the labours and researches of the little company.
Cockerell's thorough and sagacious researches and his untir-
ing activity stood the illustrated publications of the Dilettanti
Society and the British Museum in good stead for nearly
half a century. Besides his later work on the temples at
Aegina and at Bassae, Cockerell was engaged with Donald-
son, Jenkins, Kinnard and Railton on the continuation of the
Antiquities of Athens[242]; while Francis Bedford and John
P. Gandy, guided by W. Gell, were working by commission
of the Dilettanti Society towards the completion of that
fundamental work, as well as of the *Ionian Antiquities* (A.D.
1811—1813)[243]. It happened sometimes in these travels
and researches that here and there an original fragment
came to the hands of the explorers. With praiseworthy
unselfishness they gave up all they found to the British
Museum. This institution is, for example, indebted to
Cockerell for a piece of the Parthenon frieze, and to Gandy
for some interesting sculptures from Rhamnus[244].

*Lord
Elgin's
under-
takings.*

74. The great undertakings of LORD ELGIN (A.D. 1766
—1841), which form so splendid an inauguration of the new
century, threw all other acquisitions of original works into
the shade[245]. Urged by the architect Harrison, the young
lord, when he had been named ambassador to the Porte (A.D.
1799), resolved to have drawings and casts made of all the
Athenian sculptures that were accessible for the purpose.
An attempt to interest the Government in the scheme, and

[242] *Antiquities of Athens and other
places in Greece, Sicily, &c. Supplementary to the Ant. of Ath. by Stuart
and Revett.* London, 1830.
[243] *The Unedited Antiquities of
Attica.* London, 1817. *Antiquities
of Ionia*, vol. III. London, 1840.
[244] Parthenon, south frieze, slab 1.
(*Mus. Marbles*, VIII. Pl. 56). *Unad.
Ant. of Attica*, ch. VI. pref., ch. VII.
Pl. 1 (*Synopsis*, 63 ed., 1856, p. 127,
nos. 300, 325, fragment of head of
Nemesis, 325*, statue of 'Themis,'
326, p. 129, no. 368).
[245] The chief authorities on Lord

Elgin are Hamilton's Memorandum
(notes 370, 378) and the report of the
Parliamentary Commission with the
Minutes of evidence (note 387). Cf.
Anc. Marbles Brit. Mus. VII. p. 22,
and the narrative founded on the original documents in my *Parthenon*, p.
74—87. Besides this I have made use
of the letters in the *Gentleman's Magazine*, LXXIII., 1803, II. p. 723 (Rome);
LXXX., 1810, II. p. 333 (London);
Tom Taylor, *Life of B. R. Haydon*,
London, 1853, vol. I.; Haydon, *Correspondence and Table-talk*, London,
1876, 2 vols.

to obtain a small grant of public money, proved a failure, for Pitt hesitated to authorize such an outlay,—a hesitation easily accounted for by the enormous expenses incurred during the long and burdensome years of war. Lord Elgin therefore decided to undertake the work at his own cost. By the advice of the experienced Sir William Hamilton, who was then in Sicily, he entrusted the artistic guidance of the enterprise to the Neapolitan painter Don Tita Lusieri, while his secretary, W. R. Hamilton, engaged the rest of the artists, a draughtsman, two architects, and two *formatori*, in Rome[346]. With this suite the ambassador proceeded to Constantinople. He did not himself go near Athens, but after the necessary preparations had been made, despatched the little party thither under the direction of Hamilton. In consequence of Bonaparte's successes in Egypt at this time, British influence in Constantinople was very slight, and it was impossible to obtain permission to do more than make drawings. The Athenian authorities showed themselves most ingenious in intrigues, evasions, and hindrances of all kinds; entrance to the Acropolis, for example, cost a daily douceur of almost five pounds. Accordingly for nine months the undertaking had only very small results. A change then occurred in Egyptian affairs, and the influence of England became again predominant at the Porte. Elgin instantly availed himself of the favourable turn. A new firman at once permitted the erection of scaffolding and the taking of plaster casts (May A.D. 1801). Work began in good earnest on the Acropolis, entrance to which no longer entailed a daily payment, although there was even now no lack of incivility and vexatiousness on the part of the garrison. A personal visit paid by Lord Elgin to Athens[347] convinced him of these facts, and he consequently applied for further powers. He was soon enabled to arrange for the purchase and demolition

---

[346] Hamilton's letter to Haydon, 1840, Dec. 25, in Haydon's *Corresp.* I. p. 425.

[347] Lord Elgin's visit is clear from the *Gentl. Mag.* LXXX., II. p. 333. Cf. *Report of Comm.* p. 42.

of two houses next to the Parthenon. Under one was discovered a rich booty of costly fragments of pediment figures :
under the other nothing at all. The Turkish owner pointed
with a sardonic smile to the lime in the city wall, which had
been made from the sculptures that once stood there ! This
was not the only experience of the kind. It was impossible
to ignore the fact that the ruin of the noblest works of art
in the world was progressing with giant steps. Since the
drawings of Dalton, Stuart, and Revett had been taken
half a century before, much had vanished and much had
been destroyed. In the year 1787 the French Vice-Consul,
Fauvel, had abstracted a metope and a slab of the frieze from
the Parthenon for his ambassador, Count Choiseul-Gouffier,
and the same enterprising agent was accused of cherishing
schemes far more extensive. Year after year also travellers
had been coming in increasing numbers, and taking away
larger or smaller fragments by way of keepsake. The sad-
dest fate, it was clear, awaited the buildings of Athens and
the sculptures of Phidias : they would be gradually broken
up, and dispersed to every nook and corner of the world[348].

The new Firman and its consequences.

75. Meanwhile Hamilton was engaged in travelling
through Asia Minor, Syria and Egypt. The chaplain to
the embassy, Dr Philip Hunt, was the life and soul of the
undertakings at Athens ; he was more often to be found in
that city and on other classic spots than in Constantinople[349].
At his suggestion Lord Elgin in A.D. 1801 obtained that
firman which has become so celebrated, by which full
liberty is granted to his work-people "in going in and
out of the citadel of Athens ; or in fixing scaffolding
around the ancient Temple of the Idols ; or in modelling
with chalk or gypsum the ornaments and visible figures
thereon, or in measuring the fragments and vestiges of
other ruined edifices, or in excavating, when they find it

[348] Elgin's opponents endeavoured
to deny this danger. Cf. however the
facts given in my *Parthenon*, p. 72,
75.

[349] Hunt's assertion in the *Report
of Committee*, p. 140—147. *Gentl.
Mag.* LXXII., ii. p. 725. I have not
had access to Dr Hunt's 'Journal.'

necessary, the foundations, in search of inscriptions among the rubbish;" finally it is commanded "that they be not molested, and that no one meddle with their scaffolding or implements, nor hinder them from taking away any pieces of stone *(qualche pezzi di pietra)* with inscriptions or figures." The elastic final clause of this memorable permit was so luminously expounded by Hunt to the governor of Athens, the interpretation being backed up by an appropriate present of brilliant cut-glass lustres, firearms, and other articles of English manufacture, that the governor at once gave leave for a metope to be taken from the Parthenon. Hunt was prudent enough to have this forthwith put on board ship and sent off to England. "The facility with which this had been obtained induced Lord Elgin to apply for permission to lower other groups of sculpture from the Parthenon, which he did to a considerable extent, not only on the Parthenon, but on other edifices in the Acropolis[350]." The result of these labours, which employed between three and four hundred men for about a year, is well known. The principal pedimental figures, fifteen metopes and fifty-six slabs of the frieze from the Parthenon (without including numerous fragments), one of the sculptured 'Korai' from the Erechtheion, four slabs from the frieze of the temple of Athené Niké, besides a number of architectural remains and more than a hundred inscribed stones, formed the precious booty. Many of these had not been taken from their original places without difficulty; in particular the removal of several metopes, and of the statue from the Erechtheion, had severely injured the surrounding architecture; at the same time the fact must not be forgotten that a great part of the sculptures had long been severed from their connections, that they had been scattered over the whole surface of the fortress, and sometimes built over with miserable hovels, or else let into walls, and that they now owed their collection and preservation to the zeal of Lord Elgin's agents.

[350] Hunt's own words, *Rep. of Comm.* p. 142.

It may be doubted whether Lord Elgin was quite discreet in thus using the influence of his official position to further his private undertakings; or whether the interpretation of that firman, made with the connivance of the Athenian magistrates, was in accordance with the views of the Turkish Government—if indeed the elasticity of the wording had been made altogether clear to them[301]. But only blind passion could doubt that Lord Elgin's act was an act of preservation, and that he took the only possible steps to keep together the remains of the most comprehensive creation of Phidias, and guard from further disfigurement so much as had been lucky enough to survive all preceding disasters, from Morosini's bombardment to Fauvel's partial depredation[302].

Transport of the marbles to England.   76. In the year 1803 Lord Elgin was recalled from his post. On his way home he visited Athens, where he found the most important part of his work finished and two hundred chests full of marbles ready for transportation. Lusieri remained behind in Athens to look after the shipping of these chests and to superintend some arrears of work, while Lord Elgin and the other artists went to Italy. In Rome the drawings aroused Canova's highest admiration, and prompted the advice never to have these masterpieces, the renovation of which Elgin proposed to him, touched by the hands of a restorer. While continuing his journey the Earl himself was taken prisoner by the French, contrary to all international law, and confined in Paris for two years. In the year 1805, on account of a denunciation from Athens, he was actually shut up in the fortress of Melun. While

---

[301] It is singularly characteristic of Turkish duplicity that the Turkish Government subsequently (1811) "entirely disavowed ever having given any authority to Lord Elgin for removing any part of his collection, and did still refuse to allow the removal of so ne articles remaining behind" (Lord Colchester, *Diary and Corresp.* II. p. 327). As a matter of fact, the firman

only speaks of taking away, not of removing. Cf. also the anecdotes in Fellows' *The Xanthian Marbles*, p. 12 note.

[302] As standard witnesses, because certainly not partial, for Lord Elgin, I mention only Choiseul-Gouffier, *Voyage pittor.* II. p. 86, Quatremère de Quincy, *Lettres à Canova*, pp. 5, 18, 30.

Lord Elgin was thus unlucky, his art treasures met with misfortunes of another kind. The majority of them reached England in various ships, but in the absence of the owner and his family the chests remained unclaimed in sundry English harbours. About a dozen large chests were shipped in Athens on board the brig 'Mentor,' in which Hamilton, who had returned from his travels, also took ship. Near the island of Cerigo the vessel sprang a leak, struck upon a rock just at the entrance of the harbour, and sank. Hamilton's energy succeeded in rescuing in the same year four chests, which were brought up by skilful divers from Kos and Syme. Further costly endeavours to raise the whole ship by the aid of two frigates were unsuccessful; and it was not until two years later, when the vessel had fallen to pieces, that the same divers rescued the remaining chests from the bottom of the sea and brought them again to the light of day[353]. This freight could now be brought to England. Meanwhile Lusieri had to withstand other dangers in Athens. War having been declared against England by the Porte in A.D. 1807, he was forced to leave the city. Lord Elgin's marbles, which were stored in magazines, were seized by the French and taken to the Piraeus, where they were threatened with the fate of shipment to France. Thus they seemed likely to be dispersed again. But England held supremacy at sea, and so no secure opportunity for their transportation was found. The hostile preparations were closed by a hasty peace, and Lusieri soon found himself again in possession of all the property. Not however till A.D. 1812 was this last freight, consisting of about eighty chests, sent off to England.

77. Immediately after his capture by the French Lord *Opposition* Elgin had sent instructions to England that his whole collec- *to the Elgin* tion was to be handed over unconditionally to the Govern- *marbles.* ment, but these directions were not attended to. At last, *Knight.* *Payne*

---

[353] *Memor.* p. 22. *Rep. of Comm.* II. p. 726. Hamilton in Haydon's App. p. xviii. *Gentl. Mag.* LXXIII. *Corresp.* I. pp. 424, 425.

in A.D. 1806, he was liberated and enabled to return home.
At the cost of much trouble he collected his scattered chests
and brought them to London, intending to exhibit his treasures to the public. A peculiarly unlucky star seemed however to hang over the expatriated gods[324]. In the space of
a few years the marbles had to change their home four
times. First they sought shelter in the mansion of the
Duchess of Portland, then they were taken to Richmond
Gardens, thence to Lord Elgin's residence in Park Lane,
and finally to Burlington House. And another far heavier
cloud hung over them yet ; inasmuch as PAYNE KNIGHT,
before one of the chests had been opened, before he had
seen a single specimen with his own eyes, pronounced on
the unknown gods sentence of excommunication. About a
hundred and thirty years previously, the traveller Jacob
Spon, after a single visit to the Acropolis, had hazarded
the opinion that two of the figures of the west pediment
resembled the Emperor Hadrian and his consort Sabina ;
upon this Spon had founded the theory that all the pedimental sculptures were a later addition to the temple[325].
Knight, who, as we have seen, considered that magnitude and
beauty could not be found together, took his stand upon this.
At the first dinner party at which Lord Elgin met him, he
cried out in a loud voice: " You have lost your labour, my
Lord Elgin, your marbles are over-rated ; they are not
Greek, they are Roman of the time of Hadrian[326]." Great
as was Payne Knight's authority in matters of taste, it
would have been incomprehensible how such an absurdity
could meet with any supporters, had not other travellers,
who had been present in Athens during the operations
attendant upon the removal of the marbles, spoken much
of the reckless behaviour of Lord Elgin's agents at that

[324] Cf. Michaelis, die Aufnahme der Elgin Marbles in London, in Im neuen Reich, Leipzig, 1877, t. pp. 81–94, 135–150.
[325] Voyage d'Italie, &c., Lyon, 1678, II. p. 146. Cf. Wheler, Journey into Greece, London, 1682, p. 361.
[326] Haydon's own words; cf. Life of Haydon, I. p. 272.

time. The severe censure which these agents deserved was
naturally visited on their master[357]. Lord Elgin's long in-
voluntary absence had made it impossible for him to dissi-
pate prejudices of this kind, and "*les absents ont toujours
tort*[358]." Thus the Earl, who could not possibly hold himself
responsible for the violence of his agents, found the tone of
critical circles unfavourable and even inimical to him, inasmuch as opinion in these circles was led by the Society
of Dilettanti, who in their turn took their cue in such
matters from Payne Knight. The fashionable disfavour
was transferred from Lord Elgin to his marbles. The
worst of all was an attack which Knight allowed himself
to make in his Introduction to the *Specimens of Antient
Sculpture*, A.D. 1809, published in the name and under the
sanction of the Society, in which he said of the friezes and
metopes of the Parthenon: "as these are merely architectural sculptures, executed from Phidias' designs and under
his directions, probably by workmen scarcely ranked among
artists....they can throw but little light upon the more
important details of his art........They are....evidently the
works of many different persons, some of whom would not
have been entitled to the rank of artists in a much less
cultivated and fastidious age[359]." Harmless as such idle
judgments would have been in ordinary times, they helped
to prejudice public opinion in the then position of
affairs[360].

78. Thus ill appreciated by the aristocratic public of
London, the Athenian deities lay for many years in a "damp
dirty pent-house" in the court of the house in Park Lane[361].
Their owner, who had thought to do valuable service to
his country by his exertions and great pecuniary sacrifices,

Champions of the Elgin marbles. West, Fuseli, Haydon.

[357] Clarke, *Travels*, II. II. pp.
48,5, &c. Dodwell, *Class. Tour*, I. p.
322, &c. Hughes, *Travels*, I. p. 261.
Eustace, *Tour in Italy*, I. p. 269,
rails from a distance without having
been in Athens.
[358] This judgment of Hamilton's is
given in Haydon's *Corresp.* I. p. 425.
[359] *Specimens*, vol. I., *prelim.
dissert.* p. xxxix.
[360] Woods, J., *Antiq. of Athens*,
IV. p. 28, shows how Elgin took his
revenge.
[361] *Life of Haydon*, I. p. 84.

could only feel deeply hurt by the partial tone taken by a
misguided but influential coterie. Still there were some
more judicious critics to be found, especially among artists.
The venerable President of the Royal Academy, BENJAMIN
WEST, unreservedly acknowledged the hitherto undreamt-of
greatness of these works, and tried at once to turn them to
account for modern art by employing them in his own
compositions[302]. The keeper of the Academy, HENRY
FUSELI, was of the same opinion[303]. The enthusiasm of
the younger generation expressed itself even more vigorously, being represented especially by the talented but
unfortunate BENJAMIN ROBERT HAYDON[304]. From the
first moment that these marvellous works were presented
to his sight (A.D. 1808) he recognised their full value, their
peculiar character, and their great superiority over the
whole crowd of late Greek and Roman works which had
hitherto been valued as the highest form of antique art,
and which filled the galleries of the English Dilettanti.
He regarded it as certain "that it was the greatest blessing
that ever happened to this country their being brought
here[305]." For three months he kept copying the originals
till he made them quite his own, and thought and dreamt
of nothing else. He entreated Lord Elgin to permit young
artists to have access to them as much as possible, as they
were the true School of Art[306]. So enthusiastic a spirit as
Haydon, and one so well able to handle the pen, could not
fail to come forward as the public champion of persecuted
beauty, and harbinger of the new gospel of art[307]. Stout
comrades in arms seem to have stood by him, like Elmes
and the architect John Soane[308]. However neither criticism,

[302] West to Lord Elgin, 1809,
Feb. 6, 1811, March 20, in the
Memorandum, App. A. Cf. Life of
Haydon, i. p. 86–88.
[303] Knowles, J., Life and Writings
of Henry Fuseli, London, 1831, I p. 294.
[304] Haydon regarded his acquaintance with the Elgin marbles as the
turning-point of his activity as an
artist. See especially Life, i. pp. 82,
&c. The reader cannot help being
infected by his enthusiasm.
[305] Haydon, Life, i. p. 89.
[306] Haydon to Lord Elgin, 1808,
Dec., in the Corresp. i. p. 256.
[307] The Examiner, 1812, Jan. 26,
Feb. 2, 9.
[308] The account is derived from

nor scorn, nor enthusiasm could dissuade the aristocratic
circle from swearing by the word of their lord and master,
and the Elgin marbles remained as unfashionable and as
much under excommunication as ever. What was the good of
these headless and armless statues and these defaced reliefs?
They could not possibly be used for decorative purposes.

79. Under such unfavourable circumstances did Lord *Attempts*
Elgin find himself obliged to contemplate a sale of his *to sell the
collection.*
treasures. The Athenian works had cost him £25,700, *Byron.*
the transport £2,500, the salvage of the sculptures sunk at
the shipwreck £5,000, the task of collecting, housing, and
guarding them in England £6,000, making a total of
£39,200, and besides these expenses he experienced a loss
of interest extending over many years and reckoned at
£23,240[369]. The Earl received hints that he should offer
his marbles for sale in Paris, where they would be incorporated into the *Musée Napoléon* together with the booty
gained by the Napoleonic armies. He paid no heed to
this suggestion, for in all his undertakings he had had the
honour and interest of his own country exclusively before
his eyes. The British Museum naturally presented itself as
the most appropriate institution to fulfil these views and
wishes. The nucleus of a national collection of antiques
had been formed by Sir William Hamilton's vases, Townley's
Graeco-Roman sculptures, and by the capture from the
French of the booty they had gathered on the Egyptian
Expedition, and it seemed that this nucleus would be completed in the happiest way by the remains of the art of the
Athens of Pericles. At the beginning of the year 1811
W. R. HAMILTON, Lord Elgin's former secretary, wrote a
"Memorandum on the subject of the Earl of Elgin's pur-

Böttiger, *Denkschrift uber Lord
Elgin's Erwerbungen*, Leipzig, 1817,
p. 54, and refers to letters of Elmes
to Th. Hope, in Valpy's *Pamphleteer*,
III., 1814, p. 329, and of Soane in
Prince Hoare's "The Artist." But
there seems to be a mistake in our way,
as according to information furnished

by Mr A. S. Murray, nothing of the
kind exists there.
  [369] Elgin to Long, 1811, May 6, in
the *Report of Comm.* App. pp. vii.—
xiv. Cf. also the letters to Bankes,
1816, Feb. 29, March 13 (pp. xv.—
xxi.).

suits in Greece[370]," which described briefly and skilfully all
that the Earl had done and the value of his acquisitions.
It was perhaps not without an afterthought in regard to
them that Hamilton about this time joined the Dilettanti
Society[371]. In April A.D. 1811 Elgin asked compensation
for his expenses, trial of the artistic worth of his collection
by a competent tribunal, and the recognition that by his
trouble he had rendered a service to his country. He
believed this to be due to his honour, which had been
attacked by the ill-feeling of the Dilettanti. The premier,
Perceval, without causing any detailed valuation of the
sculptures to be made, only offered Lord Elgin the inade-
quate sum of thirty thousand pounds; and instead of any
recognition of his services, doubts were raised as to whether
the marbles were his own property, or whether, on account
of the official position he held at the time of his acquiring
them, they did not rather belong to the State. In this unworthy treatment the influence of the disfavour prevailing
among the aristocratic Dilettanti is distinctly perceptible.
Lord Elgin naturally broke off the negotiations ; for they
only brought him the scoffing nicknames of "stone-monger,"
"marble-dealer," and even "marble-stealer[372]." The rod
seemed finally to break over the head of the "modern
Pict" when in the summer of A.D. 1812 there appeared those
burning lines in which Childe Harold lamented seeing

> "The walls defaced, the mouldering shrines removed
> By British hands, which it had best behoved
> To guard those relics ne'er to be restored,"

and discharged his full hatred upon "the last, the worst
dull spoiler" of the Greek temples[373]. Again, all who should
venture to admire the Greek treasures by the Thames were

[370] London and Edinburgh, 1811.
The first rare edition only contains
three appendices, West's letter to Lord
Elgin, *Notes on Phidias and his School*,
and Millin, *Description d'un bas relief
du Parthénon, actuellement au Musée
Napoléon.*

[371] He was elected Jan. 6, A.D.
1811.
[372] Horace Smith quizzes Haydon
with "your friend the marble-stealer"
(Haydon, *Corresp.* I. p. 319).
[373] Canto II. str. 11—15.

plunged into the same condemnation by the "Curse of
Minerva[374];" for the goddess was obliging enough to appear
in phantom shape to the noble English poet in order to
stir up his hatred against his Scotch compeer, and to
shower down a rich cornucopia of far from Olympian
curses.

> "Meantime, the flattering feeble dotard, West,
> Europe's worst dauber and poor Britain's best,
> With palsied hand shall turn each model o'er,
> And own himself an infant of fourscore:
> Be all the bruisers call'd from all St Giles,
> That art and nature may compare their styles;
> While brawny brutes in stupid wonder stare,
> And marvel at his lordship's *stone-shop* there."

The foolish condemnations of Payne Knight were not
dangerous for long, and soon passed into oblivion: but LORD
BYRON with his words of flame became Elgin's most
dangerous enemy, since even to the present day his judgment is often adopted by the ill-informed. It is well known
that the poet is always considered to be in the right, and
the more strongly he lays on his colours, the more credence
does he gain. What availed it that Byron's travelling companion, Hobhouse, showed a very different comprehension,
one that was both more impartial and more true? Besides,
Hobhouse's book did not appear till a year later[375].

80. Who knows how much longer the incomparable *Foreign aid.*
collection, increased meanwhile by the contents of those *Visconti.*
eighty chests which had been so long detained in Athens, *Lord Elgin's renewed proposals.*
would have remained unappreciated in the sheds of Bur-
lington House, if unexpected and favourable circumstances
had not arisen? The immediate cause of change was the
judgment of two foreigners, very competent judges, who
opposed the opinion prevailing in England. After the
conclusion of the Peace of Paris (May 30, A.D. 1814)
LUDWIG, CROWN PRINCE OF BAVARIA, came thence to

---

[374] This libellous poem, written at
Athens in March, A.D. 1811, was, as
is well known, not intended for publication. The effect of poison is not
lessened if it be privately adminis-
tered.
[375] *Journey through Albania*,
London, 1813, I. p. 340. &c.

London. Himself an excellent connoisseur and successful
collector, having only a short time before this obtained the
marbles from Aegina, the Prince showed no limit to
his admiration of the sculptures, and extolled them, the
reliefs particularly, as the perfection of art[376]. The similar
verdict of ENNIO QUIRINO VISCONTI, the Director of
the *Musée Napoléon*, who shortly after came from Paris to
study Lord Elgin's collection, carried with it even greater
weight. What could be said in opposition to the judgment
of the recognised leader among living archæologists, when
he expatiated upon the significance of those works for the
culture of modern art, as much as upon their beauty and
historical importance? Lord Elgin's opponents could only
be thankful that this view was not yet made public in official
form[377]. Lord Elgin began to think he had a better prospect of carrying out his former plan with success. Hamilton was now Under Secretary of State, and his Memorandum
appeared at the beginning of the year 1815 in a new edition
intended for a larger public[378]. He also opened negotiations
respecting the placing of the marbles in the British Museum,
as the sale of Burlington House made it necessary
to remove them thence (March 21). The Trustees of the
Museum could not entertain the proposal immediately, they
too being hampered by want of space ; but they showed
themselves inclined to recommend the purchase of the
collection. Government seemed also disposed to buy, and
on the eighth of June Lord Elgin presented a petition to
the State to purchase his marbles, proposing, as the basis
for determining the price, not his own expenses, but a
valuation to be decided by a commission. The proposition
was laid before the House of Commons on the fifteenth of

[376] Letter to M. Wagner, 1814,
June 17, in Urlichs, *Die Glyptothek Sr.
Maj. des Königs Ludwig I von Bayern*,
Munich. 1867. p. 53.
[377] *Lettre de E. Q. Visconti à un
Anglais* (W. R. Hamilton), Paris,
1814, Nov. 22 : in the second edition
of the *Memorandum*, pp. 78–84.
[378] *Memorandum*, &c. Second
edition, corrected. London. John
Murray. 1815. There are in addition
Visconti's letter and a letter from an
anonymous person to a friend of Lord
Elgin's, January. 1815.

June, and was not received without eager and immediate
opposition: the Battle of Waterloo and the adjournment of
the House (July 12) prevented the matter being then
brought to a conclusion[379].

81. This time, however, the delay worked favourably. *The Phi-*
In the autumn of the year 1815 the reliefs from Phigalia at *galia marbles.*
last arrived in England. They had been purchased in *Canova's*
Zante by the Prince Regent on the first May A.D. 1814, for *Select*
£15,000. In consequence of this purchase universal at- *committee.*
tention was turned to the remains of Greek sculpture, and
it was moreover inevitable that comparisons should be
instituted between the friezes that the State had thus
obtained and the marbles which were offered to it by
Lord Elgin. It is unnecessary to add that Payne Knight
spoke as loudly in favour of the Prince Regent's acquisition
as he continued to do in condemnation of Lord Elgin's[380]:
but the truth was irresistibly making way. Its final triumph
was assured when a new authority, and one from which
opinion at that date allowed no appeal, pronounced in
favour of the Elgin marbles. CANOVA came to Paris to
recover for the Vatican the art-treasures that had lately
been carried off. Visconti's unqualified approval of the
Athenian sculptures might well determine him the more
readily to accept an invitation from the sculptor Rossi to
visit him in London. He came in November. Hamilton
conducted him to see the marbles; Haydon, who was then
occupied in taking the first casts of them, acted as *cicerone.*
Canova's expectations had been pitched high, but he found
them far surpassed. In his opinion these sculptures put all
other antiques, the Apollo Belvedere not excepted, quite
in the shade; it was worth a journey from Rome only to

---

[379] Lord Colchester, *Diary and
Corresp.* II. p. 534, 546, 547. *Report
of Comm.* p. 53. Hansard's *Parliam.
Debates,* XXXI. pp. 828—830.
[380] In the *Morning Chronicle.*—
Contradictions followed in the *Cham-*
pion, by the editor, John Scott, and
by Haydon. Thus according to
Böttiger, *Denkschrift.* p. 55, who besides refers to the *New Monthly
Magazine,* 1816, April, pp. 247—
249.

see them ; they must necessarily work a great revolution in
modern sculpture. Canova himself regretted that he had
not been able to study from them in his youth : "Oh! that
I were a young man, and had to begin again, I should
work on totally different principles from what I have done,
and form, I hope, an entirely new school." He spent all
his spare time during his short visit in studying them most
carefully. Everywhere he sounded their praise, and pronounced that if £15,000 had been paid for the Phigalian
frieze, this collection was certainly worth £100,000[381]. Such
expressions, from such a mouth, naturally made a great
impression on the public at large and on the Government :
while Payne Knight, and those who had blindly followed
him, were much perplexed[382]. This change in the general
tone was particularly valuable to Lord Elgin just now, as
he was entangled in a vexatious literary controversy, which
though not directly connected with his marbles, yet concerned his honour[383]. In February A.D. 1816 he again
presented his petition to the Lower House, and a week
later a Select Committee was appointed "to enquire whether
it be expedient that the collection should be purchased on
behalf of the public, and if so, what price it may be reasonable to allow for the same[384]." The constitution of the
Committee, of which Henry Bankes was elected chairman,
was supposed to be inimical to Lord Elgin, and not quite
without reason, for Bankes had repeatedly in Parliament
expressed doubts as to the right of Lord Elgin to the

[381] Canova to Elgin, London, 1815,
Nov. 10 (Visconti, *Deux mém.* p. 1).
Haydon, *Life,* I. pp. 293–297.
Corresp. I. pp. 321–323, 424, II. p.
19. Rossi in the *Report of Comm.* p.
88. Planta in Lord Colchester's
Diary, II. p. 564. *Morgenblatt,*
Tübingen, 1816, nos. 51, 52.
[382] Haydon, *Life,* I. pp. 297, 298.
[383] *Remains of the late John
Tweddell,* ed. by Robert Tweddell,
London, 1815, Appendix. Lord Elgin,
Letter to the Editor of the Edinburgh

Review, &c., London, 1816, and *Post-
script to a Letter, &c.* Hunt, Philip,
*A Narrative of what is known re-
specting the Literary Remains of the
late John Tweddell,* London, 1816.
Quarterly Review, XIV. no. XXVII. art.
"Elgin." Tweddell, R., *Addenda to
the Remains of J. Tweddell,* London,
1816, and *Account of the Examination
of the Elgin-box at the Foreign Office,
on 7th Nov.,* 1816, Manchester.
[384] Hansard, *Parliam. Deb.* XXXII.
pp. 577, 823–828.

sculptures as exclusively his private property[285]. The success of Lord Elgin's petition was even regarded in many
circles as so doubtful, that the Crown Prince of Bavaria,
it was rumoured, secretly lodged thirty thousand pounds
with his London agents for immediate advance to Lord
Elgin if opportunity offered[286].

82. The course of the deliberations of the Committee *Delibera-*
did not justify such apprehensions, and Bankes proved him- *tions of the Committee.*
self a thoroughly impartial president[287]. On the twenty- *Literary*
ninth of February the hearing of witnesses began, Lord *warfare.*
Elgin being the first. He, Hamilton, and Hunt, as having
been most immediately concerned, were regarded as the
chief witnesses for the establishment of the facts. A
second group consisted of travellers who were called upon
to confirm the degree of danger which had threatened the
sculptures in Athens. Morritt in particular described this
danger very impressively; in addition to him were heard
Lord Aberdeen, Wilkins the architect, and Fazakerley.
The third and largest group was composed of artists
and connoisseurs. Among the latter the most interesting
witness was Payne Knight. His judgment in art did no
honour to the purity of his taste—only the metopes finding
favour in his eyes—but we can distinctly perceive his feeling that he is struggling for a lost cause. Wilkins expressed
himself with great coldness ; Lord Aberdeen with far more
freedom from prejudice, although he had been regarded in
public as a leading opponent of the purchase[288]. The testimonies of the artists have a very different tone, particularly
those of the sculptors, Flaxman, Chantrey, Westmacott,

[285] Haydon, *Corresp.* I. p. 94.
Hansard, *Parliam. Debates*, XXXI. p.
829, XXXII. p. 823.
[286] Haydon, *Corresp.* I. p. 94.
Ellis, *Elgin Marbles*, I. p. 10.
[287] *Report from the Select Committee of the House of Commons on the
Earl of Elgin's Collection of Sculp-
tural Marbles*, London, 1816. The
report is dated March 23, 1816; the

official edition was ordered to be
printed 30th April, 1816. The report itself, without the extremely
interesting minutes of evidence and
official documents, has often been
reprinted.
[288] Haydon, *Life*, I p. 303, 304.
In the *Examiner*, no. 435, 1816, Apr.
28, there appeared a satiric poem on
Knight and Aberdeen.

Rossi; the eccentric old Nollekens was less communicative. Different as were their modes of answering this or that separate question—Flaxman gave the Committee a set lecture on the history of art—they were unanimous in the opinion that the Elgin marbles belong to the very highest class of all known antiques, and that they not only far excel Townley's Graeco-Roman sculptures, but deserve to be preferred before the friezes of Phigalia. Such had already been the opinion of Canova, and so now said the painters West and Lawrence, and the art-dealer, Day. It was a pitched battle between the old and the new periods of taste, but the victory of the latter was a foregone conclusion. Haydon would also most willingly have given his testimony. Lord Elgin had proposed him as a witness, but he was put off day after day, till at last his evidence was altogether dispensed with "out of delicacy to Mr Payne Knight." He then sent forth his voice abroad in a fulminating article which appeared in two weekly papers on the next Sunday after the hearing of witnesses had concluded (March 13): "On the judgment of connoisseurs being preferred to that of professional men." The article created a tremendous sensation; replies and rejoinders followed; it was translated into foreign languages, and went the round of Europe as the writ of a new art-gospel[389]. Then came just at the twelfth hour the two masterly treatises of Visconti which he had read before the Paris Academy in the preceding autumn. Lord Elgin received them just in time to have them printed, together with a letter of Canova's, both in the original languages and in English[390]. The book appeared in May. The Earl's skill,

[389] Haydon, *Life*, I. pp. 306—313. *Corresp.* i. pp. 94—96. *Examiner*, 1816, no. 429, March 17. Reply by "J. W." in the same paper, no. 432, Apr. 7. Rejoinder by Mariette, no. 434, Apr. 21. Haydon's fiery article appeared at the same time in the *Champion*.

[390] *Lettre du chev. A. Canova : et deux Mémoires lus à l'Institut Royal de France* [1815, Oct. 21 and Nov. 10] *sur les ouvrages de sculpture dans la collection de Mylord Comte d'Elgin, par le chev. E. Q. Visconti.* London, 1816 (reprinted in Paris 1818, and in Visconti's *Opere varie*, III. p. 84). A

in thus marshalling in battle array his native troops and
his foreign auxiliaries exactly at the right moment, elicited
no small admiration[321].

83. The seventh of June was the memorable day of *The
purchase
of the
Elgin
marbles
for the
British
Museum.*
the parliamentary debate, which placed the official seal on
a complete revolution in taste[322]. The report of Bankes'
Committee proved the legality of the claim of ownership,
enlarged on the value of the collection both for its own
sake and for the culture of art in England, and proposed in
conclusion, in accordance with a valuation made by Lord
Aberdeen, and agreeably to Perceval's former offer, a purchase sum of thirty-five thousand pounds. This proposal
should have contented those who considered that Lord
Elgin was at the most entitled to indemnification for his
expenses, and that anything obtained by an ambassador belonged half to the nation; for Elgin's bare costs had in the
meantime risen to £51,000, and the interest on the capital he
had laid out was reckoned, as we have said, at £23,240; so
that the sum proposed would not cover the half of his total
expenses. But, although the value of the collection was
hardly called in question—such had been the impression
produced by the hearing of the witnesses and all the inci-
dental discussion—yet the peculiar character of the acquisition on the one hand, and on the other the impoverished
state of the national finances, gave excuse to the opposition
party for long debate, till they could at last retire with
honour and give way to a majority of eighty-two voices
against thirty. The ratification of the resolution, on the
part of the public journals, even those of the opposition,
followed immediately[323]; and when soon after (A.D. 1817)
the newly acquired sculptures were exhibited in the rooms
of the Museum, the value of the treasure that had at last

Letter, &c., and two Memoirs, &c.,
London, 1816.
[321] *Denkschrift über Lord Elgin's
Erwerbungen in Griechenland. Mit
einer Vorrede von C. A. Böttiger*,
Leipzig and Altenburg, 1817, p. 53.
[322] Hansard, *Parliam. Debates*,
XXXIV. p. 1027—1040.
[323] *Times* and *Morning Chronicle*,
1816, June 8.

been happily housed, was recognised by the public at
large ; from the riding-master who recommended to his
pupils the study of the Panathenaic horsemen[304], up to the
circle of the most gifted artists, who eagerly drew upon the
newly opened resources of study[305], and even to the royal
and august personages who visited London from abroad[306].
The excitement caused by the whole affair extended far
beyond England's boundaries. The venerable GOETHE,
brought up with quite different views of art, longed to see
those works "in which alone law and gospel were united ;"
he considered himself happy to have at least lived to see
this event, and sketched a plan for every German sculptor
in future to come and study for a time in the British Museum[307]. Plaster casts, taken first from Haydon's models,
and then from other sources, were rapidly circulated through
Europe, even to the Neva and the Tiber[308], and they caused
the sculptor DANNECKER to give utterance to the just observation, "these works seem moulded from the life, and yet
he had never had the good fortune to see in the life such
perfection[309]." But the most inspired prophet was the gifted
QUATREMÈRE DE QUINCY, then sixty-three years of age,
whose seven letters, written to Canova in the year 1818,
bear witness in the most eloquent manner to the complete
change wrought in the general view of the history and
aesthetics of Greek art[400]. At one stroke the British Museum had become the most distinguished museum of anti-

[304] Smith, J. Th., *Nollekens*, I. p.
316 note. Cf. Haydon, *Corresp.* I. p.
ix. note 3. Northcote judged very
differently (Hazlitt, *Conversations of
J. Northcote*, London, 1830, p. 255).
[305] Haydon, *Corresp.* I. p. 106,
336. *The Elgin Marbles*, London,
1816. Lyons, Edwin, *Outlines of the
E. M.*, London, 1816. Burrow, *The
E. M.*, I. London, 1817. Lawrence,
E. M. from the Parthenon of Athens,
London, 1818.
[306] Haydon, *Corresp.* I. p. 103.
[307] Goethe to Sartorius, 1817, July
30 (see *Neue Freie Presse*, Vienna,

1878, Jan. 8). Id. *Werke*, XXXII. p.
171, XLIV. p. 36. Haydon, *Corresp.*
I. p. 382.
[308] Petersburg : Haydon, *Corresp.*
I. pp. 323-329, II. p. 64. Rome,
Canova : Haydon, *Life*, I. p. 297.
Corresp. I. pp. 321—323. Thorvaldsen : ib. II. p. 173.
[309] Dannecker to Welcker, 1819,
July 26 (see *Im neuen Reich*, Leipzig,
1877, I. p. 147).
[400] *Lettres écrites de Londres à
Rome, et adressées à M. Canova, sur
les Marbres d'Elgin*. Rome, 1818.

quities in the world, and with the secure prospect of always remaining such. The splendid publication of the *Museum Marbles*, published by Taylor Combe, Hawkins, and others, under the direction of Planta, was the outward sign that the institution was both conscious and proud of its new position ; the sculptures of Phigalia and Athens, drawn by the master-hand of H. Corbould, were here reproduced in an exemplary manner[401]. By the legacy of PAYNE KNIGHT (A.D. 1824) the section devoted to bronzes and Greek coins was soon enriched to such a degree that henceforth in this respect too the museum needed to shun no comparison.

84. *Tantae molis erat Elgini condere signa.* The only persons who, in this affair, had suffered serious damage were the DILETTANTI. Still it would be unjust to judge them only according to the unlucky part which Payne Knight's mistaken persistency had betrayed them into playing. It must not be forgotten that in A.D. 1811, soon after the publication of the first volume of *Specimens of Antient Sculpture*, the Greek expedition under the conduct of W. Gell was fitted out. It cost over £6,500. Again in the year 1816, at the suggestion of Sir Henry Englefield, and with a view to the publication of the results of that journey, an "Ionian Fund" was founded, to which every member contributed ten guineas for five years. They were in consequence in a position to publish in A.D. 1817 the *Unedited Antiquities of Attica*, in A.D. 1821 to follow this up by a new and improved edition of the first volume of the *Antiquities of Ionia*, and finally in 1840 A.D. to complete this work with the third volume[402]. All these undertakings contributed towards the more intimate knowledge of Greece and Greek art, and they in this way moved in the same direction as Lord Elgin's activity. When Payne

The activity of the Society of Dilettanti.

[401] *A Description of Ancient Marbles in the British Museum,* vol. IV. 1820 (Phigalia). VI.—VIII. 1830 —1839 (Parthenon). IX. 1842 (Elgin Miscellanies). The remaining volumes, I.—III., V., X., XI., relate to the Townley Sculptures.
[402] [Hamilton] *Hist. Notices Soc. Dil.* pp. 46—51, 111. Cf. above, notes 342, 343.

Knight was dead (A.D. 1824) and Hamilton had undertaken the secretaryship of the society (A.D. 1830), there was
a hope of peace; for the society elected Lord Elgin as a
member without his knowledge in A.D. 1831. But flatter-
ing as was the form of the proposal, the Earl could not
bring himself to accept the honour. In a polite but decided
letter to the secretary (July 25, 1831), he referred to his
former exertions, the result of which "will never cease to be
a matter of the utmost gratification to me. If, when it was
made known to the public, twenty-five years ago, or at any
reasonable time afterwards, it had been thought that the
same energy would be considered useful to the Dilettanti
Society, most happy should I have been to have contributed every aid in my power. But as such expectation
has long since past, I really do not apprehend that I shall
be thought fastidious, if I decline the honour now proposed to me at this my eleventh hour[103]." While this effort
to atone for an old fault failed, the society was zealously
exerting itself to win new honours. It supported Sir William Gell, now its "Resident Plenipotentiary in Italy," in
the publication of his *Topography of Rome and its Vicinity* (A.D. 1834)[104]; by means of a subscription raised partly
among its own members and partly among other lovers of
art, the imposing sum of £834. 16. 6 was obtained, and
was given to the British Museum to enable it to compass
the purchase from Chevalier Bronsted of the so-called
bronzes of Siris, consummate examples of Greek metal-
work (A.D. 1833), and also to provide for their appropriate
publication (A.D. 1836)[105]. Finally, in A.D. 1835, after many

---

[103] *Hist. Notices*, p. 101. *Edinburgh Review*, CV., 1857, p. 504.
[104] 2 vols. London, 1834. A new
edition, revised by E. H. Bunbury,
1846. The Society awarded Gell, who
regularly sent in to it a report from
Italy, a honorarium of £200 for the
volume (*Histor. Notices*, pp. 94–97).
[105] Broendsted got £1000 for the
originals and £100 for the engravings

of the *Bronzes of Siris, now in the
Brit. Mus., an archaeological essay* by
P. O. Br., 1836; subsequently expanded under the title *Die Bronzen von Siris,* Copenhagen, 1837. The pedigree of
the bronzes is very doubtful, as the Neapolitan vendor Michele de' Crescenzi
stated to Broendsted that the place of
their discovery was Saponara, not far
from Siris, to E. Braun (*Bullett. dell'*

years' preparation, appeared the second volume of *Specimens of Antient Sculpture*, the earliest plates of which had been already executed before the publication of the first volume[405]. Unfortunately the second volume does not deserve the same praise as its predecessor. The work opens with an introductory treatise by W. S. Morritt, of no great importance, after which the society thought themselves bound to add Payne Knight's *Inquiry into the Symbolism of Greek Art and Mythology*, which had already been twice printed[407]. In fact it paid more regard to piety towards a departed and meritorious member, than to scientific investigations which had in the meantime established stronger claims to soundness and perspicuity. The execution of the fifty-eight plates is far inferior to the workmanship of the earlier ones and in its weak smooth elegance shews disadvantageously on the whole by the side of the work of the British Museum. In the choice of sculptures, the lion's share has fallen on the British Museum, as eight specimens from Townley's collection, ten from Knight's and four others make a total of twenty-two from this source. The remaining thirty examples are taken from no less than sixteen different private collections, in strong contrast to the more exclusive character of the selection in the first volume. Christie, Hope and Westmacott, as well as Knight, contributed to the text.

85. Handsome, then, as this volume was, still the question could not fail to suggest itself whether such a collected publication of single specimens, mostly of second and third rank, was as appropriate now as it had been six and twenty years ago; for by this time the national institution could and did publish complete connected series of sculptures of the first order. The treasures of the Golden Age of Greece,

Minor collectors. Westmacott, Rogers.

Inst. 1841, p. 136) and to Welcker (MS. Note) Armento, to K. O. Müller (*Zeitschr. f. d. Alt.-Wiss.* 1845, p. 108) Vulci. James Millingen also mistrusted these statements.

[406] *Hist. Not.* pp. 16—19. The expenses amounted to about £4,000.
[407] At first printed for private circulation A.D. 1818, then reprinted in the *Class. Jour.*, vols. XXIII.—XXVII.

which were collected in that museum, assuredly weighed heavily against the private collections, which were mostly Graeco-Roman and lent to their publication an almost preponderating personal interest. Certainly the new volume proved that Payne Knight had exaggerated when he had stated before the Commission on the Elgin marbles that there are no collectors in this country[408]. Besides the Egremont, Hope and Lansdowne collections, which had already been represented in the first volume, besides those at Holkham, Ince, Marbury, Newby, Strawberry Hill and that of Mr Hawkins, all of which dated their origin from the last century, new names were to be found, chiefly from the circle of the Dilettanti themselves. Such were LEAKE and DRUMMOND HAY, each of whom had contributed a bronze[409]. W. J. BANKES, of Kingston Hall, appeared as the possessor of a few heads, which had been brought by Consul Baldwin from Egypt and in A.D. 1828 put up to auction. W. R. HAMILTON contributed a head of the same origin and a beautiful fragment that Canova had given to him[410]. The sculptor RICH. WESTMACOTT, who possessed a small collection of not very important marble statues, was represented in the volume by a small bronze Athene[411]; the poet SAM. ROGERS by an excellent marble head which owed its origin to the excavations of Fagan at Ostia. Rogers' collection, in the formation of which James Millingen had been active, consisted mainly of painted vases, sometimes of considerable value. Besides these there were fifty specimens of bronzes of all kinds and as many gold ornaments; also some objects in glass and terra cotta, and lastly about eighty Egyptian antiquities. The whole collection enjoyed great fame for the taste with which it had been formed[412]. The last new name in the second volume of the *Specimens* was that of the Duke of Bedford.

---

[408] *Report of Comm.* p. 100.
[409] Leake's Herakles is now in Cambridge, Hay's Herakles (*Mon. dell' Inst.* I. Pl. 17) in the British Museum.
[410] See Cat., art. London.
[411] See Cat., art. London.
[412] Waagen, *Treas.* II. p. 81.

86.   In the time of the first of the Stuarts we find that *The Duke of Bedford.* a Countess of Bedford had interested herself in ancient coins, and about the middle of the last century Francis, Marquis of Tavistock, had brought a few marble statues home with him from Rome[112]. A very splendid specimen, the so-called Lante vase, and a beautiful sarcophagus relief from Sicily were obtained by his eldest son, Francis, the seventh Duke (*d.* A.D. 1802), at Lord Cawdor's sale (A.D. 1800)[113]. But his younger brother, JOHN, SIXTH DUKE OF BEDFORD (A.D. 1766—1839), is the real founder of the celebrated collection of Woburn Abbey.   During travels in Italy in the year 1815 he made numerous purchases, among which a number of unusually large sarcophagus slabs from the Villa Aldobrandini in Frascati deserve particular mention.   They were not brought to England without difficulty. The Rondanini Palace, the painter Camuccini, and also James Millingen contributed other specimens; and the results of the newest excavations, of those in Hadrian's Villa for example, were not passed over.   The Duke was present at an excavation at Pompeii, and the dantiest find, a bronze satyr, was immediately presented to the illustrious stranger by Queen Caroline.   In England, where the Duke joined the Society of Dilettanti in the year 1819, his collection was increased by several purchases; nor were plenty of presents wanting.   His second son, Lord George William Russell, the father of the present Duke, brought with him a few specimens from Italy; others were presented to the head of the Russell family by personal and political friends, like Lord Holland and Sir George Hayter. The whole collection was then (A.D. 1820) placed in a splendid situation in the large, bright hall that had originally

---

Catalogue of the very celebrated Collection of Works of Art, the property of Sam. Rogers, Esq., deceased. Messrs Christie and Manson. Apr. and May, 1856. Cf. *Archaeol. Anzeiger,* 1856, pp. 247—254. For Miss Rogers' col-lection see Waagen, II. p. 271.
[112] Cf. above, notes 29, 210. Woburn, nos. 171, 210.
[113] For details see Cat., art. Woburn.

been intended for a conservatory. There is a particular
charm (which may be compared in a small way to that of
the Campo Santo at Pisa) in the close contiguity of the
antiquities to masterpieces of modern sculpture, by Canova,
Thorwaldsen, Flaxman, Chantrey and Westmacott, to numerous copies of celebrated old and modern sculptures, and
to busts of the heads of the Whig party. The Woburn
Abbey collection must take a place of honour among
English sculpture-galleries, and the Duke himself was
busily engaged in preparing to make this evident by a
splendid publication, the plates of which were drawn by
Corbould, while the text was by Dr Hunt, once Lord
Elgin's chaplain and agent, but now Dean of Holkham[415].
This work appeared in A.D. 1822, but the purchases by no
means ceased then. Pieces of a mosaic flooring and a
couple of Assyrian reliefs were added later, the last-named
undoubtedly after the death of Duke John (A.D. 1839). To
shew the direction of the latter's taste, it is worthy of mention that he caused the riding school at Woburn Abbey to
be adorned with casts from the equestrian procession of
the Parthenon; homage was paid to his elegant taste by
the dedication to him of Inwood's great work on the
Erechtheion at Athens[416].

87. The example of the Duke of Bedford shews that

Collectors
at Rome.
Duke of
Bucking-
ham. Lord
Kinnaird.
Disney,
&c.

Rome, in spite of a long pause, had not lost her old power
of attraction. The English, indeed, had now no longer the
sole control of the market of antiques in that city. Besides
the French (among whom both the Government and private
individuals were active, such as General Miollis and Prince
Lucien Bonaparte) and some few Russians, the Crown
Prince Ludwig of Bavaria was collecting through his agent
Martin Wagner with great success for the proposed *Glyptothek* at Munich. After the Restoration Prussia soon
entered the competition on behalf of the Berlin Museum;

415 *Outline Engravings and De-
scriptions of the Woburn Abbey*   *Marbles.* 1822. fol.
416 London, 1827. fol.

the Duke of Blacas, Count Pourtalès, Durand and other
Frenchmen, developed a most zealous activity; and above
all the Papal Government took a great share in the purchases on behalf of the Chiaramonti Museum, and later of
the Lateran Museum. The Archaeological Commission,
with the watchful Carlo Fea at their head, did everything
to hinder the exportation of the better specimens[417]. The
Barberini Faun, for example, afterwards a chief ornament
of the Munich *Glyptothek*, had already been sold once
for about £2,850 (13,000 scudi) to an Englishman; but its
removal from the city was at that time forbidden[418]. Fagan,
who had increased his Roman supply by valuable purchases from Sicily, tried in a measure to replace Hamilton
or Jenkins; but he died as early as A.D. 1816[419]. Edward
Dodwell and James Millingen did some business in antiques, and did not restrict themselves to purchasers among
their own countrymen[420]. Many of the latter instituted
excavations on their own account. THE DUCHESS OF
DEVONSHIRE, a daughter of that Earl of Bristol, whose
collections had suffered so much at the hands of the French,
earned gratitude by clearing out the Forum round the
column of Focas, and that not at all for her own benefit (A.D.
1817)[421]. The excavations undertaken by RICHARD, MAR-
QUIS OF CHANDOS, afterwards DUKE OF BUCKINGHAM
AND CHANDOS (A.D. 1776—1839), on the Via Appia and

[417] Much material is contained in
the little volume by L. Urlichs, *die
Glyptothek Sr. Maj. des Königs Ludwig I von Bayern nach ihrer Geschichte und ihrem Bestande*. Munich,
1867.

[418] Urlichs, *Glyptothek*, p. 26.

[419] *Ib.* pp. 69, 70.

[420] Dodwell sold, for example, to
the Crown Prince of Bavaria the remarkable bronze reliefs from Perugia
(*Glypt.* nos. 32—38), and an archaic
head of a warrior (*ib.* no. 40); see Urlichs, *Glypt.*, pp. 77, 95. For the rest
cf. note 338. The excellent Millingen
had collected and brought to England
many beautiful or interesting works;

for instance a bronze candelabrum
belonging to S. Rogers, Woburn,
no. 99, *Anc. Marbl. Brit. Mus.* XI.
Pl. 45. The vases and terracottas
which he left behind him passed, A. D.
1847, into the possession of the British
Museum (*Archaeol. Anzeiger*, 1847,
pp. 154—156). A celebrated little
"marble figure" from Smyrna, (*Arch.
Zeitung*), 1849, Pl. 1, came into Lord
Vernon's possession; but it has since
been proved to be a modern fabrication in biscuit-ware.

[421] *Bullett. dell' Inst.* 1829, p. 30.
She had four paid workmen, while
the Papal Government placed ten
convicts at her disposal.

at the Villa of Hadrian, and also in Rome by the baths
of Agrippa, were set on foot rather for private interests.
The booty was applied to the adorning of the princely seat
at Stowe, where nearly half a century before Earl Temple
had applied some antiques to the decoration of the famous
park[422]. Even richer treasures fell to the share of Stowe
after the Duke's second journey to Italy, made in the years
1828 and 1829, before undertaking which he had joined the
Dilettanti. In Italy he partly bought old antiques and
partly obtained them from excavations instituted by himself on the Via Appia, at Roma Vecchia, and at the tomb
of Caecilia Metella. A sarcophagus, found in the last-
named place, served after A.D. 1837 as a coffin for the
Duke's aged pet dog, and was placed in the midst of the
flower garden. But the great curiosity of all was a funeral
inscription purporting to be that of Paris the son of Priam![423]
More modest was the selection made by CHARLES, EIGHTH
LORD KINNAIRD (b. A.D. 1807—d. A.D. 1878), during a prolonged residence in Rome from about A.D. 1820 to 1825. It
consisted chiefly of fragments of sculpture and inscriptions,
which were deposited by him in his mansion of Rossie
Priory[424]. He and the Duke of Bedford divided between them
a mosaic pavement found in the neighbourhood of Rome
in A.D. 1822. Lord Kinnaird's name is specially connected
with the Warrior's Tomb in Corneto, the chief part of the
contents of which came into his possession ; it was the first
grave found there quite untouched, and in consequence of
its discovery an impulse was given for numberless excavations in the neighbourhood, some of which proved very
successful. ALEXANDER BARING, afterwards Lord ASHBUR-
TON (b. A.D. 1774—d. A.D. 1848), bought single marbles, partly

[422] Forster, H. R., the Stowe Catalogue, London, 1848, p. 44, no. 697,
699, p. 48, no. 748. Cf. above, note
264.
[423] Stowe Catal. p. 43, no. 684,
p. 264, no. 17 (statue of Lucius Verus

from the Braschi collection), p. 265,
nos. 30, 31 (Hamilton), p. 271, nos.
106 (Hertz, Catal. p. 154, no. 56), 113
(Lowther, no. 108), 117.
[424] See Cat., art. Rossie Priory.

in competition with the Crown Prince of Bavaria[425]. JOHN
DISNEY inherited the old collection of Thomas Hollis, in
endeavouring to perfect which, towards A.D. 1830, he shewed
more zeal than knowledge or criticism[426]. The number of
valuable sculptures is small, while that of inferior or spurious
specimens is very large. Flaxman, Combe and Christie were
polite enough to mention the latter in terms of praise in
referring to the amiable owner. The collection—of trash
rather than treasure—was bequeathed by Disney to the
Cambridge University, while his smaller antiquities remained in the Hyde. Vases and other small antiques were
collected somewhat later by ROBERT HENRY, TWELFTH
EARL OF PEMBROKE (A.D. 1791—1862), and by SPENCER-
JOSHUA-ALWYNE, SECOND MARQUIS OF NORTHAMPTON
(A.D. 1790—1851); coins and engraved gems by Dr NOTT[427].
Still later, between the years 1840 and 1850, GENERAL
RAMSAY formed a small collection in Rome, which came
by inheritance into the possession of Lord Murray[428].
About the same time the banker THOMAS BLAYDS brought
home a fine collection of vases from his Italian travels, in
which was incorporated, among other things, a considerable
portion of the Pizzati collection at Florence. For a time
this collection was housed at Englefield Green, Surrey, but
in A.D. 1849 it came under the hammer and was scattered;
a small number of specimens was obtained by the British
Museum[429].

88. The post of English ambassador at Naples was *Sir William Temple.*
filled for many years by SIR WILLIAM TEMPLE, the
younger son of the collector, Viscount Palmerston, who had *Collectors*

---

[425] Urlichs, *Glyptothek*, p. 84
(colossal bust of Titus).
[426] *Museum Disneianum*, London,
1849, fol. See Cat., art. Cambridge,
Hyde.
[427] Gerhard, *Archaeolog. Intelligenzblatt zur allg. Literatur-Zeitung*,
Halle, 1833, pp. 11, 14, 15, 16. Lord
Pembroke's and Dr Nott's collections
have been sold; that of the Marquis

of Northampton has for the most part
come into the British Museum. See
Cat., art. Castle Ashby.
[428] See Cat., art. Edinburgh. Cf.
Bullett. dell' Inst., 1844, pp. 35, 155.
[429] *Archaeol. Zeitung*, 1846, p.
295. *Arch. Anzeiger*, 1849, pp. 97—
101. Another part of the Pizzati collection had been already sold to St
Petersburg.

at Athens,
Lord
Guilford,
Burgon,
Lady
Ruthven.

inherited the artistic tastes of his father. The result of his exertions in that city, in which traffic in small antiquities has always been very briskly carried on, was a collection of over fourteen hundred specimens. Among these we may notice specially the first-rate series of smaller bronzes, which are worthy to be mentioned beside Payne Knight's collection. Painted vases, among which was the magnificent Hippolytus vase, terracottas, glass vessels, and gold ornaments completed the collection ; the sculptures, coins, and other small works of art, were of less importance. When the owner had returned home, he made over the whole collection to the national museum, which thereby in several departments received most valuable completion (A.D. 1856)[430]. In Greece there was a very considerable roll of active collectors. Athens, where Lusieri and the French consul Fauvel had excellent collections, offered particularly rich booty. Contemporary with the explorers we have just mentioned above (§ 73), the following collectors must be placed : Frederick North, afterwards fifth Earl of Guilford, Lewis Richard, third Lord Sondes, Messrs Thomas Burgon, Sandford Graham, and Thomas Legh[431]. The first of these, LORD GUILFORD (A.D. 1766—1827), a nephew of that Bishop of Winchester who had collected antiquities in Rome (§ 59), was Chancellor of the University of the Ionian Islands, and had been since A.D. 1790 a member of the Dilettanti Society. Fortune favoured him particularly, for besides specimens of less value he obtained two marbles of the first rank. These were the fragment of an unusually beautiful sepulchral stélé from Acharnae, and the celebrated puteal with reliefs in a fine archaic style which Dodwell had seen in Corinth, still used

---

[430] *Arch. Anzeiger*, 1857, p. 27. It is said that Lord Palmerston, on his brother's asking him what disposition he desired to be made with respect to the collection, had on his part renounced all claim to it.

[431] Stackelberg, *Gräber der Hel-*

lenen, Berlin, 1837, p. 26. Graham and Lord Sondes, see *ib.* Pl. 35, 2, 3. Millingen, *Anc. Uned. Mon.* I. pl. 15. Legh was one of the owners of the Phigalia frieze. He joined the Dilettanti A. D. 1816.

as the mouth of a well, but turned the wrong side upwards,
and which was then brought safely to Zante. The antiques
were stored in Lord Guilford's London house (23, St
James' Place), which, having been sold at his death with
almost all its contents, was forty years later pulled down.
The fate of the rest is veiled in obscurity. The sepulchral relief has re-appeared at Lowther Castle, but, in
spite of all inquiries, not the slightest trace has as yet been
discovered of the sculptured puteal, a specimen of high
importance to the history of art[432]. A few works of art
obtained by DR MACMICHAEL in Athens, and brought
by him to England, have vanished in the same manner[433].
The collection of THOMAS BURGON was rich in smaller
works of art, not solely of Athenian origin. It contained
an old Panathenaic prize vase, the only one which has
been discovered on Attic ground, and some remarkable
terra cotta reliefs from the island of Melos, which have attained a high degree of celebrity[434]. Somewhat later LADY
RUTHVEN, who lived for a long time at Athens, had a
number of tombs opened near that city, and obtained in this
manner a fairly considerable collection of painted vases,
which are preserved, with some sepulchral reliefs, in
Winton Castle[435].

89. Among English collectors who were active in *Other
collectors
in Greece.*
parts of Greece other than Athens, particular mention must
be made of PERCY CLINTON SYDNEY SMYTHE, SIXTH
*Lord
Strang-
ford,
Borrell,
Wood-
house.*
VISCOUNT STRANGFORD (A.D. 1780—1855), who from
A.D. 1820 to 1825 filled the office of ambassador to the

---

[432] Lowther, no. 37. Dodwell,
Class. Tour, II. p. 200, note 6. Gerhard, *Hyperbor. röm. Studien,* II. Berl.
1852, p. 303. Stackelberg, *Gräber,*
Pl. 12, 3. The facts given in the text
concerning the house are derived from
a letter by Baroness North to Lady
Sheffield, communicated through Mr
Newton. What can have become
of the fruits of Lord Guilford's excavations in the temple of Zeus at
Olympia (Gerhard, *l. cit.* p. 306)?

The country-seats of the family are
Waldershare Park, near Dover, and
Glenham Hall, Suffolk.
[433] Stackelberg, *Gräber,* Pl. 3, 2;
18, 1.
[434] Millingen, *Anc. Uned. Mon.* I.
Pl. 1—3, II. Pl. 2, 3. Stackelberg,
Gräber, Pl. 11, 2; 16, 1; 45, 1; 50, 1;
56, 1; 63, 1; 66, 1. The collection
was bought A.D. 1842, after Burgon's
death, for the British Museum.
[435] See Cat., art. Winton Castle.

Porte. Among other purposes he utilized his residence in the East for founding a fine collection of antiquities, part of which he presented to Canterbury. This section consists chiefly of terra cottas from various islands in the Archipelago, and they are not all free from suspicion. The marbles were far more valuable, though few in number. Two among them, an archaic statue of Apollo after a style allied to the Aeginetan, and the fragment of a copy of the shield of the Athênê Parthenos of Phidias, became famous soon after they had passed by bequest into the possession of the British Museum[436]. The excellent numismatist H. P. BORRELL collected in Smyrna. He by no means limited himself to coins, not rejecting other small monuments, such as terra cottas and gems[437]. Finally, in the west of Greece, in Corfù, the rich merchant JAMES WOODHOUSE, who for a time held an appointment in the government of the Ionian Islands, was busy for nearly half a century in forming a very remarkable collection. He controlled the market for antiquities on the island and on the opposite mainland almost autocratically, and besides this he was often gratified by presents. Greek coins formed the staple of his collection, but gold and silver ornaments, bronzes, glass vessels, sculptures, vases, and terra cottas, as well as very valuable inscriptions, were not wanting. In the year 1866 he bequeathed it all to the British Museum, which however, even after prolonged litigation, has never come into possession of the entire legacy[438].

90. If we turn back again from Greece and Italy to England, we shall find yet a further group of amateurs who have recourse principally or exclusively to the art

Collectors in London. Edwards, Burke, Chinnery, Coghill.

[436] See Cat., art. Canterbury. *Archaeol. Anzeiger*, 1864, pp. 163, 286. *Mon. Inst. dell' Inst.* IX. Pl. 41. *Arch. Zeitung*, 1865, Pl. 19b. The marbles were long hidden in a cellar, when they were discovered by Mr Newton.

[437] E. g. Welcker, *Alte Denkm.* II. Pl. 12, 20. *Archaeol. Zeitung*, 1849, Pl. 6, 3. The collection of coins was bought for the British Museum A. D.

1833 for £1,000, some other antiquities at the sale A. D. 1852.

[438] Edwards, *Lives of the Founders*, II. pp. 702—705. Cf. the parliamentary papers for A. D. 1867: *Correspondence as to the Woodhouse-Collection of Antiquities. Appendix to "Correspondence," &c. Report from the Select Committee on the Woodhouse-Collection. Archaeol. Anz.* 1866, p. 260. *Archaeol. Zeitung*, 1868, p. 76.

market at home in the formation of larger or smaller col-   *Englefield.*
Soane,
Slade,
Fox.
lections of antiques.   Ample opportunities were afforded
by the numerous sales which took place about the end of
the last century and the beginning of this.   In this way
the bookseller, J. EDWARDS, formed a good collection of
vases in London, the gem of which came from the Cawdor
sale, and was ornamented with a scene from the legend
of Pelops, found at Lecce in the year 1790.   This large
amphora had first belonged to the King of Naples, had
then been bought by General Oudinot and sold to Lord
Cawdor for a thousand guineas ; at the sale of Edwards'
collection (A.D. 1815), it came into the hands of Soane[439].
In the year 1812 the marbles of the RT. HON. EDMUND
BURKE[440], and the mixed collection of marbles and vases
belonging to Messrs W. and G. CHINNERY[441], were put up
to auction; and some years later the same fate befel the extensive collection of vases which had been formed originally
by the Neapolitan Lalò, then purchased by the Cavaliere de
Rossi, finally bought by SIR JAMES COGHILL, and increased
by further purchases in Naples.   This collection has become
particularly well known through Millingen's publication[442].
It contributed, along with the Cawdor and Chinnery sales
and other sources, to the formation of a choice cabinet of
vases, that, namely, of SIR HENRY ENGLEFIELD, during
many years a member of the Dilettanti Society (elected
A.D. 1781), and for fourteen years its secretary.   Sir Henry's
choicest specimens have been engraved in a style of much
elegance by Henry Moses[443].   The most singular of these

[439] Goede, *England,* Dresden,
1806, IV. p. 7.   *Collection of fine
Greek vases of J. Edwards,* London,
1815.   Moses, *Collection of Antique
Vases,* Pl. 23.   Millin, *Mon. inéd.* II.
Pl. 14.   *Peintures de vases,* I. Pl. 34,
49, 50, 66.   *Archaeol. Anzeiger,* 1864,
p. 165.   Millingen, *Anc. Uned. Mon.*
I. Pl. 18, publishes a vase belonging
to Mrs C. Edwards, of Harrow.

[440] *Anc. Marbles Brit. Mus.* XI.
Pl. 23, 29, 36.   Ellis, *Townley Gallery,*
II. p. 22.

[441] Chinnery. W., *Museum Marbles,*
II. Pl. 21.   Chinnery, G., Moses,
Englefield Vases, Pl. 4—12.

[442] Millingen, J., *Peintures antiques
de Vases grecs de la collection de Sir
John Coghill, Bart.,* Rome, 1817, fol.
Moses, *Englefield Vases,* Pl. 13—28.
Payne Knight was also one of the
buyers; see *Catal. of Vases Brit.
Mus.* nos. 609, 612.

[443] *Vases from the Collection of Sir
H. Englefield, Bart., drawn and
engraved by H. Moses* (40 plates),

collections was that of the eminent architect SIR JOHN
SOANE (A.D. 1755—1837). *Non multum sed multa* appears
to have been his motto in collecting ; for there is something
of everything. Along with a few choice specimens of high
value, or at least of considerable interest, there is an im
measurable chaos of worthless fragments, of all times, from
all countries, of all kinds of art, originals and copies mixed
together. All this is crammed into the narrow limits of a
private house, and is arranged in so ingenious a manner
that no corner, however dark, is left unoccupied. In this
respect the architect has achieved marvels ; nevertheless
this labyrinth stuffed full of fragments is the most tasteless
arrangement that can be seen ; it has the same kind of
perplexing and oppressive effect on the spectator as if the
whole large stock of an old-clothes-dealer had been squeezed
into a doll's house. For an appropriate situation has not
been in all cases found for even the few good specimens.
Two only are fairly well placed, the remarkable Egyptian
sarcophagus discovered by Belzoni, and the Cawdor vase
above mentioned ; in fact, many sculptures worthy of notice
are rendered quite unavailable for enjoyment and study by
their bad position. In such a shape has this cabinet of
rarities, by the will of the collector, become the property
of the State. It seems to find admirers : and certainly it
enriches London by one curiosity the more[444]. How far
preferable to this sort of amateurship is devotion to a single
branch of collecting, we may learn by the examples of Fox
and Slade. FELIX SLADE (A.D. 1790—1868), at very considerable expense, made a collection entirely consisting of
glass, in which antique glass is very well represented, though
it does not hold the most important place. He bequeathed

London, 1820. 4to. A new and
enlarged edition (52 plates) appeared
in 1848. The collection has been, so
far as I know, dispersed ; at any rate,
a beautiful specimen from it is in the
Soane Museum. In Moses' *Collection of Vases, &c.*, London, 1814,

several vases from other private collections are represented : J. P. Ander-
ton, G. Cooke, C. H. Tatham (Pl.
1, 2, 12).
[444] See Cat., art. London, Soane
Museum.

the whole to the British Museum, to which he had already
made handsome presents, such, for example, as the so-
called sword of Tiberius[445]. On the other hand, Major-
General CHARLES FOX, a grand-nephew of the celebrated
statesman, in the course of nearly fifty years, by purchases
of smaller collections and single specimens, formed a cabinet
of eleven thousand five hundred Greek coins, which by the
rarity of many of the specimens, by the abundance of the
connected series it contained, and by the excellent state of
their preservation throughout, could challenge almost any
private collection in Europe. This precious property
passed on the death of the owner to the Royal Museum
at Berlin (A.D. 1873)[446].

91. Great as was the number of amateurs who made
collections of antiques during the first half of our century,
it is indisputable that only few of them went to work with
that magnificence which had been so much a mark of the
dilettanti of the previous century. Had such a work as
James Millingen's *Ancient Unedited Monuments* appeared
then, he would certainly not have had to complain of being
obliged to limit his work on account of lack of interest, and
of the difficulty of obtaining access to some collections. As
it was, he had reason to grumble at "the disregard entertained
in this country for archaeological pursuits," a disregard
which even amounted to scoffing at antiquarian researches
on the part of some "pretended wits[447]." *Quid placet aut odio
est quod non mutabile credas?* In the meantime a new kind
of art-passion had become dominant. The French Revolution and the Napoleonic wars had caused an immense
number of pictures from churches and convents, public
and private galleries, to be offered for sale in all the
countries of Europe, and the lion's share had fallen to
England. The sales of the Calonne (A.D. 1795) and the

Decline of classical dilettant-ism.

[445] Franks, A. W., *Catalogue of the
Collection of Glass formed by Felix Slade*,
London, 1871, 4to. Edwards, *Lives
of the Founders*, ii. pp. 706—717.

[446] Friedländer, *Archaeol. Zeitung*,
1873, pp. 99—103.
[447] Millingen, *Anc. Uned. Mon.*, ii.
London, 1826, preface.

Orleans (A.D. 1798) collections were, through the zeal of
enterprising art-dealers and agents, followed by further
acquisitions from Rome, Genoa, and other parts of Italy,
from Belgium and Holland, from Spain, and even from
France herself. For a long period London was continually
the scene of extensive sales of pictures from all countries;
great collections of Italian and French origin were put
under the hammer not in Paris, but in London. By
means of such auctions and private sales, countless paintings, including not a few masterpieces of the first rank,
were scattered among the many mansions and country-seats
of the English nobility and gentry, where they were not in-
frequently incorporated into collections of older standing[446].
Waagen's well-known book gives us a glance over these
treasures. Among the collectors we meet the names,
besides many others, of the leading members of the
Dilettanti Society. The fact is undoubted: dilettantism
had struck out in a new direction, and had turned from
ancient art to modern. The circumstances of the time, as
already mentioned, were as favourable to the latter as they
were unfavourable to the former; inasmuch as Rome was
at the beginning of the century closed to the English, and
moreover watched with a new jealousy the export of her antiques, coveted as they were on every hand; while to make
acquisitions in Greek territory, which was partly under
Turkish government and partly in open rebellion, offered to
private individuals a still more difficult task. Moreover in
the domain of sculpture the modern masters Canova and
Thorwaldsen, Flaxman, Chantrey, and Westmacott obtained
the preference.—We must point out another sign of the decay
of antiquarian dilettantism. In spite of the numerous sales
at the close of the preceding century, the majority of the
antique collections that had been found in the most flourishing period of the pursuit remained fixed in the hands of
the families of the collectors. But among all the collections

Waagen, *Treasures of Art*, I. pp. 18–28.

that were formed in the first half of the present century, there are on the contrary few which, like that at Woburn Abbey, have survived the life of their founder. Fewer still have been handed down in his family for more than one generation. Most were sold by the heirs on the death of the first collector[449], while even some of older date, like that of Horace Walpole, were at this period put under the hammer[450]. The antiquities of Stowe were scattered in the fearful bankruptcy which overtook the son of the collector soon after a visit paid by the Queen to his luxurious hereditary abode, and in which was involved the loss of all his movable property[451]. Lord Guilford's collection fell completely into oblivion. Sir John Soane converted his into a special museum; Disney's and General Ramsay's antiquities went to enrich the public museums at Cambridge and Edinburgh; Lord Strangford's were divided between Canterbury and the British Museum. Besides many smaller additions, by gift or by will, there fell to the share of the last-named museum the collections, some of them rich, of Sir William Temple, Lord Aberdeen, Slade, and Woodhouse[452].

92. Since the acquisition of the Elgin marbles and the legacy of Payne Knight, the British Museum had for a long time received no important addition. Isolated gifts had of course never ceased to come in. Some good specimens were purchased at home and abroad, or obtained by means of exchange; for example, the Apollo from the Choiseul-Gouffier collection (A.D. 1818), the relief of the Apotheosis of Homer from the Palazzo Colonna (A.D. 1819), the torso of the Richmond Venus (A.D. 1821), the Leda and the bronze Apollo from the Mimaut collection (A.D. 1837), a

Additions to the British Museum. Fellows. Sir Stratford Canning.

[449] Burke and Chinnery, 1812; Edwards, 1815; Coghill about 1818; Englefield (?); Dodwell, 1837; Burgon, 1842; Millingen, 1847; Pembroke, 1848; Blayds and Hope (see Cat., art. Deepdene), 1849; Bessborough (note 151). 1850; Borrell, 1852; Nott (?); Rogers, 1856; Fox, 1873.

[450] 1842,—see note 172.

[451] *The Stowe Catalogue priced and annotated by Henry Rumsey Forster*, London, 1848. 4to.

[452] Aberdeen,—see § 67. Lord Northampton's vases have also, to the best of my knowledge, come into the British Museum by bequest. Cf. *Cat. of Vases Brit. Mus.* no. 694.

fine Satyr from the Dresden Museum (A.D. 1838). At the
same time the list of donors, among whom were Kings
George IV. and William IV. (A.D. 1823, 1834), increased considerably[453]. But it was not until after the year 1835 that important and homogeneous additions were made in the shape
of extensive purchases of GREEK PAINTED VASES, which had
within the preceding ten years been found in undreamt-of
numbers in Southern Etruria. The Durand and Canino
(A.D. 1836, 1837) sales in Paris offered plentiful material, and
the museum reached a culminating point on the important
acquisition of a hundred choice specimens from the collection of the widowed princess of Canino (A.D. 1843)[454].
From this time forward the British Museum could stand
comparison in this department with the continental collections of vases at Paris, Berlin, or Munich. While these
vases had the effect of throwing a new light upon the lost
traditions of Greek painting, and opening up a copious in-
sight into the mythology and daily life of the race, the department of ancient sculpture was on its part remarkably
enriched by the results of the travels of Mr, afterwards
SIR, CHARLES FELLOWS (A.D. 1799—1860) in Asia Minor
(A.D. 1838—1840)[455]. The semi-Greek mountain country
of Lycia in particular revealed an extraordinary wealth of
remarkable monuments; the capital, Xanthos, alone contained a whole cycle of art history from the archaic epoch
to the time of the Roman Emperors. The directors of the
British Museum, among whom not only Hawkins, but also
W. R. Hamilton and Lord Northampton, trustees of the
institution, showed a keen interest, applied for a firman

[453] Museum Marbles, XI. Pl. 32—
35, 40. Guide to the Bronze Room,
1871, p. 12. Græco-Roman Sculpt.
no. 159. Of other donors I mention
W. R. Hamilton, 1821, 1840; A. E.
Impey, 1825; C. Standish, 1826;
J. T. Barber Beaumont and J. S.
Gaskoin, 1836; Lord Western, 1839.
Cf. notes 336, 339, 344.
[454] J. de Witte, Description des
antiques de feu M. Durand, Paris,

1836. Descr. d'une collection de vases
peints provenant des fouilles de
l'Etrurie, Paris, 1837. Notice d'une
collection de vases antiques prov. des
fouilles faites par feu M. le Prince de
Canino, Paris, 1843.
[455] Fellows, A Journal written
during an excursion in Asia Minor,
London, 1839. An account of discoveries in Lycia, London, 1841.

for removing these new treasures, and Fellows himself
conducted the undertaking. In the first months of the
year 1842 the majority of the discovered sculptures were
secured for the Museum. A second expedition followed
under the personal conduct of Fellows and completed the
acquisitions[456]. The Harpy Tomb, the vaulted tombs of
Pajava and Merehi (the 'Horse Tomb' and the 'Chimaera
Tomb'), and the extensive sculptures of the Nereid Monument (next to the Parthenon the most considerable connected series of Greek sculptures which was at that time
known to be preserved), were the principal rewards of their
exertions. The Lycian marbles received a distinguished
completion in the shape of eleven slabs from the frieze of the
Mausoleum at Halicarnassus, which, after being walled up for
three centuries in the fortifications of Budrùm, were presented in A.D. 1846 by the Sultan to the English ambassador, SIR STRATFORD CANNING, afterwards LORD
STRATFORD DE REDCLIFFE, and then by him to the British
Museum[457]. Just as the Elgin and Phigalian marbles formed
noble memorials of the fifth century B.C., so the fourth
century B.C. was now suitably represented in the British
Museum by the sculptures of Asia Minor (not to speak of
the much more ancient Harpy Tomb); equally authentic
memorials of these great epochs of Greek art were possessed
by no other museum in Europe.

93. Archaeological interest during the next following *Discoveries*
years was essentially taken up by the great discoveries *of Newton,*
Wood,
made on the site of ancient Nineveh. England received *Pullan.*
her share of the spoil through the combined exertions of
Sir Stratford Canning, Mr., now SIR, A. H. LAYARD, and
afterwards of SIR HENRY RAWLINSON, who at that time
was consul-general at Bagdad. Not long after another consular official earned the thanks of the British Museum by

[456] Fellows, *The Xanthian Marbles, the Ionic Trophy Monument excavated
their acquisition and transmission to at Xanthus,* London, 1848.
England,* London, 1843. *Account of*   [457] *Mon. dell' Inst.* V. Pl. 18—21.

procuring for it an important addition in the department of
classical sculpture from Asia Minor. Here was a field, rich
in hidden beauties and more accessible to foreign treasure-
seekers than the kingdom of Greece, which after the constitution of A.D. 1842 forbade the export of antiques.
CHARLES T. NEWTON, who had previously held an appointment in the British Museum, had filled since A.D. 1852 the
post of vice-consul in Mytilene, and had had abundant
opportunity of exploring the coasts of Asia Minor and
the neighbouring islands. In more than one place he
had already secured valuable acquisitions for the museum.
In the year 1855, while on one of his excursions, he
observed, introduced into the walls of the fort of Budrûm,
a number of lions' heads, which could only have come from
the Mausoleum. The following year Mr Newton again
stayed at this same spot and made up his mind to attempt
excavations on the field of this wonder of the world. He
was successful in obtaining the co-operation of the British
Museum and of the Government in the accomplishment of
his plans. The first stroke of the spade was made on the
1st of January, A.D. 1857, and by the spring of the year
1858 almost everything had been recovered that yet remained accessible of the masterpieces of Skopas and his
colleagues. Further undertakings at and near Knidos, and
in Branchidae not far from Miletus, turned out no less
successful. These researches were carried on till the middle
of the year 1859, and no fewer than three hundred and
eighty-four chests were despatched by Newton to the
British Museum. Thus among many other treasures the
museum obtained, in the sitting figures and the lions of
the Sacred Way of Branchidae, splendid examples of ancient
Ionic art of the sixth century B.C.; in the lion of Knidos a
grand historical monument of the time of Conon; in the
Demeter (also from Knidos) a masterpiece that may give us
an idea of the style of Praxiteles; and finally in the colossal
statues and relief-slabs from the Mausoleum the much-

desired complement of the present of Lord Stratford de Redcliffe. The architecture of the grand sepulchral monument was also represented by appropriate specimens[458]. Newton was placed, A.D. 1861, at the head of the department of Greek and Roman Antiquities in the museum, and immediately afterwards the necessary funds were voted by the trustees to enable the architect J. T. WOOD to institute excavations in Ephesus. These were begun A.D. 1863, and led to the discovery, six years later, of the site of the celebrated temple of Artemis. Nearly five more years of hard labour were required to bring the remains of the temple to light. These too have been placed in the British Museum. Besides the interesting architectural remains, the drums and square bases of columns covered with reliefs deserve particular mention as furnishing us with additional evidence of the state of Greek art in Asia Minor about the middle of the fourth century B.C.[459] Almost at the same time (A.D. 1870) the Society of Dilettanti sent the architect R. P. PULLAN, whose abilities had already been proved at Halicarnassus, to Priene, that he might examine the sanctuary of Athena Polias, dedicated by Alexander the Great, more carefully than Chandler and his companions had been able to do[460]. With its traditional liberality the Society made over the rich yield of architectural and sculptured fragments to the National Museum, which was now in possession of the most important art treasures of the chief towns of Asia Minor except Pergamos[461].

94. When returning from Halicarnassus (A.D. 1859) *Salzmann* Newton had acquired in Rhodes the collection of ancient *and Biliotti.*

[458] Newton, *A History of Discoveries at Halicarnassus, Cnidus, and Branchidae*, London, 1862, 1863, 2 vols. and plates. *Travels and Discoveries in the Levant*, London, 1865, 2 vols. In the year 1865 Newton had the good luck to purchase at Genoa a slab of the Mausoleum frieze (*Mon. Ined. dell' Inst.* v. Pl. 1—3); still later some fragments in Rhodes; also an additional excavation on the spot

in the year 1865 yielded some further addition.

[459] Wood, *Discoveries at Ephesus*, London, 1877.

[460] Pullan's account of his discoveries will appear in a forthcoming publication of the Dilettanti Society.

[461] A colossal torso from Pergamos, unearthed by Capt. Spratt, is in the museum. See *Arch. Zeitung*, 1863, p. 72.

pottery which had shortly before been dug up by Messrs
SALZMANN and BILIOTTI on the site of the town of
Kameiros. This acquisition was manifestly so important
for the pursuit of the study of the earlier development of
art, that the British Museum supported the further explora-
tions of the discoverers, and by the year 1865 a rich harvest
had been garnered. The gem of the number is a vase
painted in colours with fully developed art. Another very
remarkable specimen is a painted sarcophagus of terra
cotta[402]. From Cyprus, the most eastern of the Greek
islands, the museum received a sufficient series of sculptures of the local school, which bear for the most part the
same character, and of which so vast a yield resulted from
the excavations carried on for many years by the American
consul, General CESNOLA[403]. Already during the Crimean
War there had been obtained from the museum at KERTSCH
a considerable number of sepulchral reliefs in a rude
provincial style of art[404]. Further booty was secured on
the north coast of Africa. The undertakings of R. M.
SMITH and E. A. PORCHER on the site of ancient Cyrene
(A.D. 1860) furnished the museum with a respectable
number of sculptures, mostly of later date, and among
them a noble statue of Apollo[405]; at the same time and
from the same place an attractive selection of terracottas
were obtained for the Louvre. All the more thankworthy
are the interesting discoveries of painted vases which we
owe to the zeal and skill of Messrs WERRY, CROWE and
DENNIS, who succeeded each other as consuls in Benghazi;
they have furnished most valuable contributions to the
history of vase-painting from the fourth century B.C., par-

402 Aug. Salzmann, *Nécropole de
Camiros*. *Journal des fouilles exé-
cutées pendant les années* 1858 à 1865,
Paris, 1875. Newton in *The Fine
Arts Quarterly Review*, 1864, p. 1.
403 Cesnola, General Louis Palma
di, *Cyprus, its ancient cities, tombs,
and temples*, London, 1877. *The
Antiquities of Cyprus, discovered by*

Cesnola, *photogr. by Thompson from
a selection made by Newton. With an
Introduction by Sidney Colvin*, London, 1873, fol.
404 Macpherson, Duncan, *Antiquities of Kertch*, London, 1857, fol.
405 Smith and Porcher, *History of
the recent Discoveries at Cyrene, made
in 1860-61*, London, 1864. 4to.

ticularly in the specimens of the prize amphorae contended for at the Panathenaic games, with their deliberate imitation of an archaic style, and their exact dates indicated by the names of the Attic Archons (A.D. 1866)[406]. Before this, at the suggestion of the Government, G. Dennis had dug up an important number of valuable vases in Sicily, together with other smaller antiquities, which Earl Russell, who was then (A.D. 1863) Secretary of State for Foreign Affairs, assigned to the British Museum[407]. Finally the museum received the results of the excavations which DR NATHAN DAVIS had set going on the sites of ancient Carthage and Utica during the years preceding 1860; these belong principally to the later Roman times[408]. We have thus made it clear with what remarkable energy and consistency the British Museum undertook and discharged the task of bringing to light over the entire range of Graeco-Roman civilization, as far as it could be made accessible to the British spirit of enterprise, the treasures of art so long hidden in the bosom of the earth and of exhibiting them for study and inspection in the halls and basements of the national institution.

95. In conjunction with these acquisitions, chiefly the *Purchases of Farnese, Pourtalès, Blacas, Castellani collections, &c.* results of special enterprise, we must mention the additions which were made to the museum by judicious use of other sources, particularly the sales of older collections. Not to speak of less important purchases, which were made every year, we notice the acquisition in A.D. 1856 of a collection of Sardinian antiquities, articles of jewellery, terra cotta, and glass, all of marked provincial style[409]. Again in A.D. 1864 most of those among the FARNESE marbles which had not been carried to Naples eighty years before, but had remained in the Farnese Palace at Rome, were purchased from the ex-king of Naples. Of these an eques-

[406] Dennis, *Transact. R. Soc. Lit.* IX. N.S. *Catal. of Vases Brit. Mus.* II. pp. 249--293. A number of vases from the Cyrenaica had already, A.D. 1852, been presented by Dr Tomlinson, Bishop of Gibraltar, and in A.D.

1856 by W. J. Smith, Esq.
[407] *Guide to the First Vase Room, Brit. Mus.*, 1871, p. 29.
[408] Davis, *Carthage and her Remains*, London, 1861.
[409] *Arch. Anzeiger*, 1856, p. 271.

trian statue with the head of Caligula, a very beautiful
Hermes, and the celebrated Farnese Diadumenos are the
most important specimens, and form a noticeable complement to the section of Graeco-Roman sculpture[470]. The
following year (A.D. 1865) were added an excellent slab of
the Mausoleum frieze from a private collection at Genoa[471],
and a very fine selection from the choice collection of Count
POURTALÈS-GORGIER, which was put up to auction in Paris
and competed for by all the large museums of Europe. It
will be sufficient to make special mention, among the
marbles, of the head of the Giustiniani Apollo, and also
to point out the fine bronzes and vases which fell to the
share of the museum[472]. In the year 1866 a still more
important purchase was made: this was the entire cabinet
of the DUKE OF BLACAS, formed by two collectors of
artistic tastes, father and son. The cabinet was poor, it is
true, in sculptures, but so much the richer in bronzes, vases,
and terracottas, and above all in engraved gems. Of
the last alone there were seven hundred and forty-eight
genuine antique examples, among them far-famed and
splendid specimens from the Strozzi collection[473]. About the
same time (A.D. 1865) the museum made its first large purchase, consisting principally of Greek and Etruscan bronzes,
from the Roman dealer in antiquities, ALESSANDRO CAS-
TELLANI[474]; this purchase was followed in A.D. 1873 by a
second far more extensive and important. Among the great
number and variety of excellent works of art (bronzes, vases,
terracottas, marbles, etc.), we need only notice specially
the female bronze head, larger than life, from Armenia,
the small bronze relief of a man in a sitting posture from
Tarentum, the marble head of Hera from Girgenti, and the
wonderfully well-preserved sarcophagus in painted terra

---

[470] Graeco-Roman Sculptures, nos.
33, 45, 109, 121, 132, 134, 171.
[471] See note 458.
[472] Arch. Anz. 1866, p. 179, note
38, pp. 243—245.
[473] Newton, Guide to the Blacas

Collection of Antiquities, 1867. Edwards, Lives of the Founders, II.
pp. 689—692. The purchase money
amounted to £40,000.
[474] Arch. Anzeiger, 1866, p. 245.

cotta from Cervetri ; these will suffice to show the unusual importance of the purchase[475]. Before this, considerable acquisitions of smaller antiquities, especially of bronzes, had been made from the PULSZKY and HERTZ collections[476]. At the same time the department of coins had been enlarged by rich additions, for example, by the gift of E. WIGAN'S collection (A.D. 1864), and by the Bank of England Cabinet of coins and medals (A.D. 1865). No other museum in Europe can boast such a succession of important additions, following so quickly one upon the other. No other museum would have been able to show year after year such an uninterrupted series of presents, comprising sometimes single specimens, often whole collections, but ever bearing witness to the lively interest felt on all hands in the national institution[477]. This interest was continually kept alive through the liberality with which both every section of the museum was thrown open to gratify the public passion for sight-seeing, and every opportunity given to specialists for study in their respective departments.

96. Private individuals could make no stand in comparison with the concentrated energy of the public museum. The activity of the SOCIETY OF DILETTANTI relaxed; though, when exerted, it proved worthy of the good old traditions of the past century. The society supported F. C. Penrose in his exhaustive researches on the most beautiful buildings of Athens; it caused Cockerell to publish in a connected form his admirable observations on the

Private collectors of marbles, Lord Lonsdale, Cook, &c.

[475] The Castellani Collection, photographed by S. Thompson from a selection made by C. T. Newton, London, 1873. Murray, A. S., Academy, 1873, p. 166. Illustr. London News, 1873, Nov. 22. The acquisition of a new collection of Castellani's (Illustr. London News, 1876, March 4) was declined by the trustees, but individual purchases have since been made from the same source.

[476] Pulszky, 1856, see Arch. Anz. 1856, p. 271. Hertz, 1859, see note 489.

[477] To give only a few examples, the department of sculpture alone exhibits the following names of donors: Hudson Gurney, A.D. 1843; Smith Barry, 1850; J. Scott Tucker, 1851; W. P. Williams Freeman, 1854; S. Chambers Hall, 1855; Society of Dilettanti, 1870; Greville Chester, 1873; T. A. B. Spratt. In the department of vases the bequest of Miss Auldjo, A.D. 1859, deserves to be specially mentioned. In that of bronzes the donation of Mr Chambers Hall, A.D. 1855. Cf. besides § 91 ad fin., and note 453.

temples of Aegina and Bassae; it sent R. P. Pullan on that
expedition to Priene, the material results of which, as far
as they consisted of marble remains, were, as has been
narrated above, handed over to the British Museum[478].
Individual members seldom became collectors, as used
formerly to be the case; though as exceptions to this rule
we must mention the DUKE OF HAMILTON and LORD DE
MAULEY (A.D. 1787—1855), a grandson of the Lord Bessborough who has been previously spoken of[479]. We find
the former among the purchasers at the auction of the
Stowe collection (A.D. 1848), where he obtained three
splendid statues[480]. The catalogue of this sale shows
plainly how few regular collectors there were then in England, for most of the specimens went singly to this and
that buyer, who were apparently mere ordinary amateurs
rather than collectors properly so called. Conspicuous
among purchasers of marbles were LADY GLAMIS, who
bought a considerable number of busts[481], and WILLIAM,
SECOND EARL OF LONSDALE (A.D. 1787—1868). This
nobleman is one of the very few who take an important
position among the Epigoni of Dilettantism. Besides
the Stowe auction he zealously availed himself of other
similar opportunities for bringing together a collection
remarkable for the number and in some instances for the
value of its specimens. In the year 1866 Lord Lonsdale

[478] Penrose, *Two Letters from Athens*, 1846. *Investigation of the Principles of Athenian Architecture*, London, 1851. Cockerell's work (note 341) appeared A.D. 1860. It was furnished with a dissertation by W. W. Lloyd on the proper-tions of the Greek temple. Pullan's work is in preparation. See note 460.

[479] Waagen, *Treasures*, I. p. 37, mentions Lord de Mauley, fellow of the Society from A.D. 1821, as a col-lector. The finest specimen in his possession was the beautiful tragic female head from Ostia, which his younger son, the Hon. Ashley G. J. Ponsonby, has exhibited for a long

time in the South Kensington Museum (see Cat., art. London).

[480] See Cat., art. Hamilton Pa-lace. In the year 1803 Alexander, tenth Duke (d. A.D. 1852), and in 1833, William, Marquis of Douglas, later eleventh Duke of Hamilton (d. A.D. 1863), joined the Dilettanti.

[481] As to the subsequent fate of this collection I am not able to speak. Among other purchasers of marbles I make special mention of H.M. Queen Victoria (see 'Osborne'), the British Museum, Lord Nugent (a con-nection of the ducal family of Buck-ingham), W. Wakeford Attree, P. Norton, Mark Philipps, A. Robertson, &c.

added to his magnificent seat of Lowther Castle two splendid galleries, which formed a worthy resting-place for the antiques that had wandered so much and been collected from so many sources. The most beautiful specimens among them are a replica of the Knidian Aphrodite from Stowe, and that fragment of an Athenian sepulchral *stélé* which Lord Guilford had once brought home from Attica[482]. In still more recent years MR FRANCIS COOK has formed a collection at Richmond, independently of another which he possesses in Portugal[483]. The Richmond collection was formed from purchases in Italy, France, and England, partly from older collections and at sales, partly from the results of the latest excavations, so that the cabinet, though not large, is various, and contains, besides single marbles worthy of remark, some noticeable bronzes and gems[484]. ADMIRAL T. A. SPRATT, of Tunbridge Wells, possesses a few marbles, the fruit of personal travels in Greece, and has moreover by repeated presents earned the gratitude of the British Museum[485]. A number of sculptures from Asia Minor, belonging to MR GEORGE MCLEAY, are deposited in the South Kensington Museum during his residence in India[486].

97. Besides the marbles many bronzes were put up *Collectors* at the Stowe auctions, among the purchasers of which *of small antiques.* B. HERTZ is particularly conspicuous. For many years *Hertz,* he had been a zealous collector of smaller antiquities, not *Mayer,* only Greek and Roman, but also Oriental and American. *Forman, Auldjo,* His collection, which was begun soon after A.D. 1830, and of *&c.* which a catalogue appeared in A.D. 1851[487], was particularly rich in engraved gems, containing more than seventeen

---

[482] See Cat., art. Lowther.
[483] *Archaeol. Zeitung.* 1868, p. 84.
[484] See Cat., art. Richmond.
[485] See Cat., art. Tunbridge Wells. Cf. notes 461, 477.
[486] See Cat., art. London, South Kensington Museum.

[487] *Catalogue of the Collection of Assyrian, Babylonian, Egyptian, Greek, Etruscan, Roman, Indian, Peruvian and Mexican Antiquities, formed by B. Hertz,* London, 1851, 4to. Cf. *Archaeol. Anz.* 1851, pp. 91–96, 107–120.

12

hundred specimens of Greek, Etruscan, or Roman origin ;
next to them we must mention the bronzes and the articles
in ivory, glass, etc.; while other classes of monuments, such
as sculptures and vases, were less numerously represented.
At that time however Hertz had by no means completed
his collection. It was constantly receiving fresh additions,
particularly of gems[48], till in the year 1856 he made it all
over for twelve thousand pounds to an association of Liverpool merchants, at the head of which stood the wealthy
silversmith, JOS. MAYER. It was the intention of the purchasers to present the complete cabinet to their native
city, but either differences of opinion, or the unfavourable
circumstances of the times, led to a dissolution of the
Society two years later. The collection was put up to
auction in London (A.D. 1859)[49], and scattered far and
wide. Among the buyers were the British Museum and
some private collectors, Forman, Fortnum, Rhodes, and
others ; very little was bought in by Mayer himself. He
was, however, already the owner of a very extensive collection, of which classic antiquities formed the least important ingredient. Its great feature was a remarkable
series of ivories, which originated from the famous Fejérváry
collection, and which had been sold to Mayer by Franz
Pulszky[50]. All this rich museum, which was said to have
cost him eighty thousand pounds, the excellent man, who
has been compared to the Fuggers at Augsburg or to the
Medici, bequeathed to his native town as the foundation of a public collection. LORD CADOGAN (A.D. 1783—
1864) and LORD LONDESBOROUGH (A.D. 1805—1860) were

[48] *Arch. Anz.* 1854, pp. 432, 433.
At the Rogers sale, too (1856, April
and May), Hertz was a principal
purchaser.

[49] *Ib.* 1856, p. 271. I am
indebted for several details to a
verbal communication from a sure
source. *Catalogue of the celebrated
and well-known Collection of Antiquities, formed by B. Hertz, now the*

*property of Joseph Mayer, Esq., of
Liverpool; which will be sold by auction,* February, 1859. (It is in
essentials the older catalogue.)

[50] Pulszky, *Catalogue of the
Fejérváry Ivories in the Museum of
Jos. Mayer,* Liverpool, 1856. *Arch.
Anz.* 1856, p. 271. Cf. 1854, pp. 432,
472. See Cat., art. Liverpool.

collecting bronzes and gold ornaments[491] about the same time. MR H. FORMAN in London was also a zealous collector of objects in bronze and glass, and other minor antiquities, as well as of painted vases; he availed himself with great skill of the Rogers and Hertz sales, and of other opportunities of the antiquarian market[492]. The collection of MR C. D. E. FORTNUM at Stanmore Hill was formed from similar sources, and is rich in bronzes and particularly in rings[493]. MR AULDJO'S ruling passion was for painted vases, and his collection afterwards fell to the share of the British Museum. One of its principal ornaments, "the Auldjo vase," is a glass vessel with reliefs, something like the Portland vase[494]. But it would be labour spent in vain to try to enumerate the numberless collections of smaller objects. As has been well remarked by an observer who for a long time had opportunities of closely watching the course of art matters in England, "The numerous travellers in Italy, Greece, and Asia Minor constantly bring home such objects as mementos, but they do not form large collections, and the next generation sells them to art-dealers and jewellers[495]."

98. "The next generation"—these words precisely hit *Perils of* the danger which is inseparable from private collections. *private collection.* At the beginning of the seventeenth century the stream of classical dilettantism had poured into England for the first time, issuing from a single rich source, and in strength sufficient to bear down powerful hindrances that opposed it. During the last century this stream flowed through the whole country, carrying beauty and fertility everywhere. Its main current, to pursue the metaphor, has now been turned aside into another bed, and its diverging branches trickle in rivulets unobserved, till they are finally lost in

[491] *Arch. Anz.* 1854, p. 433. 1856, p. 271, where also other collectors and traders in objects of art are mentioned. Cf. note 242.
[492] See Cat., art. Pippbrook House.
[493] See Cat., art. Stanmore Hill.
[494] Waagen, *Treasures*, I. p. 37. Cf. note 477.
[495] Pulszky, *Archaeol. Anz.* 1854, p. 434.

the sand, or leave only puddles of stagnant water to be seen. Any one who observes the collections at country houses with unprejudiced eyes, cannot fail to notice on how few of them the glance of the present possessor rests with real affection, and how different are his feelings to those of the amateurs who collected them. In one house the marbles stand in dark rooms like warehouses; in another they are perishing in a damp summer-house; in a third they lie about disorderly in the corners; many collections cannot be found at all. Let the stranger ask for "the sculptures," a sound which would have been familiar enough in the last century; too frequently he will receive from the housekeeper, who is acting as cicerone, the counter question: "What are sculptures? I do not understand you;" or perhaps the slighting answer: "O yes! there are some marbles of the kind." Is it an unfair inference to think we may detect in this an echo, perhaps exaggerated and distorted, of the small appreciation which the owner himself feels for such things? Without much alteration we might apply to the modern public of Great Britain the words once spoken by Horace of the Greeks, and say:

> *Marmoris aut eboris fabros aut aeris amavit;*
> *Suspendit picta vultum mentemque tabella,*
> *Nunc tibicinibus gaudet gaudetque tragoedis,*
> *Nunc athletarum studiis, nunc ardet equorum.*

The safety of the costly collections seems endangered in such an altered state of feeling, for every death, every change whether in the person or the taste of the possessor, makes them the sport of blind chance, as has so often been proved by experience, and much oftener in the later than in the earlier years of this century. The treasures can only be quite safely secured from such dangers by being placed in the shelter of a public institution.

Evils of private collections. 99. A second point of view is here presented to us. It lies in the very essence of art that its works are not created for the enjoyment of a few chosen spirits alone, but have a wider and higher mission of culture, to exercise a refining and ennobling influence on the public at large. The owners of art collections have but seldom shrunk from the duty such possessions involve; we need only remember the museums and galleries of Rome. The institution of certain "show days" on which the public are marched in troops at double quick time past the works of art, and the kindness of the owners in granting permission for more intimate inspection to a select few who wish to devote special study to the subject, are both in their way deserving of our thanks; yet they very inadequately redeem the debt which is incurred by the mere ownership of such noble collections. This unfortunate state of things is felt all the more in England, because here the collections are not, as in Rome, Paris, and most other countries, kept in the town-houses of the noble and wealthy (Lansdowne House is quite a rare exception), but, removed from the smoky, foggy atmosphere of the capital, are scattered through the land to adorn its charming country-homes. Who would blame the possessors for this? The same plan was followed in ancient Rome, and villas were in the same way honoured above town residences. But there too this condition of things was felt to be an evil. We are told of the grave Agrippa, the greatest statesman of the Augustan age, that in a brilliant speech, worthy of Rome's foremost citizen, he urged that all paintings and statues should be handed over to the State, as a far fitter course than that they should remain banished in country villas[496]. If only some influential politician, endowed with the eloquence of a Brougham, would take upon himself the same task in England! He might point to the lofty duties which art-ownership brings with it; to the dangers which threaten private property; to the small sacrifice which would be entailed on many owners if they would forego in favour of the community

[496] Plin. Nat. Hist. XXXV. 26.

their private rights in possessions which they regard,
like other antiquated house-furniture, rather as cumbersome
heirlooms and survivals of an obsolete fashion than as a
source of real artistic pleasure. It will of course be understood that what has been said does not apply to all collections. For example it would be a matter for regret if
the well-lighted sculpture-gallery in Woburn Abbey, the
Pantheon in Ince Blundell Hall, the noble hall at Deepdene
with its surrounding galleries, the cloister at Wilton House,
or the niches in the saloons of Holkham Hall and Lansdowne House, were to be shorn of their beautiful marbles; nor
should we like to think of the comfortable rooms of Newby
Hall without the attraction for the eye which is supplied
by their antiques. But there are many other collections
not placed amid such favourable surroundings; and the
guardians of such treasures should above all things think
betimes of the duty entailed upon them. Very forcibly
is this duty brought home to us in Horace Walpole's
melancholy observation, which we must cite once more,
" how insecure is the permanency of heirlooms!"

Passing of private collections into public museums. 100. We need not recapitulate here the long roll of
names, increasing every year, which is inscribed in the
book of benefactors at the various public museums. Nothing appears more striking and imposing to the stranger
who visits the British Isles for the first time, than the
number of public institutions of every kind, schools, hos-
pitals, etc., which on the continent would be established
and supported by the State or by the community, but
in England owe their existence to the energetic help and
cheerful self-sacrifice of well-to-do private individuals.
In the same way the antique collections at Oxford and
Cambridge, Liverpool and Edinburgh have arisen and
flourished. The bequest of a single collector, in conjunction with a parliamentary grant, was the origin of the
British Museum. The State has ever since liberally devoted regular as well as extraordinary subsidies to this

grand national institution. With signal success it has recommended its diplomatic representatives in classic lands
to keep the interests of the British Museum ever before
their eyes, and it has liberally supported their researches.
Not unfrequently officials have been chosen with special
regard to their capacity for such work. Finally, the State
has taken care that the management of the great institution should only be entrusted to the most capable hands.
At the same time the zeal of private individuals has always kept pace with the fostering care of the Government.
Legacies and presents, generosity in every form, play a
large part in the history of the museum. It might be
thought that since the State is so active in the matter, the
help of private individuals would be less necessary to this
institution. As to this we may draw attention, by way
of example, to one point which bears directly upon the
subject of this work. The directors of the museum give
the preference, quite naturally and with perfect right, to
the original Greek sculptures of the most flourishing periods
of art, which came into the possession of the museum more
than sixty years ago, and the number of which has been
ever since increasing. But perhaps in thus acting they
somewhat neglect the less favoured epochs of antique art.
This is especially true of the after-bloom of Greek art,
which is still so rich in invention, and which fills up the
centuries of the Hellenistic or Alexandrian era, and lays
the foundation for the development of Roman art. It is
no less true of the imitative as well as of the national art
of Rome herself, which includes many copies or variations
of older works, the originals of which are lost to us. These
are works of second or third rank, but cannot be dispensed
with for filling in and correcting our survey of the development of ancient sculpture. The treasures hoarded in
the private collections of Great Britain would precisely
fill this gap, and would make up for the reserve exhibited
by the directors of the National Museum as to the acqui-

sition of copies and minor works. For all the marbles
contained in private galleries belong, with unimportant
exceptions, to this class of Graeco-Roman sculpture. May
a noble emulation on the part of individuals make ever
greater and greater efforts to remedy such defects as still
exist in the public collection, so that the latter may, out
of its own means, continue to pursue the highest aims
exclusively, and acquire nothing but the genuine masterpieces and corner-stones of Greek art ! The author of the
present work would desire nothing better than that the
following Catalogue should soon be pronounced out of
date, and should only remain as a kind of sepulchral
monument of the private galleries of antiques in Great
Britain ; that a great part of the collections it enumerates
here should vanish from its lists, while the names of
their owners should be inscribed in letters of gold on the
roll of donors to the British Museum.

APPENDIX.

LETTERS OF SIR THOMAS ROE.

EXTRACTS FROM

"The Negotiations of Sir Thomas Roe, in his Embassy to the
Ottoman Porte, from the year 1621 to 1628 Inclusive."
London, 1740, fol.

1 (p. 16).

Copy to my Lord of ARUNDEL, *Earl Marshal.*

My Lord,

I receiued your lordships letter in the Downes; and though
my imployment bee the other end of the circle, to attend new
things; yet myne owne inclynation is curious enough, to my
meanes, to look back upon antiquity, and some learnings lost and
decayed, rather, as I think, *ex industria*, then by the moth of
tyme; in which opinion the little examination I haue made in
these parts, confirms me......hereby I find no difficulty in procuring such reliques, if I could discouer them......But now I
desire only to giue your lordship an accompt of the care I haue of
your lordships commands. I moued our consul, Richard Milward
at Scio, whom I found prepared and ready. Wee conferred about
the maid of Smirna, which he cannott yet obteyne, without an
especiall command. I brought with mee from Messina, the bishop
of Andre, one of the islands of the Arches, a man of good learning, and great experience in these parts. Hee assured mee, That
the search after old and good authors was vtterly vaine......Con-
cerning antiquities in marbles, there are many in diuers parts, but
especially at Delphos [Delos], vnesteemed here; and, I doubt not,
easy to be procured for the charge of digging and fetching, which
must be purposely vndertaken. It is supposed, that many statues
are buried, to secure them from the enuy of the Turks; and that,
if leaue obteyned, would come to light, which I will endeauour as
soone as I am warme here. Coynes wilbe had from Iewes, but

very deare when enquired for. Two are giuen me by Dominico
to present to your lordship, which I haue deliuered Antony Wood,
captain of the Rainbow; the one gold, is of Alexander; the other
is brasse, and very antient, of a queen of Seruia, with hieroglyphicks now vnknowne. I haue also a stone taken out of the old
pallace of Priam in Troy, cutt in horned shape; but because I
neither can tell of what it is, nor hath it any other bewty, but
only the antiquity and truth of being a peece of that ruined and
famous building, I will not presume to send it you; yet I haue
deliuered it to the same messenger, that your lordship may see it,
and throw it away......I am a louer of those vertues which haue
made mee Your Lordship's Seruant.

Constantinople, 27 Jan. 1621 [1622].

2 (p. 154).

Extract of a Letter to my Lord of ARUNDELL.

Constant. $\frac{1}{10}$ Maij, 1623.

My Lord,

I haue receaued from your lordship two fauours, in that you
please to command mee any seruice; and though these tumultu-
ous tymes hinder mee from an exact performance, and such as
might giue your lordship full assurance of my readyness; yett I
doubt not you will accept of what you can......The command you
required for the Greek to be sent into Morea, I haue solicited two
Viziers, one after the other; but they both reiected mee, and gaue
answere, That it was no tyme to graunt such priuiledges......

Neare to the port they haue not so great doubt, and therefore
I haue preuailed for another, sent Mr. Markham, assisted with a
letter from the capten bassa, whose jurisdiction extends to all the
islands and seaports......hee hath so good experience in this
cuntry, that he knowes how to make vse of it...... I beseech your
lordship...to beleeue, that it was very difficult to procure so much;
and I hope the effects thereof will content you.

Antiquities in gold and siluer, of the antient Greeks, from
Alexander downward, and many Romans more antient, are here
to be gathered; butt so deare, by reason the last French ambassador made great search, and some Italians are ready to buy,
that I know not whether your lordship will esteeme them at such
rates. The meddels of gold, or olde quoyne, if they bee faire, and
the inscriptions ledgible, are held at twice and thrice the waight.

Some, for curiosity, I haue bought, with others pretended to be Ægiptian, Armenian, and Arabian; but my skill is not great, I iudge only by the eye; these shall serue your lordship, if you like them.

I may also light of some pieces of marble by stealth; as now I am offered a lyon to the wast, of pure white, holding a bulls head in his clawes; butt the very nose and mouth is defaced, the rest very faire, and, they say, *a l'antiqua:* I haue not yett scene it, but expect it howrely, if the shipp meet it not; it was taken vp at Lampsacum in Natolia. On Asia side, about Troy, Zizicum, and all the way to Aleppo, are innumerable pillers, statues, and tombstones of marble, with inscriptions in Greeke: these may be fetcht at charge and secrettly; butt yf wee ask leaue, it cannot be obteyned; therefore Mr. Markham will vse discretion, rather then power, and so the Turks will bring them for their proffitt.

I know the worth of Mr. Markham, now our consull, soe well, that I should wrong my selfe, if in all things I gaue him not his due......

3 (p. 319, 320).

To my Lord Archbishop of CANTERBURY.

......[p. 320]...I heare your grace hath written by one Mr. Petty, that is arriued at Smirna, ymployed by my lord of Arundell to buy books and antiquities. Hee will find, that barbarisme hath worne out all the footstepps of ciuility and learning; yett manuscripts are plenty, old Greeke books, that are litle worth; they haue bene cerned ouer by many of good iudgment, and I think the gleanings are uery poore. When hee comes, I will present and assist him......

Constantinople, $\frac{8}{19}$ Dec. 1624.

4 (p. 343, 344).

To the Duke of BUCKINGHAM.

......The antiquities which I conceiue your grace doth desire, (for curiosity in newe arts there is none here) are either columns or statues in stone, or bookes, or ancient coynes, or medalls. I confesse my ignorance in choosing or knowing any of these; yett, for the reuerence I beare to them, either as lights or reliques of antient learning, or noble sciences, I haue a litle endeauored to search, and enforme my selfe. Butt I haue found, the spight or

sordidnesse of barbarisme hath trode out all the stepps of ciuility,
or, like rust, destroyed them. For columnes, the building of so
many Mahometan moschyes hath many enquiry euen into the
rubbish of all old monuments, and into the bowells of the earth;
so that there is litle to bee hoped for by industry, if chance assist
not. Statues, or figures of beasts, because they are forbiden in
their lawe, are either defaced on purpose by them, or sought for
by others, and conueyed away, so they are become very rare.
One of that kinde I heard of, beeing a halfe lyon of white marble,
holding the head of a bull in the pawes, the neck renuersed. I
sent for it a great way, to Lamsacum in Asia, vpon report; and
when it arriued, it had no grace in my eyes; for the face was
broken off: the rest makes a showe of art, but beyond my capacity; for when the principall part was defaced, I thought it not
worthy any estimation. I did dessigne it for your grace, but haue
kept it two yeares, as not worth the portage, except there bee any
mistery in these things, that I vnder [p. 344] stand not......Medalls
and coynes in gold and siluer, of the antient Greeke kings and
emperours, Armenians and Romans, by chaunce I light vpon: of
those I will gather all that haue either bewty or antiquity; and
these, and all, and all I can performe or finde, are freely presented
to your grace. Whatsoeuer I can collect, hauing now your graces
command, added to myne owne desire, shall not goe out of the
way to Venice: I knowe as well howe to send them, and haue as
much affection to serue your grace, as any man liuing. I expect
daily here the comming of one Mr. Petty, recommended by my
lord of Arundell, I think, to the same vses. It seemes, that gentleman is better praticque, and may informe my judgment. With
his ayd, I doubt not to giue your grace satisfaction, either in
effects, or in industry: and I hope I am now fallen into a good
way by the help of the patriarch of this citty, who hath enformed
mee of a small, despised, vninhabited island, in the Arches, a
place antiently esteemed sacred, the buriall of all the Greekes, as
yett vnbroken vpp; where, hee tells mee, are like to bee found
many rare things. Your grace may please to giue order to some
shipping, that comes for this place, (if in the meane tyme I can
procure none) to take directions of mee, and a guide from hence,
and to anchor there 5 or 6 dayes, to search it; where they may
take, without trouble or prohibition, whatsoeuer they please, if
any man of judgment to make the choyce. Hee hath also assured
mee, that Alexandria, which was once the retraict and *deliciæ*

Romanorum, hath yett about it more rare peeces, then any part
within the Leuant seas; whereof, when hee was patriarch there,
he discouered many; and, among others, a statue of a Negro, of
black marble, taken vpp whole, butt by accident a thigh broken,
the forehead inlayd with a work of gold; which hee hath promised
to procure mee, and sayes it is one of the most bewtifull figures
and stone in the world, and that hee will write thither to recouer
whatsoeuer can be gotten......

Constantinople, 24 January, 1624 [1625].

5 (p. 386, 387).

To the Duke of BUCKINGHAM.

May it please your Grace,

By conference with Mr. Petty, sent hither by my lord of Arundell, I haue somewhat bettered my sckill, in such figures as your
grace hath commanded mee to secke; at least, hee hath made
mee more assured, to venture vpon some things, which I should
of my selfe haue little esteemed, for the defacings, either by age,
or accident; if I committ any great error, I must excuse my selfe
vpon him, on whose judgement I relye; yet I will, as neare as I
can, reguard the bewtye, which takes the eye, and that the principall parts bee not too much disgraced.

Wee haue searched all this cyttye, and found nothing but
vpon one gate, called antiently Porta Aurea, built by Constantine,
bewtifyed with two mighty pillars, and vpon the sides and ouer yt,
twelue tables of fine marble, cutt into historyes, some of a very
great releuo, sett into the wall, with small pillars, as supporters.
Most of the figures are equall, some aboue the life, some less.
They are, in my eye, extreamly decayed; but Mr. Petty doth so
prayse them, as that he hath not scene much better in the great and
costly collections of Italye. Your grace, for better enformation, may
view his letters to the earl of Arundell, how he hath allowed them.
There are of them but sixe that are woorth the taking downe, the
other beeing flatt Gothish bodyes, lame, and of later tymes sett vp
only to fill place of the other sixe. Two, in my opinion, (though
Mr. Petty like them) want much of excellence, great, but brute ;
and, as I coniecture, are some storye of Hercules, not mentioned
in his labors. The fower, to which I haue most affection, are
fuller of woorke: the one is (as wee comment) an Endimion carelessly sleeping by his sheepe; Luna descending from the sckye

with a torch in her hand, representing night; and a Cupid houer-
ing in the ayre, to signifye her loue. This last gentleman is much
misused, and wee can only know him; the other two want some
parts, and the faces battered; but the generall proportions are
both braue and sweete. The next is an historye I vnderstand
not, either of some race, or game; in the middest is a horse, a
young man naked running by yt, and reaching to pull another off.
Some other figures ther are, which I remember not; but it hath
beene a peice of great bewtye and art; the releuo so high, that
they are almost statues, and doe but seeme to sticke to the ground:
some leggs, and other parts, standing holow off, are broken and
lost; yet, in the whole, it hath a showe of rare antiquitye. The
third is a Pegasus, with the Nimphs or Muses; one representing
the foun [p. 387] teyne Pirenne powring out water. These figures
are many, but less then halfe the life, as I judge them, not so
much defaced, standing high, and to a vulgar eye, like myne, of
most grace and pleasure. The last is a Satyre, sckipping betweene
an Hercules, or a wild man, and a woman, which he seemes to
auoyd: the one hath a whip in his hand, the other a pott of water
held behind her, and may signifye a rescue from rauishment: these
are aboue the life, and rather great and stately, then delightfull;
but generally they haue all suffered much uiolence, both by
weather and spight: yet they are so well esteemed by this gentleman, that I will endeauor to get them. Promise to obteyne
them I cannot, because they stand vpon the ancient gate, the
most conspicuous of the cyttye, though now mured up, beeing the
entrance by the castell called the Seauen Towers, and neuer
opened since the Greeke emperors lost yt: to offer to steale them,
no man dares to deface the cheafe seete of the grand signor: to
procure them by fauour, is more impossible, such enuy they beare
vnto us. There is only then one way left; by corruption of some
churchman, to dislike them, as agaynst their law; and vnder that
pretence, to take them downe to bee brought into some priuat
place; from whence, after the matter is cold and unsuspected, they
may be conueyed. I haue practised this for the foure, and am
offered to haue it done for 600 crownes. To send them home
chested, and freight, with some other bribes att the water syde,
may cost 100 more. This is a great price, and yet I rather des-
payre of obteyning them.

  I haue sent to Angory [Ankyra] in Galatia, the seate of Midas;
and Mr. Petty is going to search some other parts of Asya, with

commands; he may discouer and choose, but can hardly bring
any thing away: that I must doe by tyme. On the other syde,
without his directions, I may committ great errors. Therfore,
that wee may not preuent one the other, I haue mooued him, and
he is well content, yf your grace and the earle marashall approoue
yt, to joyne, and whatsoeuer both can recouer, to putt into one
stocke; and so to diuide them, when they come into England, by
lotts, or any other way that shall seeme best to your grace: our
meaning is such things as both shalbe interessed in, he by dis-
couerye, I by procuring: in this poynt I humbly desire an answere. The blacke statue from Alexandria, and some other that
I hope to prouide alone, your grace will accept from your seruant....

Constantinople, ₁¹₁ May, 1625.

6 (p. 433, 434).
To the Duke of BUCKINGHAM.

May it please your Grace,

I shall render a barren reckoning of your command laid vpon
mee to prouide your grace some antient statues; yet I had rather
giue you any account of my endeauour, then by long silence to
deserue the imputation of negligence. That which hath discouraged mee, is the failing of my promise for the black goddesse
from Alexandria; which beeing giuen mee by the patriarch, confident it was yet in his garden, I sent for, in company of his ser
uant; but beeing retorned, they haue only discouered, that a
colloire left in that charge had sold it 18 moneths since, to the
French consull, for 30 dollers, who hath transported it into France,
to the exceeding displeasure of the patriarch, and my shame. Yet
I thought it fitt to aduise your [p. 434] Grace thereof: perhaps you
may there recouer it at no great charge, beeing esteemed the jewell
of all the stones in this part of the world.

I haue not left any probable city vnsearcht into, and heare of
diuers peeces; but what they will proue, I cannot yet iudge. Some
I am absolutely promised, but nothing entire; halfe bodyes, heads
and bustos. In Salonica a Jewe hath a whole marble, and antient:
I haue procured letters to the metropolitan to buy it, if mony
will preuail. From Angora I am in hope, at least, of a faire lyon.
These on *porta aurea* will not bee remoued: no man dares aduen-
ture to steale them from the principall gate, nor any fauorite of

the vizier presume to mention the defaceing of the wall; yet I will
not leaue to hope, by some art they may bee made dropp, and
that so I may gather them. Mr. Petty hath bene at the so much
famed Pergamo, and brought somewhat away, as hee writes,
meane things, not worth his charge, only as testimonyes of his
trauailes; but hee is a close and subtill borderer, and will not bragg
of his prizes. From thence hee is gone forwards into the islands,
and hath this aduantage of mee, that hee makes search with his
owne eyes, and is not sparing to spend, when hee finds content;
though hee shall not out-buy mee, if wee fall in competition. Somewhat your grace may expect with patience, that is, all that I can
find or procure; which you will accept by the measure of my
ambition to your seruice....

Halchys. 26 August, old stile, 1625.

7 (p. 444, 445).
To the Earl of ARUNDEL.

My Lord,

I haue receiued recompence enough for more seruice then I
am able to doe your lordship, by your acceptance of that litle I
haue a desire to doe, expressed in your two letters of the 10th
and 12th of May. If myne, of the first and 25. of the same
moneth, bee arriued, I hope they haue giuen your lordship more
satisfaction: since which tyme I haue bene able to doe nothing
here, beeing fled vntill the last weeke, from the great contagion,
that hath carried away in this citty, and the suburbs, neare 200000
people. Mr. Petty this wile hath visited Pergamo, Samos, Ephesus,
and some other places; where he hath made your lordship greate
prouisions, though hee lately wrote to mee, hee had found nothing
of worth. Your lordship had good experience in a man for such an
imployment, that spareth no paynes nor arts to effect his seruices.
When hee departed, I hoped wee had bene ioyned, and that hee
would haue acquainted mee freely with his proceedings: but hee
hath therein deceiued mee; for I now perceiue, your lordship (by
way of preuention) hath resolued to bee alone; and Mr. Petty, in
this space, hath preuented mee, vpon confidence, to haue sent one
with or before him, and hath aduised mee, hee can find nothing.
I am so assured in your lordships integrity and wisedome, as I
dare write you playnly according to my nature. I haue done for
Mr. Petty whatsoeuer was in my power, by giuing him forceable

commands, and letters of recommendation from the patriarch. I
haue bene free and open to him, in whatsoeuer I knewe, and so I
will continue for your lordships command : but your lordship
knowing, that I haue receiued the like from his grace the duke
of Buckingham, and engaged my word to doe him seruice, hee
might iudge it want of witt, or will, or crediit, if Mr. Petty (who
could doe nothing but by mee) should take all things before or
from mee. Therefore, to auoid all emulation, and that I might
stand cleare before two so great and honorable patrons, I thought
I had made agreement with him for all our aduantages. Therefore wee resolued to take downe those sixe mentioned releuos on
porta aurea, and I proceeded so farre as I offer'd 600 dollers for
4 of them, to bee diuided betweene his grace and your lordship,
by lotts. And if your lordship liked not the price, Mr. Petty had
his choice to forsake them ; but now I perceaue hee hath entitled
your lordship to them all, by some right, that if I could gett them,
it were an injury to diuide them. Your lordship shall neuer find
mee to write you an vntruth, nor dissemble the truth : Mr. Petty
did not discouer them. When I carried him to the patriarch, and
there discoursed with him, what places were like to furnish vs
with old statues; hee told mee of those on *porta aurea*, and wished
mee to goe see them, though hee thought the difficulty would bee
great to procure them. Whereupon I, hauing no skill, sent a
Janizary with Mr. Petty, to view them ; [p. 445] vpon whose report
of liking them, I went with him a second tyme ; and so wee
resolued to take them downe if possible ; and I was not only
content, but desirous, your lordship should haue halfe ; and so I
assured him, though I both must bee the meanes to gett them,
and to disburse the mony, which I would willingly doe for your
lordship. And this beeing the truth, and I remayning constant
in the same resolution, I hope your lordship will well accept it.
Since, hee wrote mee another letter, in manner renouncing them
at that price, and aduising mee not to spend aboue 200 dollers
for all sixe. It seemes, hee beeing better prouided at Pergamo,
or willing to leaue these for a better occasion, was content I
should not meddle with them : but when I answered him, hee
knewe I had made lardger offers, and if hee refused, would take
them for my owne account, and yet in England offer your lordship
your part; hee then wrote mee, That hee would not leaue his
interest in them, nor yet encourage mee what to spend, to procure
them : but I am sorry wee striue for the shadowe. Your lordship

beleeue an honest man, and your seruant, I haue tryed the bassa,
the capteyne of the castle, the ouerseer of the grand signors works,
the soldiours that make that watch, and none of them dare meddle:
they stand betweene two mighty pillars of marble, in other tables
of marble, supported with lesse pillars, vpon the cheife port of the
citty, the entrance by the castle called the Seauen Towres; which
was neuer opened since the Greeke emperour lost it, but a coun-
terscarfe and another wall built before it. The vizier dares not,
for his head, offer to deface the chiefest port, so many will
clamour against him: the capteyne of the castle, nor the ouerseer
of the walls, cannot doe it without a speciall command from the
grand signor: the soldiours cannot steale them, being 30 foot, and
40 foot high, made fast to the wall with iron pins; and must bee
let downe with scaffolds, and the help of at least 50 men; for if
they fall, they will breake to dust, the ground being so thinne, and
worne with age. There is then but one way left in the world,
which I will practice; and if I can procure them, your lordship
shall know my seruice by the part I send you, without Mr. Petty,
or any other helpe. Within the castle, and on that gate, is a con-
tinuall watch of 20 soldiours: it is the kings prison; and how hard
it were to take downe such things, of at least a tonne weight
apeece, from the Tower-gate of London, your lordship will easily
iudge. And if I gett them not, I will pronounce, no man, nor ambassador, shall euer be able to doe it; except also the grand signor,
for want, will sell the castle.

After all these disputes for nothing, Mr. Petty hath aduised
mee, that retorning from Samos, where hee had gotten many things,
going to Ephesus by sea, hee made shippwrack in a great storme
vpon the coast of Asia; and sauing his owne life, lost both all his
collection of that uoiadge, and his commands and letters by mee
procured; desiring mee to send him others, or else, that hee can
proceed no further. Hee was putt in prison for a spy, hauing
lost in the sea all his testimonyes; but was released by the witness
of Turks that knew him. From thence hee recouered Scio, where
he furnished himselfe againe; and is gone to the place where
hee left his boate to fish for the marbles, in hope to find them,
and from thence to Ephesus; and this is the last newes I heard
from him. To renew commands so often, giues great jealousy
to these people, hauing taken out 3, in litle more then a yeare,
for your lordship; so that with much adoe, and by force of a
bribe, I haue again procured another, and more large, for your

lordship, which is nowe by mee, and shalbee sent to Mr. Petty, so
soone as I know where he is: though I haue written to him to
leaue the sea, and to spend this winter with mee, where he shalbee
welcome.

In conclusion, I desire your lordship to bee assured, that as I
cannot faile of my duty to my lord of Buckingham, so I will doe
your lordship that seruice, that shall witnesse for mee my affection
thereto. I will in all things assist Mr. Petty, and seeing I must
goe alone in this business, I will search all Asia, but I will find
somwhat worth my labour. My mysery is, vsing others, I must
take bad and good; and I haue things sent mee from diuers
places, figures indeed, that cost mee much, but not worth the
portage. When I haue done my best, and alone, your lordship
shall haue somwhat from mee, that you shall knowe I would haue
dealt fairely, and that I had a syncere purpose to meritt your
lordships fauour....

Constantinople. $\frac{20}{30}$. October, 1625.

8 (p. 495).

To the Earl of ARUNDELL.

My Lord,

My last letters brought your lordship the aduice of Mr. Pettyes
shipwracke, and losses vpon the coast of Asya, returning from
Samos: his commands and letters of recommendation, and his
labors, togither there perished. The first I presently renewed,
and sent them to Smyrna; and the other, I thincke, he hath by
great industrye, since recouered. From that tyme, what aduentures
he hath passed his owne enclosed will giue best satisfaction; and
it shall suffice mee to say in gross, that, although he will not
boast to mee, yett I am informed hee hath gotten many things,
rare, and antient. Ther was neuer man so fitted to an imployment, that encounters all accident with so unwearied patience;
eates with Greekes on their worst dayes; lyes with fishermen on
plancks, at the best; is all things to all men, that he may obteyne
his ends, which are your lordships seruice. He is gone to Athens,
where also I haue sent; and from thence promiseth mee to visitt
this citty, wher I shalbee glad to enterteyne him, and to know the
history of his labors. I haue in my endeauour bad success, by
the ignorance of those that I am forced to employ, who send mee
heauy stones at great chardge, that prooue newe images, wher I

seeke old idolls; for such also were the Roman statues of their
emperors. From Angory I had an hal-woman, brought 18 dayes
by land, vpon change of mules, which wants a hand, a nose, a
lip; and is so deformed, that shee makes me remember an hospital: yet the malicious Turkes brought troubles on the buyers,
by a false command, accusing them of a great wealth stollen out
of the castle; it hath cost mee money to punish them, and that is
all I haue for my labor. I haue sent three seruants togither to
Tassos, Caualla, Philippi, and all the coast of Thrace; followed
Mr. Petty to Pergamo, and Troy; am digging in Asya; and, to fulfill
the prouerb, turning of all stones. Somwhat I hope to gett, to
saue my creditt; but I dare not write to his grace, vntill I am in
possession: so often I haue beene by Greekish promise deceiued.
Those on Porta Aurea stand vp, ready to fall, in spight of all my
arts, and offers; the tymes are so dangerous that I dare not uen-
ture to entreague others; but ther is an opportunity attended to
make them stoope: the gate of Constantinople inciteth me farther
then any bewtye I see in ruines, that only showe their was once
bewtye, good emblemes of one that had beene a handsome woman,
if an old woman were not a better; yet few loue them. When I
haue made my collection, I will not forgett that I was engaged by
your lordships commands; as I am assured your lordship will not
grudge mee to performe the seruice I owe the duke of Buckingham,
betweene whom, and your lordship, if ther had beene an vnion, ther
had nothing beene difficult to us both here, and many things much
cheaper....

Constantinople, 28. Mar. old stile, 1626.

9 (p. 511, 512).

To the Duke of BUCKINGHAM.

...My agents from Greece are retorned with no great fruit of
their labours, other then discoueryes of some marbles vnder
ground, which will require tyme and priuacy to take vpp, to
auoid the enuy of these people, who suspect treasure in euery
place where Christians breake the earth. I haue omitted no
search nor expence to giue your grace some testimony of my
desire to obey your first command, wherein I would not bee
judged by effects, though I doubt not also by them to bee in part
iustified.

Mr. Petty, in the islands, hath gotten many marbles: hee takes all; what they will proue, is beyond my judgment. I haue some, but I desire not to lade your grace with vngracefull stones: they shall haue some bewty with antiquity which I will present; and if there come some other, they must passe in a throng, for number, not for weight, though they bee uery heuy.

[p. 512] I haue a litle marble, a halfe woman, in releuo, excellent workmanshipp, and a stone of rare whiteness and hardness, recouered from Troy, though, I think, in those days, no such masters, but the hand of some later Roman. It will serue for a chimney, though it bee not a statue. A head of Germanicus from Angury [Ankyra], whence I expect daily a whole peece, brought vpon a litter, by fower mules. From Athens I haue no retorne; but looke this moneth to know the success. In an island called Augusto[?], neare Paris [Paros], in the Arches, I haue heard of two great marbles, and haue taken a command to fetch them, by the bishopp of Naxia. Another of Scyra hath promised mee a whole cupid, taken vpp in Delos, of white alabaster. From Tiria [Tenos] I expect a retorne of another factor. From Pergamo, by the consull of Smirna. From Morea, by the merchants of Patrass. From Aleppo and Alexandria, by the industry of Mr. Kirkham. If all these should produce nothing, I may bee ashamed, but not accused of negligence.

Those on Port *Aurea* are like to stand, till they fall with tyme: I haue vsed all means, and once bought them, and deposed, 3 moneths, 500 dollers. Without authority, the danger and impossibility were alike; therefore I dealt with the great treasurer, who in these tymes is greedy of any mony, and hee had consented to deliuer them into a boat without any hazard of my part. The last weeke hee rode himself to see them, and carried the surweigher of the citty walls with him; but the Castellano and the people beganne to mutine, and fell vpon a strange conceit; insomuch that hee was forced to retyre, and presently sent for my enterpreter, demanding if I had any old booke of prophesy: inferring, that those statues were enchanted, and that wee knew, when they should be taken downe, some great alteration should befall this citty. Hee spake of a vault vnder ground, that I vnderstand not; which, concurring with the rumour of the Cossacks, filled them with superstition, and suspition of mee; in conclusion, hee sent to mee, to think, nor mention no more that place, which might cost his life, and bring mee into trouble: so that I despair to effect therein your graces seruice: and it is true, though I could not gett the stones, yet I almost raised an insurrection in that part of the citty....

Constantinople, $\frac{8}{13}$. May, 1626.

10 (p. 534, 535).

From the Duke of BUCKINGHAM.

...I haue likewise receiued two letters from yow, concerning some buisines of my owne; the latter bearing date the $\frac{1}{10}$. May, 1626, wherein I find my selfe much obliged to an extraordinarie dilligence yow haue vsd, in search of such pieces and antiquityes, as yow guesse will be most wellcome vnto me; and I shall endeauour to deserue the paines you bestowe vpon me there, in any seruice yow shall imploye me in heere: desireing a continuance of your respect vnto mee in this kind, with this caution only, that yow laye not out much money vpon any alabaster pieces, vnlesse they be figures of exquisite curiosity: for your antique masters (as I am informd) neuer wrought vpon alabaster. Neither am I so fond of antiquitye (as you rightly coniecture) to court it in a deformed or mishapen stone: but where yow shall meete beautye with antiquitye together in a statue, I shall not stand vpon any cost your judgment shall vallew it att. For those other pieces on Porta Aurea, since they cannot be compast without difficultye and danger, I am satisfyd with the attempt of your industrie had vpon them; and shall hope for some other [p. 535] rarityes that may be purchast with less trouble....

Yorke-House, July, 19. stilo vet. 1626.

11 (p. 570, 571).

To the Duke of BUCKINGHAM.

...I expected . . your farther order how I should proceed in the search of marbles, which I haue found a quarry and stone busines....For your graces command of marbles, I haue beene so vnlucky, that with much industrie and expence, I haue yet beene able to procure none such as, I feare, your curiositye doth expect. Mr. Petty hath raked togither 200 peices, all broken, or few entyre: what they will proue, I cannot judge. Hee had this aduantage, that hee went himselfe into all the islands, and tooke all hee saw, and is now gon to Athens, where I haue had an agent 9 monethes, and haue now sent the Venice bayloes letters to his consull their resident, to assist mee, patiently attending some better issue. I haue foure bustoes, and some heades and peices collected in Asya and Paris [Paros]; but being left at Scio, I cannot commend what I haue not seene. New hopes are giuen me from Andri and Santerino, and other parts...[p. 571]...I am tyed to a residence almost to a prison; and my ignorant instruments take all figured marbles, how disgracefull soeuer, for statues, and with them haue cloyed mee......

Constantinople, $\frac{5}{15}$. Nou. 1626.

12 (p. 583).

To the Countess of BEDFORD.

Madam,

I am glad to fynd an excuse, and force an occasion to renew in your remembrance the name of an old seruant......I haue recalled my thoughts upon what your ladyship tooke the latest pleasure, that I saw yow marshalling of antient coynes and medalls, delighting in the records of vertuous tymes, vertuous men, and uertuous actions; so that I haue presumed to enterteyne yow one hower with the enclosed catalogue of such, as in this pilgrimage I haue collected: amongst which there are some so rare, that I suppose the cabinets of Paris, which muster 12000, cannot match them. This curiositye of antiquityes, though by some seuere men censured, hath yet diuers uses besides delight, not to bee contemned: they are a kind of lay humanity, teaching and inciting deuotion to morall uertue, as well, and more safely then images among the new Romans, to the contemplation of diuine misteries. They propose a liuely cronologye on the one syde, and a representation of historye, heroicque or great actions, on the other. They carry in them a shadow of eternitye, and kindle an emulation of glorye, by seeing dead men kept long among the liuing by their famous deedes. This apologye made for the generall, your ladyship will giue mee leaue to say somwhat of particulars. Foure things are required in medalls, truth, antiquitye, bewty, storye, or poetrye: for these, the mettall is one of the best wittnesses. Copper is seldome here a counterfayt, harder to woorke upon, and therfore of most esteeme......[p. 584] .....Greeke medalls, in my opinion, as they are more antient, so they are bewtifull, full

of art, and most misticall in the reuerses, alluding to their sacrifices, religions, or warrs. I haue some rare peices, a dedication
for the health or saftye of Hercules, an hierogliphicque of the
Heathen diety, a Pallas of Athens, a head in brass, not to
bee cutt in many moderne ages, in which I read almost Agamemnon. Most of these are great, braue, and bold figures, *semiunciales*,
of gold and siluer; in breife, *cose di cardinale*. To the contemplation of their inscriptions I leaue your ladyship, not doubting
yow will teach mee, when I returne, more then I can fynd of them
without helpe......

Constantinople, $\frac{9}{19}$ Decemb. 1626.

13 (p. 619).

To the Duke of BUCKINGHAM.

......I am sorry I can yet giue your grace no better account of
marbles, after a long and exquisite search; wherein Mr. Petty
hath, by his personall sckill and labour, preuented my dull instruments. My agent is returned after a 9 moneths voyadge to
Athens, and the relicques of old Greece; and hath brought me
little fruict to my contentment, but some heads and small releuo's,
antient and good worke, a feast of Jupiter, and a peice of a
sacrifice, and such like. I had drawne them in paper to send
your grace, but defer it till a better haruest. I haue bought two
statues at Zia: how they will proue, I must runne the hazard.
Some others are collected for me in the islands; but not hauing
seene them, I will not spoyle them with prayses. My last hope
is vpon another adventure to Greece, whither, vpon a new enformation of the archbishop of Lacedemon, I haue sent two moneths
since a seruant of myne owne, that hath seene many collections
in Italye, and pretends to know. I haue giuen him two rules,
beautye and hard marble. I am made beleeue that he shall fynd
braue matter, and haue furnished him with a command, the capten
bassaes letter, the patriarchs recommendation, and sufficient
credit; and I doubt not but to bring your grace good satisfaction.
I haue two antient gates of hard white marble, wrought *al' antiquo*,
fiue stones a piece, the sides, head, and thresholds: they were
gotten in the islands from an old temple, and are very fayre; and
though they are not for your graces gallery, they wilbe rich and

bewtifull in any building.   This is the ill reckoning I can yet giue
your grace of my industrye......
   [1627. February or March.]

14 (p. 647).

To the Duke of BUCKINGHAM.

May it please your Grace,

   After a long and almost dispayrefull search of marbles, hidden
in the ground, I haue fallen vpon a course, which, I hope, will
fullfill your graces expectation, and pleade my humble affections,
and industrye to doe you some seruice.   About 4 moneths since,
as I then aduised, I sent a seruant well furnished with meanes
and authoritye to trauell Morea; who hath found, as he enformes
mee, some rare peices: one whole statue, 8 foote high, not much
defaced; another wanting the head, in the old famous Corynth;
and these embarked for Zant, to be there laden for England.   He
hath digged to two more, then vpon price, and I doubt not to
haue them.   A braue head, supposed of Lucius Mummius.   I wish
they may answer his prayses: at least, the place will giue them
some estimation.   From thence he went to Athens; where whatsoeuer is to be had aboue or vnder ground, wilbe procured for
him.   From Zea, an island in the Arches, I heard last from him,
arriued there to ship away two statues, long since bought by mee,
wanting the heads; one whereof is sent to my lord of Arundell.
There are more to be gotten, if any art can take them downe.   He
is now returning to Corynth, to fetch those that were at his
departure buried, and a great vrn of braue releuo, if possible to
carry yt, and a pillar with a garland, inscribed *Pallade;* and many
other raretyes.   He proceedes to Lacedemon, to the antient
Sparta, where I heare of seauen more, and hope to possess them.
From Andros I haue receiued, at Scio, a great releuo of Bacchus;
which, vpon report, hath cost mee deare, beeing obteyned by
fauour of the bey of that island, and mined for vnder an old
foundation; but the face is battered, the feete and one hand
broken off: the rest is fayre and statelye.   From many other
places, and sundrye agents, I expect diuers other things, which
yet I haue not seene; and must be contented to take bad with
good, from those that, hauing no skill, yet spend my mony to
employ themselues.   I am this day sending a drogaman, and

Janitzarie, with an Italian to Brussia, the antient metropolis of
Bythinia, where, I am enformed, are many marbles; and I attend
a returne from Sinope on the Black Sea, in Amasia. Thus your
grace will approue my dilligence, and accept the success according to your owne benignitye. The difficultye of carriage, and
engines, and expence, is great, and the danger among these
remote habitations greater, some stones weighing aboue 20 hundred, and brought by hand to the water: yet your grace shall haue
no cause to repent the charge; for I hope to make you a noble
collection.

If you please to continew this search, there willbe found dayly
many rare matters, the poore people being sett on worke, in hope
of gayne, and all these parts full of the enquirye made by me and
Mr. Petty: all aboue ground being gone to Venice, wee must trust,
like miners, to chance; but I fynd, that the old christians, to preuent
the enuye of the Turkes, did in all Greece, and the islands, burye
theire antiquityes, which tyme and dilligence will discouer. Your
grace willbe pleased to send me herein your farther directions,
and to accept my poore man, who hath vndergone infinite paynes
and perill, and is now well practised both in the countrye and
with the inhabitants, and has sufficient language, and indefatigable
industrye, for this employment, not easely matched. His hopes
are, that seeing I cannot reward him, that your grace, which is
his ambition, will take him for your seruant: which I shall humbly
acknowledge as an high fauour, that I haue beene able to doe
one man good......

Constantinople, $\frac{19}{23}$. May, 1627.

15 (p. 692, 693).

To the Duke of BUCKINGHAM.

May it please your Grace,

My last letters were dated the 19. of May: wherein I enclosed
the forme of some peices of marble drawne in paper: and if that
be arriued to your grace, you will haue found the first fruicts of my
seruants imployment into Greece, who is not yet returned, but I
haue often heard from him. Foure statues he hath sent from
Corynth: what they will proue, I dare not spoyle by prayses and
expectations; but I am enformed, that they are such (though defaced) as in Rome (where images are gods) would be highly

esteemed. He is some monethes past gone to Achaya, Argos, Lacedemon, and Napoli di Romania, and so to the islands Cyclades: and I do expect him shortly, after hauing uisited all the places likely to yeild your graces contentment. Many other peices he hath gotten, of which, when he shall returne, I will send your grace a catalogue, as a modell of the success of my zealous endeauours to doe you humble seruice.

At *Bursia* I lost my labour and expence, not hauing one head nor foote. And from Sinope and Amasia, ther is nothing come but aduice of a tombe, which, if it could be gotten, is too heauy for any engine to carry to the sea. What I cannot performe in my owne tyme, (which now with much wearines I spinne out) I will sett in such order, that whatsoeuer is found (and our search hath begotten a diligence and care in all the inhabitants of the Arches and Morea) shalbe preserued [p. 693] for your grace; who I know doth esteeme it as much greatnes to accept of small seruices of poore men, as to command the mighty; and therfore I will take that comfort in your graces nobelnes, that I cannot fynd in my owne meritt......

Constantinople, $\frac{15}{25}$. Octob. 1627.

16 (p. 763, 764).

EXTRACT *of a Letter to the Duke of* BUCKINGHAM.

...[p. 764]...In the search of marbles, wherby I haue endeauored that your grace should measure my deuotion to your desires, I haue had many crosses, but a late one aboue all the rest. My agent, whom I presumed to recommend to your grace, and imployed in Greece, after hauing visited and searched all the famous parts of Morea, as Thebes, Athens, Lacedemon, Achaia, Corynth, and many others, and as he continually wrote me, had bought many pieces that he could not prouide suddenly to carry away, is dead in Patras; whither he had sent foure statues, and followed to ship them: of these the consull will take charge, and to recouer many other things scattered here and there, according to such notes as he left, or had formerly sent me; but this must be a new worke. He also had sought in most of the islands, where he bought such as could be found, and buried them in the sand, or left them with Greekes vntill his returne to make his full collection; but God hath preuented him. I haue in other places diuers

marbles, if I can gett them togither: what they will proue, doth
rest in your graces only acceptance and benignitye; and though
I had lost them all, yet I would not loose his testemonye, that
no diligence, care, trauell, nor expence, hath been spared to proue
my selfe, &c.

Constantinople, 22. Feb. old stile, 1627 [1628].

17 (p. 808).

To the Duke of BUCKINGHAM.

...He [Sir Thomas Roe's successor] hath seene some of my
little marbles, and flatters me with an opinion, that they wilbe
acceptable. I am sure they haue two consequences of curiosityes;
much care in getting, and their valew resting only vpon your
gratious liking. I haue lately gotten one, whose rude figure I
enclose: and being praysed by a doctor brought vp in Italye, I
will transcribe his owne words: *E di quelle statue che li gentilhuomini
Romani sogliono metere nelle bauole [tavolet], et scantie di lor libra-
rie, secondo il uso Romano, intiera, bella, et di finissimo marmo, et a
giuditio mio di bona ualuta: non staro à depingerla piu oltre.* I know
not what my *racolta* will proue: I should haue many; but the
death of my seruant on the one syde, and the difficulty to gett our
shipps to goe out of the way to take them in, will diminish the
muster of my diligence. I could haue laden shipps with such
stones as Mr. Petty diggs; but good things undefaced are rare, or
rather not to be found. Our search hath made many poore men
industrious to rippe up old ruines: so that, in this also, my successor may supply my defects; and I am aboundantly recom-
penced, if any thing I haue done shall be by your grace esteemed
in any proportion of my deuotion......

Constantinople, 15th April, 1628.

18 (p. 818).

To the Duke of BUCKINGHAM.

...I am now collecting and lading the few marbles I haue
found for your grace. Some are to be shipt from Patrass: others I
attend from Zea and the islands. If they want the expected
beautye, your grace will consider I had them out of the ground,
which is not sufficient sanctuarye from the envye of the Turkes,
and vouchsafe in them my true zeal to your seruice......

Smyrna, 27. June, 1628.

Extract from Tierney, *The History and Antiquities of the Castle and Town of Arundel.* London, 1834.

19 (II. p. 435).

The Earl of Arundel to his Countess.

...I desire you woulde presently, by some meanes, knowe what Sir Tho. Roe hath brought of antiquities, Goddes, vases, inscriptions, medalles, or such like. I thinke Sir Robert Cotton, or Mr. Dikes, were fitte to gette them. I wish it were done before Friday, for I feare my lord Chamberlayne; and nowe I thinke they might easily be had .....

Theobald's, Monday.

A CATALOGUE

OF

ANCIENT MARBLES

IN

GREAT BRITAIN,

PARTICULARLY THOSE IN PRIVATE COLLECTIONS.

" ...in un pajo di Secoli li Antiquarj avran da faticar molto sopra le Antichità uscite dalla Manifattura nostra."

G. CASANOVA, *Discorso sopra gl' Antichi*,
Lipsia 1770, p. xli.

EXPLANATION OF SOME ABBREVIATIONS.

Arch. Anz.   = *Archäologischer Anzeiger*, supplement of the *Archäologische Zeitung*, edited by E. Gerhard, 1849—1867.

Arch. Zeit.   = *Archäologische Zeitung*, ed. by E. Gerhard and others, Berlin, from 1843: in progress.

C. I. Gr.   = *Corpus Inscriptionum Graecarum*, ed. by Boeckh, Franz, Curtius, Kirchhoff. 4 vols. Berlin, 1828—1877.

C. I. Lat.   = *Corpus Inscriptionum Latinarum*, ed. by Mommsen, Henzen, Huebner and others. Berlin, from 1863: in progress.

Cavaceppi, *Racc.*   = *Raccolta d' antiche statue, &c., restaurate da Bart. Cavaceppi, scultore romano.* 3 vols. Rome, 1768—1772.

Clarac   = *Musée de sculpture antique et moderne. Par M. le Comte de Clarac.* Engravings, 6 vols., Paris, 1826—1853; letterpress, 6 vols., Paris, 1841—1853.

Cod. Coburg.   = Codex Coburgensis, ms. containing drawings from ancient sculptures made about the middle of the 16th century; described by Matz in *Monatsbericht der Akademie der Wissenschaften zu Berlin*, 1871, pp. 445—499.

Cod. Pigh.   = Codex Pighianus, a similar collection, described by O. Jahn in *Berichte der sächsischen Gesellschaft der Wissenschaften*, 1868, pp. 161—235.

Dallaway   = Dallaway, J., *Anecdotes of the Arts in England.* London, 1800. (The numbers added in brackets refer to the French translation *Les beaux-arts en Angleterre, ouvrage traduit de l'Anglois de M. Dallaway, par M***; publié et augmenté de notes par A. L. Millin.* Paris, 1807. 2 vols.)

Denkm. d. alt. Kunst = *Denkmäler der alten Kunst, nach der Auswahl und Anordnung von C. O. Müller. Zweite Bearbeitung durch Fr. Wieseler.* 2 vols. Göttingen, 1854, 1856.

Müller-Wieseler   = the same work.

M. C.   14

Overbeck, *Bildwerke* = Overbeck, J., *die Bildwerke zum thebischen und troischen Heldenkreis.* Stuttgart, 1858.

Spec. = *Specimens of Antient Sculpture, selected from several collections in Great Britain*, by the Society of Dilettanti. 2 vols. London, 1809, 1835.

Waagen, *Treas.* = Waagen, *Treasures of Art in Great Britain.* 3 vols. London, 1854, with a supplemental (IVth) volume: *Galleries and Cabinets of Art in Great Britain.* London, 1857. (The numbers added in brackets refer to the original German edition of the first work: *Kunstwerke und Künstler in England.* 2 vols. Berlin, 1837, 1838.)

At the end of each article *, *B*, *C*, *M*, *m*, *W* refer to the following authorities (see preface):

* to the Author's own observations.
B to Prof. Bernoulli's MS. notes.
C to Prof. Conze's MS. notes.
M to the late Prof. Matz's MS. notes.
m to K. O. Müller's articles.
W to Waagen, *Treasures, &c.*

The measures are given in metres and centimetres, an English foot being equal to 0·305 m.

H. = Height. L. = Length. D. = Depth. W. = Width. "L. of face" means length from the top of the forehead downwards to the chin. l. = left. r. = right.

ANCIENT MARBLES

IN

GREAT BRITAIN.

St ANN'S HILL (Surrey).

Dallaway, p. 385 (II. p. 137).

The antiques collected by HENRY FOX, who became Lord Holland in 1763, are probably now in the possession of Lady HOLLAND. Dallaway enumerates the following busts:

1. " Sappho."
2. Trajan.
3. " Cicero."
4. " Demokritos."

To these must be added

5. **Boy with pitcher.** Cavaceppi, *Racc.*, I. Pl. 4. The boy is standing with his legs wide apart; a drapery rests on his l. shoulder and hangs down his back to the ground. On the left shoulder the boy holds with both hands a large urn in a slanting position; if it is antique, water probably issued from it into a basin, and it characterises the whole work as a decoration for a fountain. The figure appears to be less than life size.

CASTLE ASHBY (Northamptonshire).

Birch, *Arch. Zeit.*, 1846, p. 340 ff. Conze, *Arch. Anz.*, 1864, p. 237* f.

The collection of the Marquis of NORTHAMPTON includes **glass vessels**, of which we have no further information, and **painted**

vases, which are treated of in the two accounts quoted. The vases seem to have been collected together after 1830 (cf. *Archäol. Intelligenzblatt*, 1833, p. 11). The collector, who himself wrote "Observations on a Greek vase discovered in Etruria, bearing the name of the fabricator Nicosthenes, in the possession of the Marquess of Northampton" (1841, 4to), died A.D. 1851; some of his vases appear to have afterwards come into the possession of the British Museum. (Introd. note 452.)

BATTLESDEN (Bedfordshire).

Since June, A.D. 1875, the celebrated collection of the Marlborough gems has found a home here. It was bought by the present owner, Mr BROOMFIELOW of Manchester, for 35,000 guineas. GEORGE SPENCER, 4th DUKE OF MARLBOROUGH, was the collector. The principal constituents were the Arundel gems, the collection of the Earl of Bessborough, and finally single purchases made by the Duke, for example from Count Zanetti in Venice. Cf. Introd. §§ 23, 50. The collection, which consists of 739 specimens, has been admirably catalogued by M. H. Nevil Story-Maskelyne, *The Marlborough Gems*, 1870. A selection of 100 of the best specimens is to be found in the magnificent publication: *Choix de pierres antiques gravées du Cabinet du Duc de Marlborough*, fol., Vol. I. 1780, with text by James Bryant; Vol. II. 1791, by W. Cole (100 copies only). In 1845 John Murray had a new impression of the plates prepared, with text by Vaughan Thomas (2 vols., fol.).

BIGNOR PARK (Sussex).

Bignor is situated on the old Roman road from Regni (Chichester) to Londinium, and is celebrated for its remains of a Roman villa with valuable Mosaics (Lysons, *Reliquiæ Brit. Rom.*, pt. III.). Not far from it is situated the country seat of Mr HAWKINS, where are preserved some antiques, collected by the well-known traveller J. Hawkins, who sold Payne Knight a portion of his bronzes; for example the valuable specimens from Paramythia (Epeiros); but kept back for himself a few beautiful examples. (Introd. §§ 67, 68.)

1. **Bronze relief** from Paramythia: Millingen, *Anc. Uned. Mon.*, II. Pl. 12. *Spec.*, II. 20. Müller-Wieseler, II. Pl. 27, 293. Aphrodite, accompanied by two Erotes, announces to her paramour, Anchises, who wears an Eastern costume, the future greatness of his

race, of which she is to be the ancestress. (Cf. the Homeric Hymn to Aphrodite.) A magnificent relief in the most beautiful and delicate style of art. Some small injuries have been repaired by Flaxman.

2. Hermes, resting in a sitting posture. By his side a cock, which has been restored. Bronze, from Paramythia. *Spec.,* II. Pl. 21.

3. Cameo: large size: representing the triumphal procession of a beardless Emperor on a quadriga. He is being crowned by a Victory, and is surrounded by eleven men, among whom are six lictors. A Cupid hovers above; at his feet sits a weeping Woman, the personification probably of a conquered country. Of late date. [Conze, *Arch. Anz.,* 1864, p. 167 *]

I am not in a position to say whether Mr Hawkins possesses any more antiques.

BIRMINGHAM.

Mr Newton informs me that Mr J. A. CRANE owns two statues which formerly belonged to the Anson collection at Shugborough (Introd. note 174), viz.:

1. Trajan, in the attitude of haranguing his army (*allocutio*), and

2. An empress, both seriously renovated. The former has been already noticed by Pennant.

BLENHEIM PALACE (Oxfordshire).

Scharf, G., *Catalogue Raisonné of the pictures in Blenheim Palace,* London, 1861, pp. 81—82. Waagen, *Treas.,* III. p. 132 (II. p. 51).

In the splendid though somewhat cumbrous palace which the English nation had built for the victorious DUKE OF MARLBOROUGH at Woodstock, are two busts which I examined in 1877.

HALL.

1. Bust of Alexander the Great, supposed to come from Herculaneum. There is no doubt about the antiquity of the head, which is excellently sculptured and of beautiful Greek marble, probably Pentelic, of particularly fine quality. It is almost perfect except the extreme tip of the nose, which has been restored in plaster; here and there small lesions appear, particularly round the left eye; finally the curls on the back of the neck have been cut off quite straight. The form of the face is compara

tively broad; the expression inclines towards sadness; the eyes are
deep set, particularly in the inner corners. The lines of the eyebrows and of the bridge of the nose, which is wide, are clearly
defined, but without any sharpness; the gently curved profile of the
nose is very fine. The lips are remarkably full; the upper lip protrudes strikingly, the lower one is round and somewhat depressed.
The lower half of the forehead projects, especially towards the
temples; the upper part is set more back, but not divided from the
lower by any definite line. In contrast to the slightly polished flesh
the hair is roughly treated, and still preserves distinct traces of
reddish colour; in a like spirit the curls are deeply undercut but
not very delicately finished. The head is surrounded by a fillet;
above it the hair, combed in rays, is only slightly defined; the curls
once fell low down on the neck; in front they are raised considerably
above the forehead, not however over the middle, but rather
over the r. eye, a peculiarity which recurs in other portraits of the
Great King. The whole face is framed by abundant curls, which
do not however in any way confine it. The head belongs to the
class of ideal portraits, and forms a strong contrast to the insipid
terminal bust from Tivoli preserved in the Louvre (Bouillon, *Mus.
des Ant.*, II., *bustes*, Pl. 4). Of the neck only a small part remains
intact, and this piece shows that the head was originally inclined
towards the l. shoulder. It is now joined by a neck-piece of spotted
marble on to a bust covered with a breast-plate. The lower half
of this breast-plate slanting down from the r. shoulder to the l.
nipple is an uninteresting modern restoration. The upper half is
excellent, comprising the open throat below the neck-pit, the upper
edge of the breast-plate with the remains of a head of Medusa, and a
piece of the chlamys in rich folds on the shoulder. Although this
portion has been broken in several places, and here and there
mended a little, there is no doubt all these pieces originally belonged together; they are of Greek marble exactly resembling that
of the head. The folds of the chlamys are of rich workmanship;
they flow from a button which is ornamented with a fine relief after
the manner of chased metal-work, and which represents, within a
beaded moulding, an eagle facing l., standing on a dead hare, and
plucking out part of its intestines with his beak. (Cf. coins from
Elis, Agrigentum, etc.) The Medusa-head is remarkable for its
abundant and bristling hair, and also for the size of its wings.
That part of the chiton which appears above the edge of the
breast-plate in the form of a richly gathered shirt-hem looks rather

modern, and might make us doubtful whether the whole of the breast-plate is antique. The form of the breast-plate on the shoulders and at the back of the neck is unusual ; it is also strange that there are no longer any traces at the back of the neck of the curls which there is every reason to believe must previously have fallen down on to it. Considering, however, the similar quality of the marble and the excellence of the work, which are equal to those of the head, I do not venture seriously to doubt the genuineness of this upper portion of the breast-plate. H. 0·75, height of head 0·31. L. of face 0·185. [*Scharf]

LIBRARY.

2. **Bronze bust of a Satyr**: of the nobler type, laughing and youthful, looking upwards r.; life size. Over the forehead two small horns, the brutish ears lying quite back. Pupils of the eyes indicated. At the back of the head, strong traces of gilding. Very peculiar is the fawn-skin (νεβρίς) fastened lightly round the neck with a border, trimmed with fringe. This fringe and some other peculiarities arouse doubts as to the ancient origin of the bust. [*]

GARDEN.

On the further side of the waterfall, and about a mile from the mansion, there stands, under a group of trees, and used as the front wall of the basin of a fountain, an—

3. **Oval sarcophagus** : front half now in great measure overgrown with moss, so that the lower half of the relief is no longer visible. Two lions' heads, now furnished with conduit pipes, divide the figure sculpture into compartments. Below the lion's head to the l. Herakles is reclining on a lion's skin, with a roll-shaped wreath (ὑποθυμίς) round his neck and the r. arm (the hand of which is missing) upraised. A small Pan supports his back, and a second (the head missing) is pouring wine from a skin into the drinking-cup (σκύφος) which Herakles holds out. The group is surrounded by a Maenad with a lyre to the l. of the lion's head (the r. arm and half of the l. forearm are missing) and a second Maenad with cymbals (κύμβαλα) by the feet of Herakles (the r. hand and the lower half of the l. arm are wanting); both wear long draperies and cloaks floating in an arch over their heads. A Satyr (who has lost his r. hand and the lower half of his l. arm) dances in the midst before Dionysos (*minus* the head and r. arm), whose lower limbs are partly hidden by his cloak. He is supported by a second Satyr, who holds a pedum in his l. arm (his head is missing) ; on the ground

crouches a female panther. Then comes another Maenad draped in a floating cloak, hurrying r. (her head, lower part of r. arm and l. hand, are gone). At her feet lies the sleeping Ariadne under the lion's head, her lower limbs draped, the upper part of the figure nude. This upper part rests in the lap of a richly dressed figure (Somnus?), the head of which is missing. A small Cupid is playing at Ariadne's feet, and a skittish little Pan is just going to uncover the sleeper still more. On the other side of the lion's face are another Maenad with a lyre, and a Satyr with a nebris, raising his r. hand. The elegant symmetrical composition, the graceful subject, the good alto-relievo deserve a better fate than to keep gradually disappearing in this romantic spot under their destructive covering of moss. The sarcophagus belonged at one time to the Massimi, and then to the Della Valle. Old drawings of it are to be found in Cod. Coburg., Matz, no. 142, in Windsor (Vol. VII. Pl. 3, 22, X. Pl. 20), in the possession of Mr Franks in London (in duplicate), and in the Library of Trinity College, Cambridge (R. 17. 3, fol. 18). L. 1·85. H. 0·64. [*]

BOYNTON (Yorkshire).

Dallaway, *Anecd.*, p. 386. *Of Statuary*, p. 340.

In Boynton, near Bridlington, now the seat of Sir WALTER STRICKLAND, are preserved some marbles, which Sir GEORGE STRICKLAND had obtained through Jenkins in Rome between A.D. 1780— 1782. Dallaway mentions only two of them :—

    1. "**Statue of Juno** [? cf. Gerhard, *Ant. Bildwerke*, Pl. 12 'Libera'], h. 4′ 10″ [1·47] carrying a faun [fawn?] under her left arm, which is encircled in a wreath of fruits and flowers suspended from the right shoulder ; in the right hand a bunch of flowers. In great preservation, and the drapery excellent. This fine statue was found in 1777, at the Torre tre teste, four miles from Rome, on the Praenestian way, laid on a tesselated pavement, probably of the temple to which it belonged.

    2. **Head of M. Junius Brutus,** large life, and of perfect and excellent sculpture."

A communication of A. S. Murray, Esq., enables me to add the following marbles :

    3. **Venus and Cupid.**   4. **Terpsichore.**   5. **Diana.**
    6. **Vase** from Villa Mattei.

BROADLANDS (Hampshire).

Dallaway, p. 344 f. (II. p. 9).

Very near the small town of Romsey in Hampshire is situated the beautiful country seat of Broadlands, belonging to the PALMER-STON family, and now in the possession of the Right Hon. W. COWPER TEMPLE. Here may be seen a small collection of antique sculptures which HENRY TEMPLE, second Viscount PALMERSTON (1739—1802), acquired in Italy in 1764 when he was a young man. An autograph memorandum by the collector gives some of the prices, which have been placed under the particular specimens so far as it can be recognised with certainty to which they refer. In 1877 I visited the collection and made a full description.

VESTIBULE.

Here, not to mention three modern busts of an Emperor, an Empress and a veiled female, are the following antique sculptures:

1. **Head of Apollo,** colossal scale : hair drawn back from the face and fastened together over the parting in a coronal. (Cf. Deepdene no. 4, Petworth no. 7.) Forehead very round, with the browline sharply defined. The good workmanship proves the value of the original head here copied. New: nose, upper lip, breast. Pentelic marble. H. of the genuine part 0·35. L. of face 0·20. Probably purchased together with no. 9 for £35. [*]

2. **Relief of a Satyr:** he dances r. on r. leg. and throws back his head. His r. hand is stretched out backwards and he grasps in it the corner of a panther skin, whereof the greater part hangs down over his l. arm which is stretched straight out. In l. hand he holds a kantharos, the contents of which he is pouring out. Very low relief, in shape of a round disk. Diameter 0·29. Purchased together with no. 4 for £22. [*]

3. **Fragment of a relief:** female flute-player draped in a chiton, with a cloak thrown over her lower limbs, l. arm and back, moving r. and blowing the double flute. From below the knee to the neck, and part of the profile of the face, old; flute and r. hand partly new. Very high relief, originally of fresh and good workmanship, but on the chiton much worn and on all other parts a good deal touched up. Fine-grained Greek marble. H. 0·73. L. 0·32. Bought for £10. [*]

4. **"Hygieia," oval relief** : evidently only the remains cut out of a much larger relief. A woman, turning somewhat r.,

wears a chiton and over it a cloak gracefully cast from her r. hip over her l. shoulder; both forearms extended at a right angle. Hair simply arranged and gathered up behind in a plait. R. forearm, with a serpent coiled round it, and l. hand, with a cup (which details explain why the female has been ticketed Hygieia), new, and so are the greatest part of the face and parts of both legs. Very high relief of elegant workmanship. The marble has black spots. H. 0·54. L. 0·35. Cf. remarks on no. 2. [*]

5. **Fragment of a relief representing three Maenads dancing**, composed of four pieces which belong to each other, and completed by two new patches. It corresponds exactly to the Albani relief in Zoega, *Bassirilievi*, II. Pl. 83, cf. London, Lansdowne House, no. 58. The first Maenad, facing l., with her head thrown back on her neck, is swinging a fawn over her l. shoulder, and in her r. hand, which is extended backwards, holding a sword upright. The second, moving in the same direction but with her head lowered, holds the sword behind her neck and half a deer in her l. hand which is lowered. The third faces r. She also holds half a fawn in her lowered l. hand, and in the r. a thyrsos vertically. In the second figure the sword blade, the upper part of l. arm with part of the cloak, the l. foot and part of the chiton are new; the third figure has been completely renewed from above the elbow upwards. High relief in the so-called Neo-Attic style. Pentelic marble. H. 0·42. L. 0·65. [*]

6. **Head of Aphrodite**, with neck: a beautiful Greek head of coarse-grained marble, probably Parian, the surface much corroded and dotted with calcined excrescences, but not restored, or retouched. Nose in perfect preservation. In the direction of its length the forehead, which is peaked and not very low, is much rounded. The hair, parted down the middle, flows in beautifully treated waving lines towards the ears, the delicate tips of which are visible, and behind falls unrestrained down the back of the neck. The upper part of the skull is missing; a flat plane sloping backwards reminds us of the lesion disfiguring the Psyche of Capua; a narrow groove in front would seem to show that the head was once crowned with a metal stephané. The brow-line over the eyes is distinctly but very delicately drawn; the eyes, which are quite oval in shape, are somewhat deep set (l. 0·04, h. 0·015; distance of the inner corners of the eyes from each other 0·03). The eyelids are very delicate, rounded more below than above, somewhat sunk in the

inner corners; all four corners of the eyes lie in a horizontal line.
The insides of the eyes were hollow and have been filled up with
plaster. The nose has a broad bridge and is almost straight, with
a pretty, delicate tip; its profile diverges somewhat from the line of
the forehead. The mouth again is very delicate and softly curved
(l. 0·05), and is slightly opened; the upper lip protrudes a little. The
chin is very long. The whole head gives one the impression of grand
and lofty beauty, more delicate than that of the goddess of Melos,
perhaps somewhat more severe than that of the Knidian Aphrodite
in the Vatican. Purchased for £5! H. 0·37. Length of face 0·21,
height of forehead 0·07, length of nose 0·07, space between the
nose and the mouth 0·015, length of chin 0·07. [*]

7. **Cinerarium**: two eagles holding an oak garland in their
beaks; above, a bird seizing a lizard by the tail. Below, the fol-
lowing inscription (*C. I. Lat.*, vi. 1, 2503): *Mettio Messori | mil(iti)
cho(ortis) III pr(aetoriae), 7 (centuria) Audacis, Claudius | Rufianus
comm aniplo b(ene) m(erenti) f(ecit)*. Found in 1735 near S. Alessio
on the Aventine. L. 0·35. H. 0·18. "Two cinerary altars (cf.
nos. 8, 30), and an urn (nos. 32? 33?) and a small basso relievo (?)"
were purchased together for £17. [*]

8. **Cinerarium**: two Ionic spiral fluted columns connected by
a garland. Below, a tablet with the inscription: *T. Aquilio | T. l(iberto)
Peloro | vestiario de hor(tis) | Volusianis | Plotia Flora | coniug(i)
b(ene) merent(i)*. The *horti Volusiani*, probably laid out by one of
the Volusii Saturnini, a family famous for its colossal wealth in the
first century of the empire (Tac., *Ann.*, 3, 30), do not appear to be
known otherwise; for *vestiarii*, with more exact description of place,
cf. Preller, *Regionen der Stadt Rom*, p. 151. Below the inscription,
folding doors, open and surmounted by a pediment. In the doorway
stand a man in tunic and pallium and a woman with a curled
wig, in stola and palla, holding out their r. hands to each other; he
lays his l. on her head and she in her l. holds an apple (?). H. 0·58.
L. 0·36. D. 0·31. Cf. on no. 7. [*]

9. **Head of Hermes**, not a portrait: hair very curly, and
covered by the petasos, the brim of which has been broken all round
and restored on too scanty a scale (cf. Lansdowne House, no. 88); the
hat held on by a riband, which passes not under the chin but round
the nape of the neck. The terminal bust has been restored. Ordinary
workmanship. Marble with grey stripes. H. of genuine parts 0·29.
L. of face 0·16. Cf. on no. 1. [*]

10. **Terminal bust of a victorious athlete** : short curly hair lying close to the head, and entwined with a round rope-like fillet, the ends of which fall over the shoulders in front. Mouth slightly opened, chin very long. The original was, to judge by this repetition, of a pure early style, and belonged probably to the close of the 5th century B. C., or to the beginning of the 4th. New : tip of the nose, a great portion of the back part of the head with pieces of the fillet, two thirds of the terminal bust. Greek (Pentelic?) marble. H. 0·39. L. of face 0·18. Can this be the "Ptolemy" (£13) of the Memorandum? Cf. however on no. 23. [*]

11. **Triangular altar**, with a top-piece of slightly raised acanthus work ending in a (modern) knob, showing that the altar was intended for ornament and not for use. On the three sides the following reliefs : (1) **Seilenos**, bearded and bald-headed, crowned with ivy, nude except for an apron about his loins and shoes on his feet; he is standing in repose facing r., holding a tympanon in his l. hand, which is lowered, and with his r. touching the plaited fan (λίκνον, *vannus*) in which the phallus is visible surrounded with fruit. (2) On the side further l., and therefore behind Seilenos, is a **female**, facing r., in a quiet pose, draped in chiton and cloak ; her r. shoulder is bare, and on the l. she carries a flat dish full of fruits, among which a long root (?) rises up high; with her r. hand she holds a flaming torch horizontally before her, directed towards an altar on which fire burns. (3) Behind her, a **Maenad** in girdled chiton which leaves the r. breast and arm free ; her head is thrown back ; her r. hand, which is lowered behind her, holds a sword, and her l., lowered in front of her, half a fawn; she is in violent action, and her chiton floats down in grand folds. The three reliefs are to be found in the drawings of dal Pozzo at Windsor, Vol. VII. Pl. 59—61. The lower architectural sections are modern. H. 0·66. L. 0·27. [*]

12. **Statue of a Nymph**, called less correctly "Melpomene," answering to that in the Vatican given in Biondi, *Monumenti Amaranziani*, Pl. 34. Clarac, IV. 752, 1830. The wide cloak is thrown round the legs, leaving the whole of the upper part of the figure nude. She stands on the r. leg, and steps, after the manner of Melpomene, with the l. foot much raised; half the l. foot and the marble block with its base have been put in incorrectly, in place of a large vase lying on the ground, as is shown in the Vatican replica. The upper part of the figure is leaning far forward, supported on the l. arm, which rests on l. knee. New : l. forearm and a piece of upper arm, also the whole of r. arm, head and part of neck.

Graceful decorative work, but touched up. Greek marble. H. 0·62. Possibly the one styled in the memorandum "small statue of Venus," which was purchased together with no. 31 for the sum of £75. [*]

HALL, 2nd compartment.

Besides a number of modern works and copies from the antique, among which is the vase with Bacchic scenes (no. 16 in Dallaway), are to be seen here:

13. **Statue of "Ceres,"** originally a portrait like those in the Florentine Loggia de' Lanzi: Cavaceppi, *Racc.*, I. Pl. 10. Clarac, III. 428, 770. The imposing figure resting on the l. leg is draped with an Attic χιτών διπλοῦς. Over this doubled chiton is a cloak which covers the l. breast, shoulder and arm, and is then drawn gracefully behind the back to the r. shoulder in folds reaching to the knee; the upper border falls down over the l. forearm, which is outstretched. New: the head, crowned with ears of wheat, the neck, the uplifted r. arm with the ears of corn, inclusive of the shoulder, the l. forearm and hand, as well as both feet and part of the flowing chiton. Good work, not however particularly fine; only slightly touched up. Pentelic marble. H. 1·19. Purchased for £90 together with no. 14. [*]

14. **Statue of Hygieia:** Cavaceppi, *Racc.*, I. Pl. 11. Clarac. IV. 557, 1181. A figure standing in repose in chiton and cloak which covers the l. arm and the greater part of the back and legs. She rests on her l. leg, the r. being retired a little behind. Beside her r. thigh a serpent rises up between her hip and elbow, and then winds round the latter, along the arm and through her hand along front of her body, towards a cup which the goddess holds in her l. hand. New: Hygieia's head and neck, some parts of the serpent (whose head is missing), and r. foot; the r. arm has been fastened on, but is antique; the l. hand and the cup are apparently so too. Decorative work. Coarse-grained Parian marble. H. 1·08. Cf. on no. 13. [*]

15. **Female portrait head:** hair gathered up in a small knot behind, and cut in short curls round the forehead without any meanness of effect. Much washed out. New: tip of nose, part of hair over r. half of forehead, bust. Height of genuine parts 0·23. L. of face 0·11. [*]

16. **Double terminal bust:** on one side, a youthful Satyr-like head, with ruffled hair, among which is an ivy wreath. The eyebrows are strongly waved and drawn up. On the other side

a similar head with a somewhat more tender expression (perhaps feminine) wearing a laurel wreath. The upper parts of all the ears are concealed. The conjunction of the wreath sacred to Apollo with that of Dionysos is worthy of notice. In a state of perfect preservation except that the busts are modern. H. of genuine part 0·20. L. of face 0·13. "A term" was bought for £5. [*]

17. Bust of a young Roman with a good open countenance, called "Scipio Nasica." Hair very smooth, combed right over the forehead, and carefully treated there only, the rest being left in a somewhat rough state. New: certainly the nose and the bust, which is covered with drapery; all the rest has been carefully smoothed over and is not quite free from a suspicion of being spurious. In artistic work. H. 0·64. L. of face 0·16. Probably bought with no. 18 as "two busts" for £22. [*]

18. Bust called "Titus": a big head, with a fillet through the hair, certainly not Titus. The pupils of the eyes are indicated. New: the nose, and the bust, which is covered with drapery. I would not undertake to vouch for the authenticity of this insignificant piece of work. H. 0·64. L. of face 0·17. Cf. on no. 17. [*]

19. Bust of Africa: Cavaceppi, Racc., i. Pl. 49. A graceful little head, somewhat in the character of a Venus, inclined gently towards its own l. This head is framed in abundant curly hair, which is deeply undercut with the drill. An elephant's hide lies on the hair (the trunk and small tusks have been restored) in thick furrows, the large ears hang down at the sides. The fertility of that quarter of the world is indicated by the wreath of corn lying on the hide, and bound together behind by a piece of riband. New: the nose; the hem of the garment in front of the neck is open to suspicion: the work as a whole, however, though somewhat defaced, appears to be antique. Visible traces of touching up to be perceived here and there, but essential parts all original. Africa appears on coins depicted in a similar manner, but without the wreath. H. 0·29. L. of face 0·12. Bought for £17. [*]

20. Youthful head, of Bacchic character: a broad fillet covers the forehead and passes through the hair, which is gathered together in a knot behind; long curls hang down to the shoulders. Hair crowned with ears of wheat. The older parts much rubbed. New: nose, mouth, chin, part of the wreath and the female bust; the head has been raised up l. with a somewhat sharp turn without any apparent reason. L. of face 0·15. [*]

21. Front of sarcophagus with the story of Meleagros, resembling that in the Casino Rospigliosi (Heger, *Meleagrides*, p. 19) more than any other. (*a*) King Oeneus, in sleeved chiton and a cloak thrown round his hips, stands under an arched gateway on the extreme l. ; he clutches his beard sadly with his r. hand, while in his l. arm he holds a sceptre. (*b*) A youthful attendant in chlamys regarding the King with a sad demeanour stands near him in the background. (*c*) The powerful Ankaios at the same time moves hurriedly r. with heavy steps; on his l. shoulder he carries a double axe, with his r. hand he leads a hound by a cord. (*d*) Artemis, exactly in the attitude of the celebrated statue of Versailles in the Louvre, hastens before him; her r. breast bare, her head inclined forwards; by her side runs a second dog. In the background (*e*) a bearded man, looking behind him, wearing the chlamys, his r. hand in front of his body; in front a third dog. (*f g*) The two Dioskouroi then follow with chlamys, cap and spear; *f* is seizing Meleagros by the arm; a horse's head is visible near *g*. (New: the forepart of the third dog and the lower part of *f*'s r. leg.) (*h*) Meleagros, with a fillet about his hair and dressed in the chlamys, is couching his lance; between his legs is a fourth dog; (*i*) Atalanta is beside him in the background, shooting off her arrow. Opposite them stands (*k*) the mighty boar, which seems just to have burst from a cavern that is but slightly indicated; he has been transfixed by Meleagros, and bitten by a fifth dog in the leg. Beyond the boar we perceive a tree, and beside it (*l*) a hunter in chlamys and hat, casting a stone at the boar. On this side of the cavern (*m*) a hunter with a fillet in his hair, dressed in chlamys and boots, is thrusting his spear against the animal; between his legs lies (*n*) a wounded youth, supporting himself on his l. hand, with his r. resting on his left shin; he also wears a chlamys and boots. The whole closes r. with (*o*) a bearded man whose expression is full of grief; he wears a chlamys and is girded with a sword; supporting himself with his l. hand on his spear, he lays his r. on his wounded l. thigh. The sarcophagus, which is of ordinary workmanship, is not mentioned in the researches concerning the Meleagros sarcophagi of Kekulé (*De fabula Meleagrea*, Berlin, 1861), Helbig (*Annali dell' Inst.*, 1863, p. 81), Matz (*ibid.*, 1869, p. 76). Though considerably broken it is yet in a state of good preservation, and with the exception of the addition made to *f* has not been restored in any way. Parts of some of the feet are missing, so are the lower half of the bow of Artemis, the r. hand of Meleagros, and the whole of his spear as far as his l. hand, the upper half of

Atalanta's bow, the point of *m*'s spear. L. 2·16. H. 0·58. Bought for £6. [*]

22.   Relief; a large slab with two figures placed far apart. To the l. a lady in a stola with a palla thrown round her legs is sitting on a chair without back, facing l.: she is supporting herself with her l. arm on the seat of the chair, her r. hand rests in her lap. She looks round towards a beardless man, with the Roman type of features, draped in tunic and toga, who is extending his r. hand as if he were speaking. New: all four corners of slab, and footstool and part of legs of woman. Sculpture in imitation of the Greek, in high relief, belonging to the first century of the empire. Of Greek marble. H. 0·61. L. 0·93. Bought for £10. [*]

23.   Bust of a boy with close-cut hair of Roman type. The pupils of the eyes are indicated. New: tip of nose, parts of the ears, r. shoulder, parts of tunic and cloak. Coarse. Possibly the "Diadumenus" of the Memorandum, bought for £10. H. 0·37. L. of face 0·10. [*]

24.   Bust of a child with joyous expression, with crisp close hair. Small size. The tip of the nose, which is broken, appears to be ancient, and so does the bust. Eyes very narrow. Of Thasian marble. H. 0·28. L. of face 0·12. Bought for £5. [*]

Ante-Room.

25.   Terminal bust of the winged Dionysos (*psilax*) crowned with ivy, the wavy hair smoothed back, the expression delicate. Small size. The tip of the nose is new. Of coarse-grained Parian marble. H. 0·27. Probably bought with no. 26 for £6, "two small busts." [*]

26.   Terminal bust of a female Satyr, laughing: small size. A broad fillet intertwined with vine-leaves is drawn over her forehead and through her hair. New: nose and lower corner. Not agreeable sculpture. Italian marble. H. 0·24. Cf. on no. 25. [*]

27.   A fat goat with full udder, lowering its head to graze. The l. hind leg and some other details are new. Rough work. H. 0·25. L. 0·28. [*]

Drawing Room.

28.   Statuette of a female; seated on a block of rock, quite enveloped in her ample cloak, the folds of which remind us somewhat of the statue of Antiocheia (*Mus. Pio-Clem.*, III., Pl. 46). She has thrown her r. leg over the l. so that it extends far out; her r. elbow is supported on her r. thigh, and her head is leaning on her hand. The l. arm describes a right angle. The head, separately wrought, has a diadem (στεφάνη); the hair is simply drawn back and gathered together in a knot behind; it shows abundant traces of a red tinge; the r. hand lay originally somewhat further back than it does now. New: nose, r. fore-arm, l. hand with the roll, and details in the folds. Workmanship rather smooth and not delicate, but the composition is very graceful and the pose of the head fine. H. 0·51. [*]

29. **Statuette of Eros.** The mighty lion's skin is spread over a rock on which the boy sleeps with his head somewhat raised. The l. arm is outstretched and lies on one wing, the r. across the breast and body. The idea of sleep is very naturally indicated in the position of the head which is sunk back; along the crown the curly hair is dressed in a kind of plait. Both legs outstretched. The torch, still burning, has fallen from the r. hand, the l. holds the broken string of the bow, both ends of which terminate in the head of a swan. The quiver lies behind the back of Eros on the ground. Near his breast crawls a lizard and another by his l. foot. New: r. foot, half the l. foot, two fingers of the l. hand, nose and upper lip. Coarse-grained Parian marble. L. 0·57. [*]

SALOON.

30. **Cinerarium,** of the period of the Flavian Emperors, at the close of the first century after Christ. On the lower part of the front surface the folding-doors of the grave, ornamented with lions' heads, on either side a dog crouching on a pedestal. Over the door hangs a wreath enclosing a tablet with the following inscription (Gruter, 601. 4): *T. Flavio Aug(usti)lib(erto) Onesimo, ministrat(ori), dec(uriarum) IIII, | dec(uria) Favoris, | T. Flavius Vitalianus | patri optimo.* Over this a plant and on either side of it an ornament consisting of a shell out of which a trident rises up, to which two dolphins are chained by the tails. In each corner is an erection like a candelabrum, ornamented with a mask below and with a double sphinx above. On each side is also a plant. Formerly in the Capodiferro (Spada) palace in Rome. H. 0·54. L. 0·42. D. 0·32. Cf. on no. 7. [*]

31. **Statuette of Athene,** in the pose of the colossal statue from Velletri in the Louvre. New: head, r. arm, l. fore-arm, feet and a great part of the folds. H. 0·68. Cf. on no. 12. [*]

DINING ROOM.

32. **Round vase,** richly ornamented: cover and handles modern, the rest much touched up. On the principal band is on one

side a pedum and a syrinx between two masks of Satyrs, one youthful
and one bearded; on the other side a cista with the serpent, and
a thyrsos between the masks of a semi-bearded Satyr and a Silenus
crowned with ivy. All the reliefs very flat. H. 0·45. Cf. on
no. 7. [*]

33. **A similar vase** ornamented round the neck with rich fine
work representing branches; the body fluted. New: lowest piece
and cover. H. 0·50. Cf. on no. 7. [*]

BROCKLESBY PARK (Lincolnshire).

Catalogue of the Pictures, etc. in the House at Brocklesby Park,
1856. 4° (very brief notices). Dallaway, p. 386 (II. p. 138). Conze,
Arch. Anzeiger, 1864, p. 215. For the Worsley Collection see
Museum Worsleyanum, London, 1794, II. fol. (English and Italian
text. The first volume appeared in 1798, the second some years
later). New ed. London, 1824, II. 4°; Milan, 1834 (only the
Italian text, which is based chiefly on the explanations of E. Q.
Visconti. I have given my references according to the London editions,
appending to them in parentheses the references according to the
edition of Milan). Dallaway, pp. 359 ff. (II. p. 110). I visited the
collection in 1873. The numbers in my list are those of the catalogue mentioned above and of the collection itself; the numbers
which are passed over belong to modern specimens.

South of Hull, distant about two miles from the Brocklesby
railway station, lies the extensive estate of the Earl of YARBOROUGH,
called Brocklesby Hall. The sculpture gallery, separated from the
dwelling-house and built under splendid lofty trees, is a plain and
very damp apartment, not at all suited for sculptures, which are
injured by the damp. In it may be seen the few antiquities collected
by the first Lord Yarborough (1749–1823. Cf. Smith, *Nollekens*, I.
p. 13. Introd. § 54), together with most of the specimens of the
celebrated collection which Sir RICHARD WORSLEY (1751–1805),
who was at that time English resident at Venice, made at great
cost on a journey through Greece and Italy 1785–87 (Introd. § 66).
Lord Yarborough inherited this collection. Since the sale of the
Worsley estate, Appuldurcombe, in the Isle of Wight, most of the
antiques have been deposited at Brocklesby; the rest are said to be
in the town house (17 Arlington Street) where, however, Waagen
(*Treas.*, IV. p. 64 ff.) mentions nothing of the kind.

2. Terminal head of "Sophocles": *Mus. Worsl.,* Cl. II. 1 (Pl. 12, 1). The head, found by Worsley himself in the ruins of the so-called Prytaneion at Athens in June 1785, is of bad workmanship of the later Roman period and has nothing to do with the great writer of tragedy. New: nose, breast and inscription. [*BC*]

5. Head of Niobe: *Spec.,* I. Pl. 35—37. Müller-Wieseler, I. 34, 142. Of the head, which with the hair and neck is antique, only a great part of the nose has been restored: it was no doubt originally intended to be let into a statue, and has now been completed by modern drapery imitated from the Florentine example. It appears to have been very little if at all touched up. The examination of the original and the comparison of a cast with the cast of the Florentine statue, leave no doubt that the head in Brocklesby is the finer of the two. The expression of grief in the deep-sunk inner corners of the eyes is somewhat more strongly marked; the mouth is very beautiful and noble; the luxuriant curly hair, which falls in rich masses over the shoulders and neck, intertwined with a fillet, is of a fine picturesque effect (cf. the Epigrams, *Anth. Plan.,* 133. 134). The marble of a beautiful yellowish tint, apparently Pentelic of the finest quality. Length of face 0·23 (forehead 0·07, nose 0·08, lower part of the face 0·08). Nollekens sold the head to the Earl of Exeter, who gave it to Lord Yarborough. (Waagen, *Treas.,* IV. p. 506, is inaccurate.) Possibly it is the same head a cast of which Winckelmann (*Kunstgesch.,* IX. 2, 27) knew of in Rome (cf. *Monum. Ined.,* p. lxxi.) and of which Fea (*Storia,* II. p. 199) says that it was in England (cf. Mengs, *Oper,* II. p. 11); according to other authorities this head went to Russia and was there utterly lost sight of (see Stark, *Niobe,* p. 233). [* *C*]

7. Terminal head of "Alcibiades": *Mus. Worsl.,* Cl. II. 2 (Pl. 12, 2). This head, of late style, dug out at the same time as no. 2, has just as little to do with Alkibiades as no. 2 with Sophokles. The features have not been recognised; they remind us a little of the so-called Persius of the Villa Albani (Zoega, *Bassir.,* Pl. 115). The hair slightly curled. New: back of head with ears, nose, a large portion of r. cheek, and breast with the inscription. [* *BC*]

8. Figure of a Kerkopithekos, cut out of the handle of a water-vase: *Mus. Worsl.,* Cl. III. 10 (Pl. 18, 2).

9. Fragment of a marble door: *Mus. Worsl.,* Cl. I. 14 (Pl. 9, 5). On the transverse framework (ζυγά, *impages*) numerous bosses (ἧλοι, *bullae*) are introduced; the lions' heads in the panels, from which the knockers hang, are among the most favourite means for warding off evil enchantments (ἀποτρόπαια).

10. **Votive relief to Asklepios and Hygieia** : *Mus. Worsl.*, Cl. I. I (Pl. I, I), "Jupiter and Minerva" (cf. Visconti, *Mus. Pio-Clem.*, v. p. 165). Found at Athens in the year 1785, apparently on the Akropolis: most likely on the southern declivity, where the Asklepieion was disinterred not long ago, and where many similar reliefs have been found (cf. particularly *Mittheilungen des Arch. Inst. in Athens*, II. Pl. 14). One of the finest works of its class, much resembling in style the Parthenon frieze. The upper surface is somewhat rubbed away, more than would appear from the illustrations. Asklepios, with the cup in his right hand, is, if we may conclude from the position of his legs, supporting himself on a staff which does not appear in the relief: behind him is Hygieia veiled, with the tankard in her hand, which is lowered. These, as deities, are represented of larger stature than a family standing opposite to them consisting of a bearded man, a woman and a child, who, with their right hands upraised, turning the palms towards the deities, make the typical gestures of adoration. Various interpretations have been suggested for the two deities : cf. Lebas, *Annali dell' Inst.*, 1845, p. 240 (Zeus and Europa). Kekulé, *Hebe*, p. 47 (Zeus and Hebe). Overbeck, *Kunstmythologie*, II. p. 576, note 110. Pentelic marble. H. 0·81. To the r. the relief is incomplete. [*]

11. **Middle portion of a sarcophagus.** The three **Graces** in the usual grouping; the two outside hold each an apple in the outside hand which is uplifted. On either side r. and l. a tall vase. H. 0·34. L. 0·33. [*CM*]

12. **Bust called "Sappho"** : *Mus. Worsl.*, Cl. II. 8 (Pl. 13, 4). The hair wound twice round the head. The nose has been restored. The appellation is arbitrary; the work insignificant; the genuineness of the whole according to Bernoulli open to doubt. [*BC*]

13. **Fragment of the sepulchral stelè of Chairion** : *Mus. Worsl.*, Cl. I. 13 (Pl. 6, 2). Only the bearded head and the breast of the principal figure are still preserved ; upon the architrave the inscription Χαιρίων Μο ..... (*C. I. G.*, 734); above it is a row of front tiles. High relief. Pentelic marble. H. 0·33. L. 0·22. [*]

14. **Fragment of a votive relief**: engraved in reverse, *Mus. Worsl.*, Cl. I. 11 (Pl. 5, 2). Three men and three women, a boy and a girl, are moving in solemn procession l. At both ends it is incomplete. Pentelic marble ; very delicately executed, but a good deal rubbed. H. 0·19. L. 0·20. From Megara. [*]

BROCKLESBY 17

15. Head of Aphroditè, of colossal scale, intended to be let
into a (draped) statue. It came originally from Greece and afterwards
from the collection of Townley into the possession of Lord Yarborough. The hair has been but little worked on the top, because,
chiefly from the size of the statue, it was originally concealed by the
metal stephanè, for which a groove is introduced; but there are no
holes for fastening it on. By this means the upper part of the face,
by itself unusually high, must once have had a still greater preponderance over the lower part of the face, which is somewhat short.
The hair is smoothed back in free waves, thus allowing the high
triangle of the peaked forehead to stand out even more than it otherwise would. These circumstances might almost raise doubts about
the appellation of Aphroditè, but they are due perhaps more to the
art standard of the epoch of the original. The cheeks show the wide
treatment of Attic heads, the eyes are directed downwards in somewhat marked manner, and this when looked at in profile does not
contrast well with the retreating forehead; the eyes and mouth have
not much expression. The whole head is decidedly inclined towards
its r. We seem to have before us a later, even copy of a peculiar
type of a good period, which certainly is far behind the head at
Holkham (no. 37). The lobes of the ears are pierced. Pentelic
marble. Length of face 0·35; from the chin to the nose 0·10, nose
0·11, forehead 0·14. [*C]

16. Relief. flat: remains of **two horsemen** galloping l.,
in chiton and chlamys; even the bridles have been executed in
marble. This beautiful relief is certainly not sepulchral. To the r.
and at the upper part perfect. H. 0·43. L. 0·41. [*]

17. Girl with two doves, sepulchral relief from the isle of
Paros, found in 1785: *Mus. Worsl.*, Cl. 1. 17 (Pl. 8, 1): the engraving
in its conventional delicacy gives no idea of the peculiar charm of
the uncommon proportions and relief style of this remarkable work,
which must be designated the pearl of the Worsley Collection. See
the accompanying woodcut, taken from a photograph. A girl, in
a Doric chiton, is standing turned r. The chiton is not girdled, and
on the r. side quite open; its diploïdion falls back and front down to
the hips. The head is inclined downwards, the l. leg slightly bent,
the whole frame in repose. On her l. hand she holds a dove (the
head has been knocked off) in the manner of a falcon: with the r.
she presses a second dove to her breast, at the same time putting
her mouth to the beak of the bird to kiss it;

Nam mellitus erat, suamque norat
Ipsam tam bene quam puella matrem,

Nec sese a gremio illius movebat,
Sed circumsiliens modo huc, modo illuc,
Ad solam dominam usque pipiabat.

By this ac ion the diploïdion, following the upward strugglings of the bird, has been gently drawn up. The bent head of the girl is full of enchanting naïveté, and its unusual size (the height of head is nearly one-fifth, and length of face (0·10) one-eighth of the whole figure) may be owing partly to the tender age of the child, partly to a peculiar feeling for proportion. The whole arrangement of the hair, as well as the treatment of its separate strands, is of almost laboured precision. The garment is composed of a heavy material, and for this reason takes only large folds; the nude portions are executed with similar simplicity. All the contours are so clearly defined that, although the treatment is flat, a very clear relief is effected. The beak of the uninjured dove is quite detached from the ground; the mutilated head of the other bird was represented in the same way in alto-relievo. A dowel-hole in the back of the first dove, between the tips of the wings, shows that there was probably a metal ornament there, perhaps a cord. The delicacy of the sentiment, the slightly archaic tranquillity of the action, the well calculated moderation in the treatment of the relief, the apparently provincial peculiarities of the style, finally the beautiful material (Parian lychnites) and its excellent state of preservation, make the relief, which doubtless belongs to the fifth century, a specimen of the first rank. The relief is bounded below by a projecting rim; to the right and left (as is generally the case with the older class of sepulchral reliefs) the slab is not framed in. On the upper surface two holes seem to show that the stele had something to crown it (ἐπίθεμα), probably a palmette (ἀνθέμιον). It may therefore be compared with a sepulchral relief of a girl in similar attire, with a casket in her hands, which also probably came from the Greek islands, and which is, or was, at Venice in the Giustiniani alle Zecchere Palace (Thiersch, *Reisen in Italien,* I. p. 260, Friederichs, *Bausteine,* no. 359; published by Mauch, *Bau-Ordnungen,* Pl. 90, 2); the two are not dissimilar in style. A sepulchral relief from Thasos, the colony of Paros, may also be compared with the one before us on account of many analogies in style (*Annali dell' Inst.,* 1872, Pl. I. Froehner, *Musées de France,* Pl. 39). H. 0·80. L. 0·39. Elevation of the relief from the field 0·03—0·035. [*C]

18. **Bust of Demosthenes,** very naturalistic in treatment, like all the portraits of the orator, which universally go back to

the statue of Polyeuktos (cf. Knole, no. 1). Modern: nose, part
of upper lip and of r. ear; the l. ear injured. [*BC*]

23. Statue of a Maenad or a dancer: below life size. She
wears an Attic chiton and a small cloak over her l. shoulder and
arm; the folds about the leg have all the air of being in motion and
are deeply worked out. Modern: the head, which is thrown back,
the lower part of the r. arm with the thyrsos, half the lower part of
the l. arm and the pendent border of the cloak. The breast, being
but slightly raised, appeared on that account to Conze not indisputably female; he also thought that the folds in the lap had
been worked over, and that a man might be disguised under the
feminine drapery. Figure well designed and not badly executed; the
back however is not finished. [*BC*]

26. Statue of Asklepias, priestess of Artemis Orthosia at
Megara, where the sculpture was disinterred. Small size. *Mus.
Worsl.*, Cl. III. 6 (Pl. 16, 2). Ordinary work of a late period. New:
head, r. fore-arm and l. hand. The inscription, which I have not
compared, runs (*C. I. Gr.*, 1064. Kaibel, *Epigr. Gr.*, 870):

'Αξομένη κούρην Λητωίδα ἐιοχέαιραν,
"Αρτεμιν 'Ορθωσίην, πόλεως περὶ τείχεα πάντα
εἰμὶ ἱερηὶς ἐγὼ 'Ασκληπιάς· ἐκ δὲ τοκήων
πατρὸς 'Εικτιμένου 'Ασκληπιάδαο γενέσθην,
5 μητρὸς σεμνοτάτης Νεικηφόριδος γένος ἐσθλὸν,
οἱ δ' εὖ γειωάμενοί μ' ἔδοσαν ἱερηίδα τῇδε θεάίρη,
βουλῆς καὶ δήμου ψηφισ(σ)αμένης περὶ ἐμείο.

The sixth line is a heptameter. The form γενάσθην in line 4 instead
of ἐγενόθην is barbarous. [*C*]

27. Terminal head of "Regulus": *Mus. Worsl.*, Cl. II. 6
(Pl. 13, 2). The name is quite unwarranted, the inscription
modern. We perceive a distant resemblance to the Scipio heads,
but certainly no identity. Hair only indicated by short lines indented.
New: breast and a piece at the back of the head. [*BC*]

28. Votive relief to Herakles: *Mus. Worsl.*, Cl. I. 3 (Pl. 1,
2). The hero is lying on the lion's skin with the skyphos in his
r. hand and a wine-skin in his l.; quiver and club are near him. The
inscription runs (*C. I. Gr.*, 473):

Τίμαιος 'Ηρα[κλεώτης? καὶ...]ης 'Ηρακλεώτης
[ὠε]ψηκάτ[ην...........ρ]όσον.

It seems to bear witness that Timaios and a fellow-countryman from Herakleia (on the Pontos?) dedicated the relief in consequence of recovery from an illness. Found at Athens in 1785.

29. Bas-relief in terra cotta: *Mus. Worsl.,* Cl. I. 15 (Pl. 7, 1). Müller-Wieseler, I. 1, 4. Purification of a terminal head by a Satyr, with the assistance of two female slaves and under the superintendence of a woman, perhaps a priestess, who carries a branch intended for the adornment of the Hermes. In a replica in the Louvre (Campana, *Opere in Plastica,* Pl. 44) a bunch of grapes is represented instead of the sponge; by the whole therefore a wreathing of the Hermes is meant. The same motive was probably originally common to both copies, and one of the two has been incorrectly restored; which it it could be learned only by exact investigation.

30. Kybele, with the lion at her side, the back of her head concealed by her cloak. No modius. The hands restored. Ordinary workmanship. [C]

31. Sepulchral relief. Attic: *Mus. Worsl.,* Cl. I. 2 (Pl. 1, 3), "Protesilaus and Laodamia." An armed warrior, of whose spear only a small part is expressed in the marble, is taking leave of his wife, who is sitting down; only scanty traces of her are preserved. A veiled female, with her head lowered, her r. hand on her cloak, stands behind the warrior. Fine bas-relief with powerful outlines. Pentelic marble. H. 0·37. L. 0·30. The restoration given in the engraving does not appear in the original. [*C]

32. Mask of a bearded warrior: it looks as if it were the corner of a sarcophagus cover, and yet it is too large. H. circa 0·48. [C]

33. Terminal bust of the youthful Herakles, crowned with ivy, with a long fillet hanging down: *Mus. Worsl.,* Cl. II. 5 (Pl. 13, 1). A beautiful head. Pentelic marble. Modern: nose, the greater part of the mouth, and a piece of the chin; also l. side of breast. [* C]

34. Fragment of a sepulchral relief, lower part: *Mus. Worsl.,* Cl. I. 4 (Pl. 2, 1). A man in chiton and chlamys is offering his hand in farewell to a woman sitting down; she is not veiled. Beside her stands another woman; while behind the chair stands a man in a cloak, his posture denoting grief. Under the chair lies a dog. Very pretty, but not particularly delicate. From Megara. Apparently of Pentelic marble. [*]

36. Painting: Glaukos and Skylla, composed in exact accordance with Ovid (*Met.,* XIII. 907 ff.): *Mus. Worsl.,* Vol. I. p. 103 (*tav. d' agg.,* no. 1). Penna, *Viaggio della Villa Adriana,* IV.

Pl. 141. *Mon. dell' Inst.*, III. 52, 6, cf. Vinet, *Annali*, 1843, p. 184. At the r. end Skylla is standing on a rocky shore, the upper part of her body nude, her legs and trunk draped in her cloak, the border of which she is raising with her l. hand; on her throat a necklace. With her r. hand she waves refusal to Glaukos, who from the sea assures her of his love. He is bearded; his feet terminate after many coils in a fish's tail. The painting is said to have been discovered in Hadrian's Villa in 1786, together with nine others which were published in 1821 by Carloni. It has either been entirely painted over, or (a hypothesis which seems to me more probable) is entirely spurious. Bernoulli shares my doubts. We must not forget that in the last century, when the Herculanean discoveries made so much stir, the fabrication and sale of so-called "antique" paintings was carried on in Rome with great energy; and we are expressly told that many of these paintings found their way to England; cf. Winckelmann, *Werke*, II. p. 46, 261. Fea, *Storia delle Arti*, III. p. 219. Azara in *Opere di Mengs*, ed. Fea, p. xxxii. It is hardly likely that so profitable a trade should have been brought to an end by the death of the chief dealer, Guerra (1761). [*B]

37. **Draped female statue**: *Mus. Worsl.*, Cl. III. 5 (Pl. 16, 1), "Venus." Clarac, IV. 591, 1294. A woman stepping forward in a graceful, almost affected manner, on the l. leg. From the r. shoulder which is somewhat lowered the chiton has slipped, and from her breast; her very ample cloak envelopes her l. arm, back and legs in its rich folds. She has lowered her r. hand to lift the cloak near her knees, and her l. lies on the border of the garment. New: the head; it is uncertain what further restorations may have been made. [B]

39. **Fragment of a votive relief**, l. end: *Mus. Worsl.*, Cl. I. 10 (Pl. 5, 1). A man, two women (the foremost veiled), two children and female slave with a large covered box on her head, are moving r., to a space probably once occupied by a dead man, rendered with heroic treatment (cf. no. 45), or else where gods were represented. Ordinary work of a good period. Pentelic marble. Found in Eleusis. H. 0·42. L. 0·29. [*]

40. **Siren**, tearing her hair with both hands: *Mus. Worsl.*, Cl. I. 7 (Pl. 3, 1). Over the arms on either side appear the upper curves of the wings, the lower tips of which, like the tail, were not fully given in the relief, but were originally only expressed by colour. The whole is a fragment of the rounded top of an Attic sepulchral stelè. The upper edge was partly defined by the

upper contour of the wings; now the piece is sawn off horizontally below and vertically on either side. (Cf., for similar adornment of sepulchral monuments, Schrader, *Die Sirenen*, p. 86. Stephani, *Compte-Rendu*, 1866, p. 41. Conze, *Sitzungsberichte der Wiener Akademie*, LXXI. p. 326.) Very bold relief. Pentelic marble. H. 0·32. L. 0·19. [*]

41. **Fragment of a child's sarcophagus, representing Cupids racing in the circus.** Only one Cupid preserved, who is riding, and beside him is a led horse. H. 0·28. L. 0·20. [*CM*]

42. **Fragment of a relief:** *Mus. Worsl.*, Cl. I. 19 (Pl. 8, 3), "Theseus." The name arises from the fact that in the engraving a lion's skin is on the head of the horseman, who is galloping r., but this skin is not in the original; in its place there is a flaw in the marble. Small size. Delicate sculpture in slight relief, in the style of the Parthenon frieze, unfortunately much rubbed; may have belonged to a sepulchral relief. Pentelic marble. "Discovered amidst some ruins in the Temple of Minerva in the Acropolis." H. 0·20. L. 0·13. [*B*]

43. **Mosaic,** of large stones: an owl in a chariot, drawn by two geese. [*BC*]

45. **Fragment of a sepulchral relief,** r. end: *Mus. Worsl.*, Cl. I. 12 (Pl. 6, 1), "Pluto." Much more likely to be the upper part of the body of a dead man to whom heroic honours are assigned, looking somewhat like Pluto. He is reclining before a table, prepared to receive the gifts and adoration of his worshippers. (Cf. no. 39.) Beside him, near a large krater, stands a youthful slave. Good alto-relievo. Pentelic marble. H. 0·34. L. 0·13. [*]

48. **Fragment of a relief.** A boy with a cloak on his back is with evident effort carrying a burden on his back. The motion of the figure is graceful; cf. the boy furthest l. in Millin, *Gal. Mythol.*, Pl. 1, 2. The face has been restored. The antique origin is not quite free from suspicion. [*C*]

49. **Fragment of a relief:** *Mus. Worsl.*, Cl. I. 25 (Pl. 9, 6), "Pisistratus." A bearded warrior and charioteer in chariot.

53. **Fragment of a sepulchral relief, Attic:** *Mus. Worsl.*, Cl. I. 5 (Pl. 2, 3). A horseman armed with breastplate and shield is galloping l. The inscription on the field cannot be completed with certainty:

.ερ.....κλῆς Πολυαρ - - 'Αλωπεκ[ῆθεν].

(*C. I. Gr.*, 580). Much defaced. [*]

55. **Small bust** with the modern inscription *Telesphorus*. [*C*]

60. Small terminal bust of Asklepios, much resembling Zeus, with a twisted roll round the head. Alabaster. The inscription *Juppiter Ol.* modern. *Mus. Worsl.*, Cl. II. 9 (Pl. 13, 5). [*BC*]

62. Statue of a boy: *Mus. Worsl.*, Cl. III. 7 (Pl. 16, 3), "Genius." He is standing in a graceful attitude on his r. leg, putting the l. foot forward; the chlamys is hung round his shoulders and l. arm, the r. arm and the l. are bent at right angles. The head let into the figure is not certainly a portrait. A riband goes through the hair, which is arranged in a top-knot over the forehead. Restorations unknown. [*B*]

64. Relief of a sacrificial ox: *Mus. Worsl.*, Cl. I. 16 (Pl. 7, 2). The ox is adorned for the sacrifice with a laurel wreath (*infula*) and a broad embroidered fillet. "Found in Magna Graecia, and thence transported to Naples, where it remained some time in the palace of His Grace Caraffa of Colubrano."

65. Sepulchral relief: *Mus. Worsl.*, Cl. I. 6 (Pl. 2, 2). In a slightly sunken field the bearded Ion is offering his r. hand in farewell to Aristokleia. She is sitting down and is fully draped, but unveiled. The little Kaphision is standing by her chair looking up to her. Above is inscribed Ἴων and Ἀριστόκλεια; in the relief field itself Καφισίων; over the field καλαί is cut in. (*C. I. Gr.*, 1091, faulty.) Style of the fourth century. Flat relief. The slab has been sawn off above and below. H. 0·35. L. 0·24. [*]

66. Cinerarium of Saenia Longina: Piranesi, *Vasi e Candelabri*, Pl. 96. The rape of Persephone is delineated above, as she is being forcibly carried off in a quadriga by Hades. The upper part of the relief and the cover are, according to Conze's opinion, modern; on the pediment of the latter may be seen a bust of Mercury between an overturned basket and a cock. Below the relief is the inscription *Saeniae Longinae* | [*fili*]*ae* [*Ge*]*rmani* [*ci*]. The letters in brackets are modern introductions. The urn is of good workmanship and comes from Rome. It was formerly at Chelsea at the house of the first Lord Yarborough's father-in-law, G. Aufrere, Esq. (cf. Welcker, *Zeitschrift für die alte Kunst*, p. 195. Förster, *Raub der Persephone*, p. 126. Overbeck, *Kunstmythol.*, III. p. 644, no. 7). H. 0·42. L. 0·41. [*CM*]

67. Fragment of a sepulchral vase; very large size: *Mus. Worsl.*, Cl. I. 14 (Pl. 6, 3). The bearded Moschos (Μόσχος), who is followed by a small attendant, is offering his hand to a lady sitting down. Of the latter figure only a very small portion is preserved. Pentelic marble. Found at Athens. H. 0·27. L. 0·17. [*C*]

69. **Small terminal head,** with the modern inscription *Sappho.* New: the whole profile and the bust. [*BC*]

70. **Small terminal head,** bearded, with the modern inscription *Ermaeus, i.e.* Hermarchos. [*BC*]

72. **Small terminal head,** with the modern inscription *Pherekydes: Mus. Worsl.,* Cl. II. 4 (Pl. 12, 4). The head is stretched forwards and somewhat upwards, the eyes are put in unevenly, the ears stand out. [*BC*]

74. **Terminal head of Herakles,** with the lion's skin over the head, the inscription *Hercules* being modern : *Mus. Worsl.,* Cl. II. 10 (Pl. 13, 6). [*C*]

76. **Marble beard,** from Athens : *Mus. Worsl.,* Cl. I. 21 (Pl. 9, 2).

79. **Foot,** covered with sandal : the twisting of the straps very distinctly indicated. [*C*]

82. **Eros,** painfully dragging at Herakles' club and lion's skin : *Mus. Worsl.,* Cl. III. 4 (Pl. 17, 2). The portion of the club which touches the head genuine ; the rest of the club and the r. arm new. [**C*]

83. **Statue of Athenè,** less than life size. She is resting on her r. leg, the l. slightly bent, her r. arm rests on her hip. She wears a girdled doubled chiton ; the aegis is divided into two rounded halves. The motive pleasing and simply worked out. Modern : the helmeted head, the r. arm (which has been correctly restored), the l. arm and the oval shield on which rests the l. hand. [*C*]

84. **Female head,** modern ; with the hair in the style of Agrippina. [*BC*]

85. **Female head,** slightly inclined l., with a double fillet in the hair : Bernoulli considers it a tolerably exact replica of the Venus of Arles in the Louvre. A delicate work. New: half the neck, the nose, the lower lip. [*BC*]

86. **Marble throne** : *Mus. Worsl.,* Cl. III. 11 (Pl. 19, 2). Originally belonging to the celebrated Fulvio Orsini, and afterwards added to the curiosities in Villa Montalto, bought by Jenkins.

87. **Marble chair,** of the same origin : *Mus. Worsl.,* Cl. III. 11 (Pl. 19, 3).

88. **Bust of "Achilles,"** modern : *Mus. Worsl.,* Cl. II. 7 (Pl. 13, 3). [**BC*]

89. **Bust of Caracalla** ; the neck and paludamentum unbroken. The back part of the head is too small. [***]

90. Dionysos and Eros: *Mus. Worsl.*, Cl. III. 1 (Pl. 14).
"Bacchus and Acratus." Clarac, IV. 690, 1626. Müller-Wieseler, II.
32, 370. Dionysos, with a fillet and an ivy wreath in his hair and
with curls falling to his shoulders, stands in repose, his l. hand
supported on his hip; a chlamys lies on his r. shoulder, falling
across his back and partly concealing his l. arm. He is laying his
r. hand on the r. shoulder of the youthful Eros, a figure of smaller
scale, who stands by him and over whose breast a nebris hangs
crosswise. Eros stands with his legs crossed, holding a goblet
to his breast with both hands and looking up at the god. Between the two is a vine-stock. The group has received important
restorations. The l. arm of Dionysos and the drapery on it (but
not the hand) are new, and so are his legs and r. arm; the portions of the chlamys which cover his back are old. The head and
neck are undoubtedly antique, but they seem somewhat too small
and perhaps do not really belong to the figure. New: the head
of Eros; his r. arm from the shoulder, with the goblet; also his
l. hand and half of the fore arm, a portion of the skin, nearly the
whole of his wings, and the lower parts of his legs: also the vine-
stock and pedestal. The nebris is a rather remarkable attribute
for Eros to bear. There is besides at the back of the loins a
round smooth circle, with an iron socket, as if a little tail had once
been fastened there, and these facts give rise to the thought whether
the Eros was not originally a Satyr. But in this case the tail would
without doubt have been made of the same piece of marble with the
statue itself; the iron socket rather goes to show that the transformation into a Satyr was due to a restorer, to whom moreover the Satyr-
like head with the bristly hair may be referred. But a more modern
restorer has very rightly filled in the wings of the young figure, for
the part of the left wing adhering to the back is undoubtedly ancient.
Now it would be difficult to admit a winged Satyr (cf. Zoega,
Bassiril., Pl. 88; Müller-Wieseler, II. 40, 479), while the Bacchic nebris
or panther's skin, is quite suitable to Eros as the companion of
Dionysos. According to this view it was right to take away the little
tail, and the regeneration should have been completed by removing
the Satyr head of the first restorer and putting instead a head of Eros.
Finally it is worth mentioning that there is no material coherence
between the two figures in their antique parts. But it would be too
sceptical on that account to raise doubts about their having originally
belonged to each other. The marble of both figures is Pentelic
of the same quality. Besides, great praise has been rightly given to

the harmonious flow of the lines; the fine grouping; the beautiful treatment of the nude, particularly in Dionysos where "the masculine energy of youth is admirably blended with female softness and virgin delicacy." The whole group is of excellent effect, and among the many similar must take a high rank. We may be reminded of Thymilos' group of Dionysos and Eros in the Street of Tripods at Athens (Paus., 1. 20. 2). H. about 1·37.   [*C]

91.   **Marble ship,** Roman: of rather clumsy construction. In front, considerably raised, a beak (*rostrum*) is introduced in the form of a bird's beak, over that is a (modern) animal's head; above the foredeck is a battlemented turret (for the most part modern). The hull of the ship has three tiers one above another; in the middle and upper ones in the forepart of the vessel are 11 holes for the oars. The after half of the uppermost tier is ornamented in the fashion of the stern of a galley with a double row of relief fields, one over the other; this adornment is varied on starboard and port respectively. In the lowest row on the starboard side next to the oar-holes is a bucranium, then an eagle, a snake, a thunderbolt; on the port side is a wreath thrice repeated. Standing somewhat out over the bucranium is a head with a crown of rays, an oar, an ornament of branches, and a capricorn; on the port a bearded head, a trident surrounded with two dolphins, ornamental branches, a sea-panther. Finally there projects a long way out from the stern a kind of balcony (on it there are two half-moons on the starboard side and one on the port); from which the aplustre (ἄφλαστον) rises up; in the lower field of the latter is a capricorn, in the upper one a crab (on the port a helmet below and a Janus head above); the uppermost portion of the aplustre is modern. Steering paddles are not indicated. [C]

96.   **Female head,** with a coif. Small size. Nicely executed but somewhat rubbed out.   [*]

97.   **Bearded head,** with the modern inscription *Anacreon: Mus. Worsl.*, Cl. 11. 3 (Pl. 12. 3). The antique head is fastened on to a modern marble slab. [BC]

98.   **Satyr head,** small and delicate, with two little horns and pointed ears. It is of the tender kind that we see for example in the statues of Cossutius Cerdo (Brit. Mus. Graeco-Roman Sculpt. No. 188, 190. *Mus. Marbl.*, 11. 33, 43). New: nose and neck. [* C]

99.   **Fragment of a sepulchral relief.** A woman is represented in complete drapery, with wavy hair. Coarse, of a late epoch. H. 0·30. L. 0·14. [*]

100.   **Head of an empress.** The style of hair points to the

beginning of the 3rd century. Said to be Julia Cornelia Paula.
New: nose, mouth, chin, r. eye. [*BC*]

101. Relief of Artemis facing r. in girdled doubled chiton,
her r. hand supported on her hip, her l. hand somewhat raised and
holding the long straight bow. To her l. a deer standing in repose.
The proportions unusually slender. Low relief. Greek workmanship,
very commonplace. H. 0·31. L. 0·17. [*]

102. Bust of Herakles. The breast new. [*C*]

103. Torso of Aphroditè, presented by the sculptor Emil
Wolff in Rome to the Earl of Yarborough.

106. Head of a Roman boy, with straight hair, designated
"Britannicus." Small size. Good work. [*B*]

108. Upper part of a beautiful female **portrait statue**
("Muse") purchased A.D. 1850 from the Bessborough collection in
Roehampton (Introd. note 151). The body is covered to the throat
by a fine cloak of which one end is thrown back and falls over the l.
shoulder. The management of the folds, which are determined
mainly by the position of the arms (the r. lies across the body, the
l. is lowered), is very graceful, and reminds us of the delicacy of
terra cotta statues. The pretty head seems to belong to the rest
(Conze thinks it modern); it is inclined somewhat forward and
towards the r. shoulder; the hair is treated simply and gathered up
in a knot behind. Nose and l. hand new. Of Greek, apparently
Pentelic, marble. [*²BC*]

108ᵃ (let into the pedestal of no. 108). **Relief** of good Roman work. Two Satyrs and a Bacchante; one of the Satyrs is
swinging a kantharos, of which he holds the handle by one finger. [*C*]

SOUTH LIBRARY.

109. Statue of an Egyptian priest: *Mus. Worsl.,* Cl. III. 8
(Pl. 3, 7). Behind the back is an obelisk with an hieroglyphic inscription. Basalt.

I cannot say where the following four specimens represented in
the engravings, but not exhibited with the other marbles, are at
present to be found.

110. Votive relief: *Mus. Worsl.,* Cl. I. 9 (Pl. 4). Müller-
Wieseler, II. 44, 555. A man, clothed in chiton and chlamys,
followed by three females also clothed, moving with light steps
before an altar of rough stones in a rocky grotto, over which Pan,
with goat's legs, is sitting. According to the ingenious explanation
of Visconti, the figures are Kekrops and his three daughters, Aglauros, Pandrosos and Herse, and the locality would be the grotto of

Aglauros, on the northern rock-declivity of the Athenian Akropolis, near the celebrated grotto of Pan (Eurip., *Ion*, 492 ff., 938, 1400). This explanation is borne out by the beard of the supposed Kekrops. But we see from the drawing that the face is entirely rubbed, and the short drapery would be very surprising in king Kekrops. We might rather incline, following the analogy of numerous similar reliefs (cf. Michaelis, *Annali dell' Inst.*, 1863, p. 311. *Archäol.-Epigraph. Mittheilungen aus Oesterreich*, i. Pl. 1), to recognise Hermes as leader of three nymphs, for it is well known that they were often worshipped with Pan. The large bearded head at the r. end would indicate a fountain, or a river. From the l. approaches a troop of worshippers, represented as of less magnitude. They lead a ram as a sacrificial offering and among them is probably the donor of the relief, who came from the Attic demos Phlya [ὁ δεῖνα-]ίππου Φλυεὺς ἀνέθηκεν, *C. I. Gr.*, 469). *Mus. Worsl.* gives no fuller information respecting the origin of the relief; Leake's assertion (*Topogr. of Athens*, p. 482, 2nd ed.) that it was found near the Akropolis of Athens is probably dictated only by Visconti's explanation.

111. **Fragment of a relief**, from Megara: *Mus. Worsl.*, Cl. I. 8 (Pl. 3, 2). "Telephus and Auge." A bearded man is sitting on a block, holding forth his r. hand; beside the block appears a small doe or fawn; near the man stands a woman. Is it votive?

112. **Small statue of Herakles**, discovered in Egypt: *Mus. Worsl.*, Cl. III. 3 (Pl. 17, 1). Clarac, v. 795, 1986. The hero, his head adorned with fillets and a wreath of flowers, is quite drunk and is moving forward with unsteady steps; he held his club on his shoulder with his r. hand; the lion's skin hangs over his outstretched l. arm; the hand is broken off, but probably held a goblet. (Cf. Margam, no. 4.)

113. **Statue of Eros stringing his bow**, in the favourite composition: *Mus. Worsl.*, Cl. III. 13 (Pl. 19, 1). Found in 1793 below Colonna (Labicum).

The **group of the Nile**, from Ostia (*Mus. Worsl.*, Cl. III. 2, Pl. 15), is said by Mr F. Cook of Richmond to be in his collection at Cintra, Portugal (Gurlitt, *Arch. Zeit.*, 1868, p. 84, no. 1).

I know not what has become of the beautiful Worsley Collection of Gems, formed in Rome, Athens, Egypt and Constantinople (*Mus. Worsl.*, I. p. 2 [p. xxxviii.]), which, it may be observed, included also Sir W. Hamilton's Gems (Visconti, *Mus. Pio-Clem.*, vi. p. 63 Mil.). Cf. *Mus. Worsl.*, Cl. IV. (Pl. 20—31).

BROOM HALL. (Scotland).

In this castle, near Dunfermline, the property of the Earl of ELGIN, may be seen a number of smaller **fragments** of **reliefs** and **inscriptions**, which have been let into the walls. The celebrated Lord Elgin brought them with him from Athens. Even although, as is Mr A. S. Murray's opinion, they are "of no consequence," still a careful examination is much to be desired on account of their origin.

CAMBRIDGE.

The principal collection at Cambridge is now located in the basement of the magnificent Fitzwilliam Museum, a smaller number in the staircase well of Trinity College Library. It is much to be wished that the latter should be deposited in the first-mentioned locality, all the more as their present place of preservation is utterly unworthy of them.

FITZWILLIAM MUSEUM.

Conze, *Arch. Anzeiger*, 1864, pp. 169 ff. Huebner, *ibid.*, 1866, p. 301.

The sculptures of this Museum are to be divided into two principal groups. One, formerly in the vestibule of the University Library, comprises the donations of E. D. CLARKE (Introd. § 67) and of some other amateurs, the objects composing which are derived from the soil of Greece. Cf. Clarke, *Greek Marbles brought from the shores of the Euxine, Archipelago and Mediterranean*, Cambridge, 1809. (The explanations here given of the several works of art are in most cases so thoroughly mistaken, that pious regard for the honoured author bids one pass them over in silence.) Spiker, *Reise durch England*, II. pp. 293–296.—The second portion originates in the will of JOHN DISNEY, who bequeathed to the University of Cambridge the sculptures of the collection of antiques founded about the middle of the last century by Thomas Hollis and Thomas Brand, and increased in the third decade of this century by Disney himself (Introd. §§ 41, 87). This collection is derived entirely from Italy. It is interspersed with much that is spurious. Cf. *Museum Disneianum, being a description of a collection of ancient marbles, &c. in the possession of John Disney, Esq.*, London, 1849, fol. (with unusually bad illustrations); Gerhard, *Arch. Zeit.*, 1847, pp. 157–160.

M. C.   16

Wieseler, *Göttingische gel. Anzeigen*, 1849, pp. 441–462.—Owing to
the entirely different origin and style of art of the two divisions it
has seemed convenient to keep them distinct from one another and
to include in one or other of them the few similar specimens of
the collection, and then in conclusion to notice a few other antiques.

SCULPTURES COLLECTED IN GREECE.

Among these the place of honour is taken by

1. (Clarke, XIV.) **Fragment of a statue of a Kistophoros**
from Eleusis, in former times generally named Ceres : colossal scale.
Its present condition is represented by the illustrations, which are
however not accurate in matters of detail, in *Museum Worsleyanum*,
Cl. III. 12 (Pl. 18, 3 Mil.), in Clarke's work, p. 24, and in Gerhard,
Antike Bildwerke, Pl. 306. 5 ; for a front view restored after Flaxman's design, see Clarke's frontispiece ; Gerhard, *l. c.*, no. 4 ;
Müller-Wieseler, II. 892.   A better illustration is given in the
accompanying plate.   Upper part of the body to about the
lower half of the breast, head and cista are preserved.   The r.
breast and shoulder are destroyed.   Professor Sidney Colvin has

FIG. 1.

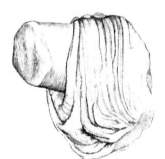

however found in Eleusis a piece of shoulder and upper arm, with
the chiton depending from them, a plaster cast of which is in
Cambridge (fig. 1).   There can be no doubt as to its belonging to
the specimen in question ; unless, indeed, we have to regard it as

CAMBRIDGE I

the fragment of a second exactly corresponding copy. The l. shoulder
together with the junction of the arm is preserved; the arm was
somewhat advanced. Chiton fastened together on the shoulder with
three buttons. Cross bands drawn slantwise across the breast;
where they cross each other, a Medusa's head carved in relief,
as a symbol to avert harm (ἀποτρόπαιον). Countenance of the statue
completely destroyed. Rich waving hair falls down behind in a not
very lengthy mass, which is in one place, on the nape of the neck,
confined by a band. On the head a very small porter's pad (τύλη,
κεφάλλον) whereon is sustained the large round vessel which people
have been inclined to designate as a κανοῦν or κάλαθος (and hence
too the bearer as Kanephoros or Kalathephoros). It is however
likely to be best, considering the general shape, the proportion of
the height to the breadth, and the horizontal division into two parts,
to regard it as the mystic κίστη (Jahn, in *Hermes*, III. pp. 317—334);
cf. the representation of this vessel on the Eleusinian Propylon
of Appius Claudius Pulcher (*Bullett. dell' Inst.*, 1860, p. 226; *C.
I. Lat.*, I. 619, III. 547; Lenormant, *Rech. archéol. à Eleusis*, p.
390), and, set on a pedestal with three feet, on a piece of entablature from Eleusis (*Uned. Antiq. of Attica*, ch. 4, Pl. 7). Cista
very richly decorated; see Fig. 2, p. 245, in which its various
courses of ornament have been restored as accurately as possible
from their unmutilated portions. Its lower margin is encircled
by a braided band (*e*), irregularly bordered below, along a short
portion of its course only, with a beaded moulding (*astragalus*) (*f*).
The next belt (*d*) exhibits in the front a vessel in the form of a
tureen, the πλημοχόη of the Mysteries (Beulé, *Monnaies d'Athènes*,
p. 156; Bötticher, in *Philologus*, XXIII. p. 234) and wands with
regular projections laid crosswise. These are too much worn away to
enable it to be said with certainty whether they are stalks of a plant
or, perhaps, decorated torches in the manner of the reliefs quoted.
Then on either side a rosette, next to which are three ears of corn,
then again a rosette, then a longish object laid slantwise, much
abraded, probably a torch of a broader kind, though this is very
uncertain. Above this belt appears (*c*) a projecting roll (*torus*) formed
of leaves, upon which are seen berries in relief; this roll is crossed
at intervals by bands, and bordered on either side with a bead and
reel moulding. This is the middle of the cista. Above this a
broad belt with beautiful palmette ornaments (*b*). Lastly (*a*) remains
of a low cymatium moulding, too much mutilated to be restored,
form the upper border of the cista. The head as well as the

cista is backed by a flat slab of marble 0·50 broad, which proves that the figure was employed in architecture. Hence it is further clear why the cista has no cover, but is flat on the top. On this an epistyle or something of the sort would rest. The restoration of the statue is to be obtained from the similar statue in the Villa Albani given by Gerhard, *Ant. Bildw.*, Pl. 94, 2; Clarac, III. 442, 807. It will have both arms raised symmetrically to the cista, the preserved remnants of the arms being perfectly conformable with this attitude. The older explanation of the figure as that of Demeter, perhaps the very image from the great temple, has been given up; Hirt (*Geschichte der Baukunst*, II. p. 21) having first regarded it as a Kanephoros; Preller (*Demeter und Persephone*, p. 375) as a Kalathephoros; while Leake (*Demi of Attica*, p. 162, 2 ed.) rightly proposed the name Kistophoros. (For the further literature of the subject cf. Gerhard, *Akad. Abhandl.*, II. p. 408, note 198; Müller-Wieseler, *Denkmäler*, II. 8, 92.) The style does not point to the Roman period, in which people are disposed to place it on the evidence of an inscribed block (cf. Wheler, *Journey*, p. 428, Boeckh, *C. I. Gr.*, 389), but rather perhaps to the fourth or third century before Christ; one might refer it to the fresh decoration of the sanctuary under Demetrios of Phaleron (Vitruv., VII. praef. 17). Execution, with deeply grooved folds, thoroughly in keeping with a figure designed for architectural decoration. Pentelic marble. H. 2·15. H. of cista 0·70 (viz. *a* 0·13, *b* 0·17, *c* 0·14, *d* 0·17, *e* 0·09), of head 0·55, of neck 0·19, of part below 0·71. With regard to the history of the monument, attention was first paid to it in A.D. 1668 (Les Monceaux in C. Le Bruyn's *Voyages*, Paris, 1725, v. p. 492); and all the allusions made to it by earlier travellers have been collected by Clarke (pp. 12—37, *Travels*, II. pp. 772—790), who in company with J. M. Cripps (also of Jesus College, Cambridge), was lucky enough (A.D. 1801) to get possession of this colossus in spite of the objections of the people of Eleusis, and to ship it with great trouble. The vessel was wrecked off Beachy Head, but the statue was rescued. [*Colvin*]

2. (Clarke, XVI.) **Fragment of a statuette of Aphroditè:** sketched by Clarke, *Travels*, II. 1, p. 130, found in some ruins at Kushunlu Tepe near Baramitsh in the Troad, where Leake (*Asia M.*, p. 274) places the site of Kebrènè, cf. Clarke, p. 127. Motive on the whole like that of the Aphroditè of Melos. The goddess stands on the r. foot, the l. leg being bent and the foot placed in a somewhat raised position on a projecting portion of the rocky base. Both legs

FIG. 2

shrouded in the cloak, one end of which falls down in copious folds, not however thrown from the hip over the l. thigh and so down its inner side, but on the outer part of the thigh. Near the l. foot a low round base, with the remains of a female statue in a long chiton and cloak preserved about as far as the knees. Of the Aphrodite itself there are still preserved the draped lower limbs and a small portion of the nude body. A hole on the top points out that the upper part was worked in a separate piece of marble. Execution ordinary. Coarse Parian marble.   II. 0·47.   Cf. Preuner, *Ueber die Venus von Milo*, Greifswald, 1874, p. 39. ·[*C]

3. (Clarke, XXXVI.) **Mother of the gods** (?) ("Ceres"). Small figure in chiton and cloak, sitting on a throne, both arms in the lap. Attributes not recognisable, the little figure being altogether much defaced. The head, originally veiled, and feet are wanting. Coarse work. Pentelic marble. H. 0·19. From Athens. [*]

4. (Clarke, XI.) **Pan**; τροπαιοφόρος, figured after Flaxman's restoration in Wilkins' *Antiq. of Magna Graecia*, p. 71. The goat-footed god stands quite straight. Upper part of the figure as far as half the thigh clad in a rather stiff cloak apparently of leather. In the lowered l. hand he holds the syrinx, the r. arm lies bent before the breast. Head missing, but remains of the long beard extant. Back set against a marble column of irregular round shape, which apparently represents the trunk of a tree. Apart from this detail our statue corresponds closely, even in size, to a second copy in the Theseion at Athens (no. 48; Müller-Wieseler, II. 43. 532; Clarac, IV. 726 F. 1736 K), found in the Peiraeus, which exhibits the god standing against a square column (cf. Wilton, no. 144). Our statue was "discovered in a garden below the grotto of Pan at the foot of the Acropolis of Athens" (Clarke, *Travels*, II. 2, p. 479). It undoubtedly served once for the decoration of a column of a balustrade, and agreeably to this the still traceable iron cramp on the top is to be explained, not as serving to fasten a tropaeon (cf. *Annali dell' Inst.*, 1863, p. 310). Pentelic marble. H. 0·75; inclusive of the basis, 0·85. [*C]

5. (Clarke, XXXIV.) **Eros.** A tall shape, most likely a tree-stem or piece of rock (certainly not a "female figure"), is hung with a large drapery, one of the depending corners of which is encircled by the r. arm of a little Eros clinging to the tree. He stands quite nude; r. leg somewhat advanced; curly head a little raised; l. arm lowered, but preserved only in its upper half. Horizontally attached to the tree behind the l. thigh a round object, broader in the middle,

in which Clarke recognised, without doubt wrongly, the torch of Eros or a club. It seems to me to be a phallus, introduced here owing to its power of averting evil. Coarse-grained marble. H. 0·40. "Found in Egypt, and taken from the House of the French Institute in Grand Cairo." Cf. Clarke, *Travels*, II. 2, p. 47. [*]

6. (Clarke, XXXII.) **Male torso,** apparently belonging to a youth; lower part of the body and l. arm in a cloak, l. hand lying on the hip and holding a corner of the cloak. Breast and body nude. Lowered r. arm preserved only where it joins shoulder. Head and legs below the mid-thigh missing. A similar motive recurs in no. 32. Good spirited execution of simple and beautiful effect; worked quite carelessly at back. Parian marble. H. 0·57. Brought from Knidos by R. Walpole and presented 1808. [*]

7. (Clarke, XXXVIII.) **Right hand** of a colossal statue, male; treatment adequate to the dimensions. Very white marble. Clarke brought the specimen from Larnaka in Cyprus; it came originally from Paphos. Cf. Clarke, *Travels*, II. 1, p. 335. [?]

8. Fragment of a column, with a cavity on the top in the capital. Before it stands a terminal figure of Dionysos with long hair and ivy-crowned. Square holes in the place of the shoulders. Dark green stone. H. 0·44. [*]

9. (Clarke, XXVI.) **Bust called "Juno,"** found on the same spot as no. 2: sketched in Clarke's *Travels*, II. 1, p. 130. A female head and neck, with a fillet in the hair, which is taken up from the sides and all gathered into a knot on the top of the head. Nose broken off, mouth much mutilated, back of the head split off. Head of good design, but superficially executed, apparently belonging to an **Aphroditè.** Greek marble. H. 0·13. l. of face 0·16. [*]

10. (Clarke, XIX.) **Comic mask:** bearded, the r. eye raised and wide open, the l. drawn down; wrinkles of the forehead much distorted; hair arranged awry; laughing mouth wide open. In the eyes traces of colour. The mask is left rough behind. H. 0·26. Br. 0·24. "Found in the ruins of the proscenium of the theatre at Stratonicea, in Asia Minor by R. Walpole, and presented by him." [*]

11. (Clarke, XXXIII.) **Fragment of a knotted club,** lower end; flattened out at the bottom so as to be capable of standing upright; apparently a votive offering, perhaps to Herakles. From Athens. Coarse-grained Parian marble. H. 0·39. [*]

12. (Clarke, XXXVII.) **Lion's paw,** large scale, resting on a tapering block, which seems to have been let in somewhere

Paw broken away above. Pentelic (?) marble. H. 0·27. From Athens. [*]

13. **Fragment** of irregular shape, broken at the top and both ends and rounded irregularly underneath. Scarcely a piece of a ship; rather, of a fish. Upon it is engraved the outline of a dolphin, and above the archaic inscription, running r. to l., [Τί]μων ἔγραφέ με. Grey marble. L. 0·68. Brought by Spratt from the neighbourhood of Eremopolis in Crete and presented to this Museum. A woodcut is given in *Journal of Class. and Sac. Philology*, Cambridge, 1855, II. p. 108. Spratt, *Travels in Crete*, II. Pl. 1, no. 20; cf. Kirchhoff, *Studien zur Gesch. des Alphabetes*, 3 ed., p. 64. Jahn in *Arch. Zeit.*, 1863, p. 65. [*]

14. **Fragment of an altar, upper part:** from Kanawát in Syria. From the square surface projects the raised rim (h. 0·06) of a well-shaped cavity sunk (d. 0·11) into the body of the altar; the bottom of this cavity is now perforated. On one side of the rim near its upper edge is a round hole. In the middle of each of the four sides of the surface is a small square hole of little depth; on each of the four corners are traces of a raised projection. The surface is surrounded by a moulding. On the body of the altar are the following reliefs. In front, head of a youthful god (Baal) with nine leaf-like rays, wearing chiton, which is furnished on both shoulders with a button. On the right, besides some architectural ornament, the lintel for a doorway, the interior of which is hollowed quite out: on the back, a female head (of Astaroth) over a crescent-moon. On the left a flower, and characters below. Coarse stone. H. 0·54. L. 0·43. D. 0·43. Presented by the executors of the late C. F. Tyrwhitt Drake, 1874. [*]

15. (Clarke, XXIX.) **Votive relief to Athenè.** Two antae with an architrave, surmounted by tiles. Athenè stands in a girdled χιτὼν διπλοῦς and with a small aegis, r. arm resting on her hip, l. arm upraised as if it held a spear, the shield leaning against her leg. The plume of her helmet reaches into the architrave and divides the name thus A Θ H N A. Two men approach her from r., the foremost wearing a cloak which leaves the breast and r. arm free. He lays his r. hand in the gesture of entreaty on the arm of the goddess. (The name on the architrave is worn away.) Next after him a warrior in breastplate, chlamys and helmet; his shield standing behind him. He rests his l. arm on his side and raises the r. with a gesture of entreaty. Of his name the last letters ΛΟΣ (ΛΛΟΣ according to Clarke) are preserved. H. 0·29. L. 0·34. Projection of relief from field 0·015. The relief, which looks like Attic work, comes

from the ruins of Sigeion (where Clarke obtained it in 1801), a
community intimately connected with Athens. [*]

16. (Clarke, xv.) **Relief of Asklepios and Hygieia.**
("Initiation of Hercules by a priestess of Ceres.") The figures are
enclosed in a frame, and both seen from the front. Asklepios is to
the l., in the usual fashion draped in a cloak ; his l. hand resting on
his side ; his staff, entwined with the snake, placed under his arm-pit.
Hygieia, in a chiton, stands r., enveloped to the knees in her cloak ;
her l. hand on her thigh and in her lowered r. hand the cup ; no
sign of a snake. Both heads destroyed. A fair relief of somewhat
coarse execution, much knocked about. H. 0·54. L. 0·43. Projection of relief from field 0·04. From Athens ; cf. Clarke, *Travels*,
II. 2, p. 529. [*C]

17. (Clarke, x.) **Left half of a votive relief,** framed. Three
rows of draped figures are turned to the right ; above are eight adult
figures, of whom four in flatter relief appear in the background.
They represent probably two men and six women ; below are two
girls and four boys. All alike are making the gesture of adoration
(cf. Brocklesby, no. 10). Pentelic marble. Rather coarse style.
H. 0·57. L. 0·36. The various degrees of projection of the three
rows of figures on the relief are interesting, 0·01, 0·04, 0·05. Found
in a garden at Athens ; cf. Clarke, *Travels*, II. 2, p. 530. [*]

18. (Clarke, xxvii.) **Sepulchral votive relief,** still provided
below with the marble peg for letting into a base. On either side
an anta, supporting an architrave with the upper surface tiled. To
the r., lying on a bed, the dead man, honoured as a hero, partly
covered by his cloak and having a modius on his head. In his
r. hand he holds a rhyton, which he is in the act of raising to pour
wine into a goblet which he holds in his l. hand. Beside the bed
at his feet sits his wife, clothed in cloak and chiton ; her r. hand
in her lap, l. raised, as if holding something. In front of both in
the foreground a low table with cakes on it. Behind the lady stands
a young servant (παῖς) with a cup in his lowered l. hand, and beside
him a mixing-bowl (κρατήρ) which stands on a draped tripod. A
bearded man stands l., also a veiled female and a little girl (the
survivors), all adoring. Above them is seen in a sunken square
panel the head of a horse, to indicate the equestrian rank of the
deceased. Delicate, rather flat execution ; relatively early. Pentelic
marble. H. 0·17 ; with projection of peg 0·22. L. 0·23. Brought
from Athens by the Earl of Aberdeen. [*]

19. Remains of a similar relief. The greater part of a

female in sitting posture is preserved, holding her cloak with her
l. hand; part of a male reclining with r. arm raised; and half of a
three-legged table with food on it standing by the couch. Ordinary
workmanship. High relief. H. 0·30. L. 0·18. [*]

20. (Clarke, XVIII.) **Upper half of a sepulchral stelè.**
("Caligula bringing his daughter, Livia Drusilla, to the protecting
Minerva.") Above, a cornice with the remains of a pediment over it.
Below, a broad belt, probably intended for the reception of an
inscription. Underneath is the sunken field of the relief without
any framing at the side. A lady completely dressed sits r. in
a comfortable easy chair, her r. hand on cloak, her l. in lap.
A girl, in chiton and cloak, stands l. before the lady, holding a
swathed infant in her hands. Both figures preserved to the knee.
A beautiful, softly rounded relief, but badly rubbed. Belongs probably to the beginning of the 4th century. Pentelic marble. H.
0·84. L. 0·35. From Athens; cf. Clarke, *Travels*, II. 2, p. 529. [*C]

21. (Clarke, XII.) **Rounded sepulchral stelè** of late character; flat at the top and encircled by a torus. Below is the
inscription Εὐκλίδας Εὐκλίδου | Ἑρμιονεύς (*C. I. Gr.*, 839); underneath
in a niche surmounted by a pediment a man enveloped in his cloak;
head missing. Rough relief. Below, roughly cut, is a dog on his
hind legs. Hymettian marble, of Roman period. H. 1·07. Diameter
0·42. "This pillar served as a horse-block in one of the streets of
Athens." Cf. Clarke, *Travels*, II. 2, p. 530. [*C]

22. **Sepulchral lekythos of Pentelic marble:** neck, foot
and handle almost entirely broken away. Upon the body in very
low relief we see r. a bearded man, in cloak, holding out his r. hand
to a youth, who is approaching him, dressed in chiton and chlamys,
his sword sheathed in his l. hand, his petasos pushed back on to
his neck. Beside him is his horse and behind him a small servant
wrapped in a cloak and holding two handsome greyhounds, one of
which looks before him attentively while the other sniffs at the
ground. Above the bearded man is written ['Η]γήμων | 'Επικηφύτι-
[ος], as supplied by Dobree (see Rose, *Inscr. Gr.*, p. 418, *C. I.
Gr.*, 2033). 4th century B.C. H. 0·84. Diameter 0·36. H. of
figures 0·44. John Spencer Smith, Minister Plenipotentiary at the
Ottoman Porte, brought home this genuine Attic vase from the
coast of the Propontis; cf. Clarke, *Travels*, II. 2, pp. 494, 528. [*C]

23. **Sepulchral votive relief,** framed by two antae and an
epistyle. A youth, honoured as a hero, lying on a couch half covered
by his cloak. He has a fillet in his hair and holds a cup with his

l. hand, stretching out his r. for a small box handed to him by a well-dressed lady, who sits at the foot of the bed, and whose hair is covered with a kerchief in the form of a cap. Near the lady's chair stands a diminutive female servant with a box. Before the bed is placed a three-legged table with food, and beside it is another diminutive servant who has filled a pitcher from a large mixing vessel on the ground. Above is a tree entwined with a snake, the symbol of heroic honours. Below is the inscription Μητρωδώρου τοῦ Ἀπολ λοδωρον, from the 2nd or 1st century B.C. (C. I. Gr. 6966). I. 0·46. II. 0·49. The relief, which is somewhat roughly executed, comes, to judge by the style of the marble, from Asia Minor (Smyrna?) or the Islands. Presented by Dr Fiott Lee. [*]

24. (Clarke, XIII.) **Sepulchral stele** with pediment, which is adorned with a rosette. Upon a couch lies a beardless man, in chiton and cloak; a roll in his l. hand. He looks at his wife, fully draped and sitting at the foot of the bed, viewed from the front. In front of the bed is a barking dog and a round three-legged table, with food. At the head of the bed stands a full-grown girl in chiton and peplos, supporting her head sadly on her r. hand. Beside her stands a diminutive female servant carrying in front of her an un-recognisable object. Below Ἀριστέας | Ζωσίμου (C. I. Gr. 2262) in late letters. The light yellow colour of the marble and the tasteless execution betray provincial art; the prettiest part is the motive of the daughter. Very low relief. H. 0·62. L. 0·41. Found upon a small rocky isle near the mouth of the harbour of La Scala in Patmos; cf. Clarke, *Travels*, II. 2, p. 372. [*]

25. (Clarke, V.) **Sepulchral stele:** much injured, and broken off at the top. L. a female in a sitting posture, r. hand in lap, l. raised towards chin. R. a smaller female, standing in full face. Coarse execution. Grey marble. H. 0·43. L. 0·33. From the ruins of Phanagoria (Taman) on the Cimmerian Bosporus; cf. Clarke, *Travels*, I. p. 404. [*]

26. (Clarke, IV.) **Sepulchral stele:** of the same kind and origin as no. 25. R., on a throne elevated on a low step, sits a fully dressed female, supporting her chin on r. hand. Before her a small figure, totally effaced, standing beside a column on which is seen a small statue of a man wearing the chiton. H. c 70. L. 0·27. [*]

27. (Clarke, VI.) **Sepulchral stele:** of the same origin as no. 25, but of better marble and slightly better workmanship. Below is a marble peg; the plinth was so placed that both sides were visible. Front: remains of a relief, which represents a horse stand-

ing, facing r.; before it two human feet. Underneath the following
inscription of Roman date, probably before the Christian Era (*C. I.
Gr.*, 2127. Kaibel, *Epigr. Gr.*, 539):

> Τειμόθεος Δασείος χαίρε.
> Τειμόθε[ο]ς, ὁ Πάτρας ὅσιος φώς, παῖς δὲ Δασείος,
> τρὶς δεκάτας ἐτέων τερματίσας ἔθανες·
> ἅ τάλαν, οἰκτείρω σε πολυκλαύστῳ ἐπὶ τύμβῳ,
> [ν]ῦν δὲ σὺν ἡρώων χῶρον ἔχοις φθίμενος.

In line 2, δεκάτας is written incorrectly for δεκάδας, in line 4, ΗΥΝ
for τὸν: the semi-barbarians permitted themselves to use σὺν *cum
genetivo* in the neighbouring Pantikapaion also (*C. I. Gr.*, 2114 *c, d*).
Patra is a place not far off (Strabo, p. 494). Back: a powerfully
chiselled relief: a man leading a horse r., behind whom is seen
a (female?) figure. Above, remains of an inscription...ΑΠΕ...
H. 0·53. L. 0·47. [°]

28. (Clarke, XXII.) **Fragment of a relief**, upper r. corner.
Upper half of the body of a youth wearing the chlamys, front view:
both arms, of which only the upper parts remain, lowered, the head
broken off; high relief. Clarke imagined that this coarsely-executed
work was a piece of a metope from the Parthenon, which is quite a
mistake. It may rather be a piece of a sepulchral relief (Huebner,
Arch. Anz., 1866, p. 301), although it is of an unusual style.
Clarke found the fragment outside the entrance to the Acropolis and
received it as a present from the governor of the citadel (*Travels*, II.
2, p. 475). Pentelic marble. H. 0·31. L. 0·35. Projection from
field 0·13. Thickness of slab 0·17. [*]

29. (Clarke, XXV.) **Round altar**, or pedestal, adorned with
four bull-heads conjoined with garlands and fillets (στέμματα, *vittae*):
in each loop a patera, or rosette. On the top a hollow perhaps
intended for the reception of a statue (?). Parian marble. H. 0·61.
Diameter 0·61. Brought from Delos by an ancestor of the Rev.
Bridges Harvey. Jesus Coll., who gave it to Clarke. [*C]

30. (Clarke, XX.) **Small fragment of base of a pilaster**:
found in the castle of Pergamos, about sixty feet from the ground.
Figured in Wilkins, *Antiq. of Magna Graecia*, frontisp. Above, a
torus with plaited straps, bordered higher still by an astragalus:
below a flat trochilus, interrupted by a relief, which displays the
winged Nikè, on a biga, driving rapidly r. H. 0·15. L. 0·29.
Brought to England by the late Captain George Clarke, R.N. [*]

31. Sarcophagus: from Arvi, on the south coast of Crete,
presented by Sir Pultney Malcolm 1835. Figured and explained

Pashley. *Travels in Crete*. II. pp. 6, 18, 19 (not yet quite complete). The latter has the merit of having collected the fragments and completed them by new excavations. (I. p. 275, II. pp. 2—20.) An accurate drawing lies before me. **Front.** Bacchic triumphal procession, moving r. To the extreme l. a nude Bacchante is dancing: she has a small cloak over her left arm and across her lap, and is beating the tympanon. In front is a two-wheeled car richly ornamented with reliefs (crouching lion; two standing figures; Eros and Pan between two columns, challenging each other to fight); on the car stands the youthful Dionysos, an ivy wreath in his long hair, a nebris round his breast. He holds the thyrsos in his l. hand sceptrewise, and rests the r., which holds a wreath, on a Satyr crouching in the car, who serves the god as his support. The car is drawn by a male and a female Centaur. The latter holds a large pine-branch in her r. arm, and lays the l., in which she has the kantharos, on her companion's shoulder: the male Centaur, who is crowned and has features like a Seilenos, is looking round: his l. arm, clothed in a skin, is thrown round his wife: his r. hand, which is uplifted, is emptying out a drinking-horn. The goat-footed Pan, who is delineated in a masterly manner, capers with brutish vivacity before the Centaurs, striking the tympanon high above his head (cf. Müller-Wieseler, II. 36, 422). Near him in the background is a pine tree, in the foreground beside him on the ground a pedum and a large kantharos. The latter seems to have fallen from the grasp of the wreathed Seilenos, who, wearing a sleeved tunic made of skins and a small cloak, staggers along, drunk. He is supported with difficulty by a Satyr in a skin apron and by a Maenad in a flowing garment: in the background is seen a Satyr crowned with pine leaves. Seilenos is speaking to Dionysos, to whom he stretches out his r. arm; in the l. he holds a bunch of grapes. Farther in advance a youth is stepping, with a boy riding on his shoulder whom he holds fast with his r. hand: across his l. arm a skin is thrown, and in his hand he holds a thyrsos: in the background is a fig tree. This group is preceded by an elephant partly draped in a long falling cloth with a carpet over it; on the carpet sit or rather lie two small Maenads and a Satyr, all draped; one of the Maenads plays the flute, the Satyr has a kantharos, the second Maenad is swinging a thyrsos in her r. hand, and resting her l., which holds a goblet, on a plaited osier basket. Next to her sits, on the neck of the elephant, a second young Satyr with the nebris and a pedum, probably intended to guide the animal. On the other side of a gap, from which something (hardly of importance) has been lost, a young Satyr is trying to hold a full wine-skin on his shoulders ; his back is covered with a skin, at his feet are a panther and a kantharos. Quite at the end is a vine.—**Right end.** A curtain is suspended from the vine and from a bare tree. In front of it a young Satyr with a skin apron on his loins and a torch over his r. shoulder, and a bearded companion with skin and torch over the l. shoulder, hold the two handles of a plaited winnowing fan (*vannus*) in which there are three apples and a crouching child, probably the young Dionysos himself, who, frightened at the shaking of the fan, seems to wish to climb out. The same design is repeated on one end of the Farnese sarcophagus (Gerhard, *Antike Bildwerke*, Pl. 111, 3 ; Müller-Wieseler, II. 44. 458), from which, as Prof. Colvin suggests, it may probably have been copied by Raphael in the drawing reproduced in a well-known engraving of Marcantonio (Bartsch, no. 230, cf. Fisher, R., *Catalogue of a Collection of Engravings, Etchings, and Woodcuts*, p. 47.)—**Left end.** Two small Erotes, one with wings and one without, are carrying away with manifest exertion, Pan, heavy with wine, drunken and ithyphallic. Behind are a pine tree and olive tree (?) over the branches of which a large cloth is stretched.

The Sarcophagus has still its original **Lid** in almost perfect preservation, which is finished off at each of the front corners with the mask of a youthful Satyr with bristling hair. **On the front of the lid** is seen a great rout of Satyrs and Maenads on a couch covered with a lion's skin ; in the background carpets are spread out. Quite l. sits a female, playing on a lyre ; opposite to her is a bearded Satyr, with a wreath in his r. hand and a goblet in his l., and behind him a youthful Satyr with a wreath in his l. hand and the r. laid upon his head ; on the ground beside them are a ladle (*simpulum*), a skyphos, a small goblet, and another skyphos. A second group represents a bearded Satyr, lying on his belly, and offering a large skyphos to a Bacchante, who holds a wreath in her left hand (cf. Clarac. II. 139, 139) : beside them is a baby Satyr sitting on the ground, devouring a bunch of grapes, and two drinking vessels. Then follows a bearded Satyr with a skyphos in his r. hand, turning to a Bacchante opposite him, who is holding up a bunch of grapes in her r. hand and has a wreath in the l.; at her feet in the background is a draped, bearded dwarf figure, with a girt-up cloak and a cap, raising a bowl to his mouth. Then a gap occurs, from which probably a figure and a half have been lost, after which comes the upper half of a naked youthful form with a goblet in the l. hand;

beside it a draped Maenad with a kerchief on her head, drinking.
Last comes a bearded Satyr with a skin apron, clapping his hands
delightedly; beside the couch two drinking vessels and a ladle. To
the extreme r. sits a Maenad, rocking an infant Satyr on her lap.—
On each of the ends, which are pediment-shaped, stands a vessel,
filled with fruits, between two crouching panthers. At the back
corners are small youthful masks, with curls and Phrygian caps.

This sarcophagus, carved in somewhat high relief, has been
reckoned with perfect justice among the best of works of the kind
which have come to us. Matz, however, is also equally correct
(*Arch. Zeit.*, 1873, p. 33) in ascribing the execution not to Crete,
but to Rome, or at all events to Italy (cf. Wiltonhouse, no. 137);
and in remarking that the celebrated Farnese sarcophagus is the
most nearly allied to it, not only because of the repetition in both of
the same scenes as above-mentioned, but also because it is of the
same refined and delicate execution, reminding us sometimes of
miniature sculpture. Many figures and groups occurring in this
composition are to be found on other Roman sarcophagi; and the
grey striped marble seems to me to resemble the marble of southern
Italy. H. 0·50. L. 2·11. D. 0·6. [*CM*]

SCULPTURES COLLECTED IN ITALY.

Among the works of this class at the Fitzwilliam Museum, which
almost all come from the Hollis-Brand-Disney collection, I shall
place the statues first, then the busts, and lastly the reliefs. The
numbers added in parentheses are those of the Disney Collection.

STATUES AND STATUETTES.

32 (50). Statuette of a youth: *Mus. Disn.*, Pl. 25. Subject
same as that of no. 6. Here too the head and r. arm are missing;
by the l. foot is a support. Poor work. Greek marble. H. with
base, 0·32. [*]

33 (2). Statuette of a youthful Satyr: *Mus. Disn.*, Pl. 26.
This is the most graceful piece of statuary in the collection. The
Satyr is sitting on a rock, leaning so far back that it seems as if he
must fall. He has a short tail behind. His right foot is crossed
lightly over the left and both legs are stretched out. He holds in
his hands a flute, which he is blowing (cf. Wieseler in *Gött. gel.
Anzeigen*, 1849, p. 448). His head, which has pointed ears and
little horns, growing from the forehead, is crowned with pine twigs.
The r. arm was broken, but is nevertheless the original arm; only

some fingers having been supplied. The whole work is badly
polished. H. 0·49. [*C]

34 (24). **Statuette of a woman with a child**: *Mus. Disn.*,
Pl. 27. "Leucothoe." The woman, draped in chiton and wide
cloak, is resting on her l. leg, the right being somewhat in advance,
the r. arm, which is hidden by her cloak, lowered; on the l. is to
be seen all that remains of a rather big boy. The head (missing)
had long curly hair and was veiled. The statue was originally not
badly executed, but the front has been so destroyed and re-worked
that only the grace of the general design can now be traced.
Greek marble. H. 0·47. [*C]

35 (5). **Statuette of Seilenos**: *Mus. Disn.*, Pl. 28. The
bearded Seilenos, crowned with ivy, sitting on a rock, playing the
flute. He has drawn up his l. foot: a cloak covers the rock and
part of the r. thigh. To the l. a dog. This dry uninteresting
little figure, although broken, appears to me to be quite modern.
H. 0·49. [*]

36 (4). **Statuette of a sitting female**: *Mus. Disn.*, Pl. 30.
"Juno." On a stuffed chair, which stands in a strangely oblique
position, sits a woman in girdled chiton and with a cloak which
covers legs, l. arm, and back, and which once veiled the head. L. foot
advanced, r. drawn back, l. forearm stretched out. New: nose,
neck, r. arm, which is lowered, as well as half the l. forearm with
the sceptre, l. foot, veil and the four legs of the chair. The veil
is modern and has been stuck on an antique head which can hardly
belong to the figure, and to which the restorer (Pigiani, an assistant
of Vescovali) has added a crown. Disney considered it a Vesta,
Westmacott, a Roma. The old parts are of good decorative work
(cf. the Terra Mater, *Bullett. municip.*, I. Pl. 3; Overbeck, *Kunstmythol. Atlas*, Pl. 14, no. 17). The marble appears to be Italian.
H. 0·65. Found in A.D. 1825 in Tivoli, opposite the Cascatelle
in the so-called villa of Quintilius Varus: bought by Disney A.D.
1826. [*]

37 (3). **Statuette of a throned goddess, called "Vesta."**
A veiled goddess sitting on a throne with a high back, like the
usual representations of Kybelè (cf. no. 3), but without any recognisable emblem; a fragment beside the l. thigh is not likely to be a
tympanon, and both forearms, which were outstretched, are missing.
The head with stephanos has been stuck on, but is antique. Other
restored pieces have fallen off again. Coarse Roman work. H. 0·45.
[*C]

38 (35). **Fragment of a double terminal figure** : *Mus. Disn.*, Pl. 29. A terminal column culminates in a double half-length, female figure, draped, and having a number of folds slanting across the breast. The arms, which are lowered on both sides, hold each the corner of the garment. Stiff curls lie on the shoulders. The double head missing. Stiff, ornamented archaism, coarsely executed. Between the forearms on either side is a square hole, probably intended to receive a beam which connected these hermae and other similar ones in a kind of railing. Found in a field at Cumae by Mr Henry Tuffnell in A.D. 1824, who gave it to Disney. H. 0·54. [*C]

39 (7). **Athenè** : *Mus. Disn.*, Pl. 1. Bust much exceeding life size ; front half only preserved ; the helmet is cut off in front and nevertheless the hair flows over the edge. The work is either completely restored or more probably quite modern. Coarse execution. Brought from Rome by Wil. Lloyd and bought of him by Hollis, in A.D. 1761. H. 0·46. L. of face 0·21. [*]

40 (21). **Portrait head** : *Mus. Disn.*, Pl. 2, "Antoninus Pius." A poor head, certainly not that of Antoninus Pius ; a much patched and plastered face and new nose. The r. half of the breast perhaps ancient, but not belonging to the rest : the l. half and the drapery new. H. 0·66. L. of face 0·18. [*]

41 (26). **Marcus Aurelius** : *Mus. Disn.*, Pl. 3. A fairly good head with a new nose ; the pupils of the eyes expressed. Neck modern and so probably all the draped bust with the wide cross stripe, usually called the *laena*. H. 0·77. L. 0·20. From the Barberini Palace, bought by Hollis A.D. 1766, purporting to have been brought from Alexandria about A.D. 1742 (?). [*]

42 (20). **"Domitian"** (?) : *Mus. Disn.*, Pl. 4. Head quite intact, crowned with oak. The pupils of the eyes expressed. Rough work. H. 0·37. L. of face 0·20. [*]

43 (13). **Head of a barbarian** : *Mus. Disn.*, Pl. 5. Perhaps a Dacian, with scanty beard and Phrygian cap. By no means free from suspicion. Striped alabaster. H. 0·29. [*C]

44 (12). **Phrygian youth**, perhaps Ganymedes : *Mus. Disn.*, Pl. 6, "Atys". A passable head with curly hair and Phrygian cap ; tip of nose new. H. 0·39. L. 0·15. Bought at the Duke of Argyle's sale, A.D. 1771. [*]

45 (19). **Roman portrait** : *Mus. Disn.*, Pl. 7, "Otho." Massive head, the forehead surrounded by a fringe of hair, strangely drawn back. Nose new. The neck has been inserted into a new bust. Insignificant work. L. of face 0·18. [*]

46 (9). **Serapis**: *Mus. Disn.*, Pl. 8. A tolerable head, on the top of which is seen the ring for the modius. New: the modius, which is wreathed with oak, and the drapery. H. 0·37. L. of face 0·11. Bought of the Abbate Clementi at Rome A.D. 1752. [*C]

47 (32). **Terminal head of Dionysos**: *Mus. Disn.*, Pl. 9. A beautiful bearded head with grave expression. The whole is executed with a moderate tendency to archaism. The beard, which is somewhat pushed aside, well treated, neither too minutely, nor too freely. The hair is worked in regular furrows, and gathered in with a narrow fillet, which, on the forehead, is delicately entwined with two long curls. The hair hung far down, but has been broken off. New: the tresses falling down to the shoulders, the bust-piece and the nose. The eyes are singularly small. Pentelic marble? H. of head 0·34. L. of face 0·17. Bought by Hollis in A.D. 1761. [*C]

48 (8). **Bacchic female head**: *Mus. Disn.*, Pl. 10, "Muse." A colossal head and neck, very broad in the proportions, apparently belonging to the Bacchic cycle. A fillet is drawn across the forehead and through the hair, which is gathered in a knot behind. Hard execution. Coarse Greek marble. H. 0·33. L. of face 0·19. "I have every reason to believe it was found in, or near to, the Acropolis at Athens." (?) Disney. [*]

49 (10). **Young girl**: *Mus. Disn.*, Pl. 11, "Sappho." No cloth or kerchief covers the hair, which is gathered into a knot behind. New: bust, neck, chin and point of the nose; the rest being restored in so uninteresting a way that it looks almost entirely modern. H. 0·18. L. of face 0·12. [*]

50 (25). **Double terminal bust.** *Mus. Disn.*, Pl. 12, "Bacchus and Ceres." On one side Seilenos, crowned with ivy, on the other a youthful head crowned with laurel, thus shewing the connection of the attributes of Dionysos and Apollo. (Cf. Broadlands, no. 16; London, Lansdowne House, no. 69.) New: busts and nose tips. Pretty. Height, of the genuine parts, 0·16. [*]

51 (22). **Double terminal bust**: *Mus. Disn.*, Pl. 13, "Bacchus and Libera". The two heads, which are strikingly narrow, are pressed very close together, perhaps because the piece of marble was not larger. On one side Seilenos, with long beard, crowned with ivy; his ears were originally covered by the hair, but the restorer has transformed them into pointed ears. On the other side a youthful head, also crowned with ivy; nose-tip restored. H. 0·28. [*]

52 (31). **Terminal bust of Pan**: *Mus. Disn.*, Pl. 15, "Silenus." Bearded head with horns, crowned with ivy. The face has a grinning expression. Modern. H. 0·35. Bought by Hollis of Mr Lloyd, A.D. 1761. [*]

53 (14). **Dionysos**? *Mus. Disn.*, Pl. 16, "Aeginetan Bacchus." Bearded head in stiff imitation of the archaic style: three rows of curls on the forehead: beard well designed: eyes filled up with some substance. New: nose and bust. H. 0·33. L. of face 0·18. [*]

54 (15). **"Hermarchos"**: *Mus. Disn.*, Pl. 17. I cannot warrant the identification, but it appears to me possible. (Cf. Visconti, *Iconogr. Gr.*, I. Pl. 26.) Head broad, no meagreness in the face; nose slightly aquiline, beard tolerably long; forehead wrinkled. Bust new; nose only slightly injured. Ordinary workmanship. Greek marble. L. of face 0·20. Bought by Disney in London. [*]

55 (6). **Terminal bust of a Satyr**: *Mus. Disn.*, Pl. 19. A very bad head, of poor, timid workmanship, for the face cannot even laugh properly. Horns over the forehead. The terminal bust of a very awkward shape. Said to have been "found in a vineyard near Rome, about two miles out of the Porta Pia, near the Church of St Agnese, in A.D. 1826, by a peasant, and brought immediately to Sig. Raim. Trentanove, of whom Disney bought it A.D. 1827." In spite of this statement as to the discovery, and of the fact that the nose has been repaired, I consider the head to be modern. H. 0·38. L. 0·14. [*]

56 (11). **Bust of a youth**: *Mus. Disn.*, Pl. 20, "Mercury, young." The orbits are hollow; the point of the nose new. "Found in Populonia, in A.D. 1828," and bought by Disney. The head appears to me to be modern. H. 0·41. [*]

57 (17). **A Roman**: *Mus. Disn.*, Pl. 21. "Found in the neighbourhood of Florence, where Disney bought it in A.D. 1829, of Sig. Trugoni." The genuineness of this bust, which is quite intact, is most doubtful. H. 0·35. L. of face 0·18. [*]

58 (29). **"Julia Sabina"**: *Mus. Disn.*, Pl. 22. Lightly waving hair adorned with stephané. The pupils of the eyes expressed. New: tip of nose. Very superficial work. Parian marble. H. 0·33. L. of face 0·15. Bought in London, A.D. 1823, by Disney. [*]

59 (24). **Double terminal bust**: *Mus. Disn.*, Pl. 23, "Bacchus and Libera." Two youthful heads with the usual stiff curls on

17   2

forehead; one is almost half modern. Sculpture of no merit. H. 0·29.
[*C]

60 (33). **Pan.** So early as in Th. Hollis's *Memoirs*, p. 821,
this bad head is ascribed to Michael Angelo; but it is hardly
necessary to mention that he is absolutely guiltless of it. Modern.
H. 0·33. [*C]

61 (16). **Female head,** adorned with stephanè, and the hair
gathered in a knot behind. Tip of nose new. We suspect the work
to be of modern origin, as it is very superficial and poor. H. 0·24.
L. of face 0·12. [*]

62 (18). **A youth** with a circlet in his hair. New: nose and
upper lip. Breast crossed by sword-band, chlamys on l. shoulder.
Insignificant sculpture. H. 0·29. Length of face 0·13. The appellation "Octavianus" quite without foundation. [*]

63 (27). **Lucius Verus.** New: nose. Very rough work.
H. 0·39. L. of face 0·17. [*]

64 (28). **"Commodus"** (?): Eyebrows and pupils expressed.
A very poor head; bust with breast-plate modern. H. 0·30. L. of
face 0·19. [*]

65 (30). **"L. Aelius Cæsar"** (?). New: nose. Bad sculpture. H. 0·40. L. of face 0·16. [*]

WORKS IN RELIEF.

66 (53). **Agamemnon and Chryses,** from *Iliad* i.: *Mus.
Disn.,* Pl. 39. Overbeck, *Bildwerke,* Pl. 16, 11. Said to have been
found at Perugia, A.D. 1826, and bought by Disney from Vescovali in Rome. The latter sold at that time many similar imitations,
the works of the Neapolitan Vinc. Monti, (*Kunst-Blatt,* 1823, no.
95, 1824, no. 30). This very low relief, nominally Greek, but of
which the modern origin is beyond all question, imposes on us more
at the first glance than after closer investigation. Cf. Wieseler, pp.
455—458, and Conze, pp. 169, 170. [*C]

67 (66). **Votive relief to Pan:** *Mus. Disn.,* Pl. 35. Within
a rocky grotto there stands Pan, full face, with a pointed beard,
horned and ithyphallic; in the l. arm, over which a small cloak
hangs, he holds a pedum, and with the right, which is lowered, he is
emptying a vessel (now destroyed) over a small Hermes with a long
beard. The latter is provided on the shoulders with quadrangular
projections, and is placed upon a low pedestal; the head is apparently
covered with a cap and the symbol of sex is not wanting. Rude
work. Apparently of Italian marble. H. 0·42. L. 0·24. [*C]

68 (70). **Greek votive relief**: *Mus. Disn.*, Pl. 88, 2. Two columns (the r. hand one has been restored) support an epistyle with tiles on the top. Zeus stands in the middle, facing r., in a cloak which leaves his r. breast and shoulders free; his lowered r. hand holds the thunderbolt (much damaged), his l., upraised, a piece of sceptre. Hera stands behind him in a doubled chiton, her r. hand resting on her side, the l. uplifted as if to hold a sceptre, which however is not represented in the sculpture; her cloak droops over both arms and down her back; her head is adorned with a stephanos. R. of Zeus more than a third of the space is left completely bare; is it possible that a painting was once introduced here? Although the relief is much rubbed, pretty motives can be traced through it. Coarse Greek marble, certainly not Attic. H. 0·47. L. 0·63. Brought to England by Brand. [*C]

69 (38). **Fragment of an Attic votive relief.** A beardless man in adoration, facing l., in a cloak of which he holds a corner in l. hand; r. hand outstretched. Pentelic marble. H. 0·41. L. 0·14. [*C]

70 (52). **Front of a marble discus**: *Mus. Disn.*, Pl. 37 1. A bearded Satyr, with a skin floating behind his back, moves quickly r. towards a rock altar. In l. hand he carries a flat dish and with r. holds out a torch towards the altar. Moderate relief. Diameter 0·26. [*]

71 (54). **Back of the same discus**: *Mus. Disn.*, Pl. 37, 2. A Seilenos in apron, carrying in both hands a winnowing fan (*vannus*), from which rises a phallus. Before him a rocky altar. Very low relief. Diameter 0·26. [*]

72 (67). **Fragment of a marble discus**: *Mus. Disn.*, Pl. 33. On one side two masks facing r.; one youthful, crowned with ivy and a fillet, the other of a female, the hair being quite hidden by a kerchief. Upon the other side a dancing Satyr, facing r., with a skin floating behind him, the thyrsos in l. arm, the r. arm outstretched. Below is all that remains of a panther snapping his teeth in the air. Edge broken away all round. Very low relief. H. 0·18. L. 0·21. Original diameter abt. 0·36. [*]

73 (68). **Two Bacchic masks**, placed opposite to each other. That to the l. youthful, wearing an ivy wreath and a fillet. Beside him a thyrsos. That to the r. bearded and bald-headed, with human ears. Common-place work. H. 0·23. L. 0·31. [*]

74 (56). **Female mask**, perhaps Medusa. Very coarse. H. 0·23. L. 0·20. [*]

75 (23). **Base of a pilaster.** A female figure terminating in and flanked on each side by branches. Delicate relief. H. 0·40. L. 0·31. D. 0·23. H. of field 0·14, L. 0·23. [*]

76 (41). **Sarcophagus representing story of Achilleus:** *Mus. Disn.*, Pl. 42 and 42 *a*. **Front.** Achilleus on Skyros. Achilleus, facing r., in the centre of the composition, is violently excited. He is clothed in a long Doric chiton, which leaves his r. leg free and which has slipped from his r. shoulder, revealing the masculine form of his breast. A waving cloak floats behind his head and round his arms, and his head is covered with a cap. In contrast to this, his l. hand is armed with the shield, and his r. with the lance; a helmet stands on the ground. The l. foot is still shod, his r. shoe lies on the ground. The glance of Achilleus is directed l., where Deïdameia, in chiton and cloak, and with a kerchief on her head, is kneeling on the ground with outstretched arms and looking up to him entreatingly. A sister, in chiton and coif, with a floating veil, hurries past her to their mother, who is sitting l. on a low seat, looking astonished at the whole scene. One sister is already standing beside her, leaning against her chair, and like the mother she is arrayed in chiton, cloak, shoes and coif. Behind the chair stand two more sisters, in simple chiton and coif, talking more calmly over the occurrence. Quite to the l. stands the bearded king Lykomedes, in long chiton (χιτὼν ποδήρης), with a broad girdle and cloak, shoes on his feet and a fillet in his hair. He rests his r. hand on a low column, and in his lowered l. holds a roll (?); his glance is directed to the group, but he is less astonished than the others, probably because he understands better what is going on. On the other side of Achilleus is another woman, much excited, draped in chiton and floating cloak, a sister of Deïdameia. She has apparently just sprung up from an easy chair and is excitedly calling for help. Instead of that Odysseus comes hurriedly up, nude except for his cloak and characteristic cap (πῖλος, *pileus*), his r. hand raised, in the l. his sword in its sheath. Near him Agyrtes, beardless, is blowing the long trumpet, with l. hand bent towards the back of his head; he is dressed in short chiton, cloak, and boots. At the r. extremity comes up the youthful Diomedes, dressed in a chlamys, stretching out his r. hand and holding his sheathed sword in l. (The interesting representation is to be added to those of O. Jahn, *Archäol. Beitrage*, p. 359; Overbeck, *Bildwerke*, p. 287.)—**Left end.** Achilleus, nude except for his helmet and shield, is running with his drawn sword in his r. hand. He looks round l. at Hektor, who has sunk to the ground and who is equipped in breast-plate, helmet, shield and sword. In the background r. the stone walls of Troy. The figure of Achilleus is only lightly sketched, that of Hektor more fully wrought.— **Right end.** Achilleus, who is depicted as on the other side, is seizing by the hair Penthesileia, who has fallen to the ground. She is clothed in a short chiton and boots; her hands are lowered, but with the r. she grasps her double axe, holding in the l. her crescent-shaped shield (*pelta*). In the background her charger, from which Achilleus has dragged her, is galloping away.—The lid is ornamented at each corner with a grinning mask of Pan. These masks are without horns, but have very long drooping ears. Upon the front the centre is indicated by a portable censer (*thymiaterion*), on each side of which crouch sphinxes, symmetrically grouped round an amphora with a cover. Each end of the lid is adorned with a thunderbolt. The reliefs of the lid are somewhat affected, particularly the masks, but they are not modern. The sarcophagus is distinguished by its perfect state of preservation. Hollis received it from William Lloyd, who had brought it from the palace of the Marchese Cavalieri in Rome. L. 1·62. H. 0·50. D. 0·46. [*CM*]

77 (46). **Bacchic sarcophagus** : *Mus. Disn.*, Pl. 41. The front is ornamented with perpendicularly waved flutings which at either end leave a narrow space and in the middle a broad space. The latter is enclosed by two Corinthian pilasters, which support a flat arch. Within stands Dionysos. Besides the wreath on his curly hair he is adorned with a second (ὑπόθυμίς) placed across on his breast. A cloak, lying on his l. shoulder, conceals his r. leg; on his feet he has high boots. The god is resting the elbow of his l. arm on the r. shoulder of a youthful Satyr, and supporting his head with his l. hand. The Satyr has a skin hanging over his l. arm and is leaning vigorously forwards. Below the corner of the skin stands a round cista of osier, from which the snake stretches up. By the side, at the feet of Dionysos, moves a panther, laying his r. fore-paw on a pedum. With the r. hand Dionysos is pouring wine from a kantharos upon a ram's head which is lying on a low altar. Above the altar, half concealed by the god, Pan appears, bearded and horned, and the artist has succeeded in giving to his countenance his particularly brutish expression. He is looking at the god and with his r. hand is supporting the latter's r. arm; he has placed his r. foot on a low mass of rock. (Cf. the very similar representation in Müller-Wieseler, II. 42, 508.) In the space at the l. end a Satyr, in a skin hung over him crosswise, is dancing, holding in his r. arm a pedum and in his

l. hand a staff. He is turning away his face from a small boy, who is hanging on his l. shoulder and embracing him. On the ground a panther is stepping on the head of a ram; and there is besides the large head of a he-goat. At the end r. a Bacchante in a long Doric chiton is dancing. Her garment leaves her l. leg and r. breast bare. She is striking the cymbals.—On the **left end** we see in very low relief a large round shield, behind which two spears are crossed. —The **right end** is left rough.—The sarcophagus is in excellent preservation, in front highly polished. Found about A.D. 1740 in the Vigna Capponi beyond S. Andrea della Via Flaminia, brought home by W. Lloyd, and in A.D. 1761 bought of him by Hollis. L. 2·15. H. 0·59. D. 0·61. [*CM]

78 (62). **Fragment** showing a female figure: *Mus. Disn.*, Pl. 36. A female in long drapery and a floating cloak moves l. Gerhard and Wieseler, p. 454, have suggested that it is Selenè going to Endymion, but this appears questionable. The fragment has been cut on all sides to make it square. H. 0·24. L. 0·15. [*C]

79 (55). **Right corner of the lid of a sarcophagus:** a mask with long curls and a radiated crown. H. 0·27. L. 0·22. [*].

80 (39). **Etruscan urn:** *Mus. Disn.*, Pl. 85. A man and a woman are holding out their hands to each other. A winged figure, in short drapery and with a lowered torch, approaches from the l. and lays his l. hand on the man. A similar figure, without wings, is hurrying up from the r. with r. hand on head and shouldering a torch with the l. arm. A similar figure with a sword in the l. arm is trying to hold her back. Greyish marble. H. 0·41. L. 0·54. D. 0·25.—The lid, which does not belong to the urn, is of *nenfro*, and represents a recumbent man of very short proportions, wreathed and with a cup in his r. hand. H. 0·39. Bought by Disney of Sig. Cinci, at Volterra, Oct. A.D. 1829, soon after it had been found. [*]

Then follow a number of Roman **cineraria**; those marked with a star are to be found figured in the plates at the end of Th. Hollis' *Memoirs*.

81 (42)*. **Round urn, fluted:** *Mus. Disn.*, Pl. 48. Inscribed on tablet: D(is) M(anibus). | T. Fl(avio) Vero Aug(usti) | lib(erto), tab(ulario) rat(ionis) | aquarior(um), co(n)iugi bene merenti Octa(via Tutis f(ecit). (Mommsen, *Inscr. R. Neap.*, 2489. Orelli-Henzen, 6570.) From Pozzuoli. H. 0·25. Diameter 0·25. [*]

82 (40)*. **Urn in the form of a pail:** *Mus. Disn.*, Pl. 49. The surface is marked to represent a stone wall, so that the whole

has the appearance of a round tower diminishing upwards. In front
is a tablet with inscription: *D(is) M(anibus)*. | *M. Aur(elio) M. f(ilio)*
Aelia Gall(ica) | *Vivinacio* | *mil(iti) coh(ortis)* IV *pr(aetoriae)* | *vixs(it)*
ann(is) XLV, *mil(itavit) ann(is)* XIII, | *Aurelia Nice* | *marito suo* | *b(ene)*
m(erenti) posuit. H. 0·24. Diameter of base 0·27, of top 0·22. [*]

83 (47)*. **Round urn (modern), antique lid** : *Mus. Disn.*,
Pl. 51. The lid is covered with foliage, and on it stands upright
a small tablet with this inscription : *hare Aeciae* | *P. f(iliae) Tulliae*
sol. ti. b. f. (Genuine ?? The last letters appear to contain a misconception of familiar formulas). [*]

84 (45). **Round urn** : *Mus. Disn.*, Pl. 52. On either side
a head serves as a handle. Inscription : *L. Sentii L. l(iberti)*
Cocceti | *v(ixit) a(nno)* I. *m(ensibus)* VI. | *nolite dolere parentes*, | *hoc faci-*
undum fuit. The inscription is a spurious imitation of one that was
once in Rome and is now in Milan (Muratori, 1213, 9. Wilmanns,
Exempla. no. 607*h*). Found A.D. 1825, near the tomb of Caecilia
Metella. H. 0·52. Diameter 0·42. [*]

85 (77)*. **Sepulchral monument** : *Mus. Disn.*, Pl. 50. In
the pediment is a wreath. Below, a relief : upon her deathbed lies
a draped female, with the stalk of a poppy in her lowered r. hand ;
on her legs lies a large wolf-hound. Below : *D(is) M(anibus)*. | *Pom-*
peiae | *Margaridi* | *fidelissimae* | *Felicio* | *coniugi suae* | *b(ene)*
m(erenti) | *posuit*. The name of the husband, Felicio, is strangely
crowded in. H. 0·62. L. 0·32. [*]

86 (44)*. **Square cinerarium** : *Mus. Disn.*, Pl. 53. On
what are usually called masks of Ammon hangs a garland, in the
curve of which is the inscription : *D(is) M(anibus)*. | *M. Ulpio* |
Aug(usti) lib(erto) | *Fortunato* | *Philetus pater* | *et Ulpia Plusias* |
coniugi b(ene) m(erenti) f(ecerunt). Below at the corners are masks in
Phrygian caps. On the lid is a trident entwined with two dolphins,
and two shells. H. 0·66. L. 0·36. D. 0·27. Bought by Hollis
of W. Lloyd, A.D. 1761. [*]

87 (1)*. **Square cinerarium** : *Mus. Disn.*, Pl. 54 and 54*a*.
On all four sides are garlands of fruits, depending from skulls
of rams, and below are two birds. On front and back there is
also a bird over the garland, and on the two sides is a Medusa
head in the same place. In front, above : *Aeli(a) Postumia verna*
fecit | *sivi t*e* [sic, instead of *et*] | *coniugi carissimo ;* below : *conquo*
vixit an(nis) XXIII, *b(ene) m(erenti)*. H. 0·15. L. 0·43. D. 0·42. [*]

88 (51)*. **Square cinerarium** : *Mus. Disn.*, Pl. 55. The
inscription runs : *Ti. Claudius Hermias* | *fecit Iuliae Anthidi* | *coniugi*

suae | carissimae et | sibi. vixit ann(is) XXXVI. All around are branches: above, a bird, seizing a snake with his beak. On the ends plants and on the lid a wreath. H. 0·36. L. 0·34. D. 0·29. [*]

89 (36)*. **Rectangular cinerarium**: *Mus. Disn.*, Pl. 56, 1. A garland hangs down from two so-called heads of Ammon, below which swans are visible, two birds above and two below. In the inside of the wreath the inscription: *Cn. Caesio | Attico | Julia Cypare | coniug(i) cariss(imo)*. H. 0·32. L. 0·27. D. 0·25. [*]

90 (58)*. **Square cinerarium**: *Mus. Disn.*, Pl. 56, 2. Within a garland the inscription: *DiIs Manibus | Q. Calidi Pothi Valeria | Ias(o) coniugi bene mereni* (sic) *| et Valeriae Maximae f(iliae) | Calidius Eleuthr. l. fecer(unt)*. Upon each of the sides a tripod. The cover does not belong to it. H. 0·22. L. 0·44. D. 0·30. [*]

91 (43)*. **Cippus**: *Mus. Disn.*, Pl. 57, 58. On two so-called heads of Ammon, below which eagles are visible, hangs a garland, within which is a lion tearing an ass. Above: *DiIs Manibus | sacrum | T. Statilio Hermeti | Statilia Philaenis | fecit coniugi | suo carissimo | et bene | merito de se*. On the two sides are l. a cup, r. an ewer, each in a garland; on the back corners a ram's head above and a swan below. Above is a round pediment with branches. H. 0·76. L. 0·46. D. 0·29. [*C]

FALSE OR DOUBTFUL RELIEFS.

In conclusion we have a number of reliefs which are not genuine, or which are in the highest degree suspicious.

92 (71). **Round relief**: *Mus. Disn.*, Pl. 31. Head of Medusa, surrounded by snakes: mouth deeply hollowed out. Low relief. Coarse grey stone. According to Hollis' *Memoirs*, p. 820, "beautiful and of Greek workmanship;" in my opinion modern. [*]

93 (58). **Piece of an antique ornament of a pilaster**, on the back of which is introduced a modern head of "Julius Caesar, seen in profile, with a fillet in the hair": *Mus. Disn.*, Pl. 32, 32a. Bought of a merchant of Naples, about the year A.D. 1755, by Hollis. [*C]

94 (69). **Low relief of Nero**, with halo of rays: *Mus. Disn.*, Pl. 34. We read in Hollis' *Memoirs*, p. 820, of this composition, which is certainly modern: "it was over a portal in Attica; the reverse a figure of Roma Triumphans," and Disney says "brought from Athens. Purchased at Venice about A.D. 1752." It is clear that trade in art was never at a loss for testimonies to origin. [*C]

95 (65). "**Agrippa.**" Head in profile, with a wreath. *Mus. Disn.*, Pl. 38. Modern. [*]

96 (63). **97** (61). "**Small male head**": *Mus. Disn.*, Pl. 40. "**Small female head.**" Similar. Modern flat relief.

98 (57). **99** (64). "**Laureate head of Philip of Macedon.**" "**Faustina.**" Similar. [*]

100 (60). **Portrait of an emperor.** Low relief, with sharp edges, like a cameo. Modern. [*C]

101 (59). **A female,** sitting on the ground, half nude. Graceful posture. Modern. [*]

Certain marbles, of which there are drawings in *Mus. Disn.*, are not in Cambridge, viz.: Pl. 14, Ivy-wreathed bust of Thalia; Pl. 18, Bust, falsely called "Corbulo"; Pl. 24, Statue of Apollo. They have probably remained with the Bronzes and other works of art in the Hyde. (See below, art. Hyde).

Besides the Marbles we have spoken of in the collections of Clarke and Disney, the Fitzwilliam Museum possesses other Antiquities, important among which is the great collection of **Greek coins,** purchased from the executors of the late Colonel LEAKE for £5000; further some **Greek vases** from the property of Col. LEAKE and Dr. CHURCHILL BABINGTON (*Archaeol. Anz.*, 1866, p. 302); for example, eleven amphorae, four hydriae, ten bowls, numerous lekythoi (with inscriptions of vase-painters Chachrylion and Hermogenes, hydria with inscriptions "Herakles" and "Triton"); some **Attic terra cottas,** among which are some of graceful design; and a collection of very handsome **Cyprian glass vessels,** obtained from Gen. CESNOLA; and finally some good **bronzes,** among which I consider the following most worthy of notice:

102. Statuette of Herakles, staggering drunken. *Spec.*, II. Pl. 31, 32. An excellent piece, 0·23 high, bought by Leake in Vrachóri in Aetolia, where it had been brought from Vlochós (Agrinion). *Travels in Northern Greece*, I. p. 325. [*]

103. Statuette of Zeus, standing on his r. leg, with the l. slightly bent, quite nude. In his r. hand he is lowering the lightning, and his l. arm is raised. His head is bent slightly downwards, looking r. Hair and beard are carefully treated and the latter is tolerably long. With this may be compared an Athenian coin (Müller-Wieseler, II. 2, 23), in which some scholars have proposed to recognise the Zeus Polieus of Leochares. H. 0·155. Leake. [*]

104. Statuette of Poseidon, placing his r. foot on a rock

and laying his r. arm on his knee, with a dolphin in his r. hand; his
l. arm is raised, and it no doubt held the trident. The head
approaches very nearly the character of Zeus. Concerning this type,
cf. Overbeck, *Kunstmythologie*, II. p. 278. Lange, *Das Motiv des
aufgesetzten Füsses*, pp. 81 ff. H. 0·10. Leake. [*]

105. **Statuette of Dionysos:** in a cloak that leaves his
r. arm and breast free. The r. arm is somewhat lowered and
stretched out, the position of the hand shows that it must have been
in the act of emptying out a cup. The l. hand held something before
the breast. The face has a noble expression, the beard is well trimmed, the hair on both sides of the forehead is confined by a fillet.
This good piece appears to be Etruscan. H. 0·26. Leake. [*]

106. **Statuette of a nude youth,** with a head surrounded
with curls, resting on his r. leg, and his l. leg bent. In his r. hand
he held something before his body; his l. arm is broken off. On
the top of the head is a broken peg. A good figure, found in Zoan
in the delta of the Nile. H. 0·17. Leake. [*]

107. **Statuette of a Satyr,** dancing forwards in moderate
movement, with the l. leg advanced; stretching out his l. arm with
extended fingers, and raising his r. hand. In both instances the
wrists are much bent, as is usual with Satyrs. The hair thin.
Round pedestal. The figure comes from Etruria. H. 0·13. [*]

I pass over some bronze figures of less consequence, two Etruscan
candlesticks and a bronze hand; also a suspicious bust of a female
and a modern Herakles (presented by Mrs Hare). There are two
Etruscan incised **mirrors** representing mythological subjects, viz.,
Tydeus, Amphiaraos, and Adrastos (Tute, Amphiare, Atrste),
Tydeus standing in the middle between Adrastos seated l. and
Amphiaraos r. This mirror, of which the figures and inscriptions
are almost obliterated with rust, belonged formerly to Gerhard, and
has been published by him. Cf. Gerhard, *Etrusk. Spiegel*, 178.

108. **A nude female figure with wings,** moving quickly r.,
with a Phrygian cap and shoes; in her lowered r. hand she holds a
cup for flowers. Cf. Gerhard, *Etrusk. Spiegel*, Pl. 31 ff.

TRINITY COLLEGE.

Conze, *Archaeol. Anzeiger*, 1864, p. 172.

In a corner downstairs close to the STAIRCASE which leads to the
LIBRARY stand several antique sculptures. Some of them, which have

their origin in the north of England, were collected by Sir ROBERT
COTTON, and kept by him at Cunnington, near Huntingdon, till
in A.D. 1750 Sir John Cotton de Stratton presented the collection
to Trinity. Cf. John Horsley, *Britannia Romana*, p. 192, Pl. 29;
Bruce, in the *Archaeological Journal*, Lond. A.D. 1855, XII. no. 47.
For the chief piece see the *C. I. Lat.*, VII, 1001.

Somewhat later some Greek marbles were added which EDWARD
WORTLEY MONTAGU (died A.D. 1761), the husband of Lady Mary
Wortley Montagu, had collected in the East while he was British
Ambassador at Constantinople (1716–1718 A.D.). Cf. Clarke,
Travels, II. 1, p. 163. Scipio Maffei saw the stones at Montagu's
house about A.D. 1733. (*Letters and Works of Lady M. Wortley
Montagu*, ed. by Lord Wharncliffe, III. p. 96.) The most celebrated
specimen was the inscription of Sigeum (*C. I. Gr.*, 3595), which
Montagu's daughter, Lady Bute, presented to Trinity in A.D. 1766,
probably together with the rest of the specimens. Some have been
added from other parts.

109. **Square sepulchral relief**, framed. Two men are lying
on a couch; the one l. half covered with his cloak, while the upper
part of his body is bare, and he holds a goblet in his l. hand. The
one r. wears his chiton and cloak, and with his r. hand, which is
raised, he pours wine from a drinking-horn (*rhyton*), with a ram's
head, into a large cup, which he holds in his l. hand. A small,
three-legged table stands by the couch with cakes on it and a small
ewer. Further r. is a side-board, with two shelves one over the other;
on the upper one are two plates, on the lower one a goblet; in front
a mixing vessel, by which a small servant stands, and between him
and the couch stands a second servant. A curtain is hung up at
the back of the whole; over it, looking l., are the necks and heads
of three horses, one behind the other, also the upper parts of the
bodies of three riders equipped with helmet and shield. From the
marble and style it may be inferred that the relief comes from Asia
Minor. H. 0·36. L. 0·46. [*C*]

110. **Sepulchral monument.** A quadrangular slab, enclosed
by two pilasters with a kind of Corinthian capitals; above is a
cornice with branches, below an architectural moulding. In the field
is a wreath with a broad riband; below, in rather late characters,
the inscription (*C. I. Gr.*, 6861):

Ἐνθάδε γῆ κατέχει νέον ἄνε μα, ᾧ πατρὶς ἦεν
καλὴ | χθὼν Δοκίμοιο, τὸ | δ' οὔνομά οἱ τόδ' ἔκειτο |
Παπίας | Πασικράτους· καθ θ

Franz reads κάθθανε, and Kaibel (*Epigrammata Graeca*, Berlin, 1878, no. 666) supplies κάθθανε δ' ἐν πολέμῳ; on the stone itself there seems never to have been more than is given above. I do not know what the long stroke after Παπίας is intended to signify. Franz has justly referred the "Land of Dokimos" to the town of Dokimia or Dokimeion, not far from Synnada in Phrygia. On the l. pilaster, in three lines one above the other, stands αϛ | Παπί αϛ (the final syllable was at first falsely written over); on the pilaster to the right χαῖρε. Coarse yellow marble, apparently Asiatic. H. 0·59. L. 0·45. [*]

111. **Fragment of Attic sepulchral column,** broken off below. Under a flat pediment is a narrow lintel on which appears (*C. I. Gr.*, 805*) εὐθυ KΡITOΣ Ξ ΛΕΛIOΣ. (In the second word, Λ appears to me to be certain, E probable; Dobree read doubtfully HΛΛIOΣ, K. O. Müller ...ΛΙΛIOΣ, Conze doubtfully ΛBAIOΣ; Böckh suggested Oὐαῖος, which cannot possibly be right; and Εἰτεαῖος can hardly be so. It is also possible to suppose that it is the name of the second man represented below. Below, on the slab itself, in characters much effaced:

'Ενθάδε τὸν πάσης ἀρετῆς ἐπὶ τ έρμα μολόντα |
[Ε]ὐθόκριτον πατρία χθὼν | ἐκάλυψε τάφῳ, |
μητρὶ φίλον καὶ πατρί, κασι[γ]νήταις τε ποθεινόν |
πᾶσ[ί] τε ἑταίροισν σύντροφον | ἡλικίας.

Below, in a sunken field, is a large amphora of graceful shape, with handles worked with volutes. On the body of the amphora another field has been sunk; on this is represented in very low relief, l. a man, apparently beardless, in a cloak; r. a nude youth with the chlamys over his arm; they are extending their hands to each other. Beside each of them is a dog; the one l. is sniffing the ground, the one r. is looking up backwards to his master. Below the body of the amphora the slab is broken off. Fine Attic style of 4th century. Pentelic marble. Brought from Athens by the Rev. H. V. Elliott and the Rev. E. B. Elliott, Fellows of Trinity College. H. 1·22. L. 0·42. [* C]

112. **Lower part of an Attic sepulchral stèlè.** Two lekythoi are represented in tolerably high relief, on the l. a small and on the r. a larger one. On the latter distinct traces of painting are preserved, above on the body a broad stripe, below a border *à la Grecque* and below that perpendicular stripes; on the field are what appear to be the outlines of a woman in a sitting posture to the l. and to the r. a man standing up, bending slightly toward her. Pentelic marble. H. 0·72. L. 0·37. [* C]

113. Colossal akroterion, with a double front, allowing a very rich palmette of acanthus to grow forth : originally the splendid capital of a large Attic stèle. It is broken on one of the lower corners and here and there in other parts. Pentelic marble. H. 1·19. L. 0·70. The relief stands out about 0·13. [* *C*]

In the LIBRARY is

114. Statuette of Asklepios, his r. shoulder supported on a staff round which a snake is entwined; he is feeding the snake. In perfect preservation. H. about 0·30. Presented by Sir Clifton Winthringham. [*B*]

The Rev. C. W. KING, M.A., Fellow of Trin. Coll., the author of the esteemed works on gems, possesses, besides a choice collection of **cut stones,** a few antique sculptures :

115. Relief representing three women, in hieratic style, arranged stiffly about a round column. (Cf. Montfaucon, *Ant. Expl.*, I. Pl. 90.) They are all placed full face, and they wear a girdled chiton with double folds (διπλοΐδιον) ; on their heads a kalathos, or modius ; plaits fall down on their shoulders. The first has both her arms lowered; in the hands holes may be observed, in which to fasten some symbol; the chiton has no sleeves. The second wears woollen sleeves reaching to her elbows ; her r. hand, in which is also a hole, lowered; l. hand raised to her breast and her first two fingers are placed as if she held something in them. The third figure is without sleeves; the hair is arranged in rows of curls on the forehead ; the l. hand, which is pierced, is lowered; the r. lies on her breast. This disposition of the hands leaves room between the first and second woman for a small Pan, moving r., horned and bearded, with chlamys thrown across his breast. He carries on his l. shoulder a flat dish of fruit ; his r. hand rests on his hip (the arm is broken). The upper part of the column is slightly hollowed out and shaped like a patera, or ἐσχάρα. The whole served probably as an altar. Commonplace workmanship. Greek marble from Alexandria. From the collection of Giovanni di Demetris. H. 0·47. [*]

116. Statue of Ceres. A draped female, bending far back, is sitting on a square seat; her cloak, of very good drapery, covers her legs, back and left arm. Her r. leg is stretched out, the l. drawn back. On the l. arm she holds a cornucopia, in the r. a bunch of ears of corn and poppies; this arm is broken in several places and is perhaps old. Of the broken head the face is entirely new, the wreath of corn perhaps old, but completely worked over. So is the right foot. The motive is pretty, but is carried out in an ordinary manner. Greek marble. H. 0·50. [*]

117. Fragment of a statue of Seilenos. Only the upper part of the body, from the navel upwards, is preserved. The head has pointed ears, and is bald, with a long beard; he is looking down kindly. The breast is stout and hairy; the halves of the upper arms, which are all that remain, are lowered. Well preserved, but polished. Good sculpture. From Smyrna. H. 0·21. [*]

ST JOHN'S COLLEGE.

118. "Apollinis ara." Huebner, *C. I. Lat.*, VII. 218. In a corner of cloister of third court is the quadrangular so-called ara, raised on a stone inscribed to the effect that it was found near "Coccium" (Ribchester), and bequeathed by T. Dunham Whitaker, LL.D. It was built into a wall at Salesbury Hall. **L. side.** Apollo in arched field resting on l. leg, r. leg crossed behind it and r. toe resting on ground; l. hand rests on lyre on piece of rock to r. of figure, r. elbow on l. hand, head on r. hand; drapery hangs down at the sides, and a piece goes over l. shoulder and slantwise across breast; figure nude with this exception. Hair long and raised over forehead. **Front.** Two draped females of somewhat smaller scale in field divided at the top into two arches, which meet in a point: under l. arch, the figure holding r. forearm straight across body towards that under r. arch, whose l. forearm is in similar position; they seem to hold some object between them. R. knee of r. figure a little advanced. Mural crowns on heads, or hair raised. R. top corner of field broken off with from three to six inches of the entire r. side of the "ara." **Back.** Within a moulding an inscription of at least ten lines, of which the middle and ends are partly legible, LEC VI occurring. Huebner has attempted its restoration.—Brownish gray stone (?). Very much worn. H. 1·66. W. 0·51. L. (original) 0·74. In centre of flat top a quadrangular hole. [Fennell].

CANTERBURY (Kent).

J. Brent, *The Egyptian, Grecian, Roman and Anglo-Saxon Antiquities in the Museum at Canterbury.* Canterb. 1875. Michaelis, *Arch. Zeit.*, 1864, pp. 121 ff., 137 ff.

Besides other antiquities this Museum possesses a collection of smaller objects, which Percy Clinton, VISCOUNT STRANGFORD,

(d. 1855), the English Ambassador at the Porte till 1825, collected in the Greek Islands, Asia Minor and Egypt, during his residence in the Levant, and which he presented afterwards to the Museum (cf. Introd. § 89). These specimens form the contents of Case H. I published some of them in 1864, from sketches by G. Scharf. The catalogue includes 175 objects, of which I select the following.

4. **Pitcher**, formed in the shape of **Dionysos**, as a boy. *Arch. Zeit.*, 1864, Pl. 182, 4. He is sitting on the ground, with a narrow nebris across his breast, a wreath on his head, a ring over the r. calf; holding a pitcher in the r. hand. Pale clay. From Naxos 1822. (No. 1 appears to be of a similar description.)

5. **Statuette in a sitting posture**, probably of **Hera**, found at Samos 1823. *Arch. Zeit.*, 1864, Pl. 182, 2. This figure is remarkable on account of the numerous traces of colour, white, blue, red, black. The old type is completely preserved, the features of the face being of archaic roughness; some rows of curls over the forehead and a polos on the head, give the same a somewhat heavy character. Terra cotta. H. 0·22. There are other similar figures in the collection, for ex. nos. 2, 3, 6, 9, 11.)

6. **A similar figure** from Samos, with a wreath round the head and a peaked cap.

7. " **Pedestal in terra cotta ; a boy** leaning against a tree or support of some description ; on the base is depicted a theatrical mask of a grinning face. Portions of an inscription may be traced to the l. of the figure, which is partially covered with a hood or shawl."

12. " **Egypto-Etruscan cippus**, representing Osiris between two ibises or cranes, which stand in an attitude of adoration. The lower part of Osiris terminates in a pillar, upon which is an Etruscan inscription. On the back of this cippus is a bilingual inscription, hieroglyphic and Etruscan. Terra cotta."

13. **Statuette of Aphroditè** in the typical pose; very ancient. *Arch. Zeit.*, 1864, Pl. 182, 1. The chiton falls in large zigzag folds over her r. arm and she is raising it a little with her l. hand. She holds to her breast with her r. hand something which in the drawing appears to be a dove, but which according to the catalogue would be a pear or pomegranate. The round, plump face, with pouting lips, eyes set in obliquely, and very large round ears, is framed by long curls ; the head is as it were drawn backwards by the full, thick mass of hair which falls down her back to her waist. The proportions very thick-set. Back very flat. Terra cotta. H. 0·25. At the back is written "Samos, 1823," at the bottom " Cyprus."

14. Female figure: in a flowing robe, in a dancing attitude. Terra cotta. From Delos, 1823.

15. Dionysos: as a youth, with an ivy wreath on his yellow hair. The god stands in repose, holding the wide cloak, which covers his l. arm and the whole of his back, with the r. hand, as if he were going to throw it round him. Terra cotta. Cf. *Arch. Zeit.*, 1864, pp. 144 *sq*. H. 0·13. [From a sketch by Scharf.]

16. Female dancer: draped in a wide ungirdled chiton which has slipped off her r. shoulder and breast and surrounds her body in flowing folds. In her lowered l. hand she holds the tympanon. Terra cotta. H. 0·16. Cf. *Arch. Zeit.*, 1864, p. 144, and the similar figure in Janssen's *Terra-Cotta's te Leyden*, Pl. 7, 32. [From a sketch by Scharf.]

17—21. 24. Heads in terra cotta.

25. Head with **laughing face**, with a **Pan's pipe**.

27. Head of a wolf, or a wolf-dog. *Arch. Zeit.*, 1864, Pl. 182, 5. Fine expression. From Argos. L. 0·05.

35. Pomegranate, cut open to shew the interior, admirably done. Hollow and very light, of a rich and pale clay; a small hole at the bottom. Found near Mount Athos, 1821 (according to the catalogue near Athens). W. 0·08. Cf. *Arch. Zeit.*, 1864, p. 144. From a sketch by Scharf.]

37—54. Lamps in terra cotta, some of them bearing the potter's name. Among them may be specially mentioned:

43. Mercury, with winged hat, holding a caduceus.

44. Jupiter's **eagle** carrying off the boy **Ganymedes**. *Arch. Zeit.*, 1864, Pl. 181, 3. The inscription at the bottom MCHRI 97 awakens suspicion.

45. Odysseus bound to the mast of his ship, looking at the **Siren**, who is portrayed in a very unusual manner: *desinit in piscem mulier formosa superne. Arch. Zeit.*, 1864, Pl. 181, 1, cf. 1865, p. 32. Cf. *Liber monstrorum*, 1, 7 (M. Haupt, *Opuscula*, II. p. 224). *Sirenae sunt marinae puellae, quae navigantes pulcherrima forma et cantus decipiunt dulcedine, et a capite usque ad umbilicam sunt corpore virginali et humano generi simillimae, squamosas tamen piscium caudas habent, quibus in gurgite semper latent.* In the ship is the steersman with a companion, who has his fingers in his ears. Terra cotta. At the bottom the potter's name, *C. Iun(ius) Bit.* On account of the unusual form given to the Siren the antique origin, either of the lamp as a whole, or of portions of it, has been seriously doubted, see Schrader, *die Sirenen*, Berlin 1868, p. 73. Heydemann, *Ann.*

dell Inst., 1876, p. 357 (who gives further references). It is not the only specimen in the collection subject to suspicion, cf. nos. 44, 155.

46. " Man bearing a pole across his shoulders, with a vessel at one end and a faun at the other. He holds a staff to support his hand."

54. High lamp, on the stem of which **Aphroditè** is depicted nude, with a drapery round l. leg. *Arch. Zeit.*, 1864, Pl. 181, 4. Traces of red colouring. From Histiaea in Euboea.

55—128. 156—170. Vessels, urns, vases of various shapes, of **terra cotta and marble**, among them are also some **painted vases** of which I think the following the most noticeable.

111. Nasiterno from Megara of "Corinthian" style, with imaginary animals.

113. Lekythos, with red figure, Nikè pouring wine on an altar.

116. Lekythos, from Athens, coloured outlines on white ground. A youth and a girl adorning a tomb with garlands. "Orestes and Electra at the tomb of Agamemnon." (Nos. 117, 118 appear to be of the same character, but the representations are much defaced.)

125. Lekythos, in the style of Nola, with yellow figure. A lady holding a mirror, and approaching a chair.

131. " Metallic mirror, from a tomb at Athens."

132—154. 171—175. Sculptures in marble or stone, many of which are fragmentary. Among them :

135. "Carved figure, in marble or stone, coloured red, from the neighbourhood of Mount Athos. The head has a hood-like covering, with cloak and robe reaching to the knees. Inscription to the left : ATHAIERUS, INOI."

136. " Horse and rider, in rough marble ; much worn." Probably a sepulchral relief.

137. "Sepulchral relief in stone. A man reclining on a couch, a female by the side, seated, holding his hand (?), and a child at her elbow ; two attendants, near a bust on a pedestal," surely a terminal bust.

140. " Relief in marble, a man holding a club, standing beside a horse. Fragmentary, and much worn. From the neighbourhood of Buyukdere," on the European side of the Bosporos.

143. Head of Bacchus, ivy-crowned, with a broad fillet round the forehead. *Arch. Zeit.*, 1864, Pl. 182, 3. Admirably worked, well moulded, and full of spirit. From Naxos. Fragmentary. The material, although not expressly mentioned, seems to be marble. L. of face about 0·15.

144—148. Small heads in marble.

149. Sepulchral relief, in marble, from Brussa. "A man on horseback in front of an altar, over which is a snake, clinging to a tree on the opposite side." Cf. the relief in Ephesus, *Mus. Worsl.*, Cl. 1. Pl. 20 (Pl. 9, 1.).

150. Relief, in marble, from Corcyra. A votive offering, hollowed for the hand to carry it. An inscription in Greek : "*Callistas* (presents this) *as a thank-offering for the prosperity of Alexander.*"

155. Terra cotta slab, said to be from Syracuse, containing an exact copy of that part of the reliefs of the Ara Casali (Wieseler, *Ara Casali*, Pl. 3, uppermost section) which is generally referred to the dragging of Hektor by Achilleus, by others to that of Troilos (Virgil, *Aen.*, 1. 474 f.). *Arch. Zeit.* 1864, Pl. 181, 2. The slab is probably a modern forgery, see Brunn, *Arch. Anz.*, 1864, p. 303.

167. A small **krater** on a pedestal, with yellow figures. Four female heads and a bird. From lower Italy (?). H. 0·08. Cf. *Arch. Zeit.*, 1864, pp. 144 f.

172. Sepulchral relief, in marble. "A man on a couch holding a ring (?, a cup, probably) in his right hand; a woman is seated by his side, and a child. A table with three legs. Below, two oxen drawing a plough. Inscription not legible."

174. Sepulchral relief. "Two figures on a couch. Below the couch, a boy with a vessel in his left hand. Greek inscription of the Christian era."

Some small **bronzes** and other small antiques are to be found in case I, Shelves 18 and 19.

In the Hall are preserved two fragments of **Mosaic pavement** of the simplest description, found at Canterbury; one of them is ornamented with a two-handled vessel.

CHATSWORTH (Derbyshire).

Marbles, Bronzes and Fragments at Chatsworth. London 1838, 4° (I had not access to this catalogue). Waagen, *Treas.*, III. pp. 365 f. (II. p. 448).

The Castle of the DUKE OF DEVONSHIRE is celebrated for its large collection of art treasures. In the splendid SCULPTURE GALLERY, among masterpieces by modern sculptors, are to be found also the following antiques.

1. "A colossal antique bust of **Alexander the Great**, with rich flowing hair disposed like that of Jupiter, and very noble features; of an idealised character, but agreeing very well in the main features with the celebrated portrait-bust in the Louvre. New: half the nose, and all from the throat downwards." [*W*]

2. "An antique **bronze**: **two greyhounds** licking each other: admirable in expression and motive, but of inferior execution in details." [*W*]

In the CONSERVATORIES Waagen observed—

3. "Tasteful Roman **cinerary urns**."

Winckelmann mentions besides (*Kunstgesch.* VII. 2. 27)—

4. **A bronze bust of Plato**, which the Duke of Devonshire is said to have received from Greece about 30 years before the completion of the *Kunstgeschichte* in 1762. I do not know whether this bust is at Chatsworth or at Devonshire House in London, or in the villa at Chiswick, or whether it is still in the possession of the ducal family at all. We shall probably not be far wrong if in the so-called "Plato" we suspect a **bearded Dionysos**.

[5. **Fragment from the Parthenon** (recognised as such by Count Léon de Laborde). At the request of Mr C. T. Newton it was presented by the late Duke to the British Museum in 1855. Mr Newton afterwards identified the head with that belonging to the torso of the vanquished Lapith from the south metope XVI (Michaelis, *Parthenon*, Pl. 3). See *Academy*, 1875, p. 365. *Guide to the Parthenon Sculptures*, p. 40. How the fragment came to Chatsworth is not known.]

LIBRARY.

A **Bronze head**, somewhat above life-size, apparently of **Apollo**; with signs of a wreath, which has disappeared. Hair very elaborately treated, and gathered at the back into clustering ringlets; eye-sockets empty; face completely preserved. The bronze is of unusual thickness, and has a beautiful bluish patina. Late, somewhat heavy workmanship. Said to have been brought by one of the recent Dukes from Smyrna ; the type is quite analogous to that figured on the obverse of a well-known group of the copper coins of that city, the so-called 'Ομήρεια, cf. Eckhel. [COLVIN.]

CHICHESTER (Sussex).

The Municipal Museum and the neighbouring Goodwood Park, which belongs to the DUKE OF RICHMOND, contain, as far as I know,

only native antiquities, and in particular Roman inscriptions.   Cf.
Huebner, *Monatsbericht der Berliner Akademie*, 1868, p. 90.

CLUMBER PARK (Nottinghamshire).

Among the "Antiquities, Sculptures and Paintings" which he
had not seen Waagen mentions those of the DUKE OF NEWCASTLE
in his original German work (II. p. 479).   On the occasion of
a later visit (*Treas.*, IV. p. 508) he confines his descriptions to paintings.   In March 1878 a fire destroyed part of the house.   On that
occasion perished *inter alia* "the collection of [antique ?] busts which
graced the entrance-hall.   A number of art-treasures from the ruins
of Pompeii, two sarcophagi, a number of vases, and several urns were
consumed." (*Illustr. London News*, Apr. 5, 1879, p. 332.)   I cannot
say whether there are any antiquities at Clumber Park now.

COLCHESTER (Essex).

Both the public Museum in the Castle and the collection of the
Rev. J. H. POLLEXFEN contain only native antiquities.   In the
Museum may be seen the remarkable so-called Colchester Vase
(*C. I. Lat.*, VII. 1335, 3); the chief ornament of Mr Pollexfen's collec-
tion was a glass vase with reliefs and inscriptions, which has lately
been placed in the British Museum, (*ibid.* VII. 1273).   See Huebner,
Monatsbericht der Berliner Akademie, 1868, pp. 86 ff.

CORFE CASTLE (Dorsetshire).

See art. Kingston Hall.

DALKEITH PALACE (Scotland).

Waagen, *Treas.*, IV. p. 436.

In this magnificent Castle of the DUKE OF BUCCLEUCH, situated
not far from Edinburgh, may be mentioned the **torso** of an antique
female statue of Parian marble, of good workmanship, especially
of the drapery.   The head is modern.   This is remarkable as having
been found in England.   [*W*]

At the beginning of the century a considerable collection of Roman
antiques, which the MARQUIS OF MONTHERMER had brought from
Italy, was to be seen in the town house of the Duke of Buccleuch,

Privy Gardens, Westminster. This mansion was afterwards pulled down and Montagu House was built for the Duke. It is possible that when this was done the antiquities were dispersed. (Cf. Introd. notes 245, 328).

DEEPDENE (Surrey).

Clarac, III. p. 64. Waagen, *Treas.*, II. pp. 112 f. (II. pp. 135 f.) Michaelis, *Arch. Zeitung*, 1874, pp. 15 f. In 1861 I merely paid a flying visit to the collection, but in 1877, by the courteous permission of the owner, Mrs Hope, I was able to examine it at leisure.

At the close of the last century and the beginning of the present one Thomas Hope formed a collection of antiques, which his son and heir afterwards increased. These rested for a long time in the London residence of the family. (Cf. Hope, *Household furniture*, London, 1807, and above Introd. § 61.) There Clarac went through the statues in 1833, while in 1835 Waagen contented himself with a superficial look at them. The whole collection was removed afterwards to Deepdene, once a seat of the Arundel family, situated in a wonderfully beautiful wooded valley not far from Box Hill, where the beauty of nature and the glorious products of art vie with each other for preeminence.

THE HALL.

On three sides of this striking room is a corridor under six arches on each side, supported by square columns, and above this corridor is a gallery adorned with Corinthian columns. In the archways, before the pillars, and in the corridors, stand groups, statues and busts, chiefly of marble, but in part also of stone and of bronze. Among them are masterpieces by modern sculptors (Thorwaldsen's Jason and Shepherd, Canova's Venus), and careful copies of celebrated antiques; besides them (beginning from the west side) the following antiquities in marble :

1. **Satyr's head**, of the refined kind like the Resting Satyr (Müller-Wieseler, I. 35, 143), originating perhaps from a copy of this. Head unusually good, in fact one of the best Satyr's heads I know. Eyelids very sharply indicated, and at the edge surrounded by a lightly incised line. Hair admirably treated. New: tip of nose, part of the pointed ears and of the hair, a part of top of head and the whole of the bust. Excellent Parian marble. Life size. [*]

2. Apollo. Clarac, III. 476 B, 905 C. Only the torso is part of the original statue. This torso does not belong to a *Sauroktonos*, but to that enigmatical type in which a cloak hangs to the ground from the uplifted l. arm and a swan is depicted beside the figure sitting on the ground, cf. Clarac, III. 479, 918; 483, 928; Dilthey in the *rheinische Jahrbücher*, LII, p. 51, note 2. This is shown by the position of the legs, which are crossed. Of good delicate work. Beautiful yellowish Parian marble. New: lower half of the r. leg, three-quarters of the l. leg, stem of tree with serpent, l. arm including the shoulder, r. arm from shoulder, and the neck. The head, which is of Greek marble and not so well executed as the body, did not originally belong to this. The hair is brushed up on both sides towards the top of the head, but not from the forehead. New: nose and chin and the hair on the top of the head. H. 1·51. [*]

3. Dionysos and Idol. *Spec.*, II. Pl. 53. Clarac, IV. 695, 1614. Müller-Wieseler, II. 33, 372. Gerhard, *Ges. Abhandl.*, Pl. 32, 5. Dionysos, in short chiton with a nebris thrown over it crosswise, is leaning his l. arm on a statue of an Aphroditè-Spes, crowned with flowers; the drapery of this statue is of an ancient style, with the well-known motive of the garment lifted with the l. hand. The nebris is very tightly confined by the girdle, and this is the more singular, as the girdle passes directly the animal's head. The main part of the group shows a close connection of the two figures and is very well executed. It is of a fine-grained marble with grey spots, and is in tolerably good preservation. New: both of Dionysos' arms from about the cloak, including the attributes (thyrsos and kantharos), lower half of the r. and the greater part of l. leg, and the edge of the drapery that falls down by the r. leg; the neck. The antique head (new: nose, mouth, chin, l. check, great part of the corymbi of the ivy), of coarse-grained Parian marble, did not belong to the figure originally. In the female statue, both of the arms, from the drapery downwards, are new; so is the uplifted corner of the drapery, half of the lower legs and the pedestal. H. 2·00. (A replica, somewhat larger, was found at Tusculum towards the close of the 17th cent.; it came into the possession of the March. Cavalieri [Buonarroti, *Medaglioni*, p. 420. Matfei, *Raccolta*, Pl. 134, p. 126. Montfaucon, *Ant. Expl.*, I. Pl. 151], was then in the Palace Lucatelli al Corso [Guattani, *Mon. Ined.*, 1785, Sept., Pl. 2. Clarac, IV. 695, 1615. Gerhard, *l. c.*, Pl. 32, 6], and is now in St. Petersburgh, Ermitage, no. 156.) [*]

4. Apollo and Hyakinthos. *Spec.*, II. Pl. 51. Clarac, III. 494 B, 966 A. Müller-Wieseler, II. 12, 139. The group has been

much restored, but there is not a doubt that the two figures originally
belonged to each other. The god is leaning mostly on his l. leg,
his body softly bent, and rests his r. elbow on the trunk of a tree,
before which his favourite (represented much smaller) is standing in
a rather calm attitude. The latter holds in his outstretched r. hand
a flat, thin object, which on the side nearest to the hand finishes in a
straight line, but the edge of which on the other side is broken off all
round and restored to a semicircular form. It has been suggested
that this is the disc which was to become so fatally important to
the boy, but if it is so it is of very unusual shape. New: Apollo's l.
shin between knee and ankle, his l. hand, r. arm, including the
shoulder, and neck; the head is of the same kind of marble, and
certainly belongs to the statue, but half the nose, the edges of the
ears, the plait at the back of the neck and the long flowing curls
have been restored; and this restoration of the hair shows plainly
that the restorer did not understand the intention of the sculptor
with regard to it, as it was originally all drawn up to the top of the
head and fastened there in a large knot (cf. Broadlands, no. 1.
Petworth, no. 7). Although Hyakinthos' l. arm, which is lowered, is
broken below the elbow, his l. hand is preserved entire with all its
fingers, these being bound together with rather strong supports. A
considerable portion of the lower half of the r. arm is mended and is
apparently new, but the hand and the part of the supposed disc
nearest to it are old (see above). The neck modern; head old,
but it does not appear to belong to the statue, as there is no trace
of the distinct coarse grain of the Parian marble of which the rest is
composed; the head has, in fact, besides the tip of the nose and
many parts of the curls (which are restored), been so much touched
up that it has now quite an affected modern character. Hyakinthos
touches Apollo only with his l. shoulder; at this point the group has
certainly been broken at one time, but there is no doubt as to the
original connection of the parts with each other; the same may be
said of many fractures of the legs. All of the trunk behind Hyakinthos, except the lowest part, is new. This group is said to have
been the particular favourite of Canova; he must however have
admired the delicate pose of Apollo more than the execution of the
whole. We are struck by a peculiar flatness in the surfaces and a
marked crudity in their transitions, (e.g. the muscles of the paunch)
which are far from pleasing. The boy is more delicate, but still
not exempt from these faults. Altogether the group is a remarkable
work. Cf. Kekulé's remarks *Bull. dell' Inst.* 1866, p. 100. Müller's

interpretation that Dionysos and his cupbearer are intended (Böttiger's *Amalthea*, III. p. 253) is certainly wrong. From Hadrian's villa. H. 2·03. [*]

5. **Zeus** (" Antoninus Pius "). There is no doubt that this grand figure was originally intended for Zeus, but got changed into Antoninus Pius by the addition of the modern head and neck. The powerful body rests on the r. leg, while the l. is slightly bent ; the r. arm is lowered (the lower part of the arm is modern, and should be held rather further forward, as is shewn by traces of a support at the thigh); the l. arm (of which the hand is restored) forms nearly a right angle, shoulder and arm are draped in a chlamys, which falls low near the god's side, (restored here and there). The legs are broken in many places, but the essential parts are old, except the foremost part of the l. and a piece of the r. foot ; the pedestal too and the eagle which stands beside the r. foot and is looking up at its master (the greater part of both wings and the beak have been restored) are old and evidently part of the original work· The body and the drapery are well treated. Thasian marble of very micaceous grain. H. 1·95. Similar figures of Zeus, without exception only statuettes, are to be seen in Overbeck's *Kunstmythologie*, II. p. 145 and *Atlas* I. Fig. 17; according to these a thunderbolt should be restored to the lowered r. hand. [*]

6. **Aphroditè.** Clarac, IV. 626 A, 1345. In all essential parts the goddess reproduces the motive of the Venus de Medici, with the exception that her ample flowing drapery encircles the backs and sides of her legs and is gathered to the lower part of her body in her l. hand. (Cf. Bernoulli, *Aphrodite*, pp. 255 f.) New : lower half of r. arm ; neck and head (with an additional new tip to the nose) and here and there small restorations. Good work in excellent preservation. Coarse-grained Parian marble. H. 1·80. [*]

7. **Hygieia.** *Spec*, I. Pl. 26. Clarac, IV. 555, 1178. Müller-Wieseler, II. 61, 780. (Cf. Lansdowne House, no. 10.) Beautiful figure draped in long chiton and also enveloped in an ample cloak which is thrown back over the l. shoulder. She stands on the r. leg, the l. being placed slightly back. A cloth wound round her head, which is lowered. A large snake coils round her l. shoulder and down her breast to the r. forearm. New : l. hand, the r. forearm with the cup, very considerable portions of the snake and several patches on the garment, particularly on the left side. The joint between the bust and the neck is somewhat repaired, but there is no doubt that the neck with the head belong to the statue ; Fea

(see below) bears the same testimony. The nose is new, and glass
eyes have been put in; the head is somewhat rubbed. The cloak is
excellently arranged and well executed; here and there perhaps
the details have received almost too much attention ; the execution
of the chiton is rather dry and finnicking. A cord, which passing
from the neck over the shoulder and drawn under the right arm,
causes a number of small folds in the chiton, is worthy of notice
(cf. one of the female figures of the eastern pediment of the Parthenon,
Mus. Marbles, VI. Pl. 11. Michaelis, *Parthenon*, Pl. 6, 16, and Wilton,
no. 159). The statue has been a good deal retouched, but is still
worthy of great praise. The marble appears to be Italian, not
Pentelic (*marmo cippolla*) as Fea states. Found in 1797 at Ostia, on
the spot Tor Bovacciano (Fea, *Viaggio ad Ostia*, p. 45), "among the
ruins of a magnificent palace, and thirty feet below the surface of the
ground, broken into fragments, and buried immediately under the
niches, in which they had been once placed." (Dallaway, *Of
Statuary*, p. 355.) II. 1·96. [*]

8. Statue of Antinous. *Spec.*, II. Pl. 52. Clarac, V. 945,
2430 B. This elegant statue is unusually well executed and although
it has been touched up here and there, it is on the whole exceedingly well preserved. The youthful Antinous is represented in slight
movement, his handsome head looking up and his r. arm stretched
out in the same direction. The restorer has added the cup in his r.
hand, and the vase in his lowered l. hand, thus imparting the
character of a Ganymede to the statue, but this character suits well
with the delicacy of form of our statue and is also in harmony
with Antinous' position as the favourite (*catamitus*) of Hadrian ;
cf. Prudentius, *In Symmachum*, I. 271 : *quid loquar Antinoum caelesti
in sede locatum ? | illum delicias nunc divi principis, illum | purpureo
in gremio spoliatum sorte virili | Hadrianique dei Ganymedem, non
cyathos dis | porgere, sed medio recubantem cum Iove fulcro | nectaris
ambrosii sacrum potare lyaeum | cumque suo in templis vota exaudire
marito ?* The breadth of chest usually given to the handsome
Bithynian is here much reduced, the hair too does not fall in such
masses at the back of the neck, and the weak and effeminate rendering of the pubes is worthy of notice. All this accords well with
its acceptation as an Antinous-Ganymedes, which may once have
been grouped with a Hadrianus-Jupiter. New : tip of the nose,
both fore-arms with their additions, the lower half of the l. leg with
the greater part of the pedestal, four toes of the r. foot and parts
of the chlamys. The last-mentioned is spread over the trunk of a

tree by the side of the r. leg. The head has never been broken; the pedestal which is constructed like the base of an Attic column, *spira*, is of irregular form. Marble, Parian somewhat stained through oxydation. Our statue is probably the one which M. Hirt saw in Rome towards the end of the last century at the sculptor Sposimo's; which came from Hadrian's Villa at Tivoli, the original home of several of our most remarkable Antinous statues. (Levezow, *Ueber den Antinous*, p. 111.) H. 1·93. [*]

9. **Statue of Asklepios.** Clarac, IV. 548, 1158 (the drawing Pl. 549, 1158, borrowed from Guattani, *Mon. Ined.*, 1784, Nov., Pl. 2, refers, as Clarac himself remarks in the text, to a totally different statue). Enveloped in the customary manner in his cloak the god stands on his l. leg, his r. leg being slightly bent; his l. arm rests on his hip, and his r. shoulder is supported by a long staff. New: the r. arm, which has been much broken, is entirely, or almost entirely, new (perhaps the elbow and the parts nearest to it are old); the club round which the snake coils except the uppermost piece under the shoulder, which looks more like the end of a thin staff; both feet and almost the whole of the casket by the l. foot, of which only one of the upper corners is antique. Many edges of the folds have also been restored. Neck and head, the long curls of which, although they have in no instance preserved their original length, yet do not touch the shoulders and the back of the neck, belong to a Serapis, of somewhat sullen, but not gloomy expression, the forehead being much shaded by the curls. New: tip of nose, upper and back parts of head where the modius may once have rested. The figure appears to be of Italian marble and is well executed, particularly the folds on l. arm; the work of the head is not nearly so good. H. 2·05. [*]

10. **Quadrangular Cinerarium.** Front: on each corner is a spiral column and between them a kind of candelabrum, all of which support two wreaths, with birds; within the field formed by the curve of each wreath is a tablet with a spurious inscription, on the l.: *D M | M Nulonius | Celer | vixif* [sic] *ann | XXXXII m III*, on the r.: *D M | nlia* [sic] *Secunda | fec. L. Avillant | cond. gr. nigrae | coniug dignissi*. On each adjacent side tendrils. The lid is modern. H. 0·28. L. 0·51. [*]

11. **Round Cinerarium**, ornamented with tendrils.

12. **Antique female figure.** Standing stiffly with legs close together and both forearms outstretched. The narrow chiton is quite plain and has only a broad perpendicular fold in front between the

legs. Over the chiton is worn a woollen jacket which reaches to the hips; it is somewhat shorter in the middle of the front, and round the neck it is bordered with a plain band. The sleeves reach to the elbow. A narrow shawl lies in small parallel folds on the neck, and then flows in zigzag folds to the calf of the leg. The chest as a whole is much raised, but the breasts are very little separated from each other. Three long closely-woven plaits fall on each shoulder and down on the shawl. The head, with its artistically stiff coiffure and the stephanè, may belong to the figure, though the neck has been much pieced; the nose and other details have been restored. New: great part of r. fore-arm, the sistrum in the r. hand and the l. fore-arm. Good archaistic imitation of an old type. (Cf. Lebas, *Voyage Archéol.*, *Mon. fig.*, Pl. 2, 2.) H. 1·46. [*]

13. **Archaistic female figure**, standing with both feet straight, raising a corner of the chiton with l. hand. She wears a doubled chiton, the outer part of which lies plainly on the breast; four dowel holes in the body below this outer fold seem to indicate that a metal girdle was once attached to the figure. The legs were broken, and have been patched; r. arm (the lower half stretched out) is for the most part new; though the neck is modern, still the head, with stiff rows of curls and a stephanè, probably belongs originally to the figure. New: nose and upper lip. The affected archaism of the statue aims at the utmost simplicity possible. Coarse-grained Parian marble. H. 1·36. [*]

14. **A man's right arm**, preserved from a little above the elbow, broken above the wrist. The outer side has suffered much from the weather, the inside is almost flat, and the fingers of the clenched fist have been quite neglected inside; the hand holds a bronze tool, that is like a large nail. The marble is apparently not Pentelic; and this circumstance, together with the fact that the work is anything but remarkable, shews that the fragment certainly did not belong to a metope of the Parthenon as is stated (Michaelis, *Parthenon*, p. 124). L. 0·31, from the bend of the elbow to the wrist 0·165. [*]

GALLERY OF THE HALL.

15. **Head of a Roman lady of rank**, with a stephanè adorned with palmettes: belongs probably to the first century, and reminds us somewhat of Agrippina. A fine head with strongly, much arched nose and a very delicate mouth; the hair forms numerous

little ringlets on the forehead. New: great part of the stephanè, half the nose, and all the bust, which is draped. Life size. [*]

16. **Terminal head of a victorious youth,** with fillet of victory in his curly hair. The head, which is slightly looking up, is inclined somewhat l. after the manner of the heads of Alexander. Features very much rounded, eyes small. The whole character is Lysippian, but more in the style of an Herakles than the head of the Apoxyomenos. The nose is new, the hair has been restored in places. Good sculpture. Life size. [*]

17. **Torso of a youth,** resting on r. leg. Very small part of legs preserved; the r. arm was lowered and the l. probably formed a right angle with the elbow, which was supported on some object; only a part of the arm is preserved and even this is perhaps spurious. Indifferent sculpture. H. 0·42. [*]

18. **Statue of Seilenos as Herakles.** Clarac, v. 790 B, 1084 A. The motive of this statue is the same as the Farnese 'Resting Herakles' by Glykon, with the exception that here the inclination of the body is exaggerated even to parody, and the lion's skin (restored in many places) covers the head, a part of the back, and the upper end of the club on which the l. shoulder of the statue is supported. The face (the nose has been restored) belongs undoubtedly to a bald-headed Seilenos, who is here making a parody of Herakles, as Eros does sometimes. New: r. arm and probably also the hand behind the back, with the bunch of grapes, which takes the place of the apples of the Hesperides; l. hand, exclusive of the thumb, the lower part of the club, the lower half of both legs, the pedestal and the lowest portion of the mass of rock on which the club rests. Decorative sculpture. Greek marble. H. 0·71. (A statuette of "Hercules rusticus," "about 4 palmi" [0·88] high, formerly in the possession of the architect Carlo Antonini, is rather differently restored, but is very similar to this one, Guattani, *Mon. Ined.,* 1787, Aug., Pl. 3. Clarac v. 790 B, 1984. Can it be that the two statues are identical?) [*]

19. **Statue of Seilenos, sitting on a mass of rock.** Clarac IV. 730 B, 1755 B. Seilenos is sitting in a tolerably upright position. The original motive cannot be distinguished with sufficient certainty, as both arms, the r. with a goblet in the hand, have been restored. New also: outstretched r. leg from the half of the thigh, the l. shin between the knee and the foot (which leans towards the rock). The head, bald and ivy-crowned (nose, part of beard and of wreath have been restored), is probably original, although the

neck is a modern insertion. Good work; Greek marble, much corroded. H. 0·93. [*]

20. **Dionysos.** Clarac, IV. 696, 1619 B. The god is quite nude. He stands, resting on his r. leg, near the trunk of a tree, before which a panther is sitting, looking up at a bunch of grapes held by the god in his lowered r. hand. The l. arm singularly strained (or twisted) holds the stem of a thyrsos. The head, with long curls and vine-wreath, is inclined towards the r. shoulder. The proportions, particularly those of the legs, are somewhat heavy. The head and arms were broken, the latter in many places, but as they have been repaired with Thasian marble similar to that of the body, it is difficult to state the restorations in detail. New: without doubt the principal part of the panther, probably also the god's l. foot, almost all his l. arm and the thyrsos, and perhaps his r. hand; I also doubt the authenticity of the head. Ordinary decorative work. H. 0·81. [*]

21. **Crouching greyhound bitch:** with collar, raising r. paw: it is the counterpart to no. 23. New: mouth, ears, part of neck, parts of the forelegs. Coarse-grained Greek marble. H. 0·64. [*]

22. **Eros and Psychè.** Clarac, IV. 653, 1501 B. This group is a tolerably exact copy of the famous Capitoline Sculpture; here also we notice the absence of wings. Eros wears a top-knot on his crown and so does Psychè, she further has a plait along the parting and a fillet. Eros is certainly antique as far as his knees, and the upper part of Psychè's body to below her waist is old also; the rest of her body, though much pieced, appears to be also antique, but it is impossible to vouch for Eros' head and Psychè's forearm and hand; some trifles have been filled in. Rather smooth work. Coarse-grained Greek marble. H. 0·75. [*]

23. **Crouching hound** with a collar, companion to no. 21. The upraised head and neck are put on and perhaps modern; the l. leg certainly modern. Good work. Marble, same as no. 21. H. 0·68. [*]

24. **Statue of "Ganymedes."** Clarac, III. 410 B, 706 A. The statue is nude and from its bending posture it is probable that the l. arm rested on a support. The restorer arbitrarily made it into a Ganymede. New: almost the whole of r. leg with the eagle, three parts of l. leg, the lower part of r. arm, three parts of l. arm and the cup, also the neck. The head (of which the nose is new), slightly bent and encircled with a fillet, apparently belongs to the rest of the

figure, the ends of the fillet well joined to the tops of the shoulders.
The body is treated smoothly but without much character, the head
is worn. Apparently Italian marble. H. 1·06. [*]

25. **Egyptian Statue** with apron and calantica : l. foot
advanced, supported behind by a column. The whole statue is probably modern. Oriental alabaster. H. 0.92. [*].

26. **Statue of Hermaphroditos.** Clarac, IV. 668, 1554. The
figure is perfectly nude, it rests on the r. leg and the hip is much
curved outwards. The principal part of the torso, and the thighs
with the portion of the support adhering to the l. thigh, are antique.
The breast and hips are decidedly feminine ; the masculine member
is very weak and the navel unusually sunk. New : head and
neck, arms, together with the shoulders, part of the r. breast, and all
below the knees. Work insignificant, marble coarse-grained. H. 1·04.
Cf. Oxford, no. 34. A very similar figure in a better state of preservation is in Berlin (Clarac, v. 669, 1546 C). [*]

27. **Statue of Pan.** Spec., II., Pl. 55. Clarac, IV. 726 A,
1740 B. Pan, with his goat's legs, is leaning against a tree trunk,
a skin folded round his l. arm, which he holds behind his back,
while he uplifts his r. arm. New : the whole of r. arm with the pedum
and parts of the legs ; the head has been put on, but is antique ;
only the nose and part of the horns have been restored. The figure
is well executed in a lively manner and corresponds to the one in
Dresden, no. 57 (Clarac, III. 544, 1142). Fine-grained Greek
marble. H. 0·87. [*]

COLONNADE OF THE SOUTH FRONT, FIRST STOREY.

28. **Bust of Antinous** in Egyptian costume, with calantica
reaching below the breast. More than life size. The pupils of the
eyes and the eyebrows are indicated. Restored : nose, ears, lips, parts
of the calantica. Ordinary work. Italian marble. H. 0·67. [*]

29. **Head of Athenè** ; colossal scale ; with the so-called
Corinthian helmet, the front shield of which is ornamented with
rams' heads. The head is inclined somewhat l. ; the hair is gathered
into a plait behind. New : nose, upper and half lower lip, chin and
parts of helmet. Insignificant sculpture. [*]

30. **Statue of a Bacchante** resting on her r. leg, with the l.
leg drawn back, supporting her r. hand on her hip and lowering the
l. She is clothed in a girdled chiton that has slipped down from
her r. shoulder, and a cloak is thrown round her hips and thighs.
Near her l. leg stands a tree round which a snake is twined. New :

probably l. hand, undoubtedly the kantharos in this hand, parts of
the tree and of the snake. Neck cracked right through, but there
is no doubt that the head with its round cheeks and long curls,
adorned with an ivy wreath and fillet, is antique and belonging to
the figure ; it looks towards the l. shoulder. The tip of the nose and
details have been restored. The entire sculpture is treated quite in
a decorative style and so thoroughly re-touched that one might take
it at first for a modern work. The back is left almost rough.
Thasian marble. H. 1·30. [*]

31. **Head of a Roman**, colossal scale, bearded, nose unusually squeezed in and lower lip standing out ; the hair curly.

32. **Statuette of a female** : style of affected archaism. The
figure draped in a woollen chiton, of which we see only the sleeves
and the piece by the feet, for over it falls a cloak reaching to the
ankles, with a long piece folded over in front (*diploïdion*), and two
corners hanging in zigzag folds. L. foot is somewhat in advance.
Face surrounded by a row of round button-like curls. New : three
parts of the lowered l. arm with an ewer, lower half of r. arm (which
is advanced), half of the feet, nose and upper lip. The imitation
of archaism is very superficial. Grey-striped marble. H. 0·23. [*]

33. **Bust of Cicero** : apparently a modern copy of the
Mattei bust (London, Apsley House, no. 1). Nose restored, neck
broken. L. of face 0·24, a measurement which agrees with that of
the Mattei bust. [*]

34. **Statue of Apollo**, nude, resting on his l. leg, with r.
leg slightly bent ; beside the l. leg is the trunk of a tree. The
head, crowned with laurel, and with long curls, has been put on,
but it belongs to the figure. New : tip of nose, r. arm with quiver
(the strap of which is held by the lowered hand), lower half of the l.
arm with the fragment of a bow, upper part of r. leg, the l. foot
and the lowest portion of the trunk. An insignificant sculpture.
Thasian marble. H. 1·45. [*]

35. **Statue of a Nymph.** Cavaceppi, *Racc.*, I. Pl. 22.
Clarac, IV. 599, 1312. A replica of an oft-repeated figure, supposed
by Jahn (*Archaeol. Aufs.*, p. 27) to be Amymone, by Bernoulli
(*Aphrodite*, p. 366), to be Thetis or Amphitrite, by others to be
Aphrodite. In the above-cited engravings of the statue belonging
to "Milord Hope in England" the support beside the r. leg is
described as the trunk of a palm tree, in the copy at Deepdene
as a vase ; therefore either a new restoration has been undertaken,
or the copies are different, as other antiques of "Milord Hope"

(Introd. § 54, note 244) are certainly not at Deepdene. New parts in the Deepdene statue: lower part of r. arm, and the vase covered with a drapery (that a support, probably a dolphin, was always there, is proved by a *puntello* on the r. hip), half of the r. foot and a part of the pedestal. The neck is inserted, but the head old and apparently belonging to the figure; the hair is plaited into a large top-knot (κόρυμβος) on the crown and gathered together on the back of the neck; it falls in two long curls over the shoulders. The drapery has been mended here and there. The folds are well treated and on the l. side show a rich composition. Coarse-grained Parian marble. H. 1·40. [*]

36. **Statue of Dionysos.** Clarac, IV. 696 A, 1641 A. The god is standing in a very constrained position; upper part of his body nude, but round his waist and legs a wide cloak is thrown, the corners of which fall down in zigzag folds from his advanced l. arm. The head has been put on, but is old; the beard however is for the most part new; so also are the r. arm with the goblet, the l. forearm with the thyrsos, the feet and a part of the cloak. The imitation of archaism is very neatly carried out. H. 0·62. [*]

37. **Statue of draped female** ("Isis"). Clarac, V. 990, 2569 A. The figure stands in a constrained position with the r. foot stretched out. She wears a long chiton, over which hangs a peplos after the fashion of an ungirdled doubled chiton. This peplos, which reaches very far down, is opened on the l. side, forming slight zigzag folds. The original motive of the drapery has been misunderstood by the restorer, to whom we are indebted for the principal part of the upper half of the body, the head, the breast and both arms; also half the r. foot is new. Elegant work. H. 0·66. [*]

38. **Terminal bust of the bearded Dionysos,** crowned with ivy. H. 0·20. [*]

39. **Statue of Athenè.** *Spec.*, I., Pl. 25. II. Pl. 9. Clarac, III. 459, 850. Müller-Wieseler, II. 19, 202. Braun, *Kunstmythologie*, Pl. 59. This beautiful type, which was formerly incorrectly referred to the Parthenos of Pheidias, is the same as that of the Farnese statue

(Clarac, III. 458, 851 A), in comparison with which the Hope statue
is far behind in value. A doubled cloak, fastened on the r. shoulder
and covered above by the wide aegis divided into two parts, forms a
splendid group of folds of simple composition and rich effect ;
below, the chiton with its smaller folds is visible ; it is seen also
on the arms. The l. arm was always raised, the r. lowered and
advanced. The head, which is slightly inclined, has long curls, and
is covered by a closely-fitting "Attic" helmet ornamented above
with a sphinx, and on either side with a griffin. The execution of
this statue, which was formerly valued far beyond its worth, is merely
decorative ; the folds of the chiton have no life, those of the cloak
are treated meagrely ; the rendering of the puckered edge of the
selvage appears particularly superficial. The back is hardly more
than indicated. The part showing the best work is the head,
together with the neck. It was made separately with a view to
insertion. We should imagine the eyes to be a modern addition,
had not Fea (*Viaggio ad Ostia*, 1802, p. 45) borne witness to their
being antique "*gli occhi nel bulbo d'avorio, la pupilla incavata per
modo, che supponeva materia di altro colore; e le pennazze di lastre
d'ottone finissime.*" (This last statement is incomprehensible to me,
and is certainly not borne out by the statue.) So much of the above-
mentioned ornament of the helmet is antique as to place the sphinx
and the griffins, which are known to have adorned the helmet of
the Parthenos, beyond a doubt. The plait of hair falls down
somewhat long. The aegis is rounded at the back and goes to below
the shoulder-blades. New: both arms with a part of the chiton, the
stiff figure of Nikè on the r. hand and the spear in the l., part of the
snakes on the aegis and also the chin and nose of the Gorgon's
head ; partly also the toes on the r. foot. Carrara marble. Found
at Ostia in 1797, together with no. 7, *q. v.* H. 2·00 [*]

40. Torso of a Satyr. Clarac, IV. 709, 1671 C. The head,
with its pointed ears and small horns, is ancient except the nose, but
does not belong to the torso ; the neck is an insertion. New : both
arms with the cymbals, the r. leg, which is somewhat raised, with the
wooden shoe (κροίπεζα), the lower half of l. leg, and the principal part
of the tree trunk, with the syrinx. The torso itself, the remains of
which show that a some such movement was intended, is not so
badly executed. H. 0·61. [*]

41. Small head, like the Blacas **Asklepios** in the British
Museum. A pretty piece. The neck is so much bent that the
head, which is inclined l., can look up. (Compare the head of Zeus

19—2

on the Zulian cammeo, Müller-Wieseler, II. 1, 5.) The long curly
hair hangs far down on the neck. New: nose. Work not fine,
but effective. H. 0·14. L. of face 0·07. [*]

42. **Marble relief**: roughly sketched and of late date. With
three rows of figures, in many parts similar to the bronze plate, *Mon.
dell' Inst.*, IV. 38, 1 : *Arch. Zeit.*, 1854, Pl. 65, 3. H. 0·24. L. 0·19.—
Upper row. In the midst sits amid flames (?) a swan, or a
phœnix ; below are three busts, the middle one of which appears to
be female and is draped ; the two others have pointed beards and
pointed Phrygian caps. On either side stands a man in a similar
pointed cap: the man to the r. seen from the front, has a long staff in
his l. hand, and his r. hand rests on his side ; the man to the l. is
clothed in a chlamys, and holding a large indistinct object of the
shape of an alabastros to the l. over the trunk of a tree (?). At
either end on a low pedestal is a bust ; the one on the r. hand of a
female, on the l. seemingly of a man.—**Middle row.** In the middle
stands a female with long drapery, behind a three-legged table on
which a fish is lying ; she holds both hands out from her body at a
right angle, so that each may touch the mouth of a horse standing
quietly by. On either horse sits a rider with pointed beard and
pointed cap, short doublet and short cloak, and with the face turned
towards the spectator. Under the horse on the l. a man lies stretched
out on the ground, below him to the r. is a dog. A serpent is visible
over each rider, with its head turned to the centre towards the head
of the female ; behind each rider in the upper corner is the upper
part of a draped figure, the one to the l. with arms outstretched.—
Lower row. In the centre kneels a figure in short drapery,
seen from the front, partly hidden by a large mysterious object,
which may in some measure be described as a wide-stretched
slanting cross with all the corners and angles rounded off; each
upper arm of this object is held by a man with a pointed beard in
doublet, cloak and pointed cap. On the r. lies a bullock, and over it
a ram referring perhaps to the corresponding sacrifices Taurobolia
and Kriobolia ; on the l. stands a draped female, facing r. and
raising her r. hand to her face as if in grief; behind her a high
unrecognisable object, below a ball or a shield.— This relief has been
known at least since the middle of the seventeenth century, as we
see by a drawing at Windsor from the collection of Dal Pozzo (Vol.
II. *fol.* 30). [*]

43. **Four candelabra** and sundry **vases** and pieces of
decoration have been pieced together from antique and modern

fragments in the fashion of Piranesi. For one of these candelabra
see Moses, *Coll. of Antique Vases*, Pl. 87. [*]

BEFORE THE SOUTH FRONT OF THE HOUSE.

44. Terminal head, bearded, probably of a **Dionysos**, of
good, severe archaic style. Larger than life size. [*]

45. Similar **terminal head**, but of very vacant expression and
common style. [*]

I have not found out

46. Statue of Satyr sitting on a mass of rock. Clarac, IV.
718, 1718. R. foot placed somewhat higher than the l., which is far
advanced. The r. arm, with a syrinx, is lowered, the l. is extended
with the hand open ; the head, crowned with ivy, is directing the
glance to his l. hand. Grey marble. Clarac only expresses doubt
about the wreath and the syrinx, and says that in other respects the
statue is in a state of good preservation ; but it seems to me that the
whole figure is not free from suspicion, and even the good preservation of the arms, for instance, rather strengthens the doubts awakened
by the whole character of the composition.

The remains of a **Collection of vases**, that was once much
larger, are placed on shelves in a spacious room. The foundation of
this cabinet was formed by sixteen cases full of vases from Sir Will.
Hamilton's second collection (Introd. § 64), which Thomas Hope
purchased in 1801 for 4500 guineas, after eight other cases had
been lost in the shipwreck of the Colossus off the Scilly Isles, on
their passage from Naples to England. In 1805 Hope sold 180
of the specimens. Other purchases were made gradually from
the Cawdor, Chinnery, Edwards, Coghill, Parois, Durand, Magnon-
court, Beugnot and other collections. (Millin, *Mon. Inéd.*, II. p. 15,
Vases peints, I. p. XVIII., Dallaway, II. p. 140, note.) In 1849 a sale
of vases took place (*Arch. Anzeiger*, 1849, p. 97), and from a hurried
survey I took, it appeared to me that not many specimens of conspicuous value had remained behind, but that those which were left
were chiefly vases from Lower Italy, in which the decorative style
preponderated. It is however to be wished that a better review
should be made, particularly that a comparison be instituted with
Tischbein's *Collection of Engravings, &c.*, Naples, 1791—1803, 4
Vols., the originals of which work were taken from Hamilton's second
collection (Introd. §§ 61—64).

DENTON HALL. (Northumberland).

This estate is situated not far from Newcastle-on-Tyne, and belongs to LORD ROKEBY (the ROBINSON-MONTAGU family). I have received a communication to the effect that here is preserved the "bas-relief of Niobe and her children, found near Naples, and intended as a present from his Sicilian majesty to his brother of Spain, which was taken at sea, and purchased by the late Sir Thomas Robinson," so highly praised by Dallaway, p. 388 (II. p. 141). In fact the relief is not now at Rokeby Hall, once the property of Sir Thomas, as quoted by Volkmann (*Reisen*, IV. p. 101), and Dallaway, and no one there was able to say if it ever had been there. Thomas Robinson, who died without heirs, was a brother of Matthew, 2nd Baron Rokeby, and of Morris Robinson, whose sons, Morris and Matthew Robinson-Montagu, became successively 3rd and 4th Barons Rokeby. In this way the relief may have passed to Denton Hall, while other smaller sculptures, once in the possession of Thos. Robinson, are still to be seen at Rokeby Hall (*q. v.*). The notices probably refer to a sarcophagus relief, cf. Matz, *Arch. Zeit.*, 1873, p. 25.

DITCHLEY (Oxfordshire).

Dallaway, *Of Statuary*, p. 314, mentions that a statue of **Hygieia** from Doctor Mead's collection (*Museum Meadianum*, p. 221), was on his sale in the year 1755 (Introd. § 29) transferred to VISCOUNT DILLON'S above-mentioned country house.

DUNCOMBE PARK (Yorkshire).

Volkmann, *Reisen durch England*, IV. p. 113. Waagen, *Treas.*, IV. p. 492.

This estate, which belongs to the EARL OF FEVERSHAM (DUNCOMBE family), is near Helmsley (on a branch line of the North-Eastern Railway). Two antiques may still be seen in the HALL which were mentioned by Dallaway, pp. 389 ff., (II. pp. 143 ff.) as being in the possession of Mr Duncombe.

1. A **crouching dog**, mentioned by Winckelmann, *Kunst-gesch.*, v. 6, 23, as a beautiful specimen; large size. Purchased in Rome by a zealous dilettante, Mr Jennings of Shiplake, and after-

wards purchased for a thousand guineas at a sale at Christie's by
Mr Duncombe (cf. Dallaway, *Of Statuary*, p. 348. Introd. § 54);
it has been engraved by Cavaceppi (*Racc.*, I. Pl. 6), who had
restored the dog and who was inclined to ascribe it to no less a
master than Pheidias (Casanova, *Discorsi sopra gl' Antichi*, p. LXI.).
Cf. Winckelmann, *Werke*, IV. p. 429, note 710, where similar specimens are quoted. Hor. Walpole (*Works*, II. p. 463) reckons the dog
among the five chief statues of animals; Waagen considers it more
animated and of more careful workmanship than the Florentine
dog. New: according to Waagen and to a critic in the *Athenaeum*,
1880, Sept. 11, p. 345, only the l. forefoot; according to Casanova
(p. LXII.) also half the muzzle. Of Parian marble. [*W*]

2. Statue of a Diskobolos. Cavaceppi, *Racc.*, I. Pl. 42.
Clarac, V. 863, 2196. A replica of the Diskobolos ascribed by Visconti
to Naukydes of Argos (*Mus. Pio-Clem.*, III. p. 119 Mil.), which has
been more correctly recognised by Kekulé as Attic (*Arch. Zeit.*, 1866,
pp. 169 ff.), and brought into connection with Alkamenes' "canonical
statue" (*encrinomenos*). The Duncombe replica appears to have
belonged originally to Giambattista Vettori in Rome (see Mercurialis, *De arte gymnast.*, II, ch. 12); from the Villa Montalto, the
splendid creation of Pope Sixtus V., it passed through Cavaceppi's
hands to that wealthy dilettante Mr Locke of Norbury Park
(Introd. § 54), and Duncombe bought it out of Mr Locke's collection for £341. 5s. 0d., (cf. Visconti, p. 121. Noehden in Böttiger,
Amalthea, III. p. 12). To judge from a cast now in the Strassburg
museum and probably the only one in existence, it seems to me
a mediocre specimen not to be compared with the surpassingly
excellent Vatican statue. Such was also the opinion of Gav. Hamilton, when he described the last-named statue as "much finer than
that of Mr Lock, which makes so great a noise in the world"
(*Academy*, 1878, Aug. 17, p. 169). It appears besides that the
statue at Duncombe is disfigured by a very inappropriate head, found,
however, already in Mercurialis' engraving (1573). New: according
to Clarac only the neck and the r. hand (which is missing in Mercurialis), according to Waagen, the nose, mouth, chin, part of the neck
and the r. hand; but neither of these connoisseurs is always quite
complete in his lists of restorations, and the insertion of the neck
cannot but strengthen the conviction that the head does not belong
to the statue, though it may be ancient. According to the above-
cited article in the *Athenaeum*, the statue is "of Roman work, and,
like the dog, of Parian marble." H. 1·68. [*W*]

In Thomas Allen's *History of the county of York*, III. p. 471, we further find mentioned as being in the LIBRARY four antique statues:—

   3. **Apollo,**
   4. **Bacchus,**
   5. **Mars,** and
   6. **Mercury** ; also
   7. Two good busts of **Cicero,** and
   8. **Horace** (?).

Volkmann gives a still fuller list, for in his time (1782) the hall and the saloon were adorned with various statues, but it is not stated whether they were all antique. Nos. 1 and 2 he ignores ; but he mentions in the HALL :—

   9. **Jupiter,**
  10. **Mercury,**
  11. **Minerva,**
  12. **Mars,**
  13. **Venus,**
  14. **Diana** ;

in the SALOON he places nos. 3—7 ; in the DRAWING ROOM :—

  15. A small statue of **Antonius** ;

finally in a TEMPLE IN THE GARDEN :—

  16. **Four statues.**

The building was severely damaged by a fire in January 1879. The grand saloon and the library were destroyed ; the principal works of art, in particular the dog and the Diskobolos, were however rescued (*Athenæum*, 1879, Jan. 18, p. 96). Thus, the above-quoted critic (*Athenæum*, 1880) found in the Hall nos. 1 and 2, the life-size figures of Mercury, Apollo, and Bacchus (nos. 3, 4, 6 ?), and "a certain number of modern busts."

DUNROBIN CASTLE (Sutherlandshire, Scotland).

I have only a communication from Edinburgh stating that the DUKE OF SUTHERLAND possesses some antiques in Dunrobin Castle on Dornoch Firth, I can say nothing more definite about them. Such a collection would be the most northerly of all the antique collections in Great Britain.

EASTON NESTON (Northamptonshire).

This estate, the property of the EARLS OF POMFRET, is not far

from Towcester, and here were deposited a large portion of the
Arundel Marbles, till in 1755 the widowed Countess Henrietta
Louisa purchased them from her son and presented them to the
University of Oxford. (Cf. Introd. § 24.) We have a very clear
account of their arrangement at Easton Neston from George Vertue,
who probably inspected them in 1734. His work, *A description
of Easton Neston in Northamptonshire, the seat of the Rt. Hon. the
Earl of Pomfret*, is a sequel to the book, *A Catalogue of the Curious
Collections of Pictures of George Villiers, Duke of Buckingham*,
London, 1758, pp. 53—59. This book mentions some marbles
which are not to be found at Oxford and which perhaps were left at
Easton Neston; I therefore now append notices of them :

1, 2. "Two fine statues of the **Two Scipios** in their general's
habit, very perfect and exceeding fine." (P. 54.)

3. "A statue very noble, and bigger than the life, of **Quintus
Fabius Maximus**, in his senatorial robes (a true antique as are
both the Scipios), the l. hand is wanting, the r. held up in a speaking
posture." (P. 54.)

4. "A **sun dial**." (P. 56.)

5. "A fine statue of a **senator** in his robes." (P. 56.)

6. "A **Judith** with Holofernes's head, r. arm and l. hand wanting." (P. 56, where she is expressly mentioned among the antiques ;
perhaps a Muse with a mask ?)

Another statue belonging to the Arundel Collection, which has
disappeared, may also be mentioned here :

7. "**Paris**," Sandrart, *Sculpt. vet. admiranda*, Nürnberg, 1680,
Pl. 54, "*inter Arundeliana quondam monumenta, Londini*" (r. and
l. reversed, as in all the engravings of this book). A youth resting
on l. leg with r. knee bent ; his only drapery is the chlamys which
covers his shoulders and back, and the corner of which he holds in
his lowered r. hand. His l. hand is advanced and holds the apple,
which is like a large ball. He wears on his feet some sort of boots,
undoubtedly modern. It is difficult to believe that the l. arm is
antique and so there is no sufficient reason to believe that Paris is
intended.

EDINBURGH.

Antiquarian Museum.

*Catalogue of Antiquities in the Museum of the Society of Antiquaries
of Scotland.* Waagen, *Treas.*, IV., pp. 42) ff.

One division (E) embraces Greek, Etruscan, Roman and other antiquities. Among them are eight marble sculptures from **Cyrene**, which were probably all presented in 1830 by R. HAY, Esq., Under-secretary of State. Those worthy of mention are:

1. **Statue of Asklepios**, marble. H. 1·27.

3. **Fragment of a votive relief**, l. end: bounded on the l. by an anta, surmounted by an architrave with tiles on the top. Quite to the l. is Artemis, in long drapery, with two long torches; opposite to her is a youth half concealed by his cloak; he has a cup in his r. hand and a large empty cornucopia in his l. arm (Agathodaemon? according to Scharf Acheloos); behind is a female, draped and holding a cup. All the rest is lost. The three figures are of equal stature and very slender, and the heads are small and severe. Unfinished marble of good Greek style. Cf. *Arch. Zeit.*, 1874, p. 17. [From a sketch and notes by G. Scharf.]

12, 14, 15. **Female heads**: imperfect.

13. **Head of a warrior**, with flowing hair: imperfect.

Of the remaining marbles I may mention:

6. **Sarcophagus**, from Rhodes, with roof-like cover, as is peculiar to Greek sarcophagi in contradistinction to those of Rome. (See Matz, *Arch. Zeit.*, 1873, pp. 11 f.)

16. **Bust of Julius Caesar**, life size: brought from Italy by the late General Ramsay (from the Casali Palace in Rome?). "The nose is unusually thick, and the forms very prominent. If this bust be antique, it is probably not earlier than towards the end of the 2nd century after Christ." (Waagen, *Treas.*, IV. p. 431.)

22. **Man on horseback**, fragment from Bavay (France, Dép. du Nord), the ancient capital of the Nervii (Bagacum).

23. **Fragments of ornaments** in relief, from the Choragic monument of Lysicrates at Athens.

Of the **terra cottas** (nos. 28—117), a considerable number come from **Knidos**, e. g. nos. 49—56 figures from the temenos of Demeter, nos. 57, 58 heads, nos. 59, 60 circular weights for the loom, from the temple of Aphrodite. These antiquities are due to Mr Newton's well known excavations on the site of these temples, A. D. 1858, and were presented by him to the Museum.—Nos. 61—117 are lamps found in various places.

There are also some **vases**, but apparently none of any importance.

ARCHITECTS' INSTITUTION.

There is a "Catalogue of Antiquities in the Museum of the Archit. Inst., Edinb. 1859"; but I only know it by name.

ROYAL INSTITUTION.

In the buildings of the R. Institution are to be found, belonging to the legacy of Sir JAMES ERSKINE, some small torsos, and among them that of (1) a **draped female** in Parian marble, and also that of (2) a **man**, with the head and limbs restored. (Waagen, *Treas.*, III. p. 272.) Can the former be the charming torso from Keos which has been lost sight of, engraved in Bröndstedt, *Voy. et Recherches en Grèce*, I. Pl. 9?

A. COVENTRY, ESQ.

See London, Crichton.

LORD MURRAY'S COLLECTION.

LORD MURRAY, Gt Stuart Street, possesses, or at least did possess in 1856, the antiques (some of which are very beautiful), collected by General RAMSAY in Rome; among them Waagen, *Treas.*, IV. p. 431, singles out:

1. "**Flat relief of a horseman**, with the chlamys and the petasos. H. abt. 0·33. W. 0·51."

2. "**A relief** in Pentelic marble, a fragment of a **horse**, and of a **man** holding it; treated in the style of the frieze of the Parthenon, of rare beauty." [Sepulchral?]

3. "**Head of Bacchus**, with the fig branch; **mezzo rilievo**, in terra cotta. Very noble in character, and of broad and careful workmanship."

4. "**Bacchante** in bronze, with a wreath of vine-leaves, lightly draped, and with the nebris. Two bunches of grapes at the sides. A relief showing a very peculiar conception of the character, and of a soft workmanship truly conformable to style." [Antique?]

5. "**Bronze statuette of Venus** holding her hair in her raised l. hand, and in the r. a golden patera [mirror?]. She is decorated with a golden armlet, and gold rings round her ankles. At her feet is **Cupid**, holding in his l. hand a looking-glass, in his r., as it appears, an apple. The Venus is high, about 1·10, the (original) pedestal 0·05. The workmanship is tolerably good."

6. "Bronze vase (*praefericulum*) with the head of a youth, about ⅔ life-size, of singular delicacy and beauty of features. The treatment of the hair with little prominence is antiquated."

7. "Small head of Atys, or Adonis [?] of terra cotta."

The bust of Jul. Caesar has been incorporated into the Anti-quarian Museum, (cf. supra, no. 16).

HAMILTON PALACE (Lanarkshire, Scotland).

Waagen, *Treas.*, III., pp. 296, 298, 305 ff.

This magnificent Castle of the DUKE OF HAMILTON is situated near Hamilton, in the neighbourhood of Glasgow. Among the antiques of the palace the following deserve mention :

IN THE LARGE STAIRCASE.

1. "An admirable example of the Venus of the Capitol, in Parian marble." [*W*] Purchased by Gav. Hamilton, who writes thus to Lord Shelburne, 1776, Jan. 6. (*Academy*, 1878, Aug. 31, p. 220.) "The large Venus I had in my possession is now on its way to Scotland. The Duke of Hamilton fell in love with it the moment he saw it, and secured it immediately. It is a fine thing."

IN THE DINING SALOON.

2. "Antique bust of Venus ; new : nose and lower lip. The conception remarkable as being midway between that of the Venus of Milo and of Medici, and at the same time of a beauty of work-manship which bears witness to a Greek chisel." [*W*]

3. "Bust of the dying Alexander ; conceived exactly like the marble at Florence, and in the finest red porphyry. Wonderfully executed." [*W*] Antique ?

IN THE MARBLE STAIRCASE.

4, 5. "Porphyry busts of the Emperors Augustus and Ves-pasian ; the latter very forcible, and taken at an advanced period of life." [*W*] Antique ?

6. "Admirable bust of Vespasian ; the head of nero antico, the bust of coloured marble. Formerly at Strawberry Hill." [*W*] Hor. Walpole, *Works*, II., p. 465, says about this bust : "Ves-pasian, in basaltes ; a noble bust bought out of the collection of Cardinal Ottoboni." Cf. Introd. § 41.

Besides these antiques described by Waagen, in the "Stowe Catalogue," 1848 (cf. Introd., notes 422, 451), p. 265, the three follow-

ing "fine antique marble statues, of heroic size" are mentioned
as having been purchased by the Duke of Hamilton.

7. (No. 30.) "**Apollo**, with the attributes of the god of
Medicine. This fine statue was found in the island of Lemnos.
(£46. 6s.)"

8. (No. 31.) "A **Roman Consul** in the act of speaking
(£168). The two statues were purchased in Italy by the Duke of
Buckingham in 1829."

9. (No. 34.) "**Paris** holding out the apple of discord. This
statue was discovered near the ruins of the ancient Lanuvium, in
1771, by Gavin Hamilton (£52. 10s.)." Hamilton himself speaks of
this statue in his letters to Lord Shelburne, 1774, Jan. 16, May 1,
(*Academy*, 1878, Aug. 24). According to him the neck is modern,
but the head its own. "The statue is in the attitude of giving the
apple to Venus. The drapery is very fine. It wants the left hand
and one half of the right arm. The rest is preserved, as it came out
of the sculptor's hands." The statue was found in 1773; Hamilton
offered it to Lord Shelburne for £400.

According to a statement of R. Lanciani's (given by Matz in the
Nachrichten von der Kgl. Ges. d. Wiss. in Göttingen, 1872, p. 66), the
Duke of Hamilton possesses some volumes with original drawings
from the antique, taken from the collection of the Commend. dal
Pozzo (cf. Holkham, *ad fin.* and Windsor), but this statement has
been doubted by competent authority. Cf. Matz, *Arch. Zeit.*, 1873,
p. 34. I have not been able to obtain any more definite information
on the subject.

HILLINGDON COURT (Middlesex).

Years ago Mr Newton saw on the lawn of that place a **recumbent
bull** of Pentelic marble, a very fine work of the Athenian School.
It had been brought over from Athens, about sixty years ago, by the
late Mr Cockerell. In landing it at London the sailors contrived to
slip it into the Thames. The fishing it out cost so much that
Cockerell declined to pay the freight. The bull then went to the
London Custom House, where it remained some years, till Mr
James Bandinel got hold of it. He sold or gave it to Mr MILLS, the
owner of Hillingdon Court, nr. West Drayton. I am informed that
the marble is still existing in that place, but to what extent, being
exposed in the open air, it may have suffered from the destroying
influences of English climate, I am unable to say.

HOLKHAM HALL (Norfolk).

Mat. Brettingham, *The plans, elevations, &c. of Holkham*, London, 1761. Dallaway, pp. 275 ff. (II. pp. 7 ff.) Waagen, *Treasures*, III. pp. 413 ff. (II. pp. 494 ff.). Clarac, III. pp. 36 f. Conze, *Arch. Anz.*, 1864, pp. 213 f. Matz, *Arch. Zeitung*, 1873, pp. 30 f. 35. *Guide to Holkham*, Norwich, 1861. I have examined the collection myself minutely (in the year 1877), and in particular I verified the notices of restorations, which in some cases show striking discrepancies.

Thomas Coke, EARL OF LEICESTER (acc. 1744), is the founder of this fine collection, of the history of which a general account has been given in the Introduction §§ 34, 42. Here may be mentioned again the valuable Book of Accounts, kept by one of Mr Coke's servants on his tour through Italy (A.D. 1716, 1717), which has been discovered in the library at Holkham by the present librarian, the Rev. Alex. Napier, whose kindness has enabled me to incorporate in the following descriptions all that is interesting in that book. But the main part of the antiques was procured much later for Lord Leicester, by Matthew Brettingham, who purchased in Italy after 1755 for the decoration of the sculpture gallery, and some other rooms of Lord Leicester's newly built palace, a considerable number of statues and busts. He gives brief information about the purchase thereof in the above-mentioned book (see Hor. Walpole, *Works*, III. p. 491. Dallaway, p. 271 [II. p. 3]. Payne Knight in *Specimens of Antient Sculpture*, I. on Pl. 72). Dallaway's information rests exclusively on Brettingham's authority. Since the founder's death (1759) the collection has not been increased. The numbering given below follows the order in the rooms of the Hall.

GALLERY OF THE HALL.

Besides a number of plaster casts there are here:

1. **Statue of a Roman in toga: head of Septimius Severus** attached. Clarac, V. 966, 2481 A. New: of the head, tip of nose; of the body, all r. arm with roll and half l. forearm. Mean work. Marble of poor quality. Bought by Brettingham. H. 1·97. [*]

2. **Statue of a Satyr.** Clarac, IV. 704 B, 1671 A. Only the torso, resting on the l. leg, old. An unimportant work. A nebris falls from l. shoulder down back. New: head, both arms and r. shoulder, part of the animal's head, half the lower part of r. leg, almost all l. leg and the support. Purchased of Mr Pond by Brettingham. H. 1·61. [*]

3. **Statue of a Satyr.** Clarac, IV. 714, 1701. As both arms with the cymbals, both legs from the knees with the wooden shoe (κρούπεζα) and the whole support are new, it is hard to say what the original motive of the slim statue really was. Perhaps he held his hand over his eyes, gazing into the distance, and shading his eyes from the glare of the sun (ἀποσκοπεῖν, ἀποσκοπεύειν), a favourite motive of later vase-painters. On the youthful curly-haired head, which has never been broken off, one notices brutish ears, on the back a little tail. New: nose. Mediocre sculpture. H. 1·48. This is probably the statue bought by Mr Coke about which there is an entry in the Book of Accounts, " For the Faunus 110 Rom. crowns." [*]

4. **Statue called "Julia Mammaea."** Clarac, V. 929, 2371, "Agrippina the younger." Bad modern copy of the so-called "Pudicitia" in the Vatican Museum. Marble of the worst quality. Bought by Mr Coke at Rome. H. 1·63. [* W]

5. **Head of a female Bacchante,** falsely called "Juno." The hair is partly raised above a broad band into a sort of knot, partly it flows waving down behind, and forms a coil on the neck. The original was good; the copy however is very dry and moreover much worked over. New: tip of nose and the bust with bared l. breast. Bought at Rome by Brettingham. L. of face, 0·18. [*]

6, 7. **Two specimens of Mosaic,** made up into plates for the table. On a white ground hexagonal panels with coloured rosettes and similar ornaments, divided by black maeander patterns. Found in the Villa of Hadrian near Tivoli, and purchased of Monsignor Furietti by Brettingham. [*]

8. **Female head,** called "Julia, Titus' daughter." A large structure of curls over the forehead. Pupils of eyes expressed. New: tip of nose, parts of ears, neck and bust. Smooth, poor work. L. of face 0·15. [* B]

9. **Bust of Hadrian:** according to Bernoulli Antoninus Pius. But on the seriously mutilated and patched up bust all portions which are unsuitable to Hadrian are due to restoration, e.g. the curl falling down on the forehead. Old: only r. side of face and l. cheek. L. of face 0·18. [* B]

10. **Bust of Julia Mammaea.** Modern: nose, upper lip, and parts of drapery. Pupils expressed. It is a moderately executed replica of the heads in Paris (Mongez, *Iconogr. Rom.*, Pl. 52), and in the Vatican (Visconti, *Mus. Pio-Clem.*, VI. Pl. 57, 1). H. 0·60. L. of face, 0·16. [*B*]

11. **Head of a boy,** called "Geta," the Emperor, of which numerous replicas exist, referred by Mongez (*Iconogr. Rom.*, Pl. 42) to Annius Verus. New: tip of nose and a curl. Set on a draped bust restored in many places. H. 0·56. L. of face 0·15. [*B*]

12. **Bust of a Roman,** called "Gallienus": short curly hair brushed to the sides, and slight mustaches and whiskers. Pupils expressed. Good work. New: half the nose and the bust. The neck and part of drapery on neck and l. shoulder are old. Parian marble. L. of face 0·16. [*B*]

13. **Bust of Marcus Aurelius,** youthful. New: nose, upper lip and bust. L. of face 0·17. Bought by Lord Leicester in Rome, 1716, with no. 52 for 65 Roman crowns. [*B*]

STATUE GALLERY.

14. Modern bust of "**Junius Brutus,**" on the whole similar to the Capitoline bust of L. Brutus. Dallaway, no. 15. Bought by Brettingham. Its genuineness seemed doubtful to Bernoulli also. [*B*]

15. **Statue of a youthful Satyr.** Clarac, IV. 723, 1671 B. The slim youth of graceful form, without a tail, leans with his l. shoulder on a tree-trunk, near which the r. arm hangs down easily. Beneath, on the trunk the remains of a crook (*pedum*) are visible, the crooked end lowest, and the remains of the tie by which the staff of the crook was tied to the trunk. Further to the front of the trunk the bottom piece of the shaft of a spear which must have rested in the arm of the Satyr. Both weapons are suitable to the character of the Satyr that haunts wood and field. A great part of the body is covered in a very thin tight-fitting nebris, the head of which is seen near the l. shoulder; from which, besides, a little cloak falls down behind the trunk of the tree. The legs are crossed, l. slightly bent and in front of r. on which the body is supported. The feet are in sandals. R. arm lowered, but forearm raised; the hand may perhaps have always held the pipe. Restored by West-macott: head, neck, three quarters of l. arm, including the best part of the spear and pedum, half r. forearm with the pipe. The remainder of the statue is antique, though broken in several places.

The pedestal is much worked over. The motive is charming and well executed. Parian marble. For the source cf. on no. 16. II, 1·29. [*CII*]

16. **Statue of a youthful Satyr reposing.** Clarac, IV. 704 D, 1683 A. The motive is in general very like that of no. 15, but the l. arm does not hang down, both hands meeting before the breast. Moreover, the figure is more boyish, and the nebris, with an unusually large animal's head, is drawn in a narrower strip from the r. shoulder, slanting across the breast to the l. upper-arm. On the tree which supports the figure, the upper end of the pedum is antique. On the back a little tail. Of the numerous replicas of this figure, which is specially adapted to decorate villas and gardens, the most celebrated is the Borghese in the Louvre. New: head, three-quarters of r. arm, about half the l. forearm, the pipe, lower parts of both legs, and the lower half of the trunk of the tree. As to the source of nos. 15 and 16 (Dallaway, nos. 1, 2), Brettingham says:—"One was purchased of Cardinal Albani, and the other of Cavaceppi the sculptor (who restored them both), by Brettingham." II. 1·27. [*IV*]

17. **Head of "Seneca."** Modern copy (rather a caricature) of the well-known head. Coarse marble. Dallaway, no. 16. Bought by Brettingham. [*]

18. **Statue of Poseidon.** Clarac, IV. 744, 1796 A. The god, entirely nude, is stepping forward with the r. leg, which bears the weight of the body. The large dolphin close by, in beautifully rendered motion, indicates the sovereignty of the sea, with which the head is also in character. It is like that of Zeus, only with a slightly surly expression about the mouth: beard very curly, hair thrown back, but not falling down so dank as is usually the case with Poseidon. There is a clear trace of colour on the r. pupil. New: nose, the whole head seriously worked over. There is some patchery at the neck; still, the head, though rather small, seems to belong to the statue. This is a fairly exact replica of a considerably larger statue, found about twenty years ago in Cherchell (Algeria), the old capital of Mauritania (Iol or Julia Caesarea), engraved *Annali dell' Instituto*, 1857, Pl. E., 1 (Brunn). Overbeck, *Atlas zur Kunstmythologie*, Pl. 12, 34, cf. ib. Vol. II., pp. 287 ff. In this latter statue the head is more depressed, and on the advanced r. hand are the remains of a hippocampus (cf. Strabo, 8, p. 384). The modern r. arm of our statue ought to be restored accordingly. A dowel hole at the l. shoulder, and a few smirched places, shew that the trident

M. C.   20

in the l. arm has been rightly restored. Traces of the same are also to be observed on the statue from Cherchell. Lastly, the lower part of the l. leg has been restored. (Clarac's remarks are in part erroneous.) Parian marble. H. 1·64. Purchased by Brettingham of Carlo Monaldi, who restored the arms and the trident. Dallaway, no. 3. [*AHV]

19. Statue of Seilenos, called "Faun." *Spec.,* II. Pl. 7. Clarac, IV. 724, 1680 E. This most exquisite statue, distinguished moreover by its very fortunate state of preservation, amply deserves the celebrity which it enjoys. Not unlike in his pose to the often repeated *custos famulusque dei Silenus alumni* (cf. Wilton, No. 70), Seilenos supports himself with his l. arm on the trunk of a tree, and advances the relieved l. leg a little, while the hip of the r. bearing leg is accordingly protruded. A panther's skin knotted together before the breast, falls down behind the back; one corner of it being thrown over the advanced l. forearm. The powerfully-developed body of a grown man, not disfigured by a tail, corresponds to the bearded head, of dignified expression, more earnest and thoughtful than usual, without a trace of brutish feeling; only the goat's ears, the bristly beard, the hair standing up above the brow, and the snub nose betray Seilenos. A pine-wreath encircling the hair enhances the height of the head; the pupils are rendered, as also the updrawn eye-brows. Modern: only the tip of the nose, l. hand and perhaps the r. hand with the pedum; still this hand and the held part of the pedum may easily be old, and in any case are worked quite differently from the l. hand. The r. arm, though broken in several places, is old. The pedestal is mainly new. This first-rate figure, which would do honour to any museum, and can perhaps challenge all its fellows for the palm of merit, "was dug up in the Campagna of Rome, and first purchased by Cardinal Albani, from whom it was bought soon after, in the condition in which it was found, encrusted over with Tartar of the earth, by Brettingham; restored by Cavaceppi." H. 1·87. [*CII]

20. Statue of "Meleager." Clarac, v. 807, 2022 A. The attitude of the statue is vouched for by the genuine parts. The youth resting on the r. leg supports himself, with a considerable bending of the upper part of the body, on the l. arm, which is lowered vertically so that the shoulder is much pressed up. The r. arm lies behind the back. The curly youthful head looks l. into the distance. The elegant figure of good Roman work has been a little smoothed by Cavaceppi. He has besides restored the trunk of the

tree, with the boar's head and the l. arm supported thereon up to
the biceps, also the lower parts of both legs including the knees, and
part of the r. thigh, and finally the nose. The upper part of the head
from above the chin has been broken off, but it belongs to the statue,
and has suffered less by the working over than the rest. Coarse-
grained Greek marble. H. 1·72. Bought of Belisario Amadei.
Dallaway, no. 5. [*B.M.W.]

21. **Statue of Apollo.** Clarac, III. 494 B, 912 F. The
much-broken statue is almost entirely antique. New: three-quarters
of r. leg, altar and part of base, some fingers of r. hand, l. hand,
nose. All the other parts old, and belonging to each other. The
slim body is slightly inclined, and rests on the r. leg; l. arm supported on a tripod entwined with a snake, which stands on a mass of
rock; r. arm rests on the curly head. Ordinary superficial work.
Thasian marble. H. 1·57, with the base 1·64. Bought in Rome by
Mr Coke for 90 Roman crowns. Dallaway, no. 7. [*M.W.]

22. **Bust of the tutelary goddess of a town,** or of
Kybele. Old apparently: neck, face which is turned l. somewhat,
the stephane adorned with flowers, and the mural crown above it,
also the long hair falling down on the shoulders. New: veil, bust,
nose, chin. The bust is placed so high up that even with the help
of a high set of steps a close examination is impossible. It seems to
be of good sculpture. L. of face would be between 0·22 and 0·25.
Bought in Rome by Mr Coke together with no. 56 for 418 Roman
crowns. [*W.]

23. **Statue of Venus Genetrix.** Spec., II. Pl. 54. Clarac,
IV. 594, 1449 A. We are acquainted with several types of the divine
ancestress of the Julian gens, cf. Reifferscheid, Annali dell' Inst.,
1863, pp. 362 ff. Kekulé, Archaeol. epigr. Mitth. aus Oesterreich, III.
pp. 8 ff. Judging from the great number of at least twenty repetitions
(see Bernoulli, Aphrodite, pp. 86 ff.) the type represented in the
Holkham statue, obviously owing to its sensual, charming character,
was in later times far the greatest favourite; it may be traced
to a conception of the Hellenistic period. The goddess, with
her weight so decidedly on the l. leg, that the hip is forced out to
an unusual degree, is draped with an ungirdled chiton, only the l.
breast and shoulder being left bare, but by virtue of its fine, transparent, clinging texture it does not so much veil the full form as
reveal it with heightened charm; Cois tibi paene videre est ut nudam.
Then there is the frame as it were with which the mantle surrounds
the figure, without covering it in front, with one corner thrown

over the lowered and somewhat advanced l. arm, while the other
corner is drawn over the r. shoulder by the raised r. hand—a
graceful, but rather coquettish motive. Finally the slight inclination
of the head harmonises well with the waving line in which the
whole body as it were sways. Yet the countenance is remarkable
for its noble and almost chaste expression, and the hair, gathered
behind into a kind of net (ὀπισθοσφενδόνη), for its simple arrangement. The proportions of the figure are somewhat heavy. The
extremely fortunate state of preservation, by which this replica is
distinguished perhaps above all others, is unluckily a little impaired
by Cavaceppi's working over. He has only joined on the l. hand
with the hydria (instead of the apple on the coins of Sabina and the
two Faustina's), the fingers of the r. hand with the uppermost corner
of the cloak, and another piece of the folds of the cloak. R. arm
broken but old. Pentelic marble, with several cracks, slightly patched
up. H. 1·64, with base 1·71. Bought of Belisario Amadei by Brettingham. Dallaway, no. 6. [*W]

24. Artemis. Maffei, *Raccolta*, Pl. 145 (in the second edition.
1742, noticed as Mr Coke's property). Montfaucon, *Antiq. expli-
quée*, I. Pl. 87. 1. *Spec.*, II. Pl. 36. Clarac, IV. 563, 1203 A. The
antique parts of this imposing statue, one of the principal ornaments
of Holkham, are of very beautiful fine-grained marble, apparently
Greek, with a few faint blackish spots. They are as much distinguished by the noble simplicity of the composition as by the
good execution ; but are however worked over and polished. The
irregular shape of the base, the straight side of which is marked by a
slight ornamentation, shews that the figure should not be seen exactly
straight from the front, but as if stepping in a direction half to the
r. of the spectator. The goddess steps out with the l. leg, round
which the folds of the large chiton fall straight down; the whole body
inclines forward a little ; the r. foot is somewhat drawn back. The
chiton is doubly girded, inside and outside. so that a large row of
folds hangs down and is visible under the very edge of the diploidion.
A round cord serves as girdle. It is gracefully tied in front so that
the ends are pushed through under the cord again. The row of
hanging folds cleverly conceals a joint which divides this statue into two
separately-worked halves, the legs and the upper part of the figure.
Evidently the block of marble was not big enough for the scale of the
figure. The joint however is only visible behind. The divine huntress
is fully identified by the quiver-strap which goes from the r. shoulder
slantwise across the breast, and by a small fragment of the bow near

the l. hip; though the head and neck, the quiver and the whole of
the uplifted r. arm, and finally the l. forearm with the bow are new.
Similarly restored, as can be seen from Maffei's drawing (A.D. 1704),
the statue stood in the house of Ignazio Consiglieri at Rome, whence
it was "purchased and sent out of Rome by the Earl of Leicester;
for which offence His Lordship (known at that time by the name
of the Cavalier Coke) was put under arrest, but released soon after at
the instances of the Grand Duke of Tuscany" (Brettingham). The
book of Accounts gives no direct hint as to the trustworthiness of
this record, nor are its statements referring to the statue very clear.
It shows that Mr Coke was in Rome from June to September, 1716,
and returned thither for a short time in March 1717, after an absence
of several months spent in Pisa and Florence; at the end of April
1717, he was again in Florence. Further, there are the following
entries in reference to our statue: "1717, April 10. Paid for bringing
the statue of Diana from Pisa to Florence 4 crowns o pauls 5 bai."
From an account rendered by Mr Hobart (one of Mr Coke's companions) on April 30, 1717, "Paid for the statue of Diana 900
crowns. Paid to Lucca Corsi for a head of Diana and for his
assistance in buying the above said statue 26 cr. 8 p." Further,
"Expended by Mr Kent at Rome. Paid for a piece of marble sent
to Florence for the head of the Diana 3 cr." In a comprehensive
notice of June 25, 1718, is the final reference "Statue of Diana
900 cr....Head of Diana 26 cr." As there is no single head of
Diana in Holkham, the last entry cannot but relate to the head
which, according to Brettingham, the sculptor Camillo Rusconi put
on in place of the older restoration of the statue, although in the
Book of Accounts Lucca Corsi's name is connected with the head.
At any rate, the head is a bad work. From a comparison of Maffei's
drawing with the present condition of the statue, we must infer
that the other restorations were likewise renovated.   H. 1·79, including the old base, which is antique, 1·86.   Dallaway, no. 8: "There
is a tradition that this statue cost Lord Leicester £1500." It may
be seen from the above citations how untrustworthy such traditions
are, even if one takes into account the cost, unquestionably very
serious, of transport from Italy to England.   [*CII*]

   25. **Statue of Dionysos.** Clarac, IV. 696, 1608 A. The god,
entirely nude, stands near the trunk of a tree entwined with a vine,
the l. leg a little drawn back; his figure somewhat clumsy; workmanship poor and insignificant. New: perhaps the head crowned with
ivy (remains of the long curls and of the fillet on both shoulders cer-

tainly antique), yet the marble is the same as that of the body ;
beyond a doubt l. forearm with grapes, toes of r. foot and a piece
of l. leg between calf and ankle; apparently also r. forearm and hand,
certainly several fingers and the greater part of the hydria, the foot
of which is attached to the trunk of the tree, and is antique. Several
other parts broken, but old. Thasian marble. H. 1·52. Bought
by Brettingham of Cavaceppi, who restored the r. hand and l.
arm. [*W]

26. **Bust of Thukydides** ("Metrodoros"). Michaelis, *Die
Bildnisse des Thukydides*, Strassburg, 1877. *The Holkham Bust of
Thucydides*. *Transl. by* Alex. Napier, Cambridge, 1878 (printed for
private circulation). The nomenclature is confirmed by comparison
of the inscribed terminal bust of Thukydides in Naples (Visconti,
Iconogr. Grecque, i., Pl. 27), which corresponds in all details and
in proportions, but in the expression of the features and in the freedom of the pose of the head stands far behind our bust. This is
in capital preservation. A little damage on the tip of the nose,
which does not impair the shape of that feature, a few small flaws
on forehead, l. cheek and breast, and a few slight scratches are all
together of no consequence. Here and there the surface is somewhat rubbed, while at the back of the head remains of soil still
cling to the marble. The whole bust is antique, with the portion of
the cloak on the l. shoulder. The r. shoulder, being a little
lifted, seems to suggest the rhetorical posture of the arm on that
statue, from which our bust may have been copied (cf. the statue in
Christodoros' *Anthol. Palat.*, 2, 372). The head takes the same
direction. Its expression is exceedingly earnest. Beneath the lofty,
powerful forehead, which is surrounded by sparse crisp hair, lie eyes
of not large size, as it were oppressed by the thoughtful earnestness
of the wrinkled forehead : nose aquiline and large, mouth shut close
with markedly protruding upper lip, without a tinge of cheerfulness.
The crisp beard is clipped short. The skull, smoothly rounded,
bald on the top, and going down very straight behind. Our bust,
a capital portrait of the gravest of historians, is obviously a faithful
copy of a bronze original, to all appearance of the period soon after
the death of Thukydides. Marble very white, of extraordinarily fine
grain. From a faint lamination, which is especially manifest on the
r. temple, it seems to be Pentelic marble of peculiarly delicate
quality. H. 0·62. L. of face 0·22. Bought by Brettingham. [*B]

27. **Statue of Athenè.** Clarac, iii. 462 B, 888 A. In
general arrangement the statue resembles the Athenè of the Hope

collection (Deepdeene, no. 39), but the cloak is only once thrown
around the figure, not doubled, and its folds want the grand character
of that example. The Aegis is divided into two parts and adorned
with a Medusa's head. New: the whole r. arm, including shoulder
and r. breast as far as up to the Medusa's head, l. arm from point of
separation from the body, l. foot with a piece of the chiton, lastly the
neck and the greatest part of the collar-like raised border of the Aegis
behind the neck : still enough of it is old to determine the motive.
Of the head, as to which it is very doubtful whether it belongs to the
statue, the back, ears, helmet and tip of nose are new.   Proportions
tolerably broad.   Ordinary workmanship.   Marble perhaps Pentelic.
H. 1·54.   This statue and no. 28, obtained of Cardinal Albani
by Brettingham, were restored by Cavaceppi.   [*CH]

   28.   **Statue of Tychè** ("Ceres").   Clarac, III. 438 B, 786 D.
Over the chiton the goddess wears a cloak, the border of which,
twisted up into a thick roll, is thrown from the r. hip over the
l. shoulder.   R. breast and arm are left outside the cloak.   On the
upper part of the l. arm a small portion of the cornucopia is old, the
rest of it, and the hand new.   New also three-quarters of the r. arm,
with the ears of corn ; a steering paddle was undoubtedly the original
attribute.   Sundry parts of the drapery are restored.   The pretty
head with a garland of fruit, of Pentelic marble, does not belong to
the statue ; it is much more freely treated.   Its nose, part of the
underlip, a large portion of the garland are new.   Basement and foot,
with the sandals, antique.   Work not bad but rather mechanical.
Marble of coarse grain, apparently Greek.   H. 1·46.   Of same
origin as no. 27.   [*H]

   29.   **Bust of "Sulla."**   The features of Sulla on coins
scarcely correspond at all.   Bernoulli knows of no second copy
of this highly interesting head.   Short clipped hair covers the
skull ; under the high forehead, a little contracted above the nose,
lie sunk pretty deep small piercing eyes.   Pupils and brows
lightly indicated.   The long, thin, strongly arched nose takes a
decided bend downwards with the point ; only the extreme tip
is new.   The vigorous mouth is full of character, with its thin lips
tightly closed ; the underlip recedes considerably.   Chin tolerably
long, beardless cheeks broad.   The expression of strong will and
subtle acuteness is enhanced by the lively turn of the head to its
own l.   It has only suffered from polishing, while the breast-piece
is seriously patched up.   This signal preservation of the head
makes the work still more valuable.   Fine Carrara marble, like

alabaster. H. 0·54. Length of face 0·19. Purchased by Brettingham. [*B]

30. **Mosaic**, worked up into a plate for the table. On a
white ground vine leaves, naturally rendered, alternate with plants of
ornamental shape. Colours somewhat motley. A wand encircled by
a fillet goes all round. Found in the Villa of Hadrian near Tivoli ;
bought of Cavaceppi by Brettingham. L. 0·69. Br. 0·48. [*]

NORTH TRIBUNE.

31. **Statue of a Togatus.** Clarac, v. 957, 2459 A. The
toga is arranged in the usual fashion. New : arms from the
drapery onward, and feet with boots, also various portions of the
drapery. The head, of different marble, belongs to **Lucius Verus**;
nose, mouth, l. cheek and l. brow new. Purchased at Rome by
Kent, to whom 200 Roman crowns were sent in the year 1718, "for
the Consular statue ;" cf. however, no. 36. H. 2·02. [*BII]

32. "**Philippus Arabs**," bust of a **young Roman** : of the
second or third century. Hair slightly curly. Brows and pupils
indicated. New : nose. Neck and bust broken and much patched,
but belonging to the head. Over the tunic lies a cloak with a fringe.
A tablet with slight ornamentation is preserved beneath the bust.
H. 0·62. L. of face 0·16. Bought by Brettingham. [*BIV]

33. **Fragment of a draped statue of a female** called
"**Juno.**" Clarac, v. 992, 2575 A ("Isis"). It was a fragment
belonging to Cardinal Albani, restored by Cavaceppi, and purchased
by Brettingham. Cavaceppi has proceeded in a very arbitrary
manner, inasmuch as the r. arm and the whole motive, suggesting
the lifting up of the cloak, are to be traced to him alone. Consequently the whole drapery originally peculiar has now been made
inexplicable. The cloak fell with its one edge straight down
behind the l. shoulder, so that only one corner thereof came in front
and covered the breast. The arm was lowered ; only the shoulder
and the junction of the arm are old. The cloak hung down behind
the back, and was drawn from the r. to the front round the body and
the legs, then again behind the back slantwise up to the r. shoulder,
from which the edge fell down behind, but a small corner was
drawn forward slantwise over the breast, and was tied in a knot with
the somewhat raised front portion of the drapery. The very end of
this corner hangs straight down in front. The edges of the drapery
are at various places restored, other portions retouched. The unusual

motive is well carried out, and the folds are effectively executed.
Another arbitrary freak of Cavaceppi's has affected the girdled chiton,
for he has thoroughly worked over the whole portion thereof on the
r. breast, and brought it into a very unantique shape. It originally
covered this part of the body, and was fastened on the shoulder.
The lowest portion of the chiton, feet and base, and a large piece on
the r. knee are restorations. The back is only a very little worked.
A broad mass of hair on the neck, and a part of the curls on the l.
shoulder are old. The whole body is of Pentelic marble. The
head, apparently of Italian marble, is connected with it by a neck of
marble spotted with black, and certainly does not belong to the body.
The head seems to be that of a Venus, with waving hair, brushed
back and well arranged, a fillet being passed through it. The knot
behind, and the tip of the nose are new. H. 2·35. Dallaway,
no. 12. [*W]

34. **Draped statue**, perhaps of **Hera**. Clarac, III. 438,
754 B. The statue has been made into a Ceres by the renovation
of the r. forearm, and the addition of a handful of ears of corn,
though a Hera type gives it its fundamental characteristics, cf.
Overbeck, *Griech. Kunstmythol.*, III. p. 121. It has further had
placed upon it by the insertion of a neck a head which passes for
that of the elder Agrippina, but neither has the hair treated like hers,
nor resembles her usual portraits. It has flat eyes, and the lower
part of the face recedes. The tip of the nose is new. A stephanè
crowns the veiled head. Of the body itself the nude part of the r.
arm, details of the drapery, and toes of the feet are new. The chiton
is left somewhat rough, and has preserved manifest traces of reddish
colour on the r. side. The cloak is treated more smoothly, the very
deeply undercut folds suggesting some tolerably fine material. The
whole treatment is careless. The body is of Parian marble, the head
of a different kind. H. 2·15. Bought by Brettingham as a companion to no. 33 of Belisario Amadei, who procured it from the Villa
Ginnetti at Velletri. Dallaway, no. 13. [*BW]

35. **Bust of "Faustina the younger"**: more likely from
the treatment of the hair to be a lady of the period of the Flavian
Emperors. Several bands of hair are laid over one another horizontally, the uppermost being tied together in front. Good head,
smoothly treated. New: tip of nose, chin, ears, the greater part of
the drapery. No pupils. Beautiful Greek marble. H. 0·55. Length
of face 0·16. Bought by Brettingham. [*BW]

36. **Statue of "Lucius Antonius" in a toga**. Maffei,

Raccolta, Pl. 147. Clarac, v. 903, 2346 A. The statue, once an ornament of the saloon of the *Congregazione dell' Archiconfraternità della SS. Annunziata* in Rome, was bought by Mr Coke. "The arms and head are finely added by Bernini" (Brettingham). A close examination of the statue has left no doubt in my mind as to the correctness of this statement, though Clarac and Bernoulli hold the head to be antique. The head, as well as the neck, quite uninjured, is let into the tunic; the short curly hair lying close to the head is treated in a thoroughly unantique way, as also are the eyes, mouth, and folds of the skin. All over the head one observes the marks of the chisel, which are afterwards polished over. Albeit the head is so excellent in its features, expression and pose, and is set so well in harmony with the motion of the r. arm, that the restoration is one of the most striking successes that I know. The dispute about the nomenclature of the head may under these circumstances be let alone. The marble of the head is Carrara. The statue itself, apparently of Pentelic marble, is of good delicate sculpture, but in many parts worked over. The toga slanting across the breast to the l. shoulder, is drawn up somewhat more tightly than usual, and is different in some other details from the ordinary type. Near the l. foot stands a round case for books (*capsa, scrinium*), with handle. New: besides head and r. arm, also half l. forearm with parts of the drapery and the roll, r. foot and several details in the folds. If this statue is meant by the "Consular Statue" mentioned on no. 31, as is probably the case, the price, 200 crowns, is very reasonable. H. 1·97. [*BH*]

DINING ROOM.

37. **Head of Aphrodite,** colossal scale: wrongly taken for Apollo by Waagen. See the annexed Plate. It is one of the most striking specimens of the collection, and richly merits being better known; being a good copy of an original of the best period. The conception stands about halfway between the Aphrodite of Melos and the Aphrodite of Knidos by Praxiteles. New: the whole of the crown of the head with a fillet, the back of the head, the back half of the neck; face and front half of neck on the other hand in perfect preservation. Forehead broad, not low; the waving hair simply brushed back on both sides, as in heads of the best period. Eyes elongated and slightly sunk towards the inner corners, upper lid convex, lower only slightly rounded. The large broad nose comes forward in profile a little from the line of the forehead; it is a

HOLKHAM Nᵒ 37.

grand design, as are the cheeks and neck, and long, broad chin.
Space between nose and mouth very small. The slightly opened
mouth is of great winningness yet with a noble expression, though
perhaps not so reserved as that of the Aphroditè of Melos.
The sublimity of the shape is toned down by a slight but effective
inclination of the head towards the r. side. This bust, rightly
designated "very capital," is one of the most beautiful of Brettingham's purchases. Dallaway, no. 17. H. 0·56. L. of face
about 0·28; the several parts have the following proportions : forehead 0·10 high, nose 0·09 long ; space between nose and mouth
about 0·025, and space from mouth to chin about 0·06 ; neck from
the chin to the hollow of the throat measures 0·10. [*BCMH]

38. Bust of Geta, turned slightly r. with crisp beard not
encroaching on the face. Head and neck old. Drapery of variegated marble, modern. Coarse work. The nose is restored. L. of
face 0·17. [*BW]

39. Bust of Marcus Aurelius, not "Antoninus Pius"
(Waagen). Only the head is old, and of that the nose is new.
Pupils indicated. Drapery same as no. 38. L. of face 0·20.
[*BW]

40. Bust of Lucius Verus, colossal scale. The sullen look
is softened and the hair somewhat less disordered than usual. Pupils
indicated. New: nose, lower part of beard, details of the hair.
This large bust, found in cleaning the port of Nettuno, was purchased
by Brettingham. Dallaway, no. 18. [*BCW]

NORTH-WEST CORRIDOR.

41. Statuette of the Nile. Clarac, IV. 749, 1814 A. The
river god reclines on his l. arm, his leg enveloped in the cloak. The
r. hand, resting on the knee, holds the fillet of a garland ; over the
whole plinth stream waves which swell from the pointed end of a
cornucopia supported by the l. arm of the god, the horn being pierced
at its end after the manner of a drinking-horn (ῥυτόν). From the
waves a small boy emerges with half his body out, drinking from the
flood : near him under Nile's arm the broad head of a hippopotamus ;
at the feet of the god crawls a little crocodile, and near it a boy
(head missing) is clambering up, a weak reminiscence of the troop
of boys in the famous Vatican Statue (Mus. Pio-Clem., I. Pl. 37 ;
Clarac, IV. 748, 1811), who symbolised the sixteen ells (πήχεις, cubitus)
of the rise of the stream. The garlanded head (nose new) is put on,

but belongs to the statue. New: upper part of cornucopia with fruits. Ordinary work. Thasian marble. L. 0·89. [*C]

42. Tyche. Clarac, v. 987, 2569 B (" Isis"). Over the chiton a fringed cloth or cloak is thrown so as to cover the whole back and both shoulders. One of its corners moreover conceals the upper part of the l. arm, the other the r. breast and the body, and then hangs down over the advanced l. forearm. In the l. arm the goddess holds a cornucopia full of fruit encircled by a knotted fillet of wool (στέμμα, *vitta*) and by a snake. New: head, with the lotos-flower, r. forearm with the vase (probably the goddess originally held a steering paddle), l. forearm, half the cornucopia and large portion of the drapery that falls down at that part, lastly the pedestal with feet and lowest part of the chiton. All antique parts worked over by Cavaceppi to such a degree that it is often difficult to recognise the restorations. H. 0·92. [*C]

43. Bust of Gordianus III., wrongly named "Saloninus." New: tip of nose and bust. There are replicas in the Louvre (Mongez, *Iconogr. Rom.*, Pl. 54), and in the Vatican (*Braccio N. No. 76,* "Alexander Severus"). Purchased by Brettingham. [*B]

LIBRARY.

44. Head of Roma. Face of a rounded contour. On the round helmet, closely fitting to the head, three figures for the most part restored, the she-wolf on the top, the twin boys on the two sides. Remains of the original figures are preserved. New: nose, also the bust of Rosso antico. Fine-grained marble. H. of genuine part 0·42. L. of face 0·14. [°C]

45. Mosaic. In the midst of rocky scenery, a lion, viewed almost from the front, is rending a panther lying on the ground. Composition effective; drawing not quite correspondingly good: colouring and technical execution very praiseworthy. Bought by Mr Coke in Rome. L. 0·88. H. about the same. [*W]

STATE BED-CHAMBER.

[**46. Bas Relief of Julius Caesar:** oval shape. From Dr Meade's collection. *Mus. Meadianum,* p. 225. Unquestionably modern.]

The following rooms on the ground floor are decorated with antiques.

BILLIARD ROOM.

47. Terminal bust of the bearded Dionysos : called "Plato." Of pseudo-archaic style. Three rows of round curls extend over the forehead, long curls fall down on to the shoulders ; behind the hair forms a broad mass. The broad beard projects decidedly. New : tip of nose. Ordinary work. It was dug up in a vineyard near the Church of St John Lateran, and purchased at Rome by Brettingham. H. 0·45. L. of face 0·18. [*CIV]

48. Portrait-head of Lysias : on a modern terminal pillar with the inscription ΛΥΣΙΑΣ (sic). The identification, however, is correct. The head resembles the Farnese (Visconti, *Iconogr. Grecque*, 1. Pl. 28), only it is less bald, corresponding in this particular more with the Capitoline bust (*Mus. Capit.*, 1. Pl. 63). The beard hangs down tolerably straight ; the little wrinkles at the outer corners of the eyes are plainly rendered. New : tip of the decidedly arched nose, a piece of the l. ear. The surface generally speaking is much washed out. Greek marble. Purchased by Brettingham. H. of genuine part, 0·35. L. of face, 0·21. [*BCIV]

49. Square cinerary urn : with the inscription *D. M. Petronio Hedychro | vix(it) an(nis) XXXV m(ens). VI d(ieb). VIII | Petronia Tpophime [sic] | contliberto, idem | coniugi suo b(ene) m(erenti) fec(it)*. At the corners richly constructed candelabra ; on their bases rams' heads, and between them a trident with two dolphins ; further up a sphinx ; quite at the top a lamp. Under the tablet for the inscription two stags' heads sustain a garland in the curved space enclosed by which the she-wolf and only one sucking boy are represented. Beneath, two birds of prey. On the sides a griffin on a high pedestal. Bought together with no. 50 for 15 Roman crowns by Kent in Rome. H. 0·59. L. 0·44. D. 0·28. [*CIV]

50. Square cinerary urn : with the inscription *C. Calpurnio | Cognito, | vix(it) an(nis) XVIII, | Calpurnia | Chrysis | mater*. A Cupid on either side of the tablet for the inscription, supporting the garland in the curved space enclosed by which a Cupid sleeping on a rock is represented, with a hound sitting at his head. Under the garland a winged Cupid on a quadriga drives r., carrying off a wingless maiden who extends both arms to heaven. A snake under the horses. On the extreme r. an olive tree. It is a transference of the rape of Proserpine by Pluto (cf. Brocklesby, no. 110) to another combination of figures (cf. O. Jahn, *Archaeol. Beitr.*, pp. 194 ff.);

a similar example is to be seen in the *Galéria Giustiniani*, II. Pl. 147.
On the sides the garland is upheld by a Cupid at the front corner,
and behind by a ram's head under which a swan is visible ; inside
the garland a hydria on one side, a cup on the other. For the source
cf. on no. 49. H. 0·63. L. 0·44. D. 0·33. [*CW*]

The setting-in of darkness prevented me from making a more
accurate examination of the following nos., 51—54.

VESTIBULE UNDER THE PORTICO.

51. "**Medallion of Carneades.** The hair and face antique
of Grecian work; the other parts restored by Cavaceppi." Brettingham.
In my opinion the antique portion comprising the chief part of the
head is of good work and of Pentelic marble, also the nomenclature
correct. [*]

AUDIT ROOM.

52. "**Medallion of a Faun** (antique), dancing as if inspired
by the god Bacchus: he holds the lituus [*i.e.* the pedum] in one
hand, and in the other a bunch of grapes ; upon the background is a
vase. It is in basso-relievo." Brettingham. Unquestionably a
disc of marble. It is perhaps the "basso-relievo" mentioned under
no. 13, or, as the servant writes on another occasion, the "bust
releif."

PORTER'S HALL. (Guard Room).

53. "**Busto** called by the name of **Lucius Lentulus.**"
Brettingham. Noticed in the Book of Accounts as "Ritratto of
Lucio Lentulo, a colossaean head," which the servant turns into a
"Colossaeum Busto of L. Lentulo." The Rev. Alex. Napier of
Holkham has the merit of having solved the riddle of this curious
nomenclature, by discovering the Holkham head to be identical with
the bust published by Th. Gallaeus (*Illustrium imagines*, Antw. 1606,
Pl. 48) as "L. Cornelius Lentulus," then in possession of Fulvius
Ursinus, and by E. O. Visconti (*Iconogr. Rom.* I., Pl. 4, 6). To say
nothing of the likeness of the features, the identity is established by
the fact, that in the said bust, according to Ursinus (see below, cf.
Faber in his notes to Gallaeus), a ring of metal was fastened at the
back of the neck, and that the Holkham bust shows at the very junction of the head and the neck a groove 0·25 long, evidently the hole
into which the ring had once been let in. The bust seems to have

been discovered in the 16th century in Tivoli, together with an inscribed bronze tablet (*C. I. Lat.*, I. 201). The inscription contains a letter of *L. Cornelius Cn. f. pr(aetor)*, in which he informs the inhabitants of Tivoli that the Roman Senate had accepted their justification, and expresses the hope that the Roman People will do the same. Judging from the palaeographical character, the inscription belongs to the 7th century of the city of Rome. Faber referred it to L. Cornelius Cn. f. Lentulus Lupus, afterwards consul in B.C. 156; Visconti was rather inclined to seek the reasons of the quarrel between Rome and Tivoli in the disturbances of the social war, B.C. 90 or 89; Mommsen recalls the movement caused by Sertorius, during which, B.C. 78, a certain L. Cornelius ... f. Sisenna was *praetor urbanus et inter peregrinos* (*C. I. Lat.*, I. 203, 1). But, as Visconti has already observed, it is questionable whether we are right to give to the bust the name mentioned in the inscription; only a very exact account of the circumstances of the discovery would enable us to judge this point with certainty. I am indebted to the kindness of Dr H. Dessau, who is preparing the edition of the inscriptions of Latium for the *Corpus Inscriptionum Latinarum*, for the following notices taken from sources partly unedited. The first mention occurs in the voluminous collectanea of Pirro Ligorio preserved in the R. Library at Turin (composed between A.D. 1566 and 1587), a copy of which exists in the Vatican Library (Cod. Ottobon. 3376, fol. 42): "*...fragmento di una Tabola di Bronzo trouata in Tibur proprio con la testa di quel Lucio Cornelio Pretore di Marmo*," &c. A somewhat more detailed account is given in the work of Antonio del Rè, *Dell' antichità Tiburtine capitolo V.*, Rome, 1611, p. 108: "*...d'vno di loro* [of the Scipios] *fù trouata vna testa di marmo, con la tauola di bronzo, nella quale era intagliato detto Senatoconsulto, in alcune rouine di muri antichi fatti ad opera reticolata, cauandosi vna cantina non lunge dalla Chiesa di S. Lorenzo, vicino al luogo detto la Forma*" (or "*le Forme*," cf. Cabral and del Rè, *Delle ville, &c. di Tivoli*, Rome 1779, p. 34). Other antiquaries preferred to see in the head not one of the Scipios, but a *praetor Tiburtinus* called L. Lentulus. From these accounts it does not appear likely that the head should have been found at its original place; nor does the *opus reticolatum*, the network used in the 8th century of Rome, agree well with the epoch of the inscription. It is, in consequence, very doubtful whether the head has any connection with the inscription, and more particularly, whether it was meant to represent the praetor L. Cornelius who sent the Senatusconsultum to the people of Tivoli. These doubts will be the more strengthened if Mr Napier is right in identifying the countenance of the Holkham bust with that of another terminal bust, published by Lafrérie, *Industr. virorum vultus*, Rome 1569, Pl. 34, which is now in Florence (probably Uffizi, no. 319, or no. 543 of Duetschke's catalogue). Be this as it may, the bronze tablet, apparently together with the marble bust, was sold by the discoverer for 25 scudi to Curzio Alessio, canon of St John in Lateran, and by this man for 100 scudi to Fulvius Ursinus (Ant. del Rè, in Cod. Barberin. LIII, 53), in whose possession it was when Gallaeus made his drawing. Ursinus thought so highly of these two pieces that in his will (Jan. 21, 1600) he bequeathed "*senatui populoque Romano caput marmoreum L. Cornelii Praetoris, cui a tergo pendet anulus aereus, idem faciens appensum olim fuisse in aliquo publico loco ciuitatis Tiburtinae, cum aenea tabella.... cupiens eam in Capitolio reponi cum supradicto capite marmoreo eo potissimum loco, quo Bruti caput aeneum hodie seruatur.*" (Castalio, *Vita Ful. Ursini*, Rome 1657, p. 24.) It appears, however, that this bequest came to no effect; at least Ant. del Rè (*l. cit.*) was told of the inscription having passed into the possession of Ursinus' protector, the Cardinal Farnese; and, in point of fact, in the 18th century it was in the Barberini collection (see Ficoroni, *Le vestigia di Roma*, Rome 1744, II. p. 54; Visconti, *l. c.*); since that time it has been utterly lost sight of. About the fate of the bust nothing certain can be said except that, according to the book of accounts at Holkham, more than a century after the death of Ursinus the architect Kent bought it in Rome for Mr Coke for a sum of 25 crowns. [*]

54. "A fine antique **consular bust on a pedestal**, both of one piece of marble; incognito." Brettingham.

CONSERVATORY.

Here there stands, in a most unfavourable situation, hidden behind a broad palm tree, the colossal statue (no. 55), for which Kent had designed the place of honour over the staircase of the Hall (see Walpole, *Anecd. of Painting*, IV. p. 110).

55. Statue of "**Zeus**," colossal scale. Clarac, III. 396 D, 678 B. Bought by Mr Coke in Rome together with no. 22 for 418 Roman crowns, and restored by Wilton. As the neck, including the hollow of the throat, is an insertion, and the head is of different marble from that of the rest of the statue, they must both be treated separately. The splendid body, of Greek (Pentelic?) marble

of inferior quality, has been accommodated to the character of Zeus by
the following restorations. New: r. arm including a piece of shoulder,
with sceptre, l. hand from the drapery with the cup : also part of the
much broken lower parts of legs, feet, lowest piece of palm, and
parts of the drapery depending therefrom. There is left the torso of
a powerful man resting on r. leg, quite nude towards the upper part,
draped round hips and thighs with a broad cloak in rich folds, one
end of which falls down over the advanced l. arm ; near r. leg a
palm tree with dates, serving as a support. Though there are
statues of Zeus of similar design (cf. Overbeck, *Griech. Kunstmythologie*, II. pp. 140 ff.), yet a palm tree for a support for a Zeus is
unheard of. It seems to me therefore reasonable to suppose that our
torso once belonged to a statue of a Caesar in the habit of Zeus (cf.
ibidem, p. 574).

It is otherwise with the head, of the finest Pentelic marble,
worked far more exquisitely than the body, and in fact of rare
beauty. New: only part of the tip of nose. Hair not massed over
the brow, but parted and brushed sideways at first almost flat in soft
curly waves, further down it falls smoother, on the neck short. The
whole back of the head is negligently treated. Lower half of brow
projects somewhat. Eyes, of a very beautiful oval, do not, however,
lie deep. The fine, long nose comes out a little from the line of the
profile of the brow. Small mouth a little open, cheeks somewhat
dissimilar, the l. being a little too flat. Beard tolerably long. In
style I might especially compare the beautiful head to the fragment
in the Louvre (Bouillon, *Mus. des Ant.* I., Pl. 1), yet it is more soft
in execution. It would seem to belong to the younger Attic school,
standing midway between the sublime simplicity of the Zeus of
Pheidias on the frieze of the Parthenon and on coins of Elis, and
the effective display of refined art in the Blacas head in the British
Museum, the Mask of Otricoli, and other representations of Zeus and
kindred divinities by the school of Lysippos. The extremely mild
expression of the features, which forms the chief trait in the character,
joined with the short hair on the neck, makes Waagen's and Matz's
identification as an Asklepios probable ; yet one cannot as yet with
certainty distinguish between this god and a mild Zeus (Ζεὺς ἥπιος),
considering the difference of the schools of art. The head highly
deserves to have a cast made from it. Dallaway, no. 14. H. 2·23.
[*BCMW*]

In the PARK, in another GREENHOUSE are 56, 57. **Two busts**:
modern. One, no. 57, with the pretended features of **Maecenas**
borrowed from a gem (Visconti, *Iconogr. Rom.*, I. Pl. 13); besides
these on the

SEAT ON THE MOUNT

58. Sarcophagus: oval shaped, fluted, with the inscription
D(is) M(anibus) T. Flabio Hermae Ti. coiugi. [*M*]

Two more heads may here be mentioned which are temporarily
(1877) in the vestibule of Lord Leicester's town house, 19 Grosvenor
Square, but which belong to the Holkham Marbles.

59. Head of the youthful Apollo. Thick, wavy hair parted
over the brow, and falling back in a thick bunch. It is encircled
with a fillet. The fine features remind one slightly of an archaic
model. One can recall the Apollo shooting with the bow in bronze
from Pompei (Müller, *Denkm. d. alt. Kunst*, II. Pl. 11, 125).
Lips shut close; eyes flat. New: a small piece of the tip of the
nose, neck and bust. Parian marble (*lychnites*) of unusual transparency. Work not quite as good as the material. H. of head 0·21.
L. of face 0·15. [*]

60. Portrait-head of a Roman girl. Hair slightly waved,
at the back tied up into a flat coil of tresses. Features somewhat
blunt and stiff, mouth thick; nose a little cocked up; eyes (pupils
expressed) looking upwards. Expression earnest, almost sad. Hair
superficially treated. New: tip of nose, and the whole bust except
a piece of the neck. Italian marble. H. 0·25. L. of face 0·17. [*]

Beside its marble originals Holkham possesses, amongst the
valuable manuscripts and rare books in which the library is so rich,
a special treasure, namely some *volumes of drawings from antiques*,
which Mr Coke purchased in Italy.

61. A small volume of drawings by Rafael: small folio.
Formerly in the possession of Carlo Maratta in Rome, bought there
by Mr Coke, Aug. 29, 1716: "Paid for a book of the drawings of
Rafael 50 Rom. crowns." The sketches are really for the most part
drawn by Rafael, especially architectural details, which may pertain
to the studies of the antiquities of Rome in the artist's later years.
A particular account of the contents is given by Passavant, *Rafael
von Urbino*, II. pp. 586 ff., cf. Matz, *Arch. Zeitung*, 1873, p. 35. [*M*]

62. Two volumes of drawings by both the Bartolis,
the father Pietro Sante, the son Francesco. The latter is often mentioned in the Book of Accounts, Mr Coke having employed him on drawings after antiques. E.g. "1716, Aug. 4. Paid to signor Bartoli for an Antique Painting of the Volta of a temple of Bacchus 20 cr." "Aug. 31. Paid to signor Bartli for Antick painting and for the uolte of the uel. palace di Tito 30 cr. 1 p. 5 bai." Bartoli's name also occurs in reference to other services : "1717, March 17. Paid to Signor Bartoli for seuerale Licences two send awais pictures and statues 7 cr. 2 p." Lastly there is mentioned in a brief notice without Bartoli's name, "Book of antique paintings 60 old Louis." Evidently by this "book" are indicated the two volumes in question. Unfortunately the drawings, for the most part very delicately coloured, have been bound up in no order into two magnificent volumes, large folio, of which one contains 77, the other 65 leaves. They are most of them original sketches for Pietro Sante Bartoli's *Pitture antiche del sepolcro de' Nasonii* (Rome, 1680), and *Pitture antiche delle grotte di Roma*, by Bartoli father and son (Rome, 1706), but a considerable number of antiques from other quarters are mixed up with them, such as drawings for the *Antichi Sepolcri*, the Vatican Virgil, the *Admiranda*, &c. On Vol. II., Pl. 29. "Fran[ces]co Barto[li]" is named as the artist. A series of leaves contains the light original sketches in outline, the instructions for the colours only appended in words ; these are copied on the other leaves, and filled in with simple, unbroken colours. Cf. Matz, *Göttinger Nachrichten*, 1872, pp. 68 f., and *Arch. Zeitung*, 1873, p. 35. His conjecture that the Holkham drawings are derived from the legacy left by Dr Mead is confuted by the Book of Accounts (cf. Introd. § 29, and Windsor Castle, Vol. XIX). Unfortunately my time at Holkham did not allow me to make a detailed inventory of the single drawings ; it may be hoped that Mr Napier one day will publish a list of them and of the places in which each of them, respectively, has been published. [*M*]

HOUGHTON HALL (Norfolk).

Aedes Walpolianae, or a description of the collection of pictures at Houghton Hall. 1747, 1752. (Horatio Walpole, *Works*, II. pp. 221—278.) Dallaway, pp. 271, 291 f., 384 (II. pp. 3 f., 27 f., 136).

This country seat of the MARQUIS OF CHOLMONDELEY, situated

near Fakenham (Gt. Eastern Ry., between Wymondham and Wells) was adorned with a number of busts by Sir ROBERT WALPOLE, afterwards EARL OF ORFORD, most of which the younger Brettingham (cf. Holkham) had collected for him in Italy (Introd. § 41). Horatio Walpole (*l. c.*, pp. 264 f.) gives the following list of the busts.

THE HALL.

1. A woman, a most beautiful antique, and
2. Roman Empress; brought from Mrs Vernon's at Twickenham Park.
3. Marcus Aurelius.
4. Trajan.
5. Septimius Severus, and
6. Commodus; given to General Churchill by Cardinal Alexander Albani, and by him to Sir Robert Walpole.
7. A young Hercules.
8. Faustina Senior.
9. A young Commodus.
10. Jupiter.
11. A Philosopher.
12. Hadrian.
13. Pollux.

THE PORCH.

14. Philosopher.
15. Julia Pia Severi.
Dallaway adds—
16. A small bust of Venus.

HOVINGHAM (Yorkshire).

Volkmann (*Reisen*, IV. p. 121) mentioned as being at this country seat then belonging to Mr WORSLEY—

1. "An antique bas-relief of Bacchantes," perhaps a Bacchic relief from a sarcophagus.
The two following groups in bronze are hardly antique—
2. Herakles and Antaeos.
3. Herakles and the stag.

CASTLE HOWARD (Yorkshire).

Volkmann, *Reisen*, IV. pp. 122 ff. Dallaway, pp. 295 ff. (II. pp. 31 ff.). Waagen, *Treas.*, III. pp. 326 ff. (II. pp. 420 ff.). Clarac, III. p. 115 (Clarac was not there himself). Conze, *Arch. Anz.*, 1864, pp. 216 ff.

On the railway from York to Scarborough (North-Eastern) there lies, somewhat out of the way, between wooded hills, the seat of the EARL OF CARLISLE, whose antiques had been collected so early as the first decades of the last century by HENRY HOWARD, 4th EARL OF CARLISLE (1694—1758), a zealous and tasteful dilettante, who lived much in Rome (Introd. § 35). The collection is the oldest in England after those in Oxford, and at Wilton House. The number of its specimens seems to be in excess of its richness in notable antiques. A few additions have been made recently. I do not know whether a fire, which some years ago took place at the castle, has injured the antiques. Of the statues Dallaway only names no. 7; Clarac has had drawings made of 16 specimens; Volkmann has already given a very full description. I was unfortunately prevented from visiting this collection, and therefore find myself merely citing the notices of the above-quoted authorities. As Clarac did not himself visit Castle Howard, he gives no remarks on restorations.

1. **Statue of a female.** Clarac, III. 438 A, 774 A ("Ceres"). She rests on her l. foot; over the girdled chiton, a cloak covering both legs, the end of which is thrown over the l. forearm. The head crowned with laurel has been added to the statue. New: neck, more than half the r. arm, nude part of l., and the attributes of Ceres, torch and ears of corn, in the two hands, l. breast and legs from above the knee. H. 1·35.

2. **Statue of a female.** Clarac, III. 438 A, 774 B ("Ceres"), according to Waagen an empress as Ceres. Draped much like no. 1, resting on the r. leg. The statue in the pose of the arms presents the usual motive of Pietas (*Mus. Pio-Clem.*, II. Pl. 47); the antique portrait head does not belong to it. New: half of both forearms, so also the ears of wheat in the r. hand. Of little importance. H. 1·75. [*W*]

3. **Statue of Fortuna.** Clarac, III. 438 B, 823 B ("Abundantia"). Upon a chair, to the r. side of which a cornucopia is represented, the goddess sits in a chiton, which leaves both arms perfectly free; legs covered in a cloak. Head (with a stephanè), of which the

fine features, according to Waagen, have much the character of a Venus, re-joined, but according to Clarac's letter-press, belonging to the statue. New: nose, neck, half l. forearm with cup, half r. hand with cluster of grapes, on which it rests, and also some patches here and there. Well-designed figure of ordinary execution. H. 1·73. [*CW*]

4. **Statue of Athenè.** Clarac, III. 462 B, 888 C. The goddess rests on her l. leg; the prettily-arranged cloak is thrown around body and thigh, and also round the l. arm, which is supported on the side; a narrow aegis covers a portion of the breast. There are several copies in existence, e.g. Ince, no. 10, Oxford, no. 20, in the Villa Pamfili (Clarac, IV. 552 B, 1186 D), also one once at Cavaceppi's (*Racc.*, I. Pl. 18; Clarac, III. 471, 900), which was bought and sent to England, but is hardly identical with our statue, rather with that in the Ince collection. New: head, r. arm, l. foot and part of r. The rest well preserved, and of good, simple work. H. 1·52. [*CW*]

5. **Statue of Hygieia.** Clarac, IV. 552, 1172 A. Standing in repose in chiton and wide cloak. R. arm, entwined by snake, approaches a cup held in the l. hand. New: snake from the hand. Head does not belong to the statue; it has the features of Julia Mammaea. A good work with delicate drapery. H. 1·60. [*W*]

6. **Statue of a boy, probably Eros.** Clarac, IV. 650 A, 1467 A. He rests on the r. leg, l. shoulder much raised, r. correspondingly lowered, head thrown back. The quiver-strap over the breast has given occasion for the pleasing restoration, as though he had shot an arrow, and is looking after it. New: arms, lower parts of legs, trunk of tree and pedestal; whether the head also is new is not to be made out in the present position of the statue. H. 0·66. [*C*]

7. **Statue of Eros, fastening the string to his bow.** Clarac, IV. 650 C, 1471 B. Dallaway, no. 1. A good torso of the favourite figure, restored with a head that does not belong to it. New: nose, neck, both arms with the bow, lower parts of both legs. H. 1·22. [*CW*]

8. **Statue of Dionysos.** Clarac, IV. 678 B, 1619 C. The god leans with l. arm on the trunk of a tree, entwined with a vine. Head, crowned with ivy, turned with a gentle inflection toward the r., on which side he pours out with lowered r. hand the contents of a kantharos on a panther sitting at his feet. A nebris drawn over the breast; feet encased in high boots. Much pieced together. New: panther's head. H. 1·55. [*C*]

9. **Group of boy riding on a goat** (Bacchus?) Clarac, IV. 694 A, 1610 B, "Bacchus enfant sur un bouc." Dallaway, p. 298. The boy wears a garland slantwise across his breast and tries to drive the animal on with a stick in his r. hand. According to Waagen, the group is beautiful and spirited in motive, of good style and vigorous character; according to Conze of inferior work. New: of the boy, head, l. arm which holds the goat's horn, l. and half of r. foot; of the goat, legs, ears, horns. H. 0·92. [*CW*]

[10. **Small statue of sleeping Seilenos.** Clarac, IV. 738, 1762 A. Serves as cover of the sarcophagus, no. 48. Modern, see Dallaway, p. 298, confirmed by Conze.]

11. **Bearded river-god.** Clarac, IV. 749, 1821 B. He sits on the ground, supported on l. hand, a shell in r. Bluish grey stone. The composition of the figure itself as well as the form of the plinth arouse strong suspicion against its genuineness.

12. **Statue of Serapis.** Clarac, IV. 758, 1851 B. Probably wrongly described by Waagen, p. 329, as a bust. Usual motive. Insignificant execution. The two side heads of the Kerberos are small in proportion and turn backwards. New: of the Serapis, head, l. arm, with upper half of sceptre, r. forearm and hand, half of l. foot; of the Kerberos pieces of the head and r. foreleg. H. 1·00. [*C*]

13. **Statue of a youthful Roman in the toga.** Clarac, V. 904, 2313 A. New: both forearms and the wrongly restored portion from the ankles downwards. H. 1·47.

14. **Augustus.** Clarac, V. 913, 2331. The Emperor is represented in Greek style, nude but for the chlamys, which is fastened together on r. shoulder and leaves the whole r. side and r. arm free. Head admirable, other parts much repaired. H. 1·75. [*W*]

15. **Statuette of a nude youth,** Clarac, V. 927, 2354 B. (Probably the figure described by Waagen, p. 328, as Apollo, with many repairs.) Leaning l. on the trunk of a tree. Hair curly. Certainly not a portrait-figure. Modern? H. 0·64.

16. **Statue of "Marcus Aurelius."** Clarac, V. 952, 2445 B. Beardless, youthful. Nude, but for the chlamys which covers the breast and partly the l. arm. Of good workmanship. New: r. leg, r. arm with staff, l. hand with globe, probably head also, lastly the inscription AVR. CAES. on the pedestal. H. 1·60. [*CW*]

17. **Statuette of Athenè.** Yellow stone (oriental alabaster?). Black extremities. Probably modern. [*C*]

18. **Elder Pan** attacking a younger. Perhaps antique. [*C*]

19, 20. **Two groups of a lion tearing a bull:** spirited

design, indifferent workmanship. Many parts restored. About one-fourth the size of life. [*CW*]

The number of **busts** is extraordinarily large, and includes many Roman portraits, but also many modern specimens. The identification of the descriptions of the different authorities is not always to be managed with certainty.

21. Bust of Minerva or **Rome.** Dallaway, no. 12. Wrongly described as a statue by Waagen, p. 297. New: face. Helmet ornamented with figures on horseback, Amazons according to Dallaway, horsemen according to Waagen. [*W*]

22. Large mask of bearded Bacchus. Dallaway, no. 13.

23. Bust of Bacchus: crowned with grapes and ivy-berries. Of the type of the Capitoline head ("Ariadne"). Dallaway, no. 8. New: nose. Very noble. Admirably executed. [*CW*]

24. Head with Phrygian cap. Inclined l. Slightly pained expression. Hair luxuriant. Dallaway, no. 9, "Atis." Waagen, p. 331, "Paris." New: nose, mouth, chin: much patched on cap and hair. Good head. [*CW*]

25. Head of Io. Life-size. Meant to be let into a statue. Out of the waving hair, on which a stephané is visible, spring two little horns over the forehead. Well preserved. Character and work unimportant. [*C*; undoubtedly identical with Waagen's "Attes or Atys," p. 328.]

26. Female head, small scale. Graceful, of delicate, hieratic style. Openings of eyes quite narrow. Traces of red colour visible on hair, which falls in regular curls over the forehead, in broader, flatter masses on the ears, then down behind the neck. A strange kind of helmet covers the head. It is surrounded by an ornamental wreath of flowers on the lower rim, shows remains of decoration above and behind (an animal above), and is furnished behind with a guard for the neck. New: breast-piece of oriental alabaster. Conze compares a head at St Petersburg, probably Ermitage, no. 182. H. 0·13. [*CW*; apparently identical with Dallaway's no. 14, "Isis."]

27. Youthful Herakles. Of unusual beauty. New: nose, piece of chin, r. ear, breast and neck. Parian marble. [*CW*]

28. "Silenus" (Dallaway, no. 11): rather some ancient poet according to Waagen. Long beard. Head crowned with vine-leaves and ivy-berries. New: nose. Spirited, excellent work. [*W*]

29. Dioskuros. New: nose. Dallaway, no. 10.

30. "**Junius Brutus.**" Larger than life. Of decided character. Beard merely indicated by scratches on the marble. New: one ear entirely, the other half. Dallaway, no. 15. [*H'*]

31. **Scipio Africanus Major.** New: nose. Good workmanship. [*H'*]

32. "**Cicero.**" New: nose. Otherwise of very good workmanship. [*H'*]

33. **Bust of Agrippina.** Hair disposed in rows of detached curls. New: bust. Dallaway, no. 7.

34. **Otho.** Larger than life. Beard only indicated by scratches. [*H'*]

35. **Domitian.** Larger than life. Of good workmanship, but much broken and restored. [*H'*]

36. **Hadrian.** New: nose. Very well executed. [*H'*]

37. **Bust of Antoninus Pius.** Dallaway, no. 5. New: r. shoulder and nose. Very well executed. [*H'*]

38. **Bust of Commodus,** when young. Dallaway, no. 6. Very well executed and admirably preserved, drapery polished. [*H'*]

39. **Septimius Severus.** The same. [*H'*]

40. **Geta.** Hair treated in the manner of a bronze. Workmanship and preservation the same. [*H'*]

41. **Baldheaded man.** New: nose. Very good workmanship. [*H'*]

The end of a gallery is adorned with two rows of ancient and modern **busts.** The following are perhaps among these.

42. **Boy:** unknown. Hair minutely picked out. New: bust. Dallaway, no. 2.

43. **Man.** Hair, beard and fringe of drapery remaining fresh from the tool, face and drapery highly finished. Antique? Dallaway, no. 3.

44. "**Domitius Ahenobarbus**": the same. Dallaway, no. 4. The **reliefs** are far fewer in number.

45. **Nike.** Smacks of the hieratic style. Antique: upper part of body to about middle of thighs, with greater part of wings, r. arm inclusive of hand and fillet, and l. arm as far as the wrist. A fillet of peculiar shape is thrown around the waving hair which falls down in plaits. Leaving the wings out of account the figure corresponds with tolerable accuracy in drapery, pose, treatment and even in the movement of the hands to the priestess decorating the tripod on the three-sided pedestal in Dresden (no. 106. *August-cum*, Pl. 7. Millin, *Gal. myth.*, Pl. 16, 56. *Arch. Zeit.*, 1858,

Pl. 111, 3), which is also repeated on a relief in the Louvre (Bötticher, *Grab. d. Dionysos*, Berlin, 1858, fig. 2). Perhaps on our relief too a tripod should be restored instead of the modern tropaeon. It would be dedicated by the goddess of Victory as a symbol of a victory won in some games in honour of Dionysos or of Apollo. [*CW*]

46. Fragment, **Bacchante and youth.** Similar style to no. 45, but higher relief. Old: only upper parts of both figures. The full-draped Maenad stands l., the long thyrsos resting on l. shoulder and r. hand advanced with fingers spread out. Opposite her, r., a youth nude but for a small shawl, with hair tied up (κρω-βύλος) on his neck, l. hand lowered, in raised r. a (modern) cup being lifted to the mouth. Space between the two figures rubbed. Girl's l. hand belongs to the modern lower piece. Delicate work. H. about 0·75. [*CW*]

47. **Sepulchral relief.** Youth by a horse; an attendant near him ; on the other side a tree entwined by a snake. Poor work. [*C*]

48. **Child's sarcophagus,** oval shape ; with four lions' heads as apotropaea, which have each a ring in its mouth. Bacchic procession executed by children. **Front side :** Dionysos relatively grown up, like a youth, supported by a boy, follows a young girl who is striking the tympanon. **L. end.** Five figures. Near a basket, from which the head of a snake seems to protrude, a Satyr boy with pointed ears, with pedum, moves l. ; before him a young girl with tympanon ; touching her a bearded Pan, whom a Centaur playing the lyre faces ; finally a young girl playing the double flute. **Back :** three children treading grapes. **R. end :** quite r. a tree, then a boy with pointed ears, with pedum ; a boy with a lyre and one blowing a German flute (πλάγιος αὐλός), faced on l. side by a female Centaur playing the double flute. (With regard to the lid cf. no. 10.) [*CW*]

49. **Relief representing a ploughman :** small size. Old : only the lower piece, part of stem of a tree, both oxen except the horns, part of plough, a suggestion of the loosened earth, the lower parts of the ploughman's legs with long drapery. (Cf. O. Jahn, *Arch. Zeit.*, 1861, pp. 145 ff., and Ince, no. 293). [*C*]

Of the large number of **cineraria, urns, cippi,** &c. the following may be specially noticed.

50. **Cippus of P. Aelius Aug. lib. Taurus :** with a fine ox (*taurus*) on it. Cf. the tombstone of T. Statilius Aper with the boar

(*aper*), *Mus. Capit.*, IV. Pl. 9, and the bank dedicated by M. Nigidius Vaccula, ornamented with cow heads and cow feet, *Mus. Borbon.*, II. Pl. 54. [*CW*]

51. Double urn of M. Vigellius Logus and Vigellia Jucunda, and also Vigellia Anthusa, the inscriptions on two tablets on the front. Between these and on each of the front corners a head with Satyr's ears and ram's horns like a head of Ammon, (see Jahn, *Lauersforter Phalerae*, Bonn, 1860, pp. 10 f.), connected by garlands, in the field enclosed by which, below the inscriptions, are representations of—l. fight of a bird with a snake,—r. two birds pecking a locust (cf. Michaelis, *Arch. Zeit.*, 1866, pp. 142 f.). Below at each of the corners a double sphinx with only one head (Jahn, *l. c.* p. 9). [*C*]

52. Round cinerarium in the shape of a box. Moses, *Collection of Antique Vases*, &c., Pl. 121. In front, below, a low candelabrum, a Cupid on either side whose legs run into vine-shoots which rise high on both sides. On the tablet the inscription: *D(is) M(anibus) | P. Murrio | Epigono | Murria Procula | f(ilia) et Abascantus | et Amianthus | patrono b(ene) m(erenti) f(ecerunt)*.

53. Round pedestal of a tripod : with three holes on the top-surface. Front half polished ; rest rough. Simple mouldings. Brought by Nelson from Delphi. H. 0·98. Diameter 0·74. [*CW*]

Of the numerous small **bronzes** the following are worthy of mention.

54, 55, 56. , Jupiter, Victory, Telesphoros. [*W*]

57. Hercules. Very delicate. H. 0·06. [*W*]

58. Etruscan warrior. Of the well-known slender type. Dallaway, no. 18, " Mars." [*W*]

59. Venus. Estimable. H. about 0·20. [*W*]

60. Fury, sleeping with a serpent in each hand, as well as serpents and wings in her hair. Features expressive of sorrow ; design very noble, workmanship good but not delicate. The rock restored in wood. Dallaway, no. 17. " Nemesis or Medusa." Is the figure undoubtedly antique ? H. about 0·13. [*W*]

61. Archaic figure of a nude man, stepping forward with l. leg : both lowered arms somewhat bent. Apparently with cap on head. A Dioskuros ? [*C*]

62, 63. Two figures of Minerva and Hercules ; of barbaric roughness. Former in full armature, latter found in Naworth Castle, Cumberland. [*C*]

There are also two **Mosaics,** according to Waagen pretty, but repaired in many places:

64. Pan. Sitting with a wine-skin in r. hand, and letting the jet from a drinking-horn held in l. flow into his mouth. On a leafless tree hangs a cup. At the bottom, two male masks, one on a krater against which a tympanon leans. Dull colours. [C]

65. Aphroditè or **Galateia** : with red drapery floating in the form of an arch, driving in a chariot drawn by dolphins. R. a Triton blowing a shell, l. a female Triton with a branch of coral. [C]

Among the seventeen **painted vases** (Waagen, p. 327) only one seems to be important.

66. Krater of Python (Πύθων ἔγραφε). *Ann. de l'Institut Archéol., sect. franç.,* Pl. 10. Vol. 1., pp. 487 ff. Pl. B. (J. Millingen). The vase is as noteworthy for the variety of the colours as for the subject. On a high funeral pyre, which "Amphitryon" and "Antenor" are trying to ignite with two torches each, sits "Alkmene," r. arm advanced in entreaty to "Zeus," who is above, l., with half his body visible, and seems to be giving an order with his l. hand. He has hurled down two thunderbolts by Antenor and Amphitryon. Two goddesses of rain, in gray draperies spotted with white, pour down water from amphoras on the pyre and Alkmene, who is surrounded by rain like flakes of snow. A rainbow of divers colours forms an arch over her. Above in the r. corner "Aos," with a mirror in her r. hand, is looking on. The inscriptions containing the names of the figures are scratched on the surface. **Back :** Dionysos between two Maenads. Over him Pan and two Satyrs with only the upper parts of the bodies visible. H. about 0·55. Probably of Lucanian origin; formerly in Naples in the royal collection (Hirt, *Gesch. d. Künste,* p. 264, *Bilderbuch,* p. 21) or in the royal manufactory of porcelain (Matthison in the *Morgenblatt,* 1811, p. 651. Welcker, *Alte Denkm.,* III. p. 300), then brought by the artist Mr Tresham from Italy to England. [CW]

Lastly the collection contains a considerable quantity of various antique articles such as **metallic mirrors, sistra, bronze and terra-cotta lamps** as well as a fine collection of **gems.** [W]

Among the lamps I may mention

67. Pegasos flying up : his bridle held by a youth who is running by him in lively movement, with an animal's skin over l. arm. Large lamp. [C]

THE HYDE (Essex).

In this country house, the residence of the late JOHN DISNEY, Esq., near Ingatestone (Gt. Eastern Ry., not far from Chelmsford), are still preserved the **bronzes, terra-cottas, glass objects, vases,** &c. of his collection, chiefly collected by Thomas Hollis and Thomas Brand in Italy, while the marbles have been bequeathed to the Fitzwilliam Museum at Cambridge, with the exception, as it appears, of a few specimens (see Cambridge, after no. 101). Those small articles are sketched in the *Museum Disncianum*, Lond. 1848, Vol. II. and III., Pl. 59—127; cf. Gerhard, *Arch. Anz.*, 1849, pp. 55 ff., 125 ff. [Conze, *Arch. Anz.*, 1864, p. 169.]

ICKWORTH (Suffolk).

For the collection, which FREDERICK AUGUSTUS, Fourth EARL OF BRISTOL, Bishop of Derry (1730-1803), had laid the foundation of in Rome with a view to the adornment of his magnificent mansion at Ickworth, cf. Introd. § 62. This collection having been dispersed, only a very few antiques seem to exist at Ickworth. J. Gage (*Hist. and Antiq. of Suffolk, Thingoe Hundred*, Lond. 1838, p. 307) mentions as being in the dining-room:

1. **Bust of Hercules**, colossal scale,
2. **Bust of Lucius Verus**, the same ;

in the library :

3. **A frieze of Bacchanalian figures**, presumably, if antique at all, a relief from a sarcophagus.

INCE BLUNDELL HALL (Lancashire).

An **Account** *of the Statues, Busts, Bass-relieves, Cinerary Urns, and other Ancient Marbles, and Paintings, at Ince. Collected by H. B.* Liverpool: printed by McCreery, 1803, 4to. (332 pages).—**Engravings** *and Etchings of Sepulchral Monuments, Cinerary Urns, Gems, Bronzes, Prints, Greek Inscriptions, Fragments, &c. in the Collection of Henry Blundell, Esq., at Ince*, 1809. 2 vols. fol. (158 plates and 3 frontispieces). Dallaway, pp. 357 f. (II. pp. 107 ff. He only gives 12 numbers.) Spiker, *Reise*, I. pp. 396—403. Clarac, III. pp. cccxxxvii f. Waagen, *Treas.*, III. pp. 242 ff. Conze, *Arch.*

Anz., 1864, pp. 220 ff., Matz, *Arch. Zeit.*, 1873, pp. 31 ff. Michaelis, *ibid.*, 1874, pp. 20 ff. I examined a large portion of the collection in the years 1873 and 1877.

The Railway northward along the coast from Liverpool takes one to Hightown (9 m.) from which station one gets by road to Ince Blundell, about 3 miles inland. The collection of antiques there appears to be the largest private collection, unless the former Townley collection equalled or just surpassed it, which England ever possessed (the catalogue gives 553 numbers, among which not many are modern), though it is inferior to others in the number of remarkable specimens. It is exclusively the work of HENRY BLUNDELL (b. 1728, d. 1810). "Mr Blundell had nearly attained to his grand climacteric, when having accompanied Mr Townley to Rome, he was present when, through the agency of Jenkins, the marbles of the Villas Mattei and d'Este were offered for sale. An opportunity so alluring, of becoming possessed of well-known antique statues, and of a collection, without a gradual and tedious acquirement, was a temptation not to be resisted by Mr Blundell." Dallaway, *Of Statuary*, p. 352. For another version see Spiker, *Reise*, 1. p. 399. The earliest purchases were made in the year 1777 (no. 44), among which were also copies of antiques which our description passes over. The purchases soon increased prodigiously. The above-mentioned collections of the Villa Mattei on the Caelian and the Villa d'Este at Tivoli proved especially productive. Other specimens were furnished by the Palaces and Villas Altieri, Borioni, Capponi, Lante, Negroni, and by the art dealers and restorers Albaccini, Boni, Cavaceppi, Ant. d'Este, Gavin Hamilton, Jenkins, Lisandroni, Pacetti, Nice. la Piccola (keeper of the Capitoline Museum), Piranesi, Volpato, &c. It was Thorpe for the most part, a ci-devant Jesuit father, who is said to have been also actively engaged on Townley's behalf, who advised the purchases and looked after them in Rome. The majority were accumulated before the end of the last century, but were even further increased in England during the next few years. In May 1800, 45 chests of objects of art were sold by auction at Christie's, which had been carried off by the French from the Pope's apartments (see on no. 220); and of these Blundell bought 10 specimens. In June of the same year he purchased 8 at Lord Cawdor's sale; in April 1801 at that of Lord Bessborough of Rochampton 22; in May 1802 at that of Lord Mendip at Twickenham in his villa, formerly Mr Pope's, 7 specimens (cf. besides nos. 50, 64, 140, 141, 144, 228). Even after the publication of the "Account" (1803) the collection was still augmented by some few specimens. The marble bust of the owner at the age of eighty years prepared by Bullock in the year 1804, a representation of which is the frontispiece to the "**Engravings**," gives an idea of the energy by which such a result was attained.

The fame of the new collection soon drew a multitude of visitors from the neighbouring town of Liverpool, which was annoying to the inhabitants of the house. On this account Blundell had a large hall with a cupola and circular skylight, the "Garden Pantheon," built near his house for the reception of the choicest specimens. There is an engraving of it on the title-page of the first volume of the "Engravings." It was afterwards brought into immediate connection with the dwelling-house by a passage. Three large, four medium-sized and eight smaller niches, walls, tables, pedestals and lastly the floor in this building received the bulk of the antiques, arranged, nowadays at least, in tolerably motley confusion. The Staircase moreover is richly adorned with antiques of all sorts, while individual specimens also stand in the Picture Gallery. A further considerable storehouse is a garden house called "the Garden Temple," a spacious square edifice with the corners cut off, the walls furnished with niches. (A view of the front is on the title-page of the second volume of the "Engravings".) This very dilapidated building, lately however in course of restoration, serves in the mean while as a lumber room, nor is it easy to thread one's way through—to say nothing of studying accurately—the stores which are crowded together and piled one on another. Through the "Temple" lies the way to the Greenhouse, in which again several antiques are arranged. After enjoyment of the collection by the public had not been allowed with the same liberality as in its early days, at least for a time while Mr Blundell's son controlled it (see Clarac's complaint, III. p. cccxxxvii, while Spiker had occasion to praise Blundell's amiability), the present owner Mr THOMAS WELD-BLUNDELL with exceeding liberality permits the undisturbed study of his treasures; indeed he has gone so far as very kindly to allow not merely photographs to be taken (by his gardener, a learned photographer !) but even casts of some specimens (nos. 15, 154, 179, 259, 267). Still many others deserve to be similarly multiplied, especially nos. 30 and 43. and also perhaps nos. 33, 110, 121, 177, as well as sundry reliefs. The "Account" like the "Engravings" only published for private presentation, being of the greatest rarity and scarcely to be met with, I have here communicated all matter-of-fact indications from both works and have supple-

mented or corrected them by my own observations and some other
aids, especially Prof. Bernoulli's notes. As to the explanations
offered in these volumes, they being more than curious, I have
thought it better to set them aside. It must here however be observed
that the identification of the busts named in the "Account," indeed
even of those represented in the "Engravings," is often very difficult, and therefore some errors committed in referring the notices
before me to particular specimens of the collection may have crept in.

It was impossible to follow the present order, partly because in
many points it is not definitive, partly because my notices are not
complete enough for it. In the "Account" there is no ruling system,
so that there would be no sense in following that. My arrangement
divides first of all the different classes of sculptures. Among the
statues those come first which Clarac has had copied, and indeed
according to the order of his work. For the rest in the several
classes of monuments those take precedence which are figured in the
"Engravings" and then come the rest according to the numbering of
the "Account." By this means it is in particular made easy as far
as possible to find out a published specimen. The numbers of the
"Account" are placed in brackets after the consecutive numbers,
so too as far as possible is the indication of the place where the
specimen is kept. In these brackets G. means the greenhouse with
the adjoining localities. P. the "Pantheon" with its vestibule, S.
the staircase, T. the garden temple.

The following grouping of numbers may serve for more convenient use on the spot.

PANTHEON. Statues no. 1. 2. 8. 9. 11. 12. 14. 22—24. 28. 29.
31. 33. 34. 36. 37. 40. 43—45. 52. 53. 56. 63. 71. 74. 78. 81. 82.
Busts no. 89. 90. 92. 94. 95. 101. 104—106. 108. 110. 111. 113. 115
—117. 119—122. 127. 128. 137. 152. 155. 164. 178. 182—185. 193.
214. 216. 217 f. Reliefs no. 221. 227. 241. 246. 259. 267. 271. 272.
281. 282. 288. 289. 295. 303—310. 371 a. 393. 395.

PICTURE GALLERY. Busts no. 96. 114. 170. 189.

STAIRCASE. Statues no. 3. 4. 17. 21. 26. 27. 54. 55. 68—70.
Busts no. 123. 126. 148. 205 a. Reliefs no. 218. 224. 228. 245.
247—251. 256—258. 260. 262—265. 269. 270. 274. 374. 378. 396.
398. Mosaics no. 410. 413.

GARDEN TEMPLE. Statues no. 5—7. 13. 15. 16. 18. 20. 25. 30.
32. 38. 39. 42. 46. 48. 59. 83. Busts no. 84—88. 91. 93. 98—100.
102. 112. 124. 125. 133. 139—141. 154. 160. 168. 176. 216 a. 217
a. b. c. Reliefs no. 261. 273. 278. 287. 290. 296. 298. 375—377. 391.

GREENHOUSE. Statues no. 10. 41. 49—51. Busts no. 217. d. e. Reliefs no. 223. 225. 229. 243. 255. 397.

STATUES.

1 (56. P). **Ceres.** Clarac, III. 396 C, 662 A. *Engr.*, 31. "Cybele." *Mon. Matth.*, I. 71, "*Sacerdos Cereris sacrificans.*" The fully-draped, veiled goddess sits on a broad stool, holding out a cup in her r. hand. Near her r. leg a circular altar, covered with a sheep-skin, close to it a cow or an ox, on it a tympanon ; to her l. a small round cista, apparently with a lid, by it a pig. The animals are those preeminently sacred to Demeter, to whom, it is true, the tympanon only pertains through a confusion with Rhea or Kybele. Cf. Overbeck, *Kunstmythologie*, III. p. 459, and the similar statue in the *Collegio Romano* (Gerhard, *Ges. Abhandl.*, II. p. 397). New : head of cow, l. hand of goddess, parts of r. hand and of the cup, neck and veil, nose and chin ; the rest of the face old, but not belonging to the statue, of different marble. Italian marble. Decorative work. H. 0·50. [*CII*]

2 (4. P). **Statue of Zeus.** Clarac, III. 396 D, 681 A. *Engr.*, 4. Entirely nude, r. arm lowered, l. raised. The general expression is rather grand, the execution is however not above the ordinary standard, moreover the whole surface is sadly smoothed over. Head, with curly hair and beard, of noble features, but indifferent expression, has never been detached from the trunk. New : r. hand, l. arm with sceptre, lower part of l. leg, three quarters of r. leg, besides trunk of a tree and eagle. A strong plug of lead near r. wrist served probably to fasten on the thunderbolt. On the back under the shoulder-blades two small drilled holes. From Hadrian's Villa, afterwards in the Villa d'Este. H. 2·14. [*C*]

3 (10. S). **Draped female figure.** Clarac, III. 421, 743. *Engr.*, 10, 1, "Juno." Over a chiton, the folds of which fall down over the girdle as far as the lap, the figure wears a cloak which fully covers back, head, upper parts of body and of arms, and which would enfold the whole body, if both forearms did not raise up a part of the cloak. New : veiled head and neck, both hands, the r. with a pome-granate. According to Clarac one of the best statues of the collection ; it really is executed, though not at all delicately, still in a very powerful decorative style. Thasian marble. From Hadrian's Villa, afterwards in the Villa d'Este. H. 1·78. [*]

4 (18. S). **Draped female statue.** Clarac, III. 428, 769.

M. C.   22

Engr., 18, 2, " Ceres." Cavaceppi, *Racc.*, II. 36. Very ordinary statue in chiton and cloak which leaves r. breast and arm free. New: r. forearm with ears of corn, half l. forearm ; the head has been broken off but is old and perhaps its own. Found in some ruins a little way out of Rome, and bought from Antonio d'Este. H. 1·07. [*]

5 (59. T). **Statuette of Silvanus.** Clarac, III. 449, 820 A. *Engr.*, 26, 1. Exhibits quite the usual type of the rural god (cf. Reitferscheid, *Annali*, 1866, pp. 210 f.), only that instead of the skin filled with fruits there appears a small cloak with nothing in it (cf. *ibid.*, Pl. K, 2); it is more distinguished by tolerable preservation than by goodness of the work. New: only l. hand with the branch of a pine tree, r. arm (which should be more bent) with the knife, lower parts of legs, which are therefore without the boots. H. 0·69. [*C]

6 (22. T, portico). **Statuette of a boy,** carrying flowers and ears of wheat in the lap of his tunic, probably **representing the season of spring and summer** (cf. Marbury, no. 8). Clarac, III. 449, 816 A. *Engr.*, 19, 1, " Vertumnus." New: head and neck, lower parts of both legs with corresponding piece of drapery falling down behind as far as the ground ; l. forearm and both hands wanting. Coarse work. H. 0·88. [*]

7 (54. T). **Statuette of Tychè.** Clarac, III. 454, 834 A. *Engr.*, 44, 1, " Fortuna Navalis." Draped in chiton and cloak, sitting on a throne, r. hand on the steering paddle, large cornucopia in l. arm. New, according to Clarac: paddle, cornucopia, l. arm: to myself all essential parts seem to be antique. The head seems to be a portrait and may belong to the statue. Very ordinary work. From the Villa Borioni. H. 0·73. [*]

8 (1. P). **Statue of Athenè.** Clarac, III. 473, 899 A. *Engr.*, 1. *Account*, Pl. 1. The goddess in girdled Doric chiton stands on r. foot, l. being somewhat retired. Preservation excellent. Head never broken off. New: apex of helmet above the brow and the sphinx, tip of nose, r. forearm with owl (cf. Newby, no. 23), thumb, first finger and part of middle finger on l. hand, two toes of l. foot, trifles in the drapery. In l. hand traces of the groove intended for the spear. The drapery shows the motive of the Parthenos ; folds deeply undercut ; the small aegis almost entirely invisible behind the back ; on the other hand the long coil of the hair of the Parthenos is retained. Selvage of chiton still recognisable. The inclined head however indicates a later type, though less sentimental than many other heads (*e.g. Mon. dell. Inst.*, IV. Pl. 1). Good, though somewhat dry Roman work. Pentelic marble. Found in Ostia ; from the Palazzo Lante it passed

through Volpato's hands to Jenkins, from whom it came to Blundell.
H. 1·98 without the sphinx.　[*C W]

9 (S. P).　**Statue of Athenè.** Clarac, III. 473, 899 P.　*Engr.*, 8.
Account, Pl. 8.　Pose of the figure and arrangement of chiton correspond to the statue no. 8; aegis reaches down from r. shoulder
to l. hip in a slanting direction; on the l. shoulder lies a piece
of the cloak.　New: r. arm, l. arm from above the elbow with
the shield, about a third of the parts of the legs below the knee, besides
details in the folds, on the head the whole r. half of face including
the nose, mouth, chin and part of the l. brow, the guard of the helmet
(the ram's-horns l. old) and the sphinx but for a part of the attachment.
Work in no respect remarkable, folds on body very flat while they
are as marked and deeply cut in on the r. bearing leg, as if there
were no solid leg underneath.　Coarse-grained Parian marble.
According to the "Account" the statue was got from the Villa
Negroni.　According to Thorpe however (*ibid.*, p. 281) the head was
found near the church of S. Croce in Gerusalemme and came into
Cavaceppi's possession ; the torso found at the church of S. Susanna
on the Quirinal was purchased from Albaccini, and Canova directed
the further restorations.　H. 1·93.　[*C]

10 (13. G).　**Statue of Athenè.** Clarac, III. 473, 899 C.
Engr., 13, 2.　Insipid enough, but not belying a good original
(cf. Castle Howard, no. 4).　New: head and r. arm.　From the
Villa Mattei.　H. 1·47.　[*]

11 (518. P).　**Torso of an Athenè in hieratic style.** Clarac,
III. 473, 899 D.　*Engr.*, 38.　The large aegis with a powerful
Medusa-head in old style is girt with a lion's skin, the head of which,
disproportionately small, appears in front in an unusual manner as a
kind of buckle to the girdle.　In Clarac's doubt as to the antiquity
of this rare dress I entirely participate.　I regard the frigid, over-
refined torso of Italian marble as modern.　On it is set an insignificant antique head of yellowish marble ; the so-called Corinthian
helmet is furnished with a very lofty crest.　New : arms, and legs
from the knees downwards.　Bought at Lord Cawdor's sale.　H. 1·30.
[*W]

12 (P).　**Statue of Apollo Sauroktonos.** Clarac, III. 476 B.
905 B.　*Engr.*, 36.　Torso antique, also the uppermost quarter of
both legs and the piece of r. arm from above elbow to wrist.　The
antique head (new : nose, chin, neck) has not the ingenuous expression of the Sauroktonos, but somewhat the character of a Venus, and
seems to be of different marble from the torso.　Work good, but not

eminently so; according to Clarac the statue is polished over. Found near Rome by G. Hamilton and sold to Mr Rob. Heathcote and sent to England. H. 1·38. [*CH*]

13 (12. T). **Statue of Apollo in repose.** Clarac, III. 488, 946. *Engr.*, 12. New: lower parts of both legs, both arms, lyre and stem of tree. Head antique, but seriously restored, and not belonging to the statue. Work, flat decorative. The statue was got from the Villa Mattei and is probably identical with *Mon. Matth.*, I. 8, Clarac, III. 476, 912 E; rather than with *Mon. Matth.*, I. 4, Clarac, III. 490, 954 B. H. 1·45. [*]

14 (76. P). **Statue of Apollo,** Clarac, III. 488, 946 A. *Engr.*, 23, 2. The graceful, but by no means finely executed body rests on r. leg. The quiver-strap goes slantwise over the breast, but there are no traces of the quiver on the back. Long curls fall down on the shoulders. New: head, both arms, tripod, l. thigh and half the lower part of the leg, both feet. Greek marble. H. 1·34. [*C*]

15 (530. T). **Statue of Apollo, of archaistic style.** Clarac, III. 488, 946 B. *Engr.*, 39. *Arch. Zeit.*, 1874, Pl. 2. This very interesting statue is most closely related in style to the Vatican Apollo (Gerhard, *Ant. Bildw.*, Pl. 11. Clarac, III. 483, 931), but is distinguished by its wonderfully perfect preservation. New: only a small piece of tip of nose, r. hand, uppermost point of bow, part of pedestal. The god, quite nude, has his weight on both feet equally, l. foot a little advanced. L. arm (antique throughout) hangs down freely close to the body: r., likewise lowered, is a little advanced. Bow and arrow on the laurel tree determine the subject as Apollo. Fingers of l. hand in such a position as shows them to have once had some object in their grasp. It is the old type, as it begins in the famous statue of Tenea and its congeners and later on has been remodelled and improved in different ways, especially in the Choiseul-Gouffier Apollo in the British Museum (*Spec.*, II. Pl. 5, *Mus. Marbles*, XI. Pl. 32, *Journ. Hell. Stud.*, I. Pl. 4, Clarac, III. 482 B, 931 A) and the replica thereof from the theatre of Dionysos at Athens (Conze, *Beitr. zur Gesch. d. griech. Plastik*, Pl. 3—5). In the broad prominent breast and deeply hollowed back and loins one discerns a reminiscence of the archaic style, but the whole treatment of the form is modernised and badly flattened. There is an especially distressing contrast between the archaic type and the modern execution of the head, which compared with the rest of the body seems needlessly stiff and devoid of expression. The hair with an old-fashioned roll (κρωβύλος), which is raised at the back of the neck and looped in a head-band, is no less superficially treated. The lobes of the ears are of comparatively small curvature, the eye-balls indicated by a circle. The statue, which is throughout much poorer than the so-called Stephanos figures which are akin to it in many traits (see Margam, no. 5), is perhaps the latest and weakest imitation of that ancient type; but it is interesting, because it shows how long that type maintained its currency. Pentelic marble. H. 1·53 (without pedestal). Bought from the Bessborough collection. [*CIV]

16 (52. T). **Statue of sitting Apollo.** Clarac, III. 494 A, 959 C. *Engr.*, 44, 2. He sits on a block of rock on which a lizard crawls. Upper part of body nude, legs enveloped in cloak. It is very seriously patched up, and is besides of a poor style of art. From the Villa Mattei. H. 0·76. [*]

17 (74. S). **Statue of Muse?** Clarac, III. 515, 1041 B. *Engr.*, 10, 2, "Thalia." The delicate chiton is entirely ungirt, the cloak lies in a rather meaningless manner on the r. thigh which is a very little bent forward, and covers back and r. arm. The pleasing original from which this copy was taken must have been in the manner of the Venus genetrix in Coan drapery (see Holkham, no. 27); the copy before us is executed with little care. New: ivy-crowned head, neck, three-quarters of r. arm with the mask, l. fore-arm with pedum, part of drapery, the pedestal. Bought from the sale of property left by La Piccola together with nos. 30, 32, 411. H. 1·22. [*]

18 (23. T, portico). **Statuette of Muse?** Clarac, III. 516, 1053 A. *Engr.*, 20, "Melpomene." The richly draped figure supports itself with the l. elbow on a column. Chiton girt high up, enveloped on the thighs by a cloak of which the folds fall down near the l. hip over the column. New: head, greater part of breast, r. and almost all l. arm with the mask, l. foot and part of the column. Badly executed. Bought from Cavaceppi. H. 0·89. [*]

19 (19). **Statuette of Muse?** Clarac, III. 533, 1110 C. *Engr.*, 14, 2, "Urania." Clarac takes the hands with globe and style to be modern. In my opinion the whole of the little alabaster figure, especially in the arrangement of its cloak, quite suggests certain Christian figures of saints, so as to convey more than a mere suspicion of its genuineness. The statuette is said to have been found in the Marrana, a muddy brook which comes down from the Alban hills, and after flowing through the Circus Maximus empties itself into the Tiber. It was bought from Cochetto, a noted dealer in antiquities, and restored by Antonio d'Este. H. 0·38.

20 (5. T). **Statue of Asklepios.** Clarac, IV. 550, 1160 A. *Engr.*, 5. The statue exhibits none of the usual characteristics of Asklepios. The front corner of the cloak is thrown over the l. forearm; instead of the staff entwined by a snake the stem of a tree entwined by a snake stands near the l. leg. New: l. hand from the cloak, the three first fingers of r. hand (the arm has never been broken off), head of snake and a piece of the neck. The feet have been broken off, but are antique, and so is the pedestal. The head is put on, but almost certainly belongs to the statue. It looks up a little sideways and strongly reminds one of the Blacas Asklepios in the British Museum. Consequently the nomenclature both of the statue and the head is reciprocally verified. Work not bad, so far as the unfavourable light and position allow it to be discerned. From the Villa Mattei. H. 2·08. [*]

21 (29. S). **Statuette of Asklepios.** Clarac, IV. 551, 1160 B. *Engr.*, 18. In the case of this statuette the meaning is determined by the head with its long beard, which has never been broken off. New: nose, l. arm, half the r. with the staff entwined by a snake, r. foot and toes of l. and the pedestal. Unimportant work; expression of face meaningless. Found a little way out of one of the gates at Rome and bought from Cavaceppi. H. 0·76. [*]

22 (2. P). **Statue of Artemis.** Clarac, IV. 567, 1209 A. *Engr.*, 2. *Account*, Pl. 2. Antique: the torso with its short drapery of heavy style and the large skin girt over it (of which the head and the leg that hangs down in front are new), and part of the quiver, also the knees, r. arm, exclusive of the hand with the arrow, and a piece of the neck and back of the head, though the last is not, as is stated in the *Account*, unbroken. New: apparently l. arm; Conze describes the hand exclusive of the tip of the thumb and the forefinger as probably antique: all the rest is certainly new. "When this statue was first found it plainly appeared to have been gilt;" that is it is in many parts quite yellow, but that is scarcely to be accounted for by gilding. Found in the ruins of the Emperor Gordian's Villa, and bought by Mr Thorpe from Albaccini. Of very mediocre execution. H. 1·58. [*CII*]

23 (37. P). **Statuette of Artemis.** Clarac, IV. 580, 1237 B. *Engr.*, 28, 1. A short chiton tucked and girdled after the fashion of an Amazon covers both breasts; the quiver-strap runs slantwise across the breast. Near l. leg a stem of a tree with quiver and skull of a wild beast on it. The head is antique (nose and part of the knot of hair restored), and may belong to the statue in spite of the inserted

neck. Lobes of ears pierced. New: r. arm with shoulder, half the
l. forearm, r. leg below knee, a part of same portion of l. leg, parts
of folds of drapery and of pedestal. Composition of statuette pretty,
though execution not particularly delicate, the back indeed is left
quite rough. Very remarkable is its resemblance to the statues of
Amazons in which sometimes even the whole breast is draped, *e.g.*
in the Dresden and Vienna statuettes (Clarac, v. 810 A, 2031 B,
Berichte d. sächs. Ges. d. Wiss., 1850, Pl. 1, 2, 6), and on the Phigalia
frieze, &c., so that a doubt as to the intention can arise as well as
that which prevails in the case of a similar statue in the casino of
the Villa Pamfili (Clarac, iv. 567, 1208 B, cf. Jahn, *Berichte, l.c.* p.
46 note). If Artemis is really intended, we have before us an older
type of the goddess with short drapery. Grey marble. H. 0·56.
[*CW*]

24 (20. P). **Enigmatical Statuette.** Clarac, iv. 593, 1290.
Engr., 15, 1, "Venus Victrix." This unpleasing figure wears over
the chiton apparently a kind of woollen jacket, which, however, has
been created solely through modern working over of the pretty well
worn chiton; over that a short cloak. New: both arms (the cup with
the Victory, which is said to have been added, according to Visconti's
advice, is now no longer in existence) and the front half of both
feet, also the head with the strange cloth on it, though a part of
the face is further added separately. A corner of the drapery behind
the r. shoulder seems to have furnished the idea of the head-cloth.
Moreover the whole figure is not free from suspicion. At best it is
entirely worked over. The meaning is obscure in my judgment.
From the Villa Mattei. H. 0·84. [*C*]

25 (531. T). **Statue of sleeping Hermaphroditos.** Clarac,
iv. 628, 1425 B. *Engr.*, 41, "Sleeping Venus." The *Account*
(1803) mentions the figure under the first title as it was bought from
the Bessborough collection; "this curious figure is accompanied
with three little genii, one of which is sucking at the left breast."
Otherwise the *Engravings* (1809): "The figure was unnatural and
very disgusting to the sight; but by means of a little castration and
cutting away the little brats [crawling about its breast], it became a
sleeping Venus and as pleasing a figure as any in this collection." We
now see after this, certainly very cleverly executed, operation, only
a nude female figure, lying half on the back, half on the r. side, on a
wide drapery which merely covers the r. knee and the lower part of
the leg drawn up under it, as well as the part about the l. knee. The
upper part of the body lies raised on a block of rock covered with a

drapery, and the head is very naturally fallen back on to the r.
shoulder. Eyes closed; the widely opened mouth, from which one
fancies one can perceive breath passing, corresponds to the bent back
position of the head. A wreath of flowers tied with a bandage adorns
the hair. Very singular are the unusually developed breasts, especially
the l. which almost hangs, but in fact this peculiarity finds its explanation in the circumstance that we originally had before us a sleeping Hermaphrodite as a nursing mother, the acmè of unnatural
refinement. The work deserves no special praise. New: whole of
r. arm which hangs down, and l. from the armlet which encircles
the middle of the upper arm, half r. foot, the l. leg with foot in a shoe,
a great part of the wreath of flowers, nose and mouth. L. 1·25. H.
0·50. [*]

26 (32. S). **Statue of Cupid without wings**, with attributes
of earth and sea. Clarac, IV. 649, 1455 A from *Engr.*, 19. 2, and IV.
650 D, 1455 A from *Mon. Matth.*, I. 15. The boy, quite nude, steps
forward with l. leg. Hair curly, lying on the top of the head in the
well-known plait-like arrangement. In l. arm he carries a large bunch
of akanthos leaves with flowers and fruit; on the support near l. arm
a dolphin twines itself. New: r. arm with quince, l. hand, l. foot,
half r. and part of pedestal. Ordinary work. From the Villa Mattei.
H. 0·68. [*]

27 (31. S). **Statue of Hermes as a boy.** Clarac, IV. 655,
1506 A. *Engr.*, 24. The nude boy with winged shoes on his feet
stands in repose. Body rests on r. leg, near which is a heavy support
adorned with the caduceus. The curly child's head is put on, but
perhaps its own. New: both arms and the purse. Winged shoes
and caduceus certainly old. Ordinary work. Bought by Mr
Thorpe. [*]

28 (30. P). **Statue of Hermes.** Clarac, IV. 661, 1528 A.
Engr., 23, 1. The god stands in a tolerably reposeful attitude, r.
foot a little retired, stepping forward a little with l. foot. The chlamys
buttoned together on l. shoulder passes slantwise over the breast,
covers r. shoulder and r. arm, and from it falls down to the knee;
under it is the trunk of a tree. Head with wings facing somewhat r.
is put on; nose and l. cheek patched. New: half r. arm with tortoise, l. hand with handle of caduceus as also its upper end, and
perhaps r. foot as far as above the ankle. The statue is coarsely
worked and of clumsy proportions. From the Villa d'Este. H. 1·08.
[*C]

29 (34. P). **Statuette of Hermes.** Clarac, IV. 661, 1529 A.

Engr., 26, 3. Chlamys lies on l. shoulder and covers part of arm and back. Body, slightly bent, rests especially on r. leg, near which a clumsy support is visible, r. leg somewhat bent. The lowered r. hand holds a purse. New: head with its winged cap, half the lower parts of the god's legs with the adjoining part of the trunk of the tree and l. hand, but the middle part of caduceus antique, enough to verify the attribute. Of the he-goat by the trunk of the tree the head is old; but the rest of its body is new. The statuette is clumsy and of poor workmanship. Bought from the Palazzo Capponi. H. 0·55. [*C]

30 (75. T). **Group of Satyr and Hermaphroditos.** Clarac, IV. 672, 1735 A. *Engr.* 42. Böttiger, *Archaeol. und Kunst,* I. Plate to p. 169. Several examples of this composition, altogether or in part identical, have come down to us; namely two in Dresden (nos. 209, 210) found at Tivoli, formerly in the collection of Prince Mazarin; one from Hadrian's Villa, once in Count Fede's possession, now lost (Lipsius, *Beschr. der Antikengall. in Dresden,* p. 312); one in the British Museum (Graeco-Roman Sculpt., no. 178, *Mus. Marbles,* XI. 39). This proves the popularity of the *symplegma* (according to Stephani, *Compte-Rendu,* 1867, pp. 10 f., by Heliodoros, see Pliny *Nat. Hist.,* 36, 35). Its popularity is accounted for as much by the lubricity of the subject, which is agreeable to the taste of the Hellenistic period, as by the wonderful excellence of the lively composition. The bearded Satyr, whose sexual excitement is extremely apparent, sits on a low rise of rock and has both legs clasped round a Hermaphroditos so that the Hermaphroditos' back is turned to him. But with the suppleness of an eel the Hermaphroditos contrives to extricate himself from the embrace, by resting his r. knee on the ground in a peculiar bend and drawing his l. leg from under the l. leg of his assailant so that the next minute will find him on both knees half turned to the Satyr. He is already twisting round his lithe body and pushing aside the l. foot of the assailant with the l. hand to give himself free space for springing up and effecting his escape, and is thrusting his r. hand straight into the Satyr's face, who has to seize the arm with both hands to save himself from the thrust, and whose whole body is forced back. The Hermaphroditos, sure of victory, looks back on his too forward lover, with a mocking smile of triumph. The whole of the extremely complicated movement is carried out in a masterly manner, all one direction, one movement, the previous and the immediately following moments of the struggle connected in the most pregnant way. Agreeable to this is the exceedingly soft,

fleshy rendering of the lithe, female figure with its full roundness of breast and hip and the very sprightly lines of the bent back. The features too of the Hermaphroditos are appropriate in connection with the Satyr, borrowed as they are from a merry, robust, country-girl used to sport of the kind. The poverty of the delineation of the masculine parts stands in characteristic contrast to all the lines and curves of the body and the long hair. The naturalistic sentiment, especially in the rendering of the nude, reminding one of Dutch artists, combined with the smallness of the figures, which are about half life-size, all the more strongly emphasizes the lubricity of the motive. The same is the case with the Townley group of a Satyr and a nymph in the British Museum (Dallaway, p. 312, no. 27, Visconti, *Mus. Pio-Clem.*, I. p. 48 Mil., *Arch. Zeit.*, 1874, p. 24). The preservation is in the most important portions excellent, the head of the Hermaphroditos in particular never having been severed from the body. New: of the Hermaphroditos, l. forearm and lower parts of both legs; of the Satyr, the lower part of r. leg and half the lower part of the l. leg, l. knee-cap and a large piece on the r. knee, part of the cranium, besides insignificant patches and the bottom part of the rock. The restorer has not caught quite the right idea as to the l. hand of the Hermaphroditos, which must have grasped the foot of the Satyr otherwise, and probably not as to his r. leg, which may have been placed a little less out. The group is not executed with particular delicacy but with considerable vigour. It was found about A.D. 1760 in the *Tenuta di Salone* on the Via Praenestina this side of the *Tor de' Schiavi*, as was also no. 32, a crouching Venus and a plinth on which is said to have been the inscription Βοΰπαλος ἐποίει (Visconti, *Mus. Pio-Clem.*, I. p. 61 Mil., *Opere Varie*, II. p. 644, note 1). The Venus with a copy of the plinth, accurate even in the mouldings, went to the Vatican (*Mus. Pio-Clem.*, I. Pl. 10). Our group was united by the discoverer Nic. La Piccola (cf. no. 17) with that plinth, which undoubtedly had nothing to do with it originally. For it must have had a piece added to lengthen it to be able to receive the group (at present it is 0·70 long by 0·50 broad); again the block of rock does not consist of the same piece as the plinth but was afterwards let into it. Probably the plinth was thoroughly worked over on this occasion and so got its tolerably modern look. Moreover the inscription, which stands on the narrow side under the feet, appears very suspicious. It is faint as if scratched in with a knife thus—

ΒΟΥΠΑΛΟΣ
ΕΠΟΙΕΙ

The shape of the B, the Y slanting L, the Λ instead of Α and lastly both the Γ's without the little stroke at the top strengthen our suspicions. Visconti, considering that the palaeography has little in common with the period of the ancient Bupalos of Chios, supposed a falsification of the inscription in ancient times (cf. Phaedr. *Fab.*, 5, *prol.*), as indeed we read of a preference entertained by Augustus for this very ancient sculptor (Plin. *Nat. Hist.*, 36, 13); in my opinion it is more probably a modern forgery, as Franz also supposes (*C. I. Gr.*, III. 6141), and this in fact would not be the only instance in connection with the name Bupalos (see R. Rochette, *Lettre à M. Schorn*, p. 239). In the *Engravings* we read of this group, "La Picola...kept it up for many years at an extravagant price. The late Mr C. Townley is said to have offered a very large sum for it. At La Picola's death it became the joint property of his widow and others, when it was obliged to be sold, and was purchased for this collection." L. 0·78. H. 0·67. [*H*]

31 (14. P). **Statue of Dionysos.** Clarac, IV. 678 A, 1595 A. *Engr.*, 14, 1. *Mon. Matth.*, I. 12. The god, perfectly nude, stands with his body slightly inclined and his r. arm leaning on the trunk of a tree twined with branches of vine; l. arm hanging down on the body, r. hand resting on a bunch of grapes. This statue of medium size has been broken across the body, below the knees and across both arms. New: head crowned with vine, l. forearm with vase (both differently restored previously—a patch on l. hip still shows the old point of junction), probably r. leg from knee to ankle. The preservation of the other parts is good, as also is the work. The oval pedestal has a rough moulding in the style of the basis of an Attic column. From the Villa Mattei. H. 1·15. [*C*]

32 (73. T). **Statue of Dionysos.** Clarac, IV. 684, 1603 A. *Engr.*, 34. The youthful god with long curls, a fawn-skin hanging from the l. shoulder slantwise over the breast, rests on the r. leg, which is attached to a clumsy support: the l. leg being slightly bent and a little retired. The bent head (new: nose and lips) is encircled with a fillet. It may be the original head: the neck however is inserted. The l. hand with the kantharos and the r. hand or the forearm with the thyrsos are most probably modern, apparently also the legs below the knee with the corresponding portion of the support: still the figure is so covered with old dust that it is very difficult

actually to judge about the various parts. Found together with no. 30 and likewise bought from La Piccola's widow. H. 1·58. [*]

33 (38. P). **Female Statuette (Nemesis ?).** Clarac, IV. 698, 1646 A. *Engr.*, 26, 2, "Bacchante." A pleasing Attic figure in doubled chiton, fastened, with a mass of folds round the hips, resting on l. leg while the r. foot is a little advanced. The movement of the r. arm, which is not modern, is particularly delicate. It is raised before the breast so that the hand grasps the drapery at the throat. That it should therefore be called Nemesis, as Conze conjectures (cf. *Anthol. Palat. app. Planud.*, 223, 224, Mesomedes, *Hymn. in Nem.*, 11), is possible, but not certain (see Zoega, *Abhandl.*, p. 52); it would be certain, if indeed the lowered r. hand had held a twig of apple. The head joined on to the body by an inserted neck seems old (new according to Clarac and Conze) and may belong to the statue. New: the whole lower part nearly up to the knees and half the r. forearm with the vase; besides two iron plugs visible on the chiton prove that the hand always held an object requiring to be fastened on to it. H. 0·475. [*C]

34 (15. P). **Statue of a Bacchante ?** Clarac, IV. 698, 1696 B. *Engr.*, 15, 2. A figure in long drapery. It is assigned to the Bacchic cycle owing to the fawn-skin girt slantwise across the body. But with its full drapery, its long mass of folds hanging down, and the dignified repose of the attitude, it rather gives the impression of a goddess (Ariadne ?) than of a dancing Bacchante which is stamped upon it by the modern cymbals. New: both forearms with the cymbals, also the head and neck. Work somewhat hard, apparently a reduced copy of a good original of larger size. Greek marble. Found in Hadrian's villa, and bought by Mr Thorpe. H. 1·19. [*]

35 (57). **Group of Satyr-boy and Goat.** Clarac, IV. 709, 1670 A. *Engr.*, 32. The pretty lad, only to a small extent covered by the skin which is fastened below the breast with a cord, kneels on the r. knee and has the l. foot advanced. He holds a bunch of grapes in each hand, while his glance is directed to the goat which lies before him on the ground with its head attentively raised. The pleasing motive has a lively effect. New: r. arm and l. leg below the knee. From the Capponi palace. H. 0·46.

36 (516. P). **Statue of Aphroditè** (called "Galatea"). Clarac, IV. 746, 1802 A. *Engr.*, 13, 1. For the motive and meaning of this attractive figure see below on Newby Hall, no. 6. This copy came from Greece to Rome, where Lord Cawdor bought it. Though not very delicately worked it is still of good decorative effect. The

pierced snout of the dolphin proves that it was employed to adorn a
fountain. The head with stephanè and veil is put on, but is certainly
old and its own (Conze thinks otherwise). A mark of a join (*puntello*)
above the r. breast shows that the veil fell down so far. New: r.
arm with shoulder, l. forearm (upper arm broken, but old), upper
part of staff and dolphin; sundry pieces on under border of garment.
Well preserved in the genuine portions. Coarse-grained Parian
marble of fine yellow colour. H. 1·18. [*C*, cf. Matz, *Arch. Zeit.*,
1873, p. 23, note 3.]

37 (16. P). **Statue of Anchirrhoè.** Clarac, IV. 750, 1828.
Engr., 16. Visconti, *Mus. Pio-Clem.*, III. Pl. *a*, v. This example is
distinguished among the several replicas (Stark, *Niobe*, pp. 283 ff.) by
the undoubtedly genuine inscription (Conze indeed suspects it)
ANCHYRRHOE[1], which first recalls Neilos' daughter the wife of
Belos; the same significant name however belongs also to other
water-goddesses (Visconti, III. pp. 189, 231 Mil., Matz, *Arch. Zeit.*,
1873. p. 31, Michaelis, *ib.*, 1874, p. 24). The charming motive
of the nymph answers to the latter. She lifts her drapery slightly
over the r. knee and steps down cautiously to the well. She without
doubt once carried a hydria on the r. shoulder (see Friederichs,
Berlins ant. Bildw., I. no. 685). The body is entirely supported on
the l. leg, which is bent, while the r. foot is advanced. It is pretty
clear that the figure was originally designed to adorn a well (cf. Paus.,
8. 31, 4). Unfortunately, owing to the unintelligent restoration of the
head, which ought to look down, and to the affected elegance of the
pose of the r. arm with the tiny hydria, the impression of beauty
is seriously impaired. The restoration, after a clumsy repairing of
older date had been removed, was effected for Blundell by the
sculptors Lisandroni and Este. The r. arm and the shoulder are
correctly restored, as the folds of the cloak on the thigh prove.
R. foot and half the lower part of leg also new. The pleasing composition has, as it seems, been subsequently transferred to Muses
and other maidens. Brilliant Parian marble. Found in Hadrian's
Villa, bought from the Villa d'Este. H. 1·65. [*CMH*]

38 (51. T). **Statuette of Serapis.** Clarac, IV. 758, 1851 C.
Engr., 30, "Pluto." This statuette exhibits the usual representation

---

[1] Matz shows that this inscription was already known in the 16th century.
It subsequently disappeared, and the statue received the name Hebè. "When it
was removed from the place in the Villa d'Este, where it had stood for many
years, on the plinth of it was discovered its real name, which had been long
covered with mortar." (*Account*, p. 16.)

of the Alexandrine God, seated on a throne, draped in chiton and cloak, on the lowering head the modius decorated with a spray of olive, sceptre in l. hand, Kerberos at the r. In the original the snake shows no scales. New: both arms from the drapery, upper half of sceptre, middle and outer heads of the hell-hound. Coarse work. H. 0·86. [*]

39 (55. T). **Statuette of Serapis.** Replica of the last statuette. New: only l. arm with upper half of sceptre and the face, the greater part of the head with the modius ornamented with boughs is old. Coarse-grained Parian marble. Bought from Cavaceppi. H. 0·86. [*]

40 (28. P). **Statuette of Aphroditè-Spes.** Clarac, IV. 760, 1899. *Engr.*, 22, "Spes Etrusca." A rough Roman copy of the very old artistic device by which Greek art had at first tried to enliven the long drapery of female figures and which was then used by preference for Aphroditè, and afterwards for Spes. New: head, both forearms and lower part of the legs from below the calves. H. 0·75. [*C]

41 (G). **Statuette of Aphroditè-Spes.** A much stiffer replica of the same figure, but reversed so that the r. hand grasps the drapery, the l. holds a fruit or flower. It is so rigid that the taking up of the corner of the drapery exerts scarcely any influence on the general direction of the folds. New: nose, neck, lower part of legs and two fingers of r. hand. H. 0·74. [*H]

42 (9. T). **Statue of Phrygia**; colossal scale. Clarac, IV. 768 A, 1906 A. *Engr.*, 9, "Bithynia." This statue is executed in rather a coarse decorative style, yet is of good effect. It is worthy of attention as the only undoubted example which has come down to us of a sculptured personification of a province. A high girt chiton of stout material falls in simple folds down as far as the knee : before the breast there is fastened together the cloak, which merely covers the shoulders, upper arms and back. Head, broken, but undoubtedly its own, bearing a lofty mural crown, under which a twisted fillet, in the style of a porter's pad (κτέφαλλον, τέλη) is visible (cf. the Messenè, *Arch. Zeit.*, 1875, p. 104). This attribute indicates the general department of local personification to which the statue belongs. A large tambourine (τύμπανον) placed on the trunk of a tree, on which the l. hand rests, alludes most probably to the land of the mother of the gods. This is also the explanation of Filippo Aurelio Visconti (*Account*, p. 282), for which the nomenclature " Bithynia" in the explanatory text of the *Account* and the *Engravings* seems to be substituted by mere mistake. New: legs from drapery downwards with the pedestal and part of the tree, r. arm almost from the drapery as well as the banner, lastly sundry portions of the cloak. Marble apparently from Thasos. This statue, found in Hadrian's Villa, formerly stood in the Villa d'Este restored with ears of corn in the r. hand as Ceres or Cybele, and was only allowed to be exported after long negotiations and great expense through the mediation of the sculptor Lisandroni (1789). H. 1·80 according to Clarac, according to my memory considerably greater. [*W]

43 (3. P). **Statue of Theseus.** Clarac, v. 829, 2071 Q. *Engr.*, 3. *Spec.*, II. 19. *Arch. Zeit.*, 1874, Pl. 1 (from a Photograph). This most elegant statue is one of the principal treasures of the collection and was esteemed by Townley as the best specimen (Spiker, I. p. 400 note). It represents a youthful hero whose body rests for the most part on the l. leg, but still so that the r. leg which is advanced in a freer position shares the weight. A singularly delicate and elastic movement pervades the quiet pose of the main design, a quality characteristic of the works of Lysippos, especially the 'Scraper' (ἀποξυόμενος, destringens se) of the Vatican (cf. Kekulé, *Die Gruppe des Menelaos*, p. 36). All the other characteristics of the statue answer to the far-famed elegance of the Sikyonian master: the soft texture of the skin, the large size and the flatness of the feet, and above all the proportions (determined afresh, as is well known, by Lysippos), which in every single measurable portion thereof correspond accurately, mostly to within a centimeter, to those of the ἀποξυόμενος (cf. *Arch. Zeit.*, 1874, p. 25). There can therefore be no doubt that the statue is to be referred to Lysippos or his school. There is also little doubt that it is a creditable copy of a bronze original. In this original, where of course the stem of a tree which serves as a support might be absent, the impression of lightness and grace must have been much more conspicuous. In the present copy in marble a support was originally placed against the l. leg, as the small antique fragment of the stem on the l. calf proves. The remainder of the stem is modern. New also: l. forearm from above the elbow. It is highly probable that the arm did not originally lie on the stem of the tree (an arrangement by which the freedom and elasticity of the pose is seriously impaired) but carried a cloak or skin or else some attribute (cf. the similar Florentine Statue in Clarac, IV. 635, 1434). New again, besides many small patches, are the l. knee, a piece in front of the r. thigh including the knee, r. arm and the greater part of the club; the lower part of this, up to about the hollow of the knee, is old, though completely worked over and, now at least, no longer rounded off at the lower end. As to club and arm the restorer had his way so far indicated with certainty. It is on the other hand open to question whether in the bronze original the club was not in an easier position without resting on the ground, as e.g. in the bronze Herakles of Lysippian character in the Capitoline Museum (Righetti, Campidoglio, I. Pl. 35, Clarac, v. 802 E, 1969 B) and the bronze statuette of the British Museum (Mus. Marbles, III. Pl. 2, Clarac, v. 785, 1966). The club might designate Herakles, were not the slimness and elegance of the figure too great for a youthful Herakles even by Lysippos (cf. Schoene, Griech. Reliefs, Pl. 27, no. 113). There remains then Theseus, his Attic counterpart, who is undoubtedly represented if the head, which is very beautiful, belongs to the statue. New parts of head: nose, lips, chin, a piece of r. brow, on the round so-called Attic helmet the crest and parts of both griffins. The head agrees so admirably with the body in proportions, pose and character that one might regard it as belonging to the statue in spite of the inserted neck and the different colour of the marble. This opinion is shared by the writer of the letterpress of the Specimens, but not by Dallaway, no. 4. Head and body both certainly consist of Pentelic marble, the strata of which in both cases run in the same vertical direction, but on the head it looks like white sugar and is traversed by a few dark micaceous veins; on the body, on the other hand, it has a bright yellow hue and these veins are but little visible. To be sure the body is to a great extent seriously rubbed and owes its smoother appearance to this fact, while the head, especially the helmet and back of the head, are less affected by rubbing; and in fact on the parts of the body which are not so thoroughly abraded, the l. shoulder, the outside of the r. calf and especially on the feet, whereof the surface has suffered much by rain or some such influence, the marble presents quite a similar character to that of the head. Although, then, the original connection of the head cannot be demonstrated with complete certainty, still it is not improbable; less probable would be the supposition that in consideration of the size of the statue the head may have been originally made of a separate piece of marble. The interpretation of the statue as Ares (Dilthey, Rhein. Jahrb., LIII. p. 31) is certainly wrong. Waagen's depreciatory judgment (p. 256) is altogether unjust. Found in Hadrian's Villa; bought from the Villa d'Este, where it stood in the centre of the saloon. H. 2·035. [*CH]

44 (49. P). Statuette of a seated man, a philosopher

probably. Clarac, v. 846, 2134. *Engr.*, 29. The man enveloped in a wide cloak sits in a quiet and very characteristic attitude in a stone chair, adorned with lions' heads and feet in front, and moulded with a low back : r. leg far advanced, head supported on the r. hand, in the style of the Spada Aristotle (Visconti, *Iconogr. Gr.*, i. Pl. 20, 2); r. elbow rests on the l. hand which is laid across it. R. side of upper part of body not covered by cloak. Head inserted and of different marble. It is related to the so-called heads of Diogenes. It is bald, the long beard divided and softly flowing. Expression thoughtful. New : almost whole r. arm, l. hand, both feet inclusive of part of legs and drapery, plinth with lower part of chair. "Bought from Mr Jenkins in 1777; it was the first piece of ancient marble bought for this collection." H. 0·46. [*BCH*]

45 (33. P). **Group of boy and swan.** Clarac, v. 875, 2232 B. *Engr.*, 25. A tolerably big boy, quite nude, stands, with head inclined in rather affected fashion towards the r. shoulder, close to a large swan, which stands upright, and is putting a ribbon round its neck. Boy of Thasian marble. New : r. arm, part of legs, nose. Swan only fastened to boy's body, but of one piece with plinth and lower part of boy's l. leg and also his l. arm : his r. foot being also of same piece as plinth. All this of different marble, yet to all appearance antique, so perhaps an antique restoration. New : swan's head and neck, and piece of l. wing ; these parts of another different marble. The group stood in a temple of the Villa d'Este, from whence it was bought. H. 0·70. [*CH*]

46 (36. T). **Statue of a Roman boy.** Clarac, v. 877, 2236 B. *Engr.*, 27. Enveloped in the toga, doubtless the toga praetexta appropriate to his age, holding with both hands a pet bird to his breast ; perhaps it is a duck. New : back of boy's head, neck and nose (face antique), a small portion of the shoulders, both feet, with corresponding piece of drapery, pedestal, bird's head and neck. Ordinary work. From the Villa Mattei. H. 0·62. [*]

47 (53). **Statuette of fisherman.** Clarac, v. 881, 2243 A. *Engr.*, 28, 2. A fisherman sits on a block of rock in a short working-man's tunic (ἐξωμίς); close to him a basket of fish. New : whole upper part, head, neck, arms, with upper part of breast. H. 0·43.

48 (6. T). **Statue of a Roman in the toga.** Clarac, v. 892, 2278 A. *Engr.*, 6, "Consul, by many called a Cicero." *Mon. Matth.*, i. 73. An indifferent figure with a toga arranged in not very graceful folds. R. hand holds a corner of the toga before the breast. L. hand holds a roll. By l. foot stands the scrinium. The head bears no

resemblance to Cicero. Hair cut short. Lower part of face recedes.
On the nape of the neck a piece of marble has been left projecting.
Preservation quite perfect; but the statue is probably modern or at
least entirely worked over. H. about 1·60. [*BW]

49 (24. G). **Statue of a youth** ("Marcellus"). Clarac, v. 923,
2314 A. *Engr.*, 20, 2. A nude youth stepping forward slightly, with a
small cloak which covers l. shoulder and the hips, and falls down
over the l. forearm. R. arm raised. New: r. leg, lower part of l.
leg, r. arm, l. forearm with corner of cloak. Head fixed on and
scarcely its own (new: nose). Has long hair, and certainly belongs
to no Marcellus. Indeed it is doubtful whether it be a portrait at
all. Found in some ruins near the Forum of Rome. H. 0·85. [*B]

50 (G). **Portrait Statue** ("M. Aurelius"). Clarac, v. 952,
2446 B. *Engr.*, 35. Youthful figure, rather good, nude except for
cloak which covers hips and thighs, and falls down over advanced
l. arm. On the modern neck is placed a youthful head crowned
with ivy, with budding beard. It is too small for the statue. It is
in any case not Marcus Aurelius, but perhaps a portrait of his period.
New: r. arm, l. with shoulder and part of breast, parts of cloak, feet,
probably also the lower part of l. leg. "It was met with in a sculptor's yard at London; but how it came or from whence, could not be
discovered." H. 1·83. [*BW]

51 (515. G). **Statue of the elder Faustina.** Clarac, v. 955,
2458. *Engr.*, 37. The figure is quite enveloped in the long stola
and wide palla which also veils the head and entirely covers the r. arm.
These parts are of black marble, the feet, l. hand, head and neck of
white marble. The treatment of the hair and the features portray
that empress, though the somewhat sunken eyes do not quite suit a
woman who died so early. Nose injured. Head certainly antique,
so also apparently the rest of the figure. Bought at Lord Cawdor's
sale. H. 1·70. [*B]

52 (7. P). **Female draped statue**, with the head, it is supposed, of **Julia Pia.** Clarac, v. 965, 2482 A. *Engr.*, 7. Of elegant
but not good work, with long drapery and a cloak which covers all
the lower part of the body and the r. forearm, as well as the shoulder.
The statue has been converted into an Urania by the restoration
of both forearms with a globe in the r. hand and a style in the l.
Head including neck put on but not modern. It has only a general
resemblance to Julia Pia or to the so-called Crispina of the British
Museum (Graeco-Roman Sculpt., no. 34), and displays a beautiful
countenance with a slightly aquiline nose somewhat too sharply

restored at the tip. The arrangement of the hair is not that of Julia Pia. It is worn in artificial waves in front, and gathered up behind into a small plait, a loosened tress of hair falling down about the neck. Beautiful Parian marble. Found in Hadrian's Villa and bought from the Villa d'Este. H. 1·98. [*BC]

53 (59. P). **Female Statuette in the Egyptian style.** Clarac, v. 987, 2588 A, "Isis." Engr., 33, 3. A stiff little figure in ungirdled drapery clinging close to the body, both legs and both arms in similarly close connection. The fastening of the drapery leaves the r. breast free. Of basalt. H. 0·43. [*]

54 (11. S). **Statue of a priest of Isis.** Clarac, v. 988, 2588 B, "Isis." Engr., 11. Mon. Matth., I. 87, "Sabina Augusta." When in the Villa Mattei the upper part of the body was still without any Egyptian attributes and without the vase, both hands were crossed before the paunch. Hence Winckelmann following the prevalent opinion of his time took the statue for a "woman far advanced in pregnancy, probably a patroness of women in pregnancy and child-birth," and assigned it to the oldest Etruscan style (Gesch. d. Kunst, III. 2, 12. 22. 3, 5). But the head was modern, the body is decidedly male, and there was a hollow for the vase made in the front of the paunch. Consequently the statue was restored afresh for Blundell under the advice of E. Q. Visconti (Mus. Pio-Clem., III. p. 46 Mil.), founded on a relief (Mon. Matth., III. 26, 2. Mus. Chiaram., I. Pl. 2) and a painting (Pitt. di Ercolano, II. Pl. 60). The treatment of the drapery is of affected simplicity. Greek marble. H. 1·73. [*]

55 (27. S). **Statue of a priestess of Isis.** Clarac, v. 991, 2574 D. Engr., 21, "Isis." The statue presents altogether the usual treatment of drapery, the cloak fastened together before the breast. New: head and both forearms with sistrum and situla. Mediocre execution. Greek marble. From the Villa Mattei. H. 1·07. [*]

56 (58. P). **Egyptian Statuette, female.** Engr., 33, 1. Small figure, certainly female, holding the crook before the breast. Of basalt. A counterpart to no. 53. H. 0·46. [*]

57 (78). **Kynokephalos,** in a kind of grey spotted marble, from the Villa Mattei. Engr., 33, 2. Mon. Matth., II. 68, 1. Cavaceppi, Raccolta, III. 53.

58 (548). **Statue of Egyptian priest,** with a broad skirt about the hips. Engr., 40. Red granite. Nearly the size of life. Bought at Lord Mendip's sale.

59 (86, in front of the T). **A cock.** Engr., 43, 1. New: tail and legs. The figure has turned quite green. H. 0·45. Plastic representations of cocks are rare, see *Mus. Pio-Clem.*, VII. 26, 2. [*]

60 (77). **A sparrow-hawk.** *Engr.*, 43, 2. On the front of the pedestal there are hieroglyphics. Of black basalt. Found with no. 30 by La Piccola; bought from the sculptor Gionelli.

61 (191). **Upper part of an Egyptian idol.** *Engr.*, 45, 1. The figure wears the calantica and carries the crook before the breast. Small half-length figure in red granite; found in a well at Trastevere in Rome, when emptied to be cleansed.

62 (338 and 435. P). **A cista mystica, with a snake** which has lifted the lid and pushed it a little on to one side and is peeping out. Head and neck of snake new. Also

Lower parts of the two legs of a statue (colossal scale), probably of Dionysos, with cloak. *Engr.*, 45, 2. The fragment being very heavy and unwieldy in one piece, the cista and the feet were separated; thus in two separate pieces they are now both in the collection. Thasian marble. H. 0·53. L. of cista 0·35. [*]

63 (545. P). **Torso of Aphroditè.** *Engr.*, 145, 2. This excellent fragment recals the composition and the fulness of form of the Capitoline Venus (cf. the replicas in Stark's article in the *Bericht. d. sächs. Ges. d. Wiss.*, 1860, pp. 55 ff. Bernoulli, *Aphrodite*, pp. 226 ff.). It comprises the body from above the navel downwards and the greatest part of the thighs. On the l. thigh remains of a junction indicate the vessel with the drapery; a retouched place on the l. side of the stomach may offer a trace of the forearm. The fragment, found near the Pantheon at Rome, was formerly much admired in the museum of the celebrated Baron Stosch (there is a drawing of it in a volume of drawings once belonging to Stosch in the Grand-Ducal Museum at Brunswick). Afterwards it was reckoned the most valuable piece of sculpture in Lord Bessborough's collection. Dallaway, p. 385. Parian marble. H. 0·49. [*C]

63*a* (P). **Similar torso of Aphroditè.** Body from above the navel downwards. It is on a somewhat smaller scale than the last specimen, but more of the legs is preserved, the l. to just above the knee. Traces of junction of l. arm are visible on hip and in front of r. thigh, besides two large relics on the l. thigh. Very good work. Parian marble. H. 0·47. [*]

64. **Statue of a man, seated.** *Engr.*, 146, 2. On a lounging chair without arms is seated a man whose legs, back and l. arm are covered by a cloak, the rest of the upper part of the body is nude. Missing: head, three quarters of lowered r. arm, l. hand in the lap

and the advanced r. foot. There is a hole through the middle of the paunch. "This curious fragment of ancient sculpture was found in the river Thames, in its present mutilated state. It is supposed to have belonged to the Arundel Collection, now at Oxford, and being very unwieldy, to have been lost in the river at the unloading of it, one of that collection being missing. It was frequently bare at low water, and the boatmen finding a heavy stone, got a hole drilled through it, and by fastening a ring to it with melted lead, it served as a mooring for their small craft. The ring is taken away; but the hole through the body and the lead remain. The late Mr Banks, sculptor, hearing of it, and finding it a fragment of ancient sculpture, removed it to his yard at a great expense. At his death it was bought for this Collection." The story is related with a little variation by J. Th. Smith, *Nollekens and his times*, II. p. 201.

65. Statuette of Osiris. *Engr.*, 147, 1. A very small figure of the god seated with a large disk on his head. H. abt. 0·12.

66. Bronze Statuette of Aphroditè. *Engr.*, 147, 2. Quite nude. L. hand before the breast, r. on the tail of a large dolphin, which is moving away with a Cupid within its coils. H. abt. 0·21. The style as given in the engraving conveys a thoroughly modern impression.

67. Bronze Statuette of "Hygieia." *Engr.*, 147, 3. Fully clad in chiton, and behind the back with a cloak ; head adorned with a stephanè. She holds a cup in lowered r. hand. H. 0·20. "Said to have been cast in the Cinque cento age."

The *Account* does not notice nos. 64—67, but describes the following specimens which are passed over in the *Engravings*.

68 (21. S). Statuette of Hygieia. She rests on r. leg ; wears the chiton and is quite enveloped by the fine transparent drapery which covers the body and r. thigh and is drawn down from the l. shoulder to the l. hand, but generally clings to the body. New: lowered l. hand with snake, all the upper part of the body down from the waist, l. shoulder, head, r. arm with cup. Bought from Cavaceppi. H. 0·77. [*]

69 (25. S). Statuette of Paris. He stands in repose in chiton and cloak. Pavonazetto marble. Inserted : head and hands of white statuary. Bought from Antonio d'Este. H. 0·85. Whole figure unquestionably modern. [*]

70 (26. S). Similar Statuette. Paris leans on a trunk in chiton and trousers, without Phrygian cap. Near r. foot lies a hound looking up at his master. Put together of the same kinds of marble as no. 69 and equally modern. Bought like no. 69 from d'Este. H. 0·83. [*]

71 (35. P). **Statuette of "Hygieia."** A woman in chiton ; cloak fastened on r. shoulder runs down slantwise over breast and covers body as far as below knee. New: both forearms with cup and snake, half lower part of legs, and neck. Head an old Roman portrait of first century A. D. New: nose. H. 0·57. [*]

72 (50). **Statuette of a Consul seated**, with modern head of **Trajan.** In composition the figure answers to the statue in Petworth, no. 15, except that the cushion is less deeply quilted. Found on the Monte Mario and bought from d'Este as a companion to no. 44. [*B*]

73 (61). **Bronze Statuette of Bacchus**, with a vase in one hand, and grapes in the other. Said to be antique.

74 (72. P). **Statuette of a sleeping Cupid.** Head supported on l. hand, r. on the torch. A lizard at the feet. Along the top of the crown the head is brushed up into a sort of plait. New: Cupid's r. foot, lizard's head. Greek marble. L. 0·48. [*]

75 (79). **An Egyptian idol**, in form of a bird. Grey basalt. From Egypt.

76 (80). **Figure of Isis**, as appears from the drapery usual to her, and from the attitude which the figure stands in, with one foot before the other. It holds to its breast, what appears to be corn, or some kind of fruit. In good preservation; bought out of the Capponi palace.

77 (85). **Tigress lying down** ; in a very hard grey spotted granite. Found with two Egyptian vases (*Engr.*, 146, 1. 3), in a vineyard near the Porta Portese.

78 (87. P). **A hare** ; bought from the Villa d'Este.

79 (88). **A four-legged griffin** ("chimera"); bought from the Villa Borioni.

80 (89). **Figure of a soldier**, singular on account of his arms and attitude. Bought from the Villa Borioni.

81 (160. P). **Statuette of Diana**, in the character of Hecate, with a veil behind her, holding a lighted torch in her hand. Antique: only the upper part of the body and almost the whole of the drapery floating in an arch behind the back. New: head and neck, r. forearm with torch, l. with corner of drapery and all the lower part of the statuette. Bought from Cavaceppi. H. 0·56. [*]

82 (517. P). **Statue of "Nemesis,"** *i.e.* of **Artemis** originally. A very long stiff figure, l. leg slightly advanced. She wears a long chiton, which in front falls down before the legs in two points with zigzag folds. New: lower parts of legs, lowered r. forearm with a staff, r. arm bent upwards before the breast, r. breast and l. shoulder. Head old (nose new) and worked in a similar stiff style of affected archaism. It had a crown (στέφανος) on the brow; still it cannot originally have belonged to this body, because the tresses of hair on the two parts are worked quite differently. Bought at Lord Cawdor's sale. H. 1·24. [*]

83 (541. T). **Fragment of a Nereid,** the legs without the feet covered with drapery, sitting sideways on a hippocampus which is badly restored on the head. Much broken. Decorative work. "Venus sailing on a sea-horse," bought out of the Bessborough collection. Original L. abt. 1·00. [*]

BUSTS.

The *Engravings* contain the following busts.

84 (90. T). **Hadrian.** *Engr.*, 46 (and 55, from a bad drawing). *Mon. Matth.*, II. 16, 2. A beautiful bust, with paludamentum on r. shoulder; the sword-belt is wanting in the latter drawing. Query, is only the head antique? From the Villa Mattei.

85 (91. T). **Septimius Severus.** *Engr.*, 47. *Mon. Matth.*, II. 30, 1. Pupils indicated. From the Villa Mattei.

86 (92. T). **"Otho."** *Engr.*, 48. *Mon. Matth.*, II. 14, 1. This head encircled by a wreath is explained by Venuti as Elagabalus, by Amaduzzi as Otho. It excites in Bernoulli suspicion of a modern origin. From the Villa Mattei. [*B*]

87 (93. T). **"Claudius Albinus."** *Engr.*, 49 (very inaccurate). *Mon. Matth.*, II. 27, 2. A good bust, wrongly named, although of his period. From the Villa Mattei. [*B*]

88 (94. T). **"Cicero:"** falsely so called. *Engr.*, 50, 1 (bad). The bust is draped with a toga, and hardly belongs to the head, of which the profile, unfortunately, is mostly new. Still a very interesting head: the elderly eyes very vividly represented; abundant hair. Found in some ruins in Rome by an adventurer in canvas, from whom it was bought. [*B*]

89 (97. P). **Augustus.** *Engr.*, 50, 2 (bad). A good head to which it is doubtful whether the breastplate bust belongs. It portrays the Emperor as somewhat more youthful than the celebrated Vatican statue from Prima Porta (*Mon. dell' Inst.*, VII. 84). Bought from Volpato, who found it in one of his excavations. [*B*]

90 (105. P?). **"Antoninus Pius."** *Engr.*, 51, 1. Judging from the drawing the name is incorrect. Beard slightly curly, hair falling in curls on the brow. The head turned a little r. rests on a nude bust with the junctions of the arms. Found in some ruins near Albano. [*B*]

91 (108. T). **"Marciana."** *Engr.*, 51, 2. The hairdress forming a truncated cone constructed of plaits, places the bust in the time of Trajan, but it is not Marciana. Fine Greek marble. Found at Ostia, and bought from Cavaceppi. [*B*]

92 (165. P). **Seilenos.** *Engr.*, 52, 1. The bald-crowned head with an ivy wreath is singularly softly treated, mouth opened. New: l. ear, nose, smaller details. Bought from the Capponi palace. [*C*]

93 (107. T). **"Didia Clara."** *Engr.*, 52, 2. Very well preserved head of the beginning of the third century having the hair arranged nearly like that of the lady whose name it bears. Pupils expressed. Bought from the Villa Borioni. [*B*]

94 (130. P). **Omphale.** *Engr.*, 52, 3, "Iole." Female head with mouth slightly opened. The lion's skin serves as a veil.

95 (109. P). **Portrait of a Roman Lady,** with a fillet on the hair and a stephanè ornamented with relief work. *Engr.*, 53, "Ariadne" (gives a thoroughly false impression). [*B*]

96 (110. Pict. Gall.). **Terminal bust of Dionysos.** *Engr.*, 54, 1. Youthful with long hair, thick wreath of grapes and broad fillet on brows. The head, especially valued by Blundell on account of its softness, belonged to Gavin Hamilton; it was bought from Volpato. [*]

97 (126). **Terminal bust of Herakles.** *Engr.*, 54, 2. Bearded, adorned with wreath of vine-leaves and broad fillet. "There is a peculiar dignity and something inspired in the features. The ears, formed like those of an athlete, stand off from the head. The execution of the flesh parts is careful, while the hair and beard are little more than expressed. Modern: a part of the nose, the last part almost entirely; some of the curls are knocked off." Found on the Lavinian road; bought from Carlo Albaccini. [*W*]

98 (549. T). **Marcus Aurelius.** *Engr.*, 55, 2 (very bad). A good portrait. Bought at Lord Mendip's sale. [*B*]

99 (117. T). **"Scipio."** *Engr.*, 56 (pretty good). Head entirely bald, without representation of a wound, has a mouth quite different from the usual heads of Scipio (cf. Castle Howard, no. 31), yet has some relation to them. [*B*]

100 (118. T). "**Cicero**," wrongly so called. *Engr.*, 57, 2. This head, also quite bald except for a faint delineation of the roots of the hair by the chisel, equally reminds one of the heads of Scipio even in the wrinkles at the back of the neck, without however being identical with them. Found near Naples, and privately brought to Rome with no. 152. [*B*]

101 (115. P). "**Caesar**." *Engr.*, 57, 3. This head, with powerful straight nose and fairly thin cheeks, recals Augustus rather than Caesar, but has the eyes too hollow and hair too thin. Bust completely preserved, but of doubtful genuineness. [*B*]

102 (114. T). "**Sappho**." *Engr.*, 58, 1. Spiral curls fall down all round the neck. Found on the Via Praenestina. [*B*]

103 (179). **Portrait of a young man.** *Engr.*, 58, 2. Beardless, with earnest expression.

104 (120. P). "**Julia**." *Engr.*, 59, 1. 66, 1. Portrait of a Roman lady of the time of Vespasian. The hair forms a kind of high diadem of curls above the brow, behind it forms a wide mass of plaits.

105 (171. P, ante-room). **The "Grecian Youth**." *Engr.*, 59, 2. An ideal head with hair in long curls, taken up over the ears through a broad fillet. Bought from Cavaceppi.

106 (152. P). **Hermes**. *Engr.*, 60, 1. This pretty, delicate head represents the god as very youthful, with curly hair and a winged cap. The expression of shrewdness is excellent. New: bust. Bought from the sculptor Boni. [*C*]

107 (129). "**Flora**." *Engr.*, 60, 2. The head, which is crowned with flowers, is like well-known heads of Muses. It came out of the Villa Negroni, and was bought from Jenkins.

108 (150. P). **Isis.** *Engr.*, 60, 3. A good replica of the Vatican head (*Mus. Pio-Clem.*, VI. Pl. 17, 2), with a pleasing inclination of the head; over the brow the lotus-like knot of hair; otherwise without attributes. New: nose and bust. Found in the ruins of a magnificent villa in the *Tenuta di Salone* (compare no. 30). [*C*]

109 (132). **The elder Faustina**. *Engr.*, 61, 1, "Sabina," a false description. New: lower part of face, and bust. [*E*]

110 (192. P). "**Seneca**." *Engr.*, 61, 2. This beardless head with somewhat coarse but not distorted features has nothing in common with the ordinary so-called heads of Seneca (cf. Holkham, no. 36). It belongs to a man about sixty years old; with hair still abundant and fairly smooth, stern look, brow lightly furrowed, mouth somewhat opened and with its corners tending downwards. A certain general similarity in character to such heads as that of Pompey

in the Spada palace (Visconti, *Iconogr. Rom.*, 1. Pl. 5, 1. 2) or of Cicero in Madrid (cf. London, Apsley House) seems to indicate a Roman of the last century of the Republic, a statesman or author. Other replicas of the head are not known. New: nose, l. eye-ball, part of chin, ears and bust. Of good, somewhat feeble workmanship. [*B*]

111 (146. P). **Double terminal bust.** *Engr.*, 62, 1. A bearded and a youthful head each with a curious round helmet decorated with horns; before the ears towards the youthful head a ram's head at each side. This unpleasing specimen (cf. Gerhard, *Ant. Bildwerke*, Pl. 318) aroused no suspicion in Conze's mind. New: bust. Found in some ruins at Tivoli; bought from Pacetti. [*C*]

112 (226. T). **Double terminal bust** of a man and a woman, the latter with a raised crown of curls over the brow. *Engr.*, 62, 2. Its present position forbids an accurate examination. Bought from Cavaceppi. [*B*]

113 (143. P). **Sleeping boy,** in a cowl (*cucullus*). *Engr.*, 63, 1, "Telesphorus." A most charming head, on a modern bust, probably belonging to a statue such as that given by Clarac, IV. 882, 2247 D. One often comes across similar specimens in museums. Found at Albano; bought from the Borioni Palace. [*CH*]

114 (156. Pict. Gall.). **Youthful Herakles.** *Engr.*, 63, 2. The boyish head with long curls is covered by the lion's skin. Greek marble.

115 (151. P). **Terminal bust of Homer,** small scale. *Engr.*, 64, 1. The blind minstrel is represented with bald forehead and a small fillet round his head. Too narrow and high in the proportions. Conze describes nose and bust as modern. Bernoulli doubts the genuineness of the whole. [*BC*]

116 (144. P). **Vitellius.** *Engr.*, 64, 2 (rather bad). Bernoulli thinks this little head less suspicious than most other copies. "Very animatedly conceived and careful." [*BW*]

117 (128. P). **Head of a youth,** small scale. *Engr.*, 64, 3, "Hercules." This little head with a fillet entwined in the hair which seems to designate a victor, recals in expression and style of art the sons of Laokoon: eyes deeply sunk. New: bust, back of head, tip of nose. Found at Lunghezza on the Anio. Cf. no. 163. [*C*]

118 (145). **Portrait of a female.** *Engr.*, 65, "Iphigenia." The head dress is distinguished by an extraordinary abundance of tresses. Bought by Mr Thorpe.

119 (P). **Terminal bust of a woman.** *Engr.*, 66, 2, "Isis." Double row of curls and stephanè over the forehead, hair falling far down on the shoulders. New: back of head and bust. [*C*]

120 (147. P). **Aphroditè.** *Engr.*, 66, 3. Pretty little head, inclined sideways, with yearning expression; carefully executed. New: nose, hair for the most part and bust. Found at Lunghezza. Bought from Volpato. [*CW*]

121 (172. P). **Poseidon.** *Engr.*, 67, 1 (unusually bad). *Mon. Matth.*, II. Pl. 1, 1, "Jupiter Pluvius" (still worse). The small eyes (eyebrows not indicated) are deep sunk. The forehead more broad than high, very prominent towards the temples, reveals the capacity for wrathful excitement, but the whole effect is noble, and appropriate to the brother of Zeus. The cheeks are somewhat drawn in. The flowing hair falls down a long way behind. The rendering of the *madida barba* is of particularly good character. New: nose, lips, part of mustaches, hair over forehead with two fishes, which are as yet absent from the engraving in the *Mon. Matth.*, and were therefore no doubt added by Cavaceppi. Breast and shoulders antique, cut away to make the bust. From the Villa Mattei; bought from Cavaceppi. H. 0·40. L. of face about 0·20. [*C*]

122 (149. P). **"Commodus."** *Engr.*, 67, 2, "Aelius Caesar." *Mon. Matth.* II. Pl. 26, 1, "Commodus." The head resembles that of the Vatican statue in the *Braccio nuovo*, no. 1 (*Mus. Chiaram.*, II. Pl. 41), the reference whereof to Commodus Bernoulli thinks open to doubt. Pupils indicated. [*B*]

123 (157. S). **Terminal bust of a water-god**, colossal scale. *Engr.*, 68 (bad). The head of noble design, though of tolerably broad decorative execution, is very effective owing to the tangled hair, erect over the forehead, the opened mouth, and the exaggerated expression of the features. Scales cover the junction of the flowing beard with cheeks and chin. Satyr-like ears indicate the connection of the train of Neptune with that of Bacchus. Brows and pupils not rendered. New: nose, breast with lower part of beard: l. cheek is patched. Marble with grey spots seems to be from Lower Italy. From the Villa d'Este, where the head is said to have served as an ornament to a fountain, but a water-spout through the mouth has never been perforated. H. of head about 0·90 from top of forehead to bottom of beard. W. of head 0·60. H. 1·17. [*W*]

124 (158. T). **"Claudius,"** colossal scale. *Engr.*, 69, 1. The head certainly does not represent that emperor. So much renovated that identification is difficult. Found in some ruins near the Pala-

tine Hill. This and no. 125 were bought from Ant. d'Este.
[B]

125 (159. T). "**Domitian.**" *Engr.*, 69, 2. Dimensions, state of renovation, seller, same as for no. 124. [B]

126 (163. S). **Terminal bust of Ammon.** *Engr.*, 70. Head encircled with Bacchic fillet has a gloomy indolent expression, and belongs to the class of heads with ram's horns "which have never dreamt of Olympus and long for nothing better than license to move in the Bacchic thiasos" (E. Braun, *Kunstvorstellungen d. geflüg. Dionysos*, p. 5. Jahn, *Arch. Aufs.*, p. 82. *Lauersforter Phalerae*, p. 10, cf. Overbeck, *Griech. Kunstmythol.*, II. p. 282). Work rather superficial. New: nose, ears, curves of horns, neck, and breast. It was found at Nettuno and once belonged to Cardinal Alex. Albani. It was procured by Cavaceppi in exchange for some other marble, and was bought from him. H. 0·45. L. of face 0·18.

127 (189. P). **Bearded Bacchus**, in hieratic style. *Engr.*, 71, 1, "Jupiter." As the upper part of the head with the modius and also the bust are new, there remains a crowned Dionysos of stiff, affected style. Guattani found the bust in possession of the sculptors Alessandroni and d'Este and published it with a short notice in his *Monumenti Inediti*, 1788, Nov., Pl. 2. [C]

128 (336. P). **Sun dial.** *Engr.*, 71, 2. Guattani, *Mon. Ined.*, 1787, Apr., Pl. 22. Below the cavity a sort of medallion portrait bust is introduced, said to represent Berosos, which certainly belonged originally to the dial ; as in Guattani's work, neither in the plates nor in the accompanying text is there a trace of this bust to be found, he probably had in mind another copy. The long bearded head is covered with a cap. Found in Palestrina (Praeneste). For other examples, cf. Marquardt, *Handb. der röm. Alterth.*, v. II. p. 373. (The pedestal with inscription and relief is new ; the latter is taken from the Corsini silver vessel, Winckelmann, *Mon. Ined.*, Pl. 151. Michaelis, *Das Corsin. Silbergefäss*, Pl. 1.) [*C]

129 (190). **Ariadne ?** *Engr.* 71, 3, "Juno." Guattani, *Mon. Ined.*, 1788, Nov., Pl. 3 ; he found the head with no. 127 which it resembles in the studied simplicity of archaistic style. Female head with smooth hair falling down a long way on the forehead and neck and a stephanè.

130, 131 (212, 213). **Two tragic masks**, colossal scale. *Engr.*, 72, 1. 2. The first is female with long, smooth hair without onkos ; the other female as well with curls at the sides and a thick wreath of flowers entwined by a fillet which comes low down towards the middle of the forehead in garland fashion, and has an end hanging down on each side. From the Villa Negroni ; bought from Jenkins. H. o·91.

132 (305). **Mask of a river-god.** *Engr. 72, 4.* Beard and hair in curly waving tresses, scales fringe the checks and the upper lip against the beard.

133 (182. T, in the pediment of the portico). **Mask of Medusa.** colossal scale. *Engr. 73. Mon. Matth., II. 85, 3.* Powerful head with pupils and slightly opened mouth, encircled by abundant hair, with a top-knot on the crown : no snakes. Found in the artichoke grounds of the gardens of the Mattei Villa, whence it was bought. Parian marble. H. about o·90.

134 (209). **Tragic mask.** *Engr. 74, 2.* Mouth opened wide, pupils very deeply cut, a wig formed of parallel tresses hangs down over the forehead and by both checks. From the Villa Altieri. H. about o·90.

134*a* (210). **Tragic mask,** companion to no. 134, from the same villa.

135 (300). **Mask of Medusa.** *Engr. 75, 1.* Snakes are entwined in the hair and surround the cheeks ; the mass of wide-spread hair is of so singular a shape that a doubt of the genuineness of the whole or a suspicion of serious renovation is unavoidable.

136 (211). **Comic mask.** *Engr., 75, 2.* The bearded mask has an open mouth and is peculiar for the singular depth to which the brow is drawn down between the eyes. From the Villa Mattei.

137 (525. P). **"Sokrates."** *Engr., 76, 1* (unsatisfactory, over-compressed in the proportions). Certainly not Sokrates, but an unknown philosopher with long beard, with thin hair, hardly more than indicated by scratches with the chisel, so that he appears almost bald. Mustaches cover the whole mouth. Pupils expressed. Purchased at a sale at Mr Christie's (see on no. 221). [*B*]

138 (229). **"Euripides."** *Engr., 76, 2.* Bearded, curly-haired head which has as little to do with Euripides as with Pertinax to whom it has been ascribed by others. The head is not finished. In many places on beard and hair can be still observed the points and chisel-marks which have been left during the working out of the head from the marble. [*B*]

139 (98. T). **Vespasian,** colossal scale. *Engr., 77, 2.* Head unfortunately much restored. Bought from Volpato. [*B*]

140, 141 (T). **Two heads with long beards.** *Engr., 77, 1, 3.* Brow lofty, eyes deep sunk, cheeks thin, expression earnest.

On the whole the features rather convey the impression of late Roman portraits than of barbarians. "It is ascertained from good authority [?] that these two ancient heads were taken off Constantine's arch at Rome, and that they belong to statues of some of the kings of the captive slaves on that arch. They were bought at London."

142 (not identical with no. 102). **Female portrait.** *Engr.*, 145, 1, "Sappho." The long roll of hair is encircled once behind by a broad fillet.

143 (164). "**Livia.**" *Engr.*, 145, 3. Head with abundant hair and a stephane adorned with relief-work. From the Villa Mattei.

144 (122). "**Julius Caesar.**" *Engr.*, 149, 2. The designation is false. On a modern draped bust of white marble stands the red porphyry head with flat, bald crown and large back of head; nose aquiline. In perfect preservation, but according to Bernoulli probably entirely modern. "Bought in London at a sale of the Duke of Buccleugh's effects many years ago" (see Dalkeith). [*BW*]

The following busts given in the *Account* are not represented in the *Engravings.*

145 (95). **Apollo.** The hair is dressed in a singular manner, forming a kind of diadem. In the features there is a mixture of female grace and softness.

146 (96). "**Muse,**" so called from the chasteness of the drapery. Formerly in the Barberini palace; bought from Cavaceppi.

147 (104). "**Augustus,**" in fine Greek marble. The head was found near the Via Appia, and the bust near the tomb of Caecilia Metella. Both of them fitted together so well in all parts, as to be thought to have originally belonged to each other. Found by Volpato, from whom they were bought.

148 (106. S). "**Claudius,**" or more likely a portrait not of Claudius himself but resembling him. Profile restored. "Found near Lacus Gabinus," *i.e.* presumably in Lunghezza (cf. no. 117). [*B*]

149 (111). **Terminal bust called Pompeius,** small scale. Modern face fixed on to an antique back part of head. [*B*]

150 (112). "**Cato,**" small scale. Head of an old beardless man with eyes sunk in, a broad tightly-shut mouth and thin hair on forehead. An affinity in character with the so-called Cato of the Capitol is undeniable. The terminal piece however with the scarcely legible inscription M. CATO does not belong to the head. [*B*]

151 (113). Serapis; a head of great dignity, with a modius on it. Found in some ruins on the Appian Road.

152 (116. P). An athlete. *Arch. Zeit.*, 1874, Pl. 3. This remarkable head has been already noted by Waagen, who describes it as a Greek production shortly previous to the time of Pheidias, or, if not that, a very good imitation; Conze has added several particular criticisms. The shape of the skull is unusual. It is long but very narrow, forming a long slope on the top and thence falling off on both sides. With this shape the very high and narrow oval of the face corresponds. Short curly hair, rather carelessly executed above, carefully in front, reaches down to the neck and covers the skull and makes the already very low forehead still narrower. The lower half of the forehead projects a little. The lower line of the forehead is sharp, and underneath it the long narrow eyes lie deep sunk especially as to their inner corners. The lids are sharply worked out, the lower one traversed by a shallow furrow. Nose very long. Space between nose and upper lip narrow, the length being given to the tolerably pointed chin; this is a genuine archaic trait. The outline of the cheek is sharpened to a corresponding oval. The lower part of the face considerably overbalances the upper, if not in width, at least in height. A slight contraction of the brow, creases at the wings of the nose, and a similar line round the mouth give the expression of a somewhat morose character such as in a far higher degree is peculiar to the Farnese Hera (*Mon. dell. Inst.*, viii. Pl. 1). The head would appear not to belong to Attic art, rather to Peloponnesian; but, compared with the heads of Polykleitos' Doryphoros (Friederichs, *Der Doryphoros de Polyklet*, Berlin, 1863), it is more likely an older type. Kekulé, however, observes (*Kopf des praxitelischen Hermes*, p. 12 note 1) that there is a greater similarity between this head and those of Myron; unfortunately there exist no casts of the Massimi Diskobolos. There is another nearly allied head in Florence, in the Palazzo Riccardi (Dütschke, *Antike Bildwerke in Oberitalien*, II. p. 76, no. 163). Conze referred to a head in the Louvre, which however according to the engraving given in Frochner's *Les Musées de France* (Pl. 37) shows no great resemblance; cf. also Cavaceppi, *Racc.* II. Pl. 2, and Petworth, no. 17. The bruised and swollen ear of the pankratiast comes out a great deal. New: nose, part of r. ear, bust. The dimensions, with which those of the Doryphoros can be compared (Kekulé, *Jahrb. f. Philol.*, 1869, pp. 83 f.), are as follows: L. of forehead 0·045, of nose 0·07, of face 0·18. W. of eyes, inner

0·03, outer 0·093.   L. from nose to chin 0·07.   B. between wings of nose 0·033.   B. of mouth 0·045.   B. from root of nose to ear 0·133. H. of head abt. 0·26.   Pentelic marble.   Found near Naples, and privately brought to Rome, with no. 100.   Bought from Volpato, the engraver.   [*CII]

153 (119).   "**Telemachos.**"   "Visconti pronounced this to be a head of Telemachus; which he pretends to prove from a medal of Winckelmann's [*Gesch. de Kunst*, pref.], and confirms it by a print from another antique medal of Telemachus, which is singular on account of its having, as this has, a round close-knitted cap." Bought from Cavaceppi.

154 (123. T).   **Augustus.**   "It is doubtful whether it be, or be not, a portrait of that Emperor" (*Account*).   Bought from Cavaceppi. Probably identical with a pretty little head of the youthful Octavian, similar in age to the other one from Ostia in the Vatican (*Mus. Chiaram.*, II. Pl. 26), or the Castellani head in the Brit. Museum (Graeco-Roman Sculpt., no. 3. Newton, Castellani collection).   New: nose, lips and chin.   [*B*]

155 (127. P).   **Bust of a boy**, about 7 years old, with restored snub nose.   Good work.   [*B*]

156 (131).   **A Satyr.**

157 (133).   **Hermes,** with the petasos.   Half life size.   The character is delicately conceived, the profile very beautiful, every part, especially the curls, carefully rendered.   New: a portion of the throat and bust.   Bought from Cavaceppi.   [*W*]

158 (136).   **Nero**; a small head.

159 (137).   **Serapis,** with modius; small alabaster bust.

160 (139. T).   **Double terminal bust,** probably of the bearded **Dionysos** and **Ariadne.**   Bought from Cavaceppi.

161 (140).   **Satyr,** with a grinning countenance and erect ears. Rosso antico.   Bought by Mr Thorpe.

162 (141).   "**A Grecian priestess,**" with hair tied up with a fillet, of serious character.   Bought from Cavaceppi.

163 (142).   "**Herakles,**" small scale, very like the sons of Laokoon.   Greek marble.   Found at Lunghezza.   It seems to be a companion piece to no. 117.

164 (148. P).   **Terminal bust of Sokrates,** with name inscribed on the antique terminal shaft.   The lofty bold forehead is rounded in bullet fashion; the long beard falls down on to the breast in two separate divisions.   Nose somewhat higher than usual, restored tip not snub enough.   [*B*]

165 (153). **Terminal bust of the bearded Dionysos?** "A Philosopher. Such figures are often called Plato; sometimes Hercules Terminalis." Rosso antico.

166 (154). **Similar bust,** in Giallo antico.

167 (155). **"Juno,"** so called from the diadem. In good preservation. Greek marble. Bought from Cavaceppi.

168 (166. T). **Homer.** *Mon. Matth.*, II. Pl. 9, 4. The poet is blind, with aquiline nose, wearing a narrow fillet on the head, and less advanced in age than most of the portraits of that poet. According to Waagen the action of singing is excellently expressed in the mouth. New: nose. Bernoulli is doubtful about the genuineness. [*B II*]

169 (167). **Dionysos,** bronze. Bought from the Villa Negroni.

170 (168). **Ganymedes,** so called on account of the beauty of the figure. Bronze. From the Villa Negroni.

171 (169). **Portrait,** bronze. Found at Orvieto; belonged to the Negroni collection.

172 (170). **Trajan.** Face has suffered much by accidents. Bought from Pacetti. Probably identical with a head on a mailed bust in the Picture Gallery, the genuineness of which Bernoulli doubts. For the rest cf. no. 214. [*B*]

173 (173). **Hera.** Bought from Ant. d'Este.

174 (174). **Poseidonios.** "Visconti maintains this to be a portrait of P." (*Account.*) Visconti does not mention the bust when treating of the portraits of Poseidonios, *Iconogr. Grecque*, I. Pl. 24.

175 (176). **"Ariadne."** Has suffered much from the injuries of time.

176 (177. T). **Pompeius.** "As soon as Visconti saw this head he declared it to be a *testa rarissima di Pompeio Magno:* but it seems to have much stronger features than what are visible in the Greek medals of him." (*Account.*) The bust is at any rate allied to the Pompeius in the Palazzo Spada (Visconti, *Iconogr. rom.*, I. Pl. 5) and gives the same growth and cut of the hair, and in general the same shape of head; still the lower part of the face is more pointed towards the chin, the eyes less open, the whole character more youthful. (Cf. also no. 110.) Consequently, though the identity of the person is not indeed barred, still it is not certain. One may for instance very well compare the Menander of the double terminal bust at Bonn (*Mon. dell' Inst.*, v. Pl. 54. Welcker, *Alte Denkm.*, v. Pl. 3. Kekulé, *D. akadem. Kunstmuseum zu Bonn*, Pl. 2, 1). New: nose and bust. Bought from the Villa Borioni. [*B*]

177 (178). **A philosopher**, with a long beard, called a Diogenes.

178 (180. P). **Portrait.** *Arch. Zeit.*, 1874, Pl. 4. Called Apollo
on account of several holes, in which gilded rays were supposed
to have been fixed. There can be no doubt that the head is a portrait, and one not earlier than the time of Lysippos, as is shown
especially by the expression of individuality and the treatment of
the forehead. The forehead is not particularly high, traversed by two
slight furrows and projecting a good deal at the lower part. Beneath the sharply defined brow-line shrewd eyes glance forth a little
askance, framed in sharply cut lids. The lower lid is traversed by a
slight furrow, the pupils are slightly expressed. The cheeks form
in front a beautiful oval, from the side they seem tolerably broad.
Upper lip very delicate, the slightly opened mouth very expressive.
Expression of face delicate and spiritual. It is that of a man who
notwithstanding his youth has done and suffered much and is aware
of his importance. Hair somewhat thrown up above the forehead
and falling down on each side in slight curls as far as the ears; cut
fairly short behind. Behind the coronal of curls a slightly twisted
narrow riband encircles the hair. Between forehead and riband
six deep holes are introduced at regular intervals; behind the ears
against the neck below the riband there are on each side two similar
holes, and besides these four smaller holes irregularly placed. These
can scarcely point to anything else than the former presence of a
large metal wreath, which suggests a victory, or the honour of a crown
won in some other way. A general resemblance to Alexander the
Great is as unmistakeable as are many divergences, in the hair and
in the bent pose of head. The head in Erbach by which Stark (in
Bursian's *Jahresbericht*, 18¾¾, p. 1595) believed the nomenclature of
Alexander could be supported is essentially different, as Stark himself has subsequently conceded (*Zwei Alexanderköpfe*, 1879, p. 19).
Most probably some distinguished personage of the Alexandrian
or the early Hellenistic period. New: nose, under lip and chin, l.
ear, piece of r. cheek near ear, piece of crown of head, neck and
bust; however a slight inclination of the head to its own r. seems to
be established by an original piece of neck under l. ear. Injuries
on both cheeks. Good, free work, but not delicately executed.
Parian marble. L. of face 0·175.

179 (187). **"Alexander,"** a bust of open countenance and fine
character. Found near the tomb of Caecilia Metella. Bought from
Jenkins.

180 (188). "**Proserpine**," the head-dress, with a close cap, very singular. Identified as the goddess from the authority of an ancient Sicilian medal. Bought from Cavaceppi.

181 (193). A small head, called a **Venus**, in Peperino.

182, 183 (194, 195. P). **Two boys' heads**, with smooth hair falling on to the face, explained as Gaius and Lucius Caesar. Coarse work. Bought from Jenkins. "They were found at Lunghezza, in some ruins of a magnificent building. The Bacchus and Faun purchased by Mr Campbell, were found with these two heads...It is not known where they were found." (*Account.*) [*B*]

184, 185 (196, 197. P, portico). **Two Satyr heads**, with small horns, laughing; exactly corresponding to the so-called Faun of Winckelmann in Munich. Found in some ruins near the Via Praenestina. [*]

186 (198). "**Marcus Aurelius**." *Mon. Matth.*, II. Pl. 21, 2? Represented in his youth, with his first beard. This bust has been much fractured; but the parts are mostly its own. Bought from the Villa Mattei.

187 (199). A **portrait**, unknown, of good sculpture.

188 (200). **Aphroditè**. "This head once stood on that noted statue of Venus, now in the Chigi palace [with the name of Menophantos, *Mus. Capitol.*, IV. Pl. 68. Müller-Wieseler, II. 25, 275]. It was a patched-up head by Volpato, but not being adequate in merit to the rest of the statue, another head, more suitable, was found for it."

189 (201). **Faustina**. Bought from Cavaceppi. Probably identical with a modern head of the younger Faustina in the Picture Gallery.

190 (202). "**Hestia**," with a veil.

191 (203). A **portrait**, bearing a strong resemblance to Mr Thorpe [cf. pp. 100, 334].

192 (204). A **portrait**, of youthful, open countenance.

193 (205. P). **Eros**. Head of a statue of Eros stringing his bow, of which there are many replicas extant. A pretty, tender head with hair dressed into a plait along the parting of the hair. New: nose, lips, bust. Otherwise in very good preservation. Parian marble. Found at Lunghezza. L. of face 0·165. [*C*]

194 (206). **Female portrait**, by some called a **Venus**; has suffered much by time and accidents.

195 (214). **Lion's head**, found in taking down some ruins of the mausoleum of Augustus. Bought from Piranesi.

196 (215). **"Philippus."** "This head is remarkable for having on the right cheek some Greek letters, denoting it to be a head of Philipp, king of Macedonia, and father of Alexander"! Bought from Cavaceppi.

197 (216). **Satyr,** having a cap or pouch on his head. Bought from the Capponi palace.

198, 199 (217, 218). **Castor and Pollux.** On each of their heads are bronze stars. Found near the Lacus Gabinus [at Lunghezza?], and at the time desired in purchase by Poniatowsky.

200 (219). **Satyr,** a small head, remarkably fine.

201 (220). **A portrait,** unknown.

202 (221). **Portrait of a boy,** with a good open countenance. Perhaps identical with a head, with hair cut quite short, in the Pantheon. [*B*]

203 (222). **"Mars."**

204 (223). **"Ptolemy,"** with a helmet; so called from the likeness to other heads of Ptolemy.

205 (225). Two **lions' heads,** used as key-stones in two arches. Found near the Palatine hill.

205 *a* (269. S). **Lion's head,** of good sculpture; fixed over the back door of the staircase.

206 (227). **Double terminal bust,** female, below life-size, one head of which is named Sappho. Bought from Cavaceppi.

207 (228). **"Vestal virgin,"** with a veil.

208 (230). **Terminal head of a Greek poet or philoso pher.** Very like the supposed Hesiodos in the Brit. Mus. (Gr.-Rom. Sculpt., no. 119. *Mus. Marbles*, II. Pl. 44). The hair stands out round the brow beneath a tolerably thick fillet, somewhat longer before the ears. [*B*]

209 (231). **"Ariadne."** "This head has suffered so much from the injuries of time and accidents, that it scarcely deserves that name"!

210 (232). **A portrait,** unknown. Bought from the Villa Borioni.

211 (233). **"Ptolemy,** so called on account of the helmet, usual to those heads."

212 (234). **Small head of a boy,** in bronze. Bought from the Villa Negroni.

213 (235). **Portrait,** unknown, in bronze.

214 (410. P). **Small bust of Q. Aristaeus,** with head fixed on, and probably not belonging to it, and the following inscription :

D. M. | T. F. Qu. Aristaeo | Antesforus domino suo | benemerenti de suo | imaginem consacravit. (Genuine?) [*B*]

215 (522). "**Trajan**," "represented in his military habit. Both the head and chest seem to have suffered by time and accidents. Bought at Lord Cawdor's sale." Presumably identical with the head of an older thin Roman, in the kitchen; hair as with Trajan combed on to the face, but the proportions of the head more lofty than with that Emperor. For the rest cf. no. 172. [*B*] Waagen, p. 246, notices in the hall a "Bust of Trajan, of animated conception, but moderate workmanship; the point of the nose, upper lip, bones round the eyes, and a part of the ears, are new."

216 and **216** *a* (542. P. T). **Two porphyry heads**, on mailed busts of coloured marble, executed as pendants. By no means "Marius and Sulla," but emperors or generals. Ridge of each nose broad and depressed. Hair short, not polished. From the Bessborough collection. [*B*]

217 (552). **Caracalla.** Bought at Lord Mendip's sale. Seems to be modern. [*B*]

The following busts cannot be identified with those enumerated in the *Account.*

217 *a* (T). **Beardless Roman**, with gloomy look. Hair lying towards the front and cut off short over the forehead. [*B*]

217 *b* (T). **Otho.** on a bust in one piece with the head, with a sword belt. Outline of head flat at top and falling towards forehead: hair combed in this same direction forming waves round forehead. Profile quite straight. New: the powerful nose. The head seems to agree with that of the Vatican (*Sala dei busti,* no. 277 [311]). [*B*]

217 *c* (T). **Head of Philippus Junior**(?), colossal scale. New: l. side. [*B*]

217 *d* (G). **Portrait of a Roman**, unknown, with smooth shaven head, large nose and mouth. Very animated. [*B*]

217 *e* (G). **Seneca**, so called, of the usual type (cf. Holkham, no. 36), bronze. Antique? [*B*]

Under sundry tables in the ante-room of the Pantheon as one comes from the Picture Gallery stand seven busts, and among them:

217 *f*. **Beardless old man**, with hair like a wig and restored, coarse nose. [*B*]

RELIEFS.

The *Engravings* contain the following specimens.

218 (S). Let into a tall pillar are two figures in high relief, sawn out of one relief, *Engr.*, 27. (*a*) **Youth** stepping r., enveloped in cloak wh'ch leaves r. arm and breast free. L. hand laid on cloak, r. advanced; forearm and roll restored, as also feet and ground. (*b*) **Woman** dancing l., enveloped so thoroughly in a wide cloak that only face and feet are visible: r. arm lowered, l. supported on the side. It is a beautiful figure and proportionately popular, being repeated both in terra cotta statuettes and marble reliefs (*Ann. dell' Inst.*, 1863, Pl. L. 1, Cod. Pigh., no. 99 Jahn = Cod. Coburg., no. 77 Matz).—Both figures are prettily and freshly treated. II. 0·41. Relief raised from field 0·06. Pentelic marble. [*]

219 (207). **Tragic mask**, *Engr.*, 72, 3. Corner of lid of a sarcophagus. An actual mouth is visible through the cavity of the opened mouth of the mask. (Antique?)

219 *a* (208). **Fellow mask** from same sarcophagus.

220. Front of a cinerary urn, as it seems. *Engr.*, 74, 1. Large wreath, into the space enclosed by which a Medusa head furnished with snakes and wings is introduced to avert evil influence (ἀποτρόπαιον).

221 (523. P). **Front of a sarcophagus, "The Winds."** *Engr.*, 78. Somewhat l. of the middle of the relief the Sun-god sits on a rock, quite nude but for a cloak which covers breast, l. forearm and part of l. thigh; he rests l. arm on the rock, holding the r. before the breast (forearm with staff restored). Head, with long curly hair and antique attachments for a (restored) coronal of rays, is put on, but is apparently original. At the feet of the god lies a bearded Water-god of lesser stature, his lower parts cloaked, leaning on his r. arm, holding a snake (?) in his lap with l. hand; probably Okeanos. Behind the Sun-god l. follow the four Seasons in female form (cf. Ovid, *Met.*, 11. 23 ff.). First comes Spring in chiton and cloak, with long curls, r. breast bared, r. arm raised, holding in l. arm a large stalk of flowers (head and r. hand missing). Then comes Summer, sitting averted, with nude body, the cloak covering the legs, back, and l. arm, on which the figure is supported; with the l. hand she holds in her lap a bunch of ears of corn. New: lowered r. forearm, also the head, which is now turned towards the Sun-god. At her feet lie an ox and a sheep (head missing). Behind Summer stands Autumn fully draped (head not her own); in her l. arm a branch laden with clusters of grapes. New: almost all raised r. arm. The figure of Winter brings up the rear, entirely enveloped by the wide cloak which even covers the head, and allows the long chiton to be seen beneath. Face much

INCE BLUNDELL HALL. 224.

mutilated. R. arm is hidden under cloak, in l. she holds a stalk of
reeds. The suite of the Sun-god is completed by a female figure on
his l., which occupies about the middle of the relief. She wears a
chiton, which is slipping down from the l. shoulder, and a cloak ; the
restorer has treated the r. forearm as raising a large corner of the cloak
(still absent in the *Engravings*), without it being said whether this
restoration was indicated by the remnants. As the head is also new
and there are no attributes, the identification of the figure is uncertain. ("Isis," according to the explanation in the *Engravings*.) R.
half of relief occupied by chariot and four fiery horses of Sun-god,
the latter each held at the bridle by a man who is about to look after
the harnessing. Outside of chariot adorned with reliefs : a Victory
hurries l. with raised r. arm, and behind her lies a female with her
upper part nude resting her head on the r. arm (a local goddess). Of
the four grooms the first, third, and fourth are of Herculean frame,
bearded and long-haired, quite nude but for a skin which is thrown
over the advanced l. forearm ; the first and fourth moreover carry a
club on the arm ; as for the third the club is restored, presumably correctly. Their heads are connected with the background of the relief
by supports ; there is, however, no certain trace of wings. On the
other hand, the second groom, who is for the most part hidden by
the horses, is furnished with conspicuous wings on his head ; he is
beardless and youthful, and would be taken for Hermes if the curly
hair did not fall down in such abundance on his neck. On men and
horses are sundry renovations, but nothing to affect their purport.
(According to Visconti's explanation in the *Engravings* and in *Mus.
Pio-Clem.*, VI. p. 45 note, Mil., these "four figures of men with
wings on their heads" are called the Winds ; with regard to which
Matz cites the opening of a hymn to Helios : Ἀεροδινήτων ἀνέμων
ἐποχούμενος αὔραις, Ἥλιε χρυσοκόμα κ.τ.λ., cf. Miller, *Mélanges de
littér. grecque*, p. 442, Dilthey, *Rhein. Mus.*, XXVII. p. 405 f.) Quite
at the r. end is Tellus lying on the ground, with upper part nude,
legs and abdomen enveloped in cloak, r. hand lying on a cornucopiae
from which ears of corn hang down. The subject is bounded on
both sides by thin Corinthian columns, between which a tapestry is
stretched over the whole background to indicate the interior of the
palace of Helios, the *regia Solis*. Greek granular marble. Relief
mostly very high, so that the several figures stand out almost to
full rounding ; only the youthful groom and Tellus are in low relief. "The history of this bas-relief is rather curious. It was
found at Tivoli. There it was placed in a niche, to ornament a

fountain in the garden of the Villa d'Este, from whence it was
bought, 1790. By the continual lapse of tartarizing water, from the
Anio, over it for many years, it was so incrustated that it appeared
no better than an irregular surface, a single figure on the left hand
being the only one distinguishable. When it was brought to Rome,
and cleared of the incrustation, it turned out a very curious poetical
subject, and was so much admired, that the Pope Pius VI. expressed
a wish of its not being taken from Rome, which was a kind of prohibition. In consequence of that wish it was presented to his Holi-
ness [see Visconti, *Museo Pio-Clem.*, VI. p. 45], and in return several
handsome presents were made. The Pope was so partial to it, as to
keep it in his private apartments ; yet, strange to tell! this identical
bas-relief, a very few years after, was brought to Liverpool on sale,
with forty-five cases of marbles, tables, &c., all pillage and plunder out
of the Pope's palace by the French. These cases, consigned from
Italy to a merchant in London, whose agent had purchased them
from a Frenchman, with the ship, had been taken and retaken in the
passage four times, and at last brought to Liverpool, where the cases
being opened, and not meeting with sale, they were re-shipped for
London, and sold by Mr Christie, in May 1800, when Mr Blundell
gave 260 guineas to obtain again this bas-relief, which did not cost
him ten pounds, when bought out of the Villa d'Este " (*Account*).
To the same purchase belong nos. 137, 393, 412 and four mosaic
tables (*Account*, nos. 526, 527). L. 2'0. H. 0'63. [*MW*; the latter
erroneously calls to mind the story of Phaethon.]

222 (186). **Sepulchral monument.** *Engr.*, 78, 2. Five
portraits in high relief shown as far as the waist. (*a*) A woman, l. arm
round shoulder of (*b*) a boy with the bulla on his neck; (*c*) a man ;
(*d*) a girl round whose neck again (*e*) a woman is laying her r. arm ;
e has a little bird in either hand, *a* in the r., *d* in the l. ; two others
are flying in symmetrical positions close to *e*'s head. Inscription
illegible. Bought from the Villa Borioni.

223 (240. G). **Front of a child's sarcophagus.** *Engr.*,
79, 1. Two winged youths floating, with cloaks, hold symmetrically
the medallion (*clupeus*) with portrait of a boy. Beneath, two horns
of plenty with fruits, crossed, and on each side a panther lying
down with a bunch of grapes in its fore-paws. At each end stands a
winged boy playing on a syrinx, the burning torch turned towards
the ground. L. half beginning from the medallion, now missing
(once restored?). Extremely coarse. [*M*]

224 (249. S). **Slab of a sarcophagus.** *Engr.*, 79, 2. A

vase filled with fruits, grasped by the handle on either side by a
winged youth who lies down, representing a season, with a bundle of
ears of corn on the arm. New : in great part r. arm of l. figure and
its ears of corn. Bad work. L. 0·78. H. 0·23. [*M*]

225 (332. G). **Lid of a sarcophagus.** *Engr.*, 79, 3. On a
lion's skin lie two wreathed Bacchic masks, the one bearded, the
other youthful : close to the latter stands a vase on a pedestal. The
youthful Bacchus lies r., with wreath, half wrapped in cloak : r. arm
lies on his head, in l. rests the thyrsos. A nude Satyr with thyrsos
and syrinx lies l. At each corner a bearded mask of a Pan with
brutish ears hanging down considerably. [*M*]

226 (411). **Sepulchral monument.** *Engr.*, 80, 1. Three
portrait busts with inscriptions. Quite l. a beardless man (*C. Hel-
vius Hermes* | *patronus*) pointing with r. hand to a curly-headed man,
also beardless, the founder of the monument (*Asclepiades* | *lib. fecit*),
who stretches out r. hand to his wife, a lady with artistic coiffure
(*Arronia Restituta* | *coniunx Ascepia[dis]*). Apparently of Trajan's
time. The patron's pupils are expressed.

227 (331. P, pediment of portico). **Sepulchral monument.**
Engr., 80, 3. Four portraits close to each other, cut out in bust
fashion. (*a*) Man with beard cut short, (*b*) woman with Plotina's
coiffure, (*c*) older beardless man, (*d*) woman with hair dressed in
Marciana's style. Time of Hadrian. No pupils. [*]

228 (S). **Sarcophagus.** *Engr.*, 81. In front in the middle
a slab with the modern inscription *D. M. Portiae Iustae* | *C. Octavius
Firmus* (borrowed from *Mon. Matth.*, III. 54, 1). On each side of
this a garland hung on bulls' heads, in the semicircular fold thereof
a bacchic mask, l. of a Satyr, r. of a Seilenos. Beneath, four panthers
lying down, the two in the middle symmetrically grouped round
a basket of fruits. On each of the ends a garland. On the lid
wreaths of foliage and at each corner a tragic mask. Bought at the
Duke of St Albans' sale. [*M*]

229 (341. G). **Large oval sarcophagus,** seriously renovated.
Engr., 82. A man clad in toga in the middle is modern, except the
legs from the knees downwards and the lower half of the bundle of
books near his l. foot. Next him stands a man with short hair, similarly clad, in l. hand a roll with the name CANTENI VS (pupils expressed). Then comes a low quadrangular pillar on which stands
a square box shut ; above this a bearded attendant is visible in the
loose tunic (ἐξωμίς) supported on a staff and with head lying on
l. hand. Near r. leg of principal figure stands a child (new : head)

with girdled drapery and boots, holding a semi-cylindrical chest before his breast ; next a fully-draped matron (new : head, l. shoulder and hand), most likely the wife of the principal figure, with a roll in r. hand on which the letters EMILIANVS are preserved, but ANVS is inscribed on a joined-on piece (probably modern). Quite l., next to an olive tree, stands a matron in ungirdled stola, cloak over head and back, both arms raised with outspread hands (attendant ?) ; near her a sheep. Both wreaths near head of principal figure are new. On either side, where the rounding of the sarcophagus begins, a powerful lion, with head in high relief, is throttling a horse which it has thrown on the ground ; a half-moon, an ornament serving for an amulet (cf. Jahn, *Berichte d. sächs. Ges. d. Wiss.*, 1855, p. 42) hangs round the horse's neck. Behind each of the lions a beardless man in a tunic with short sleeves, with one hand lying on his head while the other holds a curved trumpet, which the man blows. Of the fourth century. L. 1·95. H. 0·91. [*M*]

231 (372). **Quadrangular cinerarium.** *Engr.*, 83, 1. Two bearded masks with ram's horns holding a garland of fruit, in the semicircular field of which, above two birds pecking, is the tablet for the inscription. Below at each of the corners is an eagle and another smaller bird. The inscription *D. M. Acellio*, &c., was not yet existing when the urn was in the Villa Mattei (*Mon. Matth.*, III. 71, 6) ; no more were the lid with a wreath on it and the youthful masks at the corners.

231 (365). **Quadrangular cinerarium.** *Engr.*, 83, 2. *Mon. Matth*, III. 58, 3. On either side an Ionic column with spiral fluting. In the middle the tablet, with the inscription *D. M. Sestilia Ɔ* (i.e. *Sestilia*) *(liberta) Secunda* ; over it two birds pecking from a basket of fruit, on each side a burning torch, beneath a pediment and a wreath (?). Lid, in pediment whereof pecking birds are seen round a basket, not yet to be seen in *Mon. Matth.*

232 (342). **Oval Sarcophagus.** *Engr.*, 83, 3. The field for relief work is divided into five compartments by six columns with spiral flutings. In the middle a pair of folding doors with lions' heads (without rings) ; one of the folding doors is somewhat open. In each of the two nearest compartments, a bearded man in tunic, pallium, and shoes, stretches out one hand towards the door of the sepulchre ; the one to the r. seems to be carrying something in his hand, the one to the l. wears a bulla on his neck. In each of the remaining compartments is a woman blowing the flute, on the l. with a head-cloth and the cloak gathered into a skirt about the hips ; on the

r. with long curls and clad merely in the stola. They are the necessary accessories of a funeral celebration. The roof-shaped lid is
furnished at its edge with masks, two bearded, four beardless, as
coping tiles (ἡγεμόνες, *personae*); only the third line of the four-
lined inscription, *hic situs est*, is still clearly intelligible. The unusual
ornaments on this sarcophagus caused some difficulty in getting
permission to take it out of Rome. L. 1·0. [*M*]

233 (343). **Child's sarcophagus.** *Engr.*, 84, 1. In the
middle the portrait bust of a boy framed in thick rolled ribbons. On
either side stands a winged boy with chlamys, the one on the l. with
a branch of blossoms in his r. arm and a small fillet (ὑποθυμίς) in
l. hand between two flowers shooting up from the ground; that on
the r. with ears of corn in r. hand and a sickle on l. arm between a
basket with ears of corn standing on the ground and some growing
corn. These two representations of spring and autumn stand for the
full round of seasons which are so popular on sarcophagi. On either
side a Dioskuros clad in chlamys, with pointed hat and spear each
leading by the bridle a plunging horse; these figures encroach somewhat on the sides of the sarcophagus. On the lid two Cupids
riding on dolphins from each side up to a trident which occupies the
middle. At each end a tragic mask. L. 0·84. H. of sarcophagus
0·32, of lid 0·11. Bought from Cavaceppi. [*M*]

234 (355). **Quadrangular cinerarium.** *Engr.*, 84, 2. From
two masks hangs a festoon which frames the field for the inscription
*D. M. | Pholoe vernae | bene merenti | Rasinia Glypte f(ecit). | vixit
ann. XVI. d. VII.* Beneath each mask a bird.

235 (397). **Quadrangular cinerarium.** *Engr.*, 84, 3 = 143,
1. 2. Shaped like an edifice built of square stones, with the inscrip-
tion *D. M. | Lappiae Primae f(iliae) | vix. a. XXXXIII,* which being
copied from a different urn (*Mon. Matth.*, III. 68, 1) is evidently
modern.

236 (354). **Quadrangular cinerarium.** *Engr.*, 84, 3. Un-
important ornaments surround the tablet with the inscription *D. M. |
Claudi Rufi | v(ixit) a. XXX di. II.*

237 (407). **Quadrangular cinerarium.** *Engr.*, 85. Within
a rich border of wreaths of foliage is the table with the inscription
*Dis Manibus | Iuniae M. f Marcellae | quae vixit ann. XX | sancte |
Iunia Iuniae l. Privata | patronae pi[i]ssimae | b. m. de suo.* Beneath
an altar of incense (θυματήριον), entwined by garlands with two
Cupids; over each garland an owl.

238 (408). **Cippus.** *Engr.*, 86. The inscription reads *D.*

M. | T. Aurelio Man|suetino eq(uiti) sing(ulari) | Aug(usti) tur(ma) Lucania|na, nat(ione) Noricus, | vix(it) an(nis) XXV, mil(itavit) annis VII. | P. Aelius Lucanus centurio | leg(ionis) VII C(laudiae) her(es) fac(iendum) cur(avit). Below, the dead man in short coat with spear, going behind a horse with long saddle-cloth, which he leads by the bridle. Below, two boys bearing a garland, in the semicircular field thereof a Medusa's head.

239 (409). **Gravestone.** *Engr.*, 87, 1. Girl lying on bed fully draped, close to her a pet dog; next stands a Cupid offering her a wreath. In lower part of field a low table with two vessels (?), and the inscription *Valeria M. f. Prisca, | vixit delicatissima ann. XXIII. | mater filiae fecit.*

240 (376). **Double cinerarium.** *Engr.*, 87, 2. 3. Two swans standing each on a balaustium hold at the corners two festoons laden with fruit, which are being grasped in the middle by an eagle. Eight smaller birds disposed symmetrically. On the tablet to the l. is *Claudiae Aug. l. | Quietae, | hic sita est,* on that to the r. *Ti. Claudius Qulr(ina) | Piolo filio, | situs est.* (The inscriptions are presumably spurious.) On the sides a garland held by the swan and a bearded mask with ram's horns; below the latter, an eagle; inside the garland, a swan. On the lid a wreath and unimportant ornaments. From the Villa Mattei (*Mon. Matth.*, II. p. 131).

241 (237. P). **"Candelabrum."** *Engr.*, 88, 1. 2. *Mon. Matth.*, II. 75, 76, where however the lowest part and the top piece are still wanting. A baroque enough composition of akanthos flowers and grapes, bordered on one side by a youthful tragic mask crowned with ivy, on the other by a Seilenos mask with a wreath. The utensil seems antique, though seriously renovated. From the Villa Mattei. H. 0·78. [*]

242 (289). **Side of a cinerarium.** *Engr.*, 88, 3. Medusa's head above a rich garland of fruit.

243 (238. G). **Lid of a sarcophagus.** *Engr.*, 89, 1. Bacchic figures, seven lying down, one kneeling; on the l. three half draped Maenads, first two with thyrsos, the third glancing round after a youthful Satyr who holds a syrinx (?) in his r. hand. Then comes a bald-headed long-bearded Seilenos lying on his belly, with a cup in his l. hand, into whose mouth a kneeling female is about to pour wine from a drinking horn (ῥυτόν). To the r. a half draped woman lying opposite a nude Satyr, who holds a goblet and a cup in his hands. Elegant sculpture. L. 1·15. H. 0·115. Procured at Rome by Mr Thorpe, in exchange for a microscope. [*M]

244 (246). **Lid of a sarcophagus.** *Engr.*, 89, 2. Hunting scene. From the l. three attendants carry on their shoulders a mighty net rolled up, the two hinder men carry stakes, the foremost leads a large baying hound in leash. Before them goes a bearded man with a stake, the master or an overseer, and seems to beckon them on. Then follows a double fence with nets stretched round it, therein are l. two boars, r. two stags with heads reaching out over net. R., a figure similar to that of the overseer; face rubbed away. At either end a wall. L. 2·05. H. 0·23. [*M*]

245 (404. S). **Lid of a sarcophagus.** *Engr.*, 89, 3. The Seasons. In the middle a tablet with the inscription *D. M.* | *L. Aurelii Aufidi . M. f.* (*i.e.* perhaps *Aufidiani* as Wilmanns conjectures), *vixit annis | septuaginta.* On either side a mask. In the two fields thus bounded lie four winged boys as representatives of the seasons with a small winged boy each as companion. L.: Summer, upper part nude, with a sickle(?) on r. arm, l. hand resting on a basket full of ears of corn, which the smaller boy holds; opposite is Spring, partly restored, with a basket of flowers(?), and on l. arm a shoot full of leaves. R.: Autumn in half-loosened tunic, a shoot with vine-leaves on r. arm, and with a basket full of fruits; opposite is Winter with sleeved tunic, cloak and Phrygian cap, likewise with fruit in his basket, and a stalk of reeds on his l. arm. Rough work. L. 2·07. H. 0·21. [*M*]

246 (239. P). **Front of a sarcophagus.** *Engr.*, 90. L. end of a Kalydonian boar-hunt (not given in Matz, *Ann. dell' Inst.*, 1869, p. 76). In background rich foliage-work indicates a forest. Quite l. a youth with chlamys and spear; next a second youth with sword on arm leading a horse by bridle. Before him a youth in the usual attitude of Meleagros, nude but for a small chlamys over l. shoulder and boots, hastening forward with brandished spear (spear, l. hand and r. arm correctly restored) ; between his legs a hound. Before him a youth in chlamys, the sword in l. hand, once probably brandishing a stone with r. hand (new : head and r. forearm). Further r. a mounted man in tunic and chlamys, treated as principal figure, pretty extensively restored; a hound at his feet. Underneath the horse lies a wounded man (Ankaeos), nude, lifting cloak with l. hand (cf. Zoega, *Bassir.*, Pl. 51); near him a figure with short drapery, apparently female (Atalante) with bow ; lastly remains of a youth in background, the greater part of whom together with the rest of the relief is restored. Probably the boar came here. Below the relief a rich decoration of foliage. The sarcophagus in its whole character recalls the Hip-

polytos sarcophagus of the Campana collection, now at St Petersburg
(*Mon. dell' Inst.*, VI. 1—3), and that at Girgenti. Bought from the
Villa Borioni. [*M]

247 (241. S). **Front of a child's sarcophagus.** *Engr.*, 91, 1.
Cupid's chariot-race. Four bigae, moving r. Under second pair of
horses a Cupid lies on the ground, while another on a single horse
rides close by; horses of third chariot in confusion, the driver
stoops over them. R. and l. in background very flat indications of
an architectural design. Rough work, apparently not finished. [*M*]

[**247** *a* (248. S). **Lid of a sarcophagus.** *Engr.*, 91, 2. Boys
playing at nuts and ball. Modern copy, as *Account* states and as
Braun also, *Ann. dell' Inst.*, 1857, p. 142, correctly recognised, of a sarcophagus in the Mattei collection (*Mon. Matth.*, III. 36, 1, *Annali, l.
cit.*, Pl. BC). Pentelic marble. L. 0·67. H 0·23. [*MW]]

248 (242. S). **Birth of Dionysos.** *Engr.*, 92, 1 (reversed
copy), "Birth of Hercules." The latter interpretation rests on Visconti's explanation of the very similar relief, *Mus. Pio-Clem.*, IV. Pl.
37, which however is very doubtful (cf. Zoega in Welcker's *Zeitschrift
f. alte Kunst*, p. 402); it is rather to be corrected by our relief, the
interpretation of which is supported by the companion piece no. 249.
Semelè lies on a bed, with closed eyes, the nude arms hanging down
limp, no mere newly-delivered woman but a corpse. Near her a
vessel perhaps meant for a bath. Behind the bed three females
busied with the new-born Dionysos. The middle one holds him in
her arms, a second on the l. lays her hands on him protectingly,
the third on the r. shows by a gesture her astonishment at the
babe. Behind her, quite at r. end, Hermes enters with winged
petasos and caduceus to carry away the babe and bring him to his
father Zeus (cf. the relief in the Pio-Clementine Museum and Stephani, *Compte-Rendu*, 1861, pp. 11 ff., Müller-Wieseler, II. 34, 392).
In the background a tapestry hangs up to indicate the interior of the
chamber. Quite l. in the front at foot end of bed a woman hurries
out, richly draped in chiton and cloak with diadem on forehead
(στεφάνη), looking back at Semelè with a proud, scornful expression ;
no doubt Hera, who triumphs over the death of her rival. Her
raised r. arm with the whole l. end of the relief has been cut off and
entirely lost. The companion piece is the following :

249 (243. S). **Triumph of Dionysos.** *Engr.*, 92, 2, "Triumph
of Ariadne." In this also a curtain hangs up in the background.
From the l. comes Dionysos, standing on a chariot, with long curls
and wreath, in long sleeved chiton with fawn-skin girt over it slant-

wise, stout thyrsos on r. arm. Holding reins in l. hand he drives the
two lionesses or panthers which draw the chariot. By the god standing on the chariot a young Satyr with thyrsos and the winged Nikè
with palm branch. Near the chariot a Maenad moves r. with thyrsos
and tambourine (τύμπανον); l. three female companions, of whom the
first, next the chariot, plays on the double flute, the second shakes
what are probably castanets (κρόταλα) or cymbals, the third seems to
carry a cista with phallus. Before them goes the goat-legged Pan
with pedum. Remains of at least one more female figure are still
distinctly preserved; r. end of relief totally lost. Upper r. corner has
been broken off but is genuine. Both pieces, nos. 248 and 249, are
remains of larger compositions. They are now 0·64 high, 0·57
broad. Composition generally very noteworthy, and in some particulars excellent, though not of specially good execution. Bought
from the Capponi palace. [*CM IV]

250 (245. S). **Nikè.** *Engr.*, 93, 1. *Amalthea*, III. Pl. 5 (C. O.
Müller). Only lower r. corner antique: legs of goddess as far as
up to the swell of the nates, tip of wing, lowest end of snake, greatest
part of coat of mail and shield. All the rest new. The fragment, in
hieratic style and low relief, belongs to a votive relief dedicated by a
victorious warrior. Pentelic marble. The antique fragment is 0·43
long, 0·32 high. [*M]

251 (244. S). **Woman by a candelabrum.** *Engr.*, 93, 2.
Antique: only body of fully-draped female in stiff hieratic style.
New: feet, corner of cloak hanging down before r. leg, r. forearm,
neck and head, and the whole candelabrum. Fairly coarse, decorative
work. Pentelic marble. The whole composition resembles the
Athenè of a pasticcio in the Villa Albani (Raffei, *Dissert.* II., *sopra
un bassoril. Albani*, cf. *Arch. Zeit.*, 1871, p. 138 note 6). [*]

252. **Fragment of a frieze.** *Engr.*, 94, 1. Between rich
scrolls of foliage a stag, a panther and a second stag flee l. L. and
r. of panther a boy on either side with chlamys, raising one arm to
beckon on other companions, the one on the r. holds a javelin. A
similar specimen is drawn in Cavaceppi, *Racc.*, III. 19, 1.

253 (247). **Lid of a sarcophagus.** *Engr.*, 94, 2. In the middle,
bearded head of the god of a spring with crab's claws in his dishevelled
hair, similarly to the so-called *bocca della verità* in S. Maria in Cos-
medin in Rome (cf. O. Jahn, *Berichte d. sächs. Ges.*, 1851, pp. 141 ff.).
On either side, turned toward the middle, a sea-tiger and a hippocampus; waves below. On each corner a youthful mask with long
hair and Phrygian cap. L. 2·07. H. 0·28. [M]

254 (311). **Fragment of a frieze.** *Engr.*, 94, 3. The piece
seems perfect on the l. It begins with two sea-hares (?), on one of
which a Cupid with whip rides; before them a winged sea-griffin and
a sea-stag; before these a bearded Triton with staff in r. hand. So
far the movement is from l. to r., the other half moves in the reverse
direction. The Triton seizes with l. hand a mighty winged sea-griffin
by one horn; then come two sea-lions, the hinder one bridled by a
Cupid. Of the further extent of the procession only the forelegs of a
hippocampus are still preserved (whose head and neck are restored
in the engraving). The fragment most likely belongs to a very long
frieze of which other very extensive pieces are preserved in Cod.
Pigh., no. 36 (cf. Cod. Coburg., nos. 21, 22). [*M*]

255 (283. G). **Front of a sarcophagus.** *Engr.*, 95, 1. Cupids
racing in the circus l. to r. Four bigae, each with a Cupid as driver,
while the three foremost have besides a second Cupid on l. horse.
This one looks round on victorious chariot at the driver who still
brandishes the whip. Horses of second chariot in confusion with
rider thrown on the ground, the driver looking round anxiously at
the following chariot, the third, whose driver again looks round at
the last chariot (without postillion). The spina represented in the
background by scratched lines; on it three semicircles are visible.
Quite l. rises the conical meta tapered towards the top. Behind the
last chariot a scaffolding is to be seen with two dolphins and a semicircle between them, behind the second chariot a substructure with four
ova. Below third and fourth chariots there lies on the ground a two-
handled basket (cf. Visconti, *Mus. Pio-Clem.*, v. on Pl. 38 ff.). [*M*]

256 (250. S). **One end of a child's sarcophagus.** *Engr.*,
95, 2. A Cupid rides on a horse prancing r., reins in advanced l.
hand, palm branch on r. arm. New: right end of slab. L. 0·30. H.
0·23. [*M*]

257 (251. S). **The other end of the same sarcophagus.**
Engr., 95, 3. The same subject turned l. New: l. end and a large
piece of the palm branch. Measurements same as those of no. 256.
[*M*]

258 (253. S). **Fragment of an altar or of the mouth of a
well.** Montfaucon, *Diar. Ital.*, p. 111 "(*Romae*) *in Villa Ursinia*"
(near the church of S. Croce in Gerusalemme), *Antiq. Expl.*, I. Pl.
32, 1, *Engr.*, 97, 1, "bought out of the Borioni Palace." Poseidon
sits l. on a block of rock with his body held straight, but his head,
encompassed by waving hair and adorned with a fillet, turned r., so
that clearly the composition once extended further in that direction.

New: nose, also two fingers of l. hand, with which the god supports himself on the rock. R. arm rests on thigh, a short little cloak envelopes hips and hangs down between legs. Close to him the trident stands straight up, the prongs whereof are connected with the shaft by two dolphins in decorative style. At feet of god a sea-dragon (κῆτος); quite l. above Poseidon's r. foot the fin of a second shows that the relief extended also on this side. Below, a raised moulding (torus) entwined with leaves. Very high relief. Roman work after a Greek original. Unfortunately completely worked over. H. o·84. [*M]

259 (263. P). **Archaic Relief.** Engr., 97, 2. Arch. Anz., 1864. Pl. A. 3. Arch. Zeit., 1873, Pl. 5, and see fig. 3 below. On a throne with high back, the thin arms of which end off in an unrecognisable ornament (head of animal according to Conze; according to the

FIG. 3.

Engravings, wrongly, a branch), sits a man without any attribute (Zeus?). Hair falls far down over his back in carefully dressed plaits, and forms above the forehead a broad roll of small curls arranged in several rows. Beard long and pointed. Opening of eyes very narrow, a feature made still more prominent by the strongly-marked cheek-bones. Small, straight nose, very pointed. Mouth slightly opened with a smile. On the neck one hardly notices border of long chiton which reaches down to feet, forming delicate parallel folds.

M. C.   25

Upper r. arm covered by chiton, over it lies a close sitting cloak, the
folds of which are only visible on breast and back, reaching to below
the calves. R. hand rests on arm of chair. It is extraordinarily long
and rather clumsy, without proper discrimination and combination of
the several joints. L. hand little better, slightly raised as if to give a
blessing with the fingers held in finnicking fashion. The huge length
of legs bears no proportion to the upper part of the figure and to the
very small head. The great length of feet corresponds with it. Feet
rest on a stool. The relief exhibits genuine archaic style and most
careful execution. Contour of figure sharp and slightly rounded
(rising above the field about 0·015), the upper surface rather flat
and faintly modelled, evidently with the intention that details should
be expressed in colour. Unfortunately the upper surface is much
abraded. Relief enclosed in a plain rectangular frame of which two
little pieces below the stool and on the upper margin are missing,
otherwise entire. Greek marble of fine grain, apparently Parian.
Probably it is identical with the relief "of the earliest Etruscan
style" noticed by Winckelmann (*Gesch. der Kunst*, III. 3, 5) in the
court of the Casa Capponi in Rome. Waagen and Conze assume
for this relief a position next to that of the Harpy tomb in the British
Museum and the so-called Leukothea relief in the Villa Albani.
For the treatment of the relief, those examples from Northern Greece
also may be compared (Pharsalos: Heuzey, *Mission scientifique en
Macédoine*, Pl. 23,—Thasos: *Ann. dell' Inst.*, 1872, Pl. L). H. 0·46.
L. 0·33. [*CII*]

260 (254. S). **Greek sepulchral relief.** *Engr.*, 98, 1. In the
middle, facing front, stands a beardless man of about fifty years, with
energetic, self-conscious features (new: nose), in chiton and cloak, r.
arm in cloak before breast, l. arm lowered. L. hand hidden in cloak,
a corner of which hangs down and effects a fairly artistic arrangement
of folds. In several places are marked the creases in the cloak,
which arise in consequence of its having been laid folded up a long
time: a refinement which is not rare with later sculptors. The man
wears shoes. On either side stands a little boy in chiton, an attendant, the one on the l. *en face*, supporting chin on r. hand; the
one on the r. with arms folded before the body looking up at his
master, leaning the while on a high pedestal. On this stands a
terminal image of Herakles, bearded, quite enveloped in the lion's
skin, which even covers both arms. It probably indicates a connection of the principal figure with a gymnasium. Figures all raised
in bold, high relief (0·12) from the very uneven field. Size and style

of work are considerably above the average of the large number of sepulchral reliefs derived from the Greek islands, to which the composition is most closely allied. The marble seems to be coarse-grained Parian. H. 0·90. L. 0·56. [*C]

261 (266. T). **Greek sepulchral relief.** *Engr.*, 98, 2. On a cushioned couch lies a bearded man with noble Zeus-like features, upper part enveloped in wide cloak. R. arm rests on somewhat raised r. thigh. He supports himself on his l. elbow. New: a cup in l. hand and greater part of snake which drinks out of cup; still a piece on the l. arm is antique, which cannot be an edge of drapery but can only be a piece of snake, so the restoration must be considered correct. Before couch a three-legged table with pieces of pastry. At head of bed sits a woman in chiton and cloak on a chair with cushions, feet resting on a stool. She lays l. arm on head pillow of couch, supporting r. elbow on l. hand and letting chin rest on back of r. hand. Her eyes meet the man's. As she is unveiled she can scarcely be taken for the wife, whose place moreover would be by foot end of couch; her youthfulness rather suggests a daughter. At foot end of couch there stands by a high mixing-bowl (κρατήρ) a serving boy in chiton, l. hand lowered, right arm raised over vessel. New: boy's curly head and greater part of r. hand, also upper l. corner of relief, including r. foot of principal person. The relief is distinguished above many similar specimens by freshness of sentiment, especially by the graceful movement of the woman. Unfortunately much effaced. Man in low, woman in higher, indeed in some parts of her figure in quite high, relief. Lower margin is cut away on under side with slope downwards towards back, but the two ends are left so as to look like the two feet of a chest. Coarse-grained Greek marble with large micaceous lumps, apparently from the islands. H. 0·40. L. 0·53. [*]

262 (256. S). **Right end of a sarcophagus.** *Engr*, 99, 1. *Account*, Plate to p. 88. Aphroditè in long chiton, cloak, shaped like a shawl, floating behind back, with stephanè on hair, hastens r. with lively step, holding a large palm-branch on l. arm, in r. hand holding out the apple to be displayed in Olympus on her victorious return from the contest of beauty. Before her hastens little Eros, looking back at his mother, nude and winged, torch on l. arm, lifting up a wreath in r. hand. There is a drawing of it already in Cod. Coburg., no. 202. Low relief. Poor work. Marble with black veins. H. 0·56. L. 0·49. Cf. next number. [*M*]

263 (255. S). **Left end of the same sarcophagus.** *Engr.*,

25—2

99, 2. *Account*, Plate to p. 88. Paris sits in sleeved chiton, trousers and Phrygian cap, r. on a rock, holding crook (*pedum*) on r. arm; with l. hand raising syrinx to mouth. Before r. foot on the ground lies the apple. By him sits a dog, r. a pine tree. Restored: small piece of r. margin. Clearly the moment before the arrival of the goddesses is represented. Cod. Coburg., no. 201. No doubt the front of the sarcophagus contained the judgment of Paris itself. It may be the relief which was built into the wall high up in the casino of the Villa Pamfili (Matz-Duhn, *Ant. Bildw. in Rom*, II. no. 3342) and is best drawn in the *Annali dell' Inst.*, 1839, Pl. H. At least the Cod. Coburg. likewise contains a drawing of it (no. 200, Matz). Measurements same as for no. 262. [*M*]

264 (258. S). **Right end of a sarcophagus.** *Engr.*, 99, 3. *Account*, Plate to p. 89. A nude youth with fillet in hair, the fat face resembling that of the Emperor Nero, turned to the spectator, hastens l. leading a prancing horse by bridle. L. hand holds a club, over l. arm hangs a lion's skin. (Dioskuros?) New: upper, l. and lower border, also a piece of r. border; still, except half l. foreleg and half head of horse, only unimportant parts are restored. H. 0·57. L. 0·50. Cf. the following number. [*M*]

265 (257. S). **Left end of the same sarcophagus.** *Engr.*, 99, 4. *Account*, l. cit. A bearded man of Herakles' type leads his horse r., club in l. arm. Counterpart of no. 264 in every respect, except that the lion's skin is absent. (Dioskuros?) New: all four borders including upper half of man's head and all that part which extends r. above the outline of the horse's neck. H. 0·59. L. 0·49. [*M*]

266 (286). **Child's sarcophagus of oval shape.** *Engr.*, 100, 1. Bacchic scene. Quite l. a pine. By it a Maenad in long ungirdled chiton, clashing large cymbals, and before her a nude boy (Eros?) with torch. Separated from this group by a second pine-tree comes Dionysos, nude but for cloak, which covers back, l. arm and part of legs. With r. hand he rests a long sceptre on the ground, while the l. hand, holding a cup carelessly, lies on the shoulder of a young Satyr, who serves to support the god, and whose eyes meet the god's. At the feet of the group lies a panther. Further r. a mystic cista stands on ground, out of which a snake is wriggling. A bearded Pan plants his r. goat's-foot on the lid of the cista, a skin (νεβρίς) on r. shoulder, swinging in r. hand a curved pedum and with the l. hand dragging along a refractory buck which lies on the ground. In background between the Satyr and the Pan

appears a Maenad in long drapery, playing flute. Quite r. a pine
tree concludes scene. Rough work. [*M*]

267 (264. P). **Relief representing a Centaur.** *Engr.*,
100, 2. *Arch. Zeit.*, 1874, Pl. 6, and see fig. 4 below. A bearded
Centaur gallops r., swinging a branch with mighty effort over his

FIG. 4.

head, apparently meaning to hit a tiny panther which sits quietly in
the lower r. corner turning up its head to its assailant. It is strange
that l. upper corner of relief is left quite bare, while the Centaur's
tail, which might have so conveniently filled it up, is tucked between
hind legs. This feature in the composition is of a piece with the
clumsiness in the connection of the equine and human halves of
the semibrute. A strange protuberance as well as a piece of mane
at the withers emphasises the contrast between the two natures more
than it conceals or at all facilitates their union. Human torso much
too short. Face, seen quite full, surrounded by dishevelled hair
and beard, presents characteristic but ignoble features. Eyelids
sharply expressed. Legs clumsily designed. In fine the whole
figure is angular and unwieldy. Although, however, the impression
produced by the whole work is of so little interest, still it has not the
roughness and carelessness of late Roman work turned off wholesale,
but rather of an art not yet fully developed. This incapacity may be
partly due to the general standard of art at the time when the relief
was produced, partly to the feeble powers of the individual author.

It is probably, as Matz recognised, the production of an Attic workman of the fifth century B.C. We find kindred traits of defective capacity on several of the less successful metopes of the Parthenon, though by no means to such a conspicuous extent as in this case. Very low relief (0·02), the flat treatment answering to the Attic style. The marble again is Pentelic. H. 0·41. L. 0·35. [*C.M]

268 (324). **Fight with lions.** *Engr.,* 100, 3. A youthful man in tunic and short cloak, holding a short hunting knife in his r. hand, lies on the ground by his dead, prostrate horse. He looks anxiously at a large lion, which, though mortally wounded by a spear in the breast, springs upon him and has already laid his forepaws on his shoulder. A second lion lies dying in the background. New: upper third of relief including shaft of spear, and almost the whole head and tail of attacking lion, also l. border. L. about 1·00. [M]

269 (278. S). **Mask of a Sea God.** *Engr.,* 101, 1. Above a rich festoon of fruit, the head of a sea god appears in front, with flowing hair and beard (new: nose). A wreath of large leaves of an aquatic plant adorns the head; ornamental leaves sprout from cheeks and chin and cover them in phantastic fashion. Cf. the following numbers. Judging from the engravings, one may suppose these reliefs to be ends of sarcophagi, like nos. 275 or 278. According to Waagen "the admirable decorative workmanship may belong to the time of Trajan;" Matz seems to have doubted its antique origin. [MW]

269 a (279). "This, a companion to the above, is much in the same style; but being without a beard, it is conjectured to be a female figure." *Account.*

270 (265. S). **Female mask.** *Engr.,* 101, 2. Similar relief. Head surrounded by long hair has a tragic expression, but no *onkos.* Perhaps a female marine deity; according to Matz a Medusa, cf. no. 220. [M]

271, 272 (272, 273. P, portico). **Two Dioskuri.** *Engr.,* 102. The two youths stand opposite to each other in similar attitude, only reversed, by their horses; small cloak over one shoulder; hat and spear new. Of the first relief indeed only body of horse including half hind legs, and body of Dioskuros from neck to knees, are antique; of the second only body of Dioskuros from neck to above feet and the whole of the arms, except l. shoulder, also body of horse and neck up to bridle. Workmanship good. Bought from the Villa

Altieri, where they were much noticed for their size and sculpture.
[* IV]

273 (345. T, portico). **Fragment of an oval child's sarcophagus.** *Engr.*, 103, 1. A few vertical flutings of the front
remain. On the rounded l. end a tolerably quiet lion, facing r.,
decorated with a broad ribbon round neck, stands over a roe
thrown on the ground. H. 0·39. [*M]

274 (543. S). **Fragment of an oval sarcophagus.** *Engr.*,
103, 2. A powerful lion springs forward l. and mangles a horse
overthrown on the ground. Horse wears round barrel a band enriched with ornament (of precious stones?) and a smaller collar band
round neck with a half-moon depending, which serves for an amulet
(σελήνια μηνίσκων εἰς ἀποτροπιασμόν, cf. O. Jahn, *Berichte der sächs.
Gesellsch. d. Wiss.*, 1855, pp. 42 f.). In background there looks on in
terror a youth with long curly tresses, in cloak, raising r. hand briskly,
in l. hunting spear with barbed point (*sparus*). Found in neighbourhood of Smyrna. From the Bessborough collection. H. 0·75.
[*M]

275 (277). **Front of a sarcophagus.** *Engr.*, 104, 1. *Account*, Plate to p. 89. Three charmingly drawn boys, the middle one
lifting a sheep by the tail, carry two especially rich festoons of
fruit (cf. nos. 269, 270). In l. field above festoon the inebriated
Herakles, head encircled by fillet, is led forward l., supported r. by a
wreathed youth (Satyr?) who has in r. hand a lowered burning torch,
l. by a Pan between whose feet a wreath lies on the ground. On l.
an olive tree, r. bearded terminal figure of a Priapos-Lordon. In
r. field a sleeping nymph lies in a rocky cave with upper part of
body nude (about it a small girdle passes); near her a Cupid, apparently asleep, stands leaning against the rock in pleasing pose.
The bearded Pan approaches from r. in wanton mood, advancing
his hand towards the sleeping nymph's drapery. New: merely a
small piece of upper border. Good sculpture. L. about 1·20. This
I suppose to be the relief which E. Q. Visconti mentions *à propos* of
the nymph's girdle, *Mus. Pio-Clem.* III., p. 47 Mil., as to be found
*ora in Inghilterra nella scelta collezione del signor cavaliere Blundell,
già presso gli scultori Lisandroni e d'Este.* [M]

276 (260?). **Two reliefs,** apparently **ends of a sarcophagus.** *Engr.*, 104, 2. 3. *Account*, l. cit. On each slab a griffin
standing with one fore-claw lifted on to a ram's head which lies on
ground; one looking r., the other l. (cf. Stephani, *Compte-rendu*, 1864,
p. 139).

277 (280). **Roman sacrifice of a bull.** *Engr.*, 105. The movement of the sacrificial procession is from l. to r. Quite r. stands the acolyte (*camillus*) in long tunic with casket of incense (*acerra turis plena*) in his hands. Next, a beardless sacrificer in tunic and toga, *velato capite*, with sacrificial bowl (*patera*) in lowered r. hand. On altar ornamented with a garland and narrow-necked jug (*guttus*) in relief burns the fire. On l. side of altar stands a sacrificial slaughterer (*popa*), bearded and wreathed, skirt girt up about loins, with high boots, shouldering on l. arm the axe with long handle, with r. hand he grasps a corner of the woollen fillet (*vitta*, *infula*), which adorns the large bull. Behind bull two more attendants garlanded and high-girt (*succincti*), the foremost of whom holds the bull by one horn. Behind them a second popa, accoutred like the first, carrying axe over l. shoulder. The scene is closed at l. end by a group of three youths in tunic and toga, of whom two at least carry a branch in their hands.

278 (284. T). **Front of a child's sarcophagus.** *Engr.*, 106. An eagle in the middle and a boy at each end support a rather tightly stretched festoon, above which in each field two Bacchic masks set opposite each other. A youthful ivy-crowned mask of ideal features is placed l. in each field. Opposite to it in l. compartment a bearded Satyr's head with dishevelled hair and large brutish ears, in r. a bearded long-eared Pan's head with very long horns. Work flat and rough. Cf. nos. 269, 270. [*M*]

279 (285). **Fragment of the front of a sarcophagus, right end.** *Engr.*, 107, 1. Achilleus in full armour, shield on l. arm, spear in r. hand, drives r. on a biga, looking round. New: greater part of cloak, r. foot and end of chariot; Hektor's corpse was undoubtedly once fastened thereto. Beneath chariot lies a youthful male deity (so says Matz), torso exposed, with long curled hair, raising r. hand in mourning (Skamandros or some other local god). The horses are led by Victory, winged, in Doric chiton, which lets l. leg become nude when advanced; in lowered l. hand she holds whip. For composition compare strip X of the Capitoline Tabula Iliaca (O. Jahn, *Griech. Bilderchroniken*, Taf. A*) and the corresponding piece of the Capitoline Achilleus relief, where also the Victoria appears (*Mus. Capitol.*, iv. 37, Overbeck, *Gallerie heroischer Bildw.*, Pl. 19, 5). [*M*]

280 (333). **Amazonomachia.** *Engr.*, 107, 2. From the r. a youthful warrior with long hair, a so-called Corinthian helmet on head, on r. arm a large round shield (device : a winged Medusa's head),

gallops at an Amazon sinking to the ground, who advances her
target (*pelta*) against him. R. breast not covered by chiton; on head
a Phrygian cap. R. forearm broken away. Above her appears on
horseback a female comrade in chiton and cap who, with a view to
protect her, brandishes her axe (*bipennis*) against her assailant. Quite
l., below, the remains of a horse's leg. This apparently fine relief is
broken on all sides.

281 (318. P). **Fragment of the front of a sarcophagus.**
Engr., 107, 3. Fragment of a representation of the rape of Persephonè. Antique: chariot, lower part of Pluto's body, and Persephonè
whom he holds in his arms, Athena with aegis, shield and helmet
(new: face and r. forearm), Artemis, who flees l. (new: head, l. hand,
r. arm and r. leg). Between Artemis and Athena an altar is partly
visible, an indication of the sanctity of the place where the rape took
place. Cf. Förster, *Der Raub der Persephone*, Stuttg., 1874, pp. 140.
154. [*M*]

282 (287. P). **Nymphs imploring** ("Prometheus"). *Engr.*,
108. *Account*, Frontispiece. *Arch. Zeit.*, 1858, Pl. 114. 4. Three women
standing and two kneeling, all with bodies nude and legs covered
with cloak are turned l. The last at r. end stands upright and bends
up r. hand towards shoulder, while with l. she holds cloak on hip.
Before her a dolphin plunging into the waves to be seen on both
sides of him. Behind dolphin stands a second nymph, bending forward and stretching out r. arm in entreaty. By her in the foreground
kneels the third nymph stretching forward both hands (new: l. arm
from middle of upper arm). The fourth stands in the background, in
similar attitude to the second. A fifth nymph kneels, like the third,
in the foreground; of her, head, torso and most of l. leg antique, the
rest including whole l. arm new. Besides this, upper border of relief
is restored from l. end as far as over head of second nymph, as well
as the whole figures of Hephaestos sitting, and of Prometheus lying
chained to the rock, together with the eagle above the latter, by
which the relief has been turned into an illustration of a scene in
Aeschylos' *Prometheus* (cf. Welcker, *Alte Denkmäler*, III. 197, Jahn,
Arch. Zeit., 1858, p. 186). The real state of the case, after Jahn had
extended his doubts to the genuineness of the entire relief, has been
stated by Conze, who also took the two figures on the r. to be
modern, and more accurately by Matz (*Arch. Zeit.*, 1873, p. 32).
The antique part, in Italian, slightly-veined marble, displays good
Roman work. From the Villa Altieri. L. 1.42. H. about 0.69.
[*CMW*]

283 (292). **Sepulchral relief.** *Engr.*, 109, 1. A garland hung on two bucrania; below two dolphins with tails twisted together. All round a kymation.

284 (291). **Companion piece to the above.** *Engr.*, 109, 2. Similar design; under garland sacrificial implements, ladle (*simpulum*), bowl (*patera*) and jar (*guttus*).

285 (312). **Akroterion.** *Engr.*, 111, 1. Composed of akanthos and helix. Lower border cut away to fit the ridge of a pediment.

286 (327). **Akroterion.** *Engr.*, 111, 2. Broader than no. 285. Straight low border.

287 (328. T). **Herdsman and herd.** *Engr.*, 112, 1. Between two trees a herdsman in exomis, with boots and mallet at side, stands facing r. leaning on staff, and looks at his herd. Below, a bull, above it a sheep lying down, quite at the top a sheep leaping up which is browsing on the foliage of the middle tree, there being a third tree quite r. Flat and bad. [*M*]

288 (313. P, on external frieze). **Bacchic scene.** *Engr.*, 112, 2. Quite r. a Maenad with head thrown back dancing with ecstatic movement, back and l. leg mostly bare (face and arms missing). Further l. follows a youthful Satyr, *en face*, dancing with crossed legs, a pedum on l. arm, holding in r. hand a syrinx before his breast. Then a Maenad in cloak, which leaves upper part of body partly nude, playing on a kithara. Quite l. the bearded Seilenos, tipsy, legs covered by a cloak, kept from falling by a young attendant, while he stoops after an object like a small plank. Very much mutilated but apparently free from restorations. The style seems to indicate the so-called neo-Attic art. L. about 0·50. [*]

289 (322. P). **Hygieia.** *Engr.*, 113, 1. Facing l. stands the goddess with long curls hanging down, in ungirdled chiton, encircled by a large snake. She holds in l. hand a shell-shaped cup. Antique: only the oblong piece of which the upper margin passes through the goddess' eye, the lower through the middle of her thigh, the l. is cut off just before the shell, on the r. side the genuine piece comes to the end of the relief. In lower l. corner the greater part of body and head of a cock, which looks up near the snake, is antique. Rocks and tree all modern. [*CM*]

290 (314. T). **Orpheus amongst Satyrs.** *Engr.*, 113, 2 (inaccurate). *Arch. Zeit.*, 1877, Pl. 12, 2 (Michaelis). Before a gnarled tree quite at l. border sits facing l. on a block of rock a beardless youth (Orpheus) with short hair, playing on the lyre; a

cloak covers his legs. Close before him and facing him in middle
of relief stands a group of three boys half grown up, of whom at
least the hindermost is plainly to be recognised as a Satyr by a small
tail. All three quite nude and in pretty quiet attitude. The foremost
is speaking to the musician and gesticulating with r. hand. The
middle one with snub nose, curly hair, and open mouth is only indicated in the background in quite low relief. Further r. a second
tree follows, before which a little boy sits on a block of rock. His
whole attitude strongly recalls the Capitoline *Boy looking for a
thorn*: probably this lad also is conceived as in the same occupation.
Near him, half hidden by tree, a larger boy with upper part of body
visible; he looks curiously at the principal part of the scene and
stretches out his opened l. hand above the sitting lad. From the r.
advancing a larger youth, presumably a Satyr, r. arm raised in wonder, in l. a pedum; a cloak flutters back from l. arm. Behind him
rocks conclude the scene. Above the group of three Satyr boys
the upper parts of two figures are visible on raised edge of rock
which starts abruptly from the field of the relief. They are only
a little covered by cloak, arms laid round one another's backs. The
figure on r., which rests l. hand on rock, seems to be male, that on
l. is female. She advances her r. hand and seems to have held
with it a staff or something of the kind to which a large round flat
disk was attached (tympanon? mirror?); of the presumed staff there
is a trace recognisable on the disk itself, another between it and
the woman's hand. Quite l. above the stem of the tree a male
figure, likewise half-draped, looks with curiosity over a piece of rock
at the scene below. There is a trace still extant of a similar ledge
of rock also on the r. over the youth with the pedum. Upper r.
corner missing. The whole relief, in part quite low, is in part raised
more than 0·01, indeed in a few places the figures are quite detached
from the field. It is extremely damaged by water and moreover
broken in several places. New: only part between tree on l. and
the player on the lyre. The kind of representation of landscape is
as remarkable as the rest of the conception. It is as unusual to
find Orpheus among Satyrs, as it is common to see him taming
wild beasts by his musical art. Prof. Wilamowitz however calls my
attention to the *liber monstrorum* 1, 6 (Haupt *Opuscula* II. p. 224):
Fauni enim silvicolae...quos poeta Lucanus (no doubt, in his lost
poem on Orpheus) *secundum opinionem Graecorum ad Orphei lyram
cum innumerosis ferarum generibus cantu deductos cecinit;* comp.
Horace, *De art. poet.*, 391. Besides, a Satyr listening to Orpheus

appears on a Greek vase (*Arch. Zeit.*, 1868, Pl. 3); less certain is
the name of Orpheus given to the musician of another Bacchic vase
(*Annali* 1845, Pl. M); cf. Knapp *Württemberg. Correspondenz-Blatt*,
1880. H. 0·32. L. 0·47. [*.*M*]

291. Fragment of a votive relief. *Engr.*, 114, 1. L. a
stout pine tree entwined by a snake. Two woollen fillets (*infulae*)
pass through the foliage and from one bough hangs a pair of
cymbals. Before it an altar adorned with garlands which depend
from a bucranium. By the altar stands a nude youth with long hair,
of Apolline type, emptying a cornucopiae on altar, advancing l. arm
behind which a cloak is visible. On l. and r. it is imperfect. On
upper border remains of an inscription of two lines . . .*m. antiquii*...
(?) | ...*is praest*...; on lower border the legend *de sua pecun(ia)*.

292 (84). Votive relief to Silvanus. *Engr.*, 114, 2. In an
aedicula formed by two Corinthian columns and a pediment, which
contains a crown as decoration, stands Silvanus in his usual style of
representation (cf. Reifferscheid, *Annali dell' Inst.* 1866, pp. 210 ff.).
He is bearded, bears fruits in skirt of cloak and in l. arm branches of
a pine tree. in r. the curved garden knife, with high boots on feet.
By him sits his dog. Below, the inscription *Sil(vano) sal(utari)
Celi Cortos* (?) *et Herm(es)*. Cf. *C. I. L.*, vi. 1, 3715. where
under no. 593 is a copy of the same inscription communicated to
E. Q. Visconti by d'Este and Lisandroni, which gives *sac(rum)* instead of *sal.* and *Hermes* instead of *Herm.*

293 (316). Ploughman. *Engr.*, 114, 3. A man in ungirdled
tunic, with a pileus on head, guides with l. hand a plough of the
primitive pattern, which survives even to this day in Italy, drawn by
two oxen, and pricks the ox with a short goad (*stimulus*). Small relief
with plain border. Cf. Jahn, *Arch. Zeit.*, 1861, p. 146.

294 (316). Roman architectural design. *Engr.*, 114, 4.
A low basement story decorated with six Tuscan half-columns, the
spaces between which are alternately occupied by an arch resting on
two pillars (three times) and a quadrangular ornament (twice). In the
upper story, which is higher, two large, similar half-columns support
the cornice; between them two arches resting on pillars and,
inside these, small façades of temples, the one having four columns
with an arch over door, the other having two columns. The relief
seems to be imperfect.

295 (320. P). Relief in imitation of the Egyptian style.
Engr., 115. An Egyptian with long hair, drapery reaching down to
knees, offers with both hands a large bowl or basket to an owl which

sits solemnly on a high pedestal. Antique: only man's body from
neck to knees, arms and vessel. Apparently a work of the time of
Hadrian. [* *H'*]

296 (323. T). **Cupids gathering quinces.** *Engr.*, 116. *Mon.
Matth.*, III. 18. Two Cupids busy knocking the fruit with long sticks
off a quince tree on which a bird sits. Very rich border of leaf
sprays, which belonged to the relief originally, as it is all of one
piece. Restorations very trifling. There seems to be no doubt
about the antiquity of the work. Very high relief. The relief was
fixed in an alcove in the garden of the Villa Mattei. H. 1·53.
L. 0·89. [*]

297 (325). **A wild boar.** *Engr.*, 117. The powerful brute
runs l. The field contains indications of rushes (antique?). From
the Villa Borioni.

298 (326. T). **A vintner's sign or sepulchral relief.** *Engr.*,
118 (inaccurate). *Arch. Zeit.*, 1877, Pl. 13 (from a new drawing),
with letterpress by H. Blümner. An older drawing is in the collection of A. W. Franks, Esq. (see London). On the l., on a rock above
which appears a vine, stands a woman fully draped, lifting a corner
of her cloak with l. hand and shaking hands with a bearded man
in ungirdled tunic with a small cloak over l. arm; in l. hand there
seems to be a roll. At woman's feet a vat lowered into the ground
and covered with a flat wooden lid. The comparatively large proportions point out this pair as the principal persons, the owners of the
wine-shop to which the relief may have served as a sign (for similar
signs cf. Jahn, *Berichte d. sächs. Ges. d. Wiss.*, 1861, pp. 353 ff.,
Jordan, *Arch. Zeit.*, 1871, pp. 65 ff.); unless it were supposed rather
to be a sepulchral relief, as is Blümner's opinion. Further r. leafy
shoots of several vines overrun the field, between which are six
vats with upper rim projecting, two sets of three one above the
other apparently, five of them shut by wooden lids. Above
goes a slave in short tunic, carrying on l. shoulder an amphora cased
in wickerwork, which he seems to have emptied into the topmost l.
vat. To the middle vat of l. row a slave brings a similar wicker-
covered amphora, into which another slave kneeling on edge of vat
seems to be pouring must from the open vat by means of a flagon
(rubbed away); this is however not quite clear. Behind lowest vat
of r. row stands a man in ungirdled drapery, holding in l. hand a long
staff furnished with a knob at the top, probably a ladle with a long
handle. Before him stands on the far side of the tree an apparently bald-headed figure in ungirdled tunic, the l. hand lowered,

r. raised thoughtfully to chin. Quite r. below are to be seen two
more vats, the lower apparently open, the upper closed with a
wooden cover. By it there stands at the very edge of the relief a
comparatively large youth in ungirdled tunic, bending up r. hand towards shoulder, in l. hand a roll. According to Blümner's plausible
conjecture the larger proportions of the figure indicate the son of the
married couple represented at other end, not a person employed in
the scene represented. Above his head the upper corner of the relief
is occupied by a strongly projecting tiled roof, under cover of which a
man in short tunic sits leaning very far back holding an open book
on his lap. With l. hand he turns leaves of book, the r. rests on a
low counter of usual shape, on which some indistinct objects are
visible. Between lower end of counter and the two vats stands a
little figure in ungirdled tunic holding in l. arm an opened book, with
r. hand laid on an oval plate, which stands on counter, with two round
flat objects on it. At upper end of counter stands a similar figure
unrolling a roll (*volumen*) in conversation with the sitting figure. The
whole scene seems not so much concerned with traffic as with the
reckoning up of the yield of the vintage. On the upper border two
square tablets are to be seen, perhaps sign-boards; next the roof one
with a snake rearing itself (as *genius loci*?) and above it eight *puntelli*, next the middle of the scene one divided into four square
fields, each of which exhibits a very deep circular cavity surrounded
by a rim. Blümner conjectures that it is a window. I should rather
suppose a bird's-eye view of vats, as on the sepulchral relief of M.
Vergilius Eurysaces before the Porta Maggiore at Rome. At the bottom a strip about 0·14 high is left bare, very likely for the inscription;
a narrower border goes round the top and r. side, on l. side it is wanting, instead of it appears a tolerably smooth join. As the vine moreover appears l. of the married couple as well as r., Blümner's conjecture, that this couple originally occupied the middle and then a
similar scene to that on the r. followed on the l., and lastly quite on
l. border a second child of the couple may have concluded the scene,
is more than probable. Work rather coarse and not very distinct.
H. 0·60 (field of relief by itself 0·42). L. 0·93 (field of relief
0·87). [*M*]

299 (329). **Leaf-work.** *Engr.*, 119, 1. Quadrangular slab,
presumably from a cinerarium. Two vine-shoots rise symmetrically
from broad akanthos leaves. In field four birds pecking, one with a
butterfly in beak.

300 (330). **Leaf-work.** *Engr.*, 119, 2. From a vase on which

is a lizard chasing a snail, spring up quite in ornamental style a
palmette and four vine-shoots. l., a butterfly, r. a grasshopper.

301 (334). **Corner of the lid of a sarcophagus.** *Engr.*, 120,
3. Medusa's head with wings on temples.

302 (402). **Cippus of Passienia Gemella.** *Engr.*, 121. *Mon.
Matth.*, iii. 67, 1. On FRONT within a border stands the inscription
*D(is) M(anibus) | Passieniae Gemellae coiugi et lib(ertae) | suae
carissimae | obsequentissimae et L. Passienio Doryphoro | filio et
Passienio | Sabino filio et lib(ertis) | sanctissimis.* Above, *L. Passienius
Saturninus fecit.* Above inscription between two pillars busts of
Passienia Gemella and both her sons, the one on her l. fully draped,
the one r. nude but for a cloak lying on shoulder. L. SIDE. In principal field the mother veiled embraces eldest son clad in short drapery
who stands on a somewhat higher step. Above, an eagle between
two pillars. R. SIDE. Similar scene in principal field. Mother not
veiled. Younger son on higher pedestal up to which a small flight of
steps leads. Above, eagle between two pillars. From the Borioni
collection.

303 (520. P, pediment of portico). **Front of a sarcophagus.**
Engr., 122. Fight with barbarians. At each corner a tropaeon with
a nude barbarian at its foot, sitting on the ground with hands bound
behind back. From l. to r. : a mailed horseman fully armed gallops
over a draped corpse lying on the ground at a nude foot-soldier with
helmet and sword turned in flight, who is threatened from the r.
with a sword-cut from a similar horseman. On the ground a barbarian, nude but for cloak, having been wounded in breast rolls over
his shield. Near by, on the back of his prostrate horse, lies another
barbarian, clad in tight trousers and cloak : over him a bearded foot-
soldier, with large shield ornamented with branches, raises his
short sword against the second horseman. Hard by, towards the
middle of the whole scene, a noble youth stands sinking backwards,
nude but for chlamys and shield on l. arm, with r. hand grasping
the spear which has pierced his breast. Further r. a fully-armed
horseman draws his sword against a foot-soldier in tunic, boots
and helmet and with a shield adorned with branches, who is pressing
on. On the ground lies a nude corpse on its back, the breast
transfixed by a spear, shield close by. Quite r. a fully-armed Roman
trumpeter is blowing the long tuba. Romans all beardless. A clear
and orderly composition. Restorations unimportant. H. 0·75.
L. 2·28. Bought at Lord Cawdor's sale. [*.*MW*]

304 (521. P). **Girl with garland.** *Engr.* 123. Fea, *Storia*

delle arti, III. Pl. 18, p. 495. A richly-draped girl in chiton and
cloak, her hair encircled with a fillet, moves r. in dancing step and
carries before her with both hands a garland, which hangs a good
way down. New: half r. forearm, an important piece of garland
and most of the feet. Behind her a flat architectural design of
pilasters. To r. a circular temple with roof running up to a point.
The Corinthian columns standing on a high stylobate have dolphins
on the capitals instead of volutes: of the intercolumnar spaces
one is filled up with trellis work, in the other is a door ornamented with a lion's head and bosses (now only one fold, modern
remainder as copied by Fea is now wanting). A flight of steps
leads up to door. Brilliant execution, especially in girl's figure,
which is accurately repeated in a celebrated Borghese relief in the
Louvre (S. Bartoli, *Admiranda*, Pl. 64 (75). Bouillon, *Mus. des
Antiques*, II., *rel.*, Pl. 4, 2. Clarac, II. 163, 258, the middle figure).
Bought from the Villa Negroni by Jenkins, sold by him to Lord
Cawdor, at whose sale it was purchased for 113 guineas. cf. Dallaway,
p. 388. [*W*]

305 (533. P). **Round ara.** *Engr.*, 124. *Gal. Giustin.*, II. 152?
An old drawing as early as in Cod. Coburg., no. 87. Movement
from l. to r. A small statue stands on a pillar, a nude figure with
lowered r. arm, supporting chin with l. hand (Eros?). From l. a youthful Satyr walks up to it, with waving nebris, thyrsos in l. hand, raising
r. hand and looking round after a Maenad with long drapery, dancing
ecstatically, who with head thrown back wields thyrsos in l. hand, tympanon in r. Between the two a panther following the Satyr. Pan
follows the Maenad, with flying nebris, holding syrinx to mouth. Behind him an ecstatic Maenad with cloak in waving folds, holding out
a wreath in r. hand. Fairly high relief (0·04) inclining to rectangular
treatment. Execution coarse, in part rough. Tolerably rubbed
and here and there retouched, especially round about the statue;
its motive however is certainly old. New: lowest part of plinth,
and kyma at the top. H. of old part 0·74, of field of relief 0·59.
From the Bessborough collection. [*C*]

306 (534. P). **Round Ara.** *Engr.*, 125. On a square basis
(without garland) rises a candelabrum or thymiaterion. Next on r.
stands *en face* Persephone, fully draped and with back of head veiled,
long torch in r. hand, and Pluto, whose cloak leaves upper part of
body free, long sceptre with pointed top in l. hand. Then comes
rocky ground on which the three-headed Kerberos sits, and by him
on a higher block of rock a bearded man, legs covered with cloak,

both hands in lap and with head facing the spectator (almost
the whole head new). It cannot well be Herakles, but only Aeakos,
the later gate-keeper of Hades and closest companion of Kerberos.
Behind him stands Hermes, the conductor of souls and messenger
of the under world, with modern wings on feet, chlamys, hat (wings
modern) and winged caduceus on l. arm, r. arm extended towards Aeakos. Low, coarse relief without restorations, but completely worked over and seriously disfigured. The parts of the
ara above and below relief mostly new. H. of antique part 0·72,
of field of relief 0·65, of relief from field 0·02. From the Bessborough
collection. A similar ara from the Giustiniani Palace (*Gal. Giustin.*
II. 126, 3) is now in the Rondanini Palace in the Corso in Rome, two
others with kindred subjects in the Vatican (*Mus. Pio-Clem.*, IV. 35,
36); cf. Petersen, *Bullett. dell' Inst.*, 1861, p. 83. [*CIV*]

307 (539. P). **Lid of a sarcophagus.** *Engr.* 126. FRONT.
Return from hunting; movement from l. to r. Furthest r. a bearded
and a youthful hunter, both in exomis and with boots, the first with
a stout stick forked at the top, carry on their shoulders a long pole to
which the body of a large bear is tied with straps. Between them a
large hound. There follows a group quite similar, only an ibex is
carried instead of a bear; also the younger bearer has a stick. Then
comes a bearded man with tunic, cloak and boots, two hunting
spears in l. hand, leading with r. a mule, on whose saddle lie two
hares. The fourth group consists of a bearded man in tunic and a
youth in exomis, both barefooted and with a stick forked at the top
in l. hand, carrying on shoulders, apparently on boughs with many
branches, a large heavily filled net, at the contents of which a dog which
is between them sniffs. The procession closes with a two-wheeled cart
(*plaustrum*) laden with a boar, two bears, an ibex, nets and branches,
drawn by two oxen, which bend their necks beneath the heavy yoke.
A bearded man in boots, exomis, and cloak, walks quickly before it,
driving on the beasts with a stout staff. Behind the beasts is visible
the upper part of a figure hurrying l. in tunic and small flying cloak,
r. hand lying on head to denote terror, l. advanced. Quite l. a stout
pillar with an arch over it, under which the cart is passing. At r. end
there never was a corresponding structure. At corners tragic masks,
to which on the opposite ends of the side gables akroteria with
single palmette ornaments correspond. L. SIDE: a youthful hunter
in exomis thrusts with a long pole at the snout of a large boar lying
on the ground, presumably to rouse it up. On the l. lies an ibex.
In background two trees. R. SIDE: between two trees a bearded

man wearing the exomis sits on a block of rock holding a staff. On the ground lie apparently asleep, on l. a stag with magnificent horns, on r. a panther. Pretty, animated composition, well executed. H. 0·21. L. 2·16. From the Bessborough collection. "At Roehampton is said to remain the sarcophagus from which it was taken with an inscription: *D. M.* | *C. Tutilio Rufino* | *venatore* (sic) | *T. Claudius Secundo* (? presumably *Secundio* or *Secundus*) | *amico b(ene)* *m(erenti) p(osuit).*" [*MH]

308 (319. P). **Satyr.** *Engr.*, 128, 1. A nude youthful Satyr, pedum in r. arm, holding in advanced l. hand the thyrsos, with taenia hanging from it, steps r. New: r. foot, lower part of l. leg, and l. hand. Beautiful and animated in forms of body. Large relief (measurements could not be taken). Greek work. Greek marble. [*C]

309 (321. P). **Satyr.** *Engr.*, 128, 2. Beardless Satyr, skin hanging down over back, pedum on l. arm, steals off l. half stooping, a deep cup in advanced r. hand full of honeycomb. Beside him an altar. Above, garlands hanging from bucrania, which are fastened to pillars. New: terminal bust of Pan to l., and in general the l. half from a line which runs through cup, altar, lower part of Satyr's r. leg in a slanting direction. Not originally a companion piece to no. 308, but equally large relief, considerably higher. Very good art. [*C]

310 (519. P). **Three youths.** *Engr.*, 129, *Arch. Zeit.*, 1877, Pl. 12, 1 (Eug. Petersen). In the middle on a block of rock sits a youth facing l., with a cloak spread under him, l. hand laid on a staff, r. arm laid on l. hand, and holding in advanced hand an unrecognisable object, most like a sword-hilt (new: head, l. forearm, upper part of staff and r. wrist). Before him l. stands a second youth, whose chlamys appears behind his back and on l. arm; on neck remains of a petasos; he is prepared to depart, but still leans on a staff fixed under l. shoulder; his only antique parts are the legs (about half r. foot and l. knee new), with part of torso to a line which goes up in a slanting direction from r. hip to just below l. shoulder, a piece of petasos, upper part of l. arm and fingers of l. hand. Behind the sitting youth, in similar attitude to that just described, a third youth whose chlamys hangs down from both shoulders and covers body equally before and behind, leaving both arms free. With r. hand (partly new) he holds up a long stick resting on the ground, l. arms lowered. New: head and l. shoulder, l. forearm with hat or bag and part of l. leg. L. hand seems originally to have held a similar object.

The head was originally turned outwards, obviously towards a fourth figure, of which a staff held slantwise near legs of third youth is still visible. Thus the relief is a fragment of a larger composition, which apparently represented travellers. Petersen conjectures that we have spectators of a scene which originally passed further l., and compares the design on a vase at Munich, *Arch. Zeit.*, 1860, Pl. 139. Pentelic marble. The fine Greek style, the tolerably round relief and the scene itself remind one strongly of a relief in the Villa Albani (Zoega, *Bassiril.*, II. 103), which Petersen has explained as the expedition of Theseus to Hades (*Arch. Zeit.*, 1866, p. 258, cf. 1877, p. 122). From the Cawdor collection. According to the *Account* the quarter whence the relief is derived is not known; according to the *Engravings* it came from Greece. [*M*]

The following plates of the *Engravings*, 130—143, possess neither accompanying text nor lettering on the Plates, nor indication of the corresponding numbers of the *Account*. In the copy in the Göttingen library, presented by Blundell's heir, and again in the copy at Ince Blundell Hall, one single plate is marked in writing, Pl. 140 and 141. These plates contain almost exclusively **cinerary urns**, mostly derived from the Villa Mattei; such cinerary urns are meant where nothing else is stated with respect to the following numbers, 311—372. As to the inscriptions, which I have not been able to compare, I am not in a position to guarantee either their reading in details, or their genuineness; certainly there are many spurious legends amongst them.

311 (368). *Engr.* 130, 1. Two boys holding a garland of fruit; three birds. On field for inscription: *T. Cam deni Eu tuchi.* (Genuine?) Cf. *Mon. Matth.*, III. p. 164, no. 15.

312 (358). *Engr.*, 130, 2. *Mon. Matth.*, III. 71, 2 (different lid). Two spiral-shaped fluted columns, from which a garland hangs down with an eagle. Below, two birds. Inscription: *C. Iulius | Hirmaiscus* (i.e. *Hermaiscus*) | *vIxit ann. XXI.*

313 (344). **Double cinerarium.** *Engr.*, 130, 3. *Mon. Matth.*, III. 65, 4 (different lid). Two bearded masks with ram's horns like an Ammon; below two eagles and between them a garland. Inscription I: *Lepidia M(arci) ɔ* (i.e. *mulieris) l(iberta)* | *PrI-vata.* | *vIxit ann. XV.* Inscription II: *M. Lepidius | Epigonus.*

314 (361). *Engr.*, 130, 4. *Mon. Matth.*, III. 69, 5 (different lid). Rich mouldings and frame to the field for the inscription: *Ellio Rufo | S. l. Habra fecit | et sibi et suis | Sempronia | P. l. Auge |*

Sempronius | Ol. Urbanus (spurious, still absent in the *Mon. Matth.*).

315 (351). *Engr.* 131, 1. 2. Two rams' heads support a garland, over it a butterfly, below, two birds. On side a palmette. Inscription: *D.M. | Have Euphrosyne | et vale. | Aemilia Cantria | filiae dulcissimae | posuit infelix.* The whole field for the inscription and rest of upper part of cinerarium is new. [*C*]

316 (394). **Double cinerarium.** *Engr.*, 131, 3. 4. On front three pilasters, on rounded lid an eagle, on side two arcades between pilasters. Inscription: *T. Peducaeus T. f. Quir(ina) Florus v(ixit) a(nn.) XXI.*; in field on l.: *T. Peducaeus | T. l(ibertus) Faustus | Peducaea T. l(ib.) | Daphne uxor;* in field on r.: *T. Peducaeo | T. f. Quir. | Severo filio | vix. an. VIII.*

317 (352). *Engr.*, 132, 1—3. Pilasters at the corners; between them on front a door with inscription above, and on each side of it a cypress (ears of wheat according to *Mon. Matth.*); on the sides, l. a jar (*guttus*), r. a cup (*patera*). In field of pediment two females *formosae superne, desinentes in piscem* hold a wreath. Round bolsters serve as akroteria, those on l. and r. furnished with a Medusa's head, that on the top with a flower, with a dolphin on each side. Inscription: *D(is) M(anibus) S(acrum) | Q. Curiati | Zosimi.* Cf. *Mon. Matth.*, III. p. 164, no. 11.

318 (393). *Engr.*, 132, 4—6, the front repeated 139, 4. At corners of front, spiral Corinthian columns, from the capitals whereof a garland of fruit hangs down, partly covering a door, the panels of which are adorned with Medusa heads to ward off harm. On each side of door a griffin. On each of the sides between a pilaster and the corner column an eagle setting both feet on a snake, in the background a tree. On the lid two masks at the corners, in the field of the pediment between them a wreath. Inscription over the door: *DIs Manibus Sacrum | M. Burrio Felici tairon* (i. e. *patrono*) *| bene merenti fecit | M. Burrius Hermes | M. Burrius Curius | et Burria inbamini* (perhaps *Filumene* or *Diadumene*) *| M. Burrius Vannius | M. Burrius Atticus | M. Burrius Abascanus* (i.e. *Abascantus*).

319 (396). *Engr.*, 133, 1. *Mon. Matth.*, III. 73, 2. Without special ornaments. Inscription: *D. M. | Liviae P. f. | P. Livius Fortunatus | libertae.* (Spurious.)

320 (385). *Engr.*, 133, 2. *Mon. Matth.*, III. 68, 3 (somewhat deviating in lid and ornamentation). Inscription: *Q. Laelius | Primigenius | vix. annis XX.* Is the inscription copied from the specimen in *Mon. Matth.?*

321 (353). *Engr.*, 133, 3. *Mon. Matth.*, III. 68, 5 (different lid). On either side four flutings, in the middle the inscription : *D. M. Numisiae | Primigeni ae.*

322 (392). *Engr.* 133, 4—6. *Mon. Matth.*, III. 61, 5 (different lid). Surrounded by insignificant ornaments, the inscription: *D. M. | T. Publiliu(s) Severianu(s) | fecit | Publilio Severiano | patri b(ene) m(erenti)*. On ends jar and cup.

323 (371). *Engr.* 134, 1. *Mon. Matth.*, III. 73, 5 (different lid). Two bearded heads with ram's horns like an Ammon support a garland, in the curve of which a swan walks. Below, two eagles at the corners, between them two birds pecking at a lizard. On the lid a laden basket and two birds. The field for the inscription contains in the *Mon. Matth.* only the letters *D. M.*, to which has been subsequently added *T. Flavi Aug. lib. | Zmaragdi*, borrowed from *Mon. Matth.*, III. 73, 6.

324 (373). *Engr.*, 134, 2. *Mon. Matth.*, III. 71, 4. Bucrania supporting a garland. Below at the corners, swans. Inscription : *DIs manibus | Cn. Pompei | Cn. f. Iusti | v(ix). a(nn.) XVI m(ens). VIIII.* On the lid a vase with fruits (?); on either side a panther (?).

325 (381). *Engr.*, 134, 3. *Mon. Matth.*, III. 68, 6 (different lid). From a vase, on the rim of which two birds sit, spring two sprays of ivy (*area hederacia*, Orelli-Henzen, 7359) surrounding the inscription: *DIs Manib(us) | T. Flavi Sp. f. | Eutyche | vIx. ann. V m(ens.) | d(ieb.) XXIX. fec(it) | Flavia Peloris mater*.

326 (356). *Engr.*, 134, 4. Folding doors with two rings, with a tree at each side, from which a garland hangs slantwise before the door. Above door a basket with fruits (a butterfly according to the *Account*) at which two birds peck. At the corners Corinthian spiral columns. On the lid a wreath.

327 (357). *Engr.*, 135, 1. From two bucrania a spray of ivy hangs down at which two birds peck. Above the inscription: *D. M. | Cornelia L. lib. | Staphyle | ben.* (spurious or incomplete). On the lid a double pediment with two birds in each.

328 (398). *Engr.*, 135, 2. *Mon. Matth.*, III. 69, 1 (without inscription and with different lid). Two eagles hold a garland of fruit. Spurious inscription: *Dis Manibus | Fulvano Arch.;* apparently copied from the cista, in other respects different, *Mon. Matth.*, III. 65, 1.

329 (383). *Engr.*, 135, 3. Pilasters with architrave and pediment-shaped lid. In the middle inscribed on tablet: *Q. Mllusius*

M. f. Arn. | Bassus miles | coh. VII pr(aetoriae) ꝑ (i.e. centuria) | C. Petili Bassi. | vix. ann. XXXV.

330 (370). *Engr.*, 135. 4. *Mon. Matth.*, III. 69. 2 (different lid). Two swans supporting a heavy garland sitting on two spiral-shaped fluted pedestals of stout proportions; above the garland two birds, below the same. On lower rim of lid the inscription *D. M.*, on the tablet *L. Cornelio Iasoni | et Laeliae Chariti | paren-tib(us) suis | b(ene) m(erentibus) fecit | L. Cornelius Clemens.*

331 (359). *Engr.*, 136. 1. *Mon. Matth.*, III. 60. 2 (different lid). Between two upright torches stands a bed on which a woman (face destroyed) lies in stola and palla, a fillet in l. hand, with r. hand letting a cloth fly loose. Below the inscription: *P. Etrilius Abascantus | Etriliae Danae uxori | karissimae.* H. 0·24. L. 0·35. [*M*]

332 (369). *Engr.*, 136. 2. *Mon. Matth.*, III. 58. 4 (different lid). At the corners two dolphins diving down, snapping after two little fishes. A heavy garland hangs down from their twisted tails; on it stands a bird. Above it, inscribed on tablet: *DIs Man. | Flaviae-Nysae | Astactus* (probably *Astictus*) *Aug. lib. | a cognitionibus | li-bertae bene de se meritae.*

333 (364). *Engr.*, 136. 3. Between two singularly bare sprays stands a candelabrum with a griffin sitting on each side. Above, the tablet with the surely spurious inscription: *D. M. | Rutilia | Ro-mana | animae | bene merenti.* The lid, which is not its own, dis-plays in the pediment a lion tearing its prey, and on either side a tragic mask. The whole urn conveys a suspicious impression.

334 (366). *Engr.*, 136. 4. *Mon. Matth.*, III. 65. 6 (without inscription, with different lid). At each of the corners a spiral column. The inscription on tablet encircled by a garland: *D. M. | Iuliae Merve | coniugi | karissimae | q(uae) v(ix). an. XXV m(ens). II d(iel). XI | Rufinus L. f. | fecit b(ene) m(erenti).* (Spurious.) On lid an owl, on either side a palmette.

335 (360). *Engr.*, 137. 1—3. FRONT: two Cupids grasping each other's hands for the purpose of wrestling; between them, on the ground, a palm branch. On l. a third Cupid stands looking at them, clutching at two palm branches. Before him on the ground an over-turned pitcher; above him on a pedestal a larger pitcher, and in back-ground three palm branches. On r. a fourth Cupid, holding an unrecog-nisable object before his body, is leaning as spectator on a table, on which stands an amphora. Behind it a beardless terminal bust, with fillet on hair. Before this a heavy wreath. Over principal group is inscribed on tablet: *D. M. | C. Minicius | Gelasinus | sibi posuit.*

Cf. *Mon. Matth.*, III. p. 163. L. SIDE: a wingless Cupid blowing tuba, r. hand lying on head. On l. a beardless terminal bust with fillet on hair, by it two palm branches. On r. a palm tree. R. SIDE: the prize table with lion's feet supports a large amphora and two small vessels or wreaths. On r., a palm tree laden with fruit. [*M*]

336 (363). *Engr.*, 138, 1. Bust of a child framed in a muscle shell; on either side a swan. Next on either side a tripod adorned with masks. Inscribed on tablet : *D. M. C. Q. F. Ian. | Carpidi et Q. | C. Q. F. Iusto C. | Amaryllis | mater fecit.* Inscription certainly spurious, probably also the whole urn.

337 (379). **Round urn, shaped like a band-box.** *Engr.*, 138, 2. On either side a Dioskuros with egg-shaped hat, chlamys and spear, by his horse. Below, a river-god, half covered in cloak, lying on l. arm, holding a bundle of reeds in r. hand. Above him inscribed on tablet: *D. M. | C. Iul(io) Iuli ano cohi. | mil. urb(anae) XII b . m. | fec(it) Iuli a mater | filio suo | bene mer enti.* (Spurious.)

338 (412). *Engr.*, 138, 3. Two boys bearing a rich festoon of fruit. Above them inscribed on tablet: *D. M. | L. Iulio Basso Domitia Nice | coniugi pientissimo | b(ene) m(erenti) f(ecit).* On the lid a double pediment, each part with a portrait, with a bird on each side ; bearded masks on ends.

339 (378). *Engr.*, 138, 4. A garland hangs down from two rams' heads; above, an eagle with extended wings ; below two butterflies. Inscription: *D. M. | A. Plautius Gallus | Hermeti lib(erto). | vix. an. XLI m(ens). IIII.* On lid a wreath.

340 (401). **Cippus.** *Engr.*, 139, 1. Below, inscribed on tablet : *DIs Manibus | T. Flavi Eutacti | vixit annis XXXV | Flavia Polla | coniugi karissimo fecit.* Above, bust of deceased, beardless, between flutings. From the Borioni collection.

341 (367). *Engr.*, 139, 2. A heavy garland hangs down from two richly decorated candelabra, within it an eagle with extended wings. Inscribed on tablet : *D. M. | Priscae | Augustor(um servae) | vix. an. XVII.* On lid a crown and two masks at corners.

342 (382). **Round urn shaped like a cista.** *Engr.*, 139, 3. Curved flutings running round it. In front two dolphins diving down into the waves. A heavy garland hangs down from their tails. Inscribed on tablet : *D. M. | Antoni.e | Gemellae | Diadumenus | pientissimae | fecit. | vixit annis XXXIII.*

343 (391). *Engr.*, 140, 1. *Mon. Matth.*, III. 73, 3. Within a frame the inscription (spurious): *Rubria Prima | Albaniesis | P.*

Rubrius Rev ilis (? *Reutilis* is given in *Mon. Matth.*). | *amice have et* | *vale : ego hic | situs sum.*

344 (399). *Engr.*, 140, 2 = 143, 5. 6. On a field in a frame the inscription : *D. M. | et | cineribus Q. C. | P. F.* (Spurious.)

345 (384). *Engr.*, 140, 3. *Mon. Matth.*, III. 61, 1. In a field with rich border the inscription: *DIs Manibus sacru(m)*. | *Ti. Claudio Onesimo Actes | lib. Claudia Felicula con|Iugi suo bene merenti | fecit. vixit cum eo ann is XXI.* (Suspicious.)

346 (389). **Double urn.** *Engr.*, 140, 4. Three roses both on r. and l., in middle a spiral-shaped ornament. Inscription on l. : *D. M. | Calidiae Ursiliae* (i.e. *Ursillae*) | *v(ix.) a(nn). XXXVII m(ens). VI d(ieb.) X | L. Calidius Baculus | libertae pientissim ae et incomparabili | fecit*; on r.: *D. M. | Telesphori Primitivi | vixit an. VIII men. III | diebus XVI horis X. | posuit Onesimus | pater.* (Spurious ?)

347 (386). *Engr.*, 140, 5. *Mon. Matth.*, III. 61, 3 (different lid). Inscribed on tablet : *D. M. | Aurelia Hermione fecit Aurelio In genuo coniugi | karissimo. item Au|relius Philander libertus patro no merenti.* (Suspicious.) On the lid the official cap (*apex*) of priests.

348 (385). *Engr.*, 140, 6. Two boys holding a festoon of fruit. Inscribed on tablet : *D. M. | M. Ulpio Eutyche | M. Ulpius | Philocalus | fratri b(ene) m(erenti) f(ecit).* The urn is besides richly decorated. On the lid a wreath, and at the corners palmettes.

349 (388). **Round vase.** *Engr.*, 142, 1. The body decorated with slanting flutings. Inscribed on tablet : *Hyla | vix. a(nn). I m(ens). III | Ti. Claudius | Epaphra | filio fec(it).*

350 (390). *Engr.*, 142, 2. On either side a column and a spray. Inscribed on tablet : *D. M. | M. Rufrius M. l. Philapfiphus | Rufia* (sic) *M. l. Iucun(da) soror | argundi.* (Spurious.)

351 (387). **Round vase** : slim form. *Engr.*, 142, 3. Not ornamented with any representation of figures, but mere decorative designs. (Genuine ?)

352 (375). *Engr.*, 143, 3. 4. Two bearded heads with horns of Ammon support a double garland raised in the middle over a button. Below, at each corner a swan, in the middle two smaller birds. Above them inscribed on tablet : *Severinae Procillae | ossa hic sita sunt. | L. Severinus L. f. matri fecit.* (Spurious ?) On sides a palmette, on lid two birds pecking at a twig.

353 (537). **Round vase** : cup-shaped. *Engr.*, 144, 1. 2. On front a thick border of vine-leaves round a tablet with the inscription *Ossa | Q. Licinii Felicis ;* back entirely covered with branches of ivy. In place of a handle on each side a bearded mask crowned with ivy, with broad ribbon on forehead, of elegant hieratic style. From the Bessborough collection.

The following Cineraria from the Mattei collection are not copied in the *Engravings*.

354 (348). *Mon. Matth.*, III. 61, 2. In a field with a frame the inscription *Ossa | L. Antoni | Felicis.*

355 (349). **Double cinerarium.** *Mon. Matth.*, III., 71, 1. Two inscriptions on fields with frames; l.: *D. M. | L. Manlio | Philargyro | fec. Larcia Rufina coniugi suo | b(ene) m(erenti), v(ix). a(nn). XXXXV, et sibi;* r.: *D. M. | Larcia Rufina coniugi suo b. m.*

356 (350). *Mon. Matth.*, III. 65, 3. Two bearded heads with horns of Ammon support a garland; below it at each corner a vessel full of fruits. Inscribed on tablet: *D. M. | M. Clodio Castori mater fecit | filio pientissim(o).*

357 (362). Between two griffins a tablet with the inscription *M. Saburius Ligus | Fal(erna) Albintimili* (i.e. from Albintimilium, now Ventimiglia) *| evoc(atus) Aug(usti) sal(ariorum) VI | vix. ann. XXXVIII | profecit ex coh(orte) V | pr(aetoria).* Cf. *Mon. Matth.*, III. p. 125.

358 (395). *Mon. Matth.*, III. 69, 3. On a field within a border: *Dis Manibus | M. Terentius Stephani libertus | Restitutus et Croeale liberta eius Carviliae | mammae suae bene meritae [d]e se.* (Suspicious.)

359 (416). **Inscribed slab.** *Mon. Matth.*, III. p. 139. *Dis Manib(us) | Atiliae Phlegusae | M. Herennius Felix | fecit conlugi | bene merenti.*

The following sepulchral monuments derived from other purchases are likewise not copied in the *Engravings*.

360 (346). **Cinerarium.** Inscription within a frame: *Paeti | M. Claudi | Paeti,* in three adjoining fields.

361 (347). **Double cinerarium.** Inscription, l.: *Aninia Asterio sibi et fratri suo;* r.: *C. Iulius Speratus.*

362 (374). **Double cinerarium.** Inscription, l.: *D. M. Festivae fec(it) Hermes pater;* r.: *D. M. Flaviaes Onesimes, vix. ann. XXVII.*

363 (377). **Cinerarium.** Cupids at the corners leaning on torches. Two hovering Cupids hold the tablet below them, l. a bow, r. a quiver. Above, horns of plenty. Inscription: *Oppiae Thisbe coniugi incomparabili, frugi, | integrae fidei | C. Oppius Eutyches maritus b(ene) m(erenti) f(ecit). | vix. a(nn). LV m(ens). I d(ieb). III.* Cf.

Engr., 155, 6. On each side a griffin. H. 0·20. L. 0·74. From
the Bessborough collection. [*M*]

364 (403). **Sepulchral monument.** Three busts, which
appear to be of a husband and his two wives. The inscription is
given as follows: *Mallia Mifprofula nata ann. X totidem m. II. v.
a., L. Mallius L. l. Clemens, Perpernea M. L. l. Prima.* (Spurious.)

365 (405). **Sepulchral inscription**, bulky ; on a field within
a rich border : *Ti. Claudius Rufus, vixit mensibus XXX.*

366 (406). **Sepulchral monument**, with the inscription :
Φλαουίαν Αὐρηλίαν Μα καρίαν φίλαν ὅρον γυναῖκα | Αὐρήλιος Ὑγει υιανὸς
γλυκυτάτῃ συμβίῳ. (*C. I. Gr.*, 3347.) Cf. *Engr.*, 155, 5. Probably
from Smyrna. From the Bessborough collection.

367 (413). **Relief**, given out to belong to a sarcophagus. The
ornaments and sea-horses are curious ; between them on a square
tablet : *D. M. Q. Quintio Eutychcii* (i.e. *Eutycheti*) *Quintii Euty-
chianus et Victoria ex testamento fecerunt nutritori suo. vixit ann. CV
m(ens). V d(ieb). XXVII.*

368 (414). **Inscribed slab** : *D. M. Aur. Iohinus mil(es)
coh(ortis) III pr(actoriae) [centuria] Q. Rufini. vix. an. XXX, mil(ita-
vit) an. VI, nat(ione) Bessus. Aur(dius) Martinus eq(ues) singularis
her(es) et Iulius Marcianus secundus her(es) et contubernales b(ene)
m(erenti) f(aciendum) c(uraverunt).*

369 (415). **Inscribed slab** : *D. M. Verriae Nicopolini Ti.
Iulius Epitynchanus coningi b(ene) m(erenti), cum qua vixit annis
XXXV sinae ulla querella, fecit et sibi.*

370 (417). **Inscribed slab.** *D. M. Ulpiae Sabinae coning(i)
optimae et dulcissimae et bene merenti P. Rufinus Ephestion locum con-
cessum et donatum ab heredibus Flavi Libani, quae posita est infra hanc
tricliam in long(um) p(ed). VII, in lat(um) p(ed). V.* (Suspicious.)

371 (551). **Cinerarium**, with rams' heads and two Cupids
with inverted torches. Inscription : *Dijs Manibus C. Munii Sereni
sacrum.* Bought at Lord Mendip's sale.

The *Account* further enumerates the following reliefs :

371 *a* (267. P). Modern copy of a so-called **Choragic Relief.** [*]

372 (269. S). A **lion's head.**

373 (274). A **charioteer** in the Circus running full speed in
his quadriga. There appear also the metae.

374 (275. S). **Fragment of an oval sarcophagus.** A lion
walking l. : on his neck a ribbon with a bulla. H. 0·60. [*M*]

375 (276. T). **Front of a sarcophagus.** Two hovering

Victories hold a medallion (*clupeus*) with half-length portrait of a boy. On both sides a Cupid with torch. Below the Victories horns of plenty, also on l. a bow, on r. a quiver. [*M*]

376 (281. T).   **Fragment of sarcophagus.**   Aphrodite or a Nereid sits on a sea monster, l. hand supported, looking r.   On the beast's tail sits a Cupid with a garland.   Above, a dove (?).   The *Account* further mentions a boy with inverted torch. [*M*]

377 (282. T).   **Fragment of a child's sarcophagus (oval).** A Cupid sits on a rock asleep, leaning on the inverted torch, by him a quiver.   On r. stands a Cupid with crossed legs holding before him slantwise a staff (? torch ?) with both hands.   On l. a third Cupid retires with a garland in his hands. [*M*]

378 (288. S).   **Slab of a sarcophagus.**   Two hovering Cupids support a shell with the portrait of a woman, head-dress in style of third century A.D., who holds a roll.   Under her a nude female figure, recumbent, with high stephane, a swan in her bosom (Leda ?), surrounded by four Cupids.   On her l. first Oceanus, semi-nude, with a steering paddle ; then a sea monster ; on her r. first Tellus, draped, with a cornucopiae ; then a Cupid frightening two companions by a large mask which he holds before him.   Of the two latter one covers his face with r. hand and advances l. to protect himself, the second falls on his back with fright.   (Cf. *Pitture di Ercolano*, I. Pl. 34.)   At ends trees, from which quivers are suspended.   Very rough work. [*M*]

379 (290).   **Medusa's head,** probably from a piece of architecture.

380 (294).   **Satyr's head,** with pointed ears, of savage expression.   Bought from Volpato.

381 (296).   **Eagle,** standing within a wreath of foliage, with expanded wings.

382 (297).   **A face.**

383 (300).   **Medusa.**

384 (301).   **A boar,** lying down, and having a dog at each end of it.

385 (302).   A head in porphyry, small.

386 (303).   **Medallion** in alto relievo, called Sappho.

387 (305).   A comic mask.

388 (306).   A mask of **Dionysos.**

389 (310).   Two **Medusa's** faces.

390 (317).   **Seven masks,** which are all singular in their kind.

391 (335. T).   **Relief from a sarcophagus.**   A herdsman

sits in exomis and boots, facing r., leaning on his staff, at his side the
herdsman's wallet. Beneath his seat a sheep, before him on r. three
more sheep in two planes one above the other, and three trees.
From the Villa Borioni. [*M*]

392 (340). Discus, with three masks.

393 (524. Portico of P, above the main entrance). Front of a
large sarcophagus. In the middle a powerful lion, pursued by a
hound, bounds l. towards a bearded horseman in tunic and cloak,
whose raised r. arm belongs to the restored piece of the relief.
Under the same a second bearded horseman with sleeved tunic and
cloak bounds towards the lion ; before him a bear and an ibex lie
on the ground killed. Above the lion a third horseman with waving
chlamys brandishes his sword. A fourth horseman and a helmeted
warrior further r. raise their swords against a panther springing
r. behind the lion, while below in the r. corner a bearded man in
sleeved tunic and cap cowering on the ground holds his shield
before him for protection from the danger. Very large dimensions.
The relief is derived from Hadrian's Villa. For the purchase, cf.
on no. 221.

394 (535). A small sarcophagus. "In the front is a Greek
inscription in verse ; on each side of it is a curious bas-relief." From
the Bessborough collection. (In the *Engravings*, Pl. 153, 154,
besides no. 366, are four Greek inscriptions given as derived from
this collection, but there are no verses among them. They seem
all to have come here from Smyrna, see *C. I. Gr.*, 3318, 3385,
3337, 3349.)

395 (540. P). "A square altar; doubtless of the time when the
worship of Serapis and Isis had spread into the Roman empire, for both
of these divinities are represented on it in the forms of Roman art.
The head of Serapis is wanting. [According to the *Account*, "Isis,
with a sistrum and inverted cantharus (*situla*) ?, and a male figure
with a spear in his hand, and a serpent springing up at his feet."
One might therefore suppose it to be a priestess of Isis, as they
often occur with a man also at their side on Greek sepulchral
monuments.] Besides this, each side contains, in strict architectural
arrangement, two torches, a nilometer [a sistrum according to the
Account], and a patera. Opposite is the colossal mask of Jupiter
Ammon, of common workmanship." From the Bessborough collection. The specimen serves as pedestal for no. 43. [*H*]

396 (546. S). Slab of a sarcophagus: of unusually large size;
in the middle, folding doors with Corinthian columns on both sides

which support a pediment, doors somewhat opened ; on each door a lion's head in the upper panel, in the lower a Cupid leaning on the inverted torch. On both sides curved flutings. On each end the figure of the good shepherd on a pedestal. From the Bessborough collection. [*C.M*]

The two following specimens are not in the *Account*:

397 (G). **Front of a sarcophagus.** Two hovering Victories hold a medallion with the bust of a boy. Below this a block of rock, on either side of it a snake attacking a recumbent lion. At the corners Cupids with a garland. Cf. no. 375. [*M*]

398 (S). **Middle piece of a fluted child's sarcophagus.** Bust of a boy. Below, two tragic masks. [*M*]

MISCELLANEOUS OBJECTS.

399 (307). **Support for a table slab (trapezophoron),** consisting of the fore part of a recumbent lion with l. paw laid on an animal's head. *Engr.*, 110, 3.

400 (308). **Support for a table slab (trapezophoron),** consisting of the fore part of a winged griffin ; below, ornament of vine branches. *Engr.*, 110, 3.

401 (507). **Shallow cup**; with two handles, on a square foot. *Engr.*, 110, 2. Richly ornamented, but apparently, at least for the most part, work by Piranesi, from whom the cup was bought, 1777.

402 (440). **Helmet.** *Engr.*, 120, 1. Of round shape with a sphinx on the crest, a griffin on the curved sides. The very large front piece is decorated with a ram's head. The emblems are suitable to Athena ; the helmet is supposed to have been broken off from a head of that goddess.

403 (442). **Boot.** *Engr.*, 120, 2. It seems to be a fragment of a statue of a warrior ; the boot has an overfold of leather at the top and is very richly ornamented (imitating embroidery?).

404 (270). **Vase showing Bacchic figures,** in different attitudes. It was found in a cava near Monticelli, not far from Tivoli, and was so much decayed and corroded, that it was necessary to re-work several parts, and new polish the figures ; this gave it the appearance of being modern. The repairs were made by Piranesi. Bought from Volpato.

I pass over a number of fragments (*Account*, nos. 420, &c.), columns (nos. 449, &c.), tables and miscellaneous objects (nos. 473 ff.); still the following may be briefly noticed :

405 (400). Antique glass urn. "When it was first found, it contained ashes and bones, with some lachrymatories, and a lamp, as may now be seen in it. Some ancient money was also found in it."

406 (418). Small glass urn, found in a Columbarium, near Naples. "It contained two lachrymatories, which are now in it, and some ashes."

407 (494). Three painted Greek vases, with various figures on them, bought at Naples, in 1777.

408 (495). Twelve small Greek vases, of different sizes and forms ; some are ornamented, others plain. Bought from Cavaceppi.

409 (498). A bronze lamp, hanging by a chain which is curiously wrought. Bought from Mr Clarke, at Naples.

MOSAICS.

410 (252. S). Thetis before Zeus? *Engr.,* 96. From the l. a female figure with arms advanced ("Juno"), fillet in hair, with white chiton, red cloak and blue shoes approaches Zeus, who sits on a throne with a high back standing on two steps. Near his l. foot sits the black eagle. Hair and beard of the god brown. A gray cloak covers his legs and upper part of l. arm. Zeus supports his l. hand, which raises the sceptre, against his head. In r. hand he holds the thunderbolt with which he points out the female suppliant to Nikè, who is turned away facing r. and writes something with a stylus on a yellow shield standing on a pedestal ; quite corresponding in attitude to the Victory of Brescia. She wears a white chiton and red cloak ; l. foot resting on a helmet which lies on the ground. Large gray wings visible on her back. The effect of the colouring is very simple ; the work tolerable. The representation agrees well with the scene in the first book of the *Iliad* (495 ff.), where Thetis entreats from the Father of the gods honour and fame for her sorrow-stricken son. Found in the ruins of an old villa near Torre Pignatara on the Via Labicana. H. 0·68. L. 0·63. [*II·*]

411 (448). Six pieces of mosaic, being part of the floor of a large room. "In the centre of each piece are some curious figures : on one is a jay looking into a mirror, on another is an ibis holding in its bill a serpent, &c. [According to Waagen : in the centre a bird and three fruits and a rabbit alternately, all enframed in tendrils of the same pattern.] Found in the ruins of an ancient house near Tivoli ; bought from La Piccola [cf. no. 17]. Near 1·60 square each piece." [*II·*]

412 (529). **An antique mosaic**, which now forms the slab of a table. According to Waagen a naked slave is strewing fodder before two oxen; behind is an ass looking upward. According to *Account*: buildings and cattle. Bought together with no. 221. [*II'*]

413 (S). **A female head in profile**, of colossal scale; composed of very coarse pieces, but still imposing in effect from the grandeur of the forms. [*II'*]

Gems.

Engr. 151 and 152 contain twenty-four gems belonging to the collection, for the most part of such suspicious appearance, or indeed so absolutely modern, that I do not describe them in detail. Waagen, p. 259, describes five specimens, while at the same time he states that there are several hundred intaglios, many of them of great interest and value.

KETTERINGHAM HALL (Norfolk).

Waagen, *Treas.*, III. pp. 427 f.

Not far from Wymondham, between Ely and Norwich, is situated this country seat of Sir John Boileau. Waagen enumerates the following marbles:

1. "**Marble relief** found at Nimes: a female figure with one foot on a vase holds to a woman opposite to her a mirror consisting of two circles attached together at one part, so that they could be folded together. The workmanship is moderate, but the action of the figures is very good."

2. "Small statue in marble, pronounced by Visconti to be the statue of a **Roman prince**, presented under the form of a young Hercules. Very good style, delicate execution; well preserved in the principal parts."

3, 4. "Two busts of **Emperors**, one of them a **Nero**."

KINGSTON LACY (Dorsetshire).

In this residence of W. J. Bankes, Esq. there were in 1835 when the second volume of *Specimens of Antient Sculpture* appeared, the undermentioned specimens. I have been lately informed that they are still there, in the possession of the present owner of the estate, WALTER RALPH BANKES, Esq. They are placed upon the staircase of the house.

1. **Marble bust of Arsinoë**, found in Alexandria, brought from Egypt by Consul Baldwin and sold by auction 1828. *Spec.*, II. Pl. 40, 41. Hair parted, flowing down in rich folds on both sides and leaving the open brow free. Head crowned with a stephanè pierced with several holes by way of embellishment. Lobes of ears also pierced. Back of head missing; it was worked from a separate piece, perhaps of different marble, and was very likely veiled. The bust was evidently intended to be let into a statue. Features of ideal beauty. "The style of sculpture is broad and grand, and the execution of the face and throat remarkably fleshy; it is also in good condition, and has no other part restored excepting the tip of the nose." H. 0·46.

2. **Bust of "Augustus,"** in green basalt, life size, found near Canopus in Egypt about 1780, bought from Mr Baldwin's collection. *Spec.*, II. Pl. 46. The lineaments of this narrow face, the very large nose, the arrangement of the hair, differing from what is seen in all portraits, both of the youthful and the aged Augustus, make the traditional nomenclature most improbable. Beautiful bust, in a high state of preservation, with the same kind of hard delineation and perfect polish as in the bust of Caesar carved in like material in the Berlin Museum.

KNOLE (Kent).

Dallaway, pp. 382 f. (II. pp. 134 f.). Spiker, II. p. 285. Waagen, *Treas.*, IV. pp. 337 f.

In Knole, near Sevenoaks, the ancient seat of the Dukes of Dorset, there are a few antiques which JOHN FREDERICK, THIRD DUKE OF DORSET (*acc.* 1769, *d.* 1799), had collected in Italy. The more exact date of the Duke's purchase has lately been yielded by the records which the Pope's chamberlain office has kept of the exportation of works of art (see Gori, *Archivio storico della Città e Provincia di Roma*, II. pp. 267, 268). Among them occur the two following entries: 1770, 7 *Agosto*. *Duca di Dorset: 4 colonne antiche di giallo di palmi 11; un busto imperiale buono, 2 teste parimente antiche ordinarie incognite; una piccola statuetta antica di marmo di donna ideale alta palmi 5... 28 Agosto. Il Duca Dorset: busto di Marco Aurelio antico ordinario, altro di marmo di giovane incognito con altro consimile*

*di detto, incognito ed antico ; un' erma di Socrate antica marmorea ; una
testa di marmo antica incognita ; un Amorino addormentato* [no. 5];
un Bassorilievo antico... The specifications are too vague for one to
attempt an identification of the several specimens with the marbles
at Knole, yet it seems that some of the above-mentioned specimens,
such as the small female ideal statue, are no longer to be found.
Knole was, in Waagen's time, in the possession of Lady AMHERST,
the eldest daughter of the collector, and is now the property of Lord
SACKVILLE, the collector's grandson. I visited the collection in the
year 1877.

HALL.

1.   **Statue of Demosthenes**, from the Columbrano Palace in
Naples. Visconti states that it was found in his time in Campania
(*Mus. Pio-Clem.*, III. p. 63 Mil.). Drawings of it are given in Fea,
Storia, II. Pl. 6. Schroeder, *Abbildungen des Demosthenes*, Brunsw.
1842, Pl. 2, 6. G. Scharf, *Trans. R. Soc. Litt.*, New Series, IV.
fig. 5. Cf. Fea, *l. cit.*, III. p. 458, Visconti, *Iconogr. Gr.*, I. p. 356,
O. Jahn, *Zeitschr. für die Alterthums-Wiss.*, 1844, p. 238, Scharf,
l. cit., p. 13, Michaelis, *Arch. Zeit.*, 1862, p. 239. As the drawing
in Fea is from a cast in the possession of Jenkins, who had also
bought other antiques from the Columbrano Palace, this dealer was
doubtless concerned in its purchase. The statue is a fairly exact
replica of the Vatican statue from the Villa Aldobrandini (*Braccio
Nuovo*, no. 62, *Mus. Chiaramonti*, II. Pl. 24, Pistolesi, *Vaticano*, IV.
Pl. 19), only that the stomach is rather more prominent and that the
very realistic reproduction of all external minutiae is not so thoroughly carried out. In general the work is not very delicate and
detailed, but in recompense for this the statue has remained almost
free from any retouching. In excellent preservation, with the exception that the upper part of the body, especially the upper parts of the
arms, have evidently been for a long time exposed to the rain, and
are in consequence much corroded ; the lower parts, especially the
drapery from the belly downwards, are preserved in unimpaired polish
and freshness. The head has never been broken off. Pupils are not
expressed in sculpture ; a trace of colour in their place is probably
of modern origin. New : merely nose, toes of l. foot, two first of
r. foot, and lastly, the hinder part of the irregularly-shaped pedestal.
Presumably in consequence of a fall, to which we must also ascribe
a crack in the l. forearm, both hands with the roll, the l. from above
the wrist, the r. with half the forearm, have been broken away just

where these parts stand clear of the bulk of the statue. The parts broken off are however, Waagen's testimony notwithstanding, undoubtedly antique, and have been put on again by dint of smoothing the fractured joints and of sundry small patches. The quality of the marble, as well as the condition of the surface, which accurately corresponds to that of the adjacent parts as to the destructive effects of the rain, testifies to the genuineness of these parts. Unfortunately, however, the restorer has found it necessary to work over seriously the under sides of the hands, especially in the finger joints (the latter as in the case of the *Arrotino* in Florence or the dying Gaul in the Capitol); the veins are also more prominently marked. This retouching extends to the neighbouring part of the l. forearm. The result of this investigation, in which I quite agree with Scharf's conclusions, is of some importance, as the roll is thus established as an original element of our replica. In the Vatican replica the forearms with the roll are, as is well known, restorations, and Martin Wagner has endeavoured to prove from the pose of the genuine portions of the arms that the restoration is wrong, and that the hands were originally folded (*Annali*, 1836, p. 161). In this way the statue would correspond to the bronze statue of Demosthenes, which was executed by Polyeuktos and erected in the agora of Athens at the public cost about B.C. 280, also with folded hands (Plut. *Demosth.*, ch. 31). Visconti had already conjectured that the statues were identical; subsequently, however, he abandoned this conjecture, but it has since been taken up again by others. The statue at Knole is calculated to prove that Wagner's view respecting the restoration of the Vatican statue, considering their complete agreement in all other points, is more than doubtful; and further, that these statues are at least no *direct* copies of the statue of Polyeuktos. Perhaps, however, there is something to be said in favour of their being only a slight variation on this statue, the main features of the composition being retained. With regard to this view I should not lay much stress on a terra cotta statuette in the late Campana collection, now presumably in Paris, which, while agreeing with our statues in all other points, has the hands folded; for the specimens in that collection are seldom free from tampering. The peculiar mixture, however, of a pregnant representation of the inward life with a vigorous naturalism in the treatment of all externals indicates an original of the Hellenistic period such as that of Polyeuktos. The fact that all extant portraits of the orator go back to a common original is a further proof of its celebrity. In fact this statue, so far from being of simply ideal beauty, offers us a speaking portrait of the man who, though endowed by nature with a frail body, developed his powers by dint of iron energy and the most strenuous intellectual toil, and who amid the storms of perplexing and sinister conjunctures stood his ground unflinchingly in the face of rancorous foes at home and abroad. The face furrowed by wrinkles, and the almost gloomy earnestness of the features, find a complement in the scantiness of the drapery, which is far different from the flowing drapery of the Lateran Sophokles, or the rich profusion of folds in the Neapolitan Aeschines. Exactly thus is Demosthenes depicted in the well-known epigram which stood beneath his Athenian statue (Plut. *Demosth.*, ch. 30): "had the piercing intellect and the strenuous will been supported by proportionate strength, they might have rescued his fatherland from Philip." While, consequently, the impression conveyed by this statue is in harmony with our idea of the portrait by Polyeuktos, the supposition also seems to be justified that in a later period, when Demosthenes had come to be admired more as the great author than as the afflicted patriot, the motive of folded hands was changed for the less significant, but more easily intelligible, attribute of a half-opened roll of manuscript, while the statue remained essentially unchanged in other respects. In matters of detail we may mention a hole pierced in front through a corner of the drapery which hangs down under the l. hand; for what it served is not clear. The sandals, with their straps, are rendered with especial care in all details. The marble seems to be Pentelic, and indeed of a fine-grained quality, similar to that of the Florentine group of Niobè. H. 1·95, with pedestal 2·08. [* *IV*]

STAIRCASE.

2. Statue of sleeping Nymph. She lies on her back with legs crossed. L. arm rests on a block of rock, the hand touching the rim of a large urn which lies on the ground. R. arm, adorned with an armlet, lies slantwise across the breast, hand on l. shoulder. Head sunk back; the abundant hair traversed by a ribbon. A wide drapery covers legs, back, and l. arm. New: half lower parts of legs, rock under l. arm, a great part of back and hips, probably also the l. hand, possibly the face and several minutiae besides. This statue had been broken into several pieces, and in piecing them together the surface has been so much smoothed away as to present an appearance of polish. Consequently the impression conveyed, which can never have been pleasing, has become quite disagreeable.

The antique part of the r. leg has taken a brilliant gold-brown hue owing to oxidation or to contact with some metal. Otherwise of very white marble. Found at Roma Vecchia by Gav. Hamilton. L. 1·43. [*]

3. **Head and neck of a youth.** Hair curly. Shows characteristics of Lysippos. Coarse work, and moreover very much rubbed away and spoilt. New: nose; lips injured. Back of head and of neck broken off. [*]

4. **Bust of " Brutus."** Similar in character to the late Roman heads with hair and beard close-shaved, scarcely more than indicated by punctures. Eyebrows rendered in a somewhat artificial style. New: nose. R. arm covered by a vague piece of drapery, neither tunic nor cloak. A button on r. shoulder holds up the fringed cloak which covers breast and l. shoulder. Below this shoulder near the breast there appears the upper part of a round staff furnished with a knob, beneath which the hilt and sheath of a small sword or dagger is visible; this extraordinary appendage is all the more strange as it is outside the cloak. As moreover the very thick pedestal, which on account of its shape can scarcely be antique, is of one piece with the bust and head, the entire specimen is more than suspicious. It may indeed have been the intention of the artist to represent a " Brutus with a dagger" (Dallaway). H. 1·00. H. of head 0·23, of pedestal 0·28. [*]

5. **Statue of sleeping Eros,** with attributes of Herakles. Legs crossed; head resting on l. hand, l. arm on l. wing. R. hand lies on a small club. A lion's skin serves the winged god to lie upon. By his foot creeps a little lizard. New: only tip of nose. Broken off: great toe of r. foot, part of l. wing and head of lizard. Coarse-grained Greek marble. L. 0·80, of Eros about 0·70. [*]

ANTECHAMBER TO PRIVATE APARTMENTS.

6. **Bust of Antinous,** from Hadrian's Villa, found 1769 by Gav. Hamilton, sold to the duke by Jenkins (Dallaway, p. 370). Head looks down somewhat sideways. Hair very thoroughly worked; brows slightly indicated. In place of pupils a slight flattening of the eyeball is noticeable. New: nose, head and bust. Antique parts seriously worked over. Very white marble of fine grain. L. of face about 0·23. [*]

7. **Head of a bearded Greek:** colossal scale. It may perhaps belong to the fourth or third century B.C. The fillet which

traverses the abundant hair denotes a distinguished personage. Lower half of forehead strongly developed, whole form of face broad and powerful; expression calm and clear. This remarkable head is in excellent preservation. New: merely neck, bust, part of tip of nose and details in hair. H. of genuine portion about 0·39. L. of face 0·27. [*]

8. **Roman portrait head.** Thin beard and thick, tolerably smooth hair. Bust covered with a drapery, the button of which on l. shoulder is ornamented with the bust of a warrior. Nose restored. The whole piece very suspicious. Pedestal certainly modern, pretty much like that of the so-called Brutus, no. 4. H. 0·73, without pedestal 0·54. L. of face 0·16. [*]

9. **Roman portrait head of a youth.** Beardless; with curly hair much undercut with the drill. Pupils indicated. Late period. New: nose, breast with drapery, pedestal. L. of face 0·18. [*]

10. **"Marcellus," bust including part of body** (προτομή). Pleasing, pretty, youthful head, inclined somewhat towards r. shoulder. Mouth finely cut; eyes somewhat veiled by the lids. Hair cut short in front, combed over forehead, falling down deep on the neck. The strange mannerism of the hair, which is treated as though it were straw, strongly suggests modern retouching. H. 0·62. L. of face 0·18. [*]

11. **Head of "Caesar,"** colossal scale: doubtless representing in truth a man of the latest period of the Roman republic, but certainly neither Cicero nor Caesar. The latter name is perhaps due to the likeness of its pendant (no. 12) to Pompey. A distinguishing feature is the lofty forehead traversed by a furrow. Hair short and beginning to get scanty. Deep eyes. Strong creases extend from the nose downwards. Finely modelled lips. Expression calm, earnest, almost melancholy, goodnatured and benevolent. The impression conveyed is that of a noble, thoughtful, but not very energetic man, somewhere between fifty and sixty years of age. New: nose, three quarters of upper lip, ears, bust and pedestal. Coarse workmanship. H. of genuine portion 0·40. L. of face 0·29. The head was presumably discovered with no. 12. [*]

12. **Head of "Pompey,"** colossal scale. Found 1769 by Cav. Hamilton in Hadrian's Villa, sold to the duke by Jenkins (Dallaway, p. 370). Apparently a companion to no. 11, being of similar dimensions and treatment. It has in fact some resemblance to the statue in the Spada Palace, though not strong enough to

justify the traditional nomenclature. Hair full and curly. Low forehead much furrowed, eyes in shadow. Eyebrows slightly indicated. The lower part of the face has calm features and conveys the impression that the man leads a contented existence. New: half the nose, the edge of the ears, bust and pedestal. H. of genuine part 0·38. L. of face 0·25. [*]

13. **Roman portrait head.** Of singular, wicked expression. Lower part of face projects in an extraordinary manner; this has all the stronger effect as the upper teeth seem to be wanting. Lips closely pressed together. Nose aquiline, but the tip quite obtuse. Brows wrinkled. The expression of energy is intensified by the turn of the head to its r. Antique: head, except l. ear, and neck. Very fine-grained white marble. H. of genuine portion 0·33. L. of face 0·20. [*]

GARDEN.

On the outside of the house, near the state drawing-room, there is built into the wall:

14. **Fragment of a child's sarcophagus.** Five Cupids in procession moving r., coming from a banquet. All wear little cloaks. The first (*a*) looks round at the second (*b*) who is emptying a cup on the shoulder of *a*, and holds a drinking-horn in r. arm. The third Cupid, *c*, raises l. hand and with r. lowers a torch towards *d* who lifts up a wreath with his l. hand and is tumbling back into the arms of a companion *e*, of whom only the hand supporting *d* is left. The slab is imperfect on both ends. L. 0·75. H. about 0·18. [*]

CONSERVATORY.

15. **Fragment of a relief.** Towards l. stands **Zeus**, full face, with cloak thrown over legs and l. arm, r. hand resting on hip, r. arm leaning on a stout staff. In consideration of this attribute one might suppose Asklepios to be intended, only that the goddess at whom he gazes seems to be assuredly **Hera**. She sits on the r. on a square block, draped in a chiton and cloak, which she airs in the well-known manner with r. hand as if it were a veil. Head adorned with a stephané. The fragment is broken off towards l. At the top a projecting border seems to be chiselled away to the level of the plane of the field. Apparently a Greek original is copied in this Roman relief. Treatment of relief angular. H. 0·42. L. 0·43. [*]

16. **Relief of Orpheus.** In the middle in rocky scenery sits a man, of almost childish smallness of stature, in short chiton and

with Phrygian cap, playing on a curved flute. He would be taken for a herdsman, did not the scene rather suggest an Orpheus. For about him are placed a boar listening very attentively, a goat, a ram, a lion or panther mangling a horse (?), and so evidently not yet fully tamed by the art of the musician, a bear (?). On the l. remains of a tree. On the l., and perhaps on the r. also, imperfect. Very rough; merely sketched. H. 0·27. L. 0·34. [*]

17. **End of a child's sarcophagus.** On the l. stands a herdsman in exomis, leaning on his staff, r. hand laid against head. Further to the r. two trees, then two cows and a sheep, lying down. Everything seems in repose. Rough work. H. 0·28. L. 0·40. [*]

LANSDOWNE HOUSE, *see* London.

LIVERPOOL.

Conze, *Arch. Anz.*, 1864, pp. 218 ff. I inspected the Museum, 1877.

The public museum possesses an abundance of the most varied kinds of art treasures, owing to the bequest of Mr Jos. MAYER (Introd. § 97), and to many additions besides; still it cannot boast of many antiquities of great consequence, and in particular owns only a few marbles. The multifarious connections of Liverpool trade with the Levant, give promise that the Museum will receive further additions in this department.

1. **Bronze statue of Apollo.** He rests on r. leg, which is crossed by the l. On the crown the hair forms a top-knot (κόρυμβος); long, stiff locks fall down on the shoulders; pupils hollowed out. Lowered r. arm without doubt held the plectron; l. arm rests on the lyre which with the piece of rock beneath it is modern. The broad proportions of the body are singular in connection with Apollo. Roman bronze from Arles. Not bad. H. 0·69. [*]

2. **Marble statue of Herakles.** The hero is seated leaning back on a rock on which the lion skin is spread. Bow and quiver as well as cuirass and shield are leaning against the rock. Herakles sets l. foot on another shield, the advanced r. foot on a coat of mail.

Both arms missing. In front, on the quadrangular pedestal, remains of an inscription :

HERCVLI *invicto* (?)

SACR*um*

CLAV*Dius*....

Perhaps identical with *C. I. Lat.*, VI. 1, 322, *Herculi invicto sacrum* | *M. Claudius Esychus d. d.* " *sub parva statua Herculis cum clava et exuviis.*" Very commonplace work. H. 0·45, with pedestal 0·58. [*]

3. **Statuette of a female figure**, in ungirdled chiton, the cloak wrapped round lower part of body. She rests on r. leg behind which she crosses the l. and leans with l. arm on a column in easy pose. Missing : head, raised r. arm, fingers of l. hand, front half of r. foot. Superficial workmanship. The low plinth seems to indicate that this figure was carved in Asia Minor (cf. Oxford, no. 9). H. 0·76. [*C]

4. **Torso of a boy**, or youth, including r. thigh and upper part of lowered l. arm. Missing : raised r. arm, head and the greater part of the legs. On the l. of the paunch is a trace which shows that the arm went along this part; there are moreover traces of a support behind the r. shoulder-blade and r. thigh. Good sculpture. H. 0·51. [*]

5. **Terminal figure of a youth with long curls (Apollo?)**, mutilated in the region of the virile emblem. The Term is placed against a pilaster which is somewhat expanded at the top, and has a hole in its upper surface. Dry, mean workmanship. H. of pilaster 0·85, of figure 0·78. [*]

6. **Sepulchral stelè of Herodotos.** The slab is furnished at the top with a cornice, only a little decorated. Below, the inscription Ἡρόδοτος Σκυλλίωνος. | ἡ τροφὸς ἐπέστησεν. In the relief stands Herodotos, apparently beardless, in cloak, holding out r. hand to an unveiled woman sitting to the r. On the l. behind Herodotos the faithful nurse, who has dedicated the sepulchral monument to her charge, stands in full face, veiled, head supported on l. hand. Common style of the second or last century B.C. Coarse marble. H. 0·66. L. 0·31. From the mouth of the aqueduct at Ephesos. Brought from Smyrna. Presented by E. Bibby, Esq., 1875. [*]

7. **Sepulchral stelè** with pediment. A beardless man lies on a bed with a thick fillet or wreath about his hair, draped in chiton, and with cloak round his legs. He holds a cup in l. hand and with r. is throwing something into a low three footed incense-burner

(θυμιατήριον, *turibulum*), which stands on a table supported by three
lion's legs. At the foot of the bed sits the wife, veiled, both hands
in cloak, turned away from the body of the man, her face turned
back towards him; feet resting on a broad footstool. On the l.
a diminutive attendant crowned with a wreath enters holding in
lowered r. hand as it seems a spoon (τρυηλίς, *trulla*), rather than a
rhyton or a strigil. Above in the field a horse's head, a round shield
with a Medusa's head, a corslet, collectively emblems of deceased's
rank. The monument is in good preservation. Style unusual; architectural design and relief very sharply cut, precise but dry; though
not in style, yet perhaps in the purely external technicalities of the
working of the stone, the relief may suggest Cyprian sculptures.
Perhaps this is partly the effect of the quality of the stone, which is
of very fine grain but quite full of tiny prints of shells (λίθος κογχίτης),
of yellowish colour. The specimen is derived from Egypt, and
belongs to the last centuries B.C. H. 0·70. L. 0·53. [*C*]

8. **Fragment of a Cyprian sepulchral stelè.** All that is
preserved is a piece of the border on the l. and the upper part of the
body of a woman sitting facing r. in fine chiton, veiled, with a necklace and a ring on forefinger of raised l. hand; the r. hand is grasped
by the hand of a second figure, of which only r. forearm is preserved.
An interesting imitation of the Attic composition so common in
sepulchral reliefs of the fourth century; about life size, in the peculiarly dry, frigid style of Cyprian sculptures. Nude parts especially
quite devoid of life (cf. Oxford, no. 127). Very high relief. Cyprian
limestone. H. 0·96. L. 0·46. Presented by Captain Fothergill,
S.S. Thessalia, 1872. [*M*]

9. **Sepulchral monument of Epaphroditos.** Round
column with clumsy, curious articulations at top and bottom,
furnished with a hole on the top for fastening on an ornament or a
vase. On the pillar the late inscription Ἐπαφρόδιται (αι = ε) | χρηστὲ|
χαῖρε. From Cyprus, of native limestone. H. 0·68. Diameter at
base 0·22. [*]

10. **Terra cotta sarcophagus**, quite plain, with projecting
flat border at the top. On the front is painted the inscription
Πλοπλείας καὶ καὶ Ἀγάθωνος. The first name is presumably a mis-
spelling for Ποπλείας (Ποπλίας, *Publiae*); καὶ is repeated by an
oversight. H. 0·27. l. 1·89. B. 0·50. Found near Karatash, the
ancient Mallos in Cilicia, on the gulf of Scandaroon, Dec. 1872.
Presented by Capt. Pernie, S.S. Ararat, 1873. [*]

11. **Sepulchral monument of Picaria Tertia.** Above, a

portrait head of a girl framed in a shell; on either side a dolphin.
Below the inscription: *Diis Manib(us)* | *Publicia Tertia* | *Picariae
Tertiae* | *filiae suae bene* | *merenti fecit.* | *vixit ann(os)* X. | *h(ic) s(ita)
e(st).* H. 0·56. L. 0·34. [*C*]

12. **Large Etruscan urn; Oedipus and Laios?** Oedipus (?) presses forward from l., in armour and with shield and
drawn sword, against a chariot, one horse of which is rearing high, a
second lies on the ground. In the background two Furies with
torches. Laios(?) covered by his shield is falling over the chariot,
to the r. of which three more horses are visible, one springing up,
one springing at "Laios," one thrown on to the ground. Quite r. an
armed attendant of "Laios" is fleeing off, looking at the scene of
disaster. Prof. Koerte considers the subject to be rather the death
of Hippolytos. Apparently alabaster. H. 0·60. L. 0·80. The lid,
showing a man with a cup in his r. hand, does not belong to the
urn; it is too large. [*C*]

13. **Small Etruscan urn; Eteokles and Polyneikes.**
They are killing each other. On either side a Fury. The colours, a
dull red and a greenish blue, are very well preserved. A female
figure on lid. Terra cotta. H. 0·26. L. 0·40. [*C*]

14. **Bronze relief of Athenè,** full face. *Cat. Hertz*, Pl. 3, 1,
p. 129, no. 5 (*Cat. Mayer*, no. 142). The goddess is represented
en face, head covered with a round helmet, the vizor of which stands
upward over the forehead. The aegis with gorgoneion covers the
breast; l. arm holds the large round shield, r. hand raised (to grasp
the spear). Good bronze intended for an antefixum, broken at the
feet. H. 0·13. [*C*]

15. **Small medallion** of bronze, silver-plated. Head of
Drusus. Found at Xanten (Castra Vetera) on the Rhine. [*C*]

16. **Etruscan mirror.** Nude female winged figure with
Phrygian cap, hovering towards the l.; in r. hand a ball (?apple?).
Cf. Gerhard, *Etr. Spiegel*, Pl. 32 ff. [*C*]

17. **Etruscan mirror.** Nude woman between two seated
youths; in the background an architectural design. Cf. Gerhard,
l. cit., Pl. 59. [*]

18. **Etruscan mirror.** A youth, leaning on a staff or thyrsos,
to whom a panther holds out its paw. The freedom of the delineation
arouses suspicion of the genuineness. [*C*]

19. **Mirror-case with a relief.** Paris kneeling on an altar,
a palm branch in l. hand, in r. a sword, on the l. a warrior, on the
r. a winged female figure with double axe raised to strike. Cf.
Gerhard, *l. cit.*, Pl. 21, 1. [*C*]

20. Mirror with drawing in raised outlines. **Perseus** (*First*) and **Minerva** (*Menerca*) looking at the reflection of the gorgoneion in the water. Even in the ornaments of the border an accurate imitation of the mirror in Gerhard, *l. cit.*, Pl. 123, with the sides reversed (so that Perseus holds the harp in his l. hand) and with the error MENEREA for MENERFA; the inscriptions besides running from l. to r. Undoubtedly a modern imitation. [*C*]

21. Eros sitting on a large **dolphin,** which he guides with reins. Small Greek terra cotta figure. [*C*]

22. Fragment of a terra cotta relief. Upper parts of a veiled bride and her pronuba, the latter with stephanè on hair. Exact replica of the relief in Guattani, *Monum. Ined.*, 1785, April, Pl. 3, 3. Campana, *Opere di plastica*, Pl. 64. *Arch. Zeit.*, 1851, Pl. 26, 2. [*C*]

23. Terra cotta relief. Five gods, from l. to r.; Apollo standing in repose with a lyre of modern shape; Tychè standing with cornucopiae; Hephaestos seated, in exomis, with round cap and boots, hammer in r. hand, tongs in l.; Athenè standing, with helmet, aegis, shield with gorgoneion, and cloak, r. arm raised high; an owl on her shoulder. Hermes standing, with a cock on his shoulder; he holds a purse in l. hand, and lays his r. on the herald's staff. Not restored, broken across once. Certainly modern. H. 0·33. l. 0·44. [*C*]

24. Vase with large body, from Canosa, with three openings carried up like necks (similar shape to that in Heydemann, *Vasens. in Neapel,* Pl. 3, no. 168). In front a Medusa's head, above it two Cupids; on either side of the principal opening the fore part (προτομή) of a galloping Centaur. On the top three small statues, Dolon between Odysseus and Diomedes, exactly answering to a vase-painting from Pisticci (*Bullett. Napol.*, 1. Pl. 7. Overbeck, *Bildwerke,* Pl. 17, 4). On the handle there slinks Dolon, beardless, clad in chlamys and hood, both arms raised (without weapon). On the lid of the l. opening Odysseus advances, with pointed beard, in chlamys and pointed cap (πῖλος), without a weapon in his hands; similarly on the lid of the r. opening advances Diomedes, bearded, with high helmet, boots, and floating chlamys, now without a weapon. The vase seems to have been considerably restored, though it is hardly possible to judge accurately to what extent. H. 0·65. [*C*]

25. Smaller vase from Canosa, with a Nikè and other figures on it. [*C*]

26. Pitcher (shape: Heydemann, Pl. 3, no. 137, only broader).

A youth in chlamys pursues with drawn sword a bearded old man draped in chiton and cloak, holding a sceptre, who looks round at him. Red figures. Good style. [*]

27. Kantharos (shape: Heydemann, Pl. 1, no. 43). Red figures. FRONT. Boy with chlamys, a strigil (?) in l. hand, stands before a dog; behind him a plant. Over him the inscription Χρύσιππος, not however painted on the background, but left in the original colour of the clay, as are also the figures; still, in spite of the thoroughly unusual technical process, the inscription seems genuine. BACK. A bearded man in cloak, leaning on a staff, stands before a grave, on which is a stelè with the inscription Λάι[ος]. In spite of many peculiarities and of the neighbourhood of several modern forgeries, there seems to me to be no definite ground for suspicion. [*]

28. Lamp with a head, perhaps antique; fastened as a projection on to a cubic die, the three other sides of which are ornamented with figures of deities in relief; by one is incised Τλήσων ὁ Νεάρχο(υ), by another χαῖρε καὶ πίει εὖ, two inscriptions often repeated on painted vases. This is naturally a forgery. [*]

Besides the above, the collection further contains a quantity of unimportant **painted vases, terra cottas, lamps, Samian vessels, bronzes, weights, leaden missiles for slings, gold ornaments, glass objects, amphora handles, Roman sepulchral inscriptions,** &c. &c. Of especial value is the collection of **ivory diptychs,** once belonging to Gabriel Fejérváry, subsequently bought by Jos. Mayer, and presented to the Museum. See *Catalogue of the Fejérváry ivories in the Museum of Jos. Mayer. Preceded by an essay on antique ivories by Francis Pulszky,* Liverpool, 1856. The most beautiful and celebrated specimen is the diptych with Asklepios and Hygieia, well known through Raf. Morghen's engraving (Müller-Wieseler, 11. 61, 791).

LONDON.

The existence of private collections in London is perhaps still less generally known to the public than is the case with those in other parts of the country. Since the Hope collection was removed to Deepdene, the Rogers collection sold, the Guilford collection completely lost sight of, the only large private collection still left is that in Lansdowne house, which is in truth one of the best of all. In addition there are the Soane Museum, the antiquities exhibited from time to time in the South Kensington Museum, and several smaller collections. No doubt many omissions in this section will at once strike persons who possess fuller information, and it is to be hoped they will be supplied.

ANTIQUARIES, SOCIETY OF, *see* Burlington House.

APSLEY HOUSE (Hyde Park Corner).

In the Duke of Wellington's town house there are in a vestibule, which leads to the small staircase, adorned by Canova's famous colossal statue of Napoleon, sundry Roman busts.

1. Bust of Cicero; the celebrated bust from the Mattei collection, which was a short time in possession of Cardinal Fesch (1815: cf. Urlichs, *Glyptothek*, p. 58). Drawings in F. Ursinus, *Imagines*, Pl. 146. *Mon. Matth.*, II., Pl. 10, 11. Visconti, *Iconogr. Rom.*, I. Pl. 12, 1. The bust closely resembles that in Madrid, the identification of which is established by its inscription (Huebner, *Ant. Bildwerke in Madrid*, Frontispiece); being similarly inclined a little to the l., and furnished, below the breast, with the antique inscription CICERO, which Marini ascribes to the third century. The value of this bust is, however, much diminished by the serious, though well executed, restorations; not only chin, mouth, and nose, that is to say, just the especially characteristic parts are restored, but also the whole r. half of the forehead upwards from the middle of the eye to pretty high up on the head, l. eyebrow with upper eyelid, a piece of l. part of forehead, half the ears, and lastly both shoulders. The rest has been broken in several places. Very life-like are the creases which extend downwards from the nose along the mouth, so also are the creases on the neck. The deep sunk, not very large, eyes also have an animated effect. Workmanship not very careful; curly hair only a little worked out. The bald part of the head is pretty extensive. Pupils and brows not expressed. The bust, the tablet (H. 0·04) with inscription and the low round pedestal (H. 0·08) in the form of an Attico-Ionic base are all unbroken and form one piece. Greek marble, apparently Parian; the restorations are made partly in Thasian, partly in coarse-grained Parian marble. Total H. 0·62. L. of face 0·24. [*]

2. **Bust of Athenè**, somewhat bent l. A so-called Corinthian helmet covers the hair, which is simply combed in waves to the sides, as in the case of the Amazons, and falls down on the neck tied up into a knot of moderate dimensions. Shape of face oval, but not so much so as in great part of the later heads of Athenè; similarly the expression is thoughtful, but not sentimental. New: whole neck and breast, tip of nose and part of helmet. The rest has been much broken. Beautiful Parian marble. H. of genuine parts, 0·41. L. of face 0·18. [*]

3. **Bust of Lucius Ursus**. Visconti, *Iconogr. Rom.*, I. Pl. 9, 3, 4. A bald crown with rather scanty hair at the sides and behind. Head looks r. somewhat. Forehead wrinkled, lips thin, expression of mouth energetic. New: nose and ears as well as shoulders, the bust has never been broken. Below this, a low tablet (H. 0·06); the inscription runs *L. Vrsum cos. III* | *Crescens lib.* (*C. I. Lat.*, VI. 1, 1432). L. Julius Ursus Servianus, husband of Hadrian's sister Paulina, was consul for the third time in the year A.D. 134, being the last private citizen who held the office. Two years afterwards, when 90 years old, he was put to death by the order of his brother-in-law, the Emperor (cf. Visconti, *l. cit.*, pp. 303 ff.). The expressive, but by no means delicate execution, is far removed from the laboured elegance of the busts of Hadrian. Pretty seriously worn. Italian marble. Total height 0·55. L. of face 0·20. Formerly in Rome, in Visconti's time in Paris. [*]

4. **Bust of Septimius Severus**, of little merit. Pupils expressed. New: nose, breast and pedestal. L. of face 0·22. [*]

5. **Bust of Lucius Verus**, still worse. New: nose, upper lip, neck, breast and pedestal. L. of face 0·19. [*]

6. **A bust of a warrior** with helmet, eyebrows wrinkled, and (7) a **bronze bust of Vitellius** are new, as also is (8) **Alexander the Great**, a copy of the bust at Blenheim (no. 1), which is exhibited in the Hall. [*]

9. **Statue of Eros as a child.** He sits on a rock and lets the r. leg hang down, having drawn up l. foot and set it on the rock; both hands rest on the knee. Curly hair arranged along the parting in a sort of plait. He looks down in the direction of r. leg, at something which fixes his attention. Pleasing conception. New: greater

part of wings, parts of feet, of hands and of l. knee, pieces of the pedestal.   H. 0·64.   [*]

Mr Atkinson.

Mr Atkinson, residing in the neighbourhood of St John's Wood, is said to have a number of Athenian works in marble, among which are named several **Fragments from the Parthenon**, as a gift of Lord Elgin's.   I have not hitherto been able to learn anything more specific about the matter; it seems extraordinary that Lord Elgin should himself have made his collection of sculptures from the Parthenon incomplete.

C. S. Bale, Esq.

The choice collection which Waagen found in the house of Mr C. S. Bale (*Treas.*, II. p. 332) was sold at Christie's in June, 1881. It consisted of antique **gems; Greek** and **Roman coins**, especially in gold; **gold ornaments; Etruscan candelabra**, and painted **vases**.

Burlington House (Piccadilly).

The Society of Antiquaries possesses, with the exception of Anglo-Roman remains, no Greek or Roman antiques of particular value.   Cf. A. Way, *Catalogue of antiquities, coins, pictures, and miscellaneous curiosities, in the possession of the Soc. of Ant. of London,* 1847.   Some **Attic vases** are perhaps worth noticing (Waagen, *Treas.*, II. p. 326), and the gold ornaments from Ithaka given by Dr Lee.

Colonel Maitland Crichton.

Colonel Maitland Crichton, 29, St James' Place, possesses a beautiful female portrait bust, formerly in the possession of the late Andr. Coventry, Esq., of Edinburgh, who wrote a paper on it (*Trans. R. Soc. Edinburgh*, XX. P. 3, 1852, p. 417).   It is under life size, very delicate, especially in the shape of nose and mouth and in the virginal expression.   The curly hair which surrounds the head in waving masses and forms a small knot on the neck is prettily treated. The resemblance to the "Clytia" of the British Museum (Graeco-

Roman Sculpt., no. 149. Huebner, *Bildniss einer Roemerin*, Berlin, 1873) is unmistakeable, only our head is more youthful and it has not the long curled tresses falling down on the shoulders. These very points increase the likeness to the portraits on coins of **Antonia Augusta**, younger daughter of M. Antonius and Octavia, wife of Drusus, mother of Germanicus and Claudius, which Mr R. S. Poole has recognised in the "Clytia" (*Encycl. Brit.*, 8th ed., *Numismatics*, p. 385 no e I. Huebner, p. 9). New: tip of nose and details on r. ear and hair. The head is of Parian marble. It is placed upon a draped bust of Carrara marble which is a little too large for it. H. 0.49. L. of face 0.14. Found in Tusculum by Lucien Buonaparte (1818?), sold by Capranesi to Mr J. Rhodes and thus passed to Mr Coventry, uncle of the present owner. [*]

DE MAULEY, *see* Mauley.

DEVONSHIRE HOUSE. (Piccadilly).

The DUKE OF DEVONSHIRE keeps in his town house a collection of **Gems** containing 546 specimens, some of them of the greatest value, see Waagen, *Treas.*, II. p. 78 (I. p. 95). For the rest cf. Chatsworth.

LORD ELCHO.

At LORD ELCHO's residence, 23, St James' Place, Waagen, (*Treas.*, IV. p. 64) saw the marble head of a youthful **Dionysos** with a large bandeau round his head. "The ideal conception of this god is here rendered with uncommon beauty, and, with the admirable workmanship, displays the hands of a Greek artist of no ordinary skill. The greater portion of the nose, and almost the whole lower lip, are modern." As the neighbouring house once belonged to Lord Guilford, and as I know from certain sources (cf. Introd., p. 161, note 432) that on leaving the house he left behind him several fragments of Greek sculpture that had been built into the wall, it is not impossible that this Dionysos is derived from the

Guilford collection. At any rate among the many and divers antiques which Brownlow North, Lord Bishop of Winchester, son of the first Lord Guilford and brother of the minister, Lord North, had collected in Italy and displayed in the episcopal palace in Chelsea (Introd. § 59), there is mentioned, as an especial ornament to the entrance hall, "an antique juvenile bust of Bacchus, much admired" (Faulkener, *History of Chelsea*, 1. p. 294). The bishop died in 1820, Winchester House was pulled down and its contents dispersed. At that time the bishop's nephew, Frederick, 5th Earl of Guilford, himself a zealous collector (Introd. § 88), lived in the house 24, St James' Place, so that the bust may have been taken thither.

<hr />

Richard Ford, Esq.

At the residence of RICH. FORD, Esq., Waagen (*Treas.*, 11. p. 226) saw "the **torso of an Aphroditè** in Greek marble, excavated at Rome in 1845. The goddess is youthfully conceived, of very noble and slender proportions, and of decided Greek workmanship."

<hr />

Augustus W. Franks, Esq.

AUG. W. FRANKS, Esq., F.R.S., keeper of the Department of British and Mediaeval Antiquities and Ethnography in the British Museum, possesses two collections of old drawings from Antiques (see Matz, *Arch. Zeit.*, 1873, p. 34).

I. A collection derived from CH. TOWNLEY. It now fills a very large portfolio, the drawings however have for the most part been detached from two parchment volumes (designated on the backs as *Bassirilievi diversi*), which in their externals fully correspond with Vols. XIII.—XVI. of the collection at Windsor. The green edging of the sheets still observable in many places, the consecutive numbering, the kind of paper, and the whole character of the drawings make it quite certain that they constitute fragments of the collection of the Commendatore DAL POZZO (see on Windsor), though intermingled with foreign elements. With this view, moreover, a MS. notice of Townley's falls in—"From Macgowan's Sale, Feb, 1804. Formerly in the Albani collection, and sold at Dalton's Sale at Greenwood's about 1790" (more accurately, 1791, as another

notice of Townley's shows). George III. had bought that collection
of drawings, now in Windsor, from Cardinal Albani (Introd. § 50);
in what way two volumes of it may have got into the private possession of Dalton, who died as Royal Librarian at Windsor Castle, is
not known. Mr Franks' collection is singularly rich in drawings of
Sarcophagus reliefs. The contents will not be individually
enumerated in this place ; a more exact account is left to be given on
another occasion. [*.M]

11. A Folio Volume in Red Morocco with gilt edges. These
drawings are all in pencil and crayon and contain with many other
specimens for the most part **vases in marble.** The collection was
made by Don Gasparo d' Haroeguzman Marchese del Carpio e
Heliece, Spanish ambassador in Rome 1676—1682, subsequently
viceroy of Naples ; it comprises his purchases at Rome on the sale
of the collection of Cardinal Camillo de' Massimi (cf. Fea, *Miscellanea,* i. p. cclxii.), and was meant to be published. There are in all
105 leaves. [*.M]

Guildhall.

In the library of the Guildhall is a **Roman lamp** with a relief
of the enthroned **Serapis** (cf. Sante Bartoli, *Lucerne ant.,* ii. Pl.
6), several fragments of red Samian pottery ware, &c., &c. [C]

W. R. Hamilton, Esq.

At the residence of the late W. R. Hamilton, Esq., Waagen
(*Treas.,* ii. p. 333) admired, among various antiquities of Grecian
art, the fragment of a **glass vessel,** which surpassed in beauty everything of the kind that he had seen.

In the *Specimens of Antient Sculpture,* the following marbles were
engraved and described as belonging to this gentleman :

1. **Head of Berenikè,** colossal scale, in marble, of fairly
ideal character. *Spec.,* ii. Pl. 39. Brought from Egypt by consul
Baldwin (cf. Kingston Hall). H. 0·39.

2. **Head of Nike with mask of Medusa.** *Spec.,* ii. Pl. 44,
" Perseus." *Annali,* 1839, Pl. K. " Minerva Gorgolopha" (Abeken).
Braun, *Vorschule zur Kunstmythologie,* Pl. 59. *Arch. Zeit.,* 1857, Pl.

97, "Aphrodite Parakyptusa" (Welcker). The correct interpretation is given by Helbig (*Rhein. Museum*, XXIV. p. 303), by his comparison of a Vatican statuette (*Mus. Pio-Clem.*, II. Pl. 11. Clarac,
IV. 636, 1442 ; better, Piranesi, *Vasi e Candelabri*, II. Pl. 64, 65) : it is
Nikè who has conquered the foe by holding before her face the mask
of Medusa, and now pushes up the horrible object so as to view the
field of victory with her own countenance. Found in Rome towards
the end of the last century, brought to Canova by a peasant, and
given by Canova to Mr Hamilton. The slab on which this very
beautiful head is fastened is presumably a modern addition.

HOLLAND HOUSE (1, Addison Road, Kensington).

In Holland House Heydemann saw in 1873 a **child's sarcophagus**, which he described as follows (*Berichte d. sächs. Ges. d.
Wiss.*, 1878, p. 133, note 1). FRONT: In the middle are two Cupids
holding a shield with the inscription : *D(is) M(anibus)* | *Sextio
P(ubli) f(ilio)* | *Cornelio ? Pal(atina)* | *Neptili̅ano, q(ui) v(ixit annum)
I* | *m(enses) V.* Below the shield stands a helmet. On the l. three
Cupids ; one sits holding a piece of iron on the anvil; the second,
standing opposite to him, is hammering at it with upraised arms
(forearms and hammer broken off) ; the third stands behind the
first and looks on. Behind the anvil the forge with blazing fire.
On the r. two Cupids, lifting up a long spear. ENDS: a sitting griffin
on each. Wretched workmanship. In good preservation.

LANSDOWNE HOUSE (Berkeley Square).

Dallaway, pp. 340 ff., 368 f. (II. pp. 86 ff., 120 f.). His very scanty
notices are valuable because they rest on the statements of the
librarian of Lansdowne House [see Goede, *England*, Dresden, 1806,
IV. p. 43], and therefore are perhaps derived from the records of the
purchases, which, however, are now better known from the letters
published by Lord Edmund Fitzmaurice (see below). K. O. Müller
in Böttiger's *Amalthea*, III. pp. 241 ff. (= Müller, *Kunstarchäolog.
Werke*, II. pp. 74 ff.) whom I denote by *m.* Waagen, *Treas.*, II. pp.
143 ff. (II. pp. 70 ff.). Clarac, III. p. 176. Mrs Jameson's *Companion
to the private galleries of art in England*, London, 1844, pp. 332 ff.

28—2

Michaelis, *Arch. Anz.*, 1862, pp. 333 ff. *Arch. Zeit.*, 1874, pp. 35 ff.
I have been allowed to inspect the collection, 1861, 1873, and 1877,
pretty much at leisure.

The collection of antiques at Lansdowne House, formerly called
Shelburne House, is one of the most beautiful and valuable in
England, and also one of the most admirably arranged. Its founder
was the celebrated statesman, WILLIAM, SECOND EARL OF SHEL-
BURNE (family names PETTY-FITZMAURICE), created 1784 FIRST MAR-
QUIS OF LANSDOWNE, who built the house (Introd. § 60). During a
stay in Rome, 1771, he purchased the first specimens, which were
principally derived from Gavin Hamilton's successful excavations of
1769 (Introd. § 48), in the Pantanello (Hadrian's Villa). He also
entered into correspondence with Hamilton with a view to the
extension of his gallery and appointed him his agent in chief.
Hamilton indeed projected the scheme of the whole collection and
had a plan of the Sculpture Gallery made by Panini, which was however eventually abandoned. He writes to Lord Shelburne (Jan. 18,
1772): "The use of this gallery is to be a receptacle of fine antique
statues. I should therefore advise throwing our whole strength on
this point. I don't mean a collection such as has been hitherto
made by myself and others. *I mean a collection that will make Shelburne House famous not only in England but all over Europe.*" He
has kept his word. His letters of the years 1771–1779, lately
published by Lord Edm. Fitzmaurice (*Academy*, 1878, Aug. 10, 17,
24, 31, Sept. 7), give instructive disclosures about the first stage of
the formation of the collection; the statements of fact given therein
have been used in the following notices in their several places with
citation of the particular letter[1]. Up to 1779 the greatest stress was
laid on the adornment of the Ball Room, called also the Sculpture
Gallery, a most peculiar room with a large semicircular recess like
an apse at each end. Large niches offered positions for magnificent
statues. Most of these were in their places about the year 1779, by
which time the manifold other adornments of the gallery were also sub-
stantially complete. Besides this room the Library and the Garden
are mentioned in the letters as requiring or adapted for adornment
by sculptures. It appears that about that time there came a pause in

[1] I observe that no letter is missing before Letter IV., that Letter XXX. is
dated wrong or else placed out of order, that no. XXXI. should come next after no.
XXXVI., that no. XXXII. manifestly belongs, not to 1777 but to 1774, and that the
note of "July the 12th," no. XXXV., should be placed in the year 1776, as an
enclosure belonging to no. XXVIII.

the purchases; they were however taken up again subsequently (cf. no. 61). None of the statues, for instance, in the Dining Room, belong to the older purchases managed by Hamilton, so that the scheme of adorning this room also with sculptures seems not to have been originated until a later period, when it is probable that other additional purchases were also made. It would be a good thing if communications on this point could be disinterred from among the archives of Lansdowne House. In the year 1805, Lord Lansdowne died; his eldest son and successor took over the collection of antiques for £8000 (or £7000 according to Payne Knight, whose own valuation amounted to £11000, cf. *Report from the Elgin Committee*, p. 99). He left them to his widow (1809), who again transferred them by sale to her brother-in-law, Henry, the third Marquis of Lansdowne (1780—1863). This competent connoisseur added several works to the collection, including no. 57, and some of the busts (Mrs Jameson, pp. 287, 334, xi.).

The description follows the order of the present arrangement.

ENTRANCE HALL.

1. **Fragment of an Attic sepulchral relief**, of the most beautiful style. *Arch. Zeit.*, 1880, Pl. 9, pp. 81 ff. A piece of the pediment is preserved, and below it on the epistyle the inscription ἡ δεῖνα...]ομένο(υ)ς θυγά[τηρ; below this the veiled head of a seated female, a little bent down with slightly painful expression. A triple fillet traverses the soft wavy hair. In the lobe of the l. ear a hole for an ornament. Nose somewhat impaired. This very notable relief belongs to the first half of the fourth century B.C. Pentelic marble. H. 0·67. L. 0·49. L. of face 0·18. The head projects 0·155 from the field of the relief. [*C*]

2. **Relief.** Welcker, *Alte Denkmaeler*, ii. Pl. 11, 19, "Homer." Jahn, *Griech. Bilderchroniken*, Pl. 3, 1. A man sitting on a chair covered with a cushion under a tree, in the foliage whereof a nest with birds is introduced. A snake is wound round the tree, menacing the birds. The man is in a cloak, his l. arm supported on his knotty stick, which he holds with the r. hand. Under the chair sits a griffin. This as well as the nest and the snake (cf. Homer, *Il.* B. 312) has caused the subject to be interpreted as Homer meditating the Iliad; still it is questionable whether it is not rather meant generally for a sepulchral monument in memory of a poet (cf. Michaelis in Jahn, *l. cit.*, p. 58, 123). The relief is seriously broken in the upper

part. A fracture runs over the r. shoulder through the hollow of the throat slanting across the l. upper arm and cutting off half the l. forearm; the piece above this fracture is new. The head (new: nose, parts of hair and trifling patches) is old and, like the bulk of the relief, of Pentelic marble; as however the veins of the marble in the head run vertically, in the body horizontally, it is clear the head did not originally belong to the relief (cf. Dallaway, p. 343). It is assuredly a head of Hades; a hole on the top possibly may indicate a modius, of which however no other trace survives. Nest and birds mostly antique, only the lower half of the snake, the remainder is modern. R. hand and l. arm of the man with a piece of the cloak make up a distinct fragment, but it is antique and belongs to the relief. Enough of the knotty stick is antique to determine its right to be there. Of the chair the l. corner of the cushion and the lower half of the l. foot, the griffin's forelegs and other trifles besides are new. Good Attic high relief. Relief very round, but treated somewhat superficially. Found by Hamilton in Roma Vecchia (Dallaway, p. 379); he mentions it as "Aesculapius" in a letter to Lord Shelburne, July 13, 1776. H. 1·35. L. 0·93. Relief is in some places raised as much as 0·25 from field.

3. **Statue of a "boxer."** Clarac, v. 851, 2180 A. A youth resting on r. leg; r. arm lowered, l. raised. Antique: only the torso (exclusive of the r. shoulder), the l. leg to just above the knee, r. leg to half-way down the calf, together with the upper part of the stem of a tree. The neck is inserted as a patch. Head, very much effaced, of Pentelic marble, while the torso is of Thasian. The youth may have originally been pouring oil into his r. hand. Bought from Hamilton for £20 (letter of May 30, 1775). H. 1·49. [*]

4. **Statue of Apollo,** "of the gardens of Sallust." Clarac, III. 476 A, 906 A. The god is draped with the chlamys, and extends the l. arm so that a distant resemblance to the Apollo Belvedere is produced. The head, with hair in a top-knot, is re-set and much effaced, but appears to be original. New: both arms from the shoulders, lower half of chlamys, l. leg, lower part of r. leg, and stem with quiver. Poor, bad workmanship. Thasian marble. Bought from Hamilton for £25 (letter of May 30, 1775). H. 1·50. [*]

5. **Fine torso of a powerful man,** in attitude of repose. The r. arm was lowered, the l. raised. Greek marble. Chisel marks visible all over it. The impression from a little distance is highly effective. The back also is very good. H. from hollow of throat to pubis 0·62. [*]

6. **Statuette of a warrior.** Clarac, v. 972, 2510 B. The bearded man in coat of mail with a cloak on l. shoulder and round l. arm, extends his r. hand as if for an *adlocutio*, and lets the l. hand rest on a shield, which stands on a low pedestal. The sword hangs at the l. side. New: neck, r. arm, the front of the rim of the shield. The Commodus-like head, with a thick wreath, perhaps its own (nose new). Coarse work. Presented by Hamilton (letter of July 13, 1776). H. 0·73. [*]

7, 8. **Double terminal heads of the bearded Dionysos and Ariadne,** archaistic style; two copies. All noses new. Bought for 18 crowns (more than 4 guineas) from Hamilton (letter of July 12, 13, 1776). H. 0·42 and 0·43. [*]

STAIRCASE.

9. **Statue of Artemis as a huntress.** Clarac, iv. 565, 1217 A. The goddess hastens forward with r. leg advanced, short drapery, a small cloak thrown like a shawl over l. shoulder and round the waist. The l. arm was extended straight out in horizontal direction, the r. arm probably always somewhat raised. The torso however, exclusive of r. shoulder, and the legs to below the knees, are all that is antique. The antique mask of the face (nose new) does not belong to the statue. But that there is no trace of a quiver one would be reminded of the motive of the Artemis of Versailles. Careless decorative sculpture, yet not without effect. H. 2·05. [*Cm]

10. **Statue of Hygieia.** Clarac, iv. 552, 1172 B. A slender figure, resting on r. leg, and draped with a chiton and a cloak, which covers thighs, body, l. breast and l. arm. Both arms are lowered, r. forearm and l. hand missing. The head, somewhat bent, with a headcloth (κεκρύφαλος) is antique and belongs to the statue; nose injured. The large snake is preserved as far as before the breast, and moreover on r. thigh are traces of hand and snake. The statue is a replica of that at Deepdene (no. 7), but much inferior in dimensions, proportions and execution; there is a similar torso in the British Museum (Clarac, iv. 552 B, 1186 F). H. 0·96. [*]

11 (placed under no. 10). **Ara.** In front: a Fortuna seated, seen full face, veiled, with a large cornucopiae in l. arm, a cup in r., an ewer in l. hand. H. 0·63. L. 0·30. D. 0·27. [*]

12. **Statue of Hermaphroditos.** Clarac, iv. 750, 1829 B. "Nymphe." The Hermaphrodite reclines in repose on the rocky

ground with his drapery under him, head supported on l. hand and
l. leg drawn up under him. The r. hand rests on r. thigh. A
cloak covers the greatest part of the r. leg and a piece of the l.
shin. New: l. leg below knee, and knee-cap, r. leg from half
down the thigh and almost the whole drapery, r. arm from below
the elbow, l. forearm. There are patches on the breast. The
head is antique (nose and upper lip restored), but does not belong
to the body. Body, inclining to stoutness, fine ; hips broad, effeminate. There are clear indications that the whole figure should recline
more on its l. side. Workmanship not bad. Fine Greek marble,
apparently Parian. Bought from Hamilton for £40 (letter of May
30, 1775). L. 1·49. [*]

13. **Statue of a sleeping Nymph.** Clarac, IV. 750, 1829
A · 1829 D (inaccurate). The pose is in general similar to that of
no. 12, only the Nymph supports herself on the l. forearm, which rests
on an urn, and the r. hand is laid slantwise across breast on to l.
shoulder. New: the whole rocky ground, the whole of the legs
with the drapery covering them, part of the rest of the drapery and
a piece of the urn. On each arm is an armlet which gets broader in
the middle. A fillet in the hair. Ordinary decorative work. Thasian
marble. Can this be the "statue of the Nymph Egeria turned into
a fountain" which Lord Shelburne bought of Hamilton, 1771, for
£65 ? (Memorandum no. II.) L. 1·07. [*]

14. **Bust of Zeus.** Overbeck, *Atlas zur Kunstmyth.*, Pl. 2,
13, cf. *Kunstmyth.*, II. p. 79. The forehead is very low, towards the
temples the brows project considerably over the deep sunken
eyes. The expression is mild, and indeed somewhat unintellectual.
Mouth slightly opened. Head a little inclined to its own l. Hair
rising up over forehead hangs down dankly; the curly beard too hangs
considerably. A fillet traverses the hair. It may be in fact a question as to whether Poseidon is not intended. Certainly antique and
apparently original is the bust with rich folds of the cloak on the
l. shoulder. New: nose, under lip, a piece of the neck and hair, a
few patches on the bust. Top and back of head have been broken
off, but are apparently antique. Good workmanship, but unfortunately much rubbed away. The marble seems to be Greek.
Bought for 45 crowns (about £11) from Hamilton (Memorandum
of July 12, 1776). H. 0·70. L. of face 0·20. [*BCm II']

15 (placed under 14). **Cinerary urn of Nicostratus.** Cavaceppi, *Racc.* III. Pl. 12. FRONT. In the middle a niche rounded at
the top, its edge surrounded by eight small holes which must have

served to fasten on a metal border. In the niche the nude bust of a
youth with curly hair. Pupils expressed. On either side of the niche
a figure in relief: on the l. a nude youth in lively movement, with
upper part of body thrown back and upturned gaze; with the outstretched l. arm he has tossed up a shield of a peculiar shape (see
below), and seems to wish to catch it again. In his lowered r. hand
he holds a short sword. On the r. a second youth stands in repose,
draped in the short tunic; on his lowered l. arm he carries a shield
similar to that of his companion; in the r. hand he holds up his
sword (?). Below, the inscription: *Di[s Manibus Nicostrat[i]]
Neronis Claud[l Cae[sa]ris Augus[ti] | .. ven (or vin)..... RIGHT
SIDE. A double flute and a short sword in the sheath. LEFT SIDE.
A shield as above, of the following shape

with a boss; and a syrinx. LID FRONT. Two reclining figures
turned away from each other. On the l. a bearded Pan with a
pedum on his l. arm, over the goatish legs hang two flutes crossed,
one straight, the other curved. On the r. a draped girl (legs, hand
with wreath restored). BOTH SIDES are modern. H. 0·34, with lid
0·44. L. 0·46. D. 0·45. [*CM]

16 (placed under 15). **Sepulchral ara of T. Flavius
Sedatus.** It is adorned with rams' heads which support garlands;
below, at the corners griffins, behind, eagles. In the field made
by the garland in front an eagle and the inscription: *T. Flavio
Aug(usti) l(iberto) | Sedato | Antoniano | P. Cornelius | Iaso patri |
piIssimo;* on each side a bird and above them on the r. an ewer,
on the l. a cup. H. 0·94. L. 0·64. D. 0·51. [*C]

17. **Sepulchral ara of Vicanus.** At the corners, spiral-
shaped twisted columns on each of which stands a Cupid holding a
garland. Over the latter the apparently modern inscription: *D. M. |
Vicano incoparabili ac dulci filio Nedimus | et Sintyche p(arentes)
f(ecerunt). | v(ixit) a(nnum) I m(enses) V d(ies) XVIII.* Below this
a tripod between two griffins. Above on the lid two birds and an
overturned basket of flowers. On the sides, l. a cup, r. an ewer, above,
birds. H. 0·55. L. 0·36. D. 0·33. [*C]

18, 19. Two modern round sepulchral **vases**, the one with
the inscription: *D. M. | Dis Manibus | L. Macri | Fuelpisti* (for
Euelpisti). [°]

20. **Marble throne consecrated to Apollo.** *Mon. dell'*

Inst., v. 28; cf. *Annali,* 1851, p. 102 (E. Braun). The seat is cushioned and covered over with a drapery, and is supported on four very richly ornamented legs, the tops of which terminate in eagles' heads. On the seat and the high back, which is framed by pilasters, and above by a pretty ornament, are represented in very high relief a bow (strangely, as it seems, cracked, the one half leaning towards the back, the other half lying on the seat) entwined by a large snake, and a quiver of which the broad strap is richly decorated with a palmette pattern. Elegant work; much broken, but antique, as it seems, in essentials; the dark position makes an accurate investigation difficult. H. 1·54. L. 0·63. D. 0·47. [*Cm*]

21. **Roman sepulchral monument.** Five busts (belonging to three generations) close together; an elderly man, a young woman, a young man (nude), a very old woman and a very old man. The grandam (no. 4) exhibits a head-dress not uncommon in the Augustan period, a small roll projecting over the forehead (cf. Mongez, *Iconogr. Rom.,* Pl. 19), though broken. Noses wholly or partially restored, missing on no. 5. H. 0·74. L. 1·81. [*B*]

22. **Roman sepulchral monument.** Three busts over life size, of the period of the Claudian Emperors; father, mother and son. The woman's hair is arranged in the style of the elder Agrippina. Noses restored. H. 0·66. L. 1·27. [*B*]

23. **Roman sepulchral monument.** Busts of a man and his wife in high relief, well executed, apparently somewhat retouched; noses new. Between them the inscription: *Hanc talem | coniugem, quam | praefestinas | Fatus peremit, | quam Fors tribuit, | Fortuna ademit. | casus dominatur. | quapropter hos pes, spera, pauca adpete, vive | quietus, teque hominem c000000000: | omnia despicies. | Deum Manium | sacrum. parce, | Ita te dcis superis | atque inferis | parcant. | vale.* H. 0·40. L. 0·50. For *praefestinas Fatus* (cf. Petronius, ch. 42, 71, and frequently on inscriptions) also an inscription in Castle Howard may be compared: *L. Pituani Salvi. quoniam te Fatus praecucurrit, ossa tua bene adquiescant.* [*]

24. **Sepulchral ara of M. Carienius Venustus.** Above, the bust of a boy in a semicircular field. In the field the inscription: *Dis Man(ibus) | M. Carienio M. f. | Venusto | q(ui) v(ixit) an(nos) VIII m(enses) X | M. Carienius Felix | et Carienia Venusta | infelicissimi parentes fec(erunt).* On the sides, l. the ewer, r. the cup. H. 0·87. L. 0·64. D. 0·29. [*C*]

25 (on the staircase). **Bacchic frieze.** Cavaceppi, *Racc.,* II.

Pl. 58. The upper border with ovolo pattern proves that this is not the slab of a sarcophagus, though the subject suggests it; but the distance also between the several figures is contrary to the style of sarcophagus reliefs. The procession moves from l. to r.; whether it is quite complete cannot be said as the l. end is restored. Here stands a Satyr with a skin over the l. shoulder, and holds out a drinking-horn (*rhyton*) in his r. hand to receive the precious draught from the bowl of the Dionysos. The god crowned with ivy (new: neck and l. shoulder) lies in easy attitude in a car of strange shape, rounded in the form of a tray, and only two-wheeled; the cloak covers only the legs. He holds a wreath in the l. hand, the out-stretched r. arm, with the bowl (*kantharos*) carelessly held, rests on the shoulder of a female lying in the car by the god; she wears a girdled chiton, which has slipped from the r. shoulder. Two Centaurs draw the car, one bearded, playing on the cithara (new: head, probably also the upper part of the body, and the cithara), and the other younger, blowing the double flute (new: head, r. arm, r. leg); on their backs a Cupid stands as driver, but of this figure only the torso with the thighs and the fore part of the l. foot are antique. Below the car lies a syrinx, a tympanon and a pedum. Before the Centaurs dances Pan, with a skin over his l. shoulder, with his r. foot treading on a krupezion. He stretches the r. hand forward (holding nothing), the l. up; his head he turns back, because a youthful Satyr dancing before him, with the nebris over his breast, flourishing the pedum in his l. hand, is hitting him in the face with the r. hand. Beyond, a Maenad, in chiton, dancing and striking the tympanon (new: head and lower part of r. arm). Next comes a dancing Satyr (not a Maenad) who is blowing the double flute, seen from back; then a Maenad, nearly nude, in full face, striking the tympanon. Lastly, a bearded Pan with man's legs but goat's horns, a cloak on his back. Though the whole has a good effect, still the work is rough, and might here and there arouse suspicion of modern origin, though scarcely with justice. Pretty seriously restored and much blackened, having probably indeed been coated with black paint. H. 0·50. L. 2·15. [*Mm*]

26 (over a door on the first floor). **Greek sepulchral relief.** On the r. a throne with high square back and very artistically turned legs; the arms supported in front by an eagle. On it sits a stately woman in sleeveless chiton; a cloak covers her legs and falls down with a corner over her l. arm with which the woman supports herself on the arm of the throne. She holds out the r. arm, adorned on the upper part and the wrist with armlets (ψέλια), towards a flat casket with open lid, which a little serving-maid hands her. Two holes on the casket prove that metal ornament of some kind was introduced here, perhaps ribbons, or at least some article of the toilet which the woman is about to take from the casket. The relief is excellent in its kind, rounded and raised very high (more than 0·16), and with the principal figure about half the size of life. It seems to be a good Roman imitation of an older Greek original; the place where it is let into the wall is so situated as to make close examination difficult. H. 0·93. L. 1·04. [*M]

ANTE-ROOM (on the right next the Entrance Hall).

27. Small relief, in a frame. Four hippocampi, led to the r. by a Triton; the Poseidon on the l. is restored. High relief. H. 0·21. L. of genuine part 0·37. [*]

DINING ROOM.

28. Statue of "Tiberius." Clarac, v. 925, 2356 C. A head of Tiberius in Pentelic marble (new: nose and chin) is connected by means of a modern neck with a heroic statue of Thasian marble. The powerful, almost coarse, frame steps slightly forward with the l. leg. A cloak lies on the l. shoulder and winds round the l. arm which is set akimbo. New: lowered r. arm, some fingers of l. hand, lower parts of legs, the support by the l. leg and a great part of the drapery. The l. thigh has been broken at the top but is joined on again. Coarse work. H. 1·93. [*]

29. Statue of a Roman in the toga. Clarac, v. 894, 2284. This statue is broken across the middle, but is nevertheless very well preserved except the modern neck, on which is set a coarse portrait head (a replica of the "Sulla" in the Vatican, *Braccio Nuovo*, no. 60; new: nose, pupils expressed), and except the greater part of the r. arm. L. hand with roll worked over. H. 2·05. [*B]

30. Statue of "Traian." Clarac, v. 942, 2415 A. The head of Trajan (new: nose; lips, chin) does not belong to the statue, which in its main attitude corresponds to no. 28, only that the l. arm is not akimbo. New: r. arm with sword, l. forearm and considerable portions of the cloak, lower part of r. leg, l. foot, pedestal and a large portion of the support. Ordinary work. H. 1·93. [*B]

31. Statue of Dionysos in repose. Clarac, iv. 695, 1568.
The torso is antique in essentials, with the nebris girt from the l.
shoulder slantwise across the breast, and so are the extremities so far
as to determine the movement. New: head, r. arm lying thereon
and the l. arm leaning on the stem of a tree, the stem itself, the
lower part of l. leg and three quarters of r. leg on which the body
rests. The merit of the sculpture is not in proportion to the size of
the work. Greek marble. H. 2·30. [*]

32. Statue of Apollo. Clarac, iii. 476 A, 906 C. The
figure quite nude, both arms lowered, steps forward just a little
on the l. foot. The head, never broken off, is a head of Apollo,
with wreath of laurel which lies very gracefully on the hair; the
fillet falls down on the shoulders (new: nose, lips, r. cheek). The
r. arm with arrow, all fingers of l. hand with staff, r. leg entirely,
l. leg from half way down thigh, the greatest part of the support are
restored. Common-place work. Coarse-grained Greek marble. H.
1·79. [*B]

33. Statue of Tychè. Clarac, iii. 454 B, 839 B, "Sabine
ou Plotine en Fortune." It is a noble figure in double chiton; such
as is usual in the older Attic sculpture. It rests on r. leg. Noteworthy is the strong delineation of the folds of the upper portion that
flow slantwise down towards the r. hip. R. hand with steering-
paddle is restored, and there is no indication of it in the figure itself,
but the cornucopiae in the l. hand is antique except the lower point
and the hand; hence in fact an early (Attic?) type of Tychè seems
to lie before us, perhaps belonging to the first half of the fourth
century B. C., unless we are to suppose that a favourite early motive
in drapery carving has here been at a later date transferred to
Tychè. The unknown portrait head with huge wig (belonging to the
beginning of the second century, but neither Sabina nor Plotina)
may be its own, though the neck is a modern insertion; still it is
doubtful. A few toes and various folds are restored. Drapery
rather drily, but not badly treated. Pentelic marble. H. 1·76. [*B]

34. Portrait Statue. Clarac, v. 971, 2510 A. A youth,
furnished with the chlamys, in which the body is rather framed than
covered, steps forward with the r. leg by which is a large quiver
serving as a support. New: only the greater part of l. arm. The
lowered r. arm, though broken in different places, is nevertheless
probably entirely antique. The cheerful head with agreeable
features (pupils expressed) represents neither M. Aurelius nor Geta;
it is unknown. Ordinary work. Thasian marble. H. 1·57. [*B]

35. **Statue of Hermes.** Clarac, v. 946, 2436 A, "Antinous" (wrongly without doubt). The god rests on the l. leg, r. arm lowered, with the chlamys over l. arm. The statue is in perfect preservation except the l. hand. Two large marble blocks or *puntelli* (between the calves and between the r. hip and the r. hand) as well as two smaller ones (between thumb and forefinger of the r. hand, and between member and scrotum) have contributed to its preservation. This youthful head in the style of Polykleitos, to which the "Idolino" in Florence is allied (Clarac, IV. 680, 1591), is small in proportion to the slim body of the youthful figure. The treatment of the chlamys vividly recalls that of the bronze Hermes in the British Museum (*Spec.*, II. 33. Clarac, IV. 666, 1515. Müller-Wieseler, II. 34, 314). Altogether the entire statue conveys the impression of being a conglomeration of divers reminiscences. Pentelic marble. Very good execution. H. 1·75. [*]

36. **Statue of an Athlete.** Clarac, v. 856, 2180. Cavaceppi, *Racc.*, I. Pl. 21. The figure rests on r. leg with tolerably strong inclination of the body, the l. leg being somewhat drawn back ; by r. leg the stem of a palm tree; both arms have always been outstretched. One might suggest the motive of an ἀποξυόμενος, *destringens se*, which is so popular, for both arms with the caestus are new, as also the foot and the pedestal. The head a little recalls the head of an athlete in Ince, no. 152, but it belongs to a younger development of art. New: the top of the head, tip of nose, lips. Very good work. Marble seems to be Greek. H. 1·73. [*B]

37. **Female head,** of colossal scale. *Spec.*, I. Pl. 27. The face is seriously restored ; new : nose, lips, chin. Hair parted and twisted behind into a kind of roll; a thick twisted ribbon, such as often occurs in the case of Asklepios, goes round the head. It is a Roman copy of an older original, the severe proportions of which and the sharp treatment of the edge of the brow and of the eyelids are still slightly indicated, though the effect of the copy is not happy. The bust, trimmed to a terminal shape, is new. L. of face 0·21. Bought of Gavin Hamilton for £43 as "Erma of Berenice" (letters of July 16, Dec. 26, 1772). [*B]

38. **Bust of Antinous** ; in Egyptian costume, with the calantica, which suits the character of the head admirably. The glance of the eyes goes straight forward rigidly, and is less gloomy than usual. Eyebrows expressed. New: the greater part of the calantica from above the band over the forehead, the tip of the nose, neck and breast. On the top of the head a dowel-hole (modern ?).

H. 0·59. L. of face 0·19. Found in Hadrian's Villa, 1769, bought from Hamilton for £75 (letter of Dec. 15, 1771). [*]

39. Statue of Paris. Clarac, III. 396 E, 664 I., "Atys." The beautiful youth rests the r. hand on a low stem of a tree, so that the shoulder is somewhat forced up. The r. leg is crossed in front of the l. on which the body is supported. The l. hand lies on the back. The curly head, with Phrygian cap, is gracefully bent ; the curls treated similarly to those of the Vatican Eros (*Mus. Pio-Clem.*, I. Pl. 12). The head is certainly re-set, but, according to the view of Clarac, Bernoulli and myself, is without doubt original, while Dallaway remarks (p. 340) that it is "not its own." Unhappily the statue is much mutilated. New : nose, lips, chin, peak and most of the cap, considerable pieces on the neck, and r. forearm ; l. arm patched, but apparently quite antique ; l. thigh patched ; the lower parts of both legs, broken, r. above, l. below knee, are doubtful ; the l. foot, toes of r. and part of pedestal certainly antique. The name "Paris" is not indisputably correct ; the addition of an eagle, for example, would at once make it quite as suitable for a Ganymedes (cf. *Mus. Pio-Clem.*, II. Pl. 35). The beauty of the statue, which is with justice highly praised, lies more in the fine movement and generally in the conception than in the execution, which is not excellent. The marble seems to be Greek. H. 1·56. Found by Hamilton, 1769, in Hadrian's Villa (Dallaway, p. 368), then for a long time in process of restoration (Hamilton's letter of Jan. 18, 1772), and sold to Lord Shelburne for £200 (letter of Dec. 26, 1772). [*BC*]

40 (inserted into the pedestal of no. 39). **Fragment of an ornament of branches,** very delicate. [*]

41. Statue of Apollo Sauroktonos. Clarac, III. 476 B, 905 D. Antique : torso, r. thigh to above the knee, half l. thigh, half upper part of r. and whole upper part of l. arm (attached to the stem of a tree). Work soft and very good, though not excellent. On the modern neck a pretty Apollo's head (antique) is set, with a top-knot above the forehead and a fillet (new : half the nose) ; it does not belong to the statue and also has not the right pose, as it does not look at the tree, but down before him. The restorer, to be sure, had not recognised the original motive of the torso, and had changed it into a Narkissos. After Hamilton had long busied himself to no purpose to find as pendant to the Paris (no. 39) a Venus of corresponding dimensions, as Lord Shelburne wished, he sent him this "sweet pretty statue representing a Narcissus, of the exact size with the Paris, and I imagine will suit it for a companion, without waiting for a Venus, which are very rare to be found of that small size. The price of it is £150 including all charges at Rome and Leghorn" (letter of Aug. 9, 1775). Italian marble. H. 1·46. [*BC]

42 (inserted into the pedestal of no. 41). **Ornament of branches**, pendant to no. 40.

LIBRARY.

The busts almost all stand very high on the bookcases.

44. **Head of beardless Roman** with short hair. [B]

45. **Small head of " Sappho,"** corresponding to that in the Louvre (Clarac, VI. 1114, 3520 A), in the Vatican (*Mus. Pio-Clem.*, VI. Pl. 4, 2), in Wilton, no. 128, and elsewhere. A cloth is wound several times round the head; curls hang down on the sides. New : tip of nose and bust. [*B]

46. **Female head of Antonia** probably. Bernoulli observes, "This portrait corresponds more to the pleasing type of the Roman bronze coins and to the noble picture given by historical tradition than any single bust of the Italian Museums. Cf. Wilton, no. 25." [*B]

47. **Head of a youthful Roman**, beardless, with full, curly hair. The paludamentum on the l. shoulder. Below life size. [B]

48. **Colossal head of a Roman**, beardless, somewhat of the character of the so-called Marcellus in the Capitol (*Mus. Capitol.*, II. Pl. 3). [B]

49. **Fragment of a female statue**, upper part, in the treatment of the Pudicitia, broken below the breast. The r. hand covered by the drapery, is raised towards the neck. The virginal expression is extraordinarily noble and thoughtful, the hair is smooth and encircled by a fillet. This fragment, found in Hadrian's Villa 1769, is one of Lord Shelburne's earliest acquisitions ; he bought it of Hamilton for £50 (Memorandum, no. 11). [*B]

50. **Female portrait-bust** of the period of the Flavian emperors, with a raised structure of curls pointed in the style of a tragic onkos. The face is that of a woman past her prime of youth, and is pretty plump and of proud expression. The brows are lowered towards the nose. Life size. [*B]

51. **Bust of Antoninus Pius** (?). [B]

52.   Ideal bust of a female, with fillet and top-knot. [*B*]

53.   Female head. *Spec.*, 1. Pl. 7. Bernoulli writes, "It has smooth, wiry hair, which is twisted round a fillet along the somewhat flat forehead, and behind forms a roll which stands out some way, and is combed upwards. This peculiar treatment of the hair, which scarcely ever recurs in any other head, makes it probable that it is a portrait; the simple, sharp, almost dry sculpture, renouncing all picturesque effect, indicates a rather early period, and the wire-like character of the hair suggests a bronze original. According to Payne Knight's letterpress to the *Specimens*, the hair is indeed for the most part modern; the restoration however seems to be established by replicas at Richmond (no. 53), in the Vatican (Chiaramonti, no. 363), in the British Museum (Graeco-Roman Basement Room). The head, according to Payne Knight in excellent preservation, rests on a bust with a gathered chiton, hemmed round on the neck, a piece of cloak running obliquely across the l. shoulder." Found by Hamilton in the neighbourhood of Rome. [**B*]

54.   Head of a beardless Roman, turned somewhat l., recalling Modius Asiaticus (Wilton, no. 78), but not identical therewith. Life size. [*B*]

55.   Portrait bust of an elderly Roman lady with wavy hair, gathered behind into a tolerably peaked knot, little ornamental curls in front of the ears; the hair is treated very much like that of Lucilla in Mongez, *Iconogr. Rom.*, Pl. 42. Life size. [**B*]

56.   Porphyry bust of Vitellius. Face uninjured. It corresponds to the coins better than the ordinary busts, therefore Bernoulli holds an antique origin to be at least possible; I doubt this, for example on account of the thoroughly unantique rendering of the pupils by a roundish hollow. On the back of the head a bald patch. Corslet and cloak of bronze. Over life size. [**B*]

SCULPTURE GALLERY (Ball Room).

The numbering begins with the easterly apse and then goes round the wall.

57.   Statue of a boy; travesty of Herakles in repose. Clarac, IV. 650 D, 1478 A, "Amour." Exactly in the attitude of the Farnese statue of Glykon; the lion's skin with the claws tied in front of the neck covers the head and the l. arm; the club is wrongly restored. Whether Eros is meant is not quite certain; no wings. The whole figure is pretty, the expression of the face roguish, as

M. C.

becomes the motive.   New : the whole stem, l. hand with club, parts
of skin, lower parts of both legs.   H. 0·98.   Bought by Henry, 3rd
Marquis of Lansdowne.   [*m II']

58 (under no. 57).   **Round altar with Bacchic relief.**   On
the r. side of an altar adorned with a garland (without figure-sculpture),
on which burns a small pile of wood, stands Dionysos in a long
doubled chiton (the under part, of finer material, is only visible at the
feet) and with a nebris which is tied round the waist with a girdle.   On
his feet he wears pointed shoes.   The stiff pose and archaic drapery
correspond to the pointed beard and to the arrangement of the hair
in long stiff curls.   In his lowered l. hand he carries a vessel with
handles, shaped like half an egg, and in the r. hand an ewer with
handles from which he pours a libation on the altar.   A Maenad
follows with her sword over her head, and the hind half of a kid in
her l. hand (exactly like Broadlands, no. 5, fig. 2.   Zoega, *Bassir.*,
Pl. 83, fig. 2, Pl. 84, fig. 2.   Müller-Wieseler, II. 48, 602, fig. 6).
Opposite Dionysos, next the altar, stands a second Maenad in chiton
and fluttering cloak, with a wreath in the l. hand and a corner of her
drapery in the r., her head thrown back (like Zoega, Pl. 84, fig. 5).
A third companion follows her, likewise with head thrown back on
neck, with an upright thyrsos in the r. hand and a half kid in the l.
(like Broadlands, no. 5, fig. 3.   Zoega, Pl. 83, fig. 3, Pl. 84, fig. 6.
Clarac, II. 135, 135).   The combination of full freedom of movement,
in the figures of these enthusiastic women, with archaic stiffness in
that of the god, is characteristic of the eclecticism of the so-called
New Attic School in Rome, to which corresponds also the angular
style of the execution.   Below, an ovolo and other mouldings.
Pentelic marble.   H. 0·55.   Diameter 0·38.   [*Cm IV]

59 (under no. 58).   **Attic relief of Athenè Nikè.**   Athenè
stands facing r., draped in a rich doubled chiton, which is opened on
the r. leg and forms two rows of beautiful zigzag folds ; the l. knee is
a little bent.   A simple cloak falls down behind the back (as on the
Eirenè in Munich) ; the goddess wears no aegis.   The hair falls down
far on to the nape of the neck.   The r. arm is akimbo.   The goddess
gazes at the lofty (Corinthian) helmet with magnificent plume which
she holds on her l. hand (cf. Harpocration *s. v.* Νίκη 'Αθηνᾶ).   A
large round shield stands by her l. leg, close to it a pillar on which
sits the owl.   On extreme r. a tree, manifestly the olive, entwined by
a snake (οἰκουρὸς ὄφις).   This excellent piece of the noblest style,
apparently belonging to the first half of the fourth century B.C., is
executed in low relief, only the r. forearm in high relief.   Pentelic

marble. H. 0·72. L. 0·46. As Müller does not mention the relief, it is probably one of the purchases of the third Marquis. The Archaeological Institute in Rome possesses a drawing of it. [*CH*]

60. Bust of Hadrian. New: nose, neck and breast. H. 0·32. L. of face 0·20. [*]

61. Statue of Herakles. *Spec.*, i. Pl. 40. Clarac, v. 788, 1973. This beautiful statue, always rightly considered one of the choicest ornaments of the collection, exhibits the hero as of youthful age. He rests on r. leg, holding club over l. shoulder; the lowered r. hand clasps the lion's skin, which hangs down to the ground and is adroitly used as a support for the r. leg. In spite of the powerful square-built frame, which befits a Herakles, the statue is unmistakeably in the spirit of Lysippos. The head, through the freely-treated, short, curly hair of which the fillet of a victor is drawn, displays sharp forms, especially in eyes and brows, and is of characteristic smallness. The shortness of the neck is still more remarkable in contrast with the mighty shoulders. The legs are long in proportion to the thick-set torso, the feet somewhat flat, as in all statues of the school of Lysippos (cf. Ince, no. 43). The style of this master is especially evinced in the noble unconstrained freedom of the whole movement, the freshness and elasticity of the slightly twisted pose. The *argutiae operum custoditae in minimis quoque rebus* (Plin., 34, 65) show themselves, for example, in the naturalistic rendering of the soft folds of skin between thumb and finger of the r. hand. Without doubt the statue offers one of the finest specimens, if not absolutely the best, of a Herakles according to the conception of Lysippos. The workmanship is first-rate, the marble Pentelic (not Carrara), the preservation remarkable. The head has never been broken off. New: only the tip of the nose, parts of l. forearm and club, a piece inserted on the r. forearm and the r. thumb, the l. shin between knee and ankle. H. 1·95. Found in 1790 in Hadrian's Villa, in the grounds belonging to the Marefoschi family, originally owned by the Conte Fede; purchased by Jenkins (Dallaway, p. 341). Payne Knight's account, doubtless based on Townley's statements, is as follows: "Found with the Discobolus [Townley, found 1791: *Spec.*, i. Pl. 29. *Mus. Marbles*, xi. Pl. 44. Clarac, v. 860, 2194 B] in the neighbourhood of Rome: and the late Mr Townley, to whom the choice of them was immediately offered was induced, by the drawing and description sent to him, to prefer the latter; though, when he saw them, he instantly changed his opinion: this Hercules being, with the exception of the Pan or Faun at Holkham [no. 19], incomparably the finest male figure that has ever come into this country." Zoega (in Welcker's *Alte Denkmaeler*, I. p. 422) affirms that both statues came from Hadrian's Villa, and were only bought, not exhumed, by Jenkins. Another more dramatic but less trustworthy version was given by Townley's biographer, Dallaway (in J. Nichols' *Illustrations, &c.*, III., p. 727): "Upon the receipt of a letter from Jenkins, at Townley, promising him the first choice of some discovered statues, Mr Townley instantly set off for Italy, without companion or baggage, and, taking the common post conveyance, arrived *incognito* at Rome, on the precise day when a very rich cava was to be explored. He stood near, as an uninterested spectator, till he perceived the discovery of an exquisite statue, little injured, and which decided his choice. Observing that his agent was urgent in concealing it, he withdrew to wait the event. Upon his calling at Mr Jenkins' house in the Corso, who was not a little surprised by his sudden appearance, the statue in question was studiously concealed, while the other pieces were shared between them with apparent liberality. Mr Townley remonstrated, and was dismissed with an assurance that, after due restoration, it should follow him to England. In about a year after, Mr Townley had the mortification to learn that the identical young Hercules had been sold to Lord Lansdowne at an extreme, yet scarcely an equivalent price." Lord Lansdowne paid £600, the same as for no. 65, and £100 less than Townley paid for the much inferior Diskobolos, cf. Payne Knight in the *Report from the Elgin Committee*, p. 95 : Knight himself set the value of the Herakles at £1000 (*ib.* p. 99). [*m IV*]

62. Bust of a victorious youth; by Waagen wrongly named Antinous, of whom the head reminds one less than the broad breast. The portrait character is modified, and fused with the traits of Hermes, only the forms are softer and broader, the lips fuller. The mouth is slightly opened. The angle of the brow is sharply accentuated ; above it the lower portion of the forehead projects slightly. Hair short and curly, minutely divided but not detached very freely from the head. Through it is twined the remains of a wreath of laurel, the tiny leaves of which are chiselled out delicately and with animation. Below it a broad groove for the reception of a bronze fillet, not a bronze wreath (as has been sometimes repeated on Dallaway's authority). The type is not that usual in the school of Lysippos, but can hardly be earlier. New: tip of nose and part of l. brow ; hair over forehead is re-worked ; the bust is broken but is antique in essentials. H. 0·61. L. of face 0·18.

Found by Hamilton, 1769, in Hadrian's Villa; bought, 1771, by Lord Lansdowne for £75 (Memorandum, no. 11.). [*B II*]

63. Marcus Aurelius. Clarac, v. 950, 2445 A. The emperor, almost nude, rests on the r. leg, l. being somewhat drawn back; a chlamys covers breast, shoulders, and back. In his lowered r. arm he holds a sword, the raised l. hand grasps the sceptre at the upper end. By the r. leg is a leathern corslet hung over a support. The idea of the statue is founded on a type of the god Mars (cf. Dilthey, *Rheinland. Jahrbücher*, LIII., pp. 27 ff.). New: greater part of l. foot and of the sceptre, of which however both ends are antique; the l. arm is broken and worked over, but is antique; the r. arm between shoulder and wrist seems new, and so too a great part of the sword; the hand is old but patched. The youthful head of M. Aurelius, with slight down on upper lip and chin (new: nose and half the chin), is re-set and, according to Hamilton, who found the statue in 1771 at Tor Colombaro, properly belongs to it: "The head is its own, though wanting part of the neck, as I found it near where I found the statue, as likewise both the hands, though one of them is much corroded by the nitre of the earth" (letter of March 4, 1773). According, however, to Hamilton's communications to Townley there was found close by our statue a replica of poor workmanship, broken into many pieces, and the head was said to belong to one of the two statues (Dallaway, p. 372). In Waagen's opinion the head is fine, but has been placed on an inferior statue. I have found no reason for doubting that the two belong together; the whole statue is more impressive by its size than by its artistic value. Hamilton sent it to Lord Shelburne, although aware that he was not fond of portraits in general. The price came to £300. It does credit to the taste of the Marquis, that he was somewhat dissatisfied with the statue (letters of March 4, May 7, July 1, 1773, March 13, 1774). Really it does not deserve the place of honour, in the central niche of one of the two apses, which has been given to it on account of its unusual size. H. 2·20. [*IV*]

64. Bust of Antinous, of Bacchic character. The head is somewhat inclined over to the l., the expression more thoughtful than sullen. Through the luxuriant hair runs a wreath of ivy, very much undercut, so that the several leaves are almost detached. The eyebrows are expressed in the carving. New: nose, lips, part of chin, many pieces of ivy-leaves, lastly the bust. Good, powerful sculpture. H. 0·44. L. of face 0·22. The head was found by Hamilton, 1769, in Hadrian's Villa. As the Papal licence for exportation was not granted, Hamilton had to smuggle the head away, which was managed by means of an "additional present to the under antiquarian." As to the price cf. on no. 85 (letters of July 16, Aug. 6, 1772). [*B]

65. Statue of Hermes. *Spec.*, II. Pl. 37. A replica of the Belvedere Hermes (formerly named Antinous or Meleagros), in which, since the discovery of the Hermes in the Heraeon at Olympia, we recognise the characters of the style of Praxiteles (cf. Treu, *Hermes mit dem Dionysosknaben*, Berlin, 1878, pp. 8 f.). The head reminds us especially of the Hermes of Andros in Athens (Kekulé, *Theseion*, no. 368); it exhibits the same delicate arching of the nose, the same shape of eyes and brows, the same prominence of the forehead over the nose, which disappears towards either side, so that the forehead quite recedes at an angle on the temples, lastly a similar expression of mild but earnest thought. G. Hamilton found our statue in Tor Colombaro, 1771, and at once reported to Lord Shelburne that it was of the same size and equal preservation with the Vatican statue, with head untouched. "There is as yet wanting one hand, a knee with part of the thigh, and a small part of one arm.....As yet I cannot fix a prize upon it, as I am still in hopes of having it quite complete. As it is, I rank it with the one at the Belvedere" (letter of Jan. 1, 1772). The hope of finding further fragments seems not to have been fulfilled. The head is in fact unbroken, but the tip of the nose is restored, so too are part of l. arm and some fingers of l. hand, r. hand (r. arm broken off but antique), r. leg from half way down the thigh and the stem, half lower part of l. leg, pedestal, lastly borders and corners of chlamys. The remainder, of beautiful Parian marble of yellowish colour, is in excellent preservation, the surface of the whole body is executed with very delicate feeling, the treatment throughout soft and animated; the upper part seems to bear on the legs less heavily than in the Vatican copy; with all the breadth and power the contours are yet softer, the muscles of the breast not too massive. Not a trace has been preserved of the kerykeion in the l. hand, as in the Farnese copy in the British Museum (Graeco-Roman Sculpt., no. 171. Braun, *Kunstmythol.*, Pl. 91). This really exquisite copy is said to have been praised by Canova as finer and more perfect than that of the Vatican, which has been seriously impaired by modern polishing (Mrs Jameson, p. 335). Similar judgments were expressed in Rome soon after the discovery; therefore the Pope was urged to forbid the export, but the replica already in the Vatican seemed to him to be sufficient, so that the new copy was secured for Lansdowne House at the price of £600 (not £700 as Payne Knight states, himself valuing it at £1400, cf. *Report from the Elgin Committee*, pp. 95, 99). The Diskobolos in repose which was found a few steps away from this Hermes (*Mus. Pio-Clem.*, III. 26. *Arch. Zeit.*, 1866, Pl. 20), 1, 2), would have quickly followed it, but it was bought for the Vatican and forms a conspicuous ornament of the Museum there. (Cf. Hamilton's letters of Jan. 1, 18, Feb. 18, Aug. 6, Sept. 30, Dec. 26, 1772, March 4, May 7, July 7, 1773.) H. 1·99. [*mH]

66. Bust of Marcus Aurelius. New: nose, r. eyebrow, breast. H. 0·39. L. of face 0·21. [*]

67. Statue of Artemis. Clarac, IV. 564 A, 1213 A. The goddess is draped with the Doric chiton, open at the l. leg, and its upper fold not girdled. She steps forward a little with the l. leg, whereby the folds of the drapery are determined; they are simply treated, tolerably rich on the upper part of the body. The whole impression of the figure is grand and lofty, yet this lies more in the motive than in the execution. R. arm raised, l. lowered; the nude parts however of both are new. The breadth of all parts of the figure made Müller suggest Demeter, Waagen Hera; but a strap which runs from the r. shoulder slantwise over the breast is continued on the back (which is but slightly worked) in the shape of a shallow furrow with a peg of metal in it, which was meant to hold a quiver. This establishes the interpretation of the figure as an Artemis. Moreover the figure itself is not as broad as it looks owing to the arrangement of the drapery, especially near the r. arm; the hips are fairly narrow, the stomach flat; the breast indeed is strongly developed. The statue doubtless represents a somewhat early and severe type of the goddess designed for a temple. perhaps of the 5th century B.C., and related to the later types somewhat as the Parthenos of Pheidias to the later and slenderer statues of Athené (cf. no. 33). The neck is modern, and so a doubt as to the head being original may be entertained, all the more readily as, though it is of Pentelic marble like the statue, yet it displays a finer quality. This is however not a strong objection in the case of draped statues, as the head and neck were often worked separately and inserted, not seldom also consisting of better material, *e.g.* on the Demeter of Knidos in the British Museum (cf. also Petworth, no. 5). Our head matches the statue thoroughly; we have in it an older, broader and more powerful forerunner of the heads of those statues of which the most beautiful example is the Colonna Artemis in Berlin (Müller-

Wieseler, II. 16, 167), and most nearly resembles the head of the Vatican example (*ibid.* II. 15, 162 *a*. *Mus. Pio-Clem.*, I. Pl. 29); the hair is drawn back sideways in detached waving masses, by which treatment the impression of breadth is enhanced. This head may be said to stand to those in a similar relation as does the whole statue to those more animated figures, the conception of which certainly pertains to Attic art of the 4th century B.C. Moreover a bronze pin on the top of the head, a little to the l. of the parting, can hardly be explained otherwise than as serving to fasten a half-moon, as an attribute of Artemis-Selenè. New : nose and pieces of lips and chin. H. 2·06. [*m II´*]

68. **Statue of a boy.** Clarac, IV. 763, 1877, "Harpokrates." Antique : torso, curly head, lowered r. upper-arm, l. upper-arm which lies before the breast, also l. thigh and lastly both feet and pedestal. Head re-set, but original; new are nose, parts of upper lip and of curls ; a pin over the forehead held a top-knot there, of which the join is still preserved. No sufficient evidence exists for the restoration of the characteristic motive of Harpokrates, namely the forefinger laid on the mouth. H. 1·15, with pedestal 1·23. Bought from Hamilton, 1771, for £30 (*Memorandum*, no. 11.). [*]

69 (under no. 68). **Circular ara of Apollo and Dionysos.** Four upright thyrsi, from which hang four different garlands, divide off four fields, which follow each other thus from l. to r. : (*a*) from a garland of vine-leaves hang a pedum and a small round discus on which is represented Eros dancing, with torch in lowered r. hand, and a cup (? a bunch of grapes? much defaced) in l. Below, a Bacchic panther drinking out of a large krater. (*b*) Under a garland of laurel stands the tripod of Apollo, entwined by a snake ; above, a swan swimming with out-spread wings (head and neck missing) ; on r. by the tripod the bow and quiver. (*c*) Under a garland of ivy a pine tree, on the branches of which hang a Bacchic drinking-horn with an animal's head (*rhyton*) and a double flute, straight and curved. (*d*) Under a garland of laurel sits the griffin of Apollo. All in low relief. The mingling of the symbols of Apollo and Dionysos on the same ara is interesting (cf. Cambridge, no. 50. Stephani, *Compte-Rendu*, 1861, pp. 58 ff.). H. 1·09. Diameter, 0·48. [*]

70. **Group of Eros and Psychè.** Clarac, IV. 653, 1501 A. Psychè is represented as a half-grown girl. She stands in quiet attitude, resting principally on r. leg, and is draped with a doubled chiton which has slipped down from the r. shoulder, and with a cloak which covers the middle of the body and the r. thigh, and is thrown

with its corners round the l. arm. Of her butterfly-wings the stumps
are antique, as is the advanced l. forearm with a butterfly, and the r.
arm with small torch lowered. Both attributes are in themselves
appropriate to Psychè, but still in the position and combination here
found are scarcely explicable; they would be more easily explained
if held by Eros. Psychè's neck is new, the head encircled by a
broad cloth is antique (new: nose); it seems to me after repeated
examination to be original, and so too thought Clarac and Prof. G.
Hirschfeld, who studied the group with me, while Conze leaves it
undecided and Bernoulli has strong doubts. If the head originally
belonged to the figure, the peculiarly melancholy expression of the
lowered face would suggest that an object held in the l. hand,
perhaps something broken, attracted her regretful attention. Close
to Psychè, though not absolutely leaning on her, stands Eros with
his r. arm round her back; r. leg advanced. His glance is also
directed towards Psychè's l. hand, and no doubt his l. arm was
always extended in this direction. New are lower parts of both his
legs, l. arm, the greater part of his wings, besides the whole of the
upper part of his head including eyes and nose (the lower part of the
head broken off but antique); lastly r. hand, r. shoulder and piece
of breast, while the arm itself is antique and in one piece with
Psychè's back. That the two figures belong to each other and have
been rightly put together again in their present position is indubitable. The group conveys an impression of elegance, though not to
compare with the Capitoline group. I should ascribe its invention
to Alexandrine rather than to Roman art. Conze conjectures that
the group may originally have pertained to the decoration of a grave,
representing two deceased children under the ideal figures of Eros
and Psychè, which figures are so often found on sarcophagi. Execution fair, but on the other hand not remarkably good. H. 1·03. The
group was found, 1769, in Hadrian's Villa by Hamilton, who at
first offered it to Mr Anson for £300 and thereupon sent it to
Lord Shelburne for the same price; Hamilton thought very highly
of it (letter of Dec. 15, 1771). [*BCm]

71 (under no. 70). **Cippus.** On front the inscription: *Dis
Manibus Claudio Hyllo, vix(it) ann(is) IIII mens(ibus) VII dieb(us)
V, Claudius Tauriscus pater filio karissImo.* Over it a lunette with
winged Eros, sleeping, on a rock; the r. hand laid on head which is
leaning on l. arm. On the sides, l. the ewer and r. the cup. H. 0·92.
L. 0·65. D. 0·42. [*BC]

72 (on a modern pedestal under no. 71). **Modern copy of a**

relief from the Rondanini Palace, now in the Lateran Museum, no.
245, representing an actor and a Muse (Winckelmann, *Mon. Ined.*,
II. no. 192, *Museo Lateran.*, Pl. 42, 4). A thoroughly accurate
copy, of dry workmanship, well preserved even in the parts most
delicate and liable to breakage. Carrara marble. [*C*]

73 (under no. 71). **Sepulchral monument**, with the inscription [*Quint*]*ilia A. l(ib.) Secunda, A. Quintilius A. (lib.) Ero...* Above
it two small busts, facing each other, the woman with hair arranged in
the style of the first century A.D., with fillet and plait, the man
beardless ; between the two a dog (?) with collar. On the field
behind the man a V (modern?). H. 0·19. L. 0·36. [*B*]

74 (under no. 71). **Relief with six figures.** From l. to r: (*a*)
Herakles, youthful, full face, quite in the attitude of the Farnese statue
in Naples. (*b*) Aphroditè in chiton and cloak, unveiled, going r.,
carrying with both hands a small cup with fruit. (*c*) Eros, winged, full
face, raising r. arm to Aphroditè and lowering the l. arm. (*d*) Bacchic
female, full face, in chiton and cloak ; on r. arm rests a thyrsos (?),
l. arm akimbo. (*e*) A female figure (Hebè?), turned a little l., in
chiton with sleeves and cloak, holding a cup in lowered r. hand, with
l. grasping a corner of the drapery (?). (*f*) Zeus (?), bearded, facing
l., in long chiton and cloak, carrying on l. arm a large cornucopiae, in
the r. hand raising a small thunderbolt (?). The figures *b, d, e, f*
wear fillets round their heads. Graceful composition ; delicate workmanship ; a somewhat suspicious appearance seems to arise only
from retouching. H. 0·24. L. 0·45. [*B.M*]

75 (on the wall). **Front of a sarcophagus : the Muses.**
Cavaceppi, *Racc.*, II. Pl. 58, 1. From l. to r., adopting the common
nomenclature ; (*a*) Polyhymnia, enveloped in her drapery, leaning
on a pillar ; in the background a sun-dial on a high pillar. (*b*)
Euterpè in long chiton, with two long flutes, of which one has five
holes, the other none. (*c*) Thaleia in chiton, cloak and shoes, with
a perforated staff in the r. hand and a comic mask in the l. (*d*)
Melpomenè, in broad-girdled chiton and cloak, planting with the r.
hand a pedum (not a club) on a bull's head (indistinct), on l. arm
the bearded tragic mask. (*e*) Erato, in the pose of the Aphroditè
of Melos, but with chiton, resting her lyre on a pillar. (*f*) Hermes
with petasos (wings indistinct), chlamys and herald's staff, setting r.
foot on a pedestal, on which stands a comic mask. (*g*) The deceased, apparently beardless, with hair cropped short, in tunic and
pallium, a roll in l. hand. (*h*) Athenè, fully armed except for the
shield, holding up a branch of olive in the r. hand (apparently

antique). (*i*) Kleio with the roll in her hands, and a bundle of rolls by her on the ground. In the background (*k*), the upper part of the figure of a young girl, full face, probably a relative of the deceased. (*l*) Terpsichorè with the cithara and the plectron. (*m*) Urania with the globe and stylus, on the ground a comic mask. (*n*) Kalliopè with the diptychon. All the Muses are adorned over their foreheads with the plumage of the Seirens. In the background is a hanging. Late, rather bad work in half-round relief. Restoration unimportant. L. 2·16. [*C.Jm II*]

76 (over the chimney-piece). **Relief of black marble or basalt.** *Mon. dell' Inst.*, IV. Pl. 29, cf. *Annali*, 1846, pp. 155 ff. (H. Keil). At the bottom runs a narrow strip enlivened by Tritons, dolphins, hippocampi and other fabulous sea-monsters. Twice also a little winged Eros is seen amongst them ; in one place he hovers over a fish behind a bird which holds an eel in its beak. The principal field above contains four deep semicircular niches terminating in the form of an arch at the top, with plain smooth border ; they were no doubt meant for the reception of statuettes. At each end an ornament of climbing branches ; composition almost the same on each side. Below these a figure (l. female, r. male) emerges from a calix of acanthus, above these a boy with a pedum (l. a shoot) in one arm ; above, a girl, lightly draped, in ungirdled chiton which leaves one breast exposed ; quite on the top the upper part of a boy's body springing from a calix of leaves, holding up a wreath in either hand. Between the four niches there are three rather broader fields. (*a*) In the first field, l. a ship with four oars moves l., on the stern a χηνίσκος, at the prow the figure of a dolphin ; a sail is set, but a mast is not visible. In the ship sit two nude men, apparently with arms tied (at least the one on the r.), and between them stands a third, turning up his head with the l. arm laid upon it. Above, three winged females sit on rocks, their legs covered by cloaks ; the one on the l. holds a cithara, the one on the r. probably held in the r. hand (arm missing) a flute, the third is almost hidden by her. Obviously a reference is intended to the adventure of Odysseus with the Seirens. (*b*) In the centre field moves a ship, at the stern a panther's head, at the prow a χηνίσκος, behind at the steering paddle a man sits with raised l. hand (head missing), opposite him on the right another with advanced r. hand. In the waves swims a dolphin. This can scarcely mean the transformation of the Tyrrhenian pirates into dolphins by Dionysos. Above the ship a large D in relief. Quite at the top is a tasteful spray of ivy. (*c*) In the field

on the r. again a ship adorned with χηνίσκος and human mask (Medusa's head?); in it remains of a mast with a sail (?), and two nude sailors raising the r. arm briskly. The one looks up where two birds are hovering, the one downwards, the other upwards. In the water a dolphin and another fish. Keil discerns herein the adventure of the Argonauts with the arrow-feathered birds near the island of Aretias (Apollonios Rhod., 2, 1031). At the top runs a narrow frieze, adorned with animal and hunting scenes. In one part wild beasts tear each other; in another boys or youths, here nude there lightly draped, here on foot there on horseback, take part in the struggle, or are seized by the beasts, or stand between the scenes. Here and there an isolated tree, in the middle a small wood. The representation is very animated; more graceful than the principal reliefs. Above it an ovolo ornament. The whole monument is highly polished, the reliefs raised very high and delicately worked out. The original intention of the monument is as little evident as is the meaning of the letter D. H. 0·54. L. 1·84. Found by Hamilton, 1769, in Hadrian's Villa, and sold for £50 to Lord Shelburne. [*]

If I am not mistaken there are still on the chimney-piece

76 a. Two **pseudo-Egyptian idols** of Hadrian's time, and of similar material, found at the same time and sold for £150 (*Memorandum*, no. 11.); probably also

76 b. A genuine **Egyptian terminal bust**, in green basalt, sold for £30 (letter of Aug. 6, 1772).

77 (on the wall). **Front of a sarcophagus : rape of Persephonè.** The representation is divided into three scenes (cf. Soane Museum, no. 26). FIRST SCENE (Demeter looking for her daughter). In her two-horse chariot comes Demeter, in girdled chiton, with an over-fold, a torch in her l. hand; in the r. it is now missing; head new. Before her in the chariot the wings and head of a small figure, according to Matz perhaps an Eros, according to the analogy of other replicas very likely a Hora. Above, in the background, is visible the winged Iris holding a flying drapery with both hands. The heads and necks of the horses are turned backwards in strange fashion (apparently modern). Below the horses is Tellus, half sitting, half reclining on her r. elbow. She directs her head and l. arm upwards. SECOND SCENE (Persephonè gathering flowers). Persephonè, apparently not quite finished, kneels under the forelegs of the horses, looking up l.; she raises her r. arm and lays her l. hand on a basket of flowers standing by her. On the l. stands an Eros, holding an inverted cornucopiae with both hands. THIRD SCENE (the rape).

Behind Kora we perceive a group of two females. The one, Artemis, whose nude l. leg is partly visible, hastens l., but turns her face back and grasps the other, Aphroditè, below the elbow. The latter, whose chiton has slipped down from the r. shoulder, hastens r., looking back after Artemis, and laying her r. hand on the shield of Athena, who speeds in the same direction and in her turn lays her hand on Pluto's shoulder. Pluto, with his back to the spectator, is already mounting his chariot ; r. arm broken off, l. forearm restored. Persephonè, of very small proportions, lies in his arms : especially striking is the up-raised r. arm. Remains of the legs of Pluto's horses are still preserved ; all besides missing. The slab is unusually large, the relief very high, the composition of the several parts not clearly discriminated, the work unpleasantly mannered. Cf. Gerhard, *Akad. Abh.*, II. p. 484, no. 35. Förster, *Raub der Persephone*, p. 198. Overbeck, *Kunstmythol.*, III. p. 633. Hamilton had formerly bought the slab from Adams for 100 Roman crowns and got it restored for 60 crowns ; for the latter price (about £14. 12s.) he made it over to Lord Shelburne (letter of July 12, 13, 1776).   [*CMm*]

78. Group of Leda and the swan. Clarac, III. 410 B, 1715 A. A replica of the often repeated group, which represents Leda half sitting and pressing the swan to her embrace, while the cloak held up with her l. hand is to protect him from the threatening eagle (cf. Oxford, no. 28). The chiton is very delicately and thinly worked, the deep folds of the cloak are very much undercut ; the body too is not bad. New : l. arm with cloak, r. arm as far as the wrist, sundry pieces of drapery, head and neck of swan. For the head of Leda cf. Hamilton's letter, below. Pentelic marble. H. 1·26. The specimen was found, 1775, on the Palatine in the Villa Magnani and offered by Hamilton to Lord Shelburne for £100. "For excellence of sculpture it surpasses every other ; the head though found with the statue and of the same marble, yet is doubtful whether it be its own. It is beautiful and fits it. I can affirm nothing more. The r. arm and some of the l. with some of the drapery are restored" (letters of Aug. 8, 1776, May 26, 1778, no. XXXI.). It seems that Lord Shelburne was not contented with it, and negotiations were entered into with the Bishop of Derry (cf. Ickworth, and Introd., § 62) with regard to its purchase. Ultimately Hamilton made over the piece to Lord Shelburne for £65, as a pendant to no. 70 (letter, 1779, Nov. 10). Another replica came into the possession of the Duke of Buccleuch (cf. Dallaway, p. 337. Fea, *Osservaz. sui monum. che rappr. Leda*, p. 10). [*CM*]

79 (under no. 78).　**Sepulchral ara of Terpolia Procilla.**
On the front is represented a sleeping female figure with upper part
of body nude, the hair arranged high in front.　L. hand rests on an
urn with water flowing out of it.　By it flies an Eros with wreath.　By
it the inscription *Dis Manibus sacrum.* | *Terpóvliae* (after the *o* is a
cancelled *l*) *Procillae* | *P. f(iliae), vixit annis XIIII diebus LIIIII,* |
Ti. Iulius Heraclides | *uxori carissimae* | *fecit aram et* | *monimentum*
(the two last words are a later addition) ; quite at the bottom : *et
libertis libertabus | posterisque eorum.* On the sides, l. the ewer, r. the
cup.　H. 1·20.　L. 0·79.　D. 0·50.　[*C*]

80 (above in the wall).　**Slab of a sarcophagus.**　In the
middle an Eros growing out of the calix of a flower, the hands resting
on the back of the head, at each corner stands an Eros ; all three
bear garlands.　Within each of the garlands two masks facing each
other ; l. of two Maenads crowned with vine-leaves and between
them a thyrsos ; r. of two Satyrs, one with a ragged moustache, and
between them a pedum.　Low, poor relief.　[*M*]

81.　**Terminal bust of a girl.**　Clarac, v. 779, 1933 B.　The
terminal pillar, draped towards the upper part with a double chiton,
gradually passes into the girl's body, which however remains very
square up to the neck.　The head is intentionally kept in severe
style, the hair, brushed off the face on both sides and twisted
round a fillet, falls down the shoulders in a few stiff tresses.　In
style the figure reminds one of the archaistic statues in the Villa
Ludovisi and the Villa Borghese (cf. Schreiber, *Villa Ludovisi*, no.
29).　New : almost the whole r. arm with a key, half the l. arm
with an ewer, besides the greater part of the terminal pillar.　The
genuine part is 0·78 high.　This "terminus of Isis, very elegant,"
was found by Hamilton in Hadrian's Villa and presented to Lord
Shelburne (letter of Aug. 9, 1775).　[*]

82 (under 81).　**Sepulchral ara of Serenus.**　Above, a
Medusa's head between two rams' heads, all symbols for averting
evil.　Below them the inscription : *D(is) M(anibus)* | *Sereni* | *Au-
g(usti) lib(erti)* | *a sacris* | *fecit* | *Coelia Amanda* | *marito* | *carissimo*
et sibi.　On each side a tree with a bird.　H. 0·77.　L. 0·56.　D. 0·33.
[*C*]

83.　**Statue of a wounded Amazon.**　*Spec.,* II. Pl. 10.
Clarac, v. 833 B, 2032 C.　One of the finest and best preserved specimens of that type of wounded Amazon, which is on good grounds
referred to Polykleitos (cf. Klügmann, *Rhein. Mus.,* XXI. p. 322.
Kekulé in the *Commentationes in honorem Th. Mommseni scr.,* Berlin,

LANSDOWNE 63.

1877, p. 481); there is a torso of the same type in Oxford, no. 24.
The leading motive of languid repose is expressed with especial
clearness in the weary eyes and slightly opened mouth. It is in
keeping with the wound near the r. breast consisting of a sharp cut
with ten drops of blood below it. The Amazon, then, young and
strongly built, leans with her l. elbow on a pillar; the weight of
the body rests in part also on the r. leg, the l. is somewhat drawn
back. The r. hand lies on, or rather a little above, the head, so
that the hand remains in good view from below. The head is considerably inclined sideways. It is as like the head of the Doryphoros
by Polykleitos as sister to brother. It is not so sharp in its contours
as are, for example, the heads on similar statues in Berlin (*Mon.
dell' Inst.*, ix. Pl. 12) and in the Sciarra Palace at Rome (Matz-Duhn,
Ant. Bildw. in Rom, I. no. 942), or as the head in the British Museum
(Graeco-Rom. Sculpt., no. 150. *Mus. Marbles*, x. Pl. 5), all of which
belong to the same type. The waving hair flows very softly; the
whole is an excellent translation into marble of the characteristics
of a bronze original. The broad breast recals the figures of the
pediment of the Parthenon. Knees and thighs excellent. The
arrangement of the woollen chiton is characteristic of this type.
In consequence of the unfastening on the l. shoulder it leaves both
breasts free, and forms in front of the stomach a strong mass of
vertical folds. The buckle of the girdle is represented in detail
with great care, the whole statue being generally very well executed.
The preservation of the surface is excellent. Unfortunately the
marble, which is Pentelic and is in other respects very beautiful,
contains rather strong micaceous strata. These have been the
main cause of the statue being damaged. However the head, r.
arm and r. hand for example, though broken, have been accurately
joined together again; the head is quite certainly antique. New:
half the nose, half of r. arm turned towards the spectator to wrist,
tip of thumb and the four fingers of r. hand, half l. forearm with
hand, the column from just below the piece that connects it with
the figure, both legs from below knee. (Cf. Michaelis, *Arch. Anz.*,
1862, p. 335. *Arch. Zeit.*, 1874, p. 38. Klügmann in Lützow's
Zeitschr. f. d. bild. Kunst, v. p. 75 note.) H. 1·95. According to
Dallaway, pp. 342, 373, the statue was found in Tor Colombaro by
Hamilton (1771). In reality Hamilton mentions as found there
a "fine Amazon large as life" (Jan. 1, 1772), which he subsequently
offered to Lord Shelburne; when he designated it as "one of the best
of that kind" and praised the head especially (March 4, May 7,

1773). The Earl closed with the offer for £200 (Sept. 12, 1773), but on the receipt of this and sundry other specimens (nos. 63, 87) was "somewhat dissatisfied, in particular with the Amazon" (March 13, 1774). This is scarcely comprehensible in reference to our statue, but is probably in part explained by the fact that Lord Shelburne, as he went on to inform Hamilton, already possessed an Amazon (thus clearly from another source, perhaps Jenkins or Cavaceppi), whereupon Hamilton expresses the hope "that in all probability Mr Grenville (presumably one of the Prime Minister's brothers) will take it;" he is willing to send another statue in its stead (May 1, 1774). Mr Grenville was in fact prepared to take it, but not immediately (Apr. 16, 1775); however more than a year later Hamilton again writes: "I hear that Mr Barry (of Marbury Hall?) is arrived in England. I shall desire him to take a look of the Amazon and hope he will find a place for it" (July 13, 1776). It is certain that there is no Amazon in Marbury Hall, and only one in Lansdowne House, and that to this the characteristics of Hamilton's specimen correspond; still there remains some obscurity about the whole affair. If Lord Shelburne really altered his estimate of the Amazon of Tor Colombaro at a later period and kept it, then where is the one which he possessed before? [*Cm IV].

[84. Modern copy of the beautiful head of a youth in the British Museum (Graeco-Rom. Sculpt., no. 151), found by Fagan, once in the possession of Samuel Rogers. Spec., II. Pl. 18. *]

85. Statue of Hermes. Clarac, v. 814, 2048 A, "Jason." A replica of the statue from the Villa Negroni, now in the Louvre, which was formerly called Cincinnatus and restored accordingly. From the time of Winckelmann and Visconti it kept the name Jason until lately, when the comparison of coins (Mus. Class. Antiq., II. p. 292) and other considerations have led to its recognition as a Hermes (cf. Lambeck, De Mercurii statua. Thorn, 1860). It is in fact the most speaking illustration of those Homeric verses in which Zeus gives a commission to the messenger of the gods:

> ὡς ἔφατ', οὐδ' ἀπίθησε διάκτορος Ἀργειφόντης·
> αὐτίκ' ἔπειθ' ὑπὸ ποσσὶν ἐδήσατο καλὰ πέδιλα,
> ἀμβρόσια, χρύσεια, κ.τ.λ.
>
> (Il., 24, 339. Od., 5, 43.)

Christodoros describes a bronze statue representing Hermes at this very moment (Anthol. Palat., 2, 297—302):

> ἦν δὲ καὶ Ἑρμείας χρυσόρραπις· ἱστάμενος δὲ
> δεξιτερῇ πτερόεντος ἀνείρυε δεσμὰ πεδίλου,

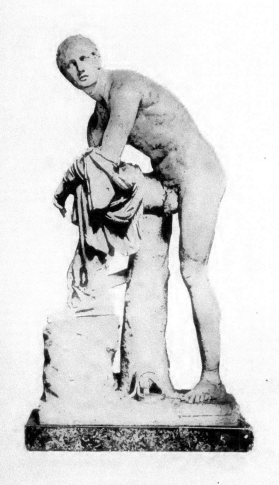

LANSDOWNE 85.

εἰς ὁδὸν ἅξαι λελιημένος· εἶχε γὰρ ἤδη
δεξιὸν ὀκλάζοντα θοὸν πόδα, τῷ ἔπι λαιὴν
χεῖρα ταθεὶς ἀνέπεμπεν ἐς αἰθέρα κύκλον ὀπωπῆς,
οἷά τε πατρὸς ἄνακτος ἐπιτρωπῶντος ἀκούων.

This description agrees on the whole so well with our statue that
first Heyne, and subsequently Müller and others, connected the two.
The slender god stands on the l. leg; he has set his r. foot on a
piece of rock and his r. hand is occupied in tying the sandal; the
l. arm rests on the r. knee, enveloped in the rich folds of the chlamys.
The whole upper part of the body is bent far forward; the head
is raised upwards with a forcible expression of strained attention.
The replica before us deviates from the other copies (in the Louvre,
in Munich, and in the Vatican, cf. Clarac, III. 309, v. 814) in this
respect, that the l. arm is not extended to the sandal like the r.,
but rests idly on the thigh (cf. Visconti, *Opere Varie*, IV. Pl. 21).
The artist has meant by this to make it evident that Hermes leaves
off tying his sandal for the moment, so as to be better able to listen;
letting the r. hand rest meanwhile among the straps.   This feature
deviates from the description of Christodoros, and must therefore be
regarded as an innovation, while the other replicas have preserved
the original motive. The artist gained by this deviation a greater
variety in the pose of the arms, and a richer development of the
folds of the chlamys; on the other hand he impaired the clearness
of the action and the close compactness of the composition. For
this comparative inferiority the statue in Lansdowne House presents
a full compensation in the preservation of the original head, while to
the copies in Paris and Munich alien heads of Parian marble have
been added, the figure in each case being of Pentelic marble. Our
head, however, proves plainly that the strained attention pertains
to the character of the whole figure. This is thoroughly appropriate
to a Hermes in the situation indicated; but just as inappropriate if
the statue be interpreted as a youth of the palaestra, in the familiar
action of tying on his sandal (cf. Konr. Lange, *Das Motiv des
aufgestützten Fusses*, Leipz. 1879, pp. 2—12). For the criticism of
the composition it is essential to observe that the original work was
in bronze, which accordingly did not need the heavy support, but
allowed the whole pose to look freer and lighter. Unfortunately
the whole statue has been much restored. New: r. forearm, r. foot,
rock, sandal, ploughshare (suggested by the "Cincinnatus" in Paris),
the support, the greater part of the plinth, l. arm from shoulder to
elbow, the l. hand, parts of chlamys, l. half of nates, lower part of

M. C.   30

l. leg between knee and ankle; the l. foot with a portion of the plinth is antique. The head is connected with the body by a narrow modern strip, but is antique (restored: nose and part of the back of the head), and to judge by the quality of the marble and the workmanship obviously belongs to the statue; the expression too is thoroughly appropriate. Its resemblance to the head discovered by Fagan (no. 84) is complete, and it is very nearly allied to the Borghese Gladiator; thus Gavin Hamilton remarked, "of the same artist that made the Gladiator at the Villa Borghese; the head is almost the same;" again Visconti, Clarac, K. O. Müller and others compare the two statues (Lange, *op. cit.*, p. 12). The "meagre treatment of the muscular body, which is not altogether noble in its modelling" (Müller in the "Amalthea"), is common to both statues, though in the Gladiator, which is moreover in part reworked, the anatomical detail is much more strongly accentuated, by reason of the strained attitude. The style of both statues alike is founded upon that of Lysippos (cf. Brunn, *Glyptothek*, no. 151), but the realism has advanced a step further: the treatment of the body is still "dryer" (*corpora sicciora*), the elastic covering of skin still more accentuated, the details generally more developed. The character of the head corresponds to the body. A head of Hermes by Lysippos would have more ideality and poetry than this meagre, sinewy head, the animation of which is, so to speak, purely of a physical, material sort. The hair is much less separated and less minutely made out than is the case with Lysippos. Lastly, the l. foot, although broad, is not so long and flat as with Lysippos (cf. no. 61, Ince no. 43). I recognise with Müller in the original of this statue—which is excellent of its kind—the work of a school of art of the Hellenistic period derived from Lysippos, presumably Asiatic (of Ephesos?). The workmanship is good, very true to nature; the surface has been largely reworked by the restorer. Pentelic marble. H. 1·54. The statue was found by Gavin Hamilton in 1769 in Hadrian's Villa; according to him "the same as that at Versailles (that is the above-mentioned replica, now in the Louvre), of better sculpture, though not so well preserved." He feared that it would have to go to the Vatican, but as the Pope declined the high price of £500, Hamilton sent it to Lord Shelburne, including also no. 64 under that price (letters of Jan. 28, July 16, Aug. 6, 1772). [*Bm W*]

85. **Head of an Ariadne**, with fillet over the forehead, crowned with ivy. New: top of head, a great part of the wreath, nose, neck. Poor head enough. L. of face 0·19. Probably the

"head of a woman" bought of Gavin Hamilton for 11 crowns = abt.
£2. 14s. (letter of July 13, 1776, Memorandum, no. xxxv.). If the
"head of Bacchus" were meant (letter of Dec. 26, 1772), the price
of £50 for this paltry head would be enormous. [*W]

87. **Female figure, seated.** Clarac, III. 420 B, 748 A,
"Juno." She is sitting with l. foot somewhat advanced, draped
in a girdled chiton, a wide cloak covering l. arm and legs; the
veiling of the back of the head is a modern addition. New also :
l. forearm with staff, the whole r. arm, r. foot, l. leg with the folds
between the legs, other portions of the drapery. The graceful head,
without indications of the characteristics of Juno, does not belong to
the body, which is of rather small value (overrated by Waagen).
Lord Shelburne had good grounds for being "somewhat dissatisfied"
with this statue, which Hamilton had sent him for £230 as a "sitting
Juno" (letters of July 16, Sept. 30, Dec. 26, 1772, March 13, 1774).
It still less deserves the place of honour in the middle of an apse
than does no. 63. H. 1·72. [*mW]

88. **Head of Hermes.** Spec., I. 51. Müller-Wieseler, II. 28,
304. Braun, Kunstmythol., Pl. 88. This fine head, inclined to the
l. shoulder, is distinguished for its delicate, soft forms, for the beautiful mouth, and the intelligent eyes, the upper lids of which project
rather decidedly. The brow is smooth and free, the curly hair not
very much detached. A round felt hat of the shape of a petasos
(cf. Yates, Textrinum antiquorum) covers the very youthful head,
which does not so much represent the crafty Hermes as patron of
trade and gain (κερδῷος, as Braun interprets), nor again the overseer
of gymnastic exercises (ἐναγώνιος), but the ideal type of well-bred
Attic youth, not indeed devoid of a touch of sentimentality, so far
from suggesting cunning. It is easily understood that the beautiful
head has become probably the most popular specimen among the
antiques of Lansdowne House. New: half the nose, parts of the
ears, almost the whole brim of the hat, and the bust. Excellent
workmanship. Pentelic marble. H. 0·29. L. of face 0·17. Found
by Gavin Hamilton, 1769, in Hadrian's Villa, and bought by Lord
Shelburne, 1771, for £55 (Memorandum, no. II.). [*Cm W]

89. **Statue of a Diskobolos after Myron**, restored as Diomedes with the palladion. Clarac, v. 829, 2085 A. Antique : only
the torso, with the junction of the l. arm, and also the r. thigh and
the (patched) l. leg as far as half-way down the shin. Following an
indication given by the muscles of the neck, the restorer, though so
decidedly mistaken in other respects, has given the head the proper

30—2

turn backwards, as in the Massimi copy of the Diskobolos (Müller-Wieseler, I. 32, 139ᵇ). The body, of coarse-grained Parian marble, is of good workmanship, though not positively excellent. On the style of Myron's work is well preserved in the small, close-lying, slightly rounded curls (Plin. 34, 58). The head is antique (new: nose), but did not originally belong to the statue. It is connected with the body by a modern neck, has whiskers, and is of a somewhat barbaric type, in some degree resembling the so-called Perseus of the British Museum (Graeco-Roman Sculpt., no. 161. *Mus. Marbles*, XI. Pl. 14); at any rate it belongs to the Hellenistic epoch of art. II. 1·75. The torso was found by Gavin Hamilton, 1772, at Ostia (Dallaway, p. 377). The restoration, which made a Diomedes of it, looks very like Cavaceppi's work. It seems to have taken a long time, and to have been conducted in profound secrecy; for not earlier than 1776 did Hamilton mention the statue to Lord Shelburne as one of the finest things he had ever had in his possession, and sent it to him as a pendant to the "Cincinnatus" (no. 85), which indeed resembles it sufficiently in style and size. He especially draws attention to the fact that the statue is beautiful looked at from every part, and that, though the legs and arms are restored, still the restoration is perfectly certain, "because it would be to the last degree absurd to suppose it anything else"! It should be borne in mind that the Massimi Diskobolos, which disposed of many wrong guesses and solved the enigma, was not discovered before 1781. The price came to £200 (letter of March 25, 1776). For other replicas and for an estimate of the worth of the statue cf. Welcker, *Alte Denkm.*, I. pp. 417—429. [*m II*]

90. **Head of a girl**, described by Hamilton as "head of a Muse in the antient Greek taste." It really is a Greek sculpture, fresh and pretty, though not executed with minute delicacy. She looks down before her. The face is rounder than that of the beautiful virgin's head in the Glyptothek in Munich (no. 89, Lützow, *Münchner Antiken*, Pl. 19), the eyes small and rounded, the cheeks broad, the mouth small with very beautiful lips, the chin high and round. A very broad fillet encircles the plain, wavy hair, which forms on the nape of the neck a loose, overflowing roll. New: nose, a piece of upper lip, bust. Greek marble. H. 0·33. L. of face 0·17. Found by Gavin Hamilton, 1769, in Hadrian's Villa, and sold for £15 (Dallaway, p. 369, Hamilton, Memorandum, no. 11.). [*B*]

91. **Terminal figure of Dionysos**, of human form down to the hips. Clarac, IV. 676, 1560. The head of the youthful god is

encircled by a fillet, and crowned with vine-leaves and grapes. It is
of delicate but ordinary type, with very narrow eyes, and much defaced. Though re-set, it belongs to the figure. New : nose and part
of under lip, both arms with cup and grapes, and the terminal shaft
from the virile emblem downwards. In my opinion it is very questionable whether this was originally a terminal figure. Tolerable
workmanship. H. 0·66. Found by Gavin Hamilton in Hadrian's
Villa and presented to Lord Shelburne as a pendant to no. 81
(letter of Aug. 9, 1775). [*W]

92 (under 91). **Sepulchral urn of Pompusidia Eutychia,**
merely furnished with an inscription. [C]

93. **Bust of Athene,** colossal scale, fragment of a statue of
the type of the Pallas from Velletri in the Louvre (Clarac, III. 320,
851), but of more perfect art, though not so good as the head from
the Villa Albani in Munich (Glypt., no. 92, Müller-Wieseler, II. 19,
198), exactly corresponding. On the high Corinthian helmet there
are still the remains of a snake, but otherwise it is without ornament. The face displays a powerful oval. All the forms of the face,
though pretty much retouched, give unmistakeable glimpses of the
sharpness of a bronze original. The outer edge of the lips is defined by a line, the eyelashes and the brow-line are very sharp.
The wavy hair, equally in the style of a bronze, is gathered on the
nape of the neck into a roll which falls a long way down. The
conception undoubtedly belongs to the best age of Greek art. Of
the bust the r. shoulder is antique, with parts of the chiton and of
the scaly aegis with the fringe of snakes, and a hole for the insertion
of the raised arm. It is much patched about the snakes. New :
fore part of bust, with aegis and gorgoneion, and l. shoulder with
cloak ; also half the nose and small portion of the lips, the extreme
tip of the roll of hair, the front points of the helmet. Greek marble,
apparently Pentelic. H. 1·08. L. of face 0·25. Found in Roma
Vecchia, bought of Gavin Hamilton, 1771, for £104 (Memorandum,
no. II. Letter of Dec. 15, 1771). [*CmW]

SIDE GALLERY OF THE BALL ROOM.

94. **Bust of Antoninus Pius.** [*B]

95. **Terminal bust of a Greek poet,** a replica of the so-
called Hesiodos in the British Museum (Graeco-Roman Sculpt., no.
119. *Mus. Marbles*, II. Pl. 44), with however a more picturesque
treatment of the beard. New : nose and terminal shaft. [*B]

96.   **Candelabrum.**   On a pedestal are four boys with garlands
of fruit.   Connected with this by a modern piece is a tall column
with a pretty relief of scrolls of foliage.   The surmounting ornament
is again modern.   H. abt. 2·40.   Probably the "fragment of a
candelabrum" which Gavin Hamilton presented to Lord Shelburne
(letter of July 12 and 13, 1776).   [*B]

CELLAR.

Here are provisionally deposited the following marbles:

97.   **Statuette of Serapis, enthroned.**   Clarac, IV. 758,
1851 A.   Quite the common type, with Kerberos by the r. leg.   Face
full and thick.   New: nose, a portion of the hair and modius, the
raised l. arm from the cloak upwards, the r. forearm, the middle
snout of Kerberos.   Ordinary sculpture.   H. 0·75.   [*]

98.   **Child's sarcophagus : Cupids as armourers.**   At the
extreme l. a Cupid sets in motion a pair of bellows to enkindle a fire
which burns on the forge with a vaulted roof.   On his r. a seated
Cupid holds with a pair of tongs an indistinct piece of armour
(greave?) on an anvil ; two Cupids are hammering at it.   In the
centre two Cupids, symmetrically disposed, hold a large helmet over
a corslet which lies on the floor ; then a similar pair holding a shield,
which a comrade, half-kneeling, bears up with both hands.   The
lower part to about the height of the knees is restored.   On each a
sitting griffin.   Pretty motives, poorly executed.   H. 0·35.   L. 1·24.
[*CM]

99.   **Child's sarcophagus : boys playing with nuts.**
On the extreme l. is indicated the door of a house.   Then come
three groups.   (a) A boy stands bending forward to the r., grasping
the bosom of his tunic with the l. hand and advancing the r.   Facing
him comes a boy, with l. hand before his breast, his r. hand laid on
the head of a weeping friend.   On the ground two nuts.   (b) A boy
kneeling facing l., his r. hand, full of nuts, on the ground.   A second
hurries up from the r., advancing r. arm and making a signal of
warning with the l. hand.   (c) A boy hurries to the l., with three nuts
in r. hand, holding the l. before his breast.   Behind him stands a
companion with a nut in his r. hand and an amphora in the l. arm.
(The same subject otherwise treated Ince, no 247ª, Newby, no. 31.)
On each side a barbarian's shield, in incised outlines.   H. 0·31.
L. 0·90.   [*M]

100.   **Front of a child's sarcophagus of Zoticè.**   Above
two crossed horns of plenty, two Cupids hold a shield with the

inscription: *Trophima* 9 *Zoticeni* | *filiae* | *b(ene)* *m(erenti)*. The mark after the first name perhaps serves as a stop. Next come both l. and r. the group of Cupid and Psyche, embracing each other, and by them a tall vase; at the end a Cupid with apron, supporting a staff on the ground with one hand. Bad workmanship. H. 0·41. L. 1·69. [*M].

101. **Small sepulchral ara of Cornelia Briseis.** Above, a bust, much corroded. Below it the inscription, which looks very suspicious: *D(is)* *M(anibus)*. | *Corneliae* | *Briseidi* | *Corn(elius) Theseus* | *Corn(elius)* *Autolycus* | *coniugI b(ene)* *m(erenti)* | *fecerunt*. On the sides ewer and cup. H. 0·63. L. 0·24. D. 0·17. [*C]

102. **Bearded head**, much impaired. [*]

103. **Head of a youth**, much mutilated. [*]

COURT AND GARDEN.

104. **Two fragments of a long, low frieze, with Tritons** and other marine creatures. H. 0·29. L. 2·30. [*]

105. **Female figure belonging to the lid of a sarcophagus.** A female figure in the stola, with the head-dress of Julia Titi, lies on a couch, her head laid on l. hand. The r. hand holds a bunch of poppies. [*M]

I cannot find out in Lansdowne House, besides the second Amazon mentioned on no. 83, the following specimens, which are mentioned in Gavin Hamilton's letters as having been sent there.

106. "**Fountain nymph**, holding an antique vase upon her knee with both hands; a very sweet figure," intended as a pendant to no. 70, for which purpose the Leda, no. 78, was subsequently determined on. It cost £200 (letters of March 4, May 7, 1773. Memorandum, no. XIX.).

107. "**Erma of two faces**," valued together with several other pieces at £60; distinct from nos. 7, 8 (letters of May 6 and 30, 1775).

108. **Statue of a Bacchus**, £15 (letter of May 30, 1775).

109. **Venus**, £15. (*Ibid.*)

110. **Sleeping Cupid**, presented by Hamilton (letter of July 13, 1776).

The four last pieces were meant for a summer-house or for the garden. Can they be at Bowood, the favourite country seat of Lord Shelburne?

LORD LEICESTER.

LORD LEICESTER kept in 1877 in his town house, 19, Grosvenor Square, two antique busts, which are described under Holkham nos. 59, 60.

GEO. McLEAY, ESQ.

See South Kensington Museum, nos. 1—17.

LORD DE MAULEY.

Among the amateurs of antique sculpture, Waagen (*Treas.* I. p. 37) mentions WILLIAM FRANCIS SPENCER PONSONBY, FIRST LORD DE MAULEY (1787—1855), the third son of the celebrated collector, Lord Bessborough (Introd. §§ 35, 71). Of his antique marbles he specifies the following (*Treas.*, II. p. 83).

1. "A female head, above the size of life, in marble, with widely open mouth, of the noblest character, of excellent style, and broad and careful in treatment. It would be difficult to decide the subject of the head, though I believe it to be a genuine Greek work of a very good period." Evidently it is the head in South Kensington Museum, no. 18, now in the possession of Lord de Mauley's second son, the Hon. Ashley G. J. Ponsonby.

2. "Head of a muse, decorated with grapes; small, but lovely in character, and tender in workmanship."

Besides these pieces Waagen mentions a cammeo, a small bust of chalcedony, and a vase. This last is probably the great bronze krater from Southern Italy now in the South Kensington Museum.

MR MELLHUISH.

MR MELLHUISH, statuary mason, Lower Tooting, S.W., possessed in 1873 a child's sarcophagus with Bacchic Cupids. The procession moves from r. to l. First of all goes a Cupid of relatively large size, striking cymbals or a tympanon. Then comes a car drawn with strong effort by a Cupid and a little Pan, on which stands a Cupid, personating Dionysos, leaning back somewhat, with each arm round the neck of a companion. By the car in the background a Cupid clashing cymbals. There follows a second car drawn by a Cupid-Centaur playing the lyre. A Cupid reposes in the car, reclining on a cushion, legs covered with a cloak. He seems to be embracing and drawing towards him an indistinct figure. L. SIDE. A quiver with opened lid. (*M*, after a photograph.)

THE HON. ASHLLY G. J. PONSONBY.

See South Kensington Museum, nos. 18, 19.

SOANE MUSEUM (13, Lincoln's Inn Fields).

[J. Soane], *Description of the House and Museum on the North side of Lincoln's Inn Fields, the Residence of Sir John Soane.* London (1835. Only 150 copies and 100 of a French edition). *A general description of Sir John Soane's Museum.* London (latest edition, 1876). Waagen, *Treas.* II., p. 320 (I. p. 450). Conze, *Arch. Anz.,* 1864, p. 165. I examined the Museum, 1877.

SIR JOHN SOANE, the architect, devised in 1833 his house and collection to the nation, which entered on possession at his death (1837). The collection, formed during a long life and consisting of the most heterogeneous curiosities and objects of art that can be conceived (Introd. § 90), is distributed over the rooms of the house, which are mostly very small and connected with one another in a strange way. A number of very narrow passages, very dark corners, and the like, impedes a steady investigation equally with the over-crowding of the rooms and the incredibly inconvenient mode in which a great part of the contents are arranged, so that the sculptures are scarcely within reach of the eye. It is not too much to say that some of the better specimens can only be seen from the back. Then again the impression conveyed by so wild a confusion of pro-miscuous fragments is necessarily bewildering and fatiguing to the visitor, and I am therefore not sure whether I have been fortunate enough to discover the principal examples during my repeated searches through all the rooms. The numbers in brackets appended to the consecutive numbers of the following catalogue are those of the collection itself, so far as they could be ascertained.

STATUES.

1 (603). **Statue of Asklepios**, in composition closely related to the Vatican statues (Clarac, IV. 549, 1157). The cloak, the border

of which is turned over, covers the legs and l. arm: the god rests
on the r. leg, the l. being advanced sideways. The l. arm is lowered
(new: hand with roll), the r. hand rests on a staff entwined by a
snake (new: upper part of staff, hand and arm, lower half of staff
antique). The head, which is re-set, and connected with the body
by a modern neck, seems to belong to the statue; it has characteristics of a Zeus, only the hair falls more heavily. Pupils expressed.
New: nose and part of the tresses. Moderate decorative work. H.
0·87, with pedestal 0·92. [*]

2 (220). Fragment of a Herakles, quite enveloped in the
lion's skin, r. forearm raised, l. before the body. It may be derived
from a terminal figure of Herakles. Black marble. H. 0·53. [*]

3 (613). **Statue of Ephesian Artemis.** New: head, neck,
l. arm including shoulder, r. forearm, the feet and all below the
lowest strip of figure sculpture (nude parts of black marble); the
torso is restored to an unusual degree, the single pieces being separately let in. On the upright disk behind the head three griffins, on
the upper part of the arm a lion. On the breastplate two Victories
holding up a wreath together, under which is a crab; above each
Victory an animal running (r. new, l. a cow?). The breastplate is
encircled by a wreath of *immortelles* and a narrower border. Underneath the numerous breasts come six strips of relief (much restored)
with five fields on each, of which the first corresponds with the fifth,
the second with the fourth, so that I only mention the third (the
foremost), the fourth and fifth. First (uppermost) strip: three deer;
upper part of the body of a winged female figure; a stag. Second
strip: three griffins; bee; griffin. Third strip: two oxen, rose; ram.
Fourth strip: roe (new); bee; hare (? new). Fifth strip: eagle (new);
flower; l. eagle, r. griffin (both new). Sixth strip: hare (new); bee;
flower. H. 1·16. [*C]

4 (769). **Statue of Cupid,** as a figure for a fountain. Cupid
sits asleep on a large urn, on which he has set his l. leg; arms and
head rest on l. knee. The r. foot rests on the ground. The wings
are partly broken off, the l. foot is missing. The urn is perforated.
(For the motive cf. Clarac, IV. 644 A, 1459 D, E.) H. 0·52, with
pedestal 0·62. [*]

5 (A). **Upper part of the body of a youth,** with l. shoulder
strongly raised, shewing that he must have supported himself on his
l. arm (cf. Clarac, III. 476 B, 906 D, or rather IV. 585, 1265). The
torso is preserved almost to the navel, and a piece of the l. arm.
Good sculpture. Pentelic marble, much corroded. H. 0·43. [*]

6 (B). **Male torso,** much damaged. The back is beautiful. H. 0·34. [*]

7 (1015). **Male torso,** powerful; of very good style. Small scale. H. 0·35. [*]

8 (322). **Torso of a man standing in repose,** with a *puntello* on the body to support the r. forearm. Very animated work. H. 0·43. [*]

There are besides a great number of torsos and fragments which it would be idle to enumerate.

BUSTS.

9 (968). **Bust of a sleeping Pan,** with open mouth, quite turned over towards l. shoulder. Hair and beard very curly. The stumps of the horns antique. New: nose, part of cheeks, of hair, &c. Highly exaggerated work. H. 0·30. [*]

10 (974). **Pretty head of a youth,** with curly hair lying close on it, looking down toward its own r. The sober character recals a fine head in the British Museum (Campanari bust, Phigaleian Saloon). New: nose and bust. L. of face 0·15. [*]

11 (1174). **Fragment of a female head,** with low stephané, of fine, simple Greek work, the eyes and broad cheeks in particular recal the style of the best period. L. of face, if perfect, abt. 0·12. [*]

12 (1175). **Fragment of a head,** apparently male, of similar style. A ribbon is wound several times round the head. Much abraded. [*]

13 (969). **Bust of a girl,** with reticulated head-dress, of pretty, good-humoured expression. Much restored. L. of face 0·11. [*]

14 (779). **Female portrait-bust,** of the period of the Claudian Emperors, in some degree resembling the "Clytie" of the British Museum (cf. London, Crichton), but older. The rich hair, daintily curled, formed a knot (*korymbos*, now missing) on the top of the head, and falls down in long curls on the neck; at the back a roll. The glance is a little lowered towards the r. The sleeve drapery leaves the l. shoulder free, and here rests on the bosom. This extremely pleasing, well executed bust, which is quite entire, is, however, somewhat abraded. Restored: only nose and a piece of hair along the parting. H. 0·53. L. of face 0·16. [*B]

15. **Bust of Felicitas,** an old woman with bony face. The hair, parted in front, is drawn up from the back in a broad, flat plait as far towards the front as the parting. The neck is broken, but

the draped bust belongs to the head.   Below it is the inscription on
a small tablet: Θεόγνωστος Φηλικείτα(ι) | τῇ(ι) συν[βίῳ], the re-
mainder missing.   (For the form of the name Φηλικίτα = *Felicitas* cf.
C. I. Gr., 1986, 5634, 6292.)   On the modern pedestal stands the
inscription "Iulia Livia Augusta."   New: tip of nose.   H. 0·41.
L. of face 0·14.   [*]

16 (775).   **Head of a beardless, lean man,** with bony
cheeks and protruding mouth.   A distant resemblance to Caesar.
The hair, which lies close to the head, forms one mass, the details
being only indicated by strokes.   Nose mutilated.   On the bust,
which does not belong to the head, are illegible remains of a Latin
inscription.   L. of face 0·16.   [*B]

17.   A large **number of portrait busts,** partly of Emperors,
of no considerable importance.

RELIEFS, &c.

18 (755).   **Fragment of an Amazon,** Greek work.   She
hastens r. in lively movement, so that the folds of the chiton flutter
lightly about the thigh and behind the back.   Both breasts are free,
the chiton being drawn up between them in narrow gathers to the l.
shoulder.   The stump of the r. arm, which was stretched out backwards, is preserved.   Missing: head, l. arm, all from the abdomen
downwards.   Nude parts treated powerfully, drapery delicately and
effectively.   The effect of the whole is rich.   The fragment recals
vividly the sculptures of the Mausoleum, and like them belongs to the
best period.   A cast of it is exhibited in the British Museum.   H.
abt. 0·24.   [*]

19 (1043).   **Fragment of Attic votive relief,** l. end.   The
anta on the l. is preserved.   By it stands a female figure in chiton,
covered rather closely in her cloak which leaves the r. arm free; the
r. hand holds slantwise before the breast a long staff (torch?), the
upper end of which rests on the raised l. hand.   Head missing.
Presumably one of the two Eleusinian goddesses.   Pentelic marble.
H. 0·41.   L. 0·25.   [*]

20 (936).   **Greek sepulchral relief,** r. end.   The anta on the
r. and a piece of the architrave with tiles on the top are preserved.
On a couch lies a male figure with modius on head, in r. hand a cup
on the lap.   At his feet on a stool sits a female figure, not veiled,
holding a cup or a small box in the raised l. hand.   By the couch a
table with food and a goblet.   To the l., behind the female figure,

are remains of an attendant with a flat cup on the l. hand. Pretty careful work; low relief. H. abt. 0·30. L. abt. 0·30. [*]

21 (1150). **Fragment of Greek sepulchral relief,** lower l. half. On a pillar to the l. leans a nude boy (much mutilated). Further r. a female figure on a throne facing r., only preserved from the abdomen downwards. On her chair leans a female attendant on a smaller scale (head and breast missing). Figures larger than usual, relief very high. From Asia Minor or the Greek Islands. H. 0·29. L. 0·35. [*]

22 (1126). **Small sepulchral relief.** In the niche-shaped field, somewhat arched at the top, sits a female figure on a folding seat (δίφρος ὀκλαδίας), her feet placed on a high footstool, extending her r. hand to a child who stands before her on a high pedestal, wearing an ungirdled chiton and offering something to the mother. Rough, provincial style, scarcely more than sketched in outline. Detail difficult to recognise. H. 0·36. L. 0·27. [*]

23 (104). **Fragment of Greek sepulchral relief,** surrounded by a flat border; broken at the top. On a couch a beardless man sits in full face, in chiton and cloak, playing on a large cithara. On the r., at the head end of the couch, stands an attendant in short chiton, with his legs crossed, holding his arms before his stomach. Late, bad style. H. 0·42. L. 0·42. [*]

24. **Altar of Herakles.** In front, lion's skin and club; on the r. side a goblet (skyphos), with sprays of ivy in relief; on the l. an ewer; behind a cup. Roman work. H. 0·61. L. 0·37. D. 0·37. From the Bessborough Collection. [*]

25 (1446). **Fragment of a votive relief to Fortuna.** The goddess, fully draped, sits facing l. on a throne by which stands a large wheel; the r. hand rests on the tiller of the steering-paddle, which is decorated below with a sphere. All from abdomen upwards missing. Below her the inscription (C. I. Lat., VI. 3174): P. Aelius Annius eq(ues) | sing(ularis) Aug(usti) Palmyrenu(s) | \ d. d. Fortunae s(anctae? salutari?). [*]

26. **Front of a sarcophagus with the Rape of Persephonè.** Engraved in Soane, Description, p. 43, Overbeck, Kunstmythologie, Atlas, Pl. 17, 23. An old drawing in the Cod. Coburg., no. 170 M. = Cod. Pigh., no. 182 J., "in aedibus Card. S. Florae", another in the collection of Mr Franks in London (cf. above). Cf. Gerhard, Akad. Abhandl., II. p. 483, no. 34. Förster, Raub der Persephone, p. 187. Overbeck, l. cit., III. p. 627. FIRST SCENE (in chronological sequence the last): Demeter searching for her lost

daughter. From the l. Demeter advances on a car drawn by a pair
of horses. Her drapery is long and the cloak waves behind her
back. In her lowered r. hand she holds a torch, of which only
the handle is yet remaining; the l. hand, raised and advanced, held
a second torch, which, together with the hand, has disappeared all
except the flame. Of an Eros hovering over the horses only the
wings are preserved (in the old drawings he is still perfect, except
the arms and the r. leg). Hard by the horses floats Iris, with long
drapery and wings, looking back at Demeter; her r. arm and l. hand
missing, the latter appearing to have held a cloak, a piece of which
is seen before the l. wing. Below the horses lies Tellus, seen from
behind, with upper part of body nude, holding in l. arm a long
cornucopiae and advancing the r. arm towards the heads of the
horses.—SECOND SCENE (chronologically the first): Persephonè surprised by Hades while she is gathering flowers. Immediately in
front of Demeter's horses a female figure (Aphroditè) kneels on the
ground, draped with long chiton, cloak floating over the head, and
with a stephanè on the head. She looks back towards the first
scene. Near by her stands a basket filled with flowers; by it slight
but unmistakeable traces of an Eros, who laid his l. hand on the
basket. At their backs stands Hades (head re-set but antique), with
a fillet running through the hair; a chlamys flows down behind his
back. His gaze is also turned towards the first scene. He holds his
r. hand before his breast, the l. arm (partly broken) is somewhat
raised. Thus he approaches the back of the kneeling Persephonè,
whose appearance is very like that of Aphroditè, only that she wears
no stephanè, her long tresses being tied up into a knot over the
forehead. She lays her r. hand on a basket filled with flowers which
lies on the ground and raises the l. forearm perhaps to grasp her
cloak. Her glance also follows the same direction to the l. On
the r. of this figure the slab is broken right through, but there is
nothing missing.—THIRD SCENE (chronologically the second): the
rape of Persephonè. Next appears Artemis, hastening l. briskly,
in short hunting dress, with her quiver on her back; more than half
of both forearms is missing, as well as the whole of the r. leg. The
glance of Artemis is directed towards Athenè, who is on the other
side of a tree, hastening rapidly r. (lower part of l. leg missing). She
is in long drapery, and wears the high helmet and the round shield
on her arm; the r. arm she advances to succour Persephonè, who
has just been seized by Hades and lifted on to his chariot. Persephonè is represented in the act of swooning; her figure is extended

at full length, so that her head hangs down from the chariot; the
r. arm (broken off) lies on the back of the horse, the l. arm rests
on the rim of the chariot. Hades has seized her round the body
with his r. arm, and with his l. hand he manages the reins of the two
horses as they both spring off. The cloak floats behind his back, his
head (re-set, but antique) is inclined towards his beauteous prey.
Above the horses hovers Eros, with a little cloak over his l. arm,
looking down on Persephonè; his r. leg and half of both his arms
missing, yet the remains of an object (torch ?) which he held in his l.
hand are still preserved on the forearm of the adjacent Hermes.
Hermes steps out before the horses, with a chlamys flung around
him, the herald's staff shouldered on his l. arm; his r. hand is laid
on the head, which is covered with a winged hat. The l. half of his
head is broken off, the l. leg restored. A much-defaced remnant at
his feet is all that remains of Kerberos. On the ground lies a
bearded Water-god (Okeanos, or the representative deity of Lake
Pergus); the raised l. hand (now missing) may have held an attribute.
Very fair but not remarkable sculpture. L. 2·10. [*CMW]

27 (744). **Fragment of a sarcophagus**, l. end. On a
chariot drawn by Centaurs (only one equine hinder-part being preserved) stands Dionysos, his legs covered in his cloak (head and
r. forearm missing); his r. arm rests on the neck of a small bearded
Satyr with an apron, the l. on that of a youthful Satyr who looks up
at the god. In his hand the god holds in careless fashion a kantharos
which one of the Satyrs supports underneath. Below the Centaurs
remains of a lion. H. 0·59. L. 0·32. [*M]

28 (482). **Fragment of a sarcophagus**, imperfect both on
the l. and the r. The god Dionysos, crowned with ivy, only slightly
covered by his cloak, with a thyrsos in his l. hand, sits turned r. on
a rock with his head turned round and supported on the r. hand.
At his feet a panther. From the l. comes a Maenad in chiton, the
cloak flying behind her back; in the l. hand she holds a lowered
torch, laying the r. hand on the breast of the god. On the l. remains
of other figures. Coarse sculpture. H. 0·26. L. 0·25. [*]

29 (923). **Fragment of the front of a sarcophagus**, r.
end. On the extreme r. a small statue of the bearded Dionysos with
long hair and a small modius on the head. He wears a long girdled
chiton with sleeves, and holds a sceptre on his l. arm, the r. being
lowered. At the foot of the statue is an altar, on which pine-cones
are burning; close by a goat lies on the ground. A Maenad steps
up to the altar, in long drapery, the cloak disposed about her like

a shawl, and is casting a roll (?) into the flames. On the l. above, near her head, the flame of a torch is preserved, which was borne by another figure now lost. H. 0·65. L. 0·30. [*M]

30 (1125). **Fragment of a sarcophagus.** All that is preserved is a youth in Phrygian costume, sitting facing r. on a high chair; the chlamys covers the seat as well. The r. leg is raised up high; on the knee rests the l. elbow; on the l. hand the thoughtful head, which is turned back, rests; the r. arm lies on the lap. Probably Paris, whom Eros is telling of Helenè (cf. Overbeck, *Bildwerke*, Pl. 11, 12; Pl. 12, 1; also Brunn, *Urne Etrusche*, 1. Pl. 19, 6). H. abt. 0·40. [*M]

31 (472). **Fragment of a sarcophagus.** Remains of a female figure lying dead or asleep, with upper part of body exposed, the legs, which are for the most part missing, covered. The r. arm lies in the lap; l. arm and head hang down over a piece of rock on which the back reclines. Presumably Klytaemnestra, from a similar sarcophagus to that given in *Mus. Pio-Clem.*, v. Pl. 22; or one of Niobe's daughters (cf. Stark, *Niobe*, Pl. 4, in the middle of the lid; Pl. 19, 1). L. 0·25. [*CM]

32 (99). **Fragment of a child's sarcophagus.** Remains of a chariot race in the Circus contested by Cupids. The horses of a chariot; close to them an overturned chariot and a Cupid thrown out on the ground. In the background two Corinthian columns bearing an architrave with six ova. [M]

33. **End of a sarcophagus.** A griffin sits facing the l., with the claw of r. fore-leg on a ram's head. H. 0·42. L. 0·43. [*]

A large number of **square cinerary urns** with inscriptions and merely decorative reliefs (*e.g.* nos. 404, 410, 419, 421—426, 429, 460), as well as **round vases** with similar adornment, are not of sufficient importance to be enumerated individually here.

34 (1132). **Fragment of a relief.** Hermes, almost full face, with the herald's staff in his l. arm, grasps with his r. hand the chlamys, which covers back and arm. Head and greater part of r. leg missing. Rather pretty. H. abt. 0·40. [*]

35 (1121). **Large flat mask,** intended for a fountain, or for use in a vapour bath. The face is surrounded by wet, waving hair. The eyes and mouth are perforated. H. 0·62. L. 0·65. [*]

36 (413). **Relief,** with flat frame. To the l. an actor with comic mask, in sleeved chiton and with cloak (shoes restored), sits on an altar hung with garlands, on which the r. arm rests; the l. hand lies in the lap. A fracture runs through the thigh, to the

r. of which it is all modern (a female figure with tragic mask speaking to him). For the genuine piece cf. the statues in Wieseler's *Theatergebäude*, Pl. 11, 8—11; Pl. 12, 5. H. 0·33. L. 0·37, of genuine piece 0·23. [*]

37 (24). **Foot of a marble seat,** consisting of a slab which is finished off in front by a winged leg of a lion (head broken off), and is further adorned all over with pretty sprays. On one side is a goat in the middle of the ornamental work. [*]

Of the various **painted vases**, for the most part unimportant, the finest is the following :

38. The " Cawdor vase," more celebrated than actually known. Conze gives a description, p. 165: the front, the principal scene of which relates to the sacrifice of Pelops and Oenomaos before the chariot race at Olympia, is engraved, though unsatisfactorily, in the *General Description*, p. 5, and in Moses' *Collection of antique Vases*, Pl. 23. This large and rich vase, about 0·80 high, found in 1790 near Lecce, was for a long time in the possession of the King of Naples, was then purchased by General Oudinot, sent to England, and sold there for 1000 guineas to Lord Cawdor ; it then passed to J. Edwards the bookseller in Pall Mall, and from him to Sir J. Soane (Introd. §§ 54, 90).

39. Lastly, I must not leave unmentioned the chief pride of the whole collection, the **Egyptian sarcophagus of alabaster,** disinterred in 1817 by Belzoni in the neighbourhood of Thebes. It is covered inside and out with figure sculptures in very low relief and is in excellent preservation. It is thought to be the coffin of the father of Ramses II.

SOUTH KENSINGTON MUSEUM.

The Museum possesses no antique marbles of its own, but specimens belonging to private persons are often exhibited here, and they naturally vary from time to time (cf. Conze, *Arch. Anz.*, 1864, p. 167; Huebner, *ibid.*, 1866, p. 301. Michaelis, *Arch. Zeit.*, 1874, p. 41). In the autumn of 1877 the following works in marble were exhibited by two owners :

I. Lent by GEORGE Mᶜ LEAY, Esq., for the time resident in India, nos. 1—17, all derived from the west coast of Asia Minor.

1. Statue of a female, in long chiton, and over it the cloak, which covers the head and the whole body as far as below the knees.

The treatment and fall of the folds resemble those in the terra-cotta figure, Clarac, v. 890 B, 2267 F, only the cloak is not thrown back over the l. shoulder, but covers the l. breast and thence falls down. The lowered l. arm is quite covered in the cloak, the upper part of the r. arm is likewise lowered, the forearm is missing, as is also the head. The figure rests on the r. leg, on the outside of the shin is a square *puntello* which suggests an attribute (torch?) or some other accessory. H. abt. 1·70. Cf. the remark on no. 2. [*]

2. **Statue of a female**, in doubled chiton and over it a cloak, completely corresponding to four of the statues of the Loggia de' Lanzi in Florence (Cavalieri, *Antiq. stat. l. I. et II.* Pl. 81; cf. Clarac, IV. 767, 1894; V. 978 B, 2524 F). She rests on the r. leg. Missing: head, r. arm, l. forearm with the folds of the drapery below it. H. abt. 1·70. Both the statues, nos. 1 and 2, stand on low irregularly shaped plinths. They are very slender in their proportions, slim in the upper part of the body, becoming broader below, with not quite common motives of drapery. Ordinary execution. They are exact counterparts of the statues at Oxford, nos. 1—9 (cf. Oxford, after no. 9). [*]

3. **Group of Ganymedes and the eagle.** The youth, nude except for a Phrygian cap and boots, stands with l. knee bent by a pillar which is partly covered by his chlamys; the outstretched l. arm lies on the pillar; of the lowered r. arm with the pedum only remnants are preserved. Ganymedes looks up at the eagle, which sits above his l. arm on the pillar (cf. *Monum. dell' Inst.*, 1856, Pl. 18). The pose of Ganymedes is somewhat stiff and affected. The whole group is backed with a pillar, and was therefore most probably meant for architectural decoration (cf. Cambridge, no. 4, Wilton, no. 144); the moderate execution falls in with this view. H. 0·76. [*]

4. **Statue of Pan.** The god stands by a tree on which hangs the syrinx. A leather apron full of fruit hangs slantwise from the r. shoulder; in the l. arm he holds a pruning-knife (blade missing). These attributes remind one of Silvanus. Head of unpleasantly brutish expression. Goat's legs. Lowered r. arm and part of l. leg below the knee missing. Late, ordinary Roman work. H. 1·01. [*]

5—12. **Eight heads**, of bad, late workmanship, and rather damaged; from Smyrna, Rhodes, &c. The following may be particularly mentioned : **5**, a head over life-size, perhaps of **Zeus**, though of a gloomy aspect, which suggests Pluto rather than Zeus ; **6**, a head of **Herakles** with curly hair and beard ; **7**, a pretty good female head. [*]

13. Relief. On a field surrounded by a frame there sits enthroned in the middle, **Zeus**, turned l., his legs covered by his cloak, the l. hand high up on the sceptre, the r., perhaps with a cup, on the thigh. To the l. before him stands, very nearly in full face, a noble **female figure** in chiton and cloak, with a long sceptre on her r. arm, the l. hand lowered; a high ornament on the head (modius?) may designate her as Hera or Demeter, or again as the tutelary goddess of a town. Behind the throne of Zeus stands **Anubis**, with the head of a dog, draped in a chlamys. Very coarse and much abraded. Below the relief a large empty space. H. 0·65. L. 0·36. From Erythrae. [*]

14. Votive relief, flanked by two antae which carry an entablature furnished with roofing tiles. On the l. stands a youth in chlamys beside a horse; before him, in about the middle of the relief, stands a female figure, in chiton, the l. arm and the lower part of the body enveloped in cloak, offering the youth a cup. Both figures are on a much larger scale than those at the r. end of the scene: a male and two female figures, and in the foreground three children (apparently two boys and a girl). These six persons approach in adoration; before them a boy, quite small, leads a ram to the altar which stands between the two principal personages. The relief is moderately low and reminds us of Attic reliefs. H. 0·41. L. 0·56. From Smyrna. [*]

15. Sepulchral stone of Sandioklos, broken into two fragments. On the r. sits a female figure completely veiled (head missing). In the background a tree, entwined by a snake. To the l. stands in full face the deceased, a bearded man, in cloak, the l. hand lowered, the r. before the breast; for his somewhat self-conscious attitude cf. Oxford, no. 89. By him a diminutive attendant, with crossed legs, the head supported on the l. hand. Below, the inscription, in characters indicating the Roman period : χαῖρε Σανδίοκλε. (For the name cf. Σανδίων, the Σάνδιος λόφος near Myus, Thuk. 3, 19, Σανδώκης of Kymè, Her. 7, 194.) Rather high relief. H. abt. 0·60. L. 0·44. [*]

16. Fragment of a sepulchral relief, broken both at top and bottom. On the l. stands a youth, full face, almost nude, holding the chlamys on the r. shoulder with r. hand, the l. lowered. Beside him a nude boy, who turns up his face and r. hand to him ; in the lowered l. hand he holds the strigil (στλεγγίς) and the alabastron. Lively execution. H. 0·32. L. 0·30. From Smyrna. [*]

17. Relief in a frame. A man in very short chiton and with boots, flourishing a whip in his r. hand and holding out a cloth in his l., advances against a tiger which springs at him from the r.   Coarse stone. H. 0·51. L. 0·66. From the amphitheatre at Pergamon. [*]

II.   Lent by the HON. ASHLEY G. J. PONSONBY, nos. 18, 19.

18. Female head, called quite inappropriately " Juno Sospita," evidently the head mentioned above (London, De Mauley, no. 1). Engraved : *Sophoclis Electra*, ed. O. Jahn, frontisp. ; better, *Arch. Zeit.*, 1880, Pl. 8 (Michaelis). This beautiful head of large, broad forms is powerfully and yet softly treated. It is covered by a cloak or cloth of very thick material, which forms soft folds over the forehead. The wavy hair is simply brushed off the face and falls far down on both sides ; a few tresses hang on the forehead, a larger one comes forward from the ear far on to the l. cheek. The hair is not very much finished ; where the drapery and the hair meet, the several marks of the drill can still be seen in the hollow. The highly tragic intensity of expression which pervades the features appears much more striking if the head, in conformity with the pose of the neck and the fall of the hair and drapery, is set up a little more inclined forward towards its own r. than it is now. New : tip of nose. On the top and at the back the head presents level surfaces, which are apparently part of the original surfaces of the block. A brown coating grievously spoils this beautiful work, and makes it impossible to determine the quality of the marble. In my opinion it is a good reproduction of a distinguished original, belonging to the Hellenistic epoch of art. The older interpretations as " mother of Hercules " or as " Omphale " are little better than that of " Juno Sospita." The common opinion now-a-days inclines to see a barbarian woman in the head, though there are no particularities able to support this interpretation ; if nevertheless it be right, the head would be of great interest as representing an ante-Roman type of female barbarian. I am rather inclined to recognise in the head the remains of a statue of a mourning woman, which may have served as the decoration of some sepulchral monument. The head is said to have been discovered at Ostia ; casts made in Rome are common. The original, after having passed through the hands of a Mr Jones and of Lord de Mauley into the possession of the present owner, attracted well-merited attention at the Manchester exhibition of 1857. H. 0·30. L. of face 0·21. [*]

19. Female head, colossal scale, called " Hera," but much rather representing an **Aphroditè**. It is very decidedly inclined to

its own r. The wavy hair, which is brushed up on the l. side and from
off the neck, once formed a top-knot on the parting. Now, the
whole top of the head is missing on the l. side, from the lower
margin of the hair and the ear. Nose and lips restored. A poor
copy of an apparently good original, the details of which however
are quite lost in this version. Owing to the brown coating the
quality of the marble is unrecognisable. H. 0·42. L. of face 0·27. [*]

STAFFORD HOUSE (St James' Palace Court).

Waagen, *Treas.*, II. p. 73 (II. p. 69).

In this town house of the DUKE OF SUTHERLAND I found the
following antiques :

1. **Statuette of Lucius Papirius.** He is draped with the
pallium, and holds the r. arm in the cloak before his breast, the l. arm
being lowered, with a box (?) in the hand. The youthful head and
the r. hand seem to be modern ; however the dark corridor in which
the work stands does not permit a certain judgment on the point.
The same must be said as to the genuineness of the inscription on the
pedestal, *L. Papirius*, which seemed to me free from suspicion (the
lower end of the semicircle of the P does not in either case come
up to the vertical stroke). However, the name L. Papirius is too
celebrated, and the youthful head suggests the young Papirius Prae-
textus (Gellius 1, 23) too closely for it to be possible to absolve the
inscription from all suspicion. H. 0·94. [*]

2. **Head of the bearded Dionysos,** of very accurate hieratic
style, over life-size. This good head, on a modern draped bust, has
surely been originally part of a terminal figure. [*W]

3. Modern copy in bronze of the **bust** in Paris of **M. Modius
Asiaticus,** cf. Oxford, no. 238. Wilton, no. 78. The copy seems
to be carefully executed. [*II]

The servant assured me (in 1877) that there were no other
antiques in the house. Waagen saw there, among other antiques,

4. **"Bust of a young Hercules."**

5. **"Bas-relief** of a woman walking, with a child on her arm ;
before her an older child. Simple and pleasing in invention, and
delicately finished." This description seems to indicate a Greek
sepulchral relief.

For other antiquities in the possession of the Duke of Sutherland
cf. Dunrobin Castle ; Trentham Hall.

LORD WEMYSS (Stratford Place).

THE EARL OF WEYMSS is, as Doran states ("*Mann*" *and manners at the Court of Florence*, I. p. 220), the present owner of the celebrated eagle, which during a century adorned the gallery of Strawberry Hill (Introd. § 41, Dallaway, *Anecd.*, pp. 293, 384). The eagle had been dug up in the garden of Boccapadugli, near the Baths of Caracalla (in 1742, according to Dallaway), a short time before Cardinal Albani introduced it to the notice of Mr Chute, a friend of Horace Mann's, the British minister in Florence. Through the mediation of Horace Mann, Mr Chute induced Mann's friend, Horace Walpole, to purchase the eagle together with its pedestal, a marble cippus with an inscription, for 100 zecchini (£50), in the summer of 1745 (cf. Doran, *l. cit.*). How much Walpole admired the "glorious fowl" when it arrived in England two years later, is evident from several passages of his letters to Mann, *e.g.* in the letter of June 26, 1747 : "There never was so much spirit and fire preserved, with so much labour and finishing." Unfortunately, "the lower part of the beak had been broken off and lost" (letter of July 28, 1747). At the sale at Strawberry Hill in 1842, this marble was sold for £210, as is stated in an annotated copy, to Lord Leicester ; but this, according to a statement of Lord Leicester himself, is an error. Doran mentions Earl Fitzwilliam as the next owner, and says that he bought it at a far higher price ; from this nobleman "the grand weird-looking bird" came into the possession of Lord Wemyss. I am unfortunately not in a position to give an accurate description of this interesting antique, as I have neither seen the original nor a print which Walpole mentions in a letter to Mann (Dec. 5, 1760).

THE LATE SIR RICHARD WESTMACOTT.

At the residence of WESTMACOTT, the sculptor, Count Clarac, in the year 1833, found a number of marbles with regard to the actual whereabouts of which I have no information to give. Clarac has published the following statues or statuettes, apparently for the most part rather seriously restored.

1. **Statuette of Serapis**, restored as Zeus.   Clarac, III. 410 A, 669 B.

2. **Melpomenè**, setting the r. foot high on a rock. Clarac, III. 506 B, 1045 A.

3. **Statuette of a drunken Satyr**, with nebris, in a rather strained attitude. Clarac, IV. 710 A, 1708 A.

4. **Group of three nude boys**, lying pressed close to each other on the ground. Clarac, V. 875, 2236 C. Antique?

5. **Small girl** in girdled chiton holding a little bird in the l. hand (antique?). Clarac, V. 878, 2236 D.

6. **Statue of "Marcus Aurelius, when young."** A youth in chlamys, by him a dog. Clarac, V. 950, 2445 C.

In the *Specimens of Antient Sculpture*, II. Pl. 48, is given and ascribed to the same ownership:

7. **Bronze Statuette of Athenè**, with chiton and cloak, so-called Corinthian helmet and aegis, both forearms advanced. The eyes of inlaid silver.

- - - -

LORD YARBOROUGH.

In LORD YARBOROUGH'S town house, 17, Arlington Street, may presumably be preserved those specimens of the Worsley collection which are not to be found in Brocklesby Park; cf. Brocklesby, nos. 110—113.

LOWTHER CASTLE (Westmoreland).

Ancient Sculpture at Lowther Castle. Penrith. (Short notices with sundry statements about the acquisition.) Matz, *Arch. Zeit.*, 1873, pp. 27 ff. Michaelis, *ibid.*, 1874, pp. 41 ff. I visited the collection in the year 1873.

The collection, which is exhibited in the beautifully situated and very fine Castle, three miles south of Penrith (Cumberland), was formed by WILLIAM, SECOND EARL OF LONSDALE (family name LOWTHER), beginning about 1848, and seems to have received no additions since the founder's death (1868), cf. Introd. § 96. The materials were furnished principally by the sales of the Bessborough Collection, the Duke of Buckingham's (Stowe) Collection, the Marquis of Hertford's, &c. Thus it was possible, though so late as the year 1850 Waagen (*Treas.*, III. pp. 260 ff.) mentions no antiques in Lowther Castle, to form the considerable collection which worthily fills two well-lighted galleries, specially erected in 1866 for this purpose by the architect, Mr Mawson, which project towards the park on the south side of the Castle. The incompleteness of my own notes and of those by Matz, together with the laconic brevity of the catalogue, are the reasons why I have not been able to give a fuller description, though I can scarcely have passed over anything of consequence. In the case of the specimens which are noticed merely on the authority of the catalogue I naturally cannot offer any guarantee for their genuineness or for the correctness of their nomenclature. Unfortunately I had not the leisure to inspect the book mentioned by Matz, with photographs and notices on the acquisition of the several specimens. I have consulted the sale catalogue of the Stowe Collection (by Henry Rumsey Forster, London, 1848); that of the Bessborough Collection (July, 1850) proved too poor to be of any use.

EAST GALLERY.

1. **Statue of the Knidian Aphroditè.** Among the many copies of this celebrated masterpiece (cf. Bernoulli, *Aphrodite*, p. 206. Michaelis, *Arch. Zeit.*, 1876, pp. 145 ff.), this example most nearly resembles the beautiful statue in Munich (no. 131. Lützow, *Münchn. Antiken*, Pl. 41. Clarac, IV. 618, 1377). As in that case, so here, the goddess lifts up the drapery from the vase, while other copies let it fall down thereon, as certainly did the original by Praxiteles; the pose of the head too seems to have originally corresponded, although the re-set and clearly modern head is rather more decidedly raised than that of the Munich statue. The figure is extraordinarily broad in the region of the hips, flatter in the breast. New: head and neck, r. arm entirely, l. almost entirely including the armlet, the legs from below the knee; toes and portions of the pedestal seem old. The antique parts of the body are of beautiful Thasian marble slightly tinged with yellow; the drapery, on the other hand, which is very much worked over, together with the vase, similarly worked over, are of Pentelic. These parts, separately let into the pedestal, appear to belong to another copy, and are joined to the torso, presumably under Hamilton's direction, by an iron rivet, which fastens the drapery to the hip. A marble *puntello* left rather further back on the hip, the prolongation of which would not meet the present drapery, proves that the drapery was originally held somewhat further back, and perhaps also a little further from the body; now, in fact, it too

much veils, from the principal point of view, the beautiful movement of the outlines of the body. This is not the case in the other copies. Good Roman work, equally finished in all parts. H. 1·96. From the Stowe Collection (*Catal.*, p. 269, no. 91), bought for 13 guineas. "The statue was found at Rome under a church now added to St Peter's [probably in 1776, when the churches of *Santa Maria della febbre* and *Santo Stefano degli Ungari* were destroyed in order to make way for the present Sacristy]. Bought by Mr George Grenville from Gavin Hamilton for Stowe, and restored like the Venus of Cnidus" (G. Scharf). [*M*]

2. **Torso of Venus**, from the Marquis of Hertford's collection.

3. **Statue of Artemis.** Cavaceppi, *Racc.*, I. Pl. 5. Clarac, IV. 599, 1311. The goddess wears a long chiton with an over-fold which is doubly girdled, once by a flat band close under the breast, then low down round the hips. The drapery has slipped down from the r. shoulder and leaves part of the bosom bare. On the l. shoulder lies a small cloak, which falls down over the arm. The figure rests on the r. leg, the l., which is a little bent, treads on a quiver which lies on the ground, a bow lying by it (certainly antique). Through this adjunct we may interpret the motive. It might be imagined that the head was originally a little lowered, the glance perhaps directed in calm admiration on the sleeping Endymion, just as the same conjecture has been made with respect to the Artemis of the Vatican (*Braccio nuovo*, no. 50. *Mus. Chiaram.*, II. Pl. 7. Clarac, IV. 577, 1244. Braun, *Zwölf Basreliefs*, p. 12), which statue is unquestionably of far greater beauty and of more animated movement. The facts that the weapons have been let fall and that the bosom is exposed accord well with this idea. The very beautiful, but much rubbed head, in the character of a Muse, does not belong to the statue, as is proved by the material, which is Parian marble. New: nose and chin, neck, r. arm from the elbow downwards, l. forearm with elbow, and the part of the cloak which hangs down. Thasian marble. H. 1·95. The statue is derived from the Spada Palace (Winckelmann, *Kunstgesch.*, V. 2, 6; VI. 1, 22. *Mon. Ined.*, I. p. 37, "Venus"; cf. Bernoulli, *Aphrodite*, p. 104). It came through Cavaceppi's hands to Petworth, where Dallaway enumerated it (p. 279. no. 6 [II. p. 14]); in this century, however, no one has seen it there. It appears accordingly to have passed from Lord Egremont to the Duke of Buckingham (cf. Petworth, introduction), and then from Stowe (*Catal.*, p. 269, no. 92) to Lowther for the sum of 17 guineas. [*M*]

4. Statue of " Hygieia." This very interesting statue, resting on the l. leg, wears a fine close-fitting chiton, which is girdled very low down on the hips. The cloak goes slantwise on the l. shoulder, laid behind the back as far as the middle of the r. thigh, and is then thrown over the l. forearm. The expression of the face is amiable, the hair in maidenly fashion tied together on the crown, while tresses fall down on the shoulders. A snake, of which the greater part is antique, curls itself round the lowered r. arm. An uncommon feature in representations of Hygieia is offered in the winged boy sitting on her l. arm, whose legs (exclusive of the l. foot), nates, and the lower part of the stomach, as also the under part of his r. wing, are antique. The boy is undoubtedly Eros, who appears in company with Hygieia on the famous ivory diptych in Liverpool (p. 428; Müller-Wieseler, ii. 61, 792 b). New : the other parts of the boy; of the female figure the l. hand from the drapery, with the cup; the head, though broken at the neck, belongs to the statue. Parian marble. Moderate workmanship. H. 1·52. From the Bessborough Collection. [*M]

5. Statuette of Euterpè, from Fould's sale at Paris.

6. Statuette of Flora.

7. Statue of Ares, colossal scale, according to Matz perhaps a *statua Achillea*. The figure is nude except for the cloak, which falls down far behind from the r. shoulder. On the l. arm rests the sword in its sheath, by the r. leg is a marble support covered with a leathern corslet. New : head and neck, r. arm which is raised up sideways, trifling portions of the l. arm. [*M]

8. Figure of Pan, standing upon an altar.

9. Bronze Statue of Hercules.

10. Fragment of a group : on some stones rests a cauldron, from which there protrudes the carcase of a boar; a hand is still to be seen on the rim of the cauldron. Replica of a well-known group in Naples (Clarac, iv. 742, 1786). H. 0·46. [*M]

11. Julius Caesar, sitting in a consular chair. From the Bessborough Collection.

12. Statue of Augustus. The figure is nude, and heroically treated, the cloak only falling down from the l. shoulder over the lowered l. arm. The head belongs to the statue. New : almost the whole r. arm, l. hand, lower parts of both legs, much unimportant detail. A good statue, over life size. Thasian marble. From the Stowe collection (*Catal.*, p. 265, no. 29). Bought for £22. 1s. [*]

13. Statue of an Emperor, restored as **M. Aurelius.**

Antique : only the torso, with corslet (of which the front and back are decorated with Nereids on sea-horses, who bear the arms of Achilles ; the one carries a helmet, the second a greave, the third a shield) for the most part covered by the paludamentum. Colossal scale. Found in the Villa of Alexander Severus, near the Via Ostiensis. From the Stowe Collection (*Catal.*, p. 264, no. 19), bought for £38. 17s. [*M*]

14.   Statue of a Roman in the toga. Bought for £21 from the Stowe Collection (*Catal.*, p. 47, no. 742, "A Roman Senator, found in Herculaneum"). H. abt. 1·50.

15.   A seated female figure. The motive is similar to that of the "Penelope" of the Vatican (Clarac, v. 834, 2090. Müller-Wieseler, I. 9, 35) or the Oxford "Clio" (Oxford, no. 32). The head rests on the r. arm, the elbow of which is supported on the r. leg which is crossed over the l. ; the l. foot stands on a stool. The l. arm is supported on the fringed cushion of a chair with twisted legs. Chiton and cloak as on the statues just mentioned. New : r. foot. The elegant head, which is that of a maiden, and is carved in Thasian marble, does not belong to the statue, which is of Pentelic. Ordinary Roman work. H. 1·16. Bought for £47. 5s. from the Stowe Collection (*Catal.*, p. 264, no. 18, "Agrippina as the Muse of History"). This and similar figures are probably sepulchral monuments, a statue in place of the usual relief ; cf. Conze, *Arch. Anz.*, 1867, p. 94*, no. 704. [*M*]

16.   Female figure.

17.   Draped female figure.

Thirty-one busts are enumerated by the Catalogue in this part of the gallery, but the notices are generally so short that nothing is to be learnt from them. Among them the following names occur :

18.   Plato,

19.   M. Pompeius,

20.   Matidia, colossal scale, all three from the Bessborough Collection.

21.   M. Aurelius, from the Stowe Collection.

22.   C. Caesar,

23.   Agrippina,

24.   Faustina, all three from the collection of the Marquis of Hertford.

25.   Janus.

26.   Sulla.

27.   Cato, probably.

28, 29.   Jul. Caesar.

30. Livia.
31. Nero, as a youth.
32. Galba.
33. Vitellius.
34. Trajan.
35. Seneca.
36. Corbulo.

Among the reliefs by far the foremost place is occupied by the pearl of the whole collection, which is the following :

37. Fragment of an Attic sepulchral stelè, large size, of choice Pentelic marble, from Acharnae, of the fourth century B. C. Fr. North, afterwards Earl of Guilford, found the stelè, and brought it to England. The engraving by Stackelberg (*Gräber der Hellenen*, Pl. 1, 3. Schnaase, *Gesch. d. bild. Künste*, II. 2 ed., p. 224), in its feeble polish, gives but a weak idea of the abundant power and animation of the original, the peculiar Attic grace of which, met with as it is in the far north, close to the borders of Scotland, exercises a double charm. With inclined head, a slight touch of melancholy in the features, sits the deceased, a female figure, her head and body quite enveloped in the wide drapery, the r. hand near the chin, while the r. elbow rests on the lap. Two fillets run through the curly hair ; two holes below the ear prove the original presence of a metal ornament. In the flow of the lines, the delicate treatment of the drapery, and the tenderness of the expression, the figure, which is over life size, ranks with the best of its kind. A Sphinx supports the arm of the high-backed chair, which is furnished with a cushion. Missing : legs from over the knee. New : nose, the two last fingers of the r. hand, details of the edges of the drapery, neck and edge of wing on the sphinx, which is restored as a griffin. Very full relief. H. 1·19. L. 0·69. An engraving of the fragment, from successful photographs, will appear in the collection of Greek sepulchral reliefs which is to be published by the Vienna Academy. [*M*]

38. Sculptured marble tablet, in frame, brought from Athens 1763.

39. Medallion head of Homer, in carved frame. Bessborough Collection.

40. Head surrounded by a garland. Bessborough Collection.

41, 42. Two Roman sepulchral reliefs, which form a pair, each framed by two pilasters surmounted by an arch adorned with medallions. On the one there stands a female figure, full face, completely enveloped in her cloak, which even covers her head ; the l.

arm is lowered, the r. hand holds a corner of the cloak near the l.
shoulder. (For the motive compare *e.g.* the daughters of Balbus,
Mus. Borb., II. Pl. 41, 42. Clarac, v. 921, 2349.   923, 2349 C.)
On the other relief, the arch of which is decorated with a garland,
stands a female figure, whose high-towering head-dress seems to
belong to Trajan's time ; her attitude, representing Venus, is not rare
on gems and coins (Bernoulli, *Aphrodite*, pp. 184 ff.). Almost nude,
with a cloak thrown round the thighs, she supports herself with the l.
arm on a pillar. In the l. hand she holds a palm branch ; the r. arm
is half raised. By the r. foot a dove. Both reliefs were already
known in Rome in the middle of the 16th century; cf. Cod.
Coburg., no. 99, Matz = Cod. Pigh., no. 115, Jahn.   They came to
Lowther from the Bessborough Collection.   [*.M*]

43.   Child's sarcophagus. Cupids hunting. On the FRONT
a bear throttling a horse, next to them an ibex ; a Cupid with two
dogs about to transfix a boar ; next another ibex ; a Cupid with four
dogs chasing a stag. At each end a tree.— R. SIDE : two panthers
mangling an ox.—L. SIDE : a panther throttling a horse. Very much
re-worked. L. 1·20. H. 0·26. Bought from the Stowe Collection
(*Catal.*, p. 45, no. 722) for £ 16. 6s.   [*.M*]

44.   Oval child's sarcophagus. *Conclamatio.* On the l. a
griffin. Then an old man seated, by him a female figure standing
with a raised MS. roll. On the r. of a doorway stands a female
figure weeping and leaning on an arm-chair in which sits a man, completely enveloped in drapery. Next a lectus with a beardless man in
tunic and pallium lying on it ; behind, the heads and hands of
two wailing professional mourners (*praeficae*) are visible. At the head
end of the bed sits a shrouded female figure behind whose chair
two more mourners are seen. Then the remains of the arch of a
doorway, and a modern female figure seated. Bad work. L. 1·00.
H. 0·22. Discovered by the Marquis of Chandos on the Via Appia,
near the tomb of Caecilia Metella, in 1817 ; bought from the Stowe
Collection (*Catal.*, p. 48, no. 748) for £16. 5s. 6d.   [*.M*]

45.   Child's sarcophagus. Cupids racing. FRONT : four
bigae with a Cupid as driver and another Cupid on horseback near
each chariot race towards the r. The foremost Cupid holds the
wreath of victory, the second falls down head over heels, as one of
his horses rears ; below the first and fourth chariot a Cupid lies on
the ground. In the background are descried the spina of the Circus,
with four ova, one obelisk, two dolphins, two metae.—SIDES : on
each a Cupid on horseback, that on the l. side with a wreath.—l.in,

from l. to r.: four empty chariots; four boys hurrying with sacks on their backs and goads in their r. hands; four boys full face, the first three with wreath and palm-branch, the fourth with palm-branch, holding a horse by the bridle; three boys with staves breaking-in wild horses. L. 1·20. H. 0·35. [*M*] Either this or the next sarcophagus is derived from the Stowe Collection, but is not to be found in the Catalogue.

46. Front of a child's sarcophagus. Cupids racing. Four Ligae, with drivers and companions on horseback, answering to those on no. 45; the foremost has no wreath : Cupids lie on the ground below the first, the last but one and the last chariots; a Cupid is helping to raise up again the horses of the second chariot which have fallen. On the spina there are visible two pointed columns, a building with four columns and a pyramidal roof, fourteen dolphins, seven ova, a Victory with a wreath, another building with four columns, and another pointed column. L. 1·35. H. 0·30. [*M*] Cf. on no. 45.

47. Front of a child's sarcophagus. Four Cupids on chariots, which are respectively drawn, in the following order, by panthers, roebucks (?), dogs, roebucks. L. 0·91. H. 0·20. [*M*]

48. Front of the lid of a sarcophagus. Boys in the palaestra. The l. end is broken off. The first boy is bending forward and holds in his hands a thick stick, probably the handle of a hoe with which he turns up the earth. Then comes a boy with jumping weights (ἁλτῆρες), at the moment of springing off the ground; then a boy running with a shield on his l. arm; after him three runners, each with one arm stretched forward. The following double inscription : *T. Aelio Maximo* and *Iun. Aelia Rufina f.*, indicates the middle of the relief ; the lost r. half may be presumed to have contained either the rest of the Greek exercises, or, possibly, those of boxing and of wrestling, which, together with running, enjoyed the greatest favour with the Romans. [*M]

49. Front of a sarcophagus. Two Victories and two Cupids (one with his feet on a sea-ox, the other on a hippocampus) bear a garland ; in the semicircular fields which it frames a Medusa's head and two tragic masks are introduced as symbols to avert evil (ἀποτρόπαια). Below the middle of the three fields the upper part of the body of a Cupid with outspread arms, in a wreath. Below, a richly ornamented zoccolo. L. 2·20. H. 1·27. Probably from the Bessborough Collection. [*M*]

50. In the catalogue there are enumerated besides, five marble

sepulchral urns from the Bessborough Collection, one of them with a cover.

51. Sun dial.

The walls of this narrow passage are covered with inscribed stones and sundry sculptures, which give it the character of a *galleria lapidaria*. The most important specimens are seven Greek sepulchral reliefs, though without exception of later style, probably all derived from Smyrna, and, to all appearance, all bought from the Bessborough Collection.

52. Stelè of Posideos and Herophanta, from Smyrna, superficially sketched in P. Lucas' *Voyage au Levant*, i. p. 152. In the field of the pediment a shield. On the stelè itself in a field stands to the l. a beardless man (Posideos), quite covered in his cloak, the hands joined before the body; by his r. leg a diminutive attendant, in short chiton, with an ewer in his lowered r. hand. To the r. stands a veiled female (Herophanta), in cloak and chiton, holding in the r. arm a large torch which occupies the middle of the scene. Her cloak shows the folds impressed on the fabric by its having been laid up a long while, a peculiarity which recurs, for example, in the Artemisia of the Mausoleum, the so called Juno Cesi in the Capitol, etc. By the torch a diminutive female attendant. Below the relief are the names of the two persons, in the accusative: Ποσίδεον | Δημοκλείους and Ἡροφάνταν | Τίμωνος; the accusatives depend on the twice repeated inscription ὁ δῆμος above the relief, in each case enclosed in a wreath, by the conferring of which the community has honoured the two personages (*C. I. Gr.*, 3245). Good, careful style of the third or second century B.C. H. 1·52. [*]

53. Stelè of Theudotos, badly engraved in Tollius, *Epist. itinerar.*, p. 20. Two pilasters which carry a straight architrave flank the field of the relief. On the r. sits a young man (Theudotos) in chiton and cloak, the l. hand in his lap, the r. raised as though he were accompanying his speech by gesture. On the l., opposite to him, sits a female figure, in chiton and cloak, which last envelopes her entirely, even her head. Leaning against her knee before her stands a boy in a short chiton, with a roll in his hands from which he seems to be reading. Below the relief an epigram of eight lines of rather inelegant style, the interpretation of which has evoked a whole literature (*C. I. Gr.*, 3328, quite correctly, cf. Kaibel, *Epigr. Graeca*, no. 240):

Ἤλυθες οὐκ ἀἴατος ἐνὶ τρισσαῖς δεκάδεσσιν.
Ὀείδωτε, τὰν ζωοῖς οἶμον ὀφειλομέναν,
καὶ σὲ τὸν ἐν σπονδαῖσι γεγαθότα πουλὺ μετ' ἀστῶν
μάτηρ αἰἀχι μιρομένα πρίτανιν.
πέτρος ὅδε ξεινοῖσι βοάεεται, ὡς αἰδαλος
ἀσφαλὲς ἀνθρώποις οὐθὲν ἔνειμε Τύχα.
εἶης τοι σὺν πατρὶ κεχαρμένος, ὄφρ' ἂν ἐς αἰῶ
Σώστρατος ἐν φθιμένοις μυρίον αἶνον ἔχῃ.

(L. 8: EXII, not EXIII.) Style of relief careful but dry. Grayish marble. H. 0·47. The stelè was formerly in the possession of G. Ulenbroek, then of the learned Dorville, both in Leyden. [*]

54. Stelè of Apollonios and Artemo. In the pediment a cup. Below, two wreaths and between them the inscription Πομπηΐα Χρυσάριον ζῶσα τὸ μνημῆον ἐποίησεν; below the wreath on the l. Ἀπολλώνιος | Μηνοφίλου, below that on the r. Ἀρτεμοῦς | Ἀπολλωνίου. These are demonstrably Smyrnaean names (*Arch. Zeit.*, 1874, p. 43). In the field Apollonios stands on the l. in chiton and cloak, Artemo on the r., veiled, both full face, quite like the figures on the reliefs at Oxford, nos. 89, 205. Artemo's l. forearm was originally put on separately, but has been lost. She has a diminutive female attendant on each side of her, of whom the one on the r. carries a large box; on the extreme l. a diminutive male attendant leans against the edge of the field of the relief. In the background a wall, which is finished at the top in a projecting listel at the height of the shoulders of the principal personages. Rather good style, probably of the second or first century B.C. H. 0·98. [*]

55. Stelè of Menekrates and Bias. Below the pediment, between two pilasters in the field a comparatively old beardless man (Menekrates) lies on a bed, completely draped, holding a cup in the l. hand and extending the r. hand to the youthful Bias, who wears only a cloak, and who seems to wish to withdraw. Before the bed a table with three feet on which food is set. At the head of Menekrates in the background a young attendant. Below the relief the inscription Μενεκράτης Βίαντος. | Βίας Μενεκράτου. Rather rough execution. H. 0·53. [*]

56. Stelè. On the l. sits a completely draped man, with his feet on a stool, holding out his r. hand to a standing female figure in chiton and cloak. To the l. by the stool stands a diminutive attendant, to the r. a female attendant leaning against a pillar, on which stands a basket. Ordinary work. The upper half of the stele is missing. H. 0·48. [*]

57. **Stele,** broken away at the top. A completely draped, beardless man, with a roll in his lowered l. hand, stands in the middle, full face. To his r. stands a diminutive attendant leaning against the edge of the field, to the l. a nude little boy sits on the ground, stretching up his arms. Rather careful execution. H. 0·60. [*]

58. **Square sepulchral relief,** of a coarse stone, lamentably corroded. Two figures lie on a couch at a table, of which the one holds out his hand to a female figure sitting at the foot end of the couch. Before the couch stands a three-legged table. H. 0·52. [*]

59. **Five more sepulchral reliefs with Latin inscriptions,** from the Bessborough Collection.

60. **Eight sepulchral urns,** five from the Bessborough Collection, one from Lord Northwick's, one from Barnes', one from Fould's sales in Paris (*Q. Gellius Chrestus,* &c.).

61. **One hundred and twenty-three Roman sepulchral inscriptions,** from the Bessborough Collection. All the Latin inscriptions have been copied by Matz and myself for the *Corpus Inscriptionum Latinarum.*

In the last section of the passage are displayed **native antiques** from various localities in the north of England; cf. also *C. I. Lat.,* VII. pp. 77 ff.

WEST GALLERY.

62. **Statue of Dionysos,** similar to the Vatican statue, Clarac, IV. 681, 1595. New: r. forearm and three-quarters of l. arm. The head, from which long curls fall down, is inclined towards the r. shoulder; from the l. shoulder there hangs down a piece of drapery, another end of which, drawn slantwise across the back, falls down from the r. elbow to the ground. On his feet the god wears high laced boots (ἐνδρομίδες). The l. arm is raised, the hand was originally grasping a thyrsos. Ordinary Roman work. H. 1·44. [*M]

63. **Group of Dionysos and Pan.** The god leans with his l. hip against the stem of a tree, the l. leg crossed over the r. In the r. arm a piece of the thyrsos is preserved, the l. forearm rests on the shoulder of an ithyphallic Pan, not particularly youthful, modelled on a considerably smaller scale as a subsidiary figure. He is bending forward the upper part of his body and looking up at the god, whose back he embraces as though he wished to pull him along with him. Thasian marble. H. 1·25. [*M]

64. Statue of Asklepios, from Lord Anson's Shugborough Collection. The god stands on his r. leg, with his r. arm akimbo and his l. arm-pit pressed heavily on the snake-entwined staff. Unimportant work. H. 1·50. [*M]

65. Statue of Paris, from the Shugborough Collection. Probably identical with the "Adonis" named by Dallaway, p. 385 (II. p. 137).

66. Figure of Eros as god of sleep, winged. He lies sleeping on his back with crossed legs, at full length on his chlamys. The head rests on one arm ; with the other hand he holds some poppy heads ; by him lies his bow, at his feet crawls a lizard. In front the inscription *Herculi sancto | Eutychianus*. From the Bessborough Collection. [*M]

67. Figure of Eros, similar to the last, with the attributes of Herakles, lying on a lion's skin, the l. hand on the club, by which a lizard is visible. From the Bessborough Collection. [*M]

68. Female portrait statue. *Mon. Matth.*, I. Pl. 23, "Cybele." Clarac, III. 396 A, 664 E. On a throne sits the richly draped lady, in whose features, as Matz rightly observes, one can recognise a portrait, perhaps of the first century A.D. (pupils not expressed). She unites the attributes of different matronly goddesses of high rank ; the mural crown under the veil and the lion by her r. leg suggest Rhea or Kybelè, a bunch of ears of corn and poppies in the r. hand Ceres, the large cornucopiae (with pineapple, apples, poppies, ears of corn, grapes) by the l. leg and the upright steering paddle on the blade of which the l. hand rests, Fortuna. So was Livia (Julia Augusta) deified as Juno, Vesta, Ceres, Diana, Isis, &c. (cf. Eckhel, *Doctr. Numm.*, VI. p. 155 ; Letronne, *Inscr. de l'Egypte*, I. p. 230). Only a closer examination of the features than I was able to undertake can determine whether perchance the likeness of this Empress is to be recognised in the present statue. Armlets adorn the exposed r. arm, bracelets both wrists. A high narrow *pantello*, which rises from the cornucopiae, serves to secure the fingers of the l. hand. The preservation is wonderful. Only the lower end of the cornucopiae is restored. Thasian marble. Rather coarse Roman work. H. 1·50. Formerly in the Mattei Collection, then in Gavin Hamilton's hands, sold by him to the first Marquis of Buckingham, and bought from the Stowe Collection (*Cat.*, p. 264, no. 21) for Lowther for £31. 10s. [*M]

69 93. The catalogue enumerates **22 busts**, among them a series of **busts of the Caesars**, which at once rouses suspicion by its completeness. 69. Julius Caesar, 70. Augustus, 71. Tiberius, 72. Caligula (from the Marquis of Hertford's Collection), 73. Claudius, 74. Nero (Hertford Collection), 75, 76. Galba, 77. Otho, 79, 80. Vespasian (one of these busts, once the property of the Right Hon. Edmund Burke, stood in his library), 90. Titus (Hertford Collection), 91. Domitian (Hertford Collection), 92. Nerva (Hertford Collection), 93. Geta. One of the other busts, placed in 1873 near the entrance to the garden, is a fine, exceedingly well preserved **portrait of a beardless Roman**, not unlike Cicero (cf. London, Apsley House, no. 1), but of a nobler and firmer countenance.

The catalogue gives besides the following miraculous item :

94. "**The Olympian Meta**, brought from Greece by the Emperor Nero, and placed in the Circus at Rome. It was purchased for a large sum by the Marquis of Hertford."

95. **Four sepulchral urns**, three from the Bessborough Collection, one with reclining figure. Probably among these are comprised the two following specimens :

96. **Etruscan urn**, of alabaster (?), with particularly well preserved remains of colouring. Battle-scene, grouped round a warrior who has sunk down on to his knee. A friend tries to make him rise from the ground, but is himself menaced by the conqueror ; on either side a warrior hastens up to succour the respective combatants. Lid. Reclining female figure, draped, with a leaf-shaped fan in her r. hand. Below her the remains of an Etruscan inscription. [*M*]

97. **Etruscan urn**, of alabaster. At the l. end remains of a female figure with torch. Then a quadriga, on which there stand besides the driver two men in long drapery, the one with a shield, the other with a helmet, and a girl. A servant with a hatchet leads the horses. From the r. two men in long drapery advance to meet them, the one with a hood, the other, who is bearded, with a small round shield. Lid. Reclining figure of a man, very short, with diptychon and apple. [*M*]

PASSAGE LEADING TO THE WEST GALLERY.

Here the catalogue mentions, presumably all as antique—

98. **Statuette of Hercules.**
99. **Bust of Epaminondas.**

100.   **Bust of Otho.**

101, 102.   **Two antique Sarcophagi** (cf. nos. 43—49. 96. 97).

103.   **Statue of Cicero.**

104.   **Statue of Aristides.**

105.   **Draped female statuette,** name unknown.

106.   **Five busts,** four male, one female.

From the Catalogue of the Stowe Collection I add moreover the following specimens bought by Lord Lonsdale at the sale there, which I am unable to identify with definite numbers of the Lowther Collection.

107.   "**An oval cistern,** of grey marble, with lions' heads and grapes." Bought for £30. 9s. (*Cat.*, p. 269, no. 89.)

108.   "**A Roman marble sarcophagus,** inscribed *D. M. G. Messis qui vixit annis XVII mesis IIII.* Found by the late Duke of Buckingham in an excavation made by him at Rome, in 1828, near the tomb of Caecilia Metella. It then contained the skeleton of the Roman youth whose name it bears. It recently stood in the flower-garden at Stowe, and in it were deposited the remains of the late Duke's favourite dog, who died of extreme old age in 1837." Bought for £8. (*Cat.*, p. 271, no. 115.)

109.   "**Three marble busts.**" Bought for £11. (*Cat.*, p. 271, no. 124.) Probably a Roman sepulchral monument.

110.   "**A male and female marble bust.**" Bought for £1. 15s. (*Cat.*, p. 272, no. 137.) See on no. 109.

MARBURY HALL (Cheshire).

Dallaway, pp. 354 ff. (II. pp. 103 ff.). *A Catalogue of Paintings, Statues, Busts, etc., at Marbury Hall,* London, 1814, and Warrington, 1819 (privately printed ; only a short indication of the articles). Spiker, I. pp. 407 f. Clarac, III. p. 22 note 2. Waagen, *Treas.*, IV. pp. 406 ff. Conze, *Arch. Anz.*, 1864, pp. 223 f. 235 ff. Michaelis, *Arch. Zeit.*, 1874, pp. 43 ff. I visited the collection in the year 1873.

This house, the country seat of the Irish family of SMITH BARRY, is situated near Northwich. The collection of antiques was made in Rome, with the assistance of Gavin Hamilton and Jenkins, by the

Hon. J. Smith Barry, about 1776, as in a letter to Lord Shelburne of July 13, 1776. Hamilton mentions "Mr Barry" as having lately returned to England (*Academy*, Aug. 31, 1878, p. 220). Several of the principal pieces were got from the Villa Mattei and the Villa d'Este at Tivoli. Unfortunately the statues and busts are very un favourably disposed in the dark Sculpture Gallery, which is more like a cellar. Two colossal statues (nos. 2 and 17) which formerly stood in two niches in the Entrance Hall, have been placed in the court, a few smaller pieces (nos. 8, 11, 14) in the saloon. Others are secluded in other rooms, to which I had not access. The printed catalogue enumerates 21 statues, 19 busts (several modern), 10 "stone vases" (several modern, others without sculpture), 6 relievos, and 9 "altars," *i.e.* cinerary urns, &c. The statues are one and all engraved in Clarac, so I give his order in numbering.

STATUES.

1. **Statue of Zeus on a throne.** Clarac, III. 396 D, 666 A. On a seat without a back but with two transverse beams (κατόχες), sits the god, his legs and back covered by a wide cloak, a corner of which lies on the l. shoulder; breast and stomach nude. The l. arm is raised, the r. hand rests in the lap, the head is slightly bent. The state of preservation is unusually good. New: nose, both eyebrows, upper lip, the ends of several tresses, the l. forearm (which, to judge by a large *puntello* on the cloak, was once placed nearer to the head), the r. hand with the thunderbolt, some small pieces of drapery, and part of the seat. Head, feet, and plinth have never been broken. The rather decided slope of the thighs towards the knees is well adapted for a large statue in a lofty position. As the back part is cut off straight, and the depth of the seat is so small that the god cannot sit comfortably, it is plain that the statue was meant to be set up against the wall of a somewhat confined room. The workmanship is merely decorative, and is best on the cloak, the deep round folds of thick, soft material being well rendered. The most insignificant part is the head with its good-natured expression (not correctly given in Clarac). The tresses of the head, which are traversed by a fillet, and of the beard are much separated from each other and mechanically curved. Coarse-grained Parian marble. H. 2·07. From the Villa d'Este. Cf. Overbeck, *Kunstmyth.*, II. p. 118. [*C IV*, *Scharf*]

2 (Court). **Draped female statue,** colossal scale. Clarac, III. 438 A, 774 C. "Cérès." *Mon. Matth.*, I. Pl. 29, "Ceres."

. Dallaway, no. 7, "Sabina." This female figure stands in a quiet attitude with the weight on the r. leg, draped in a long, girdled, doubled chiton. A head of Sabina (eyeballs expressed), of earnest expression and with careful treatment of the hair, is set on. The r. arm is akimbo, the lowered l. hand holds ears of wheat and poppies. According to Scharf the hands are antique, the whole statue being very perfect; though Clarac was of opinion that the whole r. arm and the piece of the l. between armlet (antique) and wrist are modern. In this case we may be supposed to have before us an empress (Sabina?) as Ceres. The bunch in the l. hand and indeed much besides seemed to me, upon only a cursory view, to be restored. The colossal statue is of pretty good work; the general effect is not bad. H. abt. 2·20. From the Villa Mattei. [*Scharf]

3. **Statue of Apollo.** Clarac, III. 476 A, 926 B. Mon. Mattth., I. Pl. 5. Dallaway, no. 5. The torso only is antique. It exhibits, only with the sides reversed, the movement given in the Apollo Belvedere; the r. shoulder is remarkably raised, the pose of the arms indicated by their stumps. The workmanship is not distinguished, but rather animated. Marble probably Pentelic. By means of a modern neck an antique head, of a different kind of marble, has been set on. It is crowned with a wreath of laurel; its expression empty and insignificant, the forms effeminate, the surface re-worked. New: chin and tip of nose; besides the whole r. arm, three quarters of the l., the whole cloak, which is riveted on, the member, the lower parts of both legs, the stem of a tree with quiver and snake by the l. leg. For the restorations the Vatican statue may have served as a model. The cloak was not yet in existence when the statue was in the Villa Mattei, but has been subsequently put on. H. without pedestal 1·77. [*C]

4 (not in the Gallery). **Statue of a Nymph of Artemis?** Clarac, IV. 564 A. 1208 C. In the Catalogue the figure is called "a Diana, imperfect." The chiton is buttoned along the upper parts of the arms, and reaches down a little below the knees; a cloak, folded double, is fastened on the l. shoulder and envelops the body to the knees, except the r. breast and shoulder. The figure rests on the r. leg; by the l. is the stem of a tree. The lowered r. arm is almost entirely modern, as also the l. hand with wrist, and the feet. Antique, but set on and not belonging to the statue, is the head, which is encircled above the brow by a twisted fillet or a roll of hair, while the back of the head is covered by a smooth cloth like a hood. H. 1·68. [From a sketch by Scharf]

5. Statuette of an astragalizusa. Clarac, IV. 564 D,
1248 A. This statuette, much broken and patched, is entirely modern;
it is made of a soft kind of marble much like alabaster. The r. leg
is more completely exposed than in the antique examples, except
the copy in the Louvre (Clarac, III. 323, 1425); the knuckle-bones
are missing. H. 0·26. [*]

6. Statue of "Elektra." Clarac, IV. 594, 1449 B, "Vénus
armée." Dallaway, no. 3, "Venus Victrix." The antique portions
resemble the Elektra of a group in Naples, in which she is represented in conjunction with Orestes (Clarac, V. 836, 2093. Jahn,
Berichte d. sächs. Ges., 1861, Pl. 4. 1, pp. 119 f. Kekulé, *Gruppe d.
Menelaos*, Pl. 2, 1). It does not of course follow for a certainty
that our statue should be named in accordance with this likeness.
Antique: the torso as far as the knees, three quarters of the r. arm,
l. arm except the hand which is missing; a *puntello* on the corner of
the drapery which hangs down (of which the lower half is new)
suggests that the l. hand originally held some long object. New:
lower parts of the legs and half the l. forearm with the arrow.
Antique, but not originally belonging to the statue, is the head of
Venus with fillet and a large knot of hair on the crown. The head
is of Greek marble, the body of marble with blackish spots, perhaps
from Lower Italy; a tress in the nape of the neck on the torso,
answering to one on the Elektra in Naples, is not continued in the
hair of the head. The remarkably deep girding of the chiton about
the hips allows the whole body to shew through the fine Coan
drapery; between breast and girdle it lies close on the form with
scarcely a fold, the abdomen and thighs also are hardly concealed
by the thin folds; a deep hollow on both sides of a vertical fold
which falls down from the stomach displays the shape of the legs very
clearly. The style is like that of the Venus Genetrix (cf. Holkham,
no. 23); the exposure of the l. breast also displays a similar taste.
The latter trait, and also the pose of the arms and neck, completely
deviate from the Elektra in Naples, and therefore suggest that our
statue, detached from the group, has as a single figure received
another meaning. A similar increase of refinement finds expression
in the other extant copies enumerated by Jahn (*l. cit.*). The nude
parts exhibit rather poor workmanship; the back is quite carelessly
treated. H. 1·71. The statue was found by Gavin Hamilton in
1771 during a very productive excavation near Tor Colombaro (at
the ninth milestone on the Appian road), and restored as Venus
Victrix (Dallaway, p. 373 [II. p. 126]). [*CH*]

7. **Statue of Eros.** Clarac, IV. 650 A, 1469 A. Dallaway, no. 16. The youthful god stands on the r. leg, close to which the stem of a tree has been introduced ; the l. leg is a little drawn back. The r. arm was originally raised, the l. lowered. The head is somewhat inclined towards the r. shoulder and is richly covered with curls. It seems to belong to the statue, though re-set. No trace of wings. New : the r. arm, the l. forearm with arrow, the lower parts of both legs, the stem of a tree except a junction above the knee ; no part of the bow, which is to be seen on the stem, is antique. Excellent Parian lychnite. H. 1·08. [*]

8 (Saloon). **Group of Dionysos and a Bacchante** (rather than Ariadne). Clarac, IV. 694, 1634. Dallaway, no. 12. The Bacchante strides forward in lively movement. She has on a short chiton which leaves the l. breast and shoulder exposed. A nebris girt slantwise from the l. shoulder over the breast holds up the chiton, its corners hanging down lower. She winds her r. arm round the back of the youthful god, who, heavy with wine, has laid his l. arm round her neck and leans heavily on her, while his legs move forward with difficulty. To his condition corresponds his unusual envelopment in the wide cloak, which entirely covers the whole body and the r. arm ; the legs on the contrary are for the most part left free. His l. hand holds a corner of his companion's drapery. The group is much restored, still the restorer seems in essentials to have hit upon the right treatment. This is certainly the case as to the pose of the two heads, which are turned towards each other. New : both heads, and besides, of the god, half the l. forearm with the hand and the greater part of the corner of drapery held in it, l. leg, and r. foot ; of the female figure, three-quarters of the l. arm, a piece of the r. arm behind the back of the god, the lower part of the l. leg, the r. foot with a piece of the drapery ; lastly the plinth. The engraving in Clarac is much less clear and of less favourable effect than the original. The group is full of tipsy Bacchic jollity ; its conception may pertain to the Alexandrine rather than to the Roman period. Greek, probably Parian, marble. H. 0·81. For a similar group recently found in Rome, now in the Berlin Museum, which is better preserved and executed, cf. Dressel, *Bullett. dell' Inst.*, 1872, pp. 222 ff. ; it would appear from this copy that the l. hand of the Bacchante originally lifted up part of her drapery near the l. leg. [*]

9. **Statue of boy with grapes.** Clarac, IV. 694 A, 1637 A, "Génie bacchique." Dallaway, no. 11, "patrician boy." This Roman portrait head of a boy is by means of an inserted neck set on a body

of a different marble from that of the head. Nose new. Pupils expressed. Of the body are new: only the r. hand and the feet with part of the pedestal, but the whole figure is re-worked, and in particular the ring on the fourth finger of the l. hand was first brought into being by a modern paring of the finger. In general the work is fresh, the gentle movement in the l. hip well rendered. The powerfully made boy steps out on to the r. foot; the r. arm hangs straight down. An ample cloak, fastened on the r. shoulder, covers the back almost down to the feet, also the l. arm and the breast. The l. hand holds a large bunch of grapes before the breast. The width and length of the drapery, which is strange for an ordinary boy, leads to the suggestion that the figure is a representative or **genius of vintage**, akin to the "Vertumnus" at Ince (no. 6); the r. hand may have held a pruning-knife or the like; cf. Müller-Wieseler, II. 75, 964 *d*; 965, and on the absence of wings, Petersen, *Annali*, 1861, pp. 215 ff. H. 1·14. [*]

10. **Statue of a Bacchante.** Clarac, IV. 694 B, 1623 A, "Ariane." *Mon. Matth.*, I. Pl. 68. Dallaway, no. 8? The figure rests on the r. leg, with the l. drawn back. A long, sleeved chiton with a considerable mass of fold about the hips covers the figure; a nebris is girt slantwise from the l. shoulder and partly hangs down far; a broad girdle keeps all together round the waist. Long tresses fall down on the shoulder. The upper parts of both arms are lowered, the l. forearm advanced. New: almost the whole of the l. forearm with tympanon, three-quarters of the r. arm (which, when in the Villa Mattei, held a bunch of grapes), the front corner of the nebris. The neck with the tresses by it is inserted. The head (nose new), which is crowned with ivy, does not belong to the statue. Coarse work, calculated for strong effect, especially in the deeply undercut heavy folds. Apparently Pentelic marble. H. 1·72. From the Villa Mattei. [*C]

11 (Saloon). **Group of a Satyr on an ass.** Clarac, IV. 696, 1610 A. *Mon. Matth.*, I. Pl. 13. Dallaway, no. 13. (According to all of them "Bacchus.") The ass steps out with lowered head, with a bell round his neck. On his back is spread the skin of an animal, on which sprawls a young Satyr, the l. leg lowered, the r. raised; the l. elbow resting on a leather bottle, the opening of which his l. hand grasps. The head of Bacchus, which the figure wore when in the Villa Mattei, has been appropriately changed for the head of a Satyr. New: of the Satyr, the head, almost all the r. leg, the l. foot, the r. arm with the pedum, and smaller patches

in various places; of the ass, ears, tail, parts of the legs, plinth and pieces of the stem which underprop the body of the ass. Unhappily the group is everywhere re-worked to such an extent that even the genuineness of the whole piece may seem doubtful, though scarcely with reason. In the course of the re-working the little tail of the Satyr may very likely have disappeared. Italian marble. H. with plinth 0·54. L. 0·46. From the Villa Mattei. [*]

12. **Torso of an Apollo**, restored as a Satyr. Clarac, IV. 704 A, 1683 C, "Faune." Dallaway, no. 10, "Faunus." The genuine parts belong to an Apollo of that not yet sufficiently understood type in which a swan sits at the feet of the god, who holds the lyre high above the l. shoulder (cf. Clarac, II. 479, 918. 483, 928 A. 489, 948 A. 490, 954 A. Müller-Wieseler, II. 12. 131, cf. Dilthey, *Rhein. Jahrb.*, LII. p. 51, n. 2). The placing of the l. leg before the r., the gentle flow of the elegant torso and its slender proportions, fall in exactly with that type. The work does not quite answer to the delicacy of the conception. The marble is of a very fine grain and of a yellowish tint with grey spots. There is naturally no trace of a little tail, the god having been first degraded into a Satyr in restoration. The Satyr's head, wreathed with pine, and with goat's warts (φήρεα) on the neck, is of Thasian marble, but is antique excepting the nose and under lip. Entirely new: neck, both arms, the flute, both feet, the whole support with nebris and pedum, the pedestal. H. 1·09. [*C]

13. **Statue of a Nymph**, a figure for a fountain. Clarac, IV. 750, 1831 A. *Mon. Matth.*, I. Pl. 51. Dallaway, no. 17. Half sitting on, half raising herself from a piece of rock is a girl, the lower part of her body surrounded by an ample drapery, a narrower part of which descends from her l. shoulder. Both knees are bent; the l. foot is somewhat raised on a piece of rock. Thus the l. thigh serves to support an urn which the Nymph holds with her two lowered hands. From this, water originally was to flow into a basin. On the lower part of the body there are only trifling injuries to be remarked; the upper part too, though much broken, seems to be antique in essentials. New: r. arm, three-quarters of the l., almost the whole urn inclusive of the comic mask, and the neck. The head no doubt originally looked down at the urn. The much more simple head which the figure had when in the Villa Mattei, and which the drawings show, has subsequently been inappropriately replaced by a head of a bacchante crowned with ivy, of Satyr-like forms and with rich head-dress, which also looks away to the side

(cf. the subsidiary drawing in Clarac). The deeply undercut folds by the legs, and especially those which run slantwise across the lap, are of good effect. Greek marble. H. 1·27. From the Villa Mattei. [*C]

14 (Saloon). **Group of Herakles and Antaeos.** Clarac, v. 804, 2015 A. Dallaway, no. 14. Herakles has advanced the r. leg and steps back on the l., while he lifts up Antaeos, whom he has gripped round the stomach from behind, and presses his back tightly against himself. Antaeos writhes under the mighty hug of his opponent, and tries in vain to grasp his arms with his hands; both legs are bent up at the knees, the l. thigh lowered, the r. raised. The artist has very skilfully arranged the group so that both bodies have their fronts turned towards the spectator. Powerful, somewhat coarse forms. The restorations are considerable. New: of Herakles, head and neck, l. forefinger, three last fingers of r. hand, l. knee and l. foot (the shin seems antique), r. leg from above the knee downwards, the support covered with the skin except the junction at the top, the club, the plinth; of Antaeos, head and neck, almost the whole r. arm between shoulder and wrist, a small patch inserted on the l. wrist, r. foot, and l. leg. Ordinary execution. Pentelic marble. H. 0·77. [*]

15. **Group of a male figure on horseback.** Clarac, v. 810 B, 2028 C, "Amazone," after an erroneous conjecture hazarded by Millin, who rightly objected to Dallaway's designation, "Paris Equestris" (no. 2); in the letter-press Clarac himself points out the absence of the female breast, without however altering the nomenclature. The youthful rider, whose antique parts show no trace of Phrygian costume, sits on a prancing horse, bending down to the r., only clad in an exomis, conceived as at a hunt rather than as in battle. While the l. hand holds the reins, the r. arm was originally raised as now, obviously to deal a thrust or blow. The head of the horse is turned r. The genuine parts are pretty well executed, and are very different from Clarac's bad engraving. The motive is more animated than that of the so-called Commodus of the Vatican (*Mon. Matth.* I. 93. *Mus. Chiaram.*, III. 25. Clarac, v. 962, 2475), and more like the bronze Alexander from Herculaneum (*Ant. di Ercol.*, VI. 51. Clarac, v. 840, 2105. Müller-Wieseler, I. 40, 170). There is a similar figure in Turin (Dütschke, *Ant. Bildw.*, IV. no. 81. Wieseler, *Nachrichten von der Göttinger Ges. d. Wiss.*, 1877, p. 661, no. 7). New: the head with a strange kind of Phrygian cap, the r. arm, lower parts of both legs; of the horse, head with part of neck,

legs, and tail. Pentelic marble. Present height to the point of the
cap 1·18. L. of the rider's body abt. 1·04. The statue was found
together with no. 6 in 1771, by Gavin Hamilton, at Tor Colombaro,
and passed through Jenkins' hands to Smith Barry (cf. Dallaway, p.
372 [II. p. 124]). Hamilton speaks of it in a letter to Lord Shelburne of Aug. 6, 1772 (*Academy*, Aug. 17, 1878, p. 168) in the
following terms: "I have likewise sold him [Jenkins] a young
figure with a Phrygian cap on horseback, but considering it was so
much fragmented, and well knowing what nice judges we are in
England in horse flesh, I declined sending it." [*C*]

16. Statue of a herdsman. Clarac, v. 833, 2077 A, "Paris."
Leaning towards the r. on the stem of a tree stands the youth, his
r. leg set slightly before the l. The chlamys surrounds breast,
shoulders, and part of the back, and falls down over the r. arm, on
which rests the pedum; the l. arm was probably always akimbo.
New: head with Phrygian cap and l. arm with apple, by which
symbols the conversion into "Paris" has been effected; also the
r. hand, the larger, lower part of the pedum, the lower parts of the
legs, and the pedestal. Decorative style of workmanship. Thasian
marble. H. 1·74. [*C*]

17 (Court). **Statue of Helios,** colossal scale. Clarac, v.
839, 2104, "Alexandre le Grand." In complete nudity the youthful
figure steps forward with the l. foot foremost. The body is very
powerfully made. The youthful head, which shews well-rounded
forms, is surrounded by rich, long, curly hair, not, however, arranged
in the manner characteristic of heads of Alexander, which by its
inclination towards the l. shoulder it otherwise resembles. New:
nose and parts of the lips, both arms with globe and sword, lower
parts of both legs, the stem of a palm, the weapons, and the pedestal.
The hair is to a great extent hollowed out with the drill; the treatment of the nude is coarse and clumsy, yet not out of keeping with
a colossal figure. The shoulders are unusually broad. The name
Helios is due to Scharf, who compares the head on coins of Rhodes;
we might also call to mind a Dioskuros such as those on the steps of
the Capitol. H. abt. 2·80. [*Scharf*]

18. Statue of a poet or philosopher. Clarac, v. 844,
2125. Dallaway, no. 15, "Homer." The figure rests on the r. leg.
The cloak is disposed similarly to that of the Demosthenes at
Knole (no. 1), only that the r. hand draws the corner, which hangs
down from the l. shoulder, somewhat slantwise in front of the breast,
and thus brings some life into the drapery. The l. arm is lowered;

by the l. foot stands a bundle of rolls strapped together. It is a
prettily designed statue, and is executed in good decorative style, of
better effect than the engraving leads us to suppose. New: feet and
pedestal, the lowest piece of the bundle, the l. forearm with the
volumen, the r. forearm and part of the drapery. The figure is of
Pentelic marble, likewise the head, which is set on, but with a clean
cut, and is perhaps original; at any rate it suits the figure well.
The head is bearded, the hair entwined by a twisted ribbon, the face
(new: tip of nose) of dignified aspect. It certainly has no connection with either Euripides, as Conze proposed, or Zenon, as Scharf
thinks; for Homer, too, the characteristic traits are wanting. The
head a little recals the so-called Hesiod of the Braccio Nuovo,
no. 89, in the Vatican (Pistolesi, *Vaticano,* IV. 23, 1). H. 1·14.
[*C, Scharf*]

19 (not in the Gallery). **Statue of a boy with a bird.**
Clarac, v. 878, 2236. A half-grown boy, standing in repose, with
a small cloak flung round him, which covers the loins and part of the
l. arm, holds in the l. hand a bird, which is apparently dying (antique?). He raises the r. arm. The head, with a wreath of oak on
the smooth hair, is borrowed from another statue. According to
Clarac's letterpress this would be the only alien addition; the
engraving represents the r. hand also as restored. H. 0·73. Can
this be Dallaway, no. 9, "A statue of **Trajan,** when young"?

20. **Statue of Antinous,** colossal scale. Clarac, v. 946,
2430 A. Dallaway, no. 1. It is a fairly exact replica of the Vatican
statue, Braccio Nuovo, no. 14 (*Mus. Chiaram.* II. 39. Clarac, v.
947, 2430). Both statues, which are of about the same size, come
from Ostia. The Vatican copy was discovered in 1798 at Tor Bovacciano (Fea, *Viaggio ad Ostia,* p. 48); the English example had been
found considerably earlier by Gavin Hamilton, and indeed not, as Fea
says, in 1788 near the Capanna de' Bassi, but, according to Hamilton's own account, in the year 1772 near Porta Marina (Dallaway,
p. 377 [II. p. 129], cf. Lord Edm. Fitzmaurice, *Academy,* Aug. 10,
1878, p. 142, note‡). New on our statue: r. arm, l. hand with the
bunch of ears of corn and poppies, the greater part of the lap full of
fruits, the feet, the lowest part of the support, and the pedestal. The
neck is inserted and the greater part of the head modern ; a piece,
however, comprising the chin with the l. jaw, the under lip, the r.
cheek and a great part of the tresses, is antique and, as I believe,
originally belonging to the statue. (According to Dallaway and
Waagen the whole head would not belong to the statue.) While in

the Vatican statue the lap of the cloak, so far as it is antique, contains roses, narcissuses, bell-shaped lotus and pears (*Mus. Chiaram.*, II. p. 86), and therefore suggests different seasons, in the antique parts of the English statue only autumn fruits are contained, grapes, plums, apples, quinces, a vine leaf. Both suit the conception of Antinous as Vertumnus. The body exhibits the usual merely external polish of the sculptures of the period of Hadrian ; a polish admired by a generation which saw true ideal art in this academic elegance. Greek marble. H. 2·40. [*CW*]

21. **Male torso,** rightly compared by Conze with the Borghese boxer in the Louvre. The torso, both thighs nearly to the knees, a stump of the r. arm, which was considerably bent back, are preserved. The l. arm with the whole of the shoulder is broken off, but was presumably once stretched straight forward ; for the whole of the upper part of the body is strenuously urged in this direction ; of the legs, on the other hand, the r. is advanced, the l. drawn back. A chlamys is fastened on the r. shoulder, covers breast and back in a narrow strip, and seems to have been bound round the arm instead of a shield (*bracchium clupeatum chlamyde*). The development of muscle is very powerful, especially on the beautifully curved back. Pentelic marble. H. 1·06. [*C*]

22. **Torso of a Satyr.** Only the torso with a tail, inclusive of the shoulders and the stumps of both thighs, is preserved. This however is sufficient to enable us to recognise in this specimen a replica of the Satyr stamping the krupezion of the Florentine Tribune (Clarac, v. 715, 1709. Müller-Wieseler, II. 39, 462). For other replicas cf. Matz-Duhn, *Ant. Bildw. in Rom*, no. 416 ; cf. also Richmond, no. 42. Very good work. Apparently Italian marble. H. 0·56. [*CW*]

23. "**A statue of Bacchus with a Faun.**" Dallaway, no. 4. In the Catalogue there is no entry of the kind. Can there have been a confusion made with no. 8?

24. "**A statue of Vespasian.**" Dallaway, no. 18 ; not in the Catalogue. The statue is also mentioned in the Townley papers (Bodleian Library, Oxford) as having been bought from Jenkins for £30: "A Statue of Vespasian in a Consular Habit."

BUSTS.

I was not able to take more than a cursory survey of these busts, which are for the most part of life size and of good or moderate workmanship. Scharf's notices too, which lie before me, give but few details.

25. Hadrian. Modern. [*]
26. Antoninus Pius; large life size. Dallaway, no. 20. H. 0·96. [*Scharf]
27. Antoninus Pius ; very fine. [Scharf]
28. Marcus Aurelius. Dallaway, no. 19. About the same size as no. 26. Bought from Jenkins for £80 (Townley Papers, Oxford, Bodleian Library). [*Scharf]
29. Lucius Verus. Dallaway, no. 23. [*Scharf]
30. Aelius Verus. Dallaway, no. 20. According to Scharf, more likely Commodus. [*Scharf]
31. Septimius Severus. Dallaway, no. 22. Not quite so large as no. 26. [*Scharf]
32. Unknown. Dallaway, no. 24. With short cut beard. [*]
33. "Pindar." Dallaway, no. 27. It reminds me of Metrodoros. [*]
34. Empress. Small size. Dallaway, no. 26, "Juno." The head-dress is peculiar. Stephane over forehead. New: nose. [*Scharf]
35. Satyr. Dallaway, no. 25.

RELIEFS.

36. Puteal, representing Paris and Helena. Orlandi, Le nozze di Paride ed Elena, Rome 1775, Fol. Tischbein, Homer, Pl. 5, 2. Millin, Gal. Myth., Pl. 159, 541. Spec., II. 16. Müller-Wieseler, II. 27, 295. Dallaway, no. 29. Cf. Jahn, Ber. d. sächs. Ges., 1850, pp. 184 f. Overbeck, Bildwerke, pp. 269 f. Stephani, Compte-Rendu, 1861, p. 122. According to a letter from a Neapolitan in the Townley papers at Oxford (Bodleian Library) the relief stood during two centuries and a half "Neapoli in domo M. Comitis de Matalona in ore putei." In fact, an old drawing in the collection of Mr A. W. Franks, Brit. Mus., London, shows the relief still enclosed by a simple cornice at the top and a narrow listel at the bottom. Dallaway observes : "Formerly in the Columbran Palace at Naples. The cup at the bottom and the cornice at the top, by which it becomes a vase, were added when in the possession of Mr Jenkins about the year 1772." Thus the marble became famous under the name of the "Jenkins vase." The genuine piece is 0·76 high, its upper circumference measures 2·46. Italian marble, spotted with grey. Helena sits on a seat without a back, draped with chiton and cloak, in the typical attitude of a modest bride, supporting the lowered head on the r. hand, while the l. holds a corner of the cloak in the lap; her feet rest on a stool. (New: head, r. shoulder, greater part of the r. forearm, the l. hand and the wrist.) Beside her sits Aphroditè, draped in a chiton, which has slipped down from r. shoulder and breast, and a cloak, which also veils the head. She looks at Helena, round whose neck she has laid her r. arm, and points with her outstretched l. hand to Paris. (New: nose, both thumbs, and r. foot.) Opposite these two approaches Paris-Alex-andros, in chlamys and Phrygian cap, under which rich curls issue forth. His glance is fixed in admiration on Helena's beauty; the l. hand laid on the breast gives expression to the same feeling of lingering wonder. (New: face, r. forearm with hand, l. hand partly, a piece of l. thigh and knee.) His r. hand is grasped by Eros, who with wings outspread is striving with both hands to lead forward to Helena the hesitating youth, at whom he looks up. (New: head, r. arm and shoulder, l. hand, and the two first toes of the l. foot.) The action of the Eros is considerably coarser than in a relief in Naples, which exhibits essentially the same group, interpreted by inscrip-tions, but throughout much more delicately, less unreservedly treated (Winckelmann, *Mon. Ined.*, Pl. 115. *Mus. Borb.*, III. Pl. 40. Millin, *Gal. Myth.*, Pl. 173, 540). Instead of the Peitho, who in the Neapolitan relief sits on a high pillar behind Helena, in the English relief are grouped three Muses together behind Helena's back, facing r. Next to Helena stands "Polyhymnia" leaning on a low pillar in the attitude of well-known statues, quite enveloped in the fine cloak. (New: nose, and l. hand with roll.) "Euterpè" comes after her, draped in chiton and cloak, blowing a straight and a curved flute. (New: nose, little finger of r. hand and a great part of the forearm, and the r. knee.) "Terpsichorè" or "Erato" comes last, playing on an instrument, which in size resembles the lyre rather than the cithara, but in shape and the way it is handled is more like the latter. (New: nose, r. forearm with lower half of hand, and half the r. foot.) The presence of the Muses is explained by the similarity of the whole representation to a marriage ceremony: they are raising the hymenaeal chant. Still they seem to be a later addi-tion to the original composition (cf., besides the relief in Naples, the

Vatican relief in Guattani's *Mon. ined.*, 1785, *Giugno*, Pl. 1). In a marble vase recently discovered in Rome, which repeats the same scene, the group of the Muses is due to the restorer, who was induced by a very faint remnant of a draped female figure to introduce the three musical sisters of the Jenkins vase (*Bullett. della commiss. arch. comun. di Roma*, VIII. Pl. 6–8, pp. 119 ff.). Unhappily our whole relief (it may be presumed, when being conformed to the shape of a vase) has been considerably re-worked, so that there is probably little of the original surface left. The draperies are more dryly treated than the nude parts. Nevertheless it is a good Roman work, of unusually high projection and considerable effect. Between the heads of the figures there runs in thick, rough, and clumsy letters, not however of bad shape, the following inscription, which is presumably a later addition : GRAECEIA· PF· (head of Aphrodite) RVFA (wing) POMPON (wing, into which the N is partly cut, and head of Paris), DIANAE (head of Terpsichorè) LOCᴴ (head of Euterpè, whose knot of hair has caused the smaller figure of the H) S· P· S· C· P· S. The interpretation of the inscription is difficult, cf. Gruter, no. 1011, 3. Orelli, no. 1450. Mommsen (*I.R.N.*, no. 2589 and *Ber. d. sächs. Ges.*, 1850, p. 185 note) gives the following explanation: *Graecia P(ubli) f(ilia) Rufa Pompon(i) Dianae, loc(o) h(oc) s(ibi) p(ermisso) s(enatus) c(onsulto), p(ecunia) s(ua)*; where the order *loco hoc* for *hoc loco* and the absence of a stop before H remain strange. The late Prof. Wilmanns regarded the whole piece as a sepulchral ara dedicated by Graecia Rufa to Pomponia Diana, in which her remains were to be laid (cf. Wilmanns, *Exempla Inscr. Lat.*, no. 315, l. 9, *araque ponatur ante id aedificium ex lapide Lunensi quam optimo sculpta quam optime, in qua ossa mea reponantur*. Janssen, *Inscr. Mus. Lugd.*, p. 108. *cuius ossa in ara monumenti sunt*, etc.). He knew no certain explanation of the abbreviations. [*C W, Scharf*]

37. Attic sepulchral hydria, originally with three handles; foot and lid modern. In front a scene of leave-taking, in low relief, carelessly executed. On a comfortable chair with back and curved legs sits, facing r., the bearded Smikrias of Aphidnae (ΣΜΙΚΡΙΑΣ | ΑΦΙΔΝΑΙΟΣ), with leg and back covered by the cloak, his feet set on a stool. He holds out his r. hand to Theophilè (ϴΕΟΦΙΛΗ), who, in chiton and cloak, stands before him ; she is not veiled. Behind Smikrias, leaning on his chair, stands a female figure, also unveiled, in chiton and cloak, in attitude of grief, her chin supported in her l. hand ; behind Theophilè a diminutive attendant in chiton

M. C. 33

only, a small box on her raised r. hand and another in her lowered
l. hand. Pentelic marble. H. of genuine piece 0·46, of figures 0·20.
It is very likely that this is the piece of which the Catalogue says,
"A Grecian Vase, by Apollonius"; as to this name, cf. Petworth,
no. 6. [*C]

38 (not in the Gallery). **Fragment of an Attic sepulchral
stele** ; only the upper half preserved. A female figure sits facing
r., Phanodike the daughter of Agatharchos. Relief not high. On
the upper border the inscription ΦΑΝΟΔΙΚΗΑΓΑΘΑΡΧΟ, the final O
standing for OY; the stele therefore belongs to the first half of the
fourth century B.C. Breadth of the fragment 0·38. [C]

39 (not in the Gallery). **Marble discus**, on either side a well-
composed relief of ordinary workmanship. *A.* A slender, youthful
Satyr dances with light step to the r., the pedum in the lowered l.
hand, swinging in the raised r. hand apparently a torch ; a nebris
hangs over the r. arm. He looks back. Below the nebris, near
the l. edge of the relief, a goat jumps up, turning back her face to
him. *B.* The Satyr, kneeling, with r. hand stretched out behind
and l. hand raised, fatuit capram, which stands quietly before him
looking round at him. To the l. behind the Satyr a leafless tree, to
the r. a rock. Diameter 0·37. Thickness 0·025. [C, *Scharf*]

40 (not in the Gallery). **Marble medallion**, with the bust of
Menandros ; ΜΕΝΑΝΔΡΟC on the lower border. Dallaway, no.
28. Engraved and described by G. Scharf, *Trans. R. Soc. Lit.*, Vol.
IV., new series. From the round frame the bust stands out quite in
full face. The breast is covered with a chiton, the shoulders also
with a cloak over it. Over the r. shoulder there is in the field an
open scroll meant for an inscription, but not inscribed. "The head
is the size of life and in very high relief. The face is delicate and
somewhat effeminate, the hair rather full and curled, the eyebrow
strongly marked, and the mouth full and pleasing. The nose is
delicate and the nostrils rather small, for although the tip of the nose
has been broken off and restored, enough remains to satisfy us on
these points." Eyeballs indicated. Scharf takes this medallion to
be identical with that which passed from the possession of Fulvio
Orsini (*Imagines*, Pl. 33. Gallaeus, *Illustrium imagines*, Pl. 90) to the
Farnese family, and which Visconti got drawn in the Farnesina before the collection was brought, in 1787, to Naples (Visconti, *Iconogr.
Gr.*, I. Pl. 6, 3, p. 117, note 3 Mil.). The work in question certainly
is not in Naples, but has disappeared, like the similar medallion of
Sophokles. Although, then, it is conceivable that it may have found

its way from the Farnesina to Marbury Hall, still the difference in the entire pose of the head, in the draping, in mouth and brow, in age, and the absence of the pupils and the roll in the Farnese medallion, are sufficiently remarkable to make its identity at all events questionable. H. 0·55. L. 0·48. D. 0·23. [*Scharf*]

41. Circular pedestal. A fine round altar with two Centaurs, one with syrinx, and the other playing the double flute; a lighted candelabrum between them. H. 1·07. Diam. 0·74. [*Scharf*]

42. A round altar with pretty boys and garlands. On a round shield the inscription: *Apollini | sacrum*. The whole monument seems to be modern. [**Scharf*]

43. Square Cippus, with the inscription *Dis Manibus | M. Iunio Phoebo, vix(it) ann(is) xxv, | D(is) M(anibus) | M. Iunio Anopteni (?), | vixit annis xxx | m(ensibus) iiii, fecit | Iunia Artemisia coniugi suo | carissimo b(ene) m(erenti)*. Below, a candelabrum between two griffins. [*C*]

44. Square Cinerarium. Inscription written in lines: *DIs Manibus | Iuniae Corinthidi | M. Iunius Satyr(us) | l(ibertae) suae benemerenti*. Below, a female figure lying on a rock; by her a boy blowing on the syrinx, on the l. a bird, on the r. a sleeping goat. Quite low down a Cupid on the l. seizes an overturned basket of grapes, at which a hare nibbles, but is seized from behind by another Cupid on the r. [*C*]

45. Square Cinerarium. Inscription: *D(is) M(anibus) | M. Vlpio Aug(usti) lib(erto) | Clementi Vlpia M. f(ilia) | Clementina filia | patri pi Issimo fec(it)*. On each side of the inscription a winged lion which has caught hold of on one side a ram's head, on the other a bull's head. At the corners masks with large ears and horns of Ammon, and below each a cornucopiae. [*C*]

"Among the altars of quadrangular form are some of agreeable and rich decoration." Waagen. Conze mentions swans, Cupids, rams' heads, as ornaments of such sepulchral monuments.

On the proposition of Mr Scharf, the owner generously presented, in 1850, to the British Museum a **Fragment of the frieze of the Parthenon**, which was then in his collection, namely the upper l. corner of slab xxxii of the North frieze (Michaelis, *Parthenon*, Pl. 13).

I leave unmentioned a number of **miscellaneous antiques,** seen by Waagen and Scharf, mostly unimportant; Conze notices indeed a good **mosaic** with a mask.

MARGAM (Glamorganshire, Wales).

Dallaway, pp. 346 ff. (II. pp. 93 ff.). Michaelis, *Arch. Zeit.*, 1874, pp. 48 ff.

The mansion of Margam is situated in the middle of a beautiful wood of oaks, above the picturesque ruins of the old Margam Abbey, not far from the sea, and near two railway stations, Pyle (2 m.) and Port Talbot, near Aberavon (3 m.). The property has long been in the possession of the old family of Mansel, since the middle of the last century in that of the MANSEL-TALBOT branch. The collection of antiques was made in the latter half of the last century by THOMAS MANSEL-TALBOT, Esq., having been entirely, or for the greater part, bought from Gavin Hamilton and Jenkins. It was however, I know not why, left in the packing-cases during the greater part of Mr Talbot's life (Dallaway, *Of Statuary*, p. 344). The marbles were at first placed in the Conservatory erected in 1787 (*Beauties of England and Wales*, XVIII. p. 706); lately, however, they have been brought into the fine mansion built about thirty years ago, and there disposed in "the Tower" (a staircase-hall proportioned and roofed like a tower, and hence so called), on both sides of the principal flight of stairs. The light is unfortunately insufficient, and comes too much from above. Only two colossal statues (nos. 1 and 4) still stand in front of the Orangery; four busts (nos. 10, 11, 14, 15) have received a place of honour in the Library. The numbering of the following catalogue is Dallaway's. Since his time the collection had been quite lost sight of by antiquarian writers, until I visited it in the autumn of 1873.

1 (Garden). **Statue of Lucius Verus**, colossal scale; corresponding to some extent to the Lansdowne statue, no. 63. The head, which looks straight forward, has never been separated from the trunk. The work, though not bad, still is rather empty, the drapery especially poor. New: nose and upper part of head with the hair, both arms, the stem of the tree by the r. leg for the most part, the r. leg from below, the l. from above the knee downwards; the cloak is considerably patched. Thasian marble. H. without pedestal 1·96. [*]

2. **Statue of a Roman in the toga** (Tiberius). A good statue of Carrara marble, with deeply but somewhat sharply carved drapery, and with a sinus hanging down as far as below the knees. The feet are clothed with soft shoes, of which the fastenings are

indicated by light incisions. The toga, to judge by the absence of the so-called *umbo* (a small bunch of folds near the waist) and by the direction of its upper folds, was originally drawn over the head. Conformably to this, a veil has been in modern times attached to the beautiful, youthful head of Tiberius, of Greek marble, which is connected with the body by an inserted neck. New also: nose, many details of drapery, the l. hand, the r. forearm with a cup, in the interior of which is a copy of the celebrated Rondanini head of Medusa. H. 1·88. From the Caraffa Collection in the Columbrano Palace, Naples; then in Jenkins' possession. [*]

3. Statue of a Satyr boy, with the l. arm supported on a tree, holding the l. leg before the r. (cf. Clarac, II. 296, 1670; 1671. IV. 703, 1673. 704 D, 1683 A. 705, 1676). New: r. arm, half the l. forearm with syrinx, nose, and a few trifling details. In other respects the whole figure is in excellent preservation, the head having never been broken off. It is a slender boy of full, soft forms, near the age of adolescence; the face, more childlike than that of the so-called Periboetos, with full outline and free expression, looks complacently with a slight inclination forwards, at the hands, which probably have always held a flute. The disordered hair and the brutish ears denote the Satyr, a tail is not to be found. The treatment is decorative, but good and broad; the thick skin, which is tied in a knot on the l. shoulder and passes slantwise over the breast and l. arm and then hangs down and covers the greater part of the tree, is indeed of very good, picturesque effect. The boy, 1·28 high, stands on a piece of rock, 0·11 high, by which is the stem of a tree which reaches quite down to the pedestal. This, 0·10 high, has a moulding in front. Fine, yellowish Thasian marble. H. of whole 1·49. Purchased from the Barberini Collection through Hamilton. [*]

4 (Garden). **Statue of the drunken Herakles.** With the upper part of the body very much bent over backwards, and head inclined forwards, he staggers with uncertain step. Both knees are bent, r. leg advanced. The whole weight of the heavy body bears on l. leg. It is only with difficulty that the hero preserves his equilibrium. The forms, always heavy, seem bloated by the wine; the feeble glance and protruded under lip admirably support the impression of deep intoxication. The motive indicated by Dallaway, *Hercules ebrius et areticus*, is so plainly expressed that the figure might almost be thought to be meant for a fountain. Obviously the conception was originally designed for bronze, cf. the bronze figure in Parma (*Mon. ined. dell' Inst.*, i. Pl. 44) and other similar monuments (Stephani, *Compte-Rendu*, 1869, p. 158; 1872, p. 155. *Archäol.-epigraph. Mittheilungen aus Oesterreich*, i. p. 25, no. 84). In the marble copy the effect is very much spoilt by the stem, covered over with the lion's skin, which has of necessity been joined on to the l. leg as a support. The hair forms short, crisp curls, the beard is equally crisp but longer. The face shows the influence of the Farnese type, only that the expression is coarser and more powerful. Though the execution is not uniformly delicate, the general effect is good. New: top and back of head, nose (the front half of the head had been broken off, but is antique), half the r. foot, and both arms. The r. arm seems to be correctly restored with the club (cf. Brocklesby, no. 112, and the statuette in Parma), the l. arm was always lowered and somewhat bent back, presumably in a pose which served to facilitate the equilibrium of the body. A *puntello*, of which a trace is visible on the l. thigh, may have served for the securing of the l. hand or of an attribute. Pentelic marble. H., without pedestal, 1·50. [*]

   5. Statue of a youth. According to Dallaway, "Dioscuros," or "one of the Ptolemies." The statue belongs to the series of figures lately so much discussed, of the school of Pasiteles, one of which in the Villa Albani is the work of Stephanos (cf. Kekulé, *Gruppe des Menelaos*, pp. 21 ff.). The motive and the characteristic details correspond so thoroughly to those of the youth by Stephanos (*Annali dell' Inst.*, 1865, Pl. D, Kekulé, *l. cit.*, Pl. 2, 3; Overbeck, *Plastik*, ii. 2nd ed., p. 342) and to the Orestes in Naples (R. Rochette, *Mon. inéd.*, Pl. 23. Overbeck, *l. cit.*, p. 343. Kekulé, *l. cit.*, Pl. 2, 1), that a description is unnecessary. Particularly characteristic are the small high head, with the face of a singularly long oval, the deep hollow of the throat, the square shoulders, the broad and very projecting breast, the flat but not archaically narrow stomach, the slender thighs with neat knees, and lastly the powerfully rounded back with a very deep hollow along the spine and with the loins decidedly sunk in. Of equally powerful design are the nates (cf. Conze, *Beiträge zur griech. Plastik*, Pl. 4; 6). The head had been broken off, but it certainly belongs to the statue. New: nose, under lip and chin, half the r. ear, sundry patches on the neck, besides both arms from a little below the elbow, the private parts, the l. leg from a little above, the r. from a little below the knee, the support, and the pedestal. In the other parts the preservation is excellent; the polish seems, to judge by some slight spots and corrosions on the surface, to be antique; if modern, it has at any rate not gone very deep. Only the eyes, which are small but not sunken, are deeply corroded. The example is undoubtedly one of the best of its kind, and is worthy of the place of its discovery: it was found in 1769 by Gavin Hamilton, together with nos. 9 and 11, in Hadrian's Villa (Pantanello). The proportions (*Arch. Zeit.*, 1874, p. 50) agree pretty well with those of the other copies (Kekulé, *l. cit.*, pp. 22, 26 f.). Worked in very fine-grained Parian marble, apparently lychnite. H. 1·46. [*]

6. Statue of a boy, corresponding in general with the statues in the Louvre (Clarac, III. 317, 1506) and in the Vatican (Clarac, v. 876, 2236 A. 878, 2239). The little lad stands in the most natural awkwardness equally on both legs, and with an air of embarrassment grasps with the r. hand the border of his thick shirt before the breast; the l. forearm is bent forward, and the hand must always have held something (the restorer has given it a bunch of grapes). It quite gives the impression that the boy has been stealing; in capital conformity with this idea is the head, which is a little bent down (the whole neck, to be sure, is an insertion), with the half anxious, half puzzled smile on the wide-stretched mouth. A ribbon runs through the thick, curly hair. The whole motive is exceedingly pleasing and expressive. The disposal of the little shirt is very neat; it has slipped down somewhat from the l. shoulder, and at the same time is drawn up from the r. thigh towards the l. elbow, so that its lines all converge to the l. hand. By the r. leg is a support; on both shoulders a button on the shirt. New: nose, neck, l. hand with the grapes, lower part of l. leg, r. foot, and pedestal. Greek marble. H. 0·82. [*]

7. Statue of a youth ("Ganymede"). Torso of a powerful youth, of rather poor workmanship, with both shoulders lowered (arms missing); half of the thigh of the l. leg, on which the figure rests, of the r. leg almost all the thigh, preserved. The head is peculiar; it is re-set, but certainly belongs to the statue. The round forms and cheerful expression would suit a fresh young girl far better; the long hair is brushed up, and forms a top-knot on the crown, and behind, a fairly long plait, of which the extremity is of one piece with the torso. The glance is a little raised towards the l. The combination of this effeminate head with the powerful body of a youth has a disagreeable effect. On thighs and shoulders traces of modern restoration. New: nose, lips, chin, part of the r. brow, and small patches. Thasian marble, very much polished. H. 0·98. [*]

8. **Fragment of a statue of Pan**, the upper part of the body of which is bent forward; the l. arm was raised, the r. lowered; the face has a crudely brutish expression. The whole fragment, which is much broken, and patched and scoured to such an extent that the original motive is hardly to be determined, conveys an unpleasing impression. H. 0·60. [*]

9. **Bust of Hadrian**, head and neck. New: tip of the nose. Corroded, but of good workmanship. Pentelic marble. Found in 1769 by Gavin Hamilton in Hadrian's Villa; cf. Dallaway, p. 369 (II. p. 121). [*]

10 (Library). **Bust of a noble Roman**, a beautiful specimen, with lofty brow and short-cut hair, strong upper lip, and very energetic mouth. Dallaway's designation of "Solon" rests, as Millin conjectures, on the likeness—a very slight one indeed—to a portrait-head on a gem, the inscription on which (Σόλωνος) once used to be erroneously referred to the original of the portrait ("Maecenas") instead of to the artist who engraved the gem (Visconti, *Iconogr. Rom.*, I. Pl. 13. Bernoulli, *Röm. Ikonogr.*, I. pp. 239 ff.). The breast-piece, draped in tunic and toga, is cut away in the shape of a bust and bordered below all along the front with a row of small acanthus leaves; below is the foot in the shape of an Attic pedestal (cf. E. Huebner, *Bildniss einer Roemerin* (Clytie), Berlin, 1873, p. 26. *Arch. Zeit.*, 1874, p. 138. 1877, p. 14). This splendid work of beautiful Parian marble bears no trace of modern polishing, and is quite uninjured excepting the nose, the chin, and the r. eye near the eyebrow. It seems, according to Dallaway, to have come from Hadrian's Villa. H. 0·64. L. of face 0·215. [*]

11 (Library). **Head of Sabina**, with roundish indented stephané, somewhat over life size; much corroded and of commonplace workmanship. New: tip of nose, neck, and bust. Found at the same place and time as no. 9. [*]

12. **Bust of Antoninus Pius**, a good specimen, of Pentelic marble, with hair much undercut with the drill. Rather abraded. New: tip of the nose and many details. From Hadrian's Villa. [*]

13. **Head of Athenè**, elegant, but rather insipid, of a latish type, though the oval is not overdone; a long plait of hair on the neck. New: nose, upper lip, half of the under lip. The top of the head missing. An antique bronze helmet of the high, so-called Corinthian shape, ornamented in front with two rams' heads, covers the head. The neck is antique and belongs to the head. Antique, but not belonging to head and neck, is the bust, with a very effectively treated ægis. The soft fleece covered with scales is arranged in folds and bordered with snakes, the border on the l. side being turned over so as to show the back ; the gorgoneion is drawn up towards the r. shoulder and from it the folds start, as though the skin were held together by it as by a clasp. H. of the whole, to the girdle, 0·86. L. of face 0·19. [*]

14 (Library). **Heroic head**, of strongly exaggerated pathos, allied in style to the Laokoon. Pose, eyes, and mouth recal the so-called Dying Alexander in Florence, yet it is wrath rather than pain which finds expression in the highly excited features with the mouth slightly opened. The treatment of the hair is very much ruffled. The eyebrows, which are much knit, are expressed in sculpture ; on the cheeks is a slight down. It suggests the wrathful Achilleus, though the excitement is more marked than in the well-known picture from Pompeii with the leading away of Briseïs (no. 1309 of Helbig's catalogue): if the head does not appear to be youthful enough, this may be due to the extravagance in the expression of character which is peculiar to this style. At any rate the original belonged undoubtedly to the Hellenistic period, and perhaps to the Rhodian school. It must have been a masterpiece of the virtuoso style. New: nose and upper lip, and pieces of both ears. Pentelic marble. H. of head and neck, 0·35. L. of face, 0·205. It appears to be the so-called *Hercules Agonistes*, mentioned by Dallaway, of the Mattei collection, purchased through Gavin Hamilton. In fact the bust, *Mon. Matth.*, II. Pl. 35. 1, " *Incognitus*," seems identical with our head ; though, to be sure, the engraving would be unusually mistaken even for that publication. The head has actually no bust. [*]

The following specimen is not mentioned by Dallaway :

15 (Library). **Head of a Roman child**, roundish and pretty, with long hair ; of commonplace workmanship. Pupils and eyebrows expressed. The bust shape seems to have been arranged subsequently. New: tip of nose. Life size. [*]

For the sarcophagus mentioned by Dallaway, no. 18, cf. under " Penrice Castle."

In the Tower there stand, in addition to the sculptures, two **painted vases** (*Arch. Zeit.*, 1874. p. 51):

16. Hydria, 0·44 high, with black figures. On the principal field the departure of a youth on a quadriga ; on the neck a battle scene ; below, a Seiren between two figures in cloaks.

17. **Amphora** with red figures, of beautiful style, but ordinary execution. On both sides a procession (κῶμος) of four men in all, one of whom plays the flute.

NARFORD HALL (Norfolk).

The apparently inconsiderable collection of antiques which is to be found at this country seat of the Fountaine family appears to owe its origin to SIR ANDREW FOUNTAINE, the celebrated connoisseur (1675—1753), who travelled in Italy at the beginning of the last century (cf. Introd. § 33). Pulszky (*Arch. Anz.*, 1854, p. 472) describes a **consular diptychon**, of the middle of the fifth century, A.D., unedited.

NEWBY HALL (Yorkshire).

Dallaway, pp. 349 ff. (II. pp. 97 ff.). Clarac, III. p. 62. Matz, *Arch. Zeit.*, 1873, pp. 22 ff. Michaelis, *ibid.*, 1874, pp. 51 ff. *Athenaeum*, Nov. 16, 1878, pp. 630 f. (The author of this article has partly made use of a memorandum written by me and sent to Lady Mary Vyner.) I visited the collection in the autumn of 1873.

Newby Hall is one of the estates belonging to the GREY family and is situated nearly three miles south of Ripon. The collection was made by WILLIAM WEDDELL, Esq., who visited Rome about A.D. 1765, and employed his leisure there in collecting antiques. In the export warrants (*lettere di passo*) from the papal chamberlain's office are specified under dates March 27, April 15, and May 17, 1765, 19 chests full of antiques and besides them the Venus (no. 20) as exported by Giov. Dick, British consul in Genoa, and Guglielmo Weddell (Gori, *Archivio Storico etc. di Roma*, II. p. 216). Towards the close of the last century Weddell died and left the collection to a nephew, LORD GRANTHAM, who was then a minor. From him it came to the EARL GREY, and then to the present possessor, LADY MARY VYNER, the daughter of Lord Grey. The antiques are placed in three rooms built especially for them ; a square room at either end with a small cupola room between, which opens with a little portico into the garden. These rooms are decorated in the taste recognised as antique towards the close of the last century. The sculptures are still nearly all in their original positions. Unfor-

tunately, Mr Weddell, dying suddenly, left no memorandum as to
how he obtained the individual specimens. I am indebted to the
kind information of the present owner for the completeness of the
following catalogue, which gives the antiques as they are exhibited
now.

FIRST ROOM.

1 (on the r. near the entrance). **Statue of Seilenos.** Clarac,
IV. 730 B, 1765 A. Dallaway, no. 4. The old Seilenos, with a dignified expression, a fillet in his hair, stands resting his r. leg (beside a
pillar which serves only as a material support) on a mass of rock ; a
large wine-skin well filled rests on the l. leg, and is sustained by the
god with his r. arm, while his l. grasps the opening of the wine-skin.
The statue is a graceful composition, probably intended originally
to decorate a fountain. New: only the nose, l. hand with the
extreme edge of the wine-skin, both shins from the knees to the
ankles. H. 1·00. Similar statues are very common (see Schreiber,
Arch. Zeit., 1879, p. 68, note 7) ; one such, now in the Villa Albani
(no. 924), stood about the middle of the sixteenth century in the
garden of the Cesi Palace, in the centre of a colossal marble bowl
(now in the Torlonia Museum, no. 274 ; cf. Schreiber, *ibid.*, p. 65).
[*.M*]

2. **Statue of Priapos,** of Pentelic marble. Clarac, IV.
710 B, 1729 B. Dallaway, no. 3. Clarac thought this was a "*jeune
Faunesse,*" Dallaway and Matz were nearer the mark in suggesting a
Satyr. Already Winckelmann, who saw the statue at Cavaceppi's,
had hit on the right idea, cf. his letter to Bianconi of April 30, 1763
in Fea's *Storia delle arti del disegno*, III. p. 258 (*Miscellanea*, I. p.
CLXXXIX.) : "*Un Fauno, o Priapo giovane vagamente vestito da donna,
e in atto di ballare, alzando alquanto la lunga veste talare con ambedue
le mani, come usano le zitelle, che modestamente ballano. Ma nel più
bello di volere smentir il sesso principia a rizzarsi un Priapo smisurato,
che spinge in fuori la veste. La figura è di tre palmi incirca.* (Cf. the
letter to Riedesel of April, 1763. Fea is in error in thinking that the
statue was ever at the Villa Albani, and there *ridotta alla modestia
spianandogli la veste.*) We may see that the designation Priapos is
more suitable than Satyr, or Faun, whether we look at the feminine
drapery (cf. Jahn, *Berichte der sächs. Gesellschaft d. Wiss.*, 1855, pp.
236 ff. *Rheinische Jahrbücher*, XXVII. pp. 45 ff.), or at the enormous
dimensions of that part of the body which is most characteristic in
the demi-god of Lampsakos, and which here strongly distorts the

folds of the drapery. Nor does the head, which Clarac and Matz considered as belonging to the figure, though decidedly of the Satyr type, belie the explanation ; as the whole neck is an insertion, and the head, although it is also of Pentelic marble, shows a somewhat different quality (having blackish stripes), and is rather too large for the body. New : both arms and both legs from below the drapery. H. abt. 0·60. [*.M]

3. **Group of Dionysos and a young Pan.** Clarac, IV. 693, 1632 A. Modern. [*]

4. **Statue of a Roman youth.** Clarac, V. 966, 2486 A, "Géta prétendu." Dallaway, no. 10. The youth wears a tunic and toga and round his neck a bulla. There is no foundation for the title Geta. New : both arms from the drapery onwards. [M]

5. **Statue of Ganymedes.** Clarac. III. 410 B, 704 A. Dallaway, no. 11. This is a modern copy of a beautiful torso in Florence which Benvenuto Cellini has restored as a Ganymedes, Uffizi, no. 308, copied with sides reversed in Clarac, III. 408, 704. [°]

6. **Statue of Aphrodite,** the so-called "Galatea." Clarac, IV. 628, 1364 A. Dallaway, no. 12. The figure, which is very delicate and graceful in movement, is balanced on the r. foot, while the l. is drawn somewhat far back. With her l. arm she supports herself on a dolphin, which has a small Eros on its back and is plunging in the sea, holding a fish in its mouth. This accessory and the undoubtedly Venus-like character of the head, which in the copy at Ince (no. 36) is crowned with a stephane, convince us that this is an Aphrodite, in spite of numerous other suggestions (Galatea, Nereid, etc., cf. Bernoulli, *Aphrodite*, pp. 375 ff.). The arrangement of the drapery is a little too artificial, it covers the whole of the lower part of the body, is held fast under the hollow of the l. shoulder and then drawn up over the head, from which originally an end of the drapery fell down again to the r. breast (cf. Ince, no. 36). The numerous copies of the statue testify to its celebrity (Bernoulli, pp. 372 ff.) ; in none of them unfortunately is the r. arm preserved. In the copy at Ince the snout of the dolphin is perforated, showing that the whole piece was intended for the adornment of a fountain : undoubtedly that was the original intention. The lissom form of the goddess inclined gently forward, her head bent down, and a smile on her face that is rather at delight in herself, than of a sensual character, combined with the artistic arrangement of the drapery—all perfectly suit the goddess of gracefulness looking at herself in the water and rejoicing in her own charms.

The invention does much honour to the Hellenistic period (cf. Friederichs, *Bausteine*. no. 596. Hettner, *Bildw. zu Dresden*, no. 88).
That the head belongs to the statue is shown by the direction of the
folds on the back of the neck. New: nose and chin, all the r. arm
and shoulder, r. breast and the corner of the veil grasped by the
hand, the l. forearm and a part of the dolphin's tail, the r. foot with
part of the pedestal, and finally Eros' nose, great part of both wings,
his r. foot and the lower part of his l. leg. The preservation of the
rest is good; the execution rather commonplace. Coarse-grained
Parian marble. H. 1·25. [*M*]

7. **Portrait statue** ("Epikuros"). Clarac, v. 844, 2128. The
motive is similar to the Demosthenes in the Vatican (cf. Knole, no.
1), but the statue is certainly not the great orator. The antique
head, which no doubt belongs to it, has a long beard, elderly features,
and a calm expression, not at all resembling the well-known countenance of Demosthenes. The designation Epikuros current at Newby
is also very doubtful, but not so improbable as Clarac's suggestion
that the statue represents Chrysippos. New: the whole of the r.
forearm, half the l. forearm with the roll, the feet from below the
drapery, the scrinium. H. 1·18. [*M*]

8. **Triangular pedestal.** Cavaceppi, *Race.*, III. Pl. 53. This
pedestal was early copied by draughtsmen; in Cod. Coburg., no. 76
Matz Cod. Pigh., no. 96 Jahn; on two sheets at Windsor (Dal
Pozzo collection, vol. VII. 54. 55), the sides *a* and *b* are drawn. On
each of the three sides is a figure moving to the r.: (*a*) a **Maenad**,
nearly nude, with a tympanon; (*b*) a **Satyr** blowing a flute; (*c*) a
Satyr with pedum and outspread nebris. These figures as well as
the other ornaments often reappear on such decorative monuments.
It is a specimen of the so-called Neo-Attic art, with unusually flat
treatment of the relief. Pentelic marble. [*M*]

9 (on no. 8). **Colossal head of Herakles.** Dallaway, no. 14.
It is of the Farnese type, most nearly related to the head at Basle
(*Mon. dell' Inst.*, VIII. Pl. 54; cf. *Anc. Marbl. in the Brit. Mus.*, I.
Pl. 11), but belongs apparently to a somewhat earlier period: the
expression is calmer, more moderate, with a look of thoughtfulness
rather than of pain; the beard is rounder, the curly short hair lies
closer to the head. Nose and forehead are powerfully developed,
the ears resemble those of a pankratiastes. The original movement of
the head cannot be determined, as the head itself has been broken
short off near the beard, and the neck is new. A narrow, plaited,
rather flat fillet passes through the hair. New: upper part of head,

tip of nose, parts of r. ear and of r. eyebrow. L. of face, including the beard, 0·28, from the part where the hair begins to tip of nose, 0·155. Greek (Parian?) marble. Good, but not particularly fine work. [*M]

IN THE DOORWAY.

10, 11. Two **urns.**

SECOND ROOM.

12 (by the garden door). **Head of Minerva,** in Parian marble, the casque and back part of the head restored. Dallaway, no. 16.

13. Female draped statue. Clarac, v. 888, 2274 O. Dallaway, no. 9, " Faustina." In all essential parts the statue is antique : so is the head with the wavy hair that has been joined on to it, but it is not at all certain that this head originally belonged to the figure. Over life size ; conscientious but uninteresting work. [*]

14. Colossal bust of Zeus. The most striking point about this most peculiar head—which deserves that a good copy should be made of it—is that it conveys the impression of mild resignation, verging on sadness. The lips are gently parted ; the small eyes are very deep set, particularly at their inner angles, and framed in strongly marked lids (the lower lid resembles that of the Farnese Hera, *Mon. dell. Inst.*, VIII. Pl. 1) ; on the lower part of the forehead are broad and somewhat strong protuberances ; the hair over the forehead, an interlacing, tangled mass of curls, slightly shades the brow. The hair, which once fell on the shoulders, the mustaches, and the beard, which gets narrower towards the bottom and then ends straight, hang down heavily and so serve to strengthen the above-mentioned impression. Right across the forehead is a narrow furrow. A fillet passes round the hair. The peculiarly beautiful original, which was the source of this clearly modernised copy, can hardly, to judge by the character of the expression and the very free treatment of the hair and beard, belong to a period anterior to the fourth century, B.C. ; in fact the development of the forehead with its marked protuberances might seem to indicate an epoch even later than the younger Attic school, did not the general expression militate against the assignation of so late a date. New : neck, nose, part of mustaches, the back of the head and the curls on it. Pentelic marble. H. of the antique part 0·36. L. of face 0·22. [*M]

15. A bust.

16. Statue of a nude male figure. Clarac, v. 869, 2210 A, "Gladiateur." Dallaway, no. 8, "Brutus." New: neck, r. hand with dagger and l. arm. The thin head of true Roman type, with short hair and beard, is antique but does not belong to the body. Evidently it is this statue to which refers the sarcasm of H. Blundell, *Engravings of Statues, etc. at Ince*, vol. I., preface: "a *Torso* .... by placing on it an austere head, and restoring the arms with a dagger in one hand, became a Brutus, which was artfully contrived by Mr Jenkins to suit certain people." [*M*]

17. Bust of Caracalla. Dallaway, no. 17. "A good, but rather roughly finished sculpture, remarkable for the energy of the expression. New: nose." [*Athenaeum*]

18. Statue of a Muse. Clarac, III. 503, 1002 = 538 A, 1002 A. Cavaceppi, *Racc.*, I. Pl. 30. Dallaway, no. 5. The graceful figure, robed in a chiton with sleeves and a cloak which conceals the l. arm and the legs, is sitting in a simple attitude of repose, resting her foot on a footstool. The body is of Pentelic marble. The head, of Parian marble, has been re-set, but is no doubt that of a Muse. The hair is encircled with a fillet and gathered up into a knot. New: l. hand and forearm from the drapery, r. forearm and elbow, with the flute, a piece let in to the l. knee, the four larger toes of the l. foot. Work of decorative style, but not bad. H. 1·22. [*M*]

19. Bust of Septimius Severus. "An expressive and characteristic work, and a good specimen of its time. New: nose and fore-locks." [*Athenaeum*]

20. Statue of Aphroditè. Clarac, IV. 622 B, 1394. *Spec.*, II. Pl. 13. Dallaway, no. 1. "The Venus" is rightly regarded as the grandest specimen of the collection: it is one of the best examples of the type of the well-known Medici Venus (see Bernoulli, *Aphrodite*, pp. 222 ff.), and therefore requires no description. The peculiar ornaments of this copy are an armlet on the upper part of the l. arm, adorned all round with dolphins, and a slender vessel in the form of an alabastron, on the top of which lies a flat shell. This vessel is entwined by a heavily laden vine, about which two little Erotes are climbing gracefully, plucking grapes, and a third (much smaller) is collecting apples into a basket at the foot of the vine. Grapes are hanging above over the edge of the vase. The history of the statue is very remarkable; it is given by Dallaway (*l. cit.*, cf. J. Nichols, *Illustrations of the Literary History*, III. p. 278. Dallaway, *Of Statuary*, p. 345) after the accounts of Pacili and

Hamilton; by Heyne (*Antiquar. Aufs.*, I. p. 140) after that of Casanova (*Discorso sopra gli antichi*, p. xxi.); and is alluded to by Winckelmann in many parts of his works (cf. *Werke*, II. p. 205 = *Nachrichten*, p. 38, and the letters to Wiedewelt of May 24. 1764, to Riedesel of June 23, 1764, to Fuessly of June 19, 1765, to Schlabbrendorf of June 22, 1765). Winckelmann calls the statue the "Jenkins Venus." From these authorities it appears that Gavin Hamilton discovered the statue in the cellars of the Barberini Palace, and in point of fact, an inventory of the Barberini Collection compiled in 1738 enumerates among the marbles placed in the ground-floor of the palace "*una statua al naturale rappresentante una Venere nuda con tronco a' piedi, con diversi putti di bassi rilievi, uva e frutti... stimata scudi trecento*" (*Docum. ined. per servire alla storia dei Musei d'Italia*, IV. p. 48). Hamilton gave the statue to the sculptor Pacili in exchange for some other marble. By Pacili it was restored; a head was added, and unfortunately the whole body was smoothed over, and it was then sold to Jenkins for 1000 scudi. According to another account, Jenkins bought the statue for a hundred sequins of Hamilton direct, while it was still without a head, and had it restored by Cavaceppi. Any way Jenkins brought the statue to light with its new head in 1764, without stating where it had been discovered; and asserted, as we learn from Winckelmann's first letters, that it had been found intact. In 1765 Weddell bought the statue of Jenkins according to Casanova for 16,000 scudi (about £3,500), according to Heyne for £6,000; Dallaway gives the purchase money at a different figure, and makes it, including the cost of transmission to England, more than £1,000, or, as he says in another place, £1,500. A story is current at Newby, that with regard to the price inviolable silence was promised and observed on both sides; this circumstance would account for the enormous difference of the above-given sums. In Winckelmann's last two letters the King of England is spoken of as the purchaser, but such a statement was only a blind of Jenkins, or of Mr Weddell's agent, to ensure the export of the valuable specimen from the papal government. Last, not least, it is a fact that according to the characteristic Roman way of carrying on this trade in art, the custom-house authorities were conscientiously informed of all repairs so carefully hidden from the buyer, so as to lessen the duty on the permission to export the treasure; the value of which was then only assessed at 300 scudi, the same figure which had been set on it in the Barberini inventory (cf. the entry in the Chamberlain's Office registers as published in Gori's *Archivio storico &c. di Roma*, II. p. 216: "1765, 17 maggio. *Gio. Dick per una statua di marmo alta palmi 7, figurante Venere del tutto nuda, di ottima maniera greca, con testa riportata non sua, braccia, gamba dritta, e piede sinistro, con l'intiera base di moderno lavoro: stimata scudi 300*"). Parts really new: a small portion of the curls, the r. arm from above the armlet, the l. forearm with the elbow, a piece of the l. half of the nates, the lower half of the r. leg, the two first toes of the l. foot, small details on the Erotes, the outer edge of the pedestal. The head, of a decidedly Venus-like character, but of less coquettish expression than the Medici Venus, is of a whiter marble than the body; the face is much rubbed down, so that the eyes have almost lost their form (tip of nose new). The hair, even beyond the ribbon, has been left nearly untouched, but almost all the rest has been entirely worked over, which fact confirms Dallaway's assertion that a veil was originally over the head, and has been chiselled away. There are holes in the ears as if for an ornament. The torso with its fresh, virginal bosom and neck is the most beautiful part of the statue; the hips, not too prominent, quite suit the body; the back and the legs are graceful, but they have not the same finish. There is a fine contrast between the yellowish, smooth body of the goddess (though it be now somewhat too smooth) and the dull surface of the marble vase. This is not at all re-worked; the assertion at page 17 of the *Specimens* that the front of this vase has been restored, is quite a mistake. The marble is Parian of the most beautiful quality. H. 1·63; without the pedestal 1·55. [*.M]

21. **Bust of a Roman lady**, "having a fine portrait-like aspect. Very good. New: cranium, and back of the neck." [*Athenaeum.*]

22. **Bust of Caligula** as a boy, tolerably good. [*.M*]

23. **Statue of Athenè.** Clarac, III. 462 A, 888 B. *Spec.*, II. Pl. 38. Dallaway, no. 2. The slender form of the goddess rests on the r. leg; a cloak which lies on her l. shoulder falls round her hips and thighs in handsome folds; only at their upper edge, especially on the l. hip, the folds are too crowded. The narrow aegis, which has too formidable a complication of snakes, goes slantwise from the r. shoulder across the r. breast down to the l. hip. The r. arm, adorned with a bracelet, is advanced, and although it has been broken in two places, it is undoubtedly antique (not new, as has been asserted in the *Specimens*). In her outstretched palm the goddess holds a pretty little owl. The statue is carefully and

M. C.   34

freshly, though not very delicately, executed ; it is of Thasian marble of very beautiful quality, whilst the head, which is too small for the figure, is of Parian marble. A story, characteristic of Nollekens and related by him, proves that in fact the head did not originally belong to the body (J. Th. Smith, *Nollekens and his times*, I. pp. 11 f.) : " Jenkins...had been commissioned by Mr Locke, of Norbury Park, to send him any piece of sculpture which he thought might suit him, at a price not exceeding one hundred guineas ; but Mr Locke, immediately upon the receipt of a head of Minerva, which he did not like, sent it back again, paying the carriage and all other ex- penses. Nollekens, who was then also a resident in Rome, having purchased a trunk of a Minerva for fifty pounds, found, upon the return of this head, that its proportion and character accorded with his torso. The discovery induced him to accept an offer made by Jenkins of the head itself; and two hundred and twenty guineas to share the profits. After Nollekens had made it up into a figure, or, what is called by the vendors of botched antiquities, ' restored it,' which he did at the expense of about twenty guineas more for stone and labour, it proved a most fortunate hit, for they sold it for the enormous sum of *one thousand guineas !* and it is now at Newby in Yorkshire." (Dallaway, *Of Statuary*, p. 346, says £700.) The head is superior to the body ; the delicate, sharply chiselled face has not been touched, but the hair has been entirely worked over. On the helmet are two holes for the plume. In the body the marked projection of the r. hip strikes us as unusual for Athenè, as also are the very long legs, the upper part of the body seeming rather small and insignificant. New : neck, l. forearm and spear, some of the snakes of the aegis, the forefinger on the r. hand and the tips of the two next fingers, and finally part of the l. wing of the owl, which is very nice with its full head. The r. hand is pretty, but Clarac is extravagant in his admiration when he styles it "*la plus belle main antique que je connaisse.*" H. 1·80, with the pedestal 1·88. An exact replica in bronze, about 0·20 high, is to be found at Erbach in the Odenwald, Hesse ; it has a similar head, with the so-called Corinthian helmet ; the l. arm is lowered and holds no lance, but the fingers of the hand are bent in a right angle and directed towards the thigh, as if something had been held in the hand. [*.*M]

24. **Head of Alexander**, of pavonazzetto marble. Dallaway, no. 18. Modern. [*M*]

PORTICO FACING THE GARDEN.

25. Colossal female head, akin to heads of Aphroditè, reminding one a little of the colossal head, Brocklesby, no. 15. There is much in it to suggest good though already partially degenerate Attic art. Forehead high, and surrounded by simple but beautiful wavy hair (like that of the Amazon statues), cheeks and chin round and broad, eyes comparatively small, lips unpleasantly full, neck powerful. Nose only restored. [*.M]

26. Colossal female head. Not in such good preservation as no. 25, for only the neck and face are old, and the rest of the head new; the nose also is new. It has, like no. 25, large cheeks and chin, but the mouth and the expression of the eyes are more grave, and this harmonises well with the form of face, which is better defined and less indistinct than the other. The effect is heightened by a turn to the r. given to the head. I cannot venture to suggest any certain designation. [*.M]

IN THE DOORWAY BETWEEN THE SECOND AND THIRD ROOMS.

27. Statue of a boy. Clarac, v. 877 A, 2240 B. Dallaway, no. 7. Leaning the l. arm on the trunk of a tree, stands a boy, with his legs crossed, a small cloak thrown over his arms and back : the restorer has probably been right in putting a flute in his hands. An insignificant work. New : head and neck, both hands with the flute, r. leg, three parts of the l. leg, the lower half of the trunk of the tree, and the pedestal. H. 0·64. [*]

28. Terminal figure of Eros. Cavaceppi, *Racc.*, i. Pl. 40. Clarac, IV. 639, 1448 B. Müller-Wieseler, II. 56, 719. The body of the boy is so effeminate in form, particularly about the r. breast, that the figure was mistaken either for that of a female (Winckelmann, *Mon. ined.*, II. p. 264, Cavaceppi), or of Hermaphroditos (Winckelmann's letter to Bianconi of March 26, 1763 in Fea's *Storia*, III. p. 256 = *Miscell.*, I. p. CLXXXVIII., Clarac, Wieseler) ; Matz was quite right in recognising in it an Eros. New : head and neck, both arms with their respective attributes, the wings excepting a stump of the r. one, and part of the terminal pillar. A tolerably large skin is thrown from the l. shoulder slantwise across the breast. The torso, which is antique, is delicate and pretty, and the free turn of the body as it springs out of the pillar, which shows an indication of the two legs, is particularly graceful ; the r. hip projects strongly

backwards and outwards, the l. shoulder is elevated and comes somewhat boldly to the front, the r. shoulder inclines backwards in an
analogous manner. The usual practice of giving terminal figures
a quiet pose and accommodating them, as it were, to their stiff shafts
is here abandoned, in consequence of a freer handling which would
suit the time of Tauriskos of Tralles, whose *Hermerotes* stood in the
park of Asinius Pollio (Plin. 36, 33), though it is not quite unheard of in more ancient monuments (*Mon. ined. dell' Inst.*, x. Pl.
57, 1). A somewhat kindred character is shewn by an androgynous
terminal figure in the British Museum (Graeco-Rom. Sculp., no. 167.
Anc. Marbl., x. Pl. 30. Müller-Wieseler, II. 56, 708), which is however by no means so fine. According to Winckelmann's letter the
marble appears to have been discovered in the year 1763 ("*Un altro
inglese domiciliato in Roma* [Jenkins? Hamilton?] *ha avuto la sorte
di trovare un Termine*," &c.). H. from the crown of the head to the
pubes 0.58. [*M*]

THIRD ROOM.

29. **A bust.**

30. **Bust of Augustus.** Dallaway, no. 15.

31. **Child's sarcophagus.** Dallaway, no. 22. A room is
represented by means of a curtain, and in it seven boys, all draped,
are playing with nuts (cf. Ince, no. 247 *a*). Two of them have just
fallen out, and a third is going to interfere in the quarrel; the others
are looking on, except one, who is still playing alone. On the
extreme r. is a terminal figure. R. END. One boy has his lap
already very full of things, and another boy is trying to put some
large object into it. To the r. is an arch of freestone. L. END.
A nude boy, looking round, is trying to rob another boy clad in a
tunica of eggs or nuts from his apron. On the l. is an arch. The invention is almost throughout most graceful and simple, and except for
a general polishing, the whole is in an excellent state of preservation.
Below, a Lesbian kymation runs along. L. 0·96. H. 0·30. D. 0·44.
[*From a drawing made for the German Archaeological Institute.*]

32 (on no. **31**). **Statuette of a barbarian.** Clarac, v. 854,
2161 B. Black marble, nude parts of white marble. Modern. [*]

33. **Statue of Apollo.** Clarac, III. 476 B, 906 D. Dallaway,
no. 6. The youthful god is standing with his legs crossed, his left
arm leaning on the trunk of a tree, his r. hand behind his back.
New: nose, part of l. leg, almost the whole of the arms, and nearly
the whole of the trunk. The head has been re-set, but Clarac

considered that it belonged to the statue. Much broken and
touched up. Very ordinary work. H. 1·16. [*]

34. Oval child's sarcophagus, with Bacchic scenes sculptured all round in the following order.

In the front between two lions' heads is a representation that
reminds one strongly of the celebrated Casali sarcophagus (Visconti, *Mus. Pio-Clem.*, v. Pl. C. Müller-Wieseler, II. 37, 432).
(*a*) Dionysos and Ariadne are sitting together on a rock. Dionysos,
half draped, holds in his left hand the thyrsos, and his right on his
head; a panther lies at his feet. Ariadne, in cloak and chiton
and the nebris across her breast, has a tympanon, ornamented with
the head of Seilenos, in her left hand. Both are looking down at a
wrestling match in which Eros is getting the better of Pan (cf.
Welcker, *Zeitschr. f. alte Kunst*, I. pp. 475 ff. Friedländer, *Annali*,
1856, p. 34). Beside Ariadne is a Satyr with his right hand upraised;
beside Dionysos old Seilenos and a second Satyr. Below the lions'
heads may be seen, (*f*) to the l. a youthful Satyr extracting a thorn
from Pan's foot, (*b*) to the r., Eros, playing with a lion; then on
each side comes a pedestal with a mask on it. There follow to the
r. (*c*) two Satyrs and a Maenad in lively motion; on the ground is a
mangled fawn, a cista, two panthers; (*e*) to the l. two Maenads and a
Satyr, who has rough hair and beard, a wreath round his breast,
and is dancing over a cista, out of which a snake crawls forth.
(*d*) In the middle of the back is a procession moving l., in the van
of which we see an elephant, led by a Satyr; the first of the panthers
mentioned above (*c*) is playing with its trunk. Then comes a dancing
Maenad; then a carriage drawn by a young and an old Centaur, the
old one defending himself with a torch against an Eros who has
sprung on his back with a torch and is teasing him; a panther is
running along below the Centaurs. Dionysos lies at full length in
the carriage; at his feet stands a woman nearly nude, with a sceptre,
to whom an Eros is talking. A tree forms a barrier here to the
bearded Satyr (*e*). This sarcophagus is very rich in excellently invented scenes. Unfortunately it has been injured by water and
much restored in details. L. 1·50. H. 0·43. [*From a drawing
made for the German Archaeological Institute.*]

35. **Statue of a poet or a philosopher in sitting pos-ture.** Clarac, v. 903, 2304 A, "*Marius prétendu.*" He sits as comfortably in his chair as does the Menandros of the Vatican (*Mus. Pio-Clem.*, III. Pl. 15), and only differs from him in the movement of the l. arm and the want of a chiton. New: head and neck, three parts of r. arm, half the l. lower arm (a small portion of the roll is old), r. foot from the ankle, three of the legs of the chair. Fresh, but not delicate work. Pentelic marble. H. 0·53. [*a.M*]

36. **Bust,** of basalt.

37. **Large tub,** of pavonazzetto marble, with fluted (modern?) cover shaped like an inverted basin of the usual double curvature.

Probably a bath. Dallaway, no. 21. Cf. *Athenaeum*, Nov. 16, 1878, p. 631. [*M*]

38. **Bust,** of basalt.

39. **Tripod with a cauldron.** In the inside of the cauldron may be seen a flat omphalos wrapped round by the usual woollen fillets and entwined by the Pythian snake. The omphalos is almost entirely new, but the restoration is certain. Under the cauldron is a round, massive support, richly ornamented, on which *four* feet are executed in relief. On Mr Weddell's tombstone in the cathedral at Ripon is represented this four-footed tripod, which he appears to have considered as a conspicuous ornament of his collection. [*.M*]

40 (on no. 39). **Ibis,** the size of life. Cavaceppi, *Racc.*, I. Pl. 50. Dallaway, no. 13.

41. **Triangular pedestal.** Cavaceppi, *Racc.*, I. Pl. 4: drawn already in Cod. Coburg., no. 70 Matz. (*a*) **Woman** with stephané, holding sceptre and shield, sitting; upper part of body nude. (*b*) **Victoria** placing a helmet on a tropaeum. (A drawing of *b* is also in the Dal Pozzo collection at Windsor, vol. I. fol. 88.) (*c*) **Victoria** with a palm branch and her r. hand upraised. The style of *b* and *c* is an unpleasant, artificial archaism, the work not nearly so good as that of no. 8. Pentelic marble. On this pedestal is placed Weddell's bust by Nollekens. [*.M*]

42. **Bust of Lucilla.**

43. **Bust of a negro,** of basalt.

PICTURE GALLERY.

44. Head of a Roman boy. Dallaway, no. 19. [*M*]

45. Head of a Greek maiden, connected with the so-called Sappho heads. Inferior work. Dallaway, no. 20. [*M*]

PASSAGE.

46, 47. Two statuettes of barbarians. Clarac, v. 854. 2161 A, C. Two barbarians in chiton, hose, and cloak, standing. No. 46 is 0·80 high ;—new : head and l. forearm. No. 47 is 0·84 high ;—new : head and both forearms.

ENTRANCE HALL.

48, 49. Two small reliefs, mentioned by Matz, p. 24. They are modern. [**M*]

OSBORNE (Isle of Wight).

Catalogue of the Paintings, Sculpture and other works of art at Osborne, London, 1876.

I have to thank Mr Doyne C. Bell, the author of the above-mentioned Catalogue printed for the private use of HER MAJESTY THE QUEEN, for the information about the following antique sculptures in Osborne, and for the permission to examine the photographs which have been taken from them. The marbles were collected within the years 1848—1854.

PRINCIPAL CORRIDOR.

1 (no. 379). Bust of "Marcellus." Life size. "Purchased in 1854 from the Hertz collection." [*Bell.*] It is not to be verified in the catalogue of this collection (1851). The head, which appears to be the only antique portion, has very curly hair which nearly covers the forehead and falls low down on the neck. The glance is directed straight in front. Eyebrows expressed. New : nose and bust with the sword-belt and drapery. Nomenclature by no means certain ; the head looks rather like a Satyr's head. H. 0·81. [*From a photograph.*]

2 (no. 380). Statue of Aphroditè Anadyomenè. Poor woodcut in *The Stowe Catalogue*, by Henry Rumsey Forster, London.

1848, p. 44, no. 697. The goddess, who is quite nude, rests on her l.
leg, by which a dolphin serves as a support; her r. foot is somewhat
drawn back. She is arranging her long hair with both hands; her r.
shoulder is a good deal elevated and the l. lowered, the l. forearm
however is raised. The head glances away towards the r. side of the
figure. The hair is even too abundant. The movement of the
figure is graceful and refined, but the work is said not to be of corresponding beauty. Unfortunately it is not easy to pronounce with
certainty on the restorations from the photograph. Both legs have
been broken close under the knees and the l. leg a second time
through the calf; the lower parts of the legs are probably modern.
There is a fissure across the upper part of the body just above the
bosom, which has the effect of making the head, the r. shoulder and
the r. arm and a considerable piece of the l. shoulder, form a
separate piece: whether this is only a fracture, or whether the parts
named are new, I cannot say. A great part of the l. arm appears to
be new. One can only say decidedly that the part of the figure from
above the breast to below the knees is antique. "Found in excavating the baths of Agrippa at Rome, and brought to England by
the Marquis of Chandos [afterwards Duke of Buckingham]. After
having had the injuries it had sustained by the lapse of ages carefully
repaired, it was placed in an alcove prepared for it in the Music-
room [at Stowe]. Her Majesty the Queen, when visiting Stowe, in
January, 1845, expressed her admiration of its beauties in very warm
terms; indeed, the impression it made upon the mind of the Queen,
may be gathered from the fact that, when the melancholy news of
the fall of Stowe became known, Her Majesty commissioned Mr
Gruner to purchase the statue for her Royal Consort. The lot was
knocked down to Mr Gruner at 157 guineas. A curious story is
told of the manner in which the Prince first became acquainted with
his possession of the statue. In the *Morning Post* of the day
succeeding the sale, the lot was described as purchased by Mr
Gruner for Prince Albert. The announcement being observed by
the Queen, Her Majesty handed the newspaper to the Prince, and
congratulated him on having made so valuable an addition to his
collection. His Royal Highness, having taken no step in the
matter, expressed his entire ignorance of the affair; upon which the
Queen declared her knowledge of the circumstances, and requested
her Royal Consort to accept the work as a birthday present from
herself (26th August, 1848)." [*Forster.*] II. 137. [*From a photograph.*]

3 (no. 485). **Statue of Antinous**, represented as an Egyptian, standing in repose, his l. leg in advance, both arms hanging down by his sides. In either hand he holds a short staff. Round his loins is an apron, the striped calantica conceals his hair and falls down over both shoulders on to his breast. We recognise the Bithynian youth by the mighty proportions, particularly of his breast, while his features seem to be less characteristically expressed. Beside his r. leg is the trunk of a palm tree. It would be very difficult to tell from the photograph whether there have been any restorations. The statue is very like one from Hadrian's Villa (*Mus. Capitol.*, III. Pl. 86. Re and Mori, *Mus. Cap.*, II. *Sala grande*, Pl. 30). "Captured in 1806, by the 'Impérieuse' frigate, under the command of Lord Cochrane, from a French vessel which had on board a collection of curiosities belonging to the Emperor Napoleon and King Jerome Bonaparte. This vessel was taken into Gibraltar, and the cargo sold by auction. Some Gibraltar merchants, who were under obligations to Mr George Ward, of Northwood Park, Isle of Wight, purchased it and sent it over to him as a token of their gratitude. At his death it became the property of his son, at the sale of whose property, in 1850, it was purchased by the Queen." [*Bell.*] Grey marble (*bigio*). H. 1·70. [*From a photograph.*]

4 (no. 488). **Female head**, probably Bacchic ("Flora"). New: nose and bust; in fact the whole work is not free from suspicion. A broad fillet passes across the forehead and disappears in the hair, which is very curly and all brushed back. The hair is divided by several deep partings, and in these partings have been left, unusually, numerous pieces of marble to hold them together. On the very top of the head is a wreath of flowers. Pupils expressed. The face is feeble and much rubbed down. Purchased by the Prince Consort in 1854. H. 0·50. [*From a photograph.*]

5 (no. 516). **Statue of crouching Aphrodite**, in the well-known attitude. The r. arm is elevated high, the l. lowered but then raised from the elbow-joint, and both hands are grasping her abundant hair. The figure does not appear to be a particularly good copy. The whole of the pedestal, both feet, r. arm, l. forearm, and even a portion of the hair are certainly new ; the head appears to belong to the body but is by no means remarkable as regards expression. Purchased by the Queen in 1854 from the Hertz collection (*Hertz Catal.*, p. 152, no. 8, "Parian marble"). H. 0·72. [*From a photograph.*]

6 (no. 884). **Bust of Lucilla.** Small life size. The name appears to be correct. Hair very wavy. Pupils expressed. Pretty little head; nose and bust have apparently been restored. Purchased in Rome by Mr Gruner in 1854. H. 0·38. [*From a photograph.*]

OSTERLEY PARK (Middlesex).

Waagen, *Treas.*, IV. p. 270.

Osterley is a country seat of LORD JERSEY, near Hounslow and north-west of Richmond. In the Entrance Hall of the mansion Waagen found the following specimens:

1. "A Torso of an **Athene**, in Parian marble. Originally of tolerably good workmanship, but now defaced by retouches and restorations."

2. "Torso of another **female figure**, also in Parian marble, and of good workmanship, but in no better preservation than the foregoing."

OXFORD.

H. Prideaux, *Marmora Oxoniensia*, Oxf. 1676, fol. (Maittaire,) *Marmora Arundelliana*, Lond. 1732, fol. (R. Chandler,) *Marmora Oxoniensia*, Oxf. 1763, fol. (cited by the numbers, not by the plates ; wherever no Roman number is prefixed, the reference is to the first part). *Catalogue of the several pictures, statues and busts in the Picture Gallery, Bodleian Library, and Ashmolean Museum, at Oxford*, Oxford, 1779. Volkmann, *Reisen durch England*, III. pp. 27 ff. Dallaway, *Anecdotes*, pp. 245—263 (I. pp. 272—295). Spiker, *Reise durch England*, I. pp. 22 ff. Waagen, *Treas.*, III. pp. 50 ff. Conze, *Arch. Anz.*, 1864, pp. 167 ff. Huebner, *Arch. Zeit.*, 1866, pp. 302 f. I examined the collections in 1873 and 1877.

The University of Oxford owes the first elements of its collection of antiquities to the famous JOHN SELDEN (d. 1654), who bequeathed to it his library and nine sculptures, which came mostly from Smyrna and of which eight are ornamented with figures. Then followed the gift of HENRY HOWARD, afterwards Duke of Norfolk, who in 1667 presented all the inscribed marbles still remaining of the Arundel Collection (Introd. § 21). Most of these came in like manner originally from Smyrna and the adjacent islands and towns; an account of an important portion of them had already been published in 1628 by Selden (*Marmora Arundelliana*, Lond. 1628, 4to). Smaller gifts of individual specimens, especially of inscribed stones, were afterwards added by different persons connected with the Oxford University. An account of the collection as it stood in 1676 was published by Prideaux, and the sketchy treatment of it by Maittaire (1732) was limited to the same specimens, although in the mean time the well-known traveller, GEORGE WHELER, soon after his return from Greece (1676), had presented some inscriptions that he had brought back with him, and had afterwards added to these a considerable number of reliefs. Most of these marbles came from Athens, where they had in fact been already collected by Consul Giraud (Wheler, *Journey*, pp. 399—407). A further addition to this division of the Oxford antiquities was made by HENRY DAWKINS, who presented the collection made abroad by his brother JAMES DAWKINS, the companion of Rob. Wood in his journey to Palmyra; then by THOMAS SHAW, who had travelled in Africa and the Levant, and finally by RAWLINSON, who had formed his collection, in which there was certainly a good deal of rubbish, principally at the Kemp sale (1721, Introd. § 28) and the Oxford sale (1742, Introd. § 30), cf. Chandler, p. v. Other specimens had come to the University by gift or purchase, of which the origin was not known. All this collection was placed in the vicinity of the Bodleian Library and of the Sheldonian Theatre, for about a century in the open air, afterwards in one of the Schools. At the present day the greater part of the inscribed marbles, either with sculptures or without, have been let in to the walls of the Schools; the other specimens have been placed in the basement of the Ashmolean Museum, which is close at hand. Quite lately some marbles from Ephesos and Syracuse, presented by HYDE CLARKE, Esq. (1866), and a relief from Pergamon, the gift of the Rev. J. W. BURGON (1858), have been added to the latter Museum.

Meanwhile the COUNTESS DOWAGER OF POMFRET, HENRIETTA LOUISA, had presented to the University in the year 1755 all, or nearly all, the statues, busts and reliefs which her father-in-law, Lord Lempster, had purchased in 1691 at Arundel House (Introd. §§ 22, 24). Lord Pomfret had employed an Italian sculptor, Guelfi, to restore all the marbles which had not already been restored by the direction of Lord Arundel (cf. below on no. 3), and Guelfi had done it abominably. After this restoration they had been placed at Lord

Lempster's country seat of Easton-Neston, where G. Vertue saw them in 1734 (*A Description of Easton-Neston*, cf. above, art. Easton-Neston). These sculptures, 135 in number, found a scanty home in a small room of the Schools, till they were lately removed to the magnificent University Galleries, built by Cockerell. In pursuance of Mr Newton's advice, Guelfi's restorations have been done away with for the most part, and therefore many specimens look essentially different from the illustrations in Chandler's work, which were drawn and engraved by J. Miller in a style not always true to the original, and published by the University in 1763 as a kind of catalogue of its entire collection of antiques. Only a few specimens in the University Galleries have been obtained from other sources, some from the Rev. J. W. BURGON (1858) from the collection of his father, who had been long resident in Smyrna, and some from CHAMBERS HALL, Esq.

·In the following catalogue come first the University Galleries with the larger Arundel antiques of the Pomfret presentation (AP.), then the Schools and the Ashmolean Museum, with the marbles specially styled Arundel, bequeathed by Howard (AH.), and with various other antiques, to which the names of the donors are affixed whenever they are known. Quite at the end follows the notice of a few isolated specimens preserved in different places at Oxford.

<hr>

UNIVERSITY GALLERIES.

Handbook Guide for the University Galleries, Oxford, 1862, 1865.

I have not taken the specimens in the order in which they are at present exhibited, for the arrangement is so unworthy of the treasures that it cannot exist long, but have placed the statues first, then the busts and heads, and finally the reliefs. If in enumerating the restorations, I have omitted anything or made mistakes, my excuse must be the darkness of the apartments, particularly of the basement rooms, and the deep dust lying on great part of the marbles.

STATUES.

I will begin with a number of statues, some of which are certainly and some probably of **Greek** origin, and which appear to have formed part of W. Petty's booty from Asia Minor (Introd. §§ 11, 15).

1 (AP.). **Female draped figure.** Chandler, 25. Clarac, IV. 560 B, 1294 C, "Venus." The figure, draped merely in the simple chiton, girdled under her bosom, is stepping with the r. foot forward,

so that round the r. leg the drapery falls in perpendicular folds. The head is also inclined to the r.; a broad fillet is passed through the wavy hair. Both arms are lowered. Above the girdle a fissure runs across, showing that the statue has always been put together from two pieces. New: the advanced r. forearm and the elbow; the l. arm is missing. Neck and head appear to be antique; tip of nose broken off. H. 1·47. [*]

2 (AP.). **Female draped figure.** Chandler, 28. Clarac, v. 978 D, 2524 J. The figure rests on the l. foot; the ample chiton falls in rich folds about her feet. A large cloak of stuff so fine that the chiton can be seen through it, and trimmed with fringe, almost envelopes the whole body. The l. arm is lowered, the r. rests on her bosom. The hair is very wavy in front; it is encircled by a tolerably wide fillet, and forms a plait at the back. The shoulders and neck as well as the head have been at one time sundered from the body, but they are antique and belong to it. Missing: tip of nose, r. forearm, l. hand and r. foot. H. 1·82. [*]

3 (AP.). **Female draped figure.** Chandler, 29. Clarac, v. 978 D, 2524 K. She steps slightly forwards on the r. leg, and the head turns in the same direction. On the powerful form is a girdled chiton, and over that an ample cloak, which covers the back and the greater part of the legs, and falls double over the stomach. The r. arm was raised and the l. lowered; the hand may have held the cloak by the thigh. Almost the whole of both arms and the r. breast are missing; the feet are new. The head, which has a poor expression, is quite intact, and with the neck has been let in to the drapery; it seems to be an addition of the restorer employed by Lord Arundel (Introd. § 15, no. 36), and is at any rate far superior to Guelfi's restorations; on the head-dress must be noticed an imitation of enchased gems, a favourite device of Renaissance and Rococo art. In parts much scoured away. H. 2·17. [*]

4 (AP.). **Female draped statue.** Chandler, 30. Clarac, v. 978 D, 2524 L. The figure rests on the l. foot; the chiton has ample folds, and the cloak is wide, thrown back over the l. shoulder; it is carved so as to show the peculiar creases which are caused by the stuff lying by for some time (as in the so-called Juno Cesi of the Capitol, *Mus. Capitol.*, III. 8). Surface in good preservation. The l. arm formed a right angle, the r. forearm was probably raised; both are now missing. Neck and head, with a stephane of unusual form, may be ascribed to the same restorer as in the case of no. 3. H. 2·12. [*]

5 (AP.). **Female draped statue.** Chandler, 31. Clarac, v.

978 C, 2425 B. The figure rests on the r. leg in somewhat self-conscious pose, the l. foot steps forward. The folds of the cloak, through which the chiton may be seen (cf. no. 2), conceal the r. arm, which is resting in front of the body, but the l. forearm is freed from the drapery and is raised towards the r. shoulder. Much corroded. New: head and neck, l. forearm. H. 2·03. [*]

   6 (AP.). **Female draped statue.** Chandler, 32. Clarac, v. 978 C, 2402 A. The only portion that is certainly antique is the part of the body below the bosom, which is much like no. 4. The upper part of the body has been much broken, and seems to be quite new ; there is no doubt that this is the case with the long neck and wretched head. Arms missing. H. 2·05. [²]

   7 (AP.). **Female draped statue.** Chandler, 45. A woman with her drapery girdled high up, her r. foot somewhat drawn back. Her cloak conceals her back and legs, but not her bosom and waist, below which it forms a twisted roll. A hollow has been chiselled out for neck and head, but they and both arms are missing. Cf. no. 12. Execution coarse. H. 0·84. [*]

   8 (AP.). **Female draped statue.** Chandler, 46. This figure is remarkable for its graceful movement and the web-like transparency of the chiton (*Coa vestis*), which however is treated without any exaggeration ; the l. shoulder and the part of the bosom nearest to it is quite nude. The cloak covers the back and legs, but leaves the breast and greater part of the body exposed ; it is drawn up from the r. thigh to the l. hip, which stands out very much and on which the l. arm holds the drapery, thus forming a right angle. The r. arm was raised. R. foot is somewhat drawn back. Missing : head, l. forearm, half the l. foot ; the rest has been much broken. New : r. shoulder and stump of the arm. H. 1·24. [*C]

   9 (AP.). **Female draped statue.** Chandler, 47. She stands on the l. leg and the r. is much bent. The cloak conceals her back, all the r. side of the body from below the shoulder to below the knee, including the r. breast ; from those points it is drawn in converging lines towards the l. hip, forming thus a triangle in front of the body, and is there fastened under the l. arm. Thus it can be seen that the chiton has an over-fold which falls down as far as the l. hip. The folds of the chiton can be seen through the cloak, the material of which is fine (cf. no. 2). The arms were lowered, but they and the head are missing. Coarse work, like that of no. 7. H. 1·10. [*]

These nine female figures all belong to the same style of art, and correspondingly, are all made of the same species of Greek marble. The workmanship of them is superficial, but the treatment of the drapery, sometimes delicate and always fresh, is most pleasing, and forms a strong contrast to the insipid uniformity of Roman decorative sculptures. The different character of the perpendicular folds of the ample chiton and of the slanting folds of the fine, transparent cloak, which are treated in such an effective manner, is particularly well carried out (cf. the terracotta figure in Naples, Clarac, III. 420 A, 727 A). The proportions are mostly somewhat long, the middle part of the body very massive, the upper part short and narrow; in compensation the postures are easy and good. There is a peculiarity about the pedestal, which is an exceedingly low, irregular plinth, following in shape the edges of the drapery and the position of the feet, and is not smoothed; the statues were evidently intended to be placed on some separate pedestal with architectural mouldings. We observe the same peculiarity in statues from Asia Minor (London, South Kensington Mus., nos. 1, 2), whence I suppose Petty may have obtained our statues too (cf. Introd. § 11). They are examples of the later Greek art (possibly of the last centuries B.C.) of Asia Minor and her adjacent islands, more akin to Greek terracotta figures than to Roman marble statues; though Dallaway (p. 260) simply mentions them as "Roman Ladies" (see the note referring to nos. 43—45). Exactly similar in composition and feeling for style are the women on the reliefs of certain sepulchral monuments from Smyrna (cf. nos. 89, 90, 204, 205). At one time there seem to have been more statues like these belonging to the Arundel Collection, for on the occasion of Lord Petre's excavation on the bank of the Thames in Kennington (Introd. § 22), "they discovered six statues, without heads or arms, lying close to each other; some of a colossal size, the drapery of which was thought to be exceeding fine. When they were taken up, I was surprised to find sticking to some of them a small sort of conical Babani, which convinced me they must have formerly lain in the sea [cf. Introd. § 11].... These trunks of statues were soon after sent down to Worksop, the seat of his present Grace the Duke of Norfolk, in Nottinghamshire, where they at present remain." Thus writes, in 1757, James Theobald in Ch. Howard's *Historical Anecdotes*, London, 1769, pp. 104, 105; the mansion of Worksop Manor was burnt to the ground with all its contents in 1761 (Volkmann, *Reisen*, III. p. 423).

Somewhat resembling these statues, yet differing from them in many points, are a number of other statues (10—15) all of which we may also consider with tolerable probability to be of **Greek** origin.

10 (AP.). **Female draped figure,** from a fountain. Chandler, 5. Clarac, IV. 634 D, 1294 A, "Venus." The figure, resting on the l. foot, with the r. leg drawn back, is robed only in a chiton of the finest, most transparent stuff, which almost entirely clings closely to the body. The few folds which come forth on the projecting parts of the body, thus seem all the sharper and higher, rising as they do to sharp ridges. The chief motive of the folds is caused by the drapery having once been raised by the lowered r. hand in the neighbourhood of the thigh. It would be difficult to find a better example of effective treatment of transparent drapery. All the upper part of the body from below the breast and the upraised mass of drapery by the r. thigh are missing. The simply moulded pedestal is however preserved, and on it is by the l. foot the remains of a square block, bored through perpendicularly for the reception of a water-pipe, which may have discharged its contents through the jaws of a dolphin, or some such object. Were not this figure somewhat too freely draped for such a personage, we might take it for the nymph of the fountain. H. 0·97, with the pedestal, 1·04. [* *W*]

11 (AP.). **Female draped figure.** Chandler, 10. Clarac, III. 410 H, 802 B, " Flora." The figure is standing, resting the l. elbow on the high trunk of a tree, with the l. knee slightly bent. The chiton is girdled very high under the bosom; the cloak hangs from the l. shoulder and arm far down in front, is then drawn round behind the back, and conceals the legs, the upper edge slanting from the r. hip towards the l. thigh, without being touched by the hands. New: head and neck, and perhaps all that remains of the r. arm; the l. hand missing. The rest is not broken; the round pedestal has a rough moulding. The figure is altogether not delicately executed, but has more freshness and individuality than the common Roman specimens. H. 1·16. [* *W*]

12 (AP.). **Female draped figure.** Chandler, 44 (too slim). Same subject as no. 7 ; missing: head, three parts of the lowered r. arm, half the l. arm. Commonplace work, but still perhaps of late Greek art. H. 0·66. [*]

13. **Statue of a lady,** in girdled chiton, sitting in a chair, of which the legs are missing ; the support of the chair has the form of a high basket (*kalathos*), like those which are often seen under the chair of the mistress of the house. The r. foot rests on a

footstool, the l., further advanced, on the ground. Head, lowered arms and r. knee missing. Very simple, but good, soft treatment; almost certainly Greek. Much corroded. H. 0·76. [*]

14. **Sitting female figure.** She is robed in a girdled chiton, her thighs and the lower parts of her legs are concealed by her cloak; both feet rest on a footstool. Head, arms, front parts of both feet missing. Work much stiffer and less good than in no. 13, also more injured. H. 0·81. [*]

15 (AP.). **Statue of a Roman in the pallium.** Chandler, 38 (not slender enough). The r. arm, hidden in the cloak, is raised in front of the breast, the l. is lowered. Head and r. hand, also the outer portion of the l. forearm were put on separately, as the dowel holes show; they, and the feet are now missing. Very simple style, probably Greek. H. 1·60. [*]

16 (Burgon). **Statuette of a youth,** in a cloak, standing on the l. leg, resting his l. hand on his hip as Asklepios usually stands. Head, r. arm and feet are missing. Much corroded. H. 0·40. [*]

17 (Burgon). **Fragment of a crouching lion,** only pieces of the legs. H. 0·19. [*]

The following statues belong all, or nearly all, to Lord Arundel's Italian purchases:

18 (AP.). **Statue of Zeus.** Chandler, 1. Clarac, III. 404, 692 A. The god is sitting on a rock, the upper part of his body quite nude, his legs covered by his cloak; the l. arm is lowered, the r. raised. The statue is insignificant and has been badly broken and patched up. New probably: head, both arms excepting the junctions with the shoulders, the feet and the pedestal. H. 0·94. [*]

19 (AP.). **Statue of Athenê,** colossal scale. Chandler, 2. Clarac, III. 472, 898 C. The chiton, which is girdled and has an overfold, reminds us in the chief features of its arrangement of the Parthenos (Michaelis, *Parthenon*, Pl. 15). The goddess stands on the r. leg, r. arm lowered, l. raised. The aegis, composed of two parts, is small; it hardly covers both breasts. New: the helmeted head and the neck, upper half of r. breast and the r. arm, the l. arm, which was always raised; both arms bear traces of supplementary patching; spear and shield have recently been removed. The Medusa, with raving mouth, and other parts of the aegis have been re-worked; the folds of the chiton have been patched in many places. The work is purely decorative: the r. leg is quite lost sight of in the paltry management of the folds, the perpendicular folds

M. C.   35

standing out only between the legs. On the outside of the leg are
two rows of zigzag folds, as in the Parthenos statue, but between
are perpendicular folds as if there were another garment under the
chiton. This appears to have been caused by a misconception of
the original idea on the part of the Roman workman who executed
this figure. H. 2·70. [*]

20 (AP.). **Statue of Athenè.** Chandler, 3. Clarac, III.
474 A, 899 E. Episcopius, *Signorum veterum icones*, Pl. 91. Kraus,
Sign. vet. icones, Pl. 48 (sides reversed). The composition is excellent, like the similar figure in Castle Howard, no. 4, and is neatly
and well executed, though without particular delicacy. The aegis is
without Gorgon's head or scales, but on its edge are the remains of
snakes. On her back the plait of hair is visible. R. arm, neck and
head are now missing; the head had been restored by Guelfi, and
already before that, according to Episcopius' engraving, it had been
restored in a somewhat different way. The statue may be a Greek
work. H. 1·32. [*C]

21 (AP.). **Statuette of Athenè.** Chandler, 43. Clarac,
III. 474 A, 860 D. The goddess is very slender; her chiton, which
has an overfold, is girded very high; it falls on the ground for a good
way round the feet, so that the lower part of the body preponderates
still more over the upper part. R. foot somewhat drawn back. R.
arm was raised, l. lowered. The aegis, divided, has a Gorgon's head
and a slight indication of scales. Missing: head, nearly the whole of
both arms, r. foot. H. 0·66. The figure stands on a pedestal of
elegant Renaissance style, cf. Chandler, 156. [*CIV]

22 (AP.). **Statue of Artemis.** Chandler, 9. Clarac, IV.
560 B, 1201 A. The goddess has her chiton girded twice, so that it
is lifted above her knees; a peculiarity of this arrangement is that
the lower girdle passes, as the folds show, below the stomach, round
the hips (cf. Clarac, V. 809, 2029). A skin, which hangs from the r.
shoulder across the breast, is also confined by the upper girdle. On
her back is the quiver. On her feet high boots. The goddess is
very slender. The enormously long neck is new; the head old, but
scarcely belonging to the statue; of both lowered arms only a small
portion is preserved; the dog by the l. leg and the stout support are
new. H. 1·45. With regard to composition, compare the statuette
in Dresden, no. 80, that has been so much restored (Clarac, IV. 562,
1203). [*]

23. **Pedestal of a statuette of Artemis,** about half life size.
Only the feet of the goddess, in the position of walking, are preserved;

near the r. foot sit a boar and a dog, and in front of the l. is the
remains of an aninal whose species cannot be recognised.   [*]

24 (AP.). **Torso of an Amazon.** Chandler, 17. Clarac, v.
808, 2038 A. The torso, now cleared from Guelfi's abominable restorations, is all that remains. It is of the same type as the similar
statue at Lansdowne House (London, Lansdowne House, no. 83),
which is usually ascribed to Polykleitos. The wound, made with
one incision and about which are many drops of blood, may be
seen near the r. breast. Missing: head and neck, both arms, lower
parts of both legs, the r. from the drapery, the l. somewhat deeper.
The work is ordinary, but it has not been re-worked; all the details
in the construction of the several parts of the girdle, particularly the
clasp, are carefully imitated. H. 1·04. [*C]

25 (AP.). **Statue of Aphroditè.** Chandler, 4. Clarac, iv.
634 D. 1392 C. Pricaeus, *Notae in Apuleii apologiam*, Paris, 1635,
p. 93. Torso of a statue in the position of the Medici Venus, of very
common-place work. Restorations by Guelfi: head and neck, r. arm
with the small piece of drapery in the hand, l. forearm. The legs
below the knees and the unusually plump dolphin are attributable to
an earlier restorer; for they already existed, together with a different
head and different r. arm, in Arundel House, long before Guelfi's
time, as is shown by Price's engraving. H. 1·34. [*]

26 (AP.). **Statue of Aphroditè.** Chandler, 6. Clarac, iv.
634 D, 1392 D. The legs are concealed by the cloak, which is
arranged in a broad mass round the hips, then gathered into a
kind of knot before the lower part of the abdomen, falling then
between the legs in a richly composed mass of folds. The upper
part of the body is bent slightly forwards. Head and arms are now
missing; in the back of the neck are remains of hair that once fell
there, but there is none on the shoulders, and there is just as little
trace of hands on the drapery. Sculpture good, life-like and fresh,
though not very refined; the body is treated with feeling; in some
parts the folds of the drapery are very deeply chiselled out. Surface
much corroded. Greek marble, apparently Parian. H. 1·09. [*]

27 (AP.). **Statue of Aphroditè.** Chandler, 26. Clarac, iv.
634 D, 1294 B. Statue in the taste and composition of the Venus
Genetrix (Holkham, no. 23), draped in a transparent, ungirdled chiton,
which leaves the l. breast and shoulder free, with a cloak which
falls over the lowered l. arm, and was perhaps held by the uplifted r.
arm. Missing: head, r. arm and l. forearm. Ordinary sculpture.
H. 0·80. [*]

28 (AP.). **Statue of Leda.** Chandler, 18. Originally this was not a bad specimen of the oft repeated group (Overbeck, *Kunst-mythol.*, II. p. 491), representing Leda, rising from her rocky seat and pressing the fugitive swan against her body, while with her l. hand she holds her wide cloak as a shield from the pursuing eagle. (Cf. London, Lansdowne House, no. 78.) Missing: Leda's head and neck, three parts of the l. arm with pieces of the cloak, the r. arm, and swan's neck; the rest is much broken. H. 1·10. [*]

29 (AP.). **Statuette of Tyche.** Chandler, 40. The figure, as she sits enthroned, resembles in general the statue at Ince, no. 7. A large portion of the cornucopiae in her l. arm is preserved, but nothing of the steering paddle. Missing: head and both hands; perhaps the r. forearm is new. Decidedly decorative sculpture. H. 0·44. [*]

30 (AP.). **Statue of Hygieia.** Chandler, 27. Clarac, v. 978 D, 2524 I (not good). The figure, resting on her r. leg, wears a simple, girdled chiton with an overfold; the small cloak, which hangs down from her l. shoulder, covers her back and r. thigh, and is then drawn up in a narrow stripe towards the l. hip. Noticeable is the somewhat affected arrangement of the cloak, a piece of which is drawn up by the r. thigh, and then laid over the edge of the cloak. On the upper part of the r. arm the tail end of a snake is visible, which guarantees the interpretation of the statue as Hygieia; cf. the similar statues in Florence and Brescia (Clarac, IV. 553, 1172. 560 A, 1174 A). On the front of the r. hip there remains a *puntello* for securing the r. forearm, which held the snake: the l. possibly held the cup, from which the snake wished to drink. Missing: head, r. arm from above the elbow, and half the l. forearm. H. 1·02. [*]

31 (AP.). **Statue of a Muse, sitting.** Chandler, 7. Clarac, III. 519, 1063 A. This is a replica of the Vatican "Terpsichore" (*Mus. Pio-Clem.*, I. Pl. 20. Clarac, III. 517, 1056), of decorative work, back very slightly treated. The edge of the cloak, going across the lap, is bunchy. Missing: l. hand and half the l. foot. Neck and head, latter adorned with a stephane, have been let in and are perhaps old (nose restored) but do not belong to the statue; the r. arm appears to be new, on the l. knee there has been some patching. H. 1·32. [*W]

32 (AP.). **Statue of a Muse, sitting** (Kleio?). Chandler, 8. Clarac, III. 498 A, 990 A. Episcopius, *Icones*, Pl. 98 (sides reversed). Kraus, *Icones*, Pl. 47. On a chair that has no back and almost perpendicular legs sits the Muse in girdled chiton and a cloak that conceals her l. arm and legs. The l. arm is supported stiffly on the chair, and holds the roll which is a common attribute of Kleio: the r. leg is thrown over the l. The upper part of the body leans to its r. side and the neck is considerably inclined in the same direction, showing that once the r. elbow must have rested on the r. thigh and the r. hand have supported the head; the present arm, which is new and has all the fingers in perfect preservation, does not touch either the thigh or the head. New: r. foot and a piece of the drapery, also the neck; the head appears to be antique, but it cannot have originally belonged to this figure because the hair, unbound, now lies horizontally instead of falling down. The l. foot stands on a footstool, the whole figure, including chair and footstool, on a pedestal with mouldings. The execution of the statue is only decorative, but by reason of the motive the effect is good (cf. the "Penelope," Clarac, v. 834, 2090). The figure was intended not only to be placed against a wall, for the back is perfectly smooth, but in a sloping corner, or against a sloping object, for only this supposition can explain the extraordinary design of the pedestal. The engravings

a, chair; b, footstool; c, pedestal.

do not render this correctly, and they also do not give the legs of the chair, which are almost perpendicular. The whole surface has suffered much from rain. H. 1·23, with the pedestal, 1·35. [*CIV]

33 (AP.). **Statue of Skylla.** Chandler, 132. Fragment of a group. Upper part of Skylla's body missing; behind we see the remains of entwined fishes-tails which served her as legs. Below her hips, vandyked, there issue forth, from the covering of leaves, the foreparts of the bodies of three animals; in the place of the r. leg is a dog, in place of the l. a panther, and in front between the two a third with head and neck destroyed. Each animal is seizing a nude man (a good deal injured). The ground is rocky. The execution of this very peculiar sculpture is only moderately good. Our fragment has hitherto not received any notice at the hands of writers

on the Skylla myth (see particularly Vinet, *Annali dell' Inst.*, 1843, p. 199) ; for other representations in statuary of this subject cf. Schöne, *Arch. Zeit.*, 1870, p. 57. (The Albani fragment treated by Schöne is now in the Torlonia Museum, no. 165, absurdly restored as a Milon attacked by a wild beast, cf. Schreiber, *Arch. Zeit.*, 1879, p. 63.) Fröhner, *Musées de France*, Pl. 28, 3. The description of a bronze group, once in the Hippodrome at Constantinople, which perished in 1204, may be compared, as it is given by Niketas Choniates, p. 861 ed. Bekker, καὶ τὸ ἀρχαῖον κακόν, τὴν Σκύλλαν, μέχρι μὲν ἰξύος γυναικεῖον εἶδος προφέρουσαν, καὶ τοῦτο προτενὲς καὶ ὑπερμαζῶν καὶ μεστὸν ἀγριότητος, τὰ δ' ἔκτοτε διεσχισμένον εἰς θῆρας ἐμπηδῶντας τῇ τοῦ Ὀδυσσέως νηὶ καὶ συχνοὺς τῶν ἑταίρων καταβρυχθίζοντας. H. 0·38. L. 0·73. [*]

34 (AP.).   **Statue of Hermaphroditos.** Chandler, 34. The torso corresponds exactly to the figure in Deepdene, no. 26. R. arm was lowered. Missing: head, both arms, r. leg from the knee, l. from the middle of the thigh. The proportions of the figure are slender, the bosom virgin-like, the waist narrow, the hips like those of a woman, the distinctive male feature poor. Work soft, but not particularly good. H. 0·70. [*]

35 (AP.).   **Statue of Eros?** Chandler, 14. Clarac, IV. 763. 1876 A, "Harpocrates." The boy is without wings and has a small piece of drapery on his back; he is supporting his l. shoulder on an inverted torch which stands on a mass of rock; the r. arm is bent upwards in front of the breast. New: head and the r. hand ; the fore-finger is laid on the mouth. It is possible that at one time the eyes were closed and the head rested on the hand, so that the figure represented Sleep or Death, cf. no. 36. Insignificant work. H. 0·75, the pedestal (with mouldings) 0·12. [*]

36 (AP.).   **Statue of Eros.** Chandler, 15. Clarac, IV. 650 B, 1504 A. In the well-known motive : the god supports himself on his torch and rests his r. hand on his l. shoulder, toward which his head is inclined. Antique : body, without wings, the r. arm, both legs, excepting the feet, the inverted quiver and bow fastened to it, which serves as support to the r. leg, the chin, and part of the r. cheek. New: the greater part of the head, the l. arm and the torch, both wings which are made out of one piece and let in, and the feet. The poverty of the work is specially felt because the dimensions are so big. H. 1·73. [*]

37 (AP.).   **Statue of Eros sleeping.** Chandler, 49. Clarac, IV. 644 B, 1459 F. He lies on rocky ground with flowers about him ;

a lizard and a snail are crawling near his outstretched l. leg. At
Eros' head lies the quiver; the head rests on the l. wing. The
drapery by the shoulder belongs to a restored piece of the pedestal.
Missing: r. hand, a piece of the l. arm, l. foot. Very coarse sculpture.
L. 0·70. [*]

38 (AP.).   **Group of Herakles and the lion.**   Chandler, 13.
Clarac, v. 792, 1977 A.   Herakles stands upright with his legs far
apart, and his l. foot in advance. With both hands he presses the head
of the lion that confronts him, and is grasping the hero's arms and
leg with his fore paws and r. hind paw.   New: Herakles' head and
neck, the l. foot which is treading on the l. hind paw of the lion, this
paw and half the leg belonging to it; the lower part of Herakles'
r. leg is missing.   On the rock behind Herakles sits the nymph
of the locality, Nemea, in chiton and cloak. Her l. hand is supported
on the rock, and in it she holds a wreath intended for the victor; all
the upper part of her body is missing (cf. the same scene on the
large Albani marble cup, Zoega, *Bassir.*, Pl. 62).   The work is
decorative, but not so bad as one might think from the engravings.
H. 0·81, the pedestal (with mouldings) 0·07.   [*]

39 (AP.).   **Statue of Herakles?** Chandler, 12. Clarac, v. 790,
1970 A.   A pretty good youthful torso, resting on the l. leg, with a
lion's skin over the l. arm, which is held so as to form a right angle.
The r. arm was raised.   It has been very badly restored by Guelfi.
New: head, r. arm, l. shoulder, lower part of the legs, and pedestal.
H. 1·25.   [*]

40 (AP.).   **Statue of "Dionysos."** Chandler, 11. Clarac,
IV. 678, 1580. The torso, completely nude, is certainly antique. The
god rests on his r. leg in a sinuous attitude, so that his hip projects
far out; r. shoulder is lowered, l. raised.   (The movement may be
compared with that of the Satyr pouring out wine at Petworth, no. 6.)
The statue is placed so high that it is difficult to decide whether the
youthful upward-looking head, which is more like the head of a
young athlete than Dionysos, belongs to it or not; it appears however
to be unbroken. Already Winckelmann (*Mon. Ined.*, I. p. LVIII)
was led by this head to doubt the correctness of the title Dionysos.
New: the uplifted l. arm with the bunch of grapes, almost the whole
of the lowered r. arm with grapes and bowl, three parts of the r. leg
and the trunk of the tree, and the lower part of the l. leg.   Insignificant work, exaggeratedly praised by Vertue (p. 57). H. 1·10. [*]

41 (AP.).   **Statue of a Roman in the pallium.** Chandler,
19. Clarac, v. 900 E, 2312 C. The manner in which the l. arm is

supported on the hip, is well known in statues of Asklepios, but the arrangement of the cloak is different. The r. breast is bare. The lowered r. arm is missing. New: head and neck, r. foot, and the fore part of the l. foot. H. 1·47. [*]

42 (AP.). **Male statue, nude.** Chandler, 21, "Antinous." Clarac, v. 970, 2438 B. A powerful man rests on his l. leg; beside this a support covered with a chlamys; the r. leg is slightly bent, both arms lowered. Head very small and badly disfigured; probably new. It is difficult to decide whether more than the stump of the l. arm and whether any part of the r. arm (in the hand remains of an instrument, quite unrecognisable) is antique or not. The greater part of the legs seems to be antique. The statue is completely ruined. H. 1·69. [*]

With regard to the discovery of the three following statues (43—45) Dallaway, p. 256, writes as follows: "Lord Arundel, when at Rome, procured permission to dig over the ruins of several houses, and is said to have discovered, in subterraneous rooms, the following statues, all of which are presumed to be portraits of a consular family, and not of the distinguished characters to whom they have been attributed, without enhancing their merit." As Dallaway further speaks of "so many" statues found together, he seems to suggest that also "five Roman ladies, the size of life" (p. 260) were found at the same place. These statues can scarcely be other than nos. 1, 2, 8, 9, 11. I have explained my reasons in the note on nos. 1—9, why, in this case, I cannot think Dallaway's statement to be exact.

43 (AP.). **Statue of a Roman in the pallium.** Chandler, 22, "Archimedes." Clarac, v. 848 A, 2143 C. The statue is much better than the engravings would lead one to suppose. The position of the body, which inclines strongly to the r., gives life to the figure; the cloak, arranged in broad folds, is soft and ample, executed in good decorative style. The upper part of the body, from the cloak, is made of a separate block, to which genuinely belongs the youthful head (unbroken; nose broken). The curly hair is very superficially treated, in fact little more than suggested. The features of the face give us the idea of a portrait, but they do not resemble Chandler's engraving at all. New: l. arm from the cloak, with the square (γνώμων, *norma*, which has procured for the statue the name Archimedes, cf. Vertue, p. 58), which Chandler says is of different marble, but that cannot be decided without cleaning; new also the feet and the pedestal. H. 2·21. [*]

44 (AP.). **Statue of "Marius."** Chandler, 23. Clarac, v. 900 E, 2304 B. Episcopius, *Sign. vet. icones*, Pl. 74. The statue is in excellent preservation ; head and neck have not been let in, but put on with a sharp line of division; they appear to be antique, but I cannot vouch for it. The face has no beard, the features are elderly. The working of the drapery is very superficial and remarkably flat, not soft and rounded. Much extolled by Vertue (p. 58) ; also by Horace Walpole, who writes July 21, 1753 : "The Cicero (no. 45) is fine and celebrated; the Marius I think still finer." H. 1·82. [*]

45 (AP.). **Statue of "Cicero."** Chandler, 24. *Cicero, ed. Oxon.*, 1783, frontisp. This is a statue in a toga of very fine effect, not executed perhaps very delicately, but powerfully and well, and above all not done according to the received model, but having larger masses of folds and many peculiarities in individual details. Particularly striking is the fact that the so-called *balteus* does not lie horizontally in front of the body, and the toga does not rise from it perpendicularly in a right angle to the l. shoulder, but that the toga, in the fashion of a pallium, goes from the r. hip slanting directly to the l. shoulder, and that in consequence in the place of that right angle the small round bunch of folds (*umbo*) is missing, which otherwise only is left out when the togatus is represented *velato capite* (cf. the beautiful Vatican statue, *Mus. Pio-Clem.*, III. Pl. 19 ; altogether our statue bears a general likeness in style to this example). Just as noticeable is the length and breadth of the sinus, which hangs half way down the shin. New : half the r. forearm with the small piece of drapery in the hand, the l. hand with the roll, neck and head (with closely shaven whiskers, but without beard and mustache; nose restored). A wart (*cicer*) on the right cheek has been added by the restorer in order to make the figure a portrait of Cicero. G. Vertue (p. 57) observes naively, "Marcus Tullius Cicero, bigger than life, with his handkerchief in his right hand....'Tis exquisitely fine ; my lord [Pomfret] hath been bid three thousand pounds for this noble figure." Cf. also Horace Walpole to G. Montague, May 20, 1736. July 22, 1751. H. 2·08. [*II]

46. **Statue of a Roman in the toga,** with many unusual details in the arrangement of the toga, the folds of which are very deeply undercut. R. knee much bent. Head that of an elderly man, but with long curly hair. Nose restored, hands missing. Work very effective, but the whole statue seems to be new. H. 2·20. [³]

47. **Statue of a Roman in the pallium,** in similar style, but coarser execution. The material of the cloak is very thick, the flow of the folds ample. R. hand lies before the breast, l. arm is lowered. The fingers of the l. hand with a piece of the roll have been restored, head and neck are let in. According to all appearance this is likewise the work of a very clever modern imitator. H. abt. 2·00. [*]

48 (AP.). **Statue of a barbarian.** Chandler, 20, "Paris." Clarac, v. 834 B, 2161 J, "young Dacian." A barbarian in a short chiton, twice girdled, chlamys, and hose, stands leaning against the trunk of a tree, his l. leg crossed over his r. The youthful head in Phrygian cap (nose restored) might possibly be antique, but is to be attributed with greater probability to the older restorer (cf. on no. 3). New: r. arm (at any rate the forearm), l. forearm, legs from half way down the shins. The interpretation as a barbarian is confirmed by statues such as Clarac, v. 848 B, 2161 L. 854, 2161 C. 2162. Our figure is certainly of coarse execution, but is better than one would think from the engravings. H. 1·30. [*]

49 (AP.). **Torso of an Aphroditè.** Chandler, 33. The same type as the Medici Venus. Missing: head, r. arm, l. hand, lower parts of both legs. Poor work. H. 0·53. [*]

50 (AP.). **Male torso.** Chandler, 35. The upper part of the body is bent far forward and the l. thigh is lifted high while the r. stands upright; the position therefore suggests a Satyr stamping a krupezion, but there is no little tail at the back, and the body is too powerful, too like Herakles. Missing: head, arms, legs, of which only the stumps of the thighs are preserved. H. 0·75. [*]

51 (AP.). **Torso of a youth.** Chandler, 36. He is standing very straight, resting on the r. leg, both arms lowered. Preserved: torso, stumps of both arms, and both legs to the knee. Tolerable work. H. 0·61. [*]

52 (AP.). **Male torso.** Chandler, 37. He is standing in a pose similar to that of no. 51, but the l. arm was more raised. Preserved: torso, stumps of both arms and of r. thigh. The whole is ruined. H. 0·82. [*]

53 (AP.). **Torso of a Roman in the pallium.** Chandler, 39. Noticeable is the very large three-cornered fold of the cloak in front of the stomach. The breast is almost entirely bare. Missing: head, arms and feet. Common place work. H. 0·63. [*IV]

54 (AP.). **Male torso.** Chandler, 42. The torso is completely draped; a girdled chiton with an overfold reaches to the knees (not lower); on the r. shoulder a chlamys is fastened, which leaves both arms bare, but covers breast and back. On the cloak in front just above the girdle may be seen two holes intended to hold some metallic object. The r. arm was lowered, the l. advanced horizontally. By the r. knee are the remains of a support. The torso may have belonged to the statue of a barbarian (cf. no. 48). H. 0·63. [*]

55 (AP.). **Terminal figure.** Chandler, 16. Clarac, III. 542, 1136 C, "Apollon en hermès." Body of a youth with the chlamys round his breast and back, his thighs disappear gradually in a square pillar tapering towards the base where it has a border; below this the feet, placed close together, peep forth (this lowest piece is broken, but old). The youthful head, apparently a portrait, seems to be antique, and belonging to the body (nose new). New: r. forearm with the syrinx; l. arm is missing, and no traces of a stump are to be seen. Probably Greek marble. H. 1·72. [*]

56. **Statue of a sphinx.** Chandler, 167. The sphinx, without the foot-slab, is high. H. 0·54. L. of slab 1·13. [*]

57. **Statue of a sphinx,** quite similar. H. 0·59. L. 1·10. [*]

I have not seen the following specimen:

58. **Statue of "Apollo."** Chandler, 162. On a high column (no. 130), as it had already been placed at Easton-Neston (Vertue, p. 55), stands a male statue, without definite characteristics of an Apollo. Legs and r. side of the body hidden by the cloak. The figure leans against the stump of a column; broken across the stomach, without arms. H. 1·59.

BUSTS.

In Chandler's plates nearly all the busts are very badly represented, some of them so much so as to be quite beyond recognition.

59 (AP.). **Female bust,** "the Oxford Bust." Chandler, 53, "Sappho" (abominable). An engraving of it exists by W. Hollar of the year 1645 (Vertue, v. 88. Parthey, no. 590). This bust is the fragment of a statue, cut off below the girdle; half the lowered upper parts of the arms preserved. It is hollowed out behind to make it lighter for transport. Unfortunately it is badly mutilated; not only is the neck severed right through, but the head itself has been broken in pieces. However all these pieces fit on to each other, only the nose and a piece of the l. half of the forehead are missing. The head is inclined gently towards the r. shoulder and the face is a beautiful oval, with slightly sentimental expression. The lips, now much corroded, were soft and round, the mouth beautifully formed, the cheek broad. Unfortunately the eyes are badly worn; the lines

of the brows are rather sharply defined. The rounded forehead is
beautifully framed in the wavy hair, which is encircled by a fillet
three times and then gathered into a plait at the back. Neck and
shoulders are treated in a simple, life-like manner, so is the bared
breast, which is strongly developed; all this part however is wanting
in details. It is very noticeable that the upper hem of the chiton,
which is drawn somewhat tightly from the l. shoulder downwards straight under the r. breast, does not alter the form of the
breast; it makes no indentation in the flesh, nor does it press up
the breast. The drapery is treated in a masterly way; the small,
light folds on the upper hem, and the large loose folds which fall
partly over the girdle and also where the drapery falls unconfined,
are worked with equal skill; the hollows are strongly rendered;
the whole drapery is of most artistic effect and suitable to the
material of which the same is made. On the upper part of the l.
arm the chiton is fastened together with a number of small buttons.
The surface of the marble is now rough and granulous, the whole
statue having been much injured, and in parts much corroded. No
doubt many details have been lost, but the character of the sculpture
was always broad; it is earlier than the period of Lysippos. The
great beauty of the fragment, which is probably a reproduction of a
design of the fourth century, has only lately been brought into notice
once more by Newton. Wieseler however exaggerates its merits
when he supposes it to be an original work of Praxiteles himself,
and I do not think he is right in declaring it to be a portrait of a
hetaira (*Arch. Anz.,* 1859, p. 121); it appears to me at least that
the sensual allurement of such a portrait is wanting. The marble is
undoubtedly Greek, probably from Asia Minor or from the Islands.
H. 0·66. L. of face 0·18. [*CH'*]

60 (AP.). **Colossal head.** Chandler, 81, "Apollo" (unrecognisable); it appears to me questionable whether it is not rather
a female head. Unfortunately chin, mouth, nose, greater part of the
forehead, and much of the hair are new; one can now only see that
a peculiar, comparatively early original is the foundation of the
design; there is a preponderance of the lower part of the face, and
a line of the jaw which is peculiar to Peloponnesian sculptures. A
fillet passes round the hair, which bristles up over the forehead on
both sides and is then drawn back from the temples and wound
round the fillet (cf. R. Rochette, *Mon. Inéd.,* Pl. 33, 5), falling at
last in a large heavy plait at the back of the neck. The exceedingly
poor execution of details shows that it was meant to be placed far

from the eye. Chandler states that the statue belonging to this head is probably buried under a house in Arundel Street, London (cf. Introd. § 21). H. 0·68. L. of face 0·46. [*C]

61 (Burgon). **Terminal head of Dionysos**, in hieratic style, with rows of curls and a long beard, cut off straight at the bottom. Pretty well executed. H. 0·27. [*]

62 (AP.). **Head of Niobè.** Chandler, 54. The hair is not arranged in curls, but falls in a wide mass down the back of the neck. The bust is intended to be let into a statue. Nose and upper lip restored. To me the whole head appears very suspicious. L. of face 0·22. [*]

63 (AP.). **Head of a son of Niobè**, of the one who has sunk on his knees (Welcker, *Alte Denkm.*, I. p. 227). Chandler, 55. To me the head appears modern. [*]

64 (AP.). **Bearded head.** Chandler, 50, "Faunus." Modern. [*]

65 (AP.). **Bust of an infant Satyr.** Chandler, 51, "Fauna" (unrecognisable). A child's head with fat cheeks, brutish ears, rough hair with wreath, and with a fillet falling down behind. The mouth is slightly opened, showing the teeth. Tip of nose missing; new beyond doubt is the nude, feminine bust, and the head itself is very suspicious. Life size. [*]

66 (AP.). **Beardless head.** Chandler, 58. The beardless head has a wreath of ivy in the rough hair; can it be "the busto of Pindar the poet" which was shown to Vertue at Easton-Neston (*Deser.*, p. 59)? The head was not bad originally, but it has been frightfully disfigured. New: great part of the forehead, nose, under lip and chin, and the drapery. Life size. [*]

67 (AP.). **Bearded head.** Chandler, 59. The beard is shaved short, the hair is less like a wig than would appear from Chandler's print; the expression is morose. Pupils expressed. New: nose, and various restorations. Life size. [*]

68 (AP.). **Bearded head**, perhaps of **Pupienus.** Chandler, 60. The head very high, the long beard slightly parted. New: tip of nose and bust. Much effaced. Over life size. [*]

69 (AP.). **Head of Agrippa.** Chandler, 98. In spite of the coarse execution the characteristic features of the face, which is turned sharply to the r., are not to be mistaken. Nose battered. Over life size. [*]

70 (Rawlinson). **Head of Domitian.** Chandler, 99. Badly injured, nose battered. Over life size. [*]

71 (AP.).   **Head of a youth.**   Chandler, 56 (quite a failure). Only the head with its rough curls, which reminds us a little of a head at Madrid (no. 123, "Ares," engraved in the *Berichte d. sächs. Ges. d. Wiss.*, 1864, Pl. 1), is antique.   New: nose, neck and breast. Not bad sculpture.   L. of face 0·17.   Cf. on no. 113.   [*]

72 (AP.).   **Head of a youth.**   Chandler, 62 (bad).   Nose and mailed bust new, all the rest so much worn as to be past recognition. Life size.   [*]

73 (AP.).   **Head of a youth.**   Chandler, 63.   A poor head. Head and neck only antique; nose new.   Small life size.   [*]

74 (AP.).   **Female head.**   Chandler, 64.   The hair, parted on the forehead, falls down in rich curls by the cheeks, and low down in the neck behind.   The whole is badly rubbed.   New: nose and draped bust.   Small life size.   [*]

75 (AP.).   **Female head.**   Chandler, 65.   A stout lady, well advanced in years, with wavy hair that is plaited in a round coil at the back.   Pupils and eyebrows expressed.   Much broken.   New: part of the hair, nose and upper lip, draped bust.   [*]

76 (AP.).   **Female head.**   Chandler, 105.   The hair has been adapted for the introduction of a veil, which we may suppose was new, and which is now missing; so is the nose.   Insignificant work. Below life size.   [*]

77 (AP.).   **Head of a girl.**   Chandler, 106.   The head shows a good design.   Missing now: the l. half of the back of the head; forehead and nose have been injured.   The hair is drawn back from the forehead and confined under a ribbon (not a plait); it is brushed sideways over the ears.   Over life size.   [*]

Neither in the University Galleries nor in the Ashmolean Museum have I observed the following busts belonging to the Pomfret Collection.

78 (AP.).   **Bust of Aphroditè.**   Chandler, 52.

79 (AP.).   **Bust of an elderly man,** with thin whiskers and no beard or mustaches.   Chandler, 57.   New.

80 (AP.).   **Bust of a bearded man,** with drapery on the l. shoulder.   Chandler, 61.

81 (AP.).   **Terminal bust,** youthful, with long curls.   Chandler, 91.

82 (AP.).   **Bust of bearded old man,** with bald head. Chandler, 96.

RELIEFS, &c.

We will take first those reliefs which are of undoubted **Greek** origin.

83 (Al'.), **Greek measure.** Chandler, 166. *Annali dell' Inst.*, 1874, Pl. Q, p. 192 (Matz). In a framed field in the shape of a pediment, with corners truncated, is represented the upper part of the body of a youth down to the muscles of the breast, both arms and hands, which are stretched out to the utmost, and the head turning to the r., so that the spectator sees the profile. The form of the head is high; the hair is little more than blocked out and looks something like a cap; the lower part of the face is disproportionately heavy, especially the high chin; a smile may still be seen on the mouth; the eye (much rubbed) seems to have been originally shaped as though it were seen in full face; finally the decided though not hard expression of the muscular body, and the excellent and skilful treatment of the low relief—all this shows us that our relief, as Matz first recognised, belongs to the 5th century B.C., possibly to the first half of it. The representation is completed by the relief of a l. foot, seen from the sole, over the r. upper arm. Two holes in the upper edge show that this relief slab must once have been fastened somewhere, presumably in some public place where the relief may have served as a figured standard measure, a conjecture which has been made already long ago, probably by Lord Arundel's learned friends (cf. Vertue, p. 55). We may therefore suppose with certainty that the measure of the foot and of the fathom (ὀργυιά) must be exact. According to my measurements, which, considering the importance of the matter, I am sorry not to have taken with still greater exactness, the length of the foot is 0·295, that of the fathom 2·06 (according to Conze, 2·07); the latter consequently contains exactly 7 such feet (= 2·065). Now it is known that a fathom was generally reckoned equal to 6 feet. Moreover, our foot is considerably shorter than the foot-measures which were most in use in Greece (the Attic foot being 0·308, the Samian 0·315, the larger Olympian foot 0·321, the Philetaerian 0·35). On the contrary, our foot shows a striking similarity with the Roman foot of 0·296, the direct application of which however is excluded by the epoch of our monument. The double problem thus stated has been acutely solved by Fr. Hultsch, who first (*Arch. Zeit.*, 1879, pp. 177 ff.) recognised in the foot of our marble a *modulus* used by architects. He has since (*Arch. Zeit.*, 1880, pp. 91 ff., *Heraion und Artemision*, Berlin, 1881, pp. 21 ff.) pointed out that the recent excavations of

Olympia have brought to light as the fundamental measure of most of the Olympian buildings a "smaller Olympian foot" of 0·298 (cf. Dörpfeld in *Die Ausgrabungen von Olympia*, III. pp. 26, 28 f.). This foot, which is evidently identical with the foot of the Oxford relief, is equal to two-thirds of the smaller Egyptian ell, which stands to the larger or royal Egyptian ell in the proportion of 6 to 7; thus 7 of our feet = 4 royal ells, *i.e.* one fathom, while the latter measure contains also 6 larger feet. The chief interest of our relief lies in the fact that it unites the fathom (which is the foundation of nearly all antique foot measures) but slightly reduced (2·06 instead of originally 2·10) with the smaller foot of 0·295 (similarly reduced from the original 0·30). These two measures were already used together in architecture in very early times; the dimensions of the most ancient of all the Olympian temples, the Heraion, for instance, are based on a foot of 0·298 and a fathom of 2·084. The striking coincidence of our foot with the later Roman foot is thus explained : the Romans did not invent a new foot but merely adopted a measure long used by the Greek architects. Unfortunately we know nothing of the origin of our relief. We see by the marble that it certainly does not come from Attica ; more likely from Asia Minor. (Mr Fisher, curator of the University Galleries, called my attention to the fact that, measuring only from the root of the fingers, or with arms and hands outstretched but with the fingers closed, "from palm to palm," the exact length obtained is equal to six smaller feet, 6 × 0·295 = 1·77 m.) The relief is a good deal abraded and also broken by the r. end, but the piece that is broken off has been preserved. Total length 2·10. H. 0·62. [*C*]

84.   Fragment of a frieze.   Chandler, 149 (without style and inaccurate). The relief is finished off above with a roundish moulding (κυμάτιον), below by a square border ; it is broken on the l. end and terminated on the r. by a perpendicular joint. To the l. lies a dead man, nude, on the ground, and over him a youth, in chiton and chlamys, with high boots and a " Phrygian " cap, gallops l. on his prancing charger. Then follows a nude youth, who has sunk on his knees ; another youth standing behind him in flowing chlamys, is seizing violently with both hands the upraised r. arm and the head of his adversary, and is pushing his r. knee forcibly into his back, while the adversary is trying with his l. hand to free himself from the l. hand of his assailant. No arms are visible in either of these groups. Further to the r. a youth in a chlamys is pressing with drawn sword upon a horseman, and he appears to be seizing his adversary's prancing steed by the head; the horseman, apparelled in chiton and chlamys, cap and boots, is bending far forwards to defend himself, so that a great portion of the upper part of his body is hidden by the neck of his horse. The subject is evidently a fight between Asiatics (in caps), some of whom are mounted, and Greeks. The composition is lively and is divided into smaller groups, reminding us of the frieze from the Athenian temple of Athenè-Nikè, which is only a little higher in relief. The style is more like that of the still lower reliefs of the frieze of the Lysikrates monument, but it is harder, less interesting, and more affected. Relief not flat but rounded; marble yellowish, certainly not Attic. The fragment may belong to the fourth, possibly the third century B.C. H. 0·41. L. 1·21. [*C.I.IV]

85 (Burgon). **Fragment of a relief.** Above, the terminal portion of a skirmish; a nude man lying on the ground, and the lower part of a man in a chiton pressing him hard; between them the lower edge of a large shield, belonging possibly to a defender of the fallen hero. Lower is a moulding (*kymation*), and below that again faint remains of a Greek inscription in two lines; the first line appears to end with the letters NA, and the second with Λ (Roehl, *Schedae epigraph.*, Berlin, 1876, p. 4, no. 8). The palaeographical character suggests a good period. H. 0·42. L. 0·28. [*]

85 (A.P.). **Kybelè.** Chandler, 114. Square relief, simply framed. The field is very deeply chiselled out, and on it is represented a long bench, on which sits a veiled female figure, in full face, with a lion (described by Huebner, *Arch. Anz.*, 1866, p. 303, as a sucking child) right across her lap. One end of her cloak lies in broad smooth folds across her body and falls sideways on the bench. The feet rest on a footstool. It is a very rough variation of the Attic reliefs of Kybelè (nos. 131, 132, 159). H. 0·51. L. 0·53. [*C]

87 (A.P.). **Votive seat of Archidamos.** Chandler, II. 13. Marble arm-chair with high back, on the inside of which at the top is the inscription: ὁ ἱερεὺς Ἀρχίδαμος | Φιλαιέτου | Ἴσιδι | Ὀσίριδι Ἀνούβιδι | χαριστήριον (*C. I. Gr.*, 6841). Right and left in relief is a griffin, or winged lion walking, of which the front part is missing. Grey marble. H. 0·76. [*]

88 (A.P.). **Right half of an Attic votive relief.** Chandler, 116. The pillar to the r., and the architrave with the remains of tiles on the top, are preserved. To the l. moves a procession of seven grown-up figures and two children, the men in cloaks, the women and a girl in chitons and cloaks. Quite in advance is a boy in an apron, who is bringing the flat basket (κανοῦν) for the sacrifice.

M. C.   36

Then follow a female figure, a man, a female figure, all with their r. hands upraised in adoration; beside the last female figure is a girl, and further on three female figures, all holding their r. hands concealed in their cloaks before their breasts. A female attendant with a very large box (κιβωτός) on her head closes the procession. The heads are nearly all knocked off. Cf. no. 203. Execution rather superficial, probably of the fourth century. Pentelic marble. H. 0·69. L. 0·62. [*CH*]

89 (A.P.). **Greek sepulchral relief.** Chandler, 145. Only the lower part preserved. A beardless man, in chiton and cloak, with his r. hand before his breast, holding a roll in his lowered l. hand, is standing by a female figure. She wears a chiton and cloak; the back of her head is veiled, she is raising her r. hand to her face. Their figures are nearly full face, rather turned away from each other, while their faces are turned towards each other in a life-like manner. This peculiar motive, which is almost a little coquettish, often recurs on sepulchral monuments from Smyrna (cf. below, no. 205. Lowther, no. 19. Rokeby, no. 3), and our relief also will have come from that locality. Below, to the l., is a servant in a short chiton, on either side of the female figure a girl in a chiton, the first two with their legs crossed, the latter carrying some object in the hand; all these figures are of much smaller proportions. In the background is a shelf and on it three objects, either boxes, or caskets (not given in Chandler). The head of the man has been re-set but is probably antique; the head and l. forearm of the female figure are missing now, but they have at one time been restored. Much abraded. H. 0·61. L. 0·61. [*]

90 (A.P.). **Greek sepulchral relief.** Chandler, 144. Again only the lower part is preserved. A female figure stands in full face, in long chiton and fine cloak, which serves her also as a veil; her r. arm lies across her body and she supports her l. elbow on her r. hand. The l. hand holds a part of the border of her cloak very gracefully in front of her l. shoulder. Head somewhat bent. On either side of her stands a high pillar; on the one to the l. is a trunk with an arched lid, on the one to the r. a round cista. Against each pillar leans a diminutive female attendant; the one to the l. holding a fan made of leaves and an alabastron (?), the one to the r. a round mirror, the cover of which she is folding up. Heads of both attendants missing. The relief is a good deal abraded; it comes presumably from Smyrna or the neighbourhood. H. 0·80. L. 0·46. [*CH*]

91 (A.P.). **Sepulchral relief of Menelaos.** Chandler, n. 66.

Above is an oblong field hollowed out and enclosed by two pillars; within this field are three busts in very high relief. To the l. is a beardless man in chiton and cloak; to the r. a female figure veiled and quite concealed by her drapery; between them a nude boy, or youth, who wears a fillet falling down on his shoulders. The inscription below refers to him: Μερέλας Μερελάου χαῖρε (*C. I. Gr.*, 6962), but of the first word only traces are now visible. Below is a square field with a relief that is not so high. On a bed, beside which is a three-legged table with food on it, lies the father Menelaos, full dressed, holding in his l. hand a cup and in his r. some round object. He lays his r. hand on the neck of his half grown son Menelaos, who forms the central figure of the relief. He is draped in a cloak and leaning against his father's couch. To the l. sits the mother, veiled, her r. hand raised and laid on her cloak; near her stands a little girl in chiton and cloak. There is a very similar sepulchral monument in the Louvre (Clarac, II. 157, 291). Greyish-yellow marble. The style is not delicate. H. 0·88. L. 0·67. [*C*]

92 (AP.). **Sepulchral relief.** Chandler, 135. Three men, draped, are resting on one couch; the two to the r. have no heads, the one to the l. has had his head re-set (antique?). The two to the r. hold each a goblet with handles, the one to the l. is pointing to a youth who stands by him, in full face, leaning against the couch. This youth wears a chiton and a cloak which falls in fairly ample folds. Evidently this one to the l. is the dead man (cf. no. 91). Beside him, by the couch, stands a three-legged table with a vessel on it and two cakes in the form of pyramids. On either side sits a veiled female figure, in a cushioned chair, with her feet on a footstool; their faces are turned towards the main scene and their r. hands are raised towards their faces. Beside the lady on the r. is a diminutive female attendant with a box. At the top of the field is a coiled snake; in the r. hand top corner is in a special frame a horse's head, the badge of rank of the dead man as ἱππεύς. The relief is treated somewhat hardly and is simply framed. From its style it seems to have come from Asia Minor or the Greek Islands. H. 0·48. L. 0·63. [*]

93 (Burgon). **Fragment of a sepulchral relief** from the Island of Tenos. A bearded (?) man, with a small modius on his head, lies on the bed pouring a libation out of a cup; before him is a table (quite rubbed away) and a mixing vessel (κρατήρ). To the l., remains of a seated female figure, unveiled, with a small box in her l. hand. In the background between the two figures a snake rears

itself up. Tolerably low relief. Much abraded. Dark grey marble.
H. 0·23. L. 0·28. [*]

94 (Burgon). High stele, rounded at the top in the shape of a
palmetto ornament, which however is not expressed, either in sculpture, or, apparently, in colours. The only ornament of the stele is
the representation of a full-bodied lekythos in round relief. Marble
unrecognisable; the work looks Attic. H. 0·75. L. 0·26. [*]

95 (Burgon). **Sepulchral lekythos.** Fluted. Neck, handle
and foot broken off. H. 0·36. [*]

96—104 (AP.). Nine **round altars or pedestals,** of marble,
such as are found particularly at Rheneia, the island which served as
a necropolis to the neighbouring island of Delos; they are all provided at the top with a square hole, which shows that a statue, or
some other object, must have stood on them. There is no doubt
of their being connected with sepulchres (cf. no. 209).

96. Chandler, 157. Three heads of oxen support a garland ornamented with ribbons; on the front side we see instead of the bull's
head, a youth, in chiton and cloak. r. arm before breast, l. arm
lowered; beside him a diminutive attendant in a chiton with his
legs crossed. H. 0·66. [*]

97—101. Chandler, 158. Four heads of oxen, adorned with
fillets, wear garlands; in each entwining of the garlands is a cup
(*patera*). H. 0·88; 0·79; 0·77; 0·74; 0·71. [*]

102. The same; but the cups are missing. H. 0·75. [*]

103. The same; with two shields instead of cups. H.
0·82. [*]

104. Four heads of oxen, with only rich garlands of flowers and
grapes. H. 0·66. [*]

105 (AP.). **Fragment of a Greek sarcophagus.** Chandler,
118. It appears to be the l. end of the front, injured below and on
both ends, but having on the top a rich, sculptured moulding. On
a mass of rock sits facing r. a bearded chieftain, of somewhat barbaric appearance, with a fillet in his long hair; he wears a chiton
girdled twice and a long cloak. Behind him stands a bearded companion (δορυφόρος), in chiton, chlamys and Phrygian cap, his l. hand
holding the spear, in his lowered r. hand the sword. On the other
side of the chief stands a youth with long curls, perhaps his son,
draped in the same way as the companion in arms, but without
weapons, his hands being laid one over the other; he is looking
back to the warrior. It is uncertain whether these three wear hose;
the feet of them all are broken off. The chief is stretching out one

hand towards a dish laden with fruit that is held with both her arms
by a young girl in a girdled chiton (face destroyed). Over her head
we see to the r. a nude arm, holding out a wreath or branch to the
chief; the arm very likely belongs to a Victory, and perhaps the dish
full of fruit refers to a sacrificial offering after a victory which may
have come next (cf. for example Guattani, *Monum. Ined.*, 1784,
Giugno, Pl. 2). Only here of course the victor is not a Roman
general, as we see on the specimen I have cited and other sarcophagi ; but a barbarian prince, probably from the realm of mythology, for whom however I cannot find a name. H. 0·76. L. 0·78.
[*C.M*]

106 (AP.). **Fragment of a Greek sarcophagus.** Chandler,
120. Pretty group of two boys. One of them staggering; the other,
quite nude, clasps him in his arms from behind to support him.
The former is partly covered with a little cloak ; he lays his l. hand
on the arm of his helpful companion ; his r. he holds near his head.
The upper half is broken, but I think it belongs to the rest ; according to Matz it would be probably new. Very high relief.
Above and on both sides the piece is incomplete. H. 0·76. L. 0·46.
Cf. no. 107. [*M*]

107 (AP.). **Fragment of a Greek sarcophagus.** Chandler,
121. Similar scene. One boy, with a nebris, very tipsy, is falling
backwards insensible. The second, nude, with long curly hair, is
clasping him in his arms. The movement of the group is to the r.,
where a r. hand with a torch is visible. The fragment, also incomplete
above, and both to the r. and the l., is not in such high relief as no.
106, and looking at the marble, execution, and size is not a part of
the same sarcophagus. For similar scenes on sarcophagi of Greek
origin cf. Stephani, *Der ausruhende Herakles*, pp. 95 ff. Matz, *Arch.
Zeit.*, 1872, p. 16. H. 0·69. L. 0·64. [*M*]

108 (AP.). **Fragment of a Greek sarcophagus.** Chandler,
133. From a similar scene. A drunken boy, with a fillet round
his head, on which he lays his r. hand, is stumbling along with
his l. (not r.) foot advanced, his drapery fluttering round him. His
body is falling backwards and is held by a companion whose l. hand
and forearm, with which he supports him, alone is preserved. To
the l., a boy is stepping forward, with a pedum in his l. arm and his
r. hand on his head. He is looking back at his companions. More
superficially treated than the two foregoing fragments; relief tolerably
low and badly injured ; incomplete on both sides. H. 0·71. L. 0·32.
[*M*]

It may be asserted with tolerable certainty that the following reliefs are all of **Italian** origin.

109 (AP.). **Fragment from an oval Bacchic sarcophagus.** Chandler, 119. On a square altar or pedestal lies the head of a goat; to the l. of it is visible the r. leg of a skipping Pan; over it a hand, with a pedum; further up still a tympanon and an arm. To the r. of the altar, in the middle of the fragment, a Maenad, only to a small extent covered by her fluttering cloak, is dancing in the most lively manner; in her l. hand she holds a long staff, probably a piece of a thyrsos. Further to the r. a man (Satyr?), with drapery over his r. shoulder and holding in his r. hand a large mask of Seilenos, with the mouth open, is dancing opposite to her; he has turned his head backwards so that only the flowing curls at the back of it are visible (Chandler's draughtsman mistook it for a badly-formed profile). Between the two dancers in the background is a bald-headed, bearded man, turning r., at his feet an altar with a flame. Near the altar we see the remains of a draped figure lying on the ground, over which a lion's skin (?) hangs down, held by the dancing man or by a figure now lost. The fragment is broken below and on both sides. Coarse high relief. H. 0·70. [*M]

110 (AP.). **Fragment of a Bacchic sarcophagus.** Chandler, 126. Pricaeus, *Notae in Apuleii Apologiam*, p. 47. To the r. we see the back of a woman almost entirely nude. A stout, strong man has lifted her drapery almost to her shoulders, while his r. arm is in a position as if he had raised it to strike her. His only drapery is an apron round his loins; near his r. hip is the piece of a flat staff which, however, he cannot have held. The heads are missing. The relief is very roughly executed and is badly injured; broken above, and on both ends. It is easily understood how Price came to explain that the subject is the chastisement of a female slave who has run away, or committed some other fault, the gesture of the man being too violent for the simple inspection of a slave whom he may be going to buy; Chandler also thought of *genus aliquod supplicii*. I conjecture however that rather the plump Seilenos is intended, who in exuberant sportiveness has uncovered a dancing Maenad (cf. Müller-Wieseler, II. 40, 473; 48, 601, and for the uncovering of the Maenad *Mus. Pio-Clem.*, IV. Pl. 29). The staff would belong to a figure that has been lost. There is something humorous in the fact that this relief should have been among the first published from all those in the Arundel Collection (in 1635). H. 0·55. L. 0·39. [*]

111 (AP.). **Cover of a sarcophagus with Trojan scenes.**

Chandler, 147 (very bad). Heydemann, *Iliupersis*, Pl. 2, 3, p. 31 (cf. Conze, *Göttinger gel. Anz.*, 1867, p. 599). Chandler's publication of this relief, which is by no means exact, has called forth many wrong explanations of it. The long frieze is divided into three scenes. I. From the arched gateway of the town of Troy, on the extreme l., comes the wooden horse, standing on a base provided with wheels; on its side hangs a shield, and on its head is a helmet-like head-piece, as though it had been deemed necessary to make the warlike engine itself resemble a warrior, or to symbolize the nature of its contents. Four Trojans, wearing chitons with sleeves, hose and caps, are occupied about the horse; one stands beside him, looking back at the gate and signing to those of his companions who stand outside it; the three others are drawing the horse forward with a cord; one of them is evidently exerting himself with great pains to set the horse in motion. (Cf. the Berlin fragment of a similar sarcophagus cover in Heydemann, Pl. 3, 2.) Before the Trojan goes a woman in cloak and chiton, with a branch in her l. arm, greatly excited (her upraised r. arm and her head are missing; no doubt it is Kassandra, the prophetess of ill-luck, who in vain warns her countrymen (cf. the so-called *tabula Iliaca*, in Jahn's *Griech. Bilderchroniken*, Pl. A*, p. 32).—II. The massacre of the Trojans as they are feasting follows the taking of the town (for the feast cf. Proklos' extracts from the poems of Lesches and Arktinos, also for the connecting of both scenes Brunn, *Rilievi delle urne etrusche*, 1. Pl. 68, 2). On rocky ground lie three Trojans in Phrygian dress, the middle one youthful, the two others bearded; each has a drinking vessel. To their l. stands a bearded Trojan, putting his hand to his head and showing that he is frightened; behind the first of the recumbent carousers stands another Trojan (upper part of his body destroyed); behind the next is a Greek with his sword uplifted (chief part destroyed); into the neck of the third a Greek warrior in a helmet and fluttering chlamys is thrusting his sword. (Older interpretations considered this to be either the sacrifice offered by Achilleus for Patroklos, or the murder of Priamos at the altar.)—III. The fall of Troy was the consequence of the death of Hektor: *ademptus Hector Tradidit fessis leviora tolli Pergama Grais* (Hor., *Od.*, II. 4, 10). To the r. Pelides' chariot drawn by a pair of horses and guided by a fully armed warrior (Achilleus? Automedon?) gallops fast, dragging Hektor's corpse, beyond which stands a warrior (Achilleus?), also in breastplate and chlamys, boots, helmet, shield and spear. Under the horses two Trojans lie on the ground; beside them two Greeks are visible, one

nude, with helmet and lance.—On each corner is a youthful head
with long curls and a Phrygian cap.—Very rough sculpture, but without any restorations. H. 0·28. L. 1·12. [*CM]

112 (AP.). **Amazonomachia.** Chandler, 148. A horseman
in corselet, with cloak and helmet, whose horse has been overthrown
and whose shield lies on the ground, is seizing an Amazon, who
is attacking him, by the head, and holding his sword ready in his r.
hand. The Amazon wears a short chiton, partly loose, high boots,
a helmet, and on the l. arm a small shield (*pelta*), and wields the
sword with her r. hand. This very high relief is broken in several
pieces and seems to have been much restored; particularly suspicious
is the piece with the upper part of the horseman's body, and the head
of the Amazon, whose r. arm the restorer has quite omitted. Rough
and unskilful; perhaps the side of a sarcophagus. H. 0·58. L. 0·72.
[*M]

113 (AP.). **Sarcophagus** called "Germanicus's Tomb."
Chandler, 150. There is an older drawing from the Dal Pozzo collection in Mr Franks' possession in London. FRONT. In the centre are
two Cupids holding a large round shield with a Medusa's head on it,
and below them lie two four-footed animals (heads missing). To the
r. a Cupid hurries away, putting a colossal helmet on his head; opposite him another Cupid is trying to lift a breastplate that stands on
the ground; further still to the r. a third is hurrying off with a greave.
To the l. of the central group two Cupids are trying to lift up a lance
(greater part of it missing); finally there is one with the greave of the
other leg. All the Cupids have wings, and all, except the second from
the left, wear the chlamys. Parts of their arms and legs, once
restored, are now missing.—L. SIDE. Two boys, one of whom has
wings, with short walking-sticks in their hands, carry on a yoke on
their shoulders a large breastplate.—R. SIDE. Two winged boys, in
chlamys, are making great efforts to lift up a long lance. H. 0·50.
L. 2·15. D. 0·61. The origin of the strange name of this sarcophagus is the fact that when it was in Arundel House a bust, supposed
to be of Germanicus, was placed on it (cf. Chandler, and Dallaway,
p. 256), probably that bust which Sir Thomas Roe had obtained
from Ankyra (Introd., App., p. 197); perhaps it is no. 71, or 72,
hardly Wilton, no. 123. The name thus arbitrarily given stuck to
the sarcophagus, and even after the bust no longer stood on it, in-
vested it with such peculiar glory that in Easton-Neston it was made
the centre piece of a large architectural erection, described in the following manner by G. Vertue (*Descr.*, p. 55): "At the end of the

terrace on the left hand of the house, joining to the garden wall, is
Germanicus's tomb; it is formed thus, viz. an alcove or arch is in
the middle, and upon a large oblong pedestal stands the Sarcophagus,
or tomb of Germanicus, which is long like a coffin, only strait and
square; it is of marble, and basso rilievos on the outside; upon the
tomb is set a round pedestal [Chandler 156?], and on that a marble
statue of Jupiter less than the life [no. 18]; on each side of this
pedestal are fine bustos of two women, and on each side of this arch
or alcove are doric pilasters, which support a pediment, in which
there is in basso relievo [no. 83] the figure of a man as big as the life
with his arms extended as if he was crucified, but no lower than
about his paps is seen, the cornice cutting him off as it were; and
this extension of his arms is called a grecian measure, and over his
right arm is a grecian foot; on the top of the pediment stands the god
Terminus [no. 55], and likewise on each side of this alcove are two
smaller niches, with two trunks of body in them [no. 49 &c.]. On
the outside of both these niches are dorick pilasters, which go up and
support the cornice, and at the top on each side two pedestals with
each a statue, very fine and perfect." [*M]

114 (AP.). **Oval sarcophagus.** Chandler, 151. FRONT. In
the centre two Cupids are carrying a medallion (*clipeus*) with the bust
of a Roman in the pallium, who has a roll in his l. hand; the head is
merely sketched. Below the medallion, two tragic masks; between
the feet of each of the Cupids lies a basket with flowers. To the l.
stands a Cupid with a basket (not a cornucopiae) on his r. hand, and
two geese (necks missing) in his l. hand. The corresponding Cupid
on the r. has lost his r. hand, and traces of two stumps only remain
of some long object that he held; in his l. hand he also has a basket.
All four Cupids are winged and wear the chlamys.—At either SIDE a
lion mangling a horse. Very bad work. H. 0·48. L. 1·56. D. 0·50.
[*M]

115 (AP.). **Child's sarcophagus.** Chandler, 152. FRONT.
In the centre field a Roman (child?) in the pallium, with a square
box lying near him on the ground, is standing before a curtain. On
either side an oblong field with twisted flutings. In each of the two
end fields stands a Cupid in a chlamys, having on one arm a staff and
holding up a garland in the other hand. The upper part of the body
of the Cupid on the r. is new.—On each SIDE a palm tree, near
which a Cupid, in a chlamys, is driving a hoop (*trochus*) with a stick.
H. 0·42. L. 1·24. D. 0·42. [*M]

116 (AP.). **Child's sarcophagus.** Chandler, 153. Only the

front is sculptured. In the centre a medallion with the bust of a
boy; below it two horns of plenty crossed. On either end twisted
fluting, in the corners ornamentation of vine-tendrils. Relief and
fluting very flat. According to Matz the sarcophagus is "perhaps
not Roman" (Christian? modern?). H. 0·30. L. 0·72. D. 0·34.
[*.M]

117 (AP.).   **Fragment of a relief**, perhaps of a sarcophagus.
Chandler, 122.   A female figure in girdled chiton and cloak, back of
her head veiled (head and upraised r. hand missing), holds in her l.
hand the handle of a sword (blade broken off). Beside her an altar
with a flame, in the background on a basis of freestone a round
temple with Tuscan pillars and Doric triglyphs. It may be a fragment from a representation of Iphigenia in Tauris, rather than of
Medea. The relief is tolerably high, but unfortunately much injured; it is however far better than the engraving would lead one to
imagine. H. 0·52. L. 0·42. [*.M]

118 (AP.).   **Relief**, perhaps the side of a sarcophagus.
Chandler, 123.   A shepherd, in a chiton (*exomis*), is standing with his
legs crossed, leaning on his staff. By his feet a sheep and a dog. To
the l. a tree, to the r. a rock with a tree and two more sheep. The
upper r. corner is new. Bad, flat sculpture. H. 0·62. L. 0·29. [*]

119 (AP.).   **Square cinerary urn**. Chandler, 155.   Ox-skulls
in the corners support garlands; in front a slender spray issues from
an ornamentation of vine-tendrils. On the tendrils sit two birds.
Pretty work. H. 0·45. L. 0·38. D. 0·38. [*]

120 (AP.).   **Relief representing a Nereid**. Chandler, 129.
A large sea-panther is swimming to the l., guided by a small boy who
has thrown the bridle round his own body and is gracefully pushing
against the withers of the animal with his feet. On the back of the
panther sits a Nereid, the upper part of her body nude; her cloak
covers her legs, and originally it fluttered in an arch over her head,
as we see by the way in which a corner of it is held in her r. hand,
which is supported on the body of the animal, and by another
fragment which is visible near her r. shoulder. The pose of the
Nereid, particularly the turn of her head, is very graceful; the whole
subject is skilfully and well executed in very high relief. Matz considered the whole relief to be new, but I think he was wrong. The
upper l. corner is missing now. H. to the crown of the Nereid's
head 0·50. L. 0·85. [*.M]

121 (AP.).   **Fragment of a relief**. Chandler, 104.   A
female head, veiled, rises from the field in very high relief; it is of

late but not bad sculpture; a great many rivets have been left between the curls, which are deeply undercut with the drill. Life size. [*]

122 (AP.). **Masks.** Chandler, 134. A perfect mask, half of one, a piece of one; all three but roughly sketched. Eyes and mouth are hollowed out deeply, but not perforated. H. 0·53. L. 0·72. H. of relief 0·18. [*]

123, 124 (AP.). **Two reliefs**, perhaps the fronts of capitals of pilasters. In the corners a dog's head with large ears, and a lion's head wearing garlands of oak-leaves, over them a horse's head looks out in full face. Both specimens are like one another, only the heads in corners are transposed, as is natural in counterparts. High relief, in perfect preservation; coarse marble. H. 0·26. L. 1·04. [*]

Besides these reliefs are to be seen here :

125, 126. Two Assyrian reliefs,

and the two following specimens deposited as the property of Mr Ruskin :

127. Cyprian sepulchral stele, shaped at the top like a pediment. Below, a low relief-field (h. 0·33, l. 0·53): a bearded man, completely draped, recumbent, his head supported by his l. hand; at his feet stands a diminutive attendant in a short chiton. Below again is a higher relief-field (h. 1·15, l. 0·53): a female figure, nearly life size, is sitting to the r. in a chair; she is veiled; her r. hand lies in her lap, her l. hand raised to her face; although the body is placed in profile, the feet are placed as though it were in full face. This stele is highly interesting because it combines the standard types of two different periods side by side, and so illustrates for us the eclecticism of the Cyprian plastic art; the lower relief has been suggested by similar Attic works of the best period (cf. Liverpool, no. 8), the upper one by the most favourite subject for sepulchral monuments of the later periods of the art in Asia Minor and the Islands. Native limestone. H. 1·88. L. 0·66. [*]

128. Cyprian monument. Two lions crouching on one pedestal, their backs turned to each other. L. abt. 1·40. [*]

The University Galleries also possess the following specimens.

129. A painting from Pompeii. *Museo Borbonico,* IX. Pl. 3. Zahn, *Ornamente und Gemälde aus Pompeji,* II. Pl. 62. A female figure in a red chiton, with a white cloak over it, is sitting with her legs crossed, her chin supported on her l. hand. In front of her stands Eros, opening a small box, which he holds before his breast.

From the so-called *Casa di Meleagro*. Cf. Helbig, *Wandgemälde*, no. 1430. Presented by Chambers Hall, Esq. [*]

A collection of **terra cottas**, **vases**, and **bronzes** has been lately purchased from Mr Castellani for the Museum.

I have not paid attention to the following :

130 (AP.). **Corinthian column.** Chandler, 163, 164. The column is broken in two pieces; h. with the pedestal and without the capital 5·55, the square area measure of the pedestal is 0·78, the diameter of the column is, at the base, 0·56, at the top, 0·50. The capital does not belong to it; it is formed of a double row of acanthus leaves, and above them some reed-like foliage, without volutes ; its lower diameter is 0·52, h. 0·67. Its origin in Delphi is, I am afraid, very doubtful ; perhaps Delphi is a mistake for Delos. [*C*]

THE SCHOOLS.

The majority of the inscribed marbles, which were presented by Henry Howard from the Arundel Collection (AH.), are let into the walls of one of the rooms below the Bodleian Library. Some of them are placed so high that it is very difficult to examine them closely. With these are placed a considerable number of other marbles, presents from Selden and Wheler. I only mention here those specimens which have figure ornaments.

131 (Wheler). **Kybelē.** Chandler, 113. Wheler, *Journey*, p. 405, "Ceres." Within the little temple (ναΐσκος, *aedicula*) sits Kybelē, clothed in chiton and cloak ; her hair falls down in long plaits ; on her head is a kalathos. A lion crouches in her lap; in her l. arm she holds the large tympanon, in her r. hand a cup. Pentelic marble. H. 0·31. L. 0·18. [*C*]

132 (Wheler). **Kybelē.** Chandler, 115. Similar, but incomplete above. The goddess holds the cup in her r. hand and below it crouches the lion ; in the l. arm are the remains of the tympanon. L. hand, head, and pediment missing. Very superficial sculpture. Pentelic marble. H. 0·20. L. 0·15. [*]

133 (Wheler). **Relief with Nymphs.** Chandler, 124. The r. half is preserved. The relief is bordered on the top and on the right by the rocky margin of a grotto, on which a piece of an animal, presumably of a goat, is visible. Two Nymphs in chitons, holding out their hands to each other, and dancing to the l., where one may see the remains of the drapery of a third. Probably

Hermes was the conductor of the Nymphs to the god Pan, cf.
Brocklesby, no. 110. Pentelic marble. H. 0·30. L. 0·15. [*]

134 (Wheler). **Selenè ?** Chandler, 103. Round medallion
with a female head, seen full face; the hair is entwined with a
fillet on the head, and flows down in rich curls on either side. The
eyes are hollowed out. A chiton without sleeves is buttoned on both
shoulders, below it a border is visible, also going round the shoulders,
which might possibly have been intended as a half-moon. Late
sculpture, somewhat coarse. Apparently Pentelic marble. H. 0·28.
L. 0·27. [*]

135 (Ait.). **Votive Relief to Herakles.** Chandler, II. 57.
Prideaux, no. 15. Maittaire, no. 36. Montfaucon, *Antiq. Expl.*,
Suppl., I. Pl. 54, 2. Two antae bearing an architrave flank the
relief field; the l. corner of the architrave is broken off. The rocky
ground is covered with the lion's skin and Herakles reclines on
it, supporting himself on his l. arm (forearm missing); his r. arm
(hand missing) rests on his thigh. To the l. a tree on which the bow
and quiver hang and against which the club leans. On the archi-
trave is written: [κοσμ]ητεύοντος Στα(τίου) Σεραπίωνος Χολλείδου, |
[ἀντι]κοσμητεύοντος Κασί(ου) Ἀπολλωνίου Στειριέως, | [σω]φρονιστὴς
Ἀθήναιος Σπεύδοντος Ἐλευσείνιος | [το]ῖς ἐφήβοις τὸν Ἡρακλέα ἀπὸ
τῆς ἐν Ἐλευσῖνι νείκης. Below the relief: παιδοτριβοῦντος Ἀβα-
σκάιτου | τοῦ Εὐμόλπου Κηφεισιέως ἔτος κγ' (*C. I. Gr.*, 271. *C. I. Att.*,
III. 119). It belongs to the middle of the second century A.D. Pentelic marble. H. 0·67. L. 0·78. [*C]

136 (Selden). **Bull hunt** (*Taurokathapsia*). Chandler, II. 58.
Prideaux, no. 130. Maittaire, no. 37. The movement is from r. to
l. The foremost rider gallops forward with his r. hand upraised;
he is followed by a second, who as he sits on his horse is seizing
a bull by the horns; then comes a third whose horse is prancing
very high; the fourth has thrown a bull down on his back and
seizing his horns is pressing his head against the ground; his
horse stands quietly beside him. The fifth again is sitting on his
horse and seizing a bull by the horns, but his movements are so
violent that it would appear as if he meant to throw himself on
the bull's back. All the riders have broad cloths wound several
times round their bodies after the manner of chariot drivers in the
circus, or of gladiators. Below is the inscription : Ταυροκαθαψίων
ἡμέρα β' (*C. I. Gr.*, 3212). The whole incident is explained by
Suetonius, *Claudius* ch. 21, *Thessalos equites, qui feros tauros per
spatia circi agunt insiliuntque defessos et ad terram cornibus trahunt*

(cf. Plin., 8, 182). We have ample testimony especially from Asia Minor as to the spectacle of the Ταυροκαθάψια (cf. Prideaux, and Hermann, *Gottesdienstl. Alterthümer*, 64, 34) ; our relief comes from Smyrna. Rough work. H. 0·49. L. 1·58. [*C*]

137 (Selden). **Relief.** Chandler, 127. Prideaux, no. 44. Maittaire, no. 38. The relief has three divisions, one over the other. UPPER STRIP. One man is leading by a long cord, which is wound round their necks, two other men, nude except for a narrow apron. The leader is very completely draped ; he has a jerkin with sleeves and over that a very broad cloth round his body, a cap falling down on to the back of his neck, and hose of a reticulated pattern ; he is most like certain classes of gladiators (*Samnites, Thraces*).— MIDDLE STRIP. Almost exactly the same scene.—LOWER STRIP. A lion (only in part preserved) is strangling a bull ; close by two rams are butting each other. As the engravings here show a bull, a ram, and a pig, *suovetaurilia* have been suggested ; but it is more probable that some reference is intended in this very remarkable relief to circus games. Coarse, rough sculpture. H. 0·99. L. 0·59. Supposed to be from Smyrna. [*C*]

138 (Wheler). **Fragment of the Attic sepulchral relief of Glauketes.** Chandler, II. 62. A bearded man, with a sad expression, in a cloak, supporting his head in his r. hand, leans against the pillar which finishes off the relief on the r. ; only the upper part of his body, down to the stomach, preserved. In front of him are the remains of a second figure, apparently the bust and raised l. forearm of a boy. The r. half of the pediment is preserved ; on the architrave is written Γλαυκέτης (*C. I. Gr.*, 929). Fragment of a large and handsome stele of the fourth century, in high relief. Much abraded. Pentelic marble. H. 0·65. L. 0·45. [*C*]

139 (Wheler). **Fragment of an Attic sepulchral relief.** Chandler, 136. A bearded man lying on a couch, his body and legs covered by his cloak, raising his r. arm a little; in his l. hand he holds a cup. Missing : r. hand, legs, and the rest of the relief. Good low relief of the fourth century. Pentelic marble. H. 0·27. L. 0·18. [*]

140 (Wheler). **Attic sepulchral stele of Philodemos.** Chandler, II. 63. A youth, Philodemos, in a chiton, girded very low down, the chlamys on his l. shoulder, holding his horse by the bridle with his l. hand. He gives his r. hand to a lady, Lysimachè, completely draped, who is putting her hand to her cheek. Missing : the feet of the figures and all the lower part of the stele. Low relief, not very delicately executed. Over it is the inscription in good characters [Φ]ιλόδημος Σοφίλου (the Λ, not Ν, is added over the Ο) | Χολλείδης, and then after an interval have been but slightly scratched in the lines below, which are evidently of later date, Λυσιμάχη Τιμογείτονος (written by mistake for Τιμαγείτονος) | Φρεαρρίου (*C. I. Gr.*, 800, inaccurate). Over that a moulding and then the remains of a Siren, which formed the conclusion of the upper end of the sepulchral monument (cf. Brocklesby, no. 40. Wilton, no. 109). The monument is certainly Attic, of the fourth century B.C., but it is remarkable that it is not of Pentelic but of some grey marble; it may therefore come perhaps from a place outside Attica, where Athenians had settled and introduced Attic art. H. 0·67. L. 0·38. [*C*]

141 (Wheler). **Attic sepulchral stele of Diodora.** Chandler, II. 93. The stele is now finished off at the top with a straight moulding, but above this may be observed traces of a top ornament (ἐπίθεμα, ἀνθέμιον). Below is the inscription Διοδώρα | Νικηφόρου Ἀντιόχισσα (*C. I. Gr.*, 825), perhaps of the second, or the first century B.C. Below, two large rosettes; under them a square relief. A lady, completely draped and veiled, with a small napkin in her lowered l. hand, is offering her r. hand to a beardless man in chiton and cloak. The relief is coarser than those of the common Attic stelae of the same composition. Pentelic marble. H. 0·75. L. 0·44. [*C*]

142 (AH.). **Greek sepulchral relief.** Chandler, 140. Prideaux, no. 76 (restored). Maittaire, no. 143. Montfaucon, *Ant. Expl.*, *Suppl.*, v. Pl. 8, 2. A man, fully draped (head missing), is lying on a couch holding a cup in his l. hand, his r. hand is laid on his knee. Before the couch stand two three-legged tables; on one is food, on the other vessels, and near this on the ground is a bucket; quite to the r. is a diminutive attendant in a short chiton, who holds in both hands in front of him a fan shaped like a leaf. At the foot of the bed sits a veiled female figure, her chin supported on her r. hand; her chair and footstool very high. Behind her is a diminutive female attendant with a similar fan in her l. hand. The upper part of the monument is missing. Grey marble; coarse style; considerably rubbed. Probably from Asia Minor or the Islands. H. 0·36. L. 0·51. [*C*]

143 (AH.). **Greek sepulchral relief.** Chandler, II. 67. Prideaux, no. 73. Maittaire, no. 142. Montfaucon, *Ant. Expl.*, *Suppl.*, v. Pl. 7, 2. The relief, incomplete below, is simply framed; on the upper edge is an inscription, difficult to read, of which I think I have deciphered ΝΙΚ·Σ·ΟΣ····ΟΣΟΦΑ···(*C. I. Gr.*, 6975, inaccurate). On a couch lies a man (his head battered), fully draped, holding in his l. hand a cup and with the r. hand helping himself to food from the table. Of the table only the top is left. On the border to the r. is an indistinct remnant. To the l. an attendant (only in part preserved) is holding up a cup towards which a snake is wriggling from above to drink out of it. In the background a wall, or a shelf, on which to the r. lies a helmet of unusual shape ; above, hangs a shield ; to the l. a horse's head is visible. Yellowish marble; late, coarse style ; very much effaced. H. 0·29. L. 0·35. [*C*]

144 (Wheler). **Attic sepulchral relief.** Chandler, 138. Wheler, *Journey*, p. 406. The relief is incomplete at the r. end. On a couch lies a bearded man (upper part of his body rubbed away) with a modius on his head and in his upraised r. hand a drinking-horn (ῥυτόν). On the foot-end of the couch sits a female figure fully draped, who holds a small box in her l. hand and stretches out her r. hand towards the table. From the l. worshippers are approaching bringing to the dead man, now translated among the heroes, their sacrifice ; a bearded man and a woman of larger scale, and a man and a woman of smaller scale, all making gestures of adoration; besides these comes a sacrificial servant with a pig and in his l. hand a basket (κανοῦν). In the upper corner to the l., on a slightly raised square surface, is a horse's head (cf. on no. 92). Low relief of insignificant work, very much injured. Grey marble. H. 0·18. L. 0·27. [*]

145 (Wheler). **Attic sepulchral relief.** Chandler, 137. An architrave is supported on two antae: it has seven tiles on the top. On a couch, provided with cushions and hung with tapestry, lies a bearded man with the modius on his head. His cloak leaves his breast and r. arm exposed. With his r. hand he raises the drinking-horn to pour wine into the cup in his l. hand. On the couch there also sits a female figure, fully draped, holding in her l. hand a small open box from which she seems to have taken frankincense which she is throwing on a low altar (θυμιατήριον), that stands on the table; beside it on the table are several kinds of food. To the l. stand a bearded man and a veiled female figure, also three boys enveloped in cloaks, all with their r. hands raised in adoration. Very good work, tolerably high bas-relief. Pentelic marble. H. 0·28. L. 0·41. [*]

146 (Wheler). **Attic sepulchral relief.** Chandler, 139. The architrave is supported by two antae, provided with remains of tiles on the top. On a couch lies a bearded man, exactly as in no. 145, only that there is no modius; in front of him a dish with food. The female figure sits on a chair, holding with both hands a fillet (more likely than a wreath). On the extreme r. stands a nude attendant, raising an ewer in his r. hand, near by a mixing bowl (κρατήρ) on a draped stand. To the l. stands a worshipper, bearded, in a cloak, raising his r. hand. Style like that of no. 145. Pentelic marble. H. 0·26. L. 0·36. [*]

147 (Selden). Sepulchral relief of the brothers Hikesios and Hermippos. Chandler, II. 71. Prideaux, no. 7. Maittaire, no. 40. Montfaucon, *Ant. Expl., Suppl.*, v. Pl. 4, 2. In the centre sits, facing r., an elderly lady (Metris) with a wrinkled face, veiled; she is looking sadly up at a youth (Hermippos) clothed in chiton, cloak and shoes, to whom she gives her r. hand. A second youth (Hikesios), in a cloak only, is standing behind the mother, his hands folded before his stomach. On either side a diminutive attendant in a short chiton; the one to the l. is looking round the youth, the one to the r. in a posture of grief, his legs crossed, his head laid on his l. hand. All the upper part of the stelè above the relief is missing now; below the relief, the inscription (*C. I. Gr*, 3333. Kaibel, *Epigr. Gr.*, no. 241),

Οἱ δισσοὶ συνόμαιμοι, ἰὼ ξένε, τοῖσδ᾽ ὑπὸ τύμβοι
ἄψαυστοι τέκνων κείμεθα κουριδίων·
Ἰκέσιος κἀγὼ νεαρὰν πληρούμενος ἥβαν
Ἕρμιππος κρυερὸν τόνδε ἔχομεν θάλαμον,
5 Ἄϊδαν ἐγκύρσαντες ἀλάμπετον· εὐγενέτη[ς] δὲ
Θεύδοτος οὐ στυγερὸν πένθος ἐφεῖδε πατήρ,
μήτηρ δὲ ἡ δύστηνος ὑδύρεται οἷά τις ἀκταῖς
ἀλκυονὶς γοεροῖς δάκρυσι μυρομένα,
Μητρὶς ἡ λιπάδελφος· [ἐ]ρημωθεῖσα δὲ τέκνων
10 [γ]ηραιῶμ βιοτᾶς τέρμα ἐνέπλησε κακ[ῶ]ν.

Line 5 E stands instead of Σ, line 9 Σ instead of E, line 10 Iᵗ instead of Γ, and O instead of Ω. Boeckh has emended κακῶν, and defended ἐφεῖδε, line 6, as signifying the same as ἐπεῖδε. The inscription belongs most likely to the first century B.C.; the palaeography is rather irregular (A and Λ, Π and Γᵗ, Ͱ, Σ, Ⱳ). As to the names, cf. the Smyrnaean inscription *C. I. Gr.*, 3141, l. 27—31. Our stelè also comes from Smyrna; Selden obtained it from a Mr Vernon in Essex. H. 0·94. L. 0·59. [*C]

M. C. 37

148 (AH.). **Sepulchral stele.** Chandler, 146. Prideaux, no. 67. Maittaire, no. 141. Montfaucon, *Ant. Expl., Suppl.*, v. Pl. 6. A youth in chiton and cloak, turning r., is giving his r. hand to a beardless man or youth who is sitting, also in chiton and cloak. He has shoes on his feet which rest on a footstool. Behind each of the two men stands a diminutive attendant in chiton; the one to the l. has his legs crossed and supports his head in his hand; the one to the r. folds his hands in front of his body. In the background is a shelf with four boxes. Above the relief the marble has been roughened, apparently to obliterate an inscription that may once have been there. Above, a pediment, with a rosette in the field; it is quite peculiar that the lower geison of the pediment should not be horizontal; it is arched instead, somewhat in the form of a low pediment, and not round as in Chandler's engraving. H. 0·79. L. 0·45. [*C*]

149 (Selden). **Sepulchral stele of Apollonia.** Chandler, ll. 90. Prideaux, no. 10. Maittaire, no. 34. Montfaucon, *Ant. Expl., Suppl.*, v. Pl. 5, 2. In the pediment is a shield. Below, between two rosettes, in a hollowed square a wreath surrounding the words ὁ δῆμος: below again, in larger characters, Ἀπολλωνίαν Κηφισοφῶντος (*C. I. Gr.*, 3219); thus is immortalised on the sepulchral monument the crowning of the dead lady by the community (cf. Lowther, no. 19. Wilton, no. 109). Apollonia, who is apparently a priestess, perhaps of Demeter, is clothed in chiton and cloak, the latter richly arranged; in her l. hand she holds a bunch of ears of corn and a wide fruit or flower (in form something like a broad whitewashing brush, according to Conze a poppy-head). She raises her r. hand and touches with it the top of a very long torch (cf. Lowther, no. 19) which is held in both hands by a diminutive female attendant. A second attendant, on the r. border, holds an alabastron in her l. hand, while with her r. hand she seems touching the cover of it. The monument is broken below. Probably from Smyrna. H. 0·97. L. 0·51. [*]

150 (Selden). **Sepulchral stele of Akesteime.** Chandler, ll. 92. Prideaux, no. 9. Maittaire, no. 32. Montfaucon, *Ant. Expl., Suppl.*, v. Pl. 5, 1. In the pediment is a shield. In the hollowed relief field sits the veiled Akesteime (head missing), supporting her head on her l. hand. She sits in a chair in full face and has a footstool. To the l. stands a female attendant with a box in her uplifted l. hand; to the r. a second attendant with a fan in the form of a leaf in her r. hand. Above her, in the field, is a serpent. High up in the corners, to the l. are two cymbals and to the r. a tambourine (τύμπανον); this might suggest a relation of the lady to the rites of Kybelè, or of the mother of the gods. Below, the inscription Ἀκεστείρη Δημαγόρου, γυνὴ δὲ Ἀρτεμιδώρου, χαῖρ[ε] (*C. I. Gr.*, 3262). Coarse style, mediocre work. Presumably from Smyrna, though the marble appears more yellowish than most of that used for Smyrnaean monuments. H. 0·44. L. 0·27. [*C*]

151 (Wheler). **Fragment of a sepulchral stelè.** Chandler, 125. A female figure standing, completely draped, of which the lower half is preserved : on either side is a diminutive female attendant in chiton, each holding a box with the lid open. The stelè tapers very much. It is hardly Attic; the marble and the style point rather to the Islands or Asia Minor. H. 0·21. L. 0·36. [*]

152 (Selden). **Sepulchral stelè of Nikephoros.** Chandler, II. 68. Prideaux, no. 8. Maittaire, no. 31. Montfaucon, *Ant. Expl., Suppl.*, v. Pl. 4, 1. The stelè tapers a great deal, the pediment is severely injured. The little Nikephoros, in ungirdled chiton and a small cloak, holds in his l. hand a little box (?); with the r. he offers a bunch of grapes to a bird, which is pecking at them from the ground. Below, the inscription Νικηφόρε χρηστὲ | χαῖρε (*C. I. Gr.*, 3360). Possibly from Smyrna, or from the Islands. Coarse style. H. 0·50. L. 0·26. [*C*]

153 (Wheler). **Upper part of a sepulchral stelè.** Chandler, II. 65. The pediment still has preserved the uppermost palmette as akroterion. On the frieze (ζωφόρος) is the skull of an ox, on either side a lion or panther, turning towards the centre. At each end is half a palmetto, as a top ornament. Below, an architrave in two divisions, and in the lower of the two the inscription Διόφαντε Διοφάντου χαῖρε (*C. I. Gr.*, 6915). Of the field for a relief which was below there remain only the Corinthian capitals of the two columns that framed it at either end; all the rest missing. The material is coarse limestone, the whole composition very unusual, certainly not Attic. H. 0·60. L. 0·57. [*]

154 (AH.). **Sepulchral relief of Diophantos.** Chandler, II. 64. Prideaux, no. 75. Maittaire, no. 33. Montfaucon, *Ant. Expl., Suppl.*, v. Pl. 8, 1. Square relief, simply framed. A nude youth, in full face, stands in a graceful posture : his lowered l. hand seems to hold a wreath, the r. hand holds his head. Beside him an attendant in a chiton. On the upper edge the inscription Διόφαντος Διοφάντου (*C. I. Gr.*, 6914; besides no. 153, cf. *C. I. Gr.*, 748 h, Διόφαντος Διοφάντου Πολληνεύς). The relief, belonging perhaps to the second century B.C., was once apparently good ; now it is effaced all over. Coarse, yellowish marble.   H. 0·24.   L. 0·29.   [*C]

155 (ΛΙΙ.).   **Sepulchral monument of Claudius Agathemerus and of Myrtalë.**   Chandler, II. 70.   Prideaux, no. 4.   Maittaire, no. 39.   Montfaucon, *Ant. Expl., Suppl.,* III. Pl. 9, 1.   Visconti, *Iconogr. grecque,* I. Pl. 33.   Two life-size busts side by side, to the l. an old lady with a high curled wig, veiled, to the r. a beardless man in a toga.   Below, the inscription (*C. I. Gr.,* 6197.   Kaibel, *Epigr. Gr.,* no. 554),

Κλαύδιος ἰητὴρ Ἀγαθήμερος ἐνθάδε κεῖμαι,
παντοίης δεδαὼς κραιπνὸν ἄκεσμα νόσου·
ξυνὸν τοῦτο δ' ἐμοὶ καὶ Μυρτάλῃ εἶσα συνεύνῳ
μνῆμα· μετ' εὐσεβέων δ' ἐσμὲν ἐν Ἠλυσίωι.

The style of the lady's hair suggests the second half of the first century A.D., and with that agrees well the palaeographic character of the inscription.   Hence the suggestion of Reinesius (*Synt. inscr.,* p. 610) is a very probable one, namely, that our physician is identical with the friend and fellow-pupil of the poet Persius, of whom it is said in the *vita Persii*: *usus est apud Cornutum duorum convictu doctissimorum et sanctissimorum virorum acriter tunc philosophantium, Claudii Agathemeri medici Lacedaemonii et Petroni Aristocratis Magnetis, quos unice miratus est et aemulatus, cum aequales essent, Cornuti minores et ipsi.*   The monument comes from Rome, where it was once in the possession of the sculptor Chr. Status, near the church of S. Andrea delle Fratte.   H. 0·83.   L. 0·89.   [*]

ASHMOLEAN MUSEUM.

The basement room of this Museum conceals a tolerably large collection of various sculptures ; among which the worthless element preponderates and the spurious is strongly represented.   In many instances the names of the donors are unknown ; some specimens have been separated from the pieces in the Schools to which they belong, from want of space there.   Many of the sculptures are placed very high ; all are covered thickly with dust ; the difficulty of judging with certainty about the restorations is therefore rather great.   To facilitate our survey, I will again classify the specimens into statues and statuettes, busts, reliefs, etc.

156. Group of Aphroditè with Eros and Psychè (?).
The figure of the goddess repeats in all essentials the motive of the
Venus of Melos. It exhibits also a particular correspondence in the
drapery, the tip of which is laid over the l. thigh; the l. foot is set on
a tolerably high pedestal. The r. arm is missing from the breast, the
l. shoulder is restored, arm and head are missing, on the shoulder
traces of curls are visible. Beside the l. thigh stands a pillar on
which is a cithara. This may prove that some restorer had an idea
of making the statue a Muse (cf. the Erato on the Lansdowne sarcophagus, no. 75). In front of the pillar, beside Aphroditè's l. foot,
stands a boy (Eros) quite nude, with his hands on his back; his
head is missing. Further round the corner is the lower half of some
one enveloped in a cloak, the waist bare, apparently that of a female
(Psychè), but the restorer has stuck on a male breast, arms and head.
Both children are about half the size of the principal figure. For the
association of the three figures cf. the Dresden group, Clarac, IV. 640,
1451. H. 0·58, with the pedestal 0·64. [*]

157. Statue of Aphroditè, the same motive as the Medici
Venus. New: head, r. arm, half the l. forearm; legs badly broken,
but for the most part antique. Beside her is Eros riding on a large
dolphin; his l. arm is missing, and his r. hand, which lies on his
head, new. Very rough sculpture. H. 0·74. [*]

158. Torso of a statue of Aphroditè, in similar position.
Only her body and thighs are preserved. H. 0·28. [*]

159 (H. Clarke). Statue of Kybelè, sitting in her shrine,
which has a pediment; she has a modius on her head, below which
long curls fall down; in her r. hand she holds a cup, and in the l.
hand raises a tympanon; her feet rest on a very high footstool, and
in her lap the lion crouches. H. 0·73. L. 0·27. From Ephesos.
[*]

160 (H. Clarke). Torso of a statue of Eros, including the
r. thigh. His r. arm went down slantwise in front of his breast, the
l. was advanced horizontally. Traces of wings are perceptible on
the back. H. 0·36. From Ephesos. [*]

161. Statue of Eros riding on a dolphin. Head, r. arm,
l. forearm, lower part of r. leg missing. The dolphin's mouth has
been perforated, from which we infer that the whole piece was
intended for the adornment of a fountain. H. 0·29. [*]

162 (Rawlinson). **Statue of Eros sleeping.** Chandler, 48. Clarac, IV. 644 B, 1459 G (the sides are reversed in both drawings). The boy is reposing on his cloak. Putting aside the restorations there are now missing the arms, l. leg, r. lower leg, bow and quiver ; only pieces of the wings are left. The only remarkable point about the specimen is its unusually large size ; from the crown of the head to the knee it measures 0·80. [*]

163 (Wheler). **Statue of Silvanus.** Chandler, 80. The god is standing, bearded and crowned, an apron of fruit before his breast, a large branch of a pine tree in his l. arm ; on his feet are boots. Beside his l. foot sits a dog. R. arm missing. Rough sculpture. H. 0·25. [*]

164 (Rawlinson). **Statue of Neilos.** Chandler, 73. The god is bearded and recumbent ; he leans his l. arm on the Sphinx, his r. on his thigh ; his legs are covered by his cloak. His head is crowned. Coarse work. H. 0·25. L. 0·36. [*]

165 (AH.). **Statue of a recumbent Nymph.** Chandler, 141. Prideaux, no. 126 (p. 263). Maittaire, no. 145. Upper part of the body nude. The l. arm rests on the rock, the r., which had at some time been restored, missing. The head has wavy hair and has been joined to the body with a new neck. Insignificant sculpture. H. 0·46. [*]

166 (AH.). **Statue of a recumbent female figure.** Chandler, 142. Prideaux, no. 126 (p. 264). Maittaire, no. 145. Montfaucon, *Ant. Expl., Suppl.*, III. Pl. 10. She wears a chiton and cloak, her l. arm is supported on a cushion, her r. laid on her l. shoulder. In her l. hand she holds a thick wreath (ἐποθομίς). Her head is crowned ; it has been badly battered about, but probably belongs to the statue. The figure is bad and broken in many places. It was most likely the lid of a cinerary urn. H. 0·37. L. 0·73. [*]

167. Modern statuette of a **sleeping female figure** ; nude, but crowned and holding a wreath of roses over the lower part of her body. [*]

168. **Upper half of a female draped statue,** over life-size, extending to the navel ; the lower half once formed a separate piece. The arrangement of the drapery is the same as in Wilton, no. 1ᵈ. A hole has been cut to receive the head and neck, but they are missing. Rough work, in bad preservation. H. 0·51. [*]

169. **Upper part of a female draped statuette,** preserved down to below the l. hand ; same motive as the Vatican "Pudicitia" (Clarac, IV. 764, 1879). Pretty. H. ab. 0·30. [*]

170 (Dawkins). **Fragment of a female draped statue.**
Chandler, 41. She wears a girdled chiton and a cloak before the
lower part of her body and her legs. Preserved from above the
girdle down to the r. knee. Much battered. H. 0·74. [*]

171 (H. Clarke). **Upper part of the statue of a Roman
in the pallium,** his r. arm in front of his breast. From the neck to
the middle of the thigh is preserved; a hollow has been prepared for
the head and neck. Work flat, back quite rough. H. 0·44. From
Ephesos. [*]

172. **Torso of a nude warrior,** with belt for the sword,
resting his l. hand on his hip. His head with the helmet has been
put on ; r. arm, legs, and the support have been restored. Insignificant
work. H. 0·68. [*]

173. **Statuette of a youth,** sitting on a mass of rock on which
he supports his l. hand, his r. is before his breast ; his head is missing.
Lower down on the rock are the remains of a group, representing
perhaps some local deities ; one figure reposes in the lap of another
that is sitting ; the upper part of the body of the latter has been restored. Insignificant work, very much broken. H. 0·42. [*]

174. **Statuette of a youth,** draped, with his legs crossed ; he
supports his l. side against a pillar, on which is introduced at the
bottom a comic mask with the mouth bored far through. Apparently
quite modern. H. 0·74. [*]

175. **Statuette of a boy with a bird.** A boy, standing on
his r. leg, had lowered his r. hand (arm missing) and is holding a
little bird in his l. ; a cloak hangs from his l. arm down to the
ground. A plait goes along the whole length of his hair at the
parting. H. 0·51. [*]

176. **A foot,** covered with a sandal, the straps of which may
be very distinctly seen. Chandler, 110. The upper surface of the
marble where the foot is broken and a piece of the pedestal under
the foot show that it belonged to a statue of life size, and that it is
not a votive foot. [*]

177 (Dawkins). **Terminal figure of Polydeukion,** without
a head. It comes from a church, fallen into ruins, at Kephissia,
where Herodes Atticus had an estate. It is one of the numberless
monuments erected by Herodes in honour of the favourite whom he
prematurely lost (Philostr., *Vitae sophist.*, II. 1, 12. *C. I. Gr.*, 989 ff.
C. I. Att., III. 810 ff.). The inscription, which I have not compared,
and which is written on two sides, is given thus in the *C. I. Gr.*,
989 :—

Ἥρως Πολυδευκίων, |

ταῦσδε ποτ' ἐν τρώ|δοις σὺν σοὶ ἐπε|στρεφόμην. |

Πρὸς θεῶν καὶ ἡρώω[ν], | ὅστις εἰ ὁ ἔχων τὸν χῶρον, | μήποτε μετα-
κεινήσῃ[s] | τούτων τι· καὶ τὰς τούτω[ν] | τῶν ἀγαλμάτων εἰκόνα[s] |
καὶ τειμὰς ὅστις ἢ καθέλ[οι] | ἢ μετακεινοίη, τούτῳ μ[ή]τε γῆν καρπὸν
φέρειν, μ[ή]τε θάλασσαν πλωτὴν εἶ|ναι, κακῶς τε ἀπολέσθα[ι] | αὐτοὺς
καὶ γένος. ὅστι[s] | δὲ κατὰ χώραν φυλάττω[ν] | καὶ τειμῶν τὰ εἰωθότα |
καὶ αὔξων διαμένοι, πολλ[ὰ] | καὶ ἀγαθὰ εἶναι τούτῳ καὶ | αὐτῷ καὶ
ἐκγόνοις. | λυμήνασθαι δὲ μηδὲ λω|[βή]σασθαι μηδέν, ἢ ἀπο|[κ]ρυῦσαι ἢ
συνθραῦσαι ἢ | συγχέαι τῆς μορφῆς κ[αὶ] | τοῦ σχήματος· εἰ δέ τις
ο[ὕ]|τω ποιήσει, ἡ αὐτὴ καὶ ἐ|πὶ τούτοις ἀρά.

II. Ἀλλ' ἐὰν τά τε ἐπ[ι]|θέματα τῶν μο[ρ]|φῶν ἀσινῆ καὶ ἀκ[έ]|ραια
καὶ τὰ ὑποσ[τή]|ματα τὰς βάσεις ὤ[s] | ἐποιήθησαν· καὶ ἐ[ν] | πρώτῳ γε
καὶ ἐπὶ π[ρώ]|τοις, ὅστις ἢ προσπ[ά]ξ]ειεν ἑτέρῳ ἢ γνώμη[s] | ἄρξειεν ἢ
γνώμῃ σύ[μ]|βάλοιτο περὶ το[ύ]των τι ἢ κεαγηθῆρα[ι] ἢ συνχυθῆναι.

Pentelic marble.   H. 1·55.   [*]

**178 (Dawkins).   Terminal figure of Aurelius Appianus
Chrestus.** Chandler, II. 61. Found at Athens, not far from the
" Tower of the Winds," which is situated somewhat to the west of the
former Gymnasion Diogeneion mentioned in the inscription below.
The term has no head; drapery (χλαῖνα, see below) lies round the
neck and on the l. shoulder. Below the neck is the inscription
(C. I. Gr., 427. C. I. Att., III. 751) which I have not compared :
Ψηφισαμένης τῆς | [ἐ]ξ Ἀρείον πάγου βουλῆς τὸν υἱὸν τοῦ | κοσμητοῦ
Αὐρ(ηλίου) | Ἀφφιανὸν Χρηστὸν | Μαραθώνιον οἱ περὶ τὸ Διογένειον |
συνάρχοντες | ἀρετῆς ἔνεκεν. Below the distinctive mark of male
terms follow the verses :

Ὅστις καὶ τάνος εἰμί, τά | πρόσθεν γράμματα φράζε[ι]· |
ἀμφὶ δ' ἐμῆς μοίρης πᾶς, ἐδάκρυσε λεώς,
οὕνεκεν οὐκ ἔφθην, χλαῖναν περὶ αὐχένι θέσθα[ι] |
κώμῳ ἐν ἠγαθέῳ, παισάμενος βίοτον.

The third verse refers to the cloak, which was put on too late, in fact
first put on the terminal representation. The term belongs to the
second century A.D.   Pentelic marble.   H. 1·44.   [*]

BUSTS.

179 (Rawlinson).   Bust of Zeus. Chandler, 87. Head not
bad; the hair does not encroach too much on the forehead, and it

falls low down on to the neck behind. New: tip of the nose and all the bust. Below life size. [*]

180 (Wheler). **Small head of the youthful Dionysos,** crowned. Chandler, 82. Insignificant and much bruised. [*]

181 (Wheler). **Small head of the bearded Dionysos.** Chandler, 77. With a fillet in his hair, that falls low down on his neck. Hieratic style. [*]

182. Small head of a Satyr, with rough hair. Chandler, 84. New : bust and nebris. [*]

183. Head of a laughing Satyr, with ruffled hair. Chandler, 86. New. [*]

184. The same. Chandler, 85. New. [*]

185. Head with long hair and Phrygian cap, on an unusual pedestal ; nose battered. Chandler, 88. New. [*]

186 (Rawlinson). **Head of a youth.** Chandler, 109. The peculiar arrangement of the hair and the whole character remind us of the so-called heads of Ptolemy. Broad fillet through the hair. New: neck and bust. Below life size. [*]

187. Bust of an elderly Roman. Chandler, 100. The small head, which is not bad, resembles Claudius. [*]

188 (Rawlinson). **Bald-headed Roman.** Chandler, 94. He wears a wreath. New: nose, back of the head, and bust. The rest is so injured that the only thing we can say about it with certainty is that it is not a portrait of Caesar. [*]

189 (Rawlinson). **Bust of a Roman,** in corslet. Chandler, 93. He looks wild, and his hair is disordered. Quite new. [*]

190. Bust of a Roman old man. Chandler, 97 (bad). He has a bald head, and half the back of it is missing. Bad work. [*]

191. Small bust of a Roman old man. New. [*]

192. Remains of a head of a Roman old man. Veiled. Face only preserved, and that badly knocked about. Life size. [*]

193. Modern **head,** on a modern mailed bust of dark stone. [*]

194. Small head of a boy. Chandler, 83. The nude bust is new, and a ribbon goes right across the breast. [*]

195. Child's head, of bronze, on a bust of giallo antico. New. [*]

196 (Rawlinson). **Youthful head.** Chandler, 90. Round the smooth hair and the forehead a narrow ribbon is drawn. The head is smooth, the mouth so deeply cut as to give the impression of a mask. Life size. [*]

197. Small head of an elderly lady, with her hair dressed in a roll over her forehead. Bad, and also much injured. [*]

198 (Rawlinson). **Female portrait head.** Chandler, 89 (not accurate). Hair parted and smoothed back from the forehead, somewhat thicker on the temples. A fillet passes round the hair, in which are nine deep holes, besides six similar holes close behind them for a metal wreath or some other ornament. Originally the head was not bad, but now it is much knocked about. Over life size. [*]

199 (Rawlinson). **Bust of a Roman lady.** Chandler, 107. The plaits on the top of her head resemble an inverted basket. Nose new. Bad sculpture. Life size. [*]

200 (All.). **Sulpicia Canni.** Chandler, III. 6. A massive head, more like that of a young girl than of a woman. The hair is brushed back and forms a flat plait along the parting. Pupils expressed. Nose missing. The draped bust belongs to it, so does the slab on which it rests. On this slab stands as if cut in with a knife *Sulpicia Canni* (S. consort of Cannius, or C. Annius); it appears to me very doubtful whether its origin is antique. The bust finishes below with a round disc. H. 0·51. [*]

RELIEFS, etc.

201 (Dawkins). **Altar of Zeus Labraundes.** Chandler, 11. 12. On the front the Carian double axe (λάβρυς) is depicted; below in careful writing Διὸς Λαβραύν δον, then in careless characters which also differ palaeographically, καὶ Διὸς μεγίστου (*C. I. Gr.*, 2750). H. 0·35. L. 0·29. The altar comes from a Turkish burying-place between Aphrodisias and Hierapolis in Caria. [*C]

202 (AH.). **Altar of Herakles.** Chandler, III. 9. Prideaux, no. 139. Maittaire, no. 139. Montfaucon, *Ant. Expl., Suppl.*, I. Pl. 54, I. FRONT. Herakles is represented as a child strangling the five-headed Hydra with both hands (not the two snakes). This relief is surrounded by the inscription coarsely hewn in : *D(is) M(anibus) L(ucio) Marcio | Pacato filio dulcissimo | fecit Rodope ma'ter in [f]elici ssima, | qui t(ix)it annos | XV m(enses) VIIII d(ies) VIIII.*—R. SIDE. Herakles, beardless, strikes at a large Stymphalian bird with his club, he has seized it by the neck and is holding it. —L. SIDE. Herakles, bearded, is kneeling on the back of a Centaur whom he has thrown to the ground, and whose hands are chained behind his back ; with his l. hand the victor seizes the Centaur's head, while he swings the club against him with his r. hand.—BACK.

Herakles' arms, the lion's skin and the club, the broad quiver
(γωρυτός) and the bow.—The reliefs are delicately and prettily
executed; so much the more disfiguring therefore is the inscription
on the front ; no doubt it was added afterwards, when the little altar
was to be turned into a sepulchral monument. H. 0·42. L. 0·26.
D. 0·21. [*C]

203 (Dawkins).   **Fragment of an Attic votive relief; l.
half.** Chandler, 117. Of the frame the anta on the l. and the architrave with tiles on the top are preserved. A man in a cloak and two
veiled females approach from the l., then two girls somewhat smaller
without veils, and a female attendant with a large box on her head ;
before them is a sacrificial minister in an apron, driving a pig forward,
also a boy and a girl. Of the personages to whom the sacrifice
and the adoration are offered, we see only a r. arm akimbo with
some indistinct object in the hand; the figure to which it belonged
must have been much larger and was evidently standing. We cannot therefore take it for the deceased heroically treated on his couch
(cf. nos. 144—146), but presumably it is Asklepios with his relatives
(cf. *Mittheil. des archaeol. Inst. in Athen*, 1877, Pl. 18. *Arch. Zeit.*,
1877. pp. 139 ff.), or some other god. For the rest cf. above, no.
88. Sculpture of the fourth or third century B.C. Pentelic marble.
H. 0·66. L. 0·47. [*C]

204 (AII.).   **Sepulchral stelè of Philista.** Chandler, II. 89.
Prideaux, no. 68. Maittaire, no. 35. Montfaucon, *Ant. Expl.*,
Suppl., v. Pl. 7, 1. Stelè in excellent preservation. Above, a pediment with denticulations on the geison, in the field of the pediment
a rosette. On the frieze is the inscription Φιλίσταν Μέμνονος (*C. I.
Gr.*, 3254); below, two rosettes, and in a hollowed square field a
laurel wreath enclosing the words ὁ δῆμος (cf. above, no. 149). Below this, the architrave with dentils supported by two Corinthian
pilasters. In the very deep relief field we see Philista in chiton and
a fine, transparent cloak, trimmed with fringe ; she is veiled. Her r.
forearm, concealed by the drapery, lies across her body and her l.
elbow is supported on it, her hand gracefully holds the hem of her
drapery up to her neck. The inclination of her head, and her downward look directed to the little dog (μελιταῖος) that is jumping up
by her r. foot, have a particularly charming effect. To the l. stands
a low pillar, with a basket (κάλαθος) on it; beside it a diminutive
female attendant in chiton, opening the lid of a little box. On the
r. is another pillar, somewhat higher, with a large box on it; beside it
a similar attendant (head missing) who is laying her r. hand on a

closed box. Under the relief is a high, moulded pedestal. The
relief belongs probably to the second century B.C.; it has been
executed with evident love and care, so that the architectural adornments are even extended on the sides. It is one of the best
examples of its style; also remarkable for its good preservation.
Relief very high, nearly 0·12. It comes probably from Smyrna.
Yellowish marble. H. 1·79. L. 0·80. [*]

205 (Selden). **Sepulchral stele.** Chandler, 143. Prideaux,
no. 91. Maittaire, no. 144. Montfaucon, *Ant. Expl., Suppl.*, v.
Pl. 9. Similar to no. 204, now without pediment, which was probably
sculptured out of a separate piece; the lower geison with dentil is
still extant. On either end of the frieze is a rosette and between
them two hollowed square fields with a laurel wreath each; there are
no inscriptions now, they have probably been chiselled away. On
the architrave, which is in two belts, the inscription is also destroyed.
The relief field, which is hollowed out to a considerable depth, is
enclosed on either side by Corinthian half-columns. In their relative
positions the two principal figures resemble those in no. 89: the
young man to the l., in his long chlamys buttoned on the r.
shoulder, and with a quiver and straight bow on his back, is almost
turning his body away from the female figure, he looks however
on the ground towards the centre; his r. arm is lowered, his l.
arm raised in front of his breast. The female figure, to the r., has
exactly the posture of Philista (no. 204, cf. nos. 89, 90). Between
the two stands a diminutive female attendant, with her legs crossed
and in the attitude of the Vatican Pudicitia; on the l., by the pillar,
near the man, are two diminutive attendants in short chitons, pressed
very close to each other. On the high pedestal may be seen a
round box with the lid beside it, another round box, a high goblet-
shaped vessel, a hat (?), and a high cup or a basket. A pretty good
example of this style, but not to be compared with no. 204; probably also from Smyrna. H. 1·22. L. 0·64. [*]

206. **Sepulchral stele of Leukaios.** In the pediment is
a rosette. Below the pediment, in a square slightly hollowed out, is
a wreath, without inscription: below it Λευκαῖος Καλλίππου (not in *C.
I. Gr.*). In the relief field stands Leukaios, so much knocked about
that only his cloak and shoes can be recognised. To the r. a diminutive attendant in a chiton, with his legs crossed and his arms lowered,
is leaning against a tree round which a snake is twined. To the l. is a
pedestal, before which a little dog (μελιταῖος) is jumping up. On
the pedestal is a thick slab, with three fruits on it, then a high

ithyphallic terminal figure, with demolished head and two projections
instead of arms (cf. Ince, no. 260). The whole of this group stands
on a pedestal on which a round shield and two upright oval objects
(greaves?) are depicted in relief. The monument belongs to the
second (or first?) century B.C.; it comes probably from Asia Minor
or the Archipelago. Grey marble. H. 0·72. L. 0·34. [*]

207 (H. Clarke). **Fragment of a Greek sepulchral relief.**
A man, the upper part of whose body is nude, is lying on a couch,
before which stands a high altar of incense (θυμιατήριον). He is
reaching with his r. hand for the torch with which a figure, now
almost destroyed, seems about to set light to the incense. Very
high relief, much defaced. From Ephesos. H. 0·37. L. 0·27. [*]

208 (Burgon). **Sepulchral relief.** A horseman, in a chlamys,
is riding to the r. towards a pine tree. In his r. hand he holds out a
cup to a serpent, that is twisting itself from the tree towards him.
Near the tree is a diminutive attendant in chiton and chlamys, raising
the r. and lowering the l. arm. Under the horse is a little dog. To
the l. in the field a roll and a box. Coarse white marble. From
Pergamon. H. 0·60. L. 1·02. [*]

209 (AH.). **Sepulchral altar of Q. Avilius** of Lanuvium.
Chandler, III. 7. Round altar, ornamented with four bulls' heads,
over which a thick garland is hung, adorned with fillets and laden
with grapes (cf. above, nos. 96—104). Above, the inscription : *Q
Avili C f Lanvine salve:* below: Κόιντε Αὐίλλιε Γαίου υἱὲ Ῥωμαῖε |
χρηστὲ χαῖρε (C. I. Gr., 6894). Probably from Rheneia (cf. C. I.
Lat., III. 486). H. 0·84. [*C]

210. Similar **sepulchral altar**, adorned only with bulls' heads
and garlands. H. 0·67. [*]

211 (Dawkins). **Cippus of Atika.** Chandler, II. 91. The
monument is in the form of a square altar, left rough at the back,
and without ornament on the two sides. In front is a veiled female
figure, seated, her head supported in her l. hand. In front of her
stands a female attendant offering her something. Above, in very
large letters, the inscription : Ἀτικὰ Λάμψιος | γυνὴ Ἡροδώρου (C. I.
Gr., 6893). The monument comes probably from Asia Minor or the
Archipelago. H. 0·60. L. 0·42. D. 0·42. [*]

212 (AH.). **Cippus of Fabius Rufinus.** Chandler, III. 8.
On the front Cupid is represented, holding in his raised r. hand a
stout indistinct object ; his l. hand was lowered and is knocked off.
Coarse relief. Above: *Memoriae Fabi Rufini*; below: *Fabius Iustus.*
H. 0·65. L. 0·50. D. 0·39. [*]

213 (AH.).   **Cippus.**   Chandler, 154.   Underneath a tablet.
that is almost entirely modern, may be perceived the closed entrance
to the tomb. On either side a laurel tree with birds. H. 0·52. L. 0·33.
D. 0·30.   [*]

214 (H. Clarke).   **Sepulchral monument of L. Pompeius
Marcellinus.** Above, in relief, a pediment; below, a bearded horseman, in chiton and fluttering chlamys, with his sword by his side,
galloping r. and brandishing a spear.   Underneath, the inscription
(*C. I. Lat.*, III. 435): *L. Pompeio L. filio | Fabia Marcellino | Roma,
tri(buno) coh(ortis) pri(mae) | Ligur(um), vixit annos | XX·III·* (sic)
*mens(es) V dies XI. | monumentum fecit | Flavia Marcellina | mater
et | Pompeia Catullina | soror. | h(oc) m(onumentum) [h(eredem) n(on)]
s(equitur).*   From Ephesos, whence it was brought to Smyrna; at
this place Waddington copied it.   H. 1·49.   L. 0·59.   [*]

215 (AH.).   **Cinerarium.**   Chandler, III. 11.   Two boys are
carrying a garland, and within the field it encloses is a tablet with
the inscription: *D(is) M(anibus) | Publiliae | Spei, | vix(it) an(nos)
XVI | m(enses) VIII d(ies) XVIIII.*   On each of the sides a gar-
land. On the lid are two torches, lying. H. 0·28. L. 0·33. D. 0·24.
[*]

216.   **Remains of a cinerarium,** broken off at the top.   In
the centre is a boy turning r., and at either end a girl, draped. They
support two garlands, and each garland encloses a head of Medusa.
H. 0·26.   L. 0·69.   [*]

217.   **Fragment of a relief,** perhaps from a sarcophagus.
Chandler, 130.   R. upper corner: a Cupid, with the bow in his l.
hand, and carrying on his r. shoulder a well-filled basket.   Much
abraded.   H. 0·35.   L. 0·30.   [*]

218 (H. Clarke).   **Two fragments of a sarcophagus,** with
rich mouldings above (*kymation* and *astragalos*).   I. Beardless head,
helmeted, turning l. and blowing a trumpet.   Behind, a piece of a
shield seen from the inside.   II. Bearded head, turning l., and a
shoulder. This head is larger than the other: perhaps because the
figure was sitting. Both heads, which are in very high relief, intrude
into the moulding.   These fragments come from Ephesos, and they
remind us of the Ephesian Achilleus sarcophagus in Woburn (no.
219), though they cannot belong to it.   Perhaps they are fragments
of a representation of Achilleus in the midst of the daughters of
Lykomedes, like the sarcophagi in the Capitol and the Louvre (cf.
Cambridge, no. 76.   Woburn, no. 117); possibly they are the heads
of Agyrtes the trumpeter and of Lykomedes.   H. abt. 0·21.   [*]

219 (H. Clarke). **Fragment,** apparently of a similar sarcophagus, representing a sphinx with large wings sitting to the r.
(head missing); above the wings a piece of a cloak is visible. Behind the sphinx are the remains of a maeander ornament, belonging
perhaps to a border that may have encircled the sarcophagus below.
H. 0·42. L. 0·37. From Ephesos? [*]

220 (Rawlinson). **Slab with masks.** Chandler, 111, 112.
FRONT. Three masks in high relief. To the l. a youthful Satyr
with a fillet in his hair, to the r. Dionysos with a long pointed
beard, and Ariadne. BACK. Quite low relief. Head of the bald-
headed Seilenos, turning to the l.; in front of him a piece of a
thyrsos. On the extreme l. signs of an altar and flames on it.
H. 0·18. L. 0·28. [*]

221. Fragment of a very thick marble slab. Chandler,
II. 59. To the l. the remains of a boy carrying a wreath, coarsely
executed. To the r. an inscription tablet, which contains the con-
clusion of a menace of punishment (*C. I. Gr.*, 7023): δώσει εἰς
Καίσαρος φίσκον * βφ' καὶ εἰς τὴν | πόλιν * βφ' (2500 denarii to each).
Underneath the remains of a further inscription, perhaps εἰ ρ[ὴ] etc.
H. 0·28. L. 0·48. [*]

222 (Rawlinson). **Relief of a crowned head.** Chandler, 92.
New. [*]

223 (Rawlinson). **Portrait medallion.** Chandler, 108.
New. [*]

224 (H. Clarke). **Fragment of a pilaster,** representing a
candelabrum. The pedestal is triangular, and it rests on feet which
are like those of a sphinx; draped female figures form the relief of
the pedestal. Above, rich akanthos cups and architectural mouldings are intermingled with masks, rams' heads, swans, and eagles.
Broken off at the top. H. 1·52. L. 0·35. D. 0·20. From Syracuse.
[*]

225 (H. Clarke). **The same.** The stem of a palm tree rises
from a richly ornamented round pedestal; from the tree hang dates,
and above, the palm leaves form a tuft. H. 2·24. L. 0·34. D. 0·26.
There is a projection of the depth of 0·16 intended to be let into a
groove. From Syracuse. [*]

226 (H. Clarke). **The same.** Ornamented in front with entwined vine-sprays. Behind projects a narrow perpendicular listel,
with two holes; perhaps a hand-rail or balustrade was to have been
joined on there. H. 2·24. L. 0·35. D. 0·27 and 0·15 for the projection. From Syracuse. [*]

I could not find, or have overlooked, the following specimens :

227 (Wheler). **Double terminal bust,** apparently feminine.
Chandler, 75.

228 (Th. Shaw). **Terminal bust of Dionysos,** crowned with
ivy. Chandler, 76.

229 (Th. Shaw). **Terminal bust of Hermes,** with a long
beard, and wings on his hat. Chandler, 78.

230 (Wheler). **Head of the bearded Dionysos** (?), crowned
with ivy ; not archaistic. Chandler, 79.

231 (AP.). **A piece of a moulding** with **portrait bust** of a
man over it, apparently part of a sepulchral monument (cf. nos. 91,
155). Chandler, 95.

232 (Rawlinson). **Bronze bust of Socrates.** Chandler, 101.
Suspicious.

233 (Rawlinson). **Bronze bust of Plato,** with a Latin inscription. Chandler, 102. Apparently a copy of the Florentine
bust (Visconti, *Iconogr. Gr.*, 1. Pl. 18 A).

234 (Rawlinson). **Fragment of a relief,** l. end. Chandler,
131. A young Satyr, with nebris across his breast, appears to be
quarrelling with another Satyriskos. Of the latter remain only traces
of joints and a hand, with which he is seizing his adversary by the
hair. Both arms missing.

235 (Dawkins). **Corinthian capital.** Chandler, 165. Very
similar to the one in no. 130.

236 (Dawkins). **Fragment.** Chandler, 11. 14. Underneath a
wreath is the inscription [Οὐ]ήσιος Βάργος (*C. I. Gr.*, 3683). From
Kyzikos.

There are also in the Museum a considerable number of **terra
cottas, lamps, handles of amphoras, stamped tiles,** etc.

ALL SOULS COLLEGE.

In the Library stands the following :

237. Marble stand. On a round pedestal crouch three lions ;
upon which three female figures stand in a stiff posture, seen in full face.
They wear each a long chiton, and both arms lie on their bodies ;
long plaits fall on their shoulders, and on their heads they wear each a
modius. Between their backs rises, from the centre of the pedestal,
a strong circular support contracted in the middle and having
a torus wound round it. This support is terminated above by a

round slab, which has the appearance of being carried by the women. A round hollow in the surface of the slab seems to show that a large cup, or candelabrum, or something of the kind, was to be let in here. Late, rough art. H. 0·66. Diameter, below, 0·52; above, 0·37. According to an inscription in the ante-room, Anthony Lefroy, Esq., presented to the college in 1771 this "*aram tripodem olim matri deum in templo S. Corinthi consecratam.*" [*]

CHRIST CHURCH COLLEGE.

There is now only left the following specimen in the Library :

238. Modern bronze copy of the bust of the "methodical physician" **M. Modius Asiaticus**, in Paris; cf. on Wilton, no. 78. The former possessor of the original, the Chancellor De Pont-chartrain, had it moulded by Girardon and then cast in bronze ; the copies were a perfect success (Caylus, *Recueil*, VI. p. 142). Our specimen, which was presented by the Hon. Frederick Campbell in 1809, is proved to be a copy by some mistakes which are found in the inscription. [*B]

At one time the college possessed some more **marbles**, among them :

239. A presumed bust of Cicero, and

240. A group, from Pella in Macedonia, consisting of a woman and a boy ; unfortunately its surface had been much injured (Waagen, *Treas.*, III. p. 49) ; finally several modern busts. Of these marbles only broken pieces are in existence now in one of the upper rooms of the college, for on the occasion of a bonfire made years ago in the quadrangle of the college by the students, all the busts were carried out and placed too near the fire. The marbles turned black, and, no doubt from anger at being so ill treated, sprang into pieces ; only the *aeneum pectus* of the "methodical physician" surviving this ordeal of fire.

RADCLIFFE LIBRARY.

Here are preserved, besides some plaster casts, **two large marble candelabra.** Both of them were found in fragments by Gavin Hamilton, 1769, in Hadrian's Villa, in the place called

M. C. 38

Pantanello. They were restored under the direction of Piranesi, and thus sold to Sir Roger Newdigate, who presented them to the Radcliffe Library; this happened before the year 1778, when Piranesi's *Vasi e Candelabri* appeared. Volkmann (*Reisen*, III. p. 31), Spiker (*Reise*, I. p. 25), and Waagen (*Treas.*, III. p. 50) saw them in the Library. Unfortunately my attention was directed to them too late for me to be able to examine them myself. Nevertheless, the engravings make it evident that both these specimens are seriously restored and in great part modern. They are striking examples of those pasticcios to which, as they answered the taste of that epoch, Piranesi as an art dealer owed a great deal of his reputation and of his extraordinary success; one may compare the celebrated candelabrum in the Louvre, likewise composed by Piranesi from different antique fragments in a most arbitrary way (Piranesi, *Vasi*, I. Pl. 30, 31. Bouillon, III. *Candél.*, Pl. 1. Clarac, II. Pl. 141).

241. Marble candelabrum. Piranesi, *Vasi e Candelabri*, I. Pl. 25—27. Penna, *Viaggio della Villa Adriana*, IV. Pl. 110. Dallaway, *Of Statuary*, Pl. 28. Three lions' legs and between them a stem ornamented with leaves, all of which rest on a low triangular base, support a triangular pedestal tapering towards the top. The angles of the main portion are formed by eagles in an awkward posture; between them on each side appear Bacchic masks (*a*, two Satyrs, the one youthful, the other bearded, leaning against each other; *b*, bearded head, possibly of Dionysos, in full face; *c*, unknown). Above, a kind of ornamented capital with a group of two dolphins entwined together on each of the three corners, and between them with shells and floral patterns. The latter extend at the top on an abacus, which ends in a ram's head at each of the three corners. Over each ram's head is a large crane standing upright. In the middle of the three birds a very tall stem, or capital as it were, is erected, ornamented with sprays, leaves, and Medusa's heads. On it rests a round pedestal, shaped like a *trochilus*: it supports a flat cup or basket full of snakes. In the midst of these rises a kneeling youth, of robust forms, with both arms bent behind his shoulders. He serves as a *Telamon* or *Atlas*, bearing on his head and his forearms a large, low cup, which forms the top of the whole candelabrum.

242. Marble candelabrum. Piranesi, *Vasi e Candelabri*, II. Pl. 96, 97. Penna, *Viaggio della Villa Adriana*, IV. Pl. 111. On the corners of a low triangular base are three large lions' legs ending in lions' heads which, together with a bulky, fluted stem placed in the middle of them, support a very high triangular structure tapering towards the top and composed of a rich variety of ornamental members. The undermost of these is decorated with goats' skulls, garlands and sacrificial instruments (*apex*, pail, cup, knife, etc.). Higher up, over some rows of floral ornaments, come three Sphinxes lying at the corners, their tails ending in ornamental sprays. Above them follows a rather high section looking very modern, the principal decoration of which are three huge elephants' heads. Above, a triangular pedestal of a common species (cf. Broadlands, no. 11. Newby, nos. 8, 41). On its sides are reliefs: (*a*) **Athene**, standing full face, in chiton and aegis, helmeted, holding a spear in the r. hand and a shield on the l. arm; she looks towards l.; (*b*) behind her, a **youth** (called Silvanus by Piranesi), clad in a short chiton which leaves the l. part of his breast exposed; he goes, or rather falls, towards l., with the head, which is crowned, sunk on the breast and both arms hanging down by the body; the l. hand seems to hold some object; (*c*) the youthful **Herakles**, running l., holding his club in both his hands, the lion's skin fluttering behind his back. From the upper corners of this pedestal project three rams' heads. The topmost part of the candelabrum exhibits a rich series of various round, moulded members, architecturally ornamented; the top is formed by a large, low cup. H. abt. 2·20 (10 pal. 10½ on.).

PENRICE CASTLE (Glamorganshire, Wales).

At this ancestral mansion of the MANSEL family, 12 miles from Swansea, there is, according to what I was told by the gardener at Margam, the **sarcophagus** described by Dallaway, p. 348 (II. p. 96), under no. 18 of the Margam collection, as "fluted, with cover, in the middle the group of the Graces." For other antiques see under Margam.

PENSHURST (Kent).

Dallaway, p. 382 (II. p. 134).

There exists only a faint tradition about an older collection of antiques at this seat of the SIDNEYS, hallowed by poetry and historical reminiscences, cf. Introd. § 13, note 28. At present only a number of busts, brought from Italy by Mr PERRY about 1740 (Introd. § 41) are to be found there, in the possession of VISCOUNT DE LISLE AND DUDLEY ; nothing more definite is known to me about them.

PETWORTH HOUSE (Sussex).

Dallaway, pp. 278 ff. (II. pp. 12 ff.). Volkmann, *Reisen*, I. p. 361. K. O. Müller in Böttiger's *Amalthea*, III. pp. 249 ff. (= *Kunst-archäolog. Werke*, II. pp. 81 ff. ; indicated below by an *m*). Clarac, III. p. 60. Conze, *Arch. Anz.*, 1864, pp. 238 ff. Waagen, *Treas.*, II. p. 32, devotes only a brief and undeservedly disparaging notice to the statues. I examined the collection in the year 1877, at leisure as to the statues, in a more cursory manner as to the busts.

This ancient seat of the Percys of Northumberland, to whom is due for the most part the truly princely collection of oil paintings, now in the possession of LORD LECONFIELD, stands in close contiguity to the town of Petworth. The founder of the collection of antique sculptures was SIR CHARLES WYNDHAM, from the year 1740 a member of the Society of Dilettanti, who became in 1750 SECOND EARL OF EGREMONT. In his task he availed himself of the services of the expert architect Matthew Brettingham, junr., then resident in Rome (Introd. §§ 42, 43), who, in collecting these valuable and on the whole well-preserved antiques, evinced a skill equal if not superior to that exhibited at Holkham (cf. Dallaway, p. 271; Payne Knight, letterpress to *Spec.*, I. Pl. 72). The fact that Gavin Hamilton is also mentioned as receiving commissions from the Earl on the most liberal terms (Dallaway, *Of Statuary*, p. 318; cf. no. 6) forms no contradiction to the above statement, as Brettingham and Hamilton were intimate friends (Introd. § 44). The collection was formed between 1750 and 1760, but when the collector died in 1763, "the cases containing these statues were not unpacked" (Dallaway, p. 319). The earl's son and heir GEORGE O'BRIEN WYNDHAM, THIRD EARL OF EGREMONT (d. 1837), was at that time a boy of only twelve years old. He appears to have sold some antiques at a later date, according to the following letter from Brettingham to Townley, July 31, 1778, which I found among Townley's papers in the Bodleian Library at Oxford ("Memorandums of Marbles, &c., &c., on Sale in Italy and elsewhere"):

DEAR Sᴿ,

I have a Commission from the Earl of Egremont to dispose of 5 or 6 *more* of his Lordship's Statues chiefly from Petworth, among which is a curious Silenus with a Basket on his head [no. 54], and allso ten or a dozen Bustoes......

Then follows an invitation to Townley to inspect the marbles at Pimlico ; an enclosure adds the following list :

Antique Statues and Busts belonging to the Earl of Egremont.

		Height		Valuation
		ft.	in.	£
1.	A Diana, the Arms and hands only restored . . .	5	3	200
2.	Silenus with a basket [no. 54]	5	3	100
3.	Diana Cacciatrice [no. 17?]	5	4	100
4.	A Muse [no. 11?]	5	0	80
5.	A female drapery figure carrying a rabbit and Ducks from the market [no. 16]	5	0	100
6.	Fecialis with a young pig for sacrifice [no. 53] . .	4	2	100
7.	A small Diana Cacciatrice [no. 52?] . . .	4	2	60
8.	Juno, a capital Bust of [no. 27] . . .	3	8	70
9.	Julia Mamea, a Head [no. 46? 66?] . . .			30
10.	Lucilla, a Bust			30
11.	Marciana, do. [no. 60?]			30
12.	Faustina Maggiore, do. [no. 59?] . . .			30
13.	Faustina Minore, do. [no. 67? Dall. no. 25?] . .			30
14.	A Muse, do. [no. 29?]			30
15.	A Man's Bust incognito			30
16.	Julia Pia [no. 46? 66?]			30
17.	A Head of Bacchus [no. 21? Dall. no. 50] . . .			30

Most of these statues can be identified with sufficient certainty to enable us to say that the purchase as a whole did not take place. Only no. 1 was transferred at a later date to the Buckingham Collection at Stowe, and is now to be found at Lowther Castle (no. 3). Of two statues mentioned by Dallaway, no. 9 (Matron draped, resembling Agrippina) and no. 19 (Vestal), only one can now be traced in Petworth (no. 11). On the other hand a few pieces which Dallaway in 1800 does not enumerate, have found their way here through the third Lord Egremont, notably the group no. 12 (cf. nos. 40, 46). Unfortunately this owner prevented Brotherton, Count Clarac's draughtsman, from completing the drawings of the entire collection, so that many interesting specimens are still unpublished.

As many specimens, especially busts, have had no definite place assigned to them, it seems most suitable for my purpose to classify separately the various kinds of sculptures, and so to begin with the statues. I commence at the window on the r. of the entrance.

1. **Statue of Ganymedes.** Cavaceppi, *Racc.*, 1. Pl. 13. Clarac, III. 410, 701. Dallaway, no. 10. The powerful youth, whose breast, back, and l. arm are covered by the chlamys, is resting his l. hand in a rather unnatural manner on the wing of the large eagle that stands by him. He leans so heavily in fact that his shoulder is much forced up. New: neck and head, the r. arm with the drinking-cup, the beak and half the l. wing of the eagle; otherwise the whole group is antique and unbroken. The execution is Roman and not remarkable; the youthful softness of body appropriate to a Ganymedes is wanting. Pentelic marble. H. 1·83. [*Cm*]

2. **Fragment of a female statuette**, preserved down to the stomach. The form is quite enveloped in the cloak, which covers the r. arm so that only the hand protrudes from the cloak in front of the breast. The l. arm was originally laid back. Neck and head, possibly new, are let in to the drapery; on the head a stephanè. H. 0·30. [*]

3. **Female portrait statue** ("Agrippina as Ceres"). Cavaceppi, *Racc.*, I. Pl. 12. Clarac, V. 930, 2366. Dallaway, no. 23. The figure rests on the l. leg, the r. foot being slightly drawn back. A fine, ungirdled chiton falls down to the feet; the cloak, with one corner flung over the outstretched l. arm, envelopes the body and legs. The drapery has been very little repaired and is in excellent preservation, but its treatment is dry and it has been much re-worked by Cavaceppi. The upper parts of the arms are lowered. New: the forearms from the cloak onwards, the r. hand holding ears of corn. The head and neck have been let in, but probably belong to the statue. New: nose and parts of the stephanè. In front of the high stephanè three rows of crisp curls extend over the forehead, on either side long ringlets descend to the shoulders. The face inclines slightly to the l. shoulder; it is pretty, with gentle expression. The head reminds one of the so-called Domitia in the Vatican (*Mus. Pio-Clem.*, III. Pl. 5. Clarac, V. 949, 2405), without however being identical with it. Parian marble. H. 1·87. [*BCm*]

4. **Statue of Hera**, colossal scale. Dallaway, no. 17. Most nearly allied to the beautiful Farnese statue (Clarac, III. 414, 723 B).

She rests on the l. foot, and wears an ungirdled chiton and a cloak.
The latter covers her l. shoulder, body and legs, is gathered into a
bunch in front of her stomach and then thrown over her lowered l.
arm ; the r. shoulder is raised. New: head with stephanè, the r.
arm, and the l. hand from where it issues from the drapery. Good
work. Parian marble. H. 2·05. [*Cm]

5. **Statue of Apollo** ("Apollo Egremont"). *Spec.*, I. 62 ;
II. 45. Clarac, III. 496, 966. Müller-Wieseler, II. 12, 133. Braun,
Kunstmythol., Pl. 47. Dallaway, no. 7. This celebrated statue portrays the god resting on his r. leg, with the l. leg slightly bent ; the
r. arm has always been lowered, in the l. he carries the large cithara.
The most peculiar part is the very wide cloak. This is buttoned
together on the r. shoulder as if it were a chlamys, and so falls open
along the whole length of the body. On the l. side as well it is gathered
up on to the shoulder, so as to set this arm also free for the cithara (cf.
Clarac, IV. 663, 1535). The cloak is therefore divided into what we
may call two wings, one in front, and one behind ; the folds are very
deeply undercut and in front they lie very near together, producing
a particularly rich effect ; but a more marked alternation of principal
and subordinate parts would be requisite for grandeur. On the feet
are sandals. The young, beautiful head is gently inclined to the
l. shoulder, the forehead is low, and the long hair is brushed back
from it and falls down on the neck and shoulders. The face has
an expression of composed, thoughtful inspiration, as though the god
were listening to the strains of his own music. Near the r. ear one
curl has escaped the mass of tresses. Behind the r. foot is an
omphalos entwined with woollen fillets (στέμματα, *vittae*); it is hardly
visible from the front, but serves to support the cloak behind. On
the front of the pedestal are visible the remains of a wreath of laurel
in quite flat relief. New: nose, r. arm with the plectrum, half the l.
forearm, half of the front horn (πῆχυς, *cornu*) of the cithara with
almost the whole of the upper bridge (ζυγόν), half of the lower part of
the l. leg down to the foot, and sundry edges of the folds of the
drapery. The head and neck have been let into the figure, but,
although they are of a much whiter and more finely-grained marble,
they undoubtedly belong to the statue ; for it is not at all uncommon
in draped statues that the head should be executed in finer marble than
the rest (cf. Lansdowne House, no. 67), and of the long curls one fits
exactly to the piece on the shoulder, three others having been connected by inserted pieces. Parian marble. H. 1·65, pedestal 0·10.
Very similar to, if not identical with, the statue in Cavalieri, *Antiq.*

Statuarum, l. III. *et* IV., Rome 1594, Pl. 35, "*in aedibus Victori-arum.*" [*Cm*]

6. Statue of a Satyr pouring out wine. Dallaway, no. 16.
A replica of the statue which recurs in so many examples, probably copied from Praxiteles ; we find it in London, Dresden, Villa Ludovisi, Madrid, &c. (Clarac, IV. 677, 1576 ; 712, 1695. *Brit. Museum Marbles*, XI. Pl. 40. Müller-Wieseler, II. 39, 459). The youthful Satyr is resting on his l. leg, in an extremely pleasing attitude, by a square pillar which serves him as a support. The l. arm is lowered and the outstretched l. hand held a cup into which the Satyr was pouring wine from an ewer in his upraised r. hand. A rather large tail may be seen behind. New : head, r. arm including shoulder, with the bunch of grapes in the hand, almost the whole of the l. arm with the exception of a small piece on the shoulder ; on the l. hip we see the place where the arm originally joined the leg, but the indication has been neglected by the restorer. New also : the lower part of the r. leg and the greater part of the pedestal. The l. leg and the pillar have never been separated either from the body or from the pedestal. The work is fairly soft, but not so good as in the Dresden copy (no. 114) or in the one in the British Museum (Graeco-Roman Sculpt., no. 184). The following inscription is to be seen on the front of the pillar towards the outer edge,

ΑΠΟΛΛΩΝΙΟ ⎤
Σ ⎦

It appears to me unquestionably new (cf. *Arch. Zeit.*, 1880, p. 17, n. 29). The letters look as if they had been slightly scratched in with a knife, in an unsteady and disorderly manner, without any previous arrangement as to space, for which reason the Σ had to find room below. Dallaway and Müller add ΕΠΟΙΕΙ, of which neither Friederichs, nor Conze, nor myself could find any trace ; one only sees the remains of some untidy scratches below the letters ΛΠΟ. Consequently the name of Apollonios cannot be that of the artist, but, if it were antique, it would be the hurriedly made autograph of somebody else. In the book *Of Statuary*, &c., p. 321, Dallaway only gives as the inscription ΑΠΟΛΛΩ. Fine-grained Parian marble. H. 1·60. Discovered near Rome by Gavin Hamilton. [*Cm*]

7. Statue of Apollo. Dallaway, no. 5, "Apollo or Trophonius." The statue itself is an exact replica of the principal figure in the group at Deepdene, no. 4. The head, with a thoughtful rather than a melancholy expression, is certainly old, and belongs to the statue; the long, curly hair, which is all gathered up on the top of the head, has been much re-worked, but it retains the original motive. This head-dress, like the knot in the Apollo Belvedere and other statues, has been chosen by the artist with the view of imparting to the comparatively small head an appearance of greater height. We have no trace here of the long curls continued to the shoulder, which are found in the statue at Deepdene. The face also appears to have been re-worked; the nose is new, and parts of the neck have been repaired. The whole body, which shows a beautifully soft movement, bears much to the r., where the elbow rests on the trunk of a tree. A snake is twined round the trunk, which the chlamys covers. It is unlikely that a companion figure ever belonged to this, as in the group at Deepdene. New: lowered l. arm, half of r. forearm, head and tip of tail of snake, the first four toes of r. foot, the lower half of l. leg, pedestal. All the rest is quite unbroken. Müller thought he recognised in the statue a Dionysos, but the body is too powerful and not sufficiently effeminate. Good work. Thasian marble. H. 2·02. [*Cm]

8. **Statue of a Satyr in repose.** Dallaway, no. 13. The motive is the same as that of the statue formerly known as Periboëtos (Müller-Wieseler, I. 35, 143). The head belongs to another replica of that often-repeated and very favourite figure of antiquity. The mouth is slightly opened, the ears are pointed. New: tip of nose; the whole is somewhat effaced, but otherwise good. It is of beautiful yellowish, Parian marble, with a very distinct grain. The body is of another marble, white and fine-grained, without visible grain; the work is not distinguished, and moreover the body has been polished. New: neck, l. arm, the r. arm from below the shoulder, edges of the nebris, the trunk of the tree, the legs from below the knees; the rest of the torso is entire. H. 1·73. [*Cm]

9. **Statue of an athlete.** Dallaway, no. 12. The statue resembles others in continental museums (Clarac, IV. 663, 1537; V. 855, 2167; 856, 2169; 857, 2174. *Mon. dell' Inst.*, XI. Pl. 7). The youth rests on his l. leg, the r. is placed somewhat back. He holds the l. arm at a right angle close to his body, so that the hand, of which the open palm is turned up, is in front of his stomach; the r. arm is but slightly raised, and he pours oil from a round little alabastron with his l. hand. The head bends forward and inclines to the l. shoulder. It resembles the youthful heads indirectly traceable to Polykleitos, e.g. that of the so-called Idolino in Florence. It is of oval form, and is covered with hair, the curls of which are not

quite short but lie very close to the head ; the mouth is drawn down
a little at the left corner, which gives the expression of the face a
slight touch of sentimentality ; the tip of the nose is new, the whole
head has been much re-worked. Although the neck has been
broken, there can be little doubt that the head belongs to the body.
All the forms of the body suggest in a similar manner an earlier type
(of Myron, according to Brunn, *Annali*, 1879, pp. 201 ff.) in a somewhat modernised transformation and in more slender proportions.
The front of the body is treated in a rather superficial manner.
Breast and back are vigorous, the back near the loins very hollow,
the nates powerful, with very marked hollows on their outer sides ;
the lower margin of the muscles of the belly towards the hips
very strong, the l. shoulder angular. The pubes is treated freely,
with small, crisp curls. The r. arm, which is broken where the hand
joins the wrist and in the upper arm, appears quite antique, and so
does the alabastron ; the hand is connected with the shoulder by a
support (*puntello*). The l. arm has not been broken ; only the fingers
of the hand are new. The l. thigh has been broken, but is antique
like the stem of a tree. On a branch of the stem hang by one strap
two small cylinders, each carefully wound round with a cord, which
can hardly be leaping-weights (ἀλτῆρες). They resemble rather broad
rollers of leather or of a similar flexible material. Can they have
served for boxers instead of the usual straps of hard leather (ἱμάντες)?
New : both legs from below the knee, portions of the lower part of
the stem and the pedestal. Italian marble. H. 1·68. [*Cm*]

10. **Statue of Dionysos,** declared by Müller to be "Hippo-
lytus-Virbius." The torso is antique. It is draped in a short chiton,
which only reaches to the knees. The shoulder-pieces of the chiton
resemble sleeves, and fall down to the elbows ; the chiton is girdled,
forming a bunch of folds below the girdle, and is somewhat drawn up
on the l. side. A somewhat longer under-garment appears at the neck
and on the legs. An animal's skin hangs from the l. shoulder slantwise
across the breast ; its head hangs by the god's l. hip, resembling that
of a panther, except that it has long pointed ears ; probably it is a
lynx's head. A small cloak lies on the r. shoulder and falls behind
to the loins ; it is then drawn under the l. arm and thrown back
over the shoulder, so that the corner falls down to the knee. The
figure rests on the l. leg, the r. being somewhat drawn back. New :
l. arm, which is held at a right angle, together with the shoulder and
the paw of the skin ; that part of the cloak which is detached from the
body (restored as it seems correctly), the lower part of the r. arm, r. leg

from below the knee, half the lower part of the l. leg with the corresponding piece of the stem of a tree, boots, and pedestal. The neck has been inserted in restoration. The head is much worn, and probably did not originally belong to the body, as it is too small for it; it has long curls falling down, is adorned on the top, along the parting, with several plaits, and is encircled by a ribbon. New: tip of nose and chin. The whole figure is of unpleasing and petty execution; the back has been neglected. Italian marble. H. 1·64. [*Cm]

11. **Draped female figure.** Dallaway, no. 9. Motive the same as of the statues engraved in Clarac, v. 975, 2513; 982 B, 2423 C. The female is quite enveloped in her cloak, her lowered r. arm being hidden; the l. forearm is raised a little, and the hand holds the corner of the drapery. Head veiled. New: second and fifth fingers of l. hand, neck, and parts of cloak; the head (nose new) possibly belongs to the body. The figure is in excellent preservation, but executed in a coarse, decorative style; the surface has been much worn, probably by the action of rain; and in some parts polished over. Greek marble. H. 1·96. [*Cm]

12. **Group of Pan and Olympos (Daphnis).** Clarac, IV. 726 B, 1736 E. A lion's skin is spread over a large block of rock, and on it sit the goat-legged Pan with his l. leg drawn up, and the delicate, nude youth (rather Daphnis than Olympos, cf. Stephani, *Compte-Rendu,* 1862, pp. 98 ff.). The latter sits with his l. foot tucked under his r. leg, and with lowered head he is coyly trying to evade the importunities of the lustful semi-brute. Pan is laying his l. hand on the boy's l. shoulder and his r. on the syrinx, which the youth holds in front of his breast with both hands. On the rock below the youth, where the head of the lion's skin hangs down, are two small heifers; beside Pan a herdsman's staff (*pedum*) is introduced; both attributes appear also in the Albani replica, now in the Torlonia Museum, no. 266 (Clarac, IV. 716 D, 1736 G), the pedum also in the Naples copy (Cavalieri, *Antiq. stat. l.* III. *et* IV. Pl. 81) and in another copy in Rome (Matz-Duhn, *Ant. Bildwerke in Rom,* I. no. 500). New, of Pan: r. arm and shoulder (the l. arm, though broken, is antique), the nose (which is not brutish, though the other features, particularly the bleating mouth and the small eyes, are quite like those of a goat), parts of the beard, the r. leg, the drapery, which is arranged so as to conceal the evidences of Pan's excitement. New, of Olympos: three parts of the l. arm, half the r. arm and the syrinx, patches on the legs, which have been much broken, but in essentials

are antique. The head is antique, but it did not belong originally to the body; it appears rather to be a head of Dionysos, having long hair and a fillet round the forehead. The group has been much smoothed over. It is of rather commonplace execution, and ranks far behind the example at Naples; for other replicas cf. Jahn, *Griech. Bilderchroniken*, p. 41, n. 272. Transparent Parian marble. H., incl. pedestal, 1·50. The group was purchased by the late Lord Egremont at the Bessborough sale at Roehampton in 1801, cf. Dallaway, *Of Statuary*, pp. 322, 349. [*C*]

13 (on the pedestal of no. 12). **Greek Relief**, apparently votive. In the centre, facing r., sits a veiled female figure (Hygieia?) on a cushioned chair with a footstool; her hands in her lap holding a cup, up to which a snake rears its coils. Behind the female figure stands a female attendant in a double chiton; her r. hand is lowered; on the l. she holds out a cup. On the extreme r. an altar. The r. edge is broken. Relief of coarse, angular treatment, not Attic. H. 0·35. L. 0·42. [*C*]

14. Torso, completed by restoration as a standing Dionysos with a panther. Clarac, IV. 678 D, 1619 A. Only the torso is antique, with half the r. upper arm, which is lowered, a quarter of the r. leg on which the body rests, and half of the l. leg. New: head and neck, three parts of the r. arm, l. arm with shoulder, half the breast, all the cloak (the back as well as the front), three parts of the r. and half of the l. leg, the large panther and the pedestal. Poor work. Italian marble. H. 2·07. [*C*]

15. Male portrait statue in sitting posture. Dallaway, no. 1. The motive is that of the so-called Marcellus in the Capitol (*Gall. Giustin.*, I. Pl. 113. Maffei, *Racc.*, Pl. 88. *Mus. Chiaram.*, II. Pl. 46. Righetti, *Campidoglio*, II. Pl. 367. Clarac, V. 895, 2288 = 902, 2308), the Ludovisi statue by Zenon of Aphrodisias (Perrier, *Segm. nob. stat.*, Pl. 15), and the Florentine (Clarac, V. 904, 2305). The man is sitting in a chair, draped in a tunic and over it a pallium, which covers his whole person except the r. arm and the r. half of the breast. The body leans over to its r., the r. arm lies in the lap; the l. shoulder is raised, showing that this arm, too, instead of waving freely and gesticulating with outstretched hand, originally rested with a slight bending of the elbow on the edge of the chair, where some holes are visible, as well as other indications of the original position of the arm. The lower part of the l. leg is outstretched, the r. drawn back; on the r. foot is an ornamental sandal, thickly bound. New: l. forearm from below the elbow, three parts of the r. arm with the

roll in the hand, and the l. foot. The antique head, of Parian
marble (new : tip of nose), ascribed by Müller to the time of the
Antonines, while Bernoulli declares it to be probably Gallienus, does
not belong to the statue. This head presents a feeble man with a
small beard, certainly a Roman ; while as to the figure, the presence
of the pallium instead of the toga, and the good general conception,
point to its belonging to a Greek personage. The whole surface of
the statue is much corroded. H. 1·50. Formerly in the Barberini
palace. The inventory of the Barberini Collection drawn up in 1738
gives but one article which can be identified with our marble, "*una
statua a sedere rappresentante vuomo togato antico senza testa e senza
braccia, e mancante di un piede, stimata scudi trentacinque*" (*Docum.
ined. per servire alla storia dei Musei d' Italia*, IV. p. 45). This entry
shows that really the statue was without a head when in the Barberini
Palace. [**BCm*]

   16.   Statue of a Hora—Winter (according to Müller,
Autumn). Dallaway, no. 18, "Nymph." The figure rests with
most weight on the l. foot. She wears a chiton with sleeves, which
does not quite reach to her feet and leaves the r. shoulder bare,
and over the chiton a cloak folded double, which envelopes the
l. arm, the stomach, and nearly the whole of the legs in a fairly
uniform mass ; the end of the cloak falls over the l. forearm, which
is advanced at a right angle. Sandals are on the feet. In her
lowered r. hand the girl carries three birds, apparently ducks
(new : two necks and heads), which reach down to the stem of a
tree ; in her l. hand is a hare (legs new). These attributes are
more consistent with winter than autumn ; cf. a statue in Turin
(Dütschke, *Ant. Bildwerke in Oberitalien*, IV. no. 83). New : the r.
arm from the elbow to the wrist, parts of the legs. The head has
been re-set, but appears to belong to the statue ; it is surrounded by
curls, and a head-cloth (*opisthosphendonē*) is bound round it and
knotted together over the forehead. The head looks somewhat
stiffly straight in front ; it is rather insignificant, and much worn.
The whole figure is somewhat stiff, the drapery peculiarly arranged
with more affectation than taste ; besides, the statue has been much
re-worked in a style like Cavaceppi's, but inferior. Italian marble.
H. 1·52. [**Cm*]

   17.   Statue of a " Nymph of Artemis." Clarac, IV. 564 D,
1248 B. A maiden, in a short chiton reaching to her knees, stands
supporting herself by her r. elbow on a square pillar, which is almost
entirely covered with a cloak. The chiton, the upper fold of which

covers the whole stomach, is girt high under the breast with a round cord, the ends of which fall down straight in front of the body. A ribbon, like the hand of a quiver, goes from her r. shoulder down her back to the girdle, and in front right across her breast to a little below the girdle, where it suddenly ceases: there is no trace of a quiver. The figure rests on the l. leg; the l. hip projects very much, so that the upper part of the body is quite forced to the r. side, which causes an unusual twisting of the whole figure. A part of the cloak is drawn down from the pillar and entirely covers the r. leg, which is much bent and must originally have been supported on some object. The l. hand, which is lowered, probably grasped a piece of the drapery. New: r. forearm, which is bent upwards, considerable portions of the folds of the cloak, half the l. forearm (the middle part of the arm is broken, but antique), half the lower part of the l. leg, and half the r. leg with the foot, the pose of which is elegant to excess, and just touching the ground with its toes; the pedestal, the stem of a tree that has been introduced as a support between the legs, and parts of the pillar. The neck is for the most part a new insertion, but the head appears to belong to the statue. It has the character of a youthful Aphrodite; the wavy hair is gathered in a knot behind; a low stephane was probably only intended to support a metal one, for the securing of which two holes have been made; both eyes have been restored. The figure is pleasing, much more so than is to be inferred from the engraving, and very delicately executed, but it has unfortunately suffered much at the hands of an incompetent restorer. It is very difficult to give a confident explanation of it, as the no doubt significant attribute under the r. foot is now missing. Parian marble. H. 1·53. [*Cm]

(Under no. 17 is a long **Greek Inscription**, very much rubbed and very difficult to read: it will only be possible to decipher it with the aid of a paper impression.)

18. Statue of an Amazon. Clarac, v. 808, 2031 A. Dallaway, no. 20. The statue belongs to the type of the Mattei Amazon; unfortunately it has been much re-worked. New: the entire up-raised r. arm, the lowered l. arm from the shoulder, the legs from the knees, the stem of the tree with shield and double axe, the helmet, the pedestal. The remains of a *puntello*, intended to secure the l. arm, are preserved. The quiver has been broken off behind, and the under surface has been rasped, so that there is no trace of the bow, which must once have been fastened to it. The great importance of the statue consists in its being the only specimen, among all the replicas

of this type, in which the original head is preserved ; for though it
has been broken off, the very nature of the line of breakage and the
quality of the marble left no doubt either in my mind or in that of the
late Dr Klügmann, who examined the statue in 1880, that it belongs
to the statue ; only a little piece of the tip of the nose has been
restored. The head, which has also been in great part re-worked, is
rather heavy in comparison with the body. The type of face has
much in common with that of the Lansdowne Amazon (London,
Lansdowne House, no. 83), particularly as to the eyes with their
well-defined lids. In other respects the features are less sharp ;
the mouth forms a curving line with a slight expression of sternness,
the upper lip is rather full and the under lip delicate ; the nostrils
are a little depressed. The line of the profile is Attic, inclined to
straightness, the line of the nose being only a little advanced ;
the line of the jaw forms an obtuse angle ; the chin is very distinctly
marked. The soft wavy hair is brushed back and gathered into a
small knot behind. The narrow ribbon which goes round the hair,
and the whole length of which is visible, is a characteristic mark of
this type ; it appears also on the gem engraved by Natter (Müller-
Wieseler, I. 31, 138 *b*), which repeats this type. It does not appear
doubtful to me that a good Attic type of the fifth century B.C. is at
the bottom of the somewhat modernised delineation of the head in
this comparatively mediocre example, and that Kekulé is wrong in
attributing the invention of this type to a much later period (*Comment. Mommsen.*, p. 485). H. 1·99. [*Cm*]

19. Male portrait statue in sitting posture. *Spec.*, II. Pl.
7, 8. Clarac, v. 840 C, 2143. Dallaway, no. 2. An elderly man
with bare breast, flabby soft skin, and very marked collar-bones, is
sitting on a stone seat with no back ; his thin r. arm lies in his lap,
and his l. elbow is supported by his r. hand. Legs, body, and l. arm
are partly covered by his wide cloak with rich folds, which is stretched
between the knees so as to leave scarcely any hollow. On the feet
are sandals ; the r. advanced, the l. drawn back. New : the upraised l. forearm, the neck, the r. foot from the drapery, the l. foot,
the front piece of the pedestal. To this elderly body, which would well
suit a statue of Demosthenes (cf. Knole, no. 1), there has been joined,
by the insertion of a new neck, a head which Conze and Bernoulli
take to be in truth meant for Demosthenes. But it has not the pointed
oval form of face, not the characteristic mouth with the under lip
drawn in, nor the eyes of Demosthenes, nor his hair, which in the
subject before us is soft and rather curly, thick on the top and at the

back of the head, but scanty on the forehead; the beard is too soft, not strong and not clipped, as Demosthenes' was. This head resembles that of Demosthenes only in its general character of morose gravity; the pregnant energy of the orator is wanting. New: nose. The head, like the statue, is of Pentelic marble, and they accord very well together; nevertheless it had originally nothing to do with the body, as is conclusively shown by the Inventory of the Barberini Collection compiled in 1738 (*Docum. ined. per servire alla storia dei Musei d'Italia*, IV. p. 57), for we find the statue among the "*rottami di statue*," where it is described as "*una statua a sedere, più grande del naturale, con una spalla ed un braccio nudo, senza testa e braccio manco, alta pal. 5 on. 8.*" The body is of good and very simple composition and execution, and is undoubtedly Attic. The r. thigh, as often happens with sitting figures, is enormously long. The left must be regarded as the principal side, as the drapery is richer and fuller there. The statue would show to better advantage if it stood somewhat lower. A fine bronze statuette from Brindisi, of similar composition, is to be found in the British Museum (*Guide to Bronze Room*, p. 47, no. 3. *Encyclop. Britann.*, 9th ed., art. "Archaeology," p. 365). H. 1·48. Formerly in the Barberini Palace. [*BCm*]

Then follow the **busts of the Statue Gallery**, the greater part of which in 1877 occupied a temporary situation in a corner of the room.

20. Archaistic terminal head of Apollo (according to Müller, of Dionysos). *Spec.*, I. 28. Dallaway, no. 49. Two long ringlets fall down on either side; loose curls hang over the forehead. A ribbon is drawn through the hair. New: nose and a few curls. Expression noble. Execution commonplace. Over life size. [*m*]

21. Head of the bearded Bacchus, colossal scale, crowned with ivy, with a fillet round the forehead. In good preservation. [*C*]

22. Double terminal bust representing the bearded **Dionysos** and **Ariadne**, life size. Archaistic style. New: both noses. [*Cm*]

23. Heroic Head. *Spec.*, I. Pl. 54. Dallaway, no. 43. In character and inclination the head resembles that of the Menelaus or Ajax in the Vatican (*Mus. Pio.-Clem.*, VI. Pl. 18), but is by no means identical with it. The helmet, broken off in front, is simpler, of a hardly antique shape and ornamentation, especially in the front; the plume has been for the most part restored. The eyes are remarkably

deep set : they look upwards ; their form and that of the brow and
of the forehead show a marked mannerism ; odd too is the way in
which the hair is arranged all round under and over the edge of the
helmet. The mouth is opened wide like that of the Laokoon. The
nose is nearly all restored. The beard is negligently treated in great
tufts ; below the lips all has been restored, as also have the neck and
breast. The head, praised by Payne Knight in exaggerated terms, is,
if not totally new, at least very much re-worked and amended. Bad
Italian marble. H. of head, including the helmet, 0·45. L. of face
0·22. [*BCm]

24. **Bust of a youth.** *Spec.*, I. Pl. 30 (not quite adequate, too
sharp). The head is very beautiful ; its unusually crisp curls are
delicately and carefully executed. It belongs to a statue of a victor,
as is shown by the broad fillet which almost covers the forehead ;
over either temple small sling-shaped loops of the fillet peep forth
from behind its main portions. The face is of a beautiful oval ;
eyes long and narrow, cheeks flat, mouth tender ; the nose advances but slightly from the line of the profile. This fact, and the
expression of individuality and intellect, suggest that it is the copy of
an Attic original, no doubt of the fourth century B.C. Replicas of the
head are in Rome (*Mon. dell' Inst.*, IX. Pl. 36 ; one of the loops by
mistake changed into a roll), and in Treves (*Jahrb. d. Vereins v.
Alterthumsfr. in Rheinlande*, IX. Pl. 5, 2, only a fragment) ; but they
are far behind our example, which has preserved its original polish.
As to the general character and the motive one may compare
the description in Kallistratos of the bronze Diadumenos by Praxiteles (*Stat.* 11), e.g. κόμη δὲ εἶχεν ἕλικας ταῖς ὀφρύσιν ἐπιβαίνοντας· ὃ δὲ
τῷ τελαμῶνι καταστέφων τὴν κόμην καὶ ἐκ τῶν ὀφρύων ἀπωθούμενος
τῷ διαδήματι τὰς τρίχας γυμνὸν πλοκάμων ἐτήρει τὸ μέτωπον. New : tip
of nose and bust. L. of face 0·18. [*m]

25. **Bust of a youth** with the character of Hermes. Curly
hair, expression tender and beautiful, decidedly Attic, somewhat in
the style of Praxiteles. New : nose, neck, bust ; also the top of the
head and the hair have been partly restored. Good work. Pentelic
marble. H. of the genuine part 0·26. L. of face 0·18. [*]

26. Modern copy of the head of **Hermes** (so-called Antinous)
of the Belvedere, with bust and pedestal all completely unbroken,
but much corroded ; perhaps because it has stood for a long while in
the open air. [*]

27. **Bust of a heroine.** See the annexed plate. This fragment of a colossal statue is one of the most remarkable specimens in

the collection. Unluckily it stands in a very unfavourable position
under a window. The whole head is antique except pieces behind
the ears ; the fore-part of the neck is new, but the bust as far as
below the breast is antique. So are the ends of the long curls and
the plait that falls far down, also the stump of the r. arm which is
stretched out horizontally, while the l. (for the most part new) was
lowered. Over a fine under-garment the lady wears an Attic doubled
chiton, which is buttoned together on each shoulder, where it forms
rich folds. (It is not a chlamys as may at first sight appear.) The
forehead is perpendicular, the beginning of the parting comes down
on to it, as is usually the case with colossal heads (*e.g.* the Ludovisi
Hera). The hair is parted on both sides as it were into waves,
which crowding one over the other fall down in a rich mass behind. Above the forehead and over these wavy portions of the
hair may be seen a narrow vertical circle intended probably to be
the support for a metal stephané. There are some scratches on
the face, otherwise it is in excellent preservation. The nose is wide
and straight, making no very marked angle with the line of the
profile. The mouth is excellent, lips slightly apart and gently
curved; it bespeaks, as does indeed the whole expression of the face,
surprise if not disdain, but accompanied by that self-restraint in
emotion which we admire so much in the head of Niobè. This head,
though more oval, is in fact closely related to that of Niobè, as a
counterpart and complement to whom her rival Leto naturally occurs
to the mind. Klugmann's opinion (*Arch. Zeit.*, 1869, p. 32) that
it is a replica of the Farnese head of Hera (*Mon. dell' Inst.*, viii.
Pl. 1. Overbeck, *Kunstmythol., Atlas*, Pl. 9, 1, 2) I consider
erroneous; the long curls alone contradict such an idea, and so
does the whole stylistic character of the head. In spite of this it
may be a Hera, although in the epoch in which I must place the
head, the oval form of the face in a Hera would appear very remarkable. This capital head, which is a good copy of some grand
original of the fourth century B.C., has caught something of the
brilliance of the original, and ought to be made more widely known
by means of casts. The marble is apparently Pentelic. H. 0·89.
L. of face, 0·26; forehead, 0·09; nose, 0·09; upper lip, 0·025 ;
chin, 0·055. [*Cm*]

28. Bust of Artemis? Dallaway, no. 40, "Sabina," now
marked as "Cleopatra." The head, executed after a Greek model,
seems to have originally represented Artemis with a stephané ; the
face is pretty and of fine oval form. New: nose, l. eyebrow, a piece

PETWORTH N.º 27

on the chin, neck and bust ; the stephanè has also been adorned by a restorer with a sun, two half-moons, two stars and sundry jewels. L. of face 0·17. [*]

29. **Ideal female head**, with the wavy head-dress so common on Greek female heads. Undoubtedly the head was originally very pretty, but nose, mouth, chin and neck are new. Work somewhat superficial. Nearly life size. [*]

30. **Greek portrait head**. *Spec.*, 1. Pl. 66. Its characteristics are curly hair and beard ; expression stern and thoughtful ; there is a slight resemblance to Karneades (Visconti, *Iconogr. grecque*, 1. Pl. 19). Pupils expressed. Somewhat corroded. New : nose, neck and bust. Over life size. [*]

31. **Bust of Brutus**. In character the head resembles the L. Brutus of the Capitol (Visconti, *Iconogr. rom.*, 1. Pl. 2. Bernoulli. *Röm. Ikonogr.*, 1. p. 20), without being identical with it. It is turned to the l. A Greek portrait seems to me to be the foundation of it. The surface is completely re-worked and polished. New : nose, neck and bust. Life size. [*BC]

32. **Bust of a laughing girl.** Dallaway, no. 32. The fresh young head has quite the expression of a Satyr, but it is without pointed ears : the hair is entirely drawn back from the face and gathered into a knot behind. New : nose and upper lip, also the nude bust with a nebris. The head will bear comparison with the head of the Hermaphroditos in the Malatesta group (Clarac, IV. 671, 1736). Below life size. [*C]

33. Bearded **portrait** head, with gloomy look, belonging undoubtedly to the second century, probably of **Aelius Caesar.** Perpendicular profile. Good bust, in perfect preservation. [*B]

34. **Portrait** head, like Aelius Caesar. The flesh is smoothly, the hair roughly treated. New : tip of the nose ; otherwise well preserved. [*]

35. **Bust of Marcus Aurelius.** Dallaway, no. 29. In youthful style, without beard. New : tip of nose, neck and bust. [*C]

36. **Septimius Severus.** Dallaway, no. 22 ? 34 ? New : tip of nose. [*B]

37. **Clodius Albinus**, or a head like him. New : nose and sundry details. [*B]

38. **Portrait head** of similar character, over life size. Dallaway, no. 36 ? Beard soft and even, but not long ; hair short, forehead high. The glance is directed downward to the r. New : tip of nose and bust. [*]

39. Portrait head, with curly hair and weak beard. [*]

40. Bust of a Roman youth, with curly hair and faint whiskers and mustache. Pupils and eyebrows expressed. New: nose and bust. If I am not mistaken, this head, or the foregoing one, is copied in a volume containing drawings by Cipriani in the British Museum (MS. Add. 21118 fol. 11) as having formerly belonged to Lyde Browne (Introd. § 52); it might however be a replica, cf. no. 46. [*]

41. Bust of a child with bulla. Dallaway, no. 27. The child has fat cheeks; he wears on his head along the parting a curious plait with regular knots or buttons on either side of it. The head is let in to a draped bust to which it may possibly belong, with a wide horizontal stripe (so-called *lacna*), and in the midst of it the oyster-shaped *bulla*, the hinge of which, fastened with four pins, is very carefully indicated. New: tip of nose. Smaller than life size. [*m]

42. Bust of a boy, with curly hair. The neck is antique. New: tip of nose and bust. [*]

43. Bust of a boy, with a round cap which is pointed at the top, on his slightly curly hair. Dallaway, no. 43. Neat. New: neck and bust. [*C]

44. Bust of a child, smiling, with a silly expression. Tip of nose missing. New: neck and bust. Small scale. [*]

45. Head of a Roman matron. Dallaway, no. 33? Her hair is brushed tightly back on both sides, one plait lies back over the crown. New: only the tip of the nose; all the rest is antique. Good portrait, belonging to the first century A.D. [*B]

46. Colossal bust of an Empress, of the beginning of the third century A.D., with headdress of the fashion of Julia Mammaea, though it is not this empress herself. Dallaway, no. 23, " Julia Pia." The wavy hair hangs far down behind and is then gathered up again in a plait. Eyebrows and pupils expressed. The flesh is polished. New: nose, parts of the lips, and chin. This bust, or another one exactly like it (cf. no. 66), is to be found among Cipriani's drawings (cf. under no. 40) from the collection of Lyde Browne, fol. 15, as Julia Pia. Italian marble. H. 0·52. Length of face 0·26. [*B]

47. Female portrait bust, with the hair drawn back. New: top and back of the head, and the bust. [*]

48. Girl's head, neat, with the wavy hair drawn back; on each cheek a single ringlet. [*]

49, 50. Table legs, ornamented with griffins. [*]

51. Large bronze relief. Dallaway, p. 290. To the r. the temple of Jupiter Capitolinus and three men with wreaths, on the l. the sacrifice of a bull; further r. two boys holding a large round shield. " Sent lately from Italy by the Hon. W. Wyndham, his Majesty's minister at Florence " Dallaway (1800). To Müller the relief appeared antique; Conze is sure it is new; it is fixed in a very unfavourable place, but I take it to be only a copy or imitation of the Medici relief in Florence (Uffizi, no. 29 of Dütschke's catalogue. Sante Bartoli, *Admiranda*, Pl. 43). [*Cm*]

VAN DYCK ROOM.

In the corners of this large room, brilliantly adorned with paintings by Van Dyck, stand the four following statues :—

52. Statue of Artemis. Dallaway, no. 4. The goddess rests on her r. leg, the l. is drawn back. She is robed in a short chiton with a bunch of folds hanging down; over this is an animal's skin with long, broad ears (according to Müller that of a lynx), which is gathered in with the girdle. Both arms are lowered. Near the r. leg sits a dog; on the stem of a tree behind the leg hangs a quiver. New : head, three parts of the l. arm, half the r. forearm, l. knee, part of the quiver; of the dog, head and neck. Legs and arms of the statue broken in many places, but antique. Ordinary work. Parian marble. H. 1·26. [*Cm*]

53. Statue of an attendant at the sacrifice (*camillus*). *Spec.*, i. Pl. 68. Clarac, iv. 769, 1910. The boy has long curly hair adorned with a laurel wreath. He wears a very wide tunic ungirdled; its shoulder pieces fall down below his elbows like sleeves. In front of him he holds a pig, outstretched, the fore-legs with his r., the hind legs with his l. hand. Near the l. leg is the stem of a tree on which hangs a triangular box with the wide sacrificial knife. The statue is in excellent preservation. New : only the l. forearm of the boy with the hind legs of the pig, the ears of the pig and the boy's nose. The sculpture is in a broad, good style, though somewhat poor; the pig is the most successful feature of the piece. Parian marble. H. 1·25, with the pedestal, 1·35. [*Cm*]

54. Statue of Seilenos. *Spec.*, i. Pl. 69. Clarac, iv. 734, 1770. Dallaway, no. 14. The thickset, powerful figure stands in a posture of repose, draped only in an apron round the loins and rather high boots. On his head, which is bearded, bald, and crowned with ivy, Seilenos carries a winnowing fan (λίκνον, *vannus*), which he holds with both hands. Its contents are hidden by a cloth which hangs down. Near the l. leg is a stem of a tree entwined with a vine, and a snake coiling itself up it. The figure is broken in sundry places, but is almost entirely antique : only the tip of the nose appeared to me new, but the *Specimens* enumerate " the middle parts of both legs, and of the r. arm, and a splinter from the cista." Coarse-grained Parian marble. Good decorative figure ; it may be compared as to motive with an excellent Greek bronze from Aegion, in the British Museum (*Guide to Bronze Room*, p. 46, no. 2). H. 1·60, with the pedestal, 1·68. [*Cm*]

55. **Statue of a Roman in toga.** Dallaway, no. 15. The man wears shoes; on his right stands the box with rolls (*scrinium*). New, or at any rate re-worked : the half of the lowered r. forearm with the roll in the hand; certainly new, the advanced l. forearm and neck. The head of a boy joined to the statue, a third part of which is new, is of different marble, and, setting aside the smallness of the statue, there is no reason for supposing the figure to be a boy or even a particularly young man. Italian marble. H. 1·30. [*Cm*]

MARBLE HALL (Dining Room).

56. **Statue of a man in Oriental costume.** *Spec.*, II. Pl. 56, " Marcus Aurelius." Clarac, v. 936 C, 2511 B, "*empereur romain ou prêtre.*" Dallaway, no. 11, " Helenus the priest of Apollo." The figure is a very uncommon one, and Müller is probably correct in considering it the minister of some Oriental cult. He wears a long tunic, with long narrow sleeves, trimmed at the bottom with fringe, which reaches to the middle of his shins, and over it a small cloak likewise bordered with fringe. It rests on both shoulders and covers great part of the front of the body. New : both legs from below the drapery, the l. from a little more below, so that a fragment of the high boot, with its crossed thongs and border turned over at the upper edge, belongs to the antique part ; also, half the r. forearm with the cup, and the l. arm above the elbow with the roll in the hand. On the head is a wreath, and it is difficult to believe that the head belongs to the body ; it is an unknown portrait and has a short beard ; the hair is deeply undercut with the drill. Italian marble. H. abt. 2·00. [*Bm*]

57. **Statue of a Roman in toga.** Dallaway, no. 8. A *scrinium* beside the l. foot. New : the r. forearm, the l. arm with the roll, half the r. and a portion of the l. foot, and the pedestal. Head and neck are inserted ; the tangled hair hangs partly over the forehead, the beard is shaven close ; nose new. The statue is not bad,

and belongs possibly to the age of the Antonines. H. abt. 2·00.
[*Bm]

BEAUTY ROOM.

In this room and in the staircase-well adjoining is a large number
of busts, for the most part in excellent preservation and in some
cases of remarkable beauty and great rarity. Like Bernoulli and
Conze, I was so unfortunate as only to be able to make a very cursory
inspection.

58. **Bust of Antinous,** calmer and less gloomy than he is
usually depicted. The face is polished, the hair rough. New: tip
of nose, mouth, l. eyebrow, bust. Splendid Parian marble. Life
size. [*C]

59. **Bust of the elder Faustina.** Dallaway, no. 41. The
head is very beautiful; it is turned up towards its right. The delicate nose is well preserved, and so is the neck; the bust is new.
The lobes of the ears are pierced. The form of the face is round
and full. Pupils expressed. The hair is drawn back from the face;
new: the top and the back of the head with a nest of plaits on it.
Parian marble of a warm yellowish colour; good sculpture. Life
size. [*]

60. **Bust of a Roman matron.** Dallaway, no. 39. The
head is elderly and, with the neck, is in excellent preservation; only
the bust is new. The hair is wavy and drawn away to the side
in single tresses, so that the lower gradually are lost beneath the
upper. On the top of the head is a high arrangement of plaits
resembling a basket. Fine-grained Greek marble; excellent sculpture of the 2nd century A.D. Life size. [*]

61. **Bust of an old Roman lady.** Spec., 1. Pl. 72, 73. On
the top of the back of the head are two enormous plaits. She has
a penetrating gaze. New: nose, parts of the ears, and the lower
part of the draped bust. The head is badly polished. It belongs
to the 2nd century A.D. Life size. [*m]

62. **Bust of a Roman matron,** middle aged. The hair is
simply parted and drawn back. New: tip of the aquiline nose. The
draped bust is patched. Very white marble. [*]

63. **Head of a child,** of about six years old, on a draped bust
(probably that with a so-called lacna? see Dallaway, no. 21, "perhaps Caracalla." Müller, p. 256). Well preserved. Life size. [*m]

64. **Child's head,** with pretty curly hair. The pupils are

faintly expressed. New: tip of nose. The draped bust possibly belongs to it. Life size. [*]

Inside the door opening into the staircase-well stand before the posts :

65. Head of an empress (Julia Pia ?). Her hair falls with some luxuriance on her neck. Nose restored. Fairly delicate head. Life size. [*]

66. Bust of a Roman lady, of roundish, somewhat clumsy form ; not beautiful ; expression lively, but somewhat pouting and not attractive. The wavy hair is drawn down at the back and then gathered up again in a plait. Pupils and eyebrows expressed. New: tip of nose, and bust. Life size. Cf. above on no. 46. [*]

GRAND STAIRCASE.

67—70. Four Roman female heads, with various styles of head-dress. I had not time to describe them minutely. Bernoulli believes one head, that of **the elder Faustina** (Dallaway, no. 25 ?), to be modern. [*B]

71. Bust of a youth. Dallaway, no. 30, "probably one of the nephews of Augustus" (?). A thick wreath of laurel encircles his head ; his expression is somewhat vacant. Pupils and eyebrows expressed. Much polished. New: nose, neck and bust. Life size. [*]

72. Greek Relief. A youth in a chlamys on horseback rides forward from the l. ; he is greeted by a female figure in a chiton and with a shawl round her shoulders, who offers him a cup with her r. hand and holds an ewer in her l. Behind her, on the extreme r., is a tree, round which a snake twines. Votive? All the ground of the relief, and in some measure the outlines of the figures, have been re-worked. Not important. [C]

I did not find the following specimens, neither are they mentioned by Conze and Bernoulli ; probably they are placed in some private room.

73. Head of Aphroditè. Spec., 1. Pl. 45, 46. Dallaway, no. 31. Replica of the head of the Medici statue but, according to Müller, of greater softness and roundness, and also larger in its proportions. Payne Knight goes even so far as to suppose this head to be a relic of the original of the Medici Venus and her numerous companions. Surface well preserved. Nose and part of the upper lip restored. [m]

74. Bust of Athenè? Dallaway, no. 42, "Athens." The bust is protected by a round aegis, and the head by a so-called Attic helmet, the vizor of which stands up like a diadem in front. Helmet partly new. Müller takes the face for a portrait on account of the individuality of the features. [*m*]

Besides these Müller found a number of **bronze statuettes**, among which he considered worthy of mention :

75. Poseidon, with muscular build of limb, long flowing hair and beard. With the (upraised?) l. hand he appears to have held a trident, with the r. the bridle (or a dolphin, or a hippocampus?). Excellent work, similar to that of the Zeus of Paramythia in the British Museum (*Spec.*, I. Pl. 32). A span and a half high. [*m*]

I found it impossible to identify all the busts mentioned by Dallaway with those enumerated above ; I therefore briefly mention those with which I have not succeeded.

Dallaway, no. 24.—Female bust, unknown. The hair is much swelled out on either side, and tied in a knot behind; in front are tufts of flowers. On the tessera of the pedestal is Cupid burning a butterfly with a torch.

Dall., no. 25. Female bust having the attire much like that of the **Faustinas**. Intire, but the neck has been broken off. [No. 67 ?]

Dall., no. 26. Bust resembling **Hadrian**. Intire, but of coarse sculpture.

Dall., no. 28. Bust with the "latus clavus" ["*laena*"], nose restored ; resembling **Septimius Severus** rather than Pescennius Niger.

Dall., no. 35. **Young man**, with close hair.

Dall., no. 37. One of the **Dioscuri** [with a cap made like an egg ?], upon a modern bust. From the Barberini Palace.

Dall., no. 38. **Man** unknown, with the hair and beard in massy curls.

Dall., no. 44. **Didia Clara**, on a modern bust, the nose restored.

Dall., no. 45. Female head attired like **Julia Titi**, much repaired.

Dall., no. 46. **Antoninus Pius**, with the neck upon a grey numachella bust.

Dall., no. 47. **Hadrian**.

Dall., no. 50. Head of **Bacchus** on a terminus, in his youthful or effeminate character.

Dall., p. 290 (in a private room). Bust; the face is of crystal, and the rest of porphyry. It appears to be of **Isis** or **Arsinoe**, as it has the lotus on the head. [Modern?]

PIPPBROOK HOUSE (Surrey).

Conze, *Arch. Anz.*, 1864, p. 167.

This house, situated near Dorking, contains the considerable collection made by the late Mr FORMAN, M.P., which is in the possession of his widow, now Mrs SEYMOUR BURT. In this collection Conze saw several minor works of art, such as **bronzes, glass articles, vases**, etc. ; among them ranks as the principal piece a **vase with Amazons**, from Agrigentum (Gerhard, *Auserl. Vasenbilder*, IV. Pl. 329, 330). I was unfortunately prevented in 1877 from going through the collection by an affliction in the owner's family. A letter from the late Dr Klügmann, who visited Pippbrook House in 1880, informs me that there are also a few marbles, viz. :

1. **Statuette restored as Hygieia.** H. abt. 0·90.
2. **Statuette restored as Ceres.** Same size.
3. 4. Two **double terminal half-figures**; the one composed of two men bearing a lamb (?) each, and holding bunches of grapes in the lowered r. hand. Small size.
5. Divers **single terminal busts.** Small size.
6. **Head of horse.** Size of life.
7. **Etruscan cinerary urns**, abt. 17 examples.

The **painted vases** are of all classes, from the earliest to the latest style ; besides **lamps**, and **terracottas** of every description, also gilt ; **bronzes**, implements as well as small figures, and particularly **mirrors**, some of which are already known from engravings, while others are as yet unknown.

RAMSGATE (Kent).

In the hall of Augusta Lodge, the possession of HENRY CURLING, Esq., is placed a **double terminal bust of Epikures and Metrodoros**, which was left to the present owner by the late Mr Thomas Allason, author of *Pictures and Views of the Antiquities of Pola* (London, 1819). The two busts, over life size, placed back to back, stand on a square shaft tapering downwards, which is about 1·80 high, and are surmounted by a small square marble, projecting towards its upper end and slightly ornamented, which seems to be meant to support some piece of architecture, as indeed it actually does. The names επικογροc and μητροδωροc are inscribed on the shaft, not, as is usual, directly beneath the edge of the breast-piece, but at a certain

distance below it. The whole monument in all its parts is cut from
the same marble, without any join. The heads and faces are quite
perfect; only on the shaft there are some repairs. This wonderful
state of preservation of so large a marble cannot but raise serious
doubts about its authenticity. The doubts are strengthened by the
square top ornament, for which it would be difficult to find any
sufficient analogy among ancient terminal busts; by the palaeographical character of the inscriptions, especially the short horizontal stroke
of the ϵ, and the ω with its upper extremities curved outwards; by
a rosette occupying the place of the usual mark of male terms, a
feature utterly unheard of in antique art; not to mention certain
stylistic details in the treatment of the hair and the beard. The
marble is presumed to have been found in digging the foundation of
the new Portico of S. Maria Maggiore in Rome, in 1742. This
appears to involve a confusion with the famous double terminal bust
of the same two philosophers, which really was discovered on that
occasion and passed into the Capitoline Museum, of which it still
forms a highly admired ornament (cf. *Mus. Capitol.*, I. Pl. v. Visconti,
Iconogr. grecque, I. Pl. 25, p. 292 n. 1 Mil.). As there is not the
least allusion in literature to a second similar bust found at the same
time and place, I have little doubt that the bust at Ramsgate is a
modern copy of the Capitoline bust, and that the same origin has
been ascribed to the two either by mistake or in the interest of the
trade in objects of art. [*From letters of Mr Curling, and a photograph
kindly sent by him.*]

RICHMOND (Surrey).

Michaelis, *Arch. Zeit.*, 1874, pp. 59 ff.

FRANCIS COOK, Esq., lived for many years in Portugal, and in
recognition of his liberal care for the interests of the public he was
created Visconde de Montserrat in the peerage of Portugal. At
Montserrat, near Cintra, is a section of his collection of antiques,
and it has been catalogued by Gurlitt, *Arch. Zeit.*, 1868, pp. 84 ff.;
in this section is said to be the group of the Nile, formerly in the
Worsley collection (cf. p. 240). In his English residence, Doughty
House, Richmond Hill, Mr Cook has another large collection of
remarkable and interesting specimens. I went through the collection in 1873 and 1877. Moreover I have had some notices of
Bernoulli and Matz placed at my disposal, and lately Prof. Benndorf
of Vienna supplied me with other notices made in 1880.

1. **Ivory Casket**, of a late Roman style. The box is somewhat broader above than below, and flat at both ends; the front is convex, the back consists of a flat cover, which is furnished with a projection on its upper end for greater convenience in taking hold of it and drawing it out. On the upper surface a quadrangular hollow and numerous traces of nails bear witness that some apparatus was fixed here, the use of which is as much a riddle to me as is the intention of the casket altogether. A couple of rings show that it was meant to be hung up; those parts on both sides that project most have been so much rubbed that the vessel must have been carried in such a manner as to expose it to constant friction.—CURVED FRONT. Three Bacchic figures stand in full face over a border of acanthus leaves. In the midst is Dionysos himself, crowned, the upper part of his body nude, the legs covered with his cloak. In his l. hand he grasps the thyrsos, with the r., which is lowered, he is emptying a drinking vessel (much rubbed) over a panther, which crouches on the ground and raises its head to him. To his r. stands a Maenad, with wreath on her head, wearing a long, girdled chiton; the thyrsos is in her r. arm, with her l. hand she raises the tympanon behind her head so that it looks like a nimbus. To the l. of the god a Satyr, draped with an apron of skin about the loins and a fur cloak on his back, carries a wine-skin on his l. shoulder; with the r. arm he shoulders a pedum.—FLAT BACK (cover). Fortuna in full face, robed in chiton and cloak, the cornucopiae in her l. arm, the r. hand on the tiller of a steering paddle. The head is adorned with the attribute of Isis, the feathered disc within two cow's horns. To the r. of the head floats a little Cupid, who holds a purse (?) in his r. hand and points to the rudder with his l. In the background is a curtain. H. 0·15. W. at the upper end 0·09. D. 0·05. [*]

2. **Statue of Aphroditè** ("Venus Mazarin"). There are many similar statues of Venus, but none seems to be more like this than the one copied in Maffei's *Raccolta*, Pl. 144, as in the possession of Ignazio Consiglieri, in Rome; the motive of the r. arm is however quite different, the l. leg is not so much covered, and the dolphin is nearer to the body. Cf. also Clarac, IV. 606 B, 1343 D. Bernoulli, *Aphrodite*, p. 271. The goddess stands on her l. leg; the r. leg is slightly bent, and a little in advance. Her l. hand is lowered

so as to conceal her abdomen with a corner of her fringed cloak, which covers her l. leg entirely; the cloak passes behind her body to the r. hip, and is then taken by the raised r. hand and lifted up high. Thus the r. leg and all the upper part of the body are left uncovered. The proportions of the body are full, like those of the Capitoline Venus, and by no means inclined to slenderness. The head is somewhat heavy. On the top of it is a knot of hair (half of it has been restored), and long curls fall down to the shoulders. The goddess turns her gaze somewhat towards the l.; doubtless something has attracted her attention in that direction, for which reason she has covered her l. leg. Near this leg, and reaching up it midway, is a large dolphin, connected with her thigh by a strong *puntello*; he serves less as a support than as a distinctive attribute. He is plunging in the sea and seizes a cuttle-fish with his mouth. On the dolphin's back are three marks, which suggest the probability that an Eros was there, and on the l. hip of the goddess a piece of drapery has been restored, where probably Eros touched her. The statue is in excellent preservation. Besides the restorations already mentioned we notice only a new piece on the dolphin's tail, and the breasts of the goddess seem to have been patched. Her head and the upraised r. arm holding the drapery have been broken off, but are antique, and belong to the statue. The marble is Parian, of beautiful, large grain. The nude parts of the goddess have been polished (a condition which is not merely to be ascribed to modern re-working); the drapery, the hair, and the accessories are left rough, which gives a good artistic effect; the execution is only in decorative style, and the back has been very hastily done. H. 1·80. The statue comes from Paris. Cardinal Mazarin is supposed to have possessed himself of it first, and to have presented it to the King. It may be the statue of which we find the following entry in the Agenda of the Cardinal in the year 1643 : " *Per la venere antica, compreso il porto e l' incassatura, scudi di Roma 216. sono pistole 72* " (Laborde, *Le Palais Mazarin*, p. 185). Such a price would at least seem very high for the two statuettes of Venus mentioned in the Inventory of the Mazarin Palace (nos. 89, 112, cf. under Wilton). However that may be, the statue came later into the possession of a certain Mons. de Beaujon, whose house was situated on the Champs Elysées, near the modern Arc de l'Étoile. During the Revolution it was struck by some gun-shots, the traces of which are still visible; fortunately they are all in the back, as the precaution had been taken to turn the face of the goddess to the wall. To

ensure her safe keeping she was afterwards buried in the garden of
the house, and for about forty years she lay there hidden till she was
quite forgotten. However, about the year 1855 the statue was fortunately found and disinterred, and soon afterwards came into the
possession of Mr Cook. [*]

2 a. Statue of a Nymph. Only the lower half of the body
from about the navel is preserved. The goddess rests on the l. leg.
The legs are enveloped in a wide cloak, which leaves the r. shin and
foot bare; it is gathered before the abdomen into a large mass of
folds, and over it is a shell which must have been held by the Nymph
with both hands. The upper part of the body was quite nude. The
back is merely sketched. The toes of both feet, the curved edge of
the shell, and sundry parts of the drapery have been injured. New:
only a patch at the back. White marble. H. 0·90, including the
pedestal. [*Benndorf*]

3. Group of Eros in the Vine. *Arch. Zeit.*, 1879, Pl. 13,
pp. 170 ff. (Michaelis). The principal figure (H. 0·80) stands with
the soles of both feet—not with the tips only on the ground; the
position of the legs is somewhat stiff. Eros' long hair is gathered up
into a knot over the forehead. He has no wings. He is bending
far back to reach the grapes that hang down in rich clusters from the
vine which arches over his head; for a gnarled vine, connected
with Eros by two supports, is growing behind and around him. The
branching tendrils, laden with grapes, make as it were a roof over
his head and quite encompass him. The vine forms a kind of open
work in marble; the single pieces, much broken, have been carefully
put together again, mostly with the aid of metal pegs or thin metal
pins which are much eaten away, and which have caused serious
corrosion. Those parts of the marble that have been protected,
preserve throughout their original smooth surface, in strong contrast
to the exposed parts, which have been much injured. Also the front
part of Eros himself has been almost completely worn away by the
action of water, while his back and other protected parts are perfectly
smooth. Another statue of Eros, very like this one, was once at
Whitehall (cf. Windsor, vol. XXVII. fol. 21. *Arch. Zeit.*, 1879, Pl.
14, 2), a third copy in Rome (*ibid.*, Pl. 14, 1), a fourth in the
Louvre (*ibid.*, Pl. 14, 4. Clarac, II. 282, 1460. Müller-Wieseler,
II. 53, 676). In the copy belonging to Mr Cook, we have to notice
important accessories. The head of Eros is thrown back, and his
look directed sideways so as to catch the glance of a little bearded
Pan (H. 0·50) who is skipping round him with his r. leg lifted high.

He looks up at Eros and with both hands holds over his head a flat basket into which a diminutive winged Eros (H. 0·20), sitting on the branches, is about to drop a large bunch of grapes. A second winged boy of the same size is flitting through the branches above the r. hand of the principal figure. His r. foot is supported on the outstretched l. arm of a second bearded Satyr (same size) who crouches, behind the head of the principal figure, on a branch, and holds a bunch of grapes in his lowered r. hand. There is also a bird among the branches. This vine so alive with Erotes reminds us at first sight of the "green arbours" (χλωραὶ σκιάδες), which surround the bed of Adonis in Theocritus (15, 118): Οἱ δέ τε κῶροι ὑπερπωτῶνται Ἑρωτες· Οἷοι ἀηδονιδῆες ἀεξομεναν ἐπὶ δεὶ δρων Ἡωτῶνται πτερύγων πειρώμενοι ὄζον ἀπ᾿ ὄζω. I have no doubt that the group at Richmond gives us the original conception of the figure, as every detail is explained here in the best possible manner; the idea is probably an ingenious and playful invention of an artist of the Alexandrian period (cf. Athen., v. pp. 198 D, 200 C). The execution of the group before us is only decorative and anything but delicate, in some parts it is rather superficial. It is almost miraculous that it should have been preserved entire, with no modern restoration, especially when we consider the fragility of the peculiar kind of work. The pedestal is also preserved; it is quadrangular, with slight ornamentation: L. 0·44. D. 0·28. The height of the pedestal is about 0·06, that of the group itself 1·06. Fine-grained Greek marble. It was found in 1864 in the Bagni di Roselle (Dennis, *Cities and Cemeteries*, 2 ed., II. p. 225), four miles distant from Grosseto, near the ancient Etruscan town of Rusellae (*Bullett. dell' Inst.*, 1865, p. 68); thence it was taken to Florence and very soon found its way into the possession of Mr Cook. [⁰]

3 a. Statue of Herakles, with a cornucopiae. The bearded hero, his crisp hair wreathed with vine-like leaves, rests on his r. leg in a very composed attitude; the l. leg is put a little aside, but it touches the ground with the whole sole. The r. hand which is lowered rests on the club which is placed on the ground. A lion's skin, supported by a block of marble by the l. leg, hangs over the l. forearm; the l. hand holds a large cornucopiae, containing a bunch of grapes, two ears of corn, two walnuts, a pineapple, an apple, some other fruits, a trilateral pyramid, and a disk behind it (cf. *Annali dell' Inst.*, 1869, pp. 201 ff. Matz-Duhn, *Ant. Bildw. in Rom*, I. no. 118). Two *puntelli* serve to join, one the club and the r. thigh, the other the two shins. The pedestal is semicircular.

Benndorf thinks that the statue refers to an Attic type of Herakles, anterior to the influence of Lysippos. Head, r. forearm, and shins broken, but antique ;—new ; only the middle part of the club. Good work. Back but little finished. White marble. The statue is said to come from Constantinople. H. 1·28, of the pedestal 0·09. [*Benndorf.*] Possibly the statue identical with a small statue of Herakles which Mr Newton saw years ago lying in fragments in a cellar of Lord Stratford de Redcliffe's London house. The fragments had lain there so long that his lordship had lost all recollection how he got them, but believed they came from Constantinople. By Mr Newton's advice he had the statue put together, and it was afterwards sold by auction at Christie's for £110. (*From a letter of Prof. Newton.*)

4. Small torso of a nude Aphroditè, originally with l. arm lowered and r. arm raised ; the hand may have held an alabastron. The upper part of the body is strikingly small in comparison with the very large hips and the long thighs ; the figure is altogether very slender. The body is smoothed over. The work is rather delicate, only the back is not quite so carefully finished as the front. Both arms, the legs from below the knees, and the head are missing ; by the l. hip may be seen the remains of a support. Beautiful Parian marble (*lychnites*). H., from the neck to the knees, 0·31. Said to have been found at Athens. [*]

5. Statuette of "Zeus Serapis." The god rests on his l. leg, the r. is slightly bent. The lower part of the body, the back, and the l. arm down to the wrist are covered by an ample cloak. The hand rests on the hip in a manner similar to that seen in the common statues of Asklepios, though not quite the same. A head of different marble, which is much worn (new : nose), is stuck on to the body by means of a new neck. This head is like that of a Zeus ; the modius (partly restored) on the head gives him the character of Serapis. New : r. arm, including the shoulder, and the thunderbolt ; the pedestal with the feet and an omphalos standing by the l. foot, which serves to support the cloak ; the fingers of the l. hand, small details on the drapery. Probably intended originally for a Zeus and not an Asklepios ; for the motive cf., for example, Clarac, v. 921, 2345. Italian marble. H. 0·70. From the Pulszky collection. [*]

6. Group of Dionysos and Seilenos, small scale. The god is draped in a cloak, which however only covers his legs and back, and rests lightly on the l. shoulder, leaving all the upper part of the body and the hips bare. A fillet is passed through his hair, which falls down on his shoulders in long curls. His r. arm rests on his head. The god stands on his r. leg in too straight and stiff a position, his l. foot being in advance, and supports himself on a much smaller Seilenos, round whose neck and shoulders he has thrown his l. arm. Seilenos is draped in a coat with sleeves, which reaches nearly to his knees, and in hose, both of a shaggy stuff; he also wears shoes, and an apron round his loins. Stepping forward with the l. foot he clasps Dionysos with his r. arm, and lays the l. hand on his garment, near his l. hip. The head of Seilenos, which is thrown back on his shoulders, is bald; on his chin is a long beard, and he has a flat nose. He looks up to the god, who meets his glance with an enthusiastic look. Dionysos' r. arm is broken in several places, and is perhaps partly modern; his feet from below the garment, and a great part of the pedestal, the noses of both figures, and some trivial details have been restored. The execution of the nude parts of Dionysos is weak, almost effeminate; the body is smoothed over and rubbed, the head still more so. The rest of the group is somewhat superficially treated. The popular name of the group, "Socrates and Alcibiades," is also to be found on the drawing of a similar little group, that was in the former royal collection at Whitehall (cf. Windsor, vol. XXVII., fol. 28, no. 22). Beautiful Greek marble. H. 0·70. From the Pulszky collection. [*]

7. Statuette of Kybele. She sits on a majestic throne with a high back. She wears chiton and cloak, the latter so arranged that it forms a veil over her head and falls down her back and over her legs. Her head is surmounted by a modius. The lion lies on her lap, in her r. hand she holds a patera, in the l. arm the large tympanon. This is a late copy of a well-known Attic type, and is not of Pentelic marble. H. 0·34. [*]

8. Bust of "Caligula." Beautiful bust of a youth, the face turned r. The tip of the nose has been broken off but put on again; a piece near the r. eye has been restored. A certain likeness to Caligula cannot be questioned, but the face is broader, the form of the forehead different; instead of the gloomy and wicked expression and the pinched lips which disfigure Caligula's handsome features, we have here a goodnatured look and frank liveliness. On the upper lip and chin is a soft down. The hair is treated very superficially; in other respects the execution is very good, and the expression is remarkably well rendered. Coarse-grained Parian marble. H. 0·45. Length of face 0·19. Brought from Paris to England a few years ago. [*B]

9. Child's head: expression somewhat embarrassed, curly hair.

M. C.

40

The body is clothed in a tunic buttoned on the shoulders. Pupils expressed. Tip of nose new. Greek marble. H. 0·25. L. of face 0·10. [*]

9 a. **Two colossal busts of Claudius** and **Vitellius** ; the busts, draped, of coloured marble. Good work of the Cinquecento or Seicento. [*]

10. **Attic sepulchral relief.** Stele with pediment, below the pediment the name Τιμαρέτη (*C. I. Gr.*, 7002). The field is not framed in by pilasters. On it stands a lady, unveiled, turning l. She has a fillet in her hair, and is quite enveloped in her chiton, and in the ample cloak which almost covers her form, including the l. arm. Her head is bent and her look directed to her lowered r. hand, in which she holds a little dove. A little child, kneeling on the ground, and also dressed, stretches up both arms towards the dove. Delicate low relief of excellent art ; firm outlines with extraordinarily soft treatment of the surfaces. Pentelic marble. H. 0·82. L. above 0·35, below 0·38 ; field h. 0·56. The relief was formerly in the possession of the chemist Dodd. [*]

11. **Fragment of a round ara** of Pentelic marble : a Bac-chante, in fine doubled chiton and a wide, waving cloak, is dancing to the r. with her head lowered. She holds up a tympanon in her l. hand and has raised her r. hand to strike it. This is a favourite figure on certain so-called neo-Attic reliefs (Zoega, *Bassir.*, Pl. 84, no. 3. Müller-Wieseler, II. 48, 602 at the r. end). Below are the remains of an ornamental astragalos. The work is spirited and careful ; the figure excellently preserved ; all the rest of the relief has been cut away close round the figure. H. 0·54. H. of figure 0·48. [*]

12. **Fragment of a bas relief,** of poor Grecian style, framed in on the l., broken on the r. and at the top. *Bull. Napolet.*, v. Pl. 1, 1. A youth in a Phrygian cap, chiton and chlamys, stockings and shoes, with a long lance or staff in his l. hand, is standing, turned r., before a veiled lady, who is resting her l. elbow on her r. hand and laying her chin on her l. hand ; she is taken in the act of stepping to the r. Near her in the background is a female head with sharply defined profile and a stephane in her hair. The common explana-tion that the group represents Paris and Helena, accompanied by Aethra, or Aphroditè (cf. Overbeck, *Gall. heroischer Bildw.*, p. 372), does not seem satisfactory ; the supposed Paris is much more like a barbarian doryphoros. It may represent Medea assisting Jason in one of his feats in Colchis. H. 0·82. L. 0·51. According to

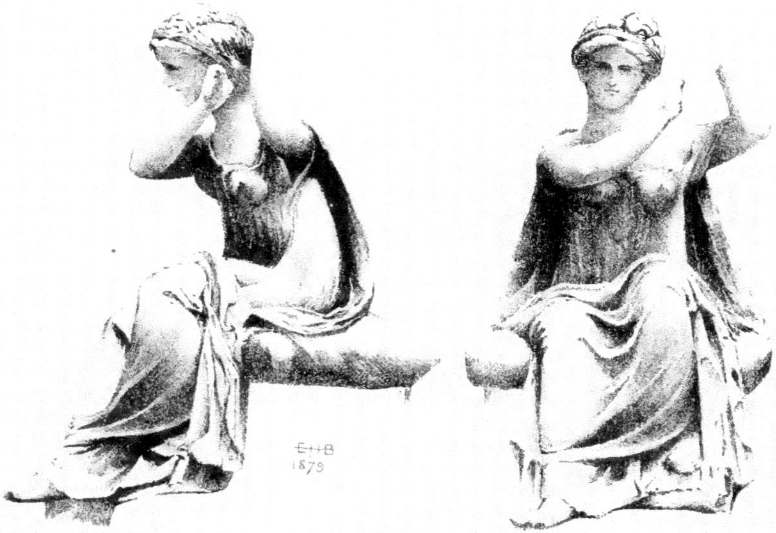

RICHMOND 14

Minervini (*l. cit.*, pp. 52 f.) the relief comes from Cumae; according to a notice of Em. Braun's on a drawing in my possession it was found at Pozzuoli in 1835. [*]

13. Large, round **bowl of red porphyry**, tolerably flat, of the grand diameter of 1·93. Obtained from the Duke of Modena. [*]

14. **Terra-cotta figure of a maiden at her toilette.** (See the annexed Plate.) A charming little figure. Front and side views equally well composed and carefully worked out, the back neglected. The maiden is sitting in a cushioned chair (legs wanting) dressed in a chiton, while a cloak entirely envelops her back and legs, and forms a frame to the body as seen from the front. The r. foot is advanced, the l. foot is drawn up and rests somewhat raised on a foot-stool. She raises her two bare arms, the l. to the side, the r. in front, to arrange the hair on the l. side of her face (the tress of hair and the l. hand have been broken off); accordingly the head is somewhat lowered and the glance directed sideways and downwards. A ribbon is drawn through the hair. The colours are in a measure preserved. The simple grace of the little figure is quite inimitable. H. 0·13. [*]

15—17. Three **terra-cotta slabs**, like metopes, representing **Herakles** with the **lion**, the **hydra**, and the **bull**. Similar terra-cotta reliefs recur in the Campana collection and elsewhere.

The **bronzes** are very numerous. I only notice the interesting examples, passing over others which are rather commonplace.

18. **Statuette of Athenè Polias**, in the attitude of combat which we see on the Panathenaic vases, only without the aegis. She advances her l. foot. Her cloak is laid across her bosom, the l. breast being only covered by the chiton, and falls down in zigzag folds. The l. arm is lowered, the r. raised, both forearms missing. On her head is a round helmet, with an upright visor in front, on the crown the remains of a plume. A tolerably broad tress of hair falls down her back. Good figure. H. 0·18. [*B]

19. **Statuette of Aphroditè**, very small. She stands in an attitude of repose, her legs hidden in her garment. Upper part of the body nude. Both arms upraised and holding long locks of hair. The head crowned with a stephanè. H. 0·04. (There is a larger copy of the same subject in which the goddess is quite nude.) [*]

20. **Statuette of Apollo**, standing upright, the r. leg slightly in advance, the r. hand lowered, in his l. arm the large cithara. He is youthful and wears a wreath on his long curls. The lower parts of the legs and the r. forearm missing. Delicate work. H. 0·05. [*]

21. **Statuette of Hermes**, with wings in his tangled hair, resting on the r. leg. His r. hand advanced and holding a large purse; the l. arm is lowered and probably once held the kerykeion. Commonplace work. H. 0·18. [*]

22. **Statuette of Hermes**, resting on his r. leg. He wears sandals; over his l. arm lies the chlamys, the hand is upraised. In the lowered r. hand is the remnant of the kerykeion. The head, without wings, inclined somewhat to the r. H. 0·16. [*]

23. **Statuette of a nude youth**, like a Hermes. The chlamys is fastened on the r. shoulder and falls over the r. shoulder and arm. A twisted hoop is passed through the hair. In the r. hand he holds a large snake; its open jaws hang down, and its head is very like that of a dragon. A small ring on the back of the head shows that the figure was destined to be hung up. The genuineness not certain. H. 0·17. [*B]

24. **Statuette of a nude youth**, remarkable for his very long, smooth hair, which is parted on the crown and terminates on the neck in light curls. He is in the act of walking, his r. foot being already advanced. The r. arm was advanced, but the lower half is broken off; the lowered l. hand is bored through and held something. The hard treatment of the hair and the large eyes suggest a modern origin, an idea which seems to be contradicted by the beautiful green patina. H. 0·21. [*B]

25. **Group of "Eros with the dolphin."** *Rheinländ. Jahrb.*, 1 (1842). Pl. 3, 1. 2, pp. 56 ff. (Urlichs). Müller-Wieseler, II. Pl. 51, 644. A powerful youth, with strong pubes, reminding us rather of Ares or Hermes than of Eros, both in the build of his body and the expression of his face. He stands on his r. leg, with the l. slightly bent. In the fashion of the *signa panthea* this youth unites in his own person the attributes of various gods. His l. hand, lowered and slightly bent, holds Poseidon's dolphin; the quiver, fastened by a ribbon, suggests Apollo, of whom, as well as of Dionysos, we are again reminded by the wreath of ivy and laurel, bound with the fillet; the helmet, shaped in the fashion of a Phrygian cap and terminating in a griffin's head, over which the high plume waves, recalls Ares, and the upraised wings Eros. The r. wing is missing, but the holes at the joint show that it must have been separately worked. It is possible that the lowered r. hand held either a kerykeion or a thunderbolt; now the arm is missing from above the elbow. The feet have been repaired. H. to the tip of the wing 0·16. This graceful and well-executed figure was found at Bonn in

1840, and belonged in the first place to Frau Sibylla Mertens-Schaaffhausen. [*]

26. **Statue of a young warrior,** in a chiton, with a short breastplate over it; on the head a low helmet. L. arm lowered. r. upraised. The disproportionately slender figure is an example of provincial art, probably from Lower Italy. H. 0·62. [*]

27. **Torso and head of a boy with long curls,** eyes having been put in. H. 0·48. From Italy. [*]

28. **Head of a boy,** broken off close under the chin, with fat, infantine cheeks. Pupils expressed. Hair gathered up in a small tuft over the forehead. H. 0·13. [*]

29. **Invalid sitting.** *Rev. archéol.*, 1 (1844). Pl. 13, pp. 458 ff. (Longpérier). A sick man sitting in a chair which has lost its feet. He is thin as a skeleton, every rib standing out. His arms and face are equally bony. The eyes have been inlaid with silver. The body is huddled together and stoops forward. A cloak covers the legs, and on it, in two rows above each knee and on the lower hem, may be read in punctured characters

which signify Εὐδαμίδας Περδίκ[κα] (*C. I. Gr.*, 6855 b). The pathological character is realistically carried out. Evidently it is a votive offering from a sick or convalescent person (cf. Paus. 10, 2, 6). H. 0·115. Found in the neighbourhood of Soissons, formerly in the possession of Vicomte de Jessaint, cf. de Witte, *Mémoires des antiq. de France*, XXXI. p. 168. Treu, *De ossium human. imaginibus*, pp. 47 ff. [*]

30. **Head,** usually called "Seneca." The realism is kept within moderate bounds, the hair very superficially treated. The genuineness does not appear to me quite indubitable. H. 0·35. L. of face 0·19. [*]

31. **Bronze weight,** representing a female head with earrings and stephanè. H. 0·12. [*]

32. **Bronze vase,** somewhat larger in the middle than at the top and bottom. It has two graceful handles, and at the joint of each is a Sphinx in high relief, crouching down and raising the l. fore-paw to the head, which is bent down and melancholy. Very delicate work, carefully chased. H. 0·40. Said to come from Pompeii. [*B]

33. **Handle of** an Etruscan **cista:** two youths in short chitons, holding a nude corpse extended to its full length. [*]

33 a. There are also a number of **handles for mirrors,** formed usually into human figures.

34. **Cover of** an Etruscan **mirror** with relief. Dionysos in a cloak and with the thyrsos over his l. shoulder is looking downwards behind him and leaning on an Eros, who looks up to him as he steps quickly forward. All the movement is to the r. A Bacchante precedes Dionysos and looks round at him, she wears a chiton and cloak and plays a cithara. Similar example in Gerhard, *Etr. Spiegel*, Pl. 21, 2. Diameter 0·16. [*B]

35. **Similar cover** with relief. Aphroditè, the upper part of her body nude, the lower part draped, is sitting to the l., with a sceptre beside her, looking up at a small Eros, who stands on a little ridge of rock. A second Eros sits at her feet. Above him we perceive a small cloaked male figure (?) whom Aphroditè touches with her right hand. Indistinct representation, badly corroded. Diameter 0·10. [*B]

36. **Etruscan mirror.** Herakles, wearing a skin as a chlamys, and carrying the club over his l. shoulder, is embracing a nude female figure with his r. hand. Behind her back is a cloak; she wears a necklace of pearls, and shoes, and is sitting on a large dolphin with a long tail. Another nude female figure to the r. is endeavouring to hold Herakles back. The scene is encircled by a wreath, below on the handle is a mouse. Diameter 0·12. L. with handle 0·25. [*]

DINING ROOM.

37. **Bronze group of Peleus and Thetis.** The pedestal, which is oval, is formed by a kind of inverted hollow box, 0·18 long, 0·07 wide, 0·12 high, adorned in front with a winged Medusa's head, resting on four animals' legs, which are high and bent outwards: over each leg a little mask. On this stands the group, 0·27 high, a repetition of the composition well known from vases. The youthful Peleus, somewhat bent, steps forward from the l., advancing his l. foot; he has curly hair and is draped only in an apron round the loins. His l. arm is round Thetis' hips, in his r. hand he holds her l. with a firm grasp. Thetis is trying to escape. She wears an ungirdled doubled chiton, the folds of which recall the zigzag style. Her long hair flows down unbound, her entreaty for help is mutely expressed by her upraised r. arm and face turned back. A panther is clambering up Peleus' r. leg which is stepping back, and bites his back near his r.

shoulder. At Thetis' l. side is a large snake with a forked tail, which raises itself from her knee up behind her back to her neck, and forces itself over the upper part of Thetis' r. arm towards Peleus and bites him in the neck. The group, which is meant to be seen only from the front, is skilfully composed. The execution is very good. It is in perfect preservation, but the surface has been badly corroded. Total height 0·39. [*]

38. **Round arched cover of bronze**, quite smooth, 0·23 in diameter. Above, a **diskobolos** serves as a handle. He steps forward on the r. leg and draws back the l., which is much bent; the upper part of the body only slightly bent forward, the head more inclined. He holds the quoit in his lowered r. hand which is slightly advanced, the l. arm is raised as if to preserve the balance, with the open hand turned up to the head. A fillet passes through the hair which falls down the back in a wide plait. A narrow band round the hips is remarkable. The motive is uncommon, and seems to be taken from a comparatively early type. H. of the figure 0·08. [*]

39. **Greek mirror.** A severely archaic Aphroditè does duty as a handle. She is in an ungirdled chiton, standing stiffly in full face, holding a flower in her much advanced r. hand, and with the l. lifting her garment near her thigh. On either side of her head hovers towards her a small draped winged figure, with legs very far apart, each stretching one arm towards the head of the goddess and holding back the other, with a small object in the hand. For similar mirrors of Greek origin see Fränkel, *Arch. Zeit.*, 1879, pp. 100 f. 204. Total height 0·39. Diameter of the mirror 0·16. H. of the group beneath it 0·20. [*]

In the cabinets of this room, besides many bronzes, are numerous **terra-cottas**, but among them none of remarkable value.

BASEMENT.

40. **Statue of Aphroditè, crouching.** Cavaceppi, *Racc.*, II. Pl. 60. Clarac, IV. 627, 1411. Well-known motive. The upper part of the l. arm is adorned with a bracelet in the form of a snake. The hair is gathered into a knot on the forehead and back of the neck; some curls fall down the back and on the l. shoulder. The head is in a very bad condition, caused by long exposure to the elements; almost the whole of the r. arm is missing and the l. hand together with the wrist. On the broken parts are pieces of iron which show that some former repairs have been made (by Cavaceppi). New: chief part of the l. foot, which has been foolishly provided

with a sandal, though the heel wears none; also toes of the r. foot.
The goddess leans her l. hip on a swan, of whose neck only part is
preserved. Behind her r. hip stands an Eros, with his l. arm on her
back and his r. arm on her body, looking up at her. His legs
are wide apart; the l. has once been restored, but now half of it
is lost. The joints of the wings are preserved. The group has
been let into a new pedestal. Coarse work, intended probably for
architectural decoration. On the body are rolls of flesh which give
it an appearance of excessive fatness. Coarse-grained Parian marble.
H. 1·15. L. of Aphrodite's face, 0·19. Through Cavaceppi's hands
the statue came into the possession of Lord Anson (see Introd.
§ 41, note 174), and probably at one time stood in the Shugborough
collection. Cavaceppi set on it an extravagant value, styling it *del
più famoso stile antico, eseguita con ammirabile morbidezza.* [*B*]

41.   **Statue of Aphroditè**, quite nude, resting on her l. leg.
Her r. hand covers her breast, her l. grasps the end of a dolphin's
tail. Remains of curls on the shoulders. New: head, fingers of r.
hand, feet and pedestal, and chief part of the dolphin. R. arm and
l. forearm have been broken off, but belong to the statue; legs
repaired. H. 0·92. [*]

42.   **Torso of a Satyr**, beating time with the wooden shoe
(*krupezion*) like the example in the Tribuna at Florence (cf. Marbury,
no. 22). Though head, legs and arms have been broken off close to
the body, the direction of each of these members can be exactly
realised. Remains of the tail are preserved. The work is altogether pretty good; the stooping back with its strong muscles is
excellent. The breast is splintered away. H. 0·59; from the hollow
of the neck to the lap 0·38. [*]

43.   **Torso of Herakles** (?), quite nude. He rests on the l.
leg; the l. arm was originally stretched out from the body horizontally
and probably rested on something, as we may infer from the stooping
position of the body. The r. leg was somewhat advanced, the r. arm
lowered. Indistinct traces in the neck hardly suggesting hair, perhaps
of a skin. H. 0·39. [*]

44.   **Upper half of a male portrait statue**, from about
the middle of the thigh, where it is cut off square; evidently the statue
was originally put together out of two pieces. The treatment of the
cloak corresponds to the Marbury statue, no. 18. The r. hand lies
on the tip of the cloak which falls down from the l. breast, the l. with
the remains of the roll is lowered. The head is missing. Somewhat
coarse work. H. 0·84. [*]

45. **Statue of a nude boy,** with curly head, the hair lies in the form of a plait along the parting. With both hands the boy holds in front of him a deep square box, in which lie round objects and a ring, probably articles of jewellery. New: the lower parts of the legs with the trunk and the pedestal, part of the l. and all the r. arm with half the box. The neck has been repaired in several places, but the head appears to belong to the statue (nose new). Decidedly decorative style. H. 0·47. [°]

46. **Statue of Zeus?** An ample cloak covers legs, back, and l. arm, one end of it is thrown in front over the l. forearm. In the lowered r. hand are the remains of a short sceptre, the head of which lies close under the hand; on the l. shoulder we see traces of a palm branch. Both attributes suggest an arbitrator of contest (*brabeutes*), perhaps Zeus as giver of victory and prizes of reward. The restorer has completed the palm branch as a sheaf of corn, and has added the l. hand, he has also put on to the statue a head crowned with ears of wheat and has added the legs from below the drapery and the pedestal. Of pavonazzetto, a material but seldom employed for sculpture; but still above suspicion. H. 0·75. [*]

47. **Double terminal bust.** **Zeus** with an oak wreath, in which are some acorns. The face is very wide and has a curly beard. Tip of nose new. On the other side **Hermes** (?), with a strange kind of hat like a helmet, which covers his cheeks; the edge juts out, and over it are two wings. Partly restored. For similar heads see Gerhard, *Antike Bildwerke*, Pl. 318. H. 0·23. [*]

48. **Double bust of the bearded Dionysos** and of **Ariadne,** both with narrow metal circlets in the hair. His hair and beard are rendered in archaic style with button-like curls. New: nose of Dionysos, nose and mouth of Ariadne. Work very poor. H. 0·30. [°]

49. **Head of Dionysos,** bearded, with an ivy wreath in his hair and a fillet straight across his forehead. The long beard forms loose, rough curls. The expression is insignificant. New: tip of nose, and terminal bust in which the neck has been inserted. H. 0·50. L. of face 0·17. [*]

50. **Bust of Athene,** with round, so-called Attic helmet, provided in front with a narrow brim that stands up, ornamented on either side with a winged griffin; traces of holes on the top suggest some adornment to the helmet, probably a plume. The hair is wavy, it falls down on the back of the neck in a round coil, on the shoulders are remains of long curls. The face is rather wide and has been very considerably restored, forehead, l. eye, nose, mouth, chin, also some hair on the l. temple being new. The bust, which is turned somewhat to its right, was intended to be let into a statue. Unfortunately it has been much rubbed and defaced. H. 0·43. L. of face 0·18. [*]

51. **Head of Artemis,** with pleasing expression. A fillet passes through the hair and a crescent fastened to it rests on the forehead. Broken at the neck. Superficial work. H. 0·24. L. of face 0·17. [*]

52. **Bust of a Roman matron,** draped and veiled, with a woollen cord in her tangled, wavy hair. Thin lips. In perfect preservation. H. 0·92. L. of face 0·18. [*B]

53. **Female bust** with the hair parted from the temples, and then drawn back in unusual fashion, and combed upward with the rest of the hair to form a knot in the shape of a ball. Just like no. 53 in Lansdowne House. New: nose, mouth, chin, neck and bust; the simplicity of the treatment reminds us of heads of Amazons. Coarse-grained marble. H. of the genuine part abt. 0·24. L. of face 0·18. [*B]

54. **Female portrait bust,** Roman, with delicate features; allied to the statue of Antonia in the Louvre. The wavy hair terminates in a plait; along the forehead it is cut short in a fringe. Behind the ears two curls fall down. New: nose, and draped bust of coloured marble. L. of face 0·14. [*B]

55. **Small head of a laughing girl,** something like a satyress, but not having pointed ears. The hair is brushed up and an ivy wreath rests on it. New: tip of nose and breast. Coarse-grained marble. H. of genuine part abt. 0·19. L. of face 0·13. [*]

56. **Greek sepulchral relief,** broken off above and on the r. edge. A lady, in somewhat high relief, is standing in full face, fully dressed, but not veiled (head broken off); r. arm is slightly bent and rests in her cloak; l. arm lowered. (Cf. Clarac, IV. 766, 1889.) At her r. stands a diminutive female servant, in much lower relief; she is holding with her r. hand a basket furnished with a handle, with the l. a fan shaped like a leaf. Broad sculpture. Coarse grey marble. H. 0·94. L. at the top 0·70, below 0·76. From Sicily. [*]

57. **Front of a sarcophagus with relief of Meleagros.** In the middle Meleagros, wearing the chlamys and having a fillet in his short, rough hair, is attacking with brandished spear the mighty boar which is almost hidden in his den, but has its r. forepaw on a dog.

Between Meleagros' legs lies a double axe. Atalantè in hunting costume, her open quiver on her back, the bow, from which she is just shooting the arrow, in her hand, comes up next to Meleagros; her hairdress is arranged in waves. Behind the den a bearded man is throwing a stone down upon the boar; then a youth, in all respects like Meleagros, hurries up with poised spear; between his legs is a dog. Next comes a tree. On the further side of this tree, at the r. end, stands a man, bearded, with a sword-strap across his breast and the chlamys behind his back. He lays his r. hand sadly on his wounded r. thigh; his l. arm, which probably grasped a spear, is almost entirely broken. To the l., behind Meleagros, approach the two Dioskuroi, each wearing the chlamys and an egg shaped cap, the foremost with the spear in his r. hand and the l. upraised. Artemis, in hunting costume, hurries away, at their approach, looking back on the scene as she runs; between her legs is a dog. Then follows Ankaeos, a huge form like a Herakles, girded in a skin and with a double axe over the l. shoulder; finally the bearded Oeneus, fully dressed and with his sceptre, appears, only partly preserved. In excellent preservation, and exhibiting unusually good treatment in the relief. H. 0·85. L. 1·88. This version of an often-repeated scene has been hitherto overlooked by those who have collated the various sarcophagi relative to Meleagros (cf. on Broadlands, no. 21); it comes from the neighbourhood of Naples. [*]

58. Front of a sarcophagus with relief of an Amazono-machia. A warrior (Achilleus) dressed in helmet, chlamys and boots, a round shield on the r. arm and a spear in the hand, stands in the centre, his l. arm thrown round an Amazon (Penthesilea), who is sinking to the ground. She, like her comrades, wears a round helmet, chlamys and boots. On the ground, at the feet of the conqueror, lies a second Amazon, dead. The conqueror's look however is not directed downwards, but backwards towards an Amazon on horseback, hurrying away, who is defending herself with drawn sword against a fully armed, bearded warrior (sign on his shield a gorgoneion). This warrior is stabbing her in the back from above with his sword; at the same time the Amazon is attacked in front with a spear by a mounted, bearded warrior in helmet, chiton, chlamys and boots. Beneath the horses on the ground lies an Amazon with her horse, both dead. On the extreme l., as a corner figure, is a winged Nikè in a long Doric chiton; one leg and her breast are bare; she shoulders her sheathed sword in her l. arm. To the r., on the further side of the principal actors, follows a perfectly symmetrically arranged group. Again a mounted Amazon, having a pelta on her l. arm, is defending herself against a bearded warrior who attacks her in the back, and is also at the same time threatened in front by a youthful horseman (badge on his shield a gorgoneion). A horse lies on the ground, also a dead and a wounded Amazon, the latter has a pelta. On the extreme r. the figure of Nikè is repeated. In excellent preservation; very good sculpture, though perhaps not quite so good as that of no. 57, in the same locality with which this sarcophagus was found. H. 0·89. L. 2·26. [*]

59. Fragment of the front of a sarcophagus. Two sea-panthers swimming towards each other, carrying on their backs nude Nereids with waving, fluttering veils and holding flying ribbons in their upraised hands. On either side traces of a similar group. H. 0·29. L. 1·17. [*.M.]

60. Terra-cotta relief. Two Amazons in Phrygian caps, rather long chitons and boots, in a half kneeling posture, are holding in symmetrical disposition a shield, adorned with a gorgoneion. Above and below, an ornamental bordering; the relief served some architectural purpose. H. 0·26. L. 0·31. There are six replicas of this in the collection. [*]

61. Etruscan sepulchral urn of terra-cotta. Between two pilasters is represented a battle scene, consisting of five figures (*e, d, a, b, c*). A youth (*a*) in a chlamys (his helmet lies on the ground) has sunk on his knee and, while he draws his sword, is protecting himself with his shield against (*b*) an advancing enemy, who approaches from the r. with fluttering chlamys and drawn sword: his shield lies on the ground. Behind *b* a comrade (*c*) provided with helmet, shield, chiton and corslet, lifts his arm for a mighty stroke. From the l. a warrior (*d*) with chlamys, shield and drawn sword hurries up to the assistance of his fallen comrade (*a*). Behind his back another (*e*) looks on at the scene without doing anything. H. 0·38. L. 0·38. D. 0·30. The **cover**, representing a female figure reposing, is too small for this urn. [*]

GARDEN MUSEUM.

62. Torso of a female draped statue (Muse?) of very elegant description. The figure is very slender; it rests on the l. leg, the r. being somewhat drawn back. The thin chiton is girded high, and has a diploïdion descending to the hips; the chiton is so long that it falls about the feet in rich graceful folds which lie on the ground. Over the chiton is thrown a thin cloak in substance like a veil; the folds of the chiton can everywhere be seen through it (in the style of the Polyhymnia of Berlin). The upper edge of the cloak, gathered into a broad mass, goes obliquely from the r. hip up to the l. shoulder; the lower edge lies nearly parallel with it, from below the r. knee to the l. hip; the tips fall in part from the l. shoulder and in part from the l. hip, although it is not quite clear how they are made to do so. The broad lines of the main divisions of the cloak, and the transparency of its tissue through which the folds of the chiton can be seen, are excellently combined. The l. arm, now missing, was worked in a separate piece; it was lowered, and pressed one tip of the cloak against the hip. The r. arm was also worked in a separate piece; it was held horizontally, as though a sceptre or something of the kind had been in the hand; of this arm only the piece by the shoulder is preserved. The head is missing; a piece has been cut straight off the r. foot, perhaps because the block of marble was too small and the foot had to be put on afterwards, perhaps in consequence of some later injury. The whole statue has been let into a modern pedestal. The back has been left quite rough, so that it is even difficult to follow the main motives of the drapery. In other respects the statue is of excellent effect, though the execution is by no means very fine. H. 1·35. Purchased in England. [*B]

63. **Bust of L. Verus.** The hair and beard are treated in a somewhat hard and dry manner, and perhaps here and there have been touched up. In other respects the bust is good and in perfect preservation. Pupils expressed. The head has never been severed from the bust, which is protected by a corslet over which falls the paludamentum. On the corslet in front is a (half-concealed) head of Medusa; on the shoulder-flap a giant with legs like serpents. Pentelic marble. H. 0·68. L. of face abt. 0·21. Found at Marathon. Purchased from Rollin and Feuardent in Paris, who also sold to the Louvre a precisely similar bust, found in the same place, of M. Aurelius. [*B]

63 a. Six **Colossal busts of Emperors,** modern.

64. **Terminal head of the bearded Dionysos,** in hieratic style. New: nose, great part of the beard, some of the hair. On the modern terminal pillar stands ΠΛΑΤΩΝ. H. of genuine part 0·22. L. of face abt. 0·15. [*]

65. **Medallion,** in diameter 0·49. From a tolerably flat field, which is framed, rises in extremely high relief a youthful portrait-

head, inclined downwards somewhat to its r., with the figure as far
as below the bust. Body nude except for a piece of a cloak that lies
on the l. shoulder. The hair, which is short and straight and brushed
to the l., is somewhat drily treated (cf. Knole, no. 10); on the
upper lip and chin a faint beard sprouts. Pupils expressed. New :
nose, great part of both ears, neck and small details. On the
field just above the l. shoulder a small square tablet, without
inscription. The head is attractive and pretty well executed; it is
likely to represent a Greek. Good Parian marble. H. 0·53. L. of
face 0·20. [*B]

66. Large mixing bowl (krater) in marble with grey stripes,
shape and ornamentation somewhat clumsy ; foot and handle new.
FRONT SIDE: two Victories, like those on the choragic reliefs, are
standing opposite each other and pouring something into a cup from
a ewer that is raised very high ; between them is a tripod round
which snakes are entwined and on which burns a flame.—REVERSE
SIDE : two girls dancing r., their drapery and head-gear like those in
the Villa Albani (Zoega, Bassir., Pl. 20; cf. Schreiber, Villa Ludovisi,
p. 102) ; they are an exact reproduction of the two figures on the
l. of that plate, even the plant growing up so high between them is
not wanting (the altar is not there).—Below each handle are two
thyrsi crossed ; the junction of the handle takes the form of an
ivy-leaf. The relief is low and has been touched up almost all
over, so that one might well doubt its antique origin, did not the
comparatively good work of the second side make this idea unlikely.
In other respects the execution is dry and insignificant. H. 0·80.
Diameter abt. 0·80. [*]

67. Sepulchral stelè of Archippos, in very perfect preservation. The architectural arrangement is very similar to that in
no. 204 at Oxford. The pediment, which has akroteria, is adorned
with a shield; the frieze below has two rosettes and between them
a wreath in a square field hollowed out; within the wreath are the
words ὁ δῆμος. On the epistyle stands Ἄρχιππον Δίωνος, the
shape of the letters being that of a good Roman period (C. I.
Gr., 3224). In the relief field which is framed in by two pilasters,
stands Archippos, beardless, draped in chiton, cloak and shoes.
He is laying his r. hand on the wreath on his head. (His nose
and a small piece of one finger have been restored.) A vase
in the form of a soup plate with a cover (πλημοχόη) stands on a
pillar in the background. To the r. and the l. a diminutive attendant
leans on each of the pillars that form the frame, the one to the l. in

a comfortable posture of repose, the one to the r. holding a little cloak over his r. arm and in his l. hand some object that may be a fillet; it is like a small triangular rule and two ears of wheat springing forth at one corner; underneath a high pedestal. Yellowish grey marble. The relief comes probably from Smyrna; it is remarkable for the carefulness of its work and the freshness of several motives, like no. 68, which in externals is precisely similar and which is derived from the same collection of the Grimani-Spago Palace in Venice (cf. Thiersch, *Reisen in Italien*, I. p. 256). H. 1.54. L. 0·62. [*]

68. Sepulchral stelè of Phila, like the last one and from the same collection. In the pediment is a rosette; on the frieze between two rosettes a low wreath with the inscription ὁ δῆμος; on the architrave Φίλαν Ἀπολλάδος (*C. I. Gr.*, 3253). On the relief field to the l. the veiled Phila is sitting on a high chair, her r. hand on her bosom, her l. on her knee and her feet on a footstool. Near her chair stands a very diminutive maid in a chiton with a spindle (?) or a top in her r. hand. A female servant on a larger scale approaches from the r. and brings her mistress an open box. In the background on an elevation stands a small cabinet with folding-doors wide open. That there were once some ornamental additions of metal is suggested by traces of several holes and remains of lead castings. H. 1·47. L. 0·63. [*]

69. Sepulchral stelè of Epiktesis. The pediment provided with akroteria is without ornament. On the architrave stands in good letters of the Roman period Ἐπίκτησις Ὀιάτου Κυθηρίου θυγάτηρ (*C. I. Gr.*, 669). In the relief field the deceased lady, unveiled, stands in full face; she has wavy hair, is draped in chiton and cloak, which she is in the act of throwing over her l. shoulder with her r. hand (cf. Clarac, v. 921, 2349); her r. hand is before her breast, her l. hand lowered. On her r. there approaches a diminutive female attendant in a chiton, carrying a box in her hand, on her head a cap like a modius. The style is better than that of most of the sepulchral reliefs from the Islands; the execution is somewhat coarse. Marble not Pentelic. H. 1·07. L. 0·65. From the same collection with nos. 67 and 68. [*B]

70. Fragment of a sepulchral relief. All that is preserved is the torso of a female, in the same attitude as that of Epiktesis (no. 69); feet and head are missing. Usual style of the Greek Islands. H. 0·47. [*]

71. Fragment of a sepulchral relief in a frame; the

relief is very low. The upper part of the body of a youth facing r. is preserved, his r. arm concealed by his cloak which covers the whole of his body, his l. arm lowered. The figure is preserved down to the thighs. The relief is rather graceful. It is an imitation, but a considerably inferior imitation, of fine Attic works (cf. Woburn, no. 100). Italian marble. H. 0·23. L. 0·17. [*]

71 a. Modern copy of the Zeus from one of the Barberini candelabra (*Mus. Pio-Clem.*, IV. 2). [*B]

72. **Fragment of a Greek sarcophagus**, partly like the relief in Stephani's *Ausruhender Herakles*, Pl. 2, 1. A tipsy boy, with the chlamys thrown in the fashion of a shawl about his neck and holding out a bunch of grapes in his l. hand, is tumbling back into the arms of a winged companion, whose hair is curled on either side, but woven into a kind of plait along the parting, a chlamys fluttering at his back. This group, in fairly high relief, occupies the l. part of the slab. To the r. a Satyr, of smaller stature and in lower relief, is hurrying further to the r. He wears a fillet in his hair, with both hands he grasps the edge of a long wine-skin (?) that rests on his l. shoulder. Above and below is a simple border. The marble is covered with plaster or colour, but it may be Pentelic. For similar compositions on Greek sarcophagi cf. Matz, *Arch. Zeit.*, 1872, p. 16. H. 0·80. L. 1·02. [*]

73. **Sarcophagus**. Bacchic Scene. In the centre the medallion of a man with an ill-humoured expression, with a closely shaven beard, in tunic and pallium. The scutcheon is held by two youthful Centaurs who, each having a bearded companion, draw a chariot; all four Centaurs crowned with fig leaves. The old Centaur to the l. is playing on a lyre; we notice on his back traces of the feet of a small boy. The old Centaur to the r. is elevating above his head a drinking-horn; his l. arm clasps a tremendous goblet into which a small boy standing on his equine back is peeping (head and l. arm broken off). On the chariot to the l. stands the youthful Dionysos, partly covered by his cloak, vine-leaves in his long hair, laying his r. hand on the thyrsos, emptying a wine-cup with his l. hand. A Maenad, in long robes, blowing the flute, goes along beside the chariot (flute and r. forearm broken off); under the chariot a panther bounds. On the chariot to the r. stands Ariadne, in a long chiton with sleeves, and a cloak, her hair adorned with a fillet and grapes, her l. hand is laid on her sceptre, with her r. she is emptying a kantharos. Beside the chariot goes a Maenad, playing the cymbals. At the feet of the chariot hurries a horned and bearded

Pan, with the pedum in his l. arm (r. forearm broken), looking round to the l.; he, like all the figures which follow, is on a much smaller scale. Under the body of the Centaur with the goblet a little boy is pouring wine from a skin into a vessel, which a second boy is seizing (r. arm missing). Below the scutcheon stand Pan and an Eros without wings, both holding their hands behind their backs, opposite each other for a wrestling match; on either side stands a boy in a cloak as arbiter of the contest, much excited. Finally under the Centaur with the lyre a boy (l. arm missing) is hurrying away frightened, as his companion, kneeling on the ground, opens the cover of a round cista and reveals a large snake.—On the two sides are shields.—Very good sculpture in excellent preservation. H. 0·68. L. 1·10. D. 0·66. [*M]

74. **Oval sarcophagus.** In the centre lies the deceased, an elderly man, beardless, and with a Roman nose. He is supporting himself on his l. arm, and his r. is thrown above his head. The upper part of his body nude, the ample cloak on which he is resting conceals his legs, back and r. arm. An Eros, winged, as are all the Erotes on this sarcophagus, hovers over him with a torch in his r. hand; he takes hold of the cloak as though he would cover up the dead man completely. A second Eros, with a torch, also hovering, touches the r. hand of the deceased. Both Erotes wear fluttering chlamydes. Below the last-named Eros, at the head of the deceased, sits an Eros on a block of rock, his head supported sadly in his r. hand; his arm rests on his knee. Behind him are two Erotes occupied in collecting fruits into a basket. Above them is a tree from which a wreath of flowers hangs down; this wreath is woven by an Eros sitting, who has more flowers lying on a low table in front of him. At the extreme r. end a laurel tree on which a quiver hangs; beside it flutes, torches, and apples.—To the l., at the feet of the deceased, a large Eros with waving chlamys approaches flying and bringing a garland in his hands. He is looking round at two smaller Erotes, who also wear the chlamys, of whom one, sitting on a mass of rock, is playing the cithara, the other blowing on the double flute (the straight and the crooked); between them is a basket with fruit. Underneath this group an Eros is kneeling in the midst of several baskets and vessels filled with fruits, and from among them he places a basket at the feet of the deceased; behind him is a hare lying in a grotto. At the l. end is another laurel tree etc., as above. —Good sculpture; in almost perfect preservation. H. 0·60. L. 2·10. [*BM]

75. **Fragment of a small sarcophagus**, broken on the r. and l. and below. Dionysos is reclining in a low four-wheeled car drawn to the r. by two panthers, his head to the spectator's r. The ample cloak on which he is lying only envelops the lower part of his legs, his r. hand rests on his head, which is crowned with a vine wreath, in his l. arm lies the thyrsos (very much injured). Eros, represented as a youth, and not as a child, and without wings, is sitting on the foremost panther; he holds the lyre in his l. hand, raising his r. arm (forearm missing), and turning his head back to the god. In the background between Eros and Dionysos appears a young Maenad, with a handkerchief round her head and a thyrsos in her l. arm; she is looking down upon the god, whom she touches with her r. hand. Beside her a Satyr is stepping briskly forwards over the necks of the panthers; he is looking round and holding in his hands a thyrsos, very much broken; he has an apron round his loins. Above Dionysos' legs appears the upper part of the body of a second Maenad without the kerchief on her head; she advances her l. arm (hand missing) towards the god, her r. rests on a vine stem heavily laden with grapes that shoots up at the feet of the god. A second Satyr is holding the stem with his l. hand, all the rest of him has disappeared except his head and his r. hand resting on it; below him are remains of a rock.—Very high relief. Ordinary work. H. 0·28. L. 0·54. [*M]

76. **Fragment of a sarcophagus**, complete on the l. side. A winged Eros with a cloak behind his back is hurrying up from the l. On the r. shoulder of a companion who is crouching down he lays a heavy ball, which the companion seizes with his r. hand. A third Eros girded with an apron and very much broken has been restored in the action of occupying himself with a flower-basket. Very graceful motives. Good work. H. 0·30. L. 0·37. [*M]

77. **Right end of a sarcophagus**. Eros, asleep, leaning on the inverted torch. H. 0·45. L. 0·26. [*]

78. **Left corner of the lid of a sarcophagus**, in the shape of a quadrant. The same subject as no. 77; beside Eros his bow and quiver. H. 0·26. L. 0·23. [*]

79. **Right corner of the lid of a sarcophagus**, in the shape of a quadrant. Mask in a Phrygian cap. H. 0·20. L. 0·34. [*]

80. **Sepulchral urn**, square, with ornamental reliefs. Inscription: *D(is) M(anibus)* | *L. Casperio* | *Epaphrodito* | *Phengis m(arito)* | *b(ene) m(erenti) f(ecit)*; to judge from the writing, the inscription is suspicious. [*]

81. Small **sepulchral monument,** rounded at the top. A
youthful horseman is piercing with his spear a lion or a bear, which is
looking forth from a grotto to the r. ; a dog is barking at it. This
sculpture is hardly a suitable one for the tomb of a child of one year
old, who is thus referred to in the inscription : *D. M.* | *Macrinio
Maximino filio* | *dulcissimo, qui vixit an. I m...* | *Macrinius Maxi-
minus* INGEN¹ | PREF....*fect.* From Sicily.   [*]

82. **Relief:** three masks, lying on the ground. (Very similar,
Müller-Wieseler, 11. Pl. 33, 388.) To the l. is a head of Herakles
with the skin drawn over it, and below, a club. Behind this a youthful head. To the r. an archaistic head of Dionysos, with pointed
beard, a knot of hair on his forehead and a tuft; underneath is a
low cista half opened. Good high relief. Greek marble. L. 0·30.
H. 0·27. [*]

Besides these marbles Mr Cook possesses an important collection
of gems, and some **painted vases,** among which is one by
Nikosthenes (*Arch. Zeit.* 1874, pp. 60, 61).

ROKEBY HALL (Yorkshire).

Volkmann, *Reisen,* IV. p. 100. Matz, *Arch. Zeit.* 1873, pp. 25 f.
Michaelis, *Ibid.,* 1874, p. 61.

This residence of Colonel MORRITT is situated in the midst of a
splendid park three miles from Barnard Castle. The collection was
made by J. B. S. MORRITT, Esq., who from the year 1798 was a
zealous member of the Dilettanti Society, and played a part in the
investigation concerning the Elgin Marbles, see *Report from the
Elgin Committee,* &c., p. 128. Cf. Introd. § 67. I visited the collection in 1873.

HALL.

1. **Sepulchral stele,** very much tapered, finished off at the
top with only a simple moulding. A female figure, unveiled, in chiton
and cloak, is holding out some small object in her l. hand to a large
snake that is winding itself round the stem and branches of a large
pine-tree. An incomprehensible object is hanging down from one
of the branches ; it can best be compared to a tent in the form of a
sentinel's box, but it is so contrived that the point of the tent is split
into two parts. (Matz thinks it may be a piece of drapery, since many

such offerings were made to the gods as votive gifts, cf. Michaelis, *Parthenon*, pp. 307 ff.) At the foot of the tree stands a round altar; between this and the principal figure are two diminutive female attendants unoccupied. At the l. end of the relief a small vase stands on a high pillar; at the foot of the pillar are two more diminutive attendants, one holding a tablet and the other a bird. Very high relief, of late but not bad style; may have come from Asia Minor or the Islands. H. 0·46. L., below 0·39; above 0·31. [*M*]

2. **Sepulchral stelè**, in a similar form and style, and probably of the same origin; broken at the top. To the l. a female figure sitting in a chair, robed in a chiton; a cloak covering her legs; her feet resting on a low, broad footstool. A little girl in a chiton with a cloak about her legs is sitting in her lap; she is looking up at her mother and laying her r. hand on her shoulder; in her l. she holds a plaything that is more like a miniature thyrsos than anything else: it is a long staff with a knob at the top, from which a ribbon goes to about the centre of the staff. The mother lays her lowered r. hand on the back of a somewhat bigger girl, who is also robed in a chiton and cloak, and who is standing on the ground and steadying herself by holding the cross bar of the chair with her l. hand, while she stretches out her r. hand to a goose. The goose is sitting in front of her on the ground, turning its head round to her and pulling at the corner of her cloak with its beak. Geese are well known to have been favourite domestic animals. This pretty family scene is made quite complete by the appearance of the father, who from the r. looks on at his children playing. He is raising his r. hand to his chin. He wears chiton, cloak and shoes. The heads of the two principal figures have been broken off with the upper piece of the slab. The marble is finer than that usually employed for the sepulchral reliefs that come from the Greek Islands. H. 0·38. L., below 0·36; above 0·31. [*]

3. **Sepulchral stelè**, much tapered towards the top. In the field a man and woman stand close together in full face, the man to the l., the woman to the r. Both are completely draped, the female figure veiled. The man holds his r. hand up to his breast in his cloak, the female figure (head knocked off) raises her l. hand to her chin, supporting her arm on her r. hand. There is something co-quettish in these movements (cf. Oxford, no. 89). Beside the man stands a diminutive attendant in a chiton, his arms and legs crossed; near the female figure is a diminutive female attendant. The upper piece, including the heads of the two principal figures, is missing.

Ordinary style of the sepulchral reliefs from Rhencia. H. 0·50.
L., below 0·45 ; above 0·39. [*]

4. **Sepulchral stele**, broken off at the top. On the sunk
field of the relief is a female figure in full face, quite enveloped in
her chiton and cloak, excepting her head. On either side, leaning
against the raised border, stands a diminutive female attendant in a
chiton ; the one to the l. carries a little box, the one to the r. is
supporting her chin on her r. hand. The coarse style is that of
the sepulchral reliefs from the Greek Islands and the coasts of Asia
Minor. Underneath is an inscription of ten lines, of which I was unable to make a copy. From two paper impressions and a photograph
my colleague, Prof. Rudolf Schoell, has with great difficulty but with
sufficient certainty deciphered the following verses :

ΔΕΙΝΗΜΕΙΣΑΙΔΗΝΜΟΙΡΗΓΑΓΕΝΟΥΘΥΓ'ΟΜΗΤΡΟΣ
ΧΕΙΡΩΝΗΜΕΛΕΗΝΥΜΦΙΔΙΟΝΘΑΛΑΜΟΝ
ΗΛΥΘΟΝΟΥΔΕΓΑΜΟΥΓΕΡΙΚΑΛΛΕΟΣΥΜΝΟΝΑΚΟΥΣΑ
ΟΥΔΕΤΕΚΝΩΝΓΛΥΚΕΡΟΝΘΡΗΝΟΝΕΜΑΞΑΓΟΤΜΟΙΣ
ΖΥΜΗΔΕΕΡΜΟΓΕΝΟΥΚΙΚΛΗΣΚΟΜΑΙΑΛΛΑΣΥΧΑΙΡΕ
ΞΕΙΝΕΟΣΟΔΟΥΒΑΙΝΕΙΣΗΔΥΤΑΤΗΝΑΤΡΑΓΟΝ
ΑΓΓΕΛΛΕΕΙΣΟΙΚΟΝΤΗΜΗΚΑΚΟΔΑΙΜΟΝΙΜΗΤΡΙ
ΚΑΙΜΗΑΕΙΛΥΓΑΙΣΚΑΙΔΑΚΡΥΟΙΣΙΦΡΕΝΑΣ
ΤΡΥΧΕΙΝΟΥΓΑΡΕΜΟΙΜΟΥΝΗΤΟΔΕΜΟΙΡΕΠΕΚΛΩΣΕΝ
ΚΗΔΟΣΟΡΩΔΕΤΕΜΟΥΚΡΕΣΣΟΝΑΣΕΙΝΑΙΔΙΑ.

On the monument the transverse stroke of the A is bent like a ν.
The interpretation would be as follows :

Δεινή μ' εἰς Ἀίδην μοῖρ' ἤγαγεν, οὔθ' ὑπὸ μητρὸς
χειρῶν ἡ μελέη νυμφίδιον θάλαμον
ἤλυθον, οὐδὲ γάμου περικαλλέος ὕμνον ἄκουσα,
οὐδὲ τέκνων γλυκερὸν θρῆνον ἔμαξα πότμοις (?).
5 [Σ]ύμη δὲ Ἑρμογένου κικλήσκομαι· ἀλλὰ σὺ χαῖρε,
ξεῖνε, ὃς ὁδοῦ βαίνεις ἡδυτάτην ἀτραπόν·
ἄγγελλε εἰς οἶκον τῇ μῇ κακοδαίμονι μητρί,
καὶ μὴ ἀεὶ λύπαις καὶ δακρύοισι φρένας
τρύχειν· οὐ γὰρ ἐμοὶ μούνῃ τόδε μοῖρ' ἐπέκλωσεν
10 κῆδος, ὁρῶ δ' ἔτ' ἐμοῦ κρέσσονας εἰν Ἀίδ[α].

The phrase in v. 4 is rather obscure, but the reading seems to be
certain. The name of Σύμη, v. 5, would well suit the Islands, Symè
being an island near the coast of Karia, and its name being derived
from Symè, the daughter of Ialysos ; the same name may be restored
C. I. Gr. 8485 instead of CIMH. V. 10, it is uncertain whether

δ' ἐτ' or δέ γ' should be preferred; at the end of the verse 'Αἴδω is more likely than 'Αἴδεω, although it would be the only Doric form (cf. Oxford, no. 147; C. I. Gr., 710; Kaibel, Epigr. Gr., no. 372, 13). The palaeographical character indicates the second or the last century B.C. H. 0·46. L., below 0·38; above 0·36. [*]

OUTSIDE THE HOUSE.

5. Fragment of a sepulchral relief, in grey marble, as is customary in the Greek Islands, but of unusually thorough execution. To the r. are the remains of a fluted column, against which, with easy flow of the lines, leans an attendant, his pretty little curly head, with its two plaits along the parting, bent, his legs crossed. He wears a chiton, with a separate border fastened on ; a shawl hangs down from his l. shoulder and is held in his r. hand, and in his l. he holds a round box. The figure is excellently conceived. On his l. hand stands an old man whose proportions are considerably larger : he has a bony face without beard, and a fillet passes through his hair; his face is full of expression. He wears a chiton and cloak. His r. hand (very well executed) lies in front of his breast on the edge of his cloak ; his l. hand, concealed by the cloak, is lowered. Below the l. hand the cloak forms several elegant, somewhat over-elaborate folds. This cloak too has a border. The r. leg from below the cloak missing, the advanced l. leg entire, except the foot. Very high relief. The fragment stands out among the many similar reliefs by the excellence of its workmanship. H. 0·66. L. 0·35. [*]

UPPER STOREY. ANTE-ROOM.

A number of **Roman statuettes** in marble, that have been very much restored, standing on consol tables.

6. Statuette of Fortuna, in a thin chiton, ungirdled, and a cloak which envelops her head, l. arm, and the lower part of her body. Hair parted and falling in two stiff curls by each cheek. She is crowned with a stephanè, over which a crescent is introduced ; behind this a high kalathos is visible, which is also covered by the drapery. (Cf. Archaeologisch-epigraphische Mittheilungen aus Oesterreich, i. Pl. 3.) The face is full and without expression. The l. hand is advanced, holding ears of wheat and poppies. The feet are covered with sandals ; near the r. foot stands a modius, over the edge of which ears of wheat hang down ; the handle of the steering paddle, which rests on the modius, is held by the r. hand. This hand and the greater part of the arm have been restored. [*1/*]

7. **Statuette of "Hermes."** A male figure standing, concealed by his long cloak, which leaves the r. half of his broad, strongly projecting chest exposed and quite hides the l. arm, which is lowered and only slightly bent. New: greater part of the r. arm with the purse, also the wings on the heels. [*M*]

8. **Statuette of Silvanus,** of the usual type (cf. Clarac, III. Pl. 448, 818). He is holding up his small cloak in the manner of a bag; in it are fruits, and in his r. hand he holds the pruning-knife; beside his r. leg is a dog (head new). [*M*]

9. **Torso of Apollo,** nude, standing with his r. leg somewhat in advance. On his shoulders are remains of long curls. With his l. hand he holds the top of a lyre that is resting against his hip, the r. arm hangs down. New: head and neck, l. arm and the lyre, r. forearm from the elbow, the lower parts of the legs including the knees, the pedestal. [*M*]

10. **Statuette of Apollo,** nude, sitting. The lower parts of the legs are somewhat drawn in, the r. thigh somewhat raised; on it rests the lyre, of which the lower part is preserved. New: all the upper part of the body from about the navel, and great part of the lower portion of the r. leg. [*M*]

11. **Statuette of Artemis,** in a chiton girt up short, stepping forward to the r. The r. leg is supported by a trunk, beside which is a dog. The goddess is turning her head somewhat towards her r. shoulder; with her r. hand she is about to take an arrow from her quiver. New: both arms. [*M*]

SALOON.

12. **Small head of Zeus ;** the hair rises up from the forehead, and a fillet is twined in it. Insignificant work. [*M*]

13. **Small bust of Serapis** with a kalathos. Nose restored. No better than no. 12. [*M*]

14. **Terminal head of Dionysos,** with a pointed beard which somewhat projects. [*M*]

For a few **Egyptian sculptures** and some unimportant **vases,** from Lower Italy, cf. Matz, *l. cit.*, p. 26.

Rokeby Hall was up to 1769 in the possession of Sir Thomas Robinson, an enthusiastic dilettante, who was not Thomas Robinson, First Lord Grantham (cre. 1761), ancestor of the Marquess of Ripon, but the eldest brother of the first Lord Rokeby. At that time the master-piece among the antique sculptures there was a large **relief of Niobe,** which is said to have come afterwards to Denton

Hall (cf. Denton).   If this really is the case, some smaller specimens mentioned by Volkmann, p. 101, may also be at Denton, viz. :

(15) a small **statue of Herakles** with the lion's skin ;

(16) **busts** of **Apollo, Diogenes, Vergil, Demosthenes,** of some **Roman emperors** and their **consorts,** among which those of **Paulina** and **Julia** are particularly beautiful ;

(17) various other antique statues and busts, and some **bas-reliefs.**

ROSSIE PRIORY (Perthshire, Scotland).

Waagen, *Treas.*, IV. pp. 445 ff. *Notes and Reminiscences of Rossie Priory.* Dundee, 1877.   4to.

The late owner of this castle, who died January, 1878, GEORGE, NINTH LORD KINNAIRD, himself compiled the above-cited catalogue of his art collection, which is considerable.   In the section which refers to the antique sculptures, descriptions made by Edm. Oldfield, late of the British Museum, have served as a foundation ; all the specimens are given in photographs.   The antiques nearly all come from Italy, where the author of the catalogue, and his father, Charles Lord Kinnaird, both lived for some time and themselves set on foot excavations and made purchases.   Since the year 1826 the collection has been in Rossie Priory.   As I have not myself visited this place, my catalogue is taken exclusively, and in great measure textually, from Lord Kinnaird's catalogue, which his lordship very kindly allowed me to use, as well as from its photographs.   With respect to some of the specimens I have asked Prof. Bernoulli's opinion.   I have kept to the numbers of the printed catalogue, but have refrained from more exact indication of the places in which they stand.

STATUES AND TORSI, GRAECO-ROMAN.

1. **Statue of Narkissos.** This statue is exactly like one in the Villa Rospigliosi (*Mon. ed Ann. dell' Inst.*, 1856, Pl. 21), and like a fragment in the vestibule of the Villa Borghese, except that the sides are reversed.   The youth is resting on his l. leg and supporting himself on his r. arm, so that his r. shoulder toward which his head inclines, is much raised ; his l. hand is behind his hip ; a little below it are attached to his figure two fragments of some object originally held in that hand.   The r. forearm, the l. leg, the greater part of the r. leg,

and the trunk of the tree covered with drapery at his r. side, were
restored by Canova; the head, though not belonging to the figure, is
antique, and is well suited to the style of the statue. It is probable
that these statues were intended to stand on the margin of some water,
so that their glance would be directed to its reflecting surface, a conception well adapted for Narkissos. H. 1·07. "Of Parian marble.
The workmanship moderate" (Waagen).

2. **Torso of a figure of Herakles**, standing on the r.
leg; round the shoulders a lion's skin, tied in a knot on the chest.
Both arms were lowered. Missing: the head, almost the whole of
both arms, three parts of the r., and half the l. leg. H. 0·69.

3. **Fragment of a small draped female figure.** Of late
Roman style. H. 0·46.

4. **Statue of Eros** as a boy, sleeping; head and arms are
lying on a small, sleeping lion. Legs incomplete. L. 0·40.

BUSTS.

5. **Bust of the youthful Dionysos**, wearing a chaplet of
ivy, entwined with vine-leaves and grapes; across the forehead a
broad diadem passing under the hair. Good work. New: nose,
chin, breast, parts of the crown. H. 0·46.

6. **Bust of Aphroditè**, figure more developed than in the
Medici statue. Much restored (nose, breast, &c.). H. 0·46.

7. **Female head** ("Persephonè?"), with a kind of cap
round it (*opisthosphendonè*). Apparently a portrait. H. 0·35.

8. **Female head** ("Muse?"), a narrow fillet entwined in
the wavy hair. The head has some connexion with a bust at Madrid
(*Memorie dell' Inst.*, II. Pl. 3), but the open mouth does not suit
the rest. It was intended to be let into a draped statue, the l. arm
of which must have been much raised. Evidently copied from a
very good original. H. 0·33.

9. **Small head of Pan**, with very brutish features. Much
mutilated. H. 0·10.

10. **Lower part of a small terminal bust of the bearded
Dionysos**, in rosso antico. Good work. H. 0·13.

11. **Double terminal bust**, of the bearded **Dionysos** and
Ariadne, in archaistic style, with ringlets, &c. Defaced; the bust
has been restored. H. 0·33.

12. **Small terminal bust of the youthful Herakles**,
covered with a lion's skin, and crowned with vine-leaves. Workmanship exaggerated. The terminal bust modern. H. 0·28.

13. **Bacchic child's head,** with wreath of grapes and fillet; mouth open. H. 0·20. To judge from the photograph the genuineness is doubtful.

14. **Bust of Pan.** Fine work, and well preserved; but is it certainly genuine? H. 0·36.

15. **Bust of "Isis."** Veiled female figure with long curls. Above the forehead is the remnant of something that may have belonged to the ornament of her head. H. 0·23.

16. **Small bust of Serapis.** Of good work. New: modius, the nose, and the terminal bust with the drapery. H. 0·23.

17. **Head of a youth,** with very rich curly hair, through which a fillet is passed, and an enthusiastic expression, reminding one of Apollo more than of any other personage. The inclination of the head towards the l. shoulder suggests Alexander the Great. In the Catalogue the head is described as female, "probably intended for Diana." Good work, but restored (tip of the nose, &c.), and the surface repolished; roughly finished behind. Heroic size. H. 0·51.

18. **Double terminal bust, of the bearded Dionysos,** his curled hair bound with intertwining sprays of vine and ivy, and of **Ariadne,** with a high wig. Superficial archaism. The work is exceptional inasmuch as the backs of the heads are wanting altogether, and little more than two masks, stuck together, can be seen. H. 0·51.

19. **Bust of a young man,** wearing a slight mustache, but no beard; the hair is arranged like that in the busts of Hadrian. Life size. The mailed bust is new. H. 0·69.

20. **Head of "Nero,"** colossal scale, with a short beard, and the indication apparently of a metal diadem formerly bound round the head, but now lost. The nose and l. side of the face were restored by Thorvaldsen. H. 0·61. The title given above from the Catalogue is certainly wrong, and can only be explained by a certain likeness to other heads which are doubtfully or wrongly attributed to that Emperor. It appears much more likely that the head is intended for Caracalla, though his wicked expression is not there; however it appears really to belong to an earlier period. [*B*]

21. **Small bust of a middle-aged man,** beardless, and with bald head, probably of the first century after Christ. Tip of nose restored. H. 0·23.

22. **Small bust of a young man,** somewhat resembling Hadrian, with whiskers, but no beard. Good work, and well preserved. H. 0·25.

23. **Small bust of a young man**, supposed, without sufficient reason, to be Marcus Aurelius at the age of adolescence. From the photograph one cannot decide whether the bust with the breastplate and paludamentum are antique. H. 0·36. [B]

24. **Small bust of a boy**, smiling. Good, and well preserved. H. 0·25.

25. **Life-sized female bust**, the hair simply gathered in a knot at the back of the head; the nose and neck restored. Eyeballs expressed. The arrangement of the hair resembles that of Faustina the younger; but the bust is certainly not intended to represent her, nor in fact any empress. H. 0·46. [B]

26. **Life-sized head**, attributed without sufficient reason to **Lucius Verus**. H. 0·41. [B]

27. **Life-sized head of a boy**, the shoulders and breast restored. H. 0·38.

28. **Life-sized female bust**, the nose restored. The front hair is brushed back, a style usual in the time of Crispina. H. 0·41. [B]

29. **Life-sized head of a little girl**; the shoulders restored. H. 0·30.

30. **Bust of a boy**, somewhat below life-size, with close-cropped hair, wearing armour and the paludamentum (antique?). Eyeballs expressed. Well preserved. In the pedestal is inserted a copper coin of **Diadumenianus**, son of the emperor Macrinus. "The features of the bust so exactly correspond with all the numismatic portraits of this Imperial child, who was killed at the age of ten, that, notwithstanding the total absence of that personal beauty which was so celebrated by Lampridius (*Antonin. Diadum. 3*), the identity of the representation cannot be doubted. A bust of this subject is of the greatest rarity" (*Catalogue*). The Capitoline bust of the same subject (*Mus. Capit. 11. Pl. 62*) is certainly rather similar; but both busts appear to be too old for a boy who only reached ten years of age. H. 0·43. [B]

31. **Life-sized bust of Otacilia Severa**, wife of the emperor Philippus Senior. Nose and shoulders restored. A similar bust is to be found in the British Museum (*Anc. Marbl.*, x. Pl. 14). H. 0·43. [B]

32. **Life-sized bust**, probably of **Marcus Aurelius**, when young. Well executed, and perfectly preserved; very similar to a bust in the Louvre (Mongez, *Iconogr. Rom.*, iii. Pl. 41, 1. 2). H. 0·56. [B]

33. Life-sized bust of **Alexander Severus** (not Septimius Severus). Eyeballs expressed. The head perfectly preserved and well executed ; the shoulders restored.   H. o·66. [B]

MISCELLANEOUS SCULPTURES.

34. **Panel** on which is sculptured a **strainer** with a handle, in shape like a patera. H. o·15. L. o·23.

35. Mutilated figure of a **tortoise** looking up, of strangely unskilful appearance. At the top in the back is a metal plug, it is conjectured for the fastening of a foot, perhaps of Hermes or of Aphroditè (?). L. o·25.

36. **Left foot** of a female statue. L. o·23.

37. Two **tragic masks**, male, bearded ; and female, placed back to back, like a bifrontal bust ; the female mask much mutilated. H. o·20.

38. **Bearded mask of a Triton**, serving as an ornament of a spout for carrying off water ; from the cornice of a building. Bold work. H. o·23.

39. **Framed relief**, rounded at the top. In it is **Athenè**, seen full face ; she is in complete armour, the shield on her l. arm, the r., with the lance, raised. H. o·41. L. o·28.

40. **Left hand** of a warrior, with part of his shield held by the strap, and ornamented outside with a winged head of Medusa. Fragment of a statue. L. o·15.

41. **Fragment of a trapezophoros**, with panther's head. Oriental alabaster. H. o·13.

42. **Bearded head**, of noble features, but with no particular expression. It bears a distant resemblance to the head of Asklepios, or Zeus, at Holkham, no. 56. The back of the head and great part of the r. half of the face are missing, the nose is restored. H. o·23.

43. **Round urn**, ornamented with masks and branches. Apparently not free from suspicion. H. o·29.

44. **Mask of an old woman**, deeply furrowed with wrinkles ; life-size. With eyes growing dim and mouth open. Apparently modern. H. o·25.

45. **Flat circular basin** ornamented with leaves ; the pedestal restored. Diameter o·74.

46. **Round urn**, ornamented outside with leaves and decorated on the rim with four rams' heads. The pedestal restored. H. 1·00.

47—50. Fragments of **pilasters and columns**, with vine-leaves trained over them.

51. **Left hand** of a person carrying a basket filled with fruit, fragment of a life-sized statue.

52. **Knee of a Pan.** L. 0·42.

RELIEFS.

54. **Corner of a sarcophagus,** fragment. At the r. end a bearded male figure with long curly hair, in tunic and pallium and wearing a sword at his side, tries to escape from an elderly, bald-headed male figure, also in tunic and pallium, who with his r. arm has seized the r. arm of the first figure. The meaning is not clear. Missing: lower halves of the figures and the continuation at the l. end. On the r. side a funeral pyre in low relief. H. 0·30. L. 0·30.

55. **Left end of the lid of a sarcophagus,** broken at the r. and underneath. Two Erotes are represented; one of them with a torch in his l. arm is employing himself about a stove (?) on which stands a kettle. H. 0·13. L. 0·27.

56—60. **Decorative reliefs,** in great part decorated with vine-sprays.

61. **Head,** resembling **Caligula,** turned r. Is now on an oval field. H. 0·30. L. 0·25. Appears suspicious.

62. **Male torso,** enveloped in an ample cloak, which falls down in rich folds from his advanced l. arm; of the relief field only a small part is preserved. Of Greek style. H. 0·39.

63, 64. **Decorative reliefs.** Architectural.

65. **Head of a Medusa,** mutilated. L. 0·20.

66. **Head of a boy,** full face; of good work. H. 0·15. L. 0·13.

67. **Bearded head,** turned to the r. Not free from suspicion. Oval. H. 0·30. L. 0·23.

68. **Youth** with Phrygian cap and flowing chlamys, pressing forward r. Arms and legs missing; broken round the edge. Graceful work. H. 0·51. L. 0·33.

69. **Head of Seilenos,** crowned with ivy. Fragment. H. 0·15. L. 0·20.

70. **Head of a young Satyr,** with ruffled hair. H. 0·20. L. 0·20.

71. **Head of a bearded warrior** in a Roman helmet. Very suspicious. Life-size. H. 0·38. L. 0·25.

72. **Fragment of a large relief,** belonging apparently to some public building. Three heads, two with slight whiskers, one with beard, mustache and whiskers; among the hair are many

traces of the auger, and the heads have hollowed chamfers round
them. On two of the figures the tunic is visible. The art lifelike
but hard, scarcely earlier than the third century A.D. H. 0·61.
L. 0·84.

73. **Fragment of an Eros**, apparently from a sarcophagus.
H. 0·28. L. 0·25.

74. **Female figure reclining**, her back exposed, the rest of
her body covered by her cloak. Probably a fragment from a Bacchic sarcophagus. H. 0·27. L. 0·38.

75. **Beardless head**, crowned with laurel, apparently a portrait from the Hellenistic period, but not free from suspicion. H. 0·33.
L. 0·30.

76. **Fragment of a sarcophagus** with a representation of the
Seasons. One of the four youths, winged, is preserved, wearing the
chlamys, a basket full of fruit in his r. hand, the attribute of the
l. hand missing. Between his legs lies a panther, near his r. leg
a small Eros runs; then comes an inverted basket and a large undis-
tinguishable object. H. 0·66. L. 0·38.

77. **Fragment of a sarcophagus.** Two boys in cloaks,
running in different directions; in front of the one running r. part of
a third is visible who carries an ewer in his r. hand. Rough work.
H. 0·32. L. 0·30.

78. **Fragment of a youth**, seated facing l., in a girdled chiton
and a cloak, a sword at his side, long effeminate curls falling down on
his shoulders. In his r. arm is a sceptre, his l. hand rests on his hip.
Probably intended for Paris, but the genuineness appears doubtful.
H. 0·28. L. 0·32.

79. **Fragment** of perhaps a later Greek **sepulchral relief.**
In the field a closed door; below it a small horse. To the r. the
remains of a comparatively tall male figure. H. 0·27. L. 0·21.

80. **Fragment of a sarcophagus.** A boar attacked by a
dog; above, the foreparts of two horses. H. 0·28. L. 0·28.

81. **Fragment with two heads** side by side looking l. One
head is bearded, and wears a round cap, fitting very tight (*pilleus*); the
other has no beard, but a fillet in his hair. Good work. Odysseus
and Telemachos have been suggested, but the expression of the
elder face is not appropriate to the character of Odysseus. H. 0·42.
L. 0·36.

82. **Fragment of a historical relief.** A chair and footstool are placed on a kind of tribune (*suggestus*), and in the chair,
turning r., sits a man in tunic and pallium (head and arms broken

off). Behind the tribune on the floor stands a beardless attendant in a short tunic. H. 0·48. L. 0·36.

83. Fragment of a sarcophagus. Columns with arches over them. In the arch to the r. stands a bearded man, apparently a shepherd in tunic and cloak, leaning upon his staff, and looking to the r. In the arch to the l. are remains of a Dioskuros with lance and horse, of the horse only parts of the fore legs are preserved. H. 0·23. L. 0·36.

84. Framed relief; a lion seizing a boar that lies on its back on the ground. H. 0·23. L. 0·43.

85. Architectural relief with foliage.

86. Bearded head, turned l., with a fillet through the hair. From the "flowing" character of the beard and of the hair on the forehead it appears to be intended for Poseidon, but the genuineness of this elegant specimen is very doubtful. H. 0·42. L. 0·36.

87, 88. Architectural fragments with foliage.

ROMAN SEPULCHRAL MONUMENTS.

Those monuments which only contain inscriptions are not reckoned here; they may be found in their place in *C. I. Lat.*, vol. VI.

91. Sepulchral altar, surmounted in front by a curved pediment, now broken, on which is sculptured in relief a figure of Mercury, holding a purse in the r. hand and a caduceus in the l., and standing between a ram and a tortoise. The inscription runs thus : *D(is) M(anibus) | M. Coccei Crescentis | vix. ann. II. m(ens). I. d(ieb). VII | et Cocceiae Auge c(oniugi) b(ene mer.) | et Cocceiae Auge f(iliae) d(ulcissimae) | et M. Ulpio Vestali f(ilio) d(ulcissimo), | v(ix). a(nn). XXVIIII. m(ens). VI, | Vestalis Aug(usti) lib(ertas) | et sibi et suis posterisq(ue) eorum.* H. 0·81. L. 0·51.

101. Square double cinerarium, ornamented with pilasters and garlands. R. : *Dis Manibus | Flaviae Zoe | Nucerinus coniugi | karissimae bene merenti, | item sibi et | Pomponiae Thallusae*; below are birds. L. : *et P. Betilieno | Cureti Carpo et | Primigenio*; below is a hare nibbling at some fruits that have fallen from an overturned basket. H. 0·25. L. 0·68.

102. Square cinerarium, with two bulls' heads to which a garland is fastened; under each head a mask. Inscription : *Dis Manibus | Selae Helidis | pater et mater | filiae pi[is]simae.*—On the lid a basket with leaves at which two birds are pecking. H. 0·23. L. 0·32.

103. Square cinerarium. On the lid a vase between two birds. Inscription, enclosed by two cypresses : *D. M.* | *ossa Meciliae Balbillae Lanuvii* | *sac(erdotis), quae in aede Iunonis S(ospitae) M(atris) R(eginae)* | *scutulum et c[l]yp(eum) et hast(am) et calc(eos)* | *rite novavit voto.* (Orelli, 1308.) Said to have come from Città Lavigna (Lanuvium), but the suspicion which Mommsen (*Bullett.*, 1853, p. 173. *N. rhein. Mus.*, IX. p. 456) entertained as to the genuineness of the inscription is fully confirmed as correct by the palaeographical character. H. 0·27. L. 0·36.

The Catalogue mentions besides the sculptures we have already noticed :

136. Fragments of a mosaic floor, " discovered near Rome in 1822, in a vineyard on Monte Rosario, about half a mile beyond the Porta Portuensis, on the r. bank of the Tiber. The centre of the pavement was destroyed ; of the portion preserved, several pieces were obtained by the Duke of Bedford, and are now at Woburn Abbey [no. 228]; the remainder is in the Rossie collection. A coloured plate annexed to the Catalogue, copied from a drawing made at the time by M. Valadier, shows the original arrangement of the entire pavement." The centre field which is oblong is completely destroyed ; it is surrounded first by a broad strip with a Triton's head in each corner, and between the heads, animals in the midst of foliage, and all on a white ground. Then follows a narrow decorative band and then a broad meander pattern which encloses square fields. These are so arranged that one field occurs at each corner (with one of the four Seasons), and between them four others down the long sides and three along the shorter sides. The further, outside stripes, are only ornamental ; towards the inside coloured, towards the edge only black and white. " The pavement is composed mainly of marble *tesserae*, with a few cubes of glass or tile ; it may be referred to the earlier half of the second century after Christ." The following fragments with representations of figures, drawn on one of two coloured plates in the Catalogue, are to be found in Rossie Priory. I. Of the inner strip : two heads of Tritons, hair and beard vanishing into sea-plants and a mushroom on the top of the head ; further a lion with a lizard over it, a stag, two panthers, one standing and one running, all entwined with foliage. II. Eight squares of the meander border ; two of them belonged to the opposite corners and each contains a female bust, one of which is crowned with flowers and the other with corn ears, thus representing Spring and Summer. The other six represent cake with almonds in an ornamental stand, a red mullet in a plate, a sweet-meat basket, a roll of bread, a cock with his legs tied together, and a purse.

Here it may be well to append the following notices of some small miscellaneous antiques, for which I have to thank Mr A. S. Murray, of the British Museum; the numbers only follow those of the present catalogue, and do not apply to the collection itself.

137. A very small head, bearded and helmeted. Marble.

138. Another male head, very small; top of head bald. A portrait. Marble. Minute cameo-like work.

139. Torso of a bronze statuette of Herakles, in fine condition, and of good workmanship.

140. Several rude bronze statuettes of Herakles.

141. A very rude bronze figure of Athenè with a gor-goneion on the breast.

142. Bronze statuette of Isis; a foot broken away.

143. Bronze mirror. Two male figures (Dioskuroi?), nude, standing face to face, and each leaning on a spear; between them a flower. The drawing is better than it usually is where such subjects occur on mirrors.

144. Fragments of a large bronze vase with a row of very rude figures. Etruscan, probably from Corneto.

145. Fragments of bronze armour, from the "Warrior's Tomb," Corneto. Cf. Mrs Hamilton Gray, *The Sepulchres of Etruria*, p. 529. *Annali d. Inst.*, 1829, pp. 95 ff.

146. A small series of Etruscan bronze fibulae.

147. Bronze stamp: P·CVRTI·P·P·L.

148, 149. Two terra-cotta lamps, probably found in the Roman Catacombs. One of them shows the Christian monogram. On the other is a ship with a figure swimming in the water beside it or after it (Jonah?).

150. A tragic mask, of terra-cotta.

The following ten numbers are gems and rings:

151. Large onyx cameo. Jupiter in a *quadriga* hurling his thunderbolt at two Giants under his horses. Very beautiful work, but of that kind as to which it is hardly possible to decide whether it is Roman or Cinquecento; it may be rather the latter.

152. Onyx cameo. A female head, to the r., with the hair

M. C. 42

plaited and twined in a knot at roots behind. A beautiful fragment.

153. Onyx cameo; a fragment. Back view of Herakles wearing a lion's skin.

154. **Carnelian intaglio**; female head to the l. Fine work.

155. **Carnelian intaglio** with scarab border. On the l. two warriors, fully armed, stand before a naked man, who has laid aside his armour, but holds a sword in his l. hand by his side.

156. **Carnelian intaglio** with scarab border; broken. Two male figures; one of them on the r. holds up by the back hair a figure of apparently a nude girl between them, while the male figure on the l. holds a sword.

157. **Carnelian intaglio**; broken. A draped female figure seated to the r. holds some object in her r. hand above her knees; her l. hand draws forward drapery from her breast.

158. **Plasma intaglio.** Jupiter, seated to the l., holds out Victory on his r. hand; on his l. hand a cornucopiae. Fine specimen.

159. **Red jasper intaglio.** Andromache holding and addressing Hektor; at their feet the child Astyanax.

160. **Small gold ring,** with intaglio of a female head to the l. Very pretty.

Finally there is

161. **A small mural painting** from Rome. Bust of a Nymph, apparently with the head thrown back. Very beautiful.

SALISBURY (Wiltshire).

In the newly-built Blackmore Museum there are, as far as I know, no Greek or Roman sculptures. Cf. Huebner, *Monatsbericht d. Berliner Akademie*, 1868, p. 90.

SHOBDEN (Herefordshire).

"A single statue of **Mercury** was acquired by the late Lord BATEMAN, and is now at Shobden. In the opinion of the late Mr Townley, it is equalled by few statues of that deity of which he had any knowledge." (Dallaway, *Of Statuary*, p. 356.)

STANMORE HILL (Middlesex).

Mr C. Drury E. Fortnum, F.S.A., the author of the valuable "Catalogue of the Bronzes in the South Kensington Museum" (1876) has himself a considerable collection of bronzes in his country house near Great Stanmore; many of them belong to the Cinquecento period. He also has a splendid collection of **antique rings**, and among them is the large portrait of Berenikè, the consort of the first Ptolemaeos, graven in gold, which is a great rarity. In 1877 Mr Fortnum kindly allowed me to look through his **bronzes**, and among them the following deserve special mention:

1. **Statuette of Aphroditè.** Engr. *Catalogue of the Collection, &c., formed by* B. Hertz, 1851, Pl. 2. The goddess, quite nude, rests on her r. leg; her l. foot is somewhat drawn back, her knee bent. Her l. arm is lowered and held away from the body, and the hand is opened in such a manner as to suggest that she has just let something fall to the ground from it. The head with a graceful curve of the neck also inclines in the same direction; the hair is simply waved. The r. hand is raised, and holds a small, broad wreath, woven very closely, and having two ribbons (ὑποθυμίς). The expression of the full face is one of maidenly grace, without a trace of coquettishness; the pose of the whole figure is very graceful. The forms of the body are full and voluptuous, and the hips, particularly when seen from behind, very broad. The l. foot is not pretty, being much too long, and the upper part of the back is not as beautiful as the rest. The surface, covered with green patina, is somewhat corroded, but the contour has not suffered on this account, and the preservation is faultless. The figure belongs undoubtedly to a good period, of Greek, and not of Roman art. H. 0·325. Found at Mogla, near Stratonikeia in Karia; purchased on the spot with a number of coins by Edw. O'Halley, Esq., for a mere trifle. In 1846 B. Hertz obtained the bronze for about £35 (*Catal. Hertz*, 1851, p. 130, no. 19); it attracted notice at the Manchester Exhibition of 1857. At Hertz' sale, 1859, the present owner purchased it (*Catal. Hertz-Mayer*, 1859, no. 150). [*]

2. **Statuette of Aphroditè.** The position of the legs is similar to that of no. 1. Both arms are held further from the body, and the upper part of the arms is only a little depressed; the r. fore-arm is advanced, and the hand turned under and opened (fingers missing), the l. bent upward (the hand missing). I do

not understand the motive of the position of the arms. The head
is inclined slightly in the direction of the r. hand. A tolerably
broad fillet is passed through the hair, which is arranged in curls
on the temples and gathered up into a plait behind. The pretty
little head is particularly well executed, but the body is also very
graceful and on the whole excellently preserved, including the pedestal
with architectural mouldings. H. 0·11, with the pedestal 0·125.
Purchased in Florence. [*]

3. **Statuette of Aphrodite**, nude, and resting on her l. leg,
her face inclined towards her r. hand. Long curls : on the hair
a stephanè with five knobs on the upper rim. Arms both lowered,
now missing. Roman work. H. 0·20. [*]

4. **Statuette of Serapis**, with the r. foot advanced. A
cloak covers the upper part of his l. arm and all the lower part of his
body ; his l. hand is held in front of his body, and in his lowered r.
hand is a fillet. The head somewhat resembles Zeus, and has rough,
curly hair falling about it ; there is a modius on the crown of the
head. Pedestal preserved. Good figure. H. 0·11, with the pedestal
0·13. From Falerii. [?]

5. **Statuette of youthful Herakles**, with the lion's skin
across his l. arm, his l. hand holding the club which he neither
shoulders nor lowers. The figure is very slim, and points to a type
of a later period than that of Lysippos. H. 0·22. [*]

6. **Statuette of a Dioskuros**, with the star on his head. His
r. hand lowered in front of his body, his cloak across his l. arm.
H. 0·08. [*]

7. **Statuette of Silvanus**, in boots, a goat's skin passed
slantwise across his breast ; he has a pine-wreath pointed like a
crown, from which long ribbons fall down on the shoulders. He
holds out a drinking-horn (*rhyton*) in his r. hand, made out of a ram's
horn, and in his l. arm he holds a large knotted club. The expression of the bearded face is goodnatured, but commonplace. H. 0·12.
Purchased in Florence. [*]

8. **Statuette of Priapos (?)**. A bearded male figure, nude, with
his l. hand resting on his hip, his r. held before his body, a cloth
wound round his head. It has been injured about the lower part
of the body ; there are traces showing that the attribute of Priapos
was once here. H. 0·08 ; with the pedestal 0·095. [*]

9. **Statuette of Commodus** on horseback, in tunic and
cloak ; the horse is very small and has crooked legs. An uncommon
kind of statuette. H. 0·05. [*]

10—12. Three Etruscan figures of a **warrior** or of **Mars**, his l. arm advanced and his r. placed in a right angle. Enormous plume on the helmet; parts of the armour chiselled out. Very slim proportions; below the feet are pegs for fastening. H. 0·30; 0·27; 0·07. [*]

13. Etruscan warrior, stepping to the r., the r. arm lowered; helmet with plume. H. 0·22. [*]

14. Bearded figure, with a large, broad nose, squatting on the ground, drinking from a cup. [*]

15. Figures of Herakles, Dionysos, a horse. From a bronze vessel. [*]

16. Archaistic Etruscan reliefs, which may have served as ornaments of a vessel: **two Gorgons**, winged, with large boots; with their knees bent they run one to the r. and the other to the l. **Bearded Satyr**, with goat's legs, large ears, reclining with his l. arm supported on a cushion. **Mask of the bearded Dionysos**, with a fillet, in grand, severe, hieratic style. [*]

17. Female bust ("Agrippina"), draped, looking somewhat to the l. Rounded off underneath, evidently a piece of a medallion (*clupeus*). Gilt bronze. From Falerii. H. 0·08. [*]

18. Terminal figure with a youthful **negro head.** Pretty. 0·20. [*]

19. A bull. [*]

20. A silver goblet, covered with delicate vine-sprays; in the shape of the rounded skyphos. The handles have been lost. [*]

St ANN'S HILL, see p. 211.

STOURHEAD HOUSE (Wiltshire).

Volkmann, *Reisen*, II. p. 34.   Dallaway, p. 384 (II. p. 136).

Dallaway commends very much the following statue found here in Sir RICHARD HOARE'S house:

1. "**Juno** or **Ceres**, which is not eclipsed by the Hercules of Ryssbrack, excellent as it is." I do not know whether this statue is identical with the following.

2. Flora, standing, from the Mead collection (*Mus. Mead.*, p. 221) which had been purchased for Stourhead (Dallaway, *Of Statuary*, p. 314).

STRATFIELD SAYE (Hampshire).

The DUKE OF WELLINGTON has kindly informed me by letter that on this estate of his, not far from Kings-Clere, there are a few **busts**, but I can give no particulars about them. Cf. London, Apsley House.

TRENTHAM HALL (Staffordshire).

This seat near Stockwood on Trent belongs to the DUKE OF SUTHERLAND. One of the servants at Stafford House told me that there were a few antique **bas-reliefs** here.

TUNBRIDGE WELLS (Kent).

Admiral T. A. B. SPRATT, C.B., the much esteemed author of the *Travels in Lycia* and the *Travels and Researches in Crete*, and the draughtsman of excellent maps, brought home some sculptures after his long residence in the East. They are kept at Tunbridge Wells, once a favourite summer residence of the last two Stuarts. Unfortunately time did not permit me to accept the owner's kind invitation to visit the sculptures. Among them I mention the following:

1.   **Statuette of Aphrodite** in marble, found at Knossos in Crete. Spratt, *Travels in Crete*, I. p. 72, with plate (I have also a larger photograph of it). It is the well-known motive of the *pseliumene*, only in the place of the leg ornament (ψέλιον) are substituted sandals which the goddess is loosening. She is just preparing herself for the bath. She stands on her r. foot, which is already uncovered, and has raised her l. foot that she may draw off the sandal with her lowered r. hand. An exceedingly large *puntello* connects the toes of the l. foot with the ground. The l. hip is leaning on the trunk of a tree, which is however only made as a material support for the marble copy; in the original, which was of bronze, it was wanting certainly, as the l. arm was supported on a pillar. The head, which was found a little afterwards about 200 yards from the statue, is turned sharply towards the r. shoulder; a fillet is passed through the wavy hair. The back of the head and nearly the whole of the l. arm are missing; all the rest is in perfect preservation. The features of the face are not purely ideal, but have an expression of their own which

is coquettish; the face seems to be somewhat rubbed, and also the rest of the figure, which when it was found was encrusted with a thick coating of carbonate of lime, and had to undergo a thorough cleansing. The proportions on the whole are exaggeratedly slender, the upper part of the body is too small in comparison with the very powerful hips. The execution of the back has been commended. H. about 0·60.

2. **Small head of Zeus**, from Crete, highly praised by Spratt, *l. cit.*, p. 75.

Admiral Spratt possesses some more specimens; others he has given away, part to the British Museum, and part to Cambridge (cf. Cambridge, no. 13).

WARWICK CASTLE (Warwickshire).

Spiker, *Reise*, I. 81. Waagen, *Treas.*, III. pp. 217 f. (II. p. 370).

The chief and superlative ornament of this celebrated old castle of the Earls of Warwick (family name Greville) stands in a conservatory:

1. **The Warwick-Vase.** Piranesi, *Vasi e Candelabri*, II. Pl. 2—4. Moses, *Vases*, Pl. 37. Penna, *Villa Adriana*, IV. Pl. 95. The vase is in the shape of a large krater, the foot having been added by Piranesi. The lower half of the main body is very much rounded, and decorated all round the foot with acanthus leaves and above with a panther's skin. Above this part the vessel is compressed so as to give the effect of a shelf covered with a skin, and on this shelf lie on either side four Bacchic masks; in the centre, on a separate, low plinth, are Dionysos himself, crowned with ivy, and the bearded Seilenos; in front of each is a short thyrsos, laid slant-wise; on the l. and the r. a bearded Satyr-head, the first crowned with ivy, the second with pine-sprays. On the opposite side, also on a low plinth, is Dionysos in the centre, bearded, without a wreath, and the bald-headed Seilenos, crowned with ivy; beside them on the l. is a pedum, on the r. a thyrsos; at either end is a bearded Satyr-head, that on the l. hand bald-headed and crowned with ivy, that on the r. hand crowned with pine-leaves. Underneath the main body of the vase are attached strong handles, which are much twisted and finally run into delicate vine-sprays, and are so continued round the uppermost edge of the vessel. The vase, of very fine marble, is 1·70 high and has a diameter of 2·11; its capacity is

81½ gallons. The work is excellent; the vine-sprays are so fine that they seem like the marble copy of a bronze original; it is well known that the manufacturer Thomason of Birmingham has had the vase in its original size copied in bronze (see Noehden in Böttiger's *Amalthea*, III. p. 418. Clarac, *Musée*, II. 1, p. 414): one of these copies is set up at Cambridge, in the space in front of the University Library. Except some of the masks, which have needed considerable repair, it is in good preservation. It was found in 1771 in Hadrian's Villa by Gavin Hamilton, was purchased from him by Sir William Hamilton and in 1774 brought to England; it was then passed on to George, Earl of Warwick. [*H*]

The other sculptures which Waagen saw in one of the rooms probably all perished in the great fire of 1871; such is certainly the case with the following:

2. **Oval sarcophagus**, with lion's heads, representing Endymion and Selene; the surface much injured. [*H*]

Besides these, Waagen mentions the following **busts**:

3. **Bust of Herakles**, colossal scale, of very noble character and excellent sculpture. New: nose, beard, and back of the head. [*H*]

4. **Bust of Scipio Africanus**, above the size of life; very characteristic, especially the mouth; of fine workmanship. The nose and ears are new. [*H*]

5. **Bust of Augustus**, rather colossal, at the age of about fifty years, beautifully executed in Parian marble. The neck and hair particularly good. The whole in capital preservation. [*H*]

6. **Bust of Trajan**, a fine work, of Carrara marble. Nose and ears restored. [*H*]

WENTWORTH CASTLE (Yorkshire).

Volkmann, *Reisen*, IV. pp. 36, 38.

In this seat, now the property of the VERNON-WENTWORTH family, the following statues were to be found towards the close of the last century, at which time it belonged to LORD STRAFFORD:

1. **Apollo**, ⎫
2. **Egyptian Priestess**, ⎬ in the Gallery.
3. **Bacchus**, ⎪
4. **Ceres**, ⎭
5. **Ceres**, in the garden, in a clump of trees.

WENTWORTH HOUSE (Yorkshire).

Dallaway, p. 385 (II. p. 137). Waagen, *Treas.*, III. p. 337 (II. p. 430).

The MARQUIS OF ROCKINGHAM, the minister, who as Lord Malton was the patron of Stuart, possessed here, according to Dallaway, several statues and busts, of which I only consider worthy of mention the **bust of Antinous** from the Mead collection (*Mus. Mead.*, p. 223. Walpole's letter to R. Bentley, March 27, 1755. Dallaway, *Of Statuary*, p. 314). A splendid cabinet of **Roman coins** is also mentioned (Volkmann, *Reisen*, IV., p. 30). The castle now belongs to the EARL FITZWILLIAM; Waagen found nothing worth mentioning except copies from celebrated antiques in the spaces between the columns of the large hall.

WILTON HOUSE (Wiltshire).

Cary Creed edited in 1731 a series of 70 plates with no printed title; the copy in the British Museum bears the manuscript title, "The Marble Antiquities, The Right Hon. the Earl of Pembroke's, at Wilton, &c." 4to. (The figures are throughout engraved without the use of a mirror, and therefore in reverse position.) Richard Cowdrie, *A Description of the Pictures, Statues, &c., at Wilton House,* 1751, translated into Italian, Florence, 1754; often republished, and partly enlarged under the title: James Kennedy, *A Description of the Antiquities and Curiosities in Wilton House,* Salisbury, 1758, 8vo; an enlarged edition in 4to, 1769, with 25 engravings (used by me), 1776, 1778, 1779 (probably identical with *A new Description of the pictures, &c., in the Earl of Pembroke's House at Wilton.* Ed. 9. Salisbury, 1779, 8vo.), 1786. *Ædes Pembrochianæ: or a critical account of the statues, bustos, relievos, paintings, medals, and other antiquities and curiosities at Wilton House. Formed on the plan of Mr Spence's Polymetis. To which is prefixed, An Extract of the Rules to judge of the Goodness of a Picture: and The Science of a Connoisseur in Painting.* By Mr Richardson. London, 1774, 8vo. (Not the whole book but only the introduction is to be referred to Mr Richardson, the rest is mainly borrowed from Kennedy; no engravings are appended.) Volkmann, *Reisen* I. pp. 478 ff. W. Gilpin, *Observations on the Western Part of England,* 1798, pp. 104 ff. Dallaway, pp. 263 ff. (I. pp. 296 ff.). Goede, *England, Wales, &c.,* V. pp. 136—150. Spiker, *Reise,* II. pp. 187 ff..

200. Waagen, *Treas.*, III. pp. 142 ff. (II. pp. 272 ff.). Clarac, III. p. 104. Newton, *Notes on the Sculptures at Wilton House*, 1849 (printed in the volume of Proceedings at the Salisbury meeting of the Archæological Institute). Conze, *Arch. Anz.*, 1864, pp. 173 ff. 209 ff. Michaelis, *Arch. Zeit.*, 1874, pp. 62 ff. I have examined the collection myself, in 1873 and 1877. The following catalogue adheres to the numbering of the collection itself from 1—179, which Newton also retains, the remaining numbers I have assigned myself. The numbers not given in my catalogue belong to such modern specimens as could not deceive a moderately practised glance; many of them, however, have received attention, if any interest attaches to them.

The collection of antiques in the ancient mansion of Wilton House, situated close by the little town of Wilton, is the exclusive work of THOMAS HERBERT, EIGHTH EARL OF PEMBROKE (1654— 1732, became Earl 1683), who had already inherited from his ancestors a fine picture-gallery, including in particular excellent Vandykes. The Earl travelled much and was well acquainted with Italian antiquaries. He was the first collector of importance after Lord Arundel and King Charles (Introd. § 25). He interested himself, as Kennedy informs us on the authority of MS. notes by the Earl, in collecting gems and bronzes, but especially busts and copies from antiques. As to reliefs, &c., and inscriptions, he only cared for notable examples. Moreover, he wished only to have objects of the best period, no mutilated specimens, no duplicates, and above all no unknown portraits! How he carried out the last intention we shall soon see.

The foundation of the collection to all appearance consisted of the busts which Lord Pembroke purchased from the gallery of ARUNDEL HOUSE, when it was broken up in 1678 (Introd. § 22); probably also a few of the other marbles came from the same place. The Arundel Collection, to judge by the remnant of it in Oxford, was entirely free, or nearly so, from modern specimens : accordingly, among the Wilton marbles of indisputable antiquity we should expect to find the specimens purchased from that collection, though we have no means of identifying them individually. We may call to mind such heads as nos. 4, 20, 25, 34, 35, 41, 47, &c., and Greek sepulchral reliefs such as nos. 17, 109, 125, 152.

A second portion of the antiques was derived from the sale of a part of the very rich GIUSTINIANI Collection in Rome (probably the contents of the Villa Giustiniani near the Porta del Popolo, which were afterwards incorporated in those of the Villa Borghese), which comprised, for example, more than a hundred busts. The choicest of these were secured by Cardinal Alessandro Albani, who completed thereby his admirable collection of busts, which was subsequently purchased for the Capitoline Museum. His fellow-purchaser was Lord Pembroke; but in this case also I am not in a position to indicate individual purchases, which would, perhaps, be made possible by comparing on the spot the engravings in the *Galleria Giustiniani* with the Wilton sculptures.

No doubt the most extensive of all the purchases which the Earl made was that of a number of marbles of all kinds from the MAZARIN Collection in Paris. The statues of this division stood there, to the disgust of visitors, in the miserable plight to which the madness of the Due de Mazarin in 1670 had reduced them (Introd. § 26), until the close of the seventeenth century. I do not know the exact date of this purchase: it was probably made in the second decade of the last century, when the Palais Mazarin was prepared for John Law's financial enterprises. Cardinal Mazarin, as in all probability Cardinal Richelieu before him, had set great store by a splendid adventitious embellishment of his gallery, which was provided with a superabundance of modern specimens. For the busts a considerable number of high pedestals of variegated kinds of marble, artistically inlaid, had been prepared in Rome; were moreover all mounted on high, clumsily moulded bases of identical proportions, the majority of variegated, several of white marble; finally the heads, which for the most part had no busts, were furnished with splendid draped or mailed busts of alabaster or other kinds of marble and other stone. Furthermore to each specimen was assigned a number, which was chiselled in some cases into the bust or statue itself, in others on the base of the bust, or again on the pedestal. These numbers are repeated in the inventory which Mazarin had drawn up in the year 1653 by no less a person than Jean-Baptiste Colbert, at that time one of his personal attendants: *Inventaire de tous les meubles du Cardinal Mazarin. Dressé en 1653, et publié d'après l'original, conservé dans les archives de Condé (par Henri Due d'Aumale).* London, 1861. It comprises 137 statues and 187 busts, while the reliefs are counted in with one or other of the two classes according to circumstances. A new inventory was prepared at the Cardinal's death, 1661, increased by about 30 statues and some 20 busts, and provided, piece by piece, with the estimated prices, which show the relatively high price of antiques at the period.

This inventory is unfortunately not printed (MS. Mélanges Colbert,
nos. 74—79); only the prices are added to the printed copy of the
older inventory.   Finally a kind of *Catalogue raisonné* seems also to
have been made subsequently with a view to the sale, as Kennedy
often avails himself of statements of the Mazarin Catalogue which
are not in the above mentioned inventory.   By the aid of this
inventory a large number of the antiques in Wilton House, among
them many of modern origin, can be proved to have come from the
Mazarin Collection ; these include not only busts, but also statues
and reliefs.   Five statues (nos. 70, 116, 144, 145, 170) still bear the
Mazarin numbers; others are sufficiently identified by the marks left
by the crazy Duke's hammering ; many more again are to be determined with more or less certainty by the statements of Kennedy or
the descriptions in the inventory.   Altogether there are no fewer
than 23 statues in Wilton House to be indicated with tolerable
certainty as having belonged to the Mazarin Collection, a fact not
without importance as showing that all these antiques were of Italian,
generally of Roman origin.   To the same source may be traced seven
reliefs, among which are two large sarcophagus slabs (nos. 61, 163).
Much larger is the number of busts which with their bases and the
costly pedestals were bought by Earl Thomas.   Here again many
can be identified by the numbers of the Mazarin collection ; still the
identification is only certain when the numbers are on the busts themselves, as the bases and pedestals have in many cases been inter-
changed, and therefore the numbers on them prove at most that
the specimens which bear these numbers in the inventory of the
Mazarin Collection are generally speaking to be found in Wilton
House.   Thus, for instance, no. 127 of the following catalogue has on
the bust the Mazarin number 52, on the base 158, on the pedestal 31 ;
and a quantity of interchanges are indicated by the fact that the
description in the inventory applying to the number which the base
or pedestal now bears, often does not suit the bust.   At any rate it
can be established with certainty or high probability from these
numbers that no fewer than 83 busts are derived from the Mazarin
collection.   In the following catalogue the designation " Maz." is in
all such cases affixed to the numbers of the several articles ; with the
numbers of the Mazarin collection in instances where they are still
recognisable on bust or statue ; with no further mark when the origin
is established from other sources; with a note of interrogation where
its assumption only rests on the peculiarities of the bust, its base or
pedestal.

A comparison of the Mazarin inventory with the nomenclature adopted in Wilton House is well calculated to show the unscrupulous and arbitrary spirit in which the christening was here undertaken. Thus no. 5, " Hercule et l'Prothée," is turned into ΗΡΑΚΛΕΣ and ΑΧΕΛΩΟΣ, &c. However, these are trifles. Far more frequently busts, which were in the Mazarin collection modestly left without names, have here been endowed with the most arbitrary, high-sounding names, in most cases quite inappropriate, generally carved on them in Latin letters, more rarely in Greek characters. In this way it was of course very easy to have "no unknown portraits." Moreover, the wildest fables were invented, to all appearance so early as to be found in the MS. notes and anecdotes of Earl Thomas, concerning the nominal origin of various specimens, especially of Roman antiques from the Mazarin collection or even of modern pieces (e.g. nos. 48, 99, 144). One of the most remarkable examples is afforded by the degree of certainty with which Kleomenes, whose name was made especially popular by the inscription of the Medici Venus, was announced as the author of four statues (nos. 124, 151, 159, 170) and one modern relief (no. 87); which Winckelmann indeed recognised as a cheat (letters to Muzel-Stosch, June or July and Oct. 4, 1760. Introd., note 118. Cf. *Arch. Zeit.*, 1880, p. 17).

A small addition to the busts at Wilton House followed on the sale of the VALLETTA Collection in Naples, the sculptures of which were sold in the year 1720 for 1100 ducats to an English doctor, and again disposed of by him (cf. Justi, *Winckelmann*, II. 2, p. 392). On some of the buyers selling again, owing to the collapse of the "South Sea" shares, Lord Pembroke came forward as a purchaser (Kennedy, p. 53). With the exception of one excellent specimen (no. 94), the addition was however only composed of modern busts (nos. 46, 192, 193, 195). Further, Lord Pembroke obtained a number of sarcophagi (nos. 60, 111, 129, 143, 155), of which on the whole there is rather a large collection in Wilton House, from HENRY SOMERSET, THIRD DUKE OF BEAUFORT, who had shared with the Cardinals Alessandro Albani and Melchior Polignac the spoils of a columbarium excavated 1726 in the neighbourhood of Rome (Gori, *Monum. libert. Liviae*, p. xx.). Other specimens came from Sir ANDREW FOUNTAINE (no. 27), or from JOHN, SECOND DUKE OF ARGYLL (no. 78). Lord Pembroke presumably bought the sarcophagus representing Triptolemos (no. 137) after the death of the former owner, Foucault (1721). Unfortunately the origin of some particularly remarkable specimens is quite unknown,

which exhibit spurious but really learned inscriptions, and thus point
to quite a different literary circle from that of Earl Thomas (nos. 1, 48).

If, in spite of a tolerably large number of interesting specimens,
some of which are beautiful or important, the connoisseur of to-day
should experience some disappointment on the inspection of the
collection, the blame must be cast on the large number of spurious
pieces, the abominable restorations, and the absurd nomenclature.
For these reasons then, although the marbles are attractively displayed in the four galleries of the cloister completed by the
twelfth earl, ROBERT HENRY (d. 1862), under the direction of
Westmacott, the visitor is not unlikely to experience a feeling of
disappointment ; and this all the more since no collection of antiques
in England enjoys such a wide-spread reputation or has evoked so
copious a literature. To be sure, the works of Cary Creed, Cowdrie
and Kennedy are models of untrustworthiness and uncritical style.
The remarks of Volkmann, Gilpin, Dallaway (who scarcely does
more than make excerpts from Gilpin), and Spiker are very
meagre ; Goede indeed is unfortunate enough to bestow his
enthusiastic laudations of antique art almost exclusively on modern
works, and among the busts he does not find a single example
even of mediocrity ! Waagen's short remarks are better. Wilton
House has, however, a great advantage over all other collections of
antiques in Great Britain in possessing a careful catalogue prepared
more than thirty years ago by Mr Newton, which with one exception
(cf. Battlesden) is the only scientific catalogue hitherto to be found
of any English collection. In it serious attention was paid for the
first time to the archæological literature of the collection, and also to
the separation of the spurious from the genuine, though still with too
sparing a hand. I have throughout thankfully used Mr Newton's
Catalogue as a foundation for my own, and at times, where my own
notices or other means of assistance did not suffice, I have given his
very words.

ENTRANCE HALL.

This room is decorated with four statues of colossal scale.

1^a. **Statue of Bonus Eventus.** Clarac, III. 438 F,
803 A = v. 970 B, 2501 E. Creed, Pl. 24, "Pantheon." The
powerful figure rests on the r. foot, the l., a little raised, treads on
a snake with a double-pointed end to its tail, its head and neck
being broken off. A wide cloak covers the l. arm, back, the whole
of the r. leg, and the l. thigh. In the l. arm (hand missing) the god

holds a cornucopiae filled with grapes, ears of wheat, pine-cones, apples, &c., accordingly with emblems of different seasons of the year. R. arm missing, shoulder somewhat raised. The curly hair, tending upwards over the forehead and falling down low on the back of the neck, reminds one of the representations of Helios or of Alexander the Great; the features of the face are ideal (new: nose, mouth and chin). The figure is good, of excellent decorative effect, and quite unbroken. No restorations except on the face. H. 2·15. [*BCW]

1^b. **Statue of Apollo.** Clarac, IV. 693, 1635 B, "Bacchus." Creed, Pl. 36. The god rests on the r. leg; the body is rather decidedly twisted; the r. hand rests on the head, the l. arm is lowered. The slightly inclined head with long curls, with a top-knot (*korymbos*) above the crown, but without any wreath or the like, is re-set, but without doubt belongs to the statue (new: nose); a piece of the r. hand on the head is also antique. New: the rest of the r. hand and the forearm, the l. hand, including the wrist, three quarters of the legs, as well as the stem of a tree with branches and a quiver. The lowered l. hand must originally have held the lyre, or bow and quiver; had it been supported anywhere, the l. shoulder must have been more decidedly raised. The whole motive is little adapted for execution on so large a scale. Pretty good work, well preserved in the antique parts. H. about 2·15. [*CW]

1^c. **Statue of Herakles.** Clarac, V. 801, 2018. Creed, Pl. 6. Kennedy, Pl. 8. The colossal figure has an unusually decided twist for a Herakles standing in repose; one might conjecture a support on his r. side, and with this the somewhat weary expression of the face would also agree best. New: both arms with their attributes, the r. entirely, as well as the club, the l. from above the elbow downwards, with the apples in the hand; also the legs (of different marble from that of the body), the feet being treated in the style of the school of Michael Angelo. The bearded head, covered with the lion's skin, is re-set but antique (except the nose), and belonging to the figure. Antique also is the skin on the back of Herakles. New, on the contrary, and separately inserted, is the knot of the lion's feet tied before Herakles' breast. Large pieces of marble are inserted in the face, breast, l. shoulder, and abdomen. The strong exaggeration of all the forms of the body, the swelling muscles, &c., rather bring to mind the Farnese Herakles. H. about 2·40. [*W]

1^d. **Statue of the elder Faustina.** Clarac, V. 949, 2443 A. Creed, Pl. 26. The motive quite resembles that of the matron from Herculaneum in Dresden (Clarac, IV. 766, 1889), and is in this instance too, owing to its good execution, of excellent effect. The head, which has never been detached, is a certain likeness of that empress, and is undamaged with the exception of the nose and chin ; the hair forms a crown of plaits on the top of the head. The lowered l. hand is not hidden in the cloak ; it holds a stalk ; for the support of the object of which the stalk formed part, two *puntelli* are introduced on the thigh, the lower with a dowel hole : Bernoulli conjectures that this object was a cluster of wheat-ears. In excellent preservation. Greek marble. H. 2·00. [*BCH*]

CLOISTERS.

1. **Round altar : Dionysos and the Horae.** This altar is furnished with architectural mouldings at the top and bottom, and has a field for a relief with a slight vertical convexity, about 0·66 high, the background of which has been completely chipped away. The relief originally contained four figures in procession on a continuous ground of rock. They were placed at the extremities of diagonals of the altar which intersect at right angles; one of them is however, as well as large pieces of the rocky ground, completely effaced. The other three figures are seriously abraded, but not re-worked. They stand very far apart from each other, and exhibit the hieratic style. They recur collectively in very similar treatment on a krater in Naples (Gerhard, *Antike Bildwerke*, Pl. 13, 2. Gargiulo, *Racc.*, Pl. 41, 42, drawn as early as in Cod. Coburg., no. 92 = Cod. Pigh., no. 112); their interpretation as Horae, not Maenads, is certified by this comparison. The first place is occupied by Dionysos with long hair and beard and a narrow fillet round his head, in long chiton and a short cloak with zigzag folds girt slantwise over it ; in the r. hand he holds out a kantharos, in the l. he holds straight upright a thyrsos adorned at the top with a fillet. (This figure also recurs exactly on a three-sided pedestal of the Villa Borghese ; cf. *Beschreibung der Stadt Rom*, III. 3, p. 241.) Behind Dionysos a pretty female panther springs up at the thyrsos ; this is designed with such freedom and softness that it decidedly deviates from the style of the figures, and seems to be an addition devised to fill the interval between one figure and another. Then follows the Hora of Spring, very stiffly designed. A woollen chiton with a broad hem at the bottom reaches down to the feet, over it another long chiton, over that again a short cloak girt slantwise, which the Hora extends before her with both arms like an apron ; what is held in it (flowers?) is not visible. Over the forehead a stephanè. (This same figure appears on the above-mentioned Borghese pedestal.) Then follows a long

blank, originally, it may be presumed, filled by the Hora of Summer and Autumn, or by a bearded figure in short drapery which recurs on kindred monuments (as the krater at Naples, the Borghese pedestal, cf. Nibby, *Mon. scelti di Villa Borghese*, Pl. 13; a relief in the Louvre, cf. Clarac, II. 132, 110). The Hora of Winter comes last, characterised by her complete envelopment in her drapery, even to the back of the head and both arms; the loose parts of the corner of her cloak are of peculiarly stiff style, while in other respects this figure is better than the others. Italian marble, not transparent, with well-marked black spots and veins. The work, though not delicate, still is better than much hieratic sculpture of the kind. The altar is finished off at the top with a low slab, on the outer moulded border of which stands the inscription (*C. I. Gr.*, 38):

MEϞΠOMΕΝ:ΔΙΟΝΥSΟΝ:ΑΜϞΑ OMΟRϘΟΝ:
ΒΑΚΧΕΥΤΟRΑ:ΞΑΝΘΟΚΑRΕΛ ΟΝ

i.e. μέλπωμεν Διόνυσον ἀγλαόμορφον, βακχεύτορα, ξανθοκάρηνον, "Let us sing the beautiful Dionysos, the reveller, the yellow-haired." The epithets here bestowed on Dionysos are taken from a late hymn which is contained in the *Anthol. Palat.*, 9. 524. The characters are scratched on the surface, rather than carved, with uncertain hand; the Α : Ξ in the two last words seem to have been written subsequently on a part of the marble already injured. From a palaeographic point of view, the strange mixture of characters of different kinds, earlier and later, is remarkable, as are also the unprecedented shapes of the letters (for Ϟ cf. no. 48), and lastly the clumsy strokes (of the Δ and Ξ). All this is so unexampled that its spuriousness is beyond a doubt; indeed the forgery is very likely of a modern rather than an ancient date (cf. Bockh, *C. I. Gr.*; Kirchhoff, *Studien zur Geschichte des griech. Alphabets*, 3rd ed., p. 101). Cf. below, on no. 48. H. 0·96. Diameter 0·57. [*CW*]

1ᶜ. Modern urn, of limestone. Apollo, accompanied by Artemis, is receiving a roll from Nikè (the well-known representation which occurs on the so-called kitharoedic votive reliefs). Behind them sits Zeus. The inscription *DM | Hor: Flacc: riis: mar: | pamph: min: fafecit* is designed to stamp the urn as the cinerary urn of Horace! It is, of course, modern, as is the entire urn. [*CW*]

2. (Maz.?) **Bust of "Alexander the Great."** Modern. [*]

3. (Maz.?) **Bust of Antoninus Pius.** The nose, lower jaw and neck restored. New also the mailed bust, of a variegated species of marble. [*]

M. C.

4.   **Head of the bearded Dionysos**, much broken; on a modern terminal bust with the inscription *Plato*.   [*B]

5.   (Maz.) **Group of Herakles fighting with a Giant.** Clarac, v. 790 A, 1094 A, "Hercules and Achelous." Creed, Pl. 41. *Arch. Zeit.*, 1881, p. 162. The group exhibits the bearded Herakles, girt with the lion's skin, with his legs astride as he grips with his l. arm a bearded male figure, whose legs end in a snake, and lifts up the r. arm to deal a blow with the club, while the foe has both arms tight round Herakles' body. The Mazarin inventory mentions under no. 43, "*Hercule qui presse et estouffe Prothée avec son bras gauche, levant de la main droite la massue pour l'assommer, haut de trois palmes, ou environ*," and under no. 44, "*Un autre semblable, de mesme posture et de mesme hauteur.*" In Wilton there is written on the pedestal, "XVII. ΗΡΑΚΛΕΣ ΑΧΕΛΩΟΣ". Newton has rightly observed that the representation does not suit Acheloos. New: of Herakles the head, both arms, the r. leg, at least from above the knee to the ankle, the l. leg from below the knee to the foot, if indeed both feet are not modern too ; of the foe, mouth and beard, and at least the greater part of the snakes. Newton regarded as probably antique the part of the snake on the l., which is attached to the r. thigh of Herakles, and perhaps the head of the other snake; still to me, as to Conze, the genuineness of the whole of the legs seems very questionable. At any rate Newton's interpretation of the figure as a snake-legged Giant is probable ; nay, certain, confirmed as it now is by comparison with a very similar group among the famous reliefs of the altar of Pergamon, now at Berlin ; this has been well shown by Furtwaengler (*Arch. Zeit., l. cit.*). The Giant has pointed ears ; the features of the face recall more than anything the Borghese and one of the Capitoline Centaurs. Unfortunately the group is much broken and disastrously re-worked. H. 0·93.   [*CII]

6.   (Maz.?) **Bust of Antoninus Pius** (according to Bernoulli), the forehead encompassed by curls and wreathed with laurel. Much corroded and restored ; variegated draped bust new. Nominally *Persius poeta* ; Newton thought of Hadrian.   [*B]

7.   **Head of a bearded Greek**, encircled with a broad fillet ; perhaps an idealized portrait. The uninjured head exhibits a strange kind of superficial treatment of the beard and hair. On the modern terminal bust the inscription *Aristoteles*. Bernoulli, *Röm. Ikonogr.*, i. p. 15, points out the likeness of this bust to the portrait of Numa on Roman coins (cf. *ibid.*, Plate of coins 1, 5). (Hardly identical with Inv. Mazarin, no. 82, "*Une teste d'Aristote, ayant une grande barbe et*

un bonnet, avec son buste sans espaulles, couvert d'une robe et d'un capuchon de marbre d'Egypte, sur son pied de mesme marbre, tout d'une pièce.") [*B*]

8. (Maz.?) **Statue of a sleeping Nymph.** Clarac, IV. 750, 1829C. Creed, Pl. 33. Attitude and drapery correspond entirely to the famous statue of Ariadne or "Cleopatra" in the Vatican (*Mus. Pio-Clem.*, II. Pl. 44); the waves on the plinth however seem to indicate a Nymph, and the statue may have been meant to be placed on the margin of water. The l. breast is exposed. On the rock on which she lies appears a lizard, a bird eating a small snake, a snail, a stork biting the tail of a lizard. Restored: only the fingers of the r. hand. Very decorative sculpture. L. 0·83. [*W*]

9. (Maz.?) **Head of Nero** with indented crown. Kennedy, Pl. 6. Modern copy of the basalt head in Florence, Uffizi, no. 65. [*B*]

10. (Maz.?) **Female draped figure.** Clarac, III. 538 B, 1122 B, "Muse." Akin in all respects to the Vatican "Nemesis" (*Mus. Pio-Clem.* II. Pl. 13. Clarac, IV. 759, 1854) and a Giustiniani statue (Clarac, IV. 773, 1925). She is stepping slightly forward with the l. foot. Her chiton is ungirdled, and she is raising its upper fold with her l. hand. Drapery, of Greek style, simple and pretty. R. arm lowered. Restored: head with stephanè, neck, both arms from above the elbow downwards, with the flute in the r. hand, and a piece of the corner of the drapery near the l. hand. Good decorative work, confining itself to the most important points. Thasian marble. H. 1·10. Cf. Inv. Maz., no. 57, "*Une femme en habit sacerdotal, avec un diadème sur la teste, soustenant son habit de la main gauche, haute de six palmes, ou environ.*" [*]

11. (Maz.?) **Bust of "Didius Julianus,"** according to Bernoulli probably of **Marcus Aurelius**, badly restored. New: nose, mouth, beard, variegated draped bust. [*B*]

11ᵃ. Head of "**Libera.**" Modern.

11ᵇ. (Maz.?) **High relief: two portrait heads,** opposite to each other, nominally M. Aurelius and Faustina, which nomenclature is erroneous, but it may express the intention of the artist, who was to all appearance modern. Inv. Maz., no. 115, "*Une médaille de marbre blanc, avec deux testes en profil qui se regardent, une de Marc Aurelle et l'autre de Faustine, enchassée d'une bordure de marbre gris.*" [*B*]

11ᶜ. **Female head,** bound with diadem, called "*Phaedra.*" The face restored.

12. (Maz.?) **Bust of "Messalina."** Head and bust modern. [*B]

12ª. **Female bust,** shoulders draped; perhaps Diana.

13. **Male torso,** of an athlete rather than of a Hermes, named on the pedestal "*Antinous.*" Clarac, v. 953, 2446 A, "Marc-Aurèle." Creed, Pl. 27. The torso exhibits the flowing position of the Belvedere Hermes, and the restorer has also caused the hand to rest on the hip. New: head, both arms, both legs from the abdomen. H. abt. 2·06. [*BW]

13ª (over the Library door). **Relief of Vesta.** Fabretti, *De columna Trai.,* p. 339. Montfaucon, *Ant. expl.,* I. Pl. 27, 1. On a chair with a high back sits Vesta, draped with chiton and cloak, which latter veils the back of the head; over the brow a stephanè. On her l. arm she holds a sceptre, in the r. hand a cup, out of which a snake drinks, raising itself from a cista under Vesta's chair (cf. Preuner, *Hestia-Vesta,* p. 242). The cista is high and round; ears of wheat hang down over the edge, and on the top lies a round loaf of bread of the form known from Pompeii and otherwise. Below, the inscription: *Vestae sacrum* | *C. Pupius Firminus et* | *Mudasena Trophime* (*C. I. Lat.,* VI. 1, 787). This Firminus was in the year A. D. 140 under Antoninus Pius, quaestor of the guild of bakers, *corpus pistorum* (*ibid.,* no. 1002); presumably he is the person who dedicated also a relief to Aesculapius and Hygia (*numinibus sanctis, ibid.,* no. 546, cf. Aldroandi, *Statue di Roma,* 1556, p. 194). Our relief was found not much before 1690 a little below the Villa Mattei. [*]

14. (Maz.?) **Torso** restored as **Hermes.** Clarac, IV. 660, 1517 A. Creed, Pl. 28. Antique: only the rather beautiful torso down to about a third of the thighs, and the shoulders (both arms lowered). H. abt. 2·06. Inv. Maz., no. 66, "*Mercure nud, un casque aislé à sa teste, tenant son caducée de la main gauche et à l'autre une bourse, haut de cinq palmes.*" [*]

15. (Maz.?) **Bust of a bearded Greek,** on the bust the inscription *Anacreon.* Modern. [*B]

16. (Maz.?) **Bust of "Asinius Pollio."** Modern copy of the so-called Aratos in Naples. [*B]

17. **Greek sepulchral relief.** Two pillars support an architrave; the r. upper corner broken off. On the r. two men lying on a couch, beardless, nude above, with cloak over legs; the face of the one to the r. destroyed: long fillets hang down on the shoulders. This one holds in the r. hand a flat plate; the other extends his

r. hand towards the food which lies on a low table. On the r. by
the table a krater stands on the ground; by it a diminutive attendant
looking up at his master, and holding an ewer in the r. hand. To
the l. of the couch an altar with burning flame; a boy in a sacrificial
apron holding on the l. hand the flat basket (κανοῦν) leads up a
fleecy ram which is to be offered to the deceased in their character
of heroes (ἀφηρωισθέντε). Round the altar three female figures
approach, the first with a wreath or twisted fillet in her hands, the
second with the r. hand raised in supplication, the third with her
hand in her drapery. Lastly a female attendant, recognisable by the
hood (κεκρύφαλος), with a cup in her r. hand, a large round box
(κιβωτός) on her head. Commonplace style of about the third
century B.C. Greek marble. H. 0·36. L. 0·53. [*C]

20. **Bust of Metrodoros.** New: nose, bust of gray marble
with the inscription *Aristophanes.* [*BC]

21. **Statuette of a boy running.** Clarac, v. 878, 2237 A.
Creed, Pl. 55. A boy hastening forwards, the l. leg in advance, with
the upper part of the figure strongly inclined forwards; the r. arm
raised, the l. lowered, both somewhat bent. The figure somewhat
reminds us of the bronze figures from Herculaneum, in Naples
(Clarac, v. 860, 2196 B; 863, 2196 A); cf. also *Mus. Chiaram.*, III. Pl.
37. The elegant curly head, with an expression of great suspense,
seems to belong to the figure; the sunk pupils enhance the effect.
New: the l. forearm, r. arm, and the feet; the figure is moreover
broken in several places. H. 0·56. [*]

22. (Maz.) **Statuette of a boy.** Clarac, v. 878, 2237 C. Creed,
Pl. 56. He stands in a quiet attitude, upper parts of both arms
lowered. Obliquely across the breast from the r. shoulder runs a
string with small amulets, one little square plate, one heart-shaped,
one triangular, one ring-shaped, one in the form of a small rectangle.
The figure much mutilated. New: neck, arms with the deeply
hollowed cymbals in the hands, and perhaps the entire legs, possibly
except the l. thigh; the curly head antique but not belonging to the
figure. H. 0·68. Inv. Maz., no. 104, "*Un enfant nud, tenant deux
gobeletz entre ses mains, haut de trois palmes, ou environ.*" [*]

24. (Maz.?) **Bust of "Coriolanus."** A Roman with scanty
beard and hair coming down on the forehead like a wig, even more
than is the case with portraits of Hadrian. Eyes staring, the corners of
the mouth drawn back, the expression stupid. Head much defaced
and of very doubtful genuineness. The bust certainly modern.
[*B]

25. Bust of Antonia. The profile rather sharper and the plait somewhat thicker than in the bust in London, Lansdowne House, no. 46. A ribbon runs through the hair. New: nose. Much polished. Of this pretty head there is a replica in the Louvre. [*B*]

27. Mosaic relief: Herakles and a Hesperid. Kennedy, Pl. 7. This specimen is an imitation of the antique fragment of a marble relief in the Villa Albani (Zoega, *Bassiril.*, Pl. 64. Braun, *Zwölf Basreliefs*, Pl. 11), which has subsequently been restored by the addition of another Hesperid, of which a slight trace had been preserved behind Herakles' back; there are early drawings of the antique portion in Cod. Coburg., no. 23 Matz = Cod. Pigh., no. 39 Jahn (copied in Beger's *Hercules ethnicorum*, Pl. 12), and in Windsor, Vol. II. fol. 45. The field of the relief is blue, the ground at the feet of the figures whitish, below that a bright greenish blue, quite at the bottom a brownish blue. On a blackish rock sits Herakles, facing r., a golden fillet in his hair ; club and chlamys brown, as also the tree, up which a greenish blue snake coils itself; on it hang four golden apples. The Hesperid who stands opposite Herakles wears a greenish blue head-cloth and under-garment, over the latter a reddish brown cloak, lastly a golden fillet in the hair ; the three apples on the twig she holds are also golden. R. and l. rather large portions of the field are fairly free. The same scene with the same technical treatment, the figures raised from the field in relief, recurs both in Madrid and in Vienna. As to the source whence our example was derived, the books on Wilton say nothing ; the statement made by Spiker and Waagen, that it came from the Arundel Collection, rests perhaps on some misunderstanding. According to Winckelmann (*Werke*, III. p. xxxiii), it came to Wilton House through Sir Andrew Fountaine, to whose friendship for Earl Thomas two busts of Sir Andrew, in Wilton, bear witness, one by Hoare, the other by Roubillac. Waagen and Conze do not doubt the genuineness of the specimen ; Newton more prudently regards it as "perhaps antique." After the thorough disquisition of R. Engelmann (*Rhein. Mus.*, XXIX. pp. 561—589) it can no longer be doubted that mosaic relief is an invention of the last century only, and that all known examples are impostures forged at that period. Again the style of the setting of the several stones, so that broad white seams of cement are to be seen between them, is not antique. H. 0·41. L. 0·33. [*CH*]

29. (Maz.?) Bust of an elderly Roman, with short-cut hair and beard, of a late period ; certainly not "*Pompeius.*" The

genuineness is not quite free from doubt.   Much battered.   Draped
bust modern.   [*B]

30. (Maz. 55) **Bust of Julia Mammaea,** or a person very
like her, nearly akin to the bust in Mongez, *Iconogr. romaine,* Pl. 52,
only that the hair behind is set up in a broad flat plait.   The eyebrows almost meet.   The head is turned r.   New: nose.   Very
good head.   Named *Cæsonia* in Wilton House.   Inv. Maz., no.
55, "*Une teste de femme, avec son buste habillé d'une chemize et d'une
drapperie...de marbre blanc.*"   [*BW*]

31. (Maz.) **Relief.** Creed, Pl. 9.   On a modern field there is
set a horseman turned r., in high relief, completely detached from
the ground.   He wears hose and a cloak; obviously a barbarian;
with this the curious details of the costume and the horse-trappings
agree.   New: of the horseman, the head and the l. leg; of the horse,
the l. fore-leg and the hind quarters.   Late sculpture; scarcely earlier
than the second half of the second century B.C.   H. 0·65.   L. 0·54.
Inv. Maz., p. 367, no. 121, "*Un bas relief de marbre blanc représentant
Marc-Aurelle à cheval, rapporté sur un fonds d'ardoise, haut de deux
palmes et demie, ou environ.*"   Kennedy tells the following story on
this (p. 57), in which he was partly anticipated by Creed, and which
probably goes back to Lord Pembroke himself.   "Equestrian Statue
of Marcus Aurelius, made at Athens and so esteemed, that the
Sculptor was sent for to Rome to make that, which is there in
Copper, as big as the Life....To prevent the breaking, Card. Mazarin
had one side cemented to a marble &c."   [*]

32. **Relief of a heroine beloved by Zeus.** On the r. sits
a female figure on a rock, nude above, draped below, laying her
r. hand on the neck of Zeus, who sits by her, similarly half covered.
Zeus holds the thunderbolt in his r. hand; his r. foot is restored.
Before him stands an altar of incense (*thymiaterion*), at which a
female figure is offering.   Below her is scratched in ANAX.   Pretty,
but no doubt modern.   [*CM*]

33. **Relief.** A bull led to sacrifice by the *popa*, and another
figure, both wreathed.   From the triangle on the horns of the bull
hangs the sacrificial fillet (*infula*).

34. **Double terminal head.** Two Bacchic female heads,
one with a fillet, the other has rows of curls over the forehead, and
the hair braided.   Noses broken, the rest in good condition.   [*]

35. **Double terminal head: Aristophanes and Menandros,** here called *Ianus et uxor.*   Replica of the double head
in Bonn (*Mon. dell' Inst.,* v. 55.   Welcker, *Alte Denkm.,* v. Pl. 3.

Kekulé, *Kunstmuseum in Bonn*, Pl. 2, 1); there is another replica in Naples (*Museo borbon.*, VI. Pl. 43. *Monum. ed Annali*, 1854, Pl. 7). Aristophanes, bearded and not bald, is distinguished by the fillet; Menandros beardless, with wrinkled forehead. The tips of both the noses are broken off. Coarse work. H. 0·27. L. of face 0·16. [*B*]

36. **Male double terminal head**: a head like Seilenos, with a beard which ends in leaves; the other head youthful. Modern. [*B*]

39. (Maz.?) **Head of "Philemon,"** somewhat like Sokrates. Modern. [*B*]

40. (Maz.?) **Bust of "Matidia,"** which nomenclature is certainly incorrect, the head-dress is however that of her time ; above, a high knot (*korymbos*), behind, a structure of plaits like a nest. Good head, neck and head in complete preservation. [*B*]

41. **Double terminal bust of Dionysos**, bearded, and both heads with stephanè, no wreath. Creed, Pl. 52. The shaft modern. H. 0·27. [*]

42. (Maz.?) **Small bust of Vitellius**, rather than *Titus* as the inscription says. Seems to be modern. [*B*]

43. (Maz.?) **Small female Bacchic head**, crowned with ivy, and with a fillet round the forehead. New: drapery. [*]

46 (Valletta). **Bust of Homer**, of the type of the Naples head (Tischbein, *Homer nach Antiken*, Pl. 1). Beneath the fillet remains of hair fall from the otherwise bald crown on to the forehead. New: nose, l. side of head from nose backwards, the whole of the back of the head, the bust; much battered besides. This very coarse copy still preserves traces of the effective, picturesque treatment of the original. On its derivation from the Valletta Collection, cf. Kennedy, p. 53, who boldly asserts that "the Emperor Constantine got the Homer from Smyrna." [*B*]

47. **Small head of a girl**, named "Annia Faustina," without warrant. The wavy hair is brushed back in several divisions which lie over each other, and is taken up behind like a bandeau. Pupils expressed. Pretty little head. The only new part is the nose. [*B*]

48. **Votive relief to Zeus**. Muratori, *Thes. Inscr.*, I. Plate facing p. 35 (Bimard de la Bastie). Engraving by Tho. Langley, 1746. Böttiger's *Amalthea*, III. Pl. 4 (K. O. Müller). Müller-Wieseler, II. 1, 9. *Annali*, 1874, Pl. P, p. 184 (Matz); this last drawing too gives no true representation of the style, which it makes appear much

too coarse. See annexed woodcut:

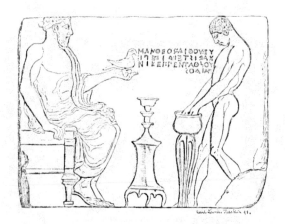

On the l. there is seated (whether the seat originally had a back or
not is uncertain, as the l. border of the relief is broken off) Zeus,
his r. hand supported on the seat, and holding an eagle on the
advanced l. hand, as is so often seen on coins. The eagle's
head is re-worked, the very sharp bend of the beak is still plainly
recognisable. A cloak covers the l. shoulder of Zeus with the
upper part of the arm, the back, stomach and legs. A fillet
traverses the hair, which is in part brought over it. The beard is
of an unusually clumsy shape, as also are the profile and the mouth;
the bad shape of the eye is due only to retouching, the inner corner
being still recognisable in its original position. The feet with soles
under them are drawn back somewhat awkwardly, and only touch
the ground with the toes, which are extraordinarily long and much
twisted. Before Zeus stands an altar for incense (*thymiaterion*), on
a three-sided pedestal supported on three feet, with several cups over
it. On the other side of it, on a high tripod with strangely bent legs,
is a cauldron (*lebes*) into which a youth dips both his hands from the r.
He is of very powerful forms, especially in the profile of his back. His
legs are wide apart, the r. advanced; the head is much bent forward.
The shape of the head is unusually high; the profile again is coarse,

especially the clumsy nose, the eye on the other hand is delicately cut. The ear stands very far back, the upper lip is short, the chin round but not very projecting, the hair only slightly rendered. The whole scene is kept in unusually low relief, and is moreover much rubbed; perhaps in consequence of this many alterations have been introduced, *e.g.* in the eye of the Zeus, also in the breast and body of the same figure, in which the sausage-like muscles and the wretchedly treated margin of the ribs have been manifestly made prominent by paring the adjacent parts; perhaps this also accounts for the absence of the youth's pudenda. This re-working, which however has not disturbed the external outlines, is certainly of ancient date; for not only is the grayish, transparent tone of the marble unaltered by it, but also the yellowish rust of oxydation, which has developed in the course of time, is in almost all parts equally distributed over the surface. Entirely different is the case with the modern re-working, by which the outlines have been in several places retraced with a sharp instrument, and consequently are here and there defaced; all these lines are as white as sugar. After all these re-workings are abstracted, I do not hesitate to agree with Conze in referring the relief to the fifth century B.C., as Matz too thought when he first examined the original (*Arch. Zeit.*, 1873, p. 30); and to some district of Greece which still lay under the influence of archaic art. The view of Müller, Newton, and Waagen, which was subsequently adopted by Matz after study of an unsatisfactory drawing (*Annali*, 1874, pp. 184 ff.), that the relief is an antique artificial imitation of really archaic art is in my opinion decidedly erroneous. The youth is angular, but excellent of his kind; the l. shoulder for example is absolutely distinguished; he recalls in stylistic feeling throughout the youths forming the handles of two bronze mirrors of Aegina and Sicily (Pinder, *Fünfkampf*, Plate. *Gazette archéol.*, 1875, Pl. 35). The long twisted toes of these youths recur in our specimen on the feet of the Zeus; his ungainly seat again recurs in the Athenè (so-called Nymph) of a metope from Olympia (Müller-Wieseler, I. 30, 129); the wave-like, rounded, parallel folds of the cloak on Zeus' lap in a certainly archaic female torso in Athens (Lebas, *Voyage archéol.*, *Mon. fig.*, Pl. 3, 2). On the Zeus again sundry details are excellently modelled, and show how effective the whole was originally. The altar for incense too is very well designed. That the character of the relief is originally archaic seems to me as certain as that it is not Attic; the whole feeling for form is un-Attic. The marble again is certainly not Pentelic, but apparently Parian or

extremely fine grain, probably lychnites. The whole seems rather to
indicate Doric art. Were not Kennedy so absolutely untrustworthy
an authority, one might give credit to his statement that the relief
"was brought out of Peloponnesus" (p. xxvi) ; only the addition
"where it was most probably made for a Victor in the Olympic
games" shows the origin of the combination, the inscription which
is set between the eagle and the youth (C. I. Gr. 34) :

MA𐤓ΘΕΟΣ:ΛΙΘΟΥ:ΕΥ
:ΙΠ Ε:ΙΙΔ: ΙΕΤ ΣΙ𐤁ΛͶ
ΝΙΚΕΙ : ΠΕΝΤΑΘͶΟΥ:
ΣΟΔΙΑͶ

i.e. Μάνθεος Λίθου εὐχαριστεῖ Διὶ ἐπὶ νίκηι πεντάθλου παιδός. This
inscription, since Maffei's discussion (*Mus. Veron.*. p. cccx) often
condemned, by others defended, either as original (Müller), or as an
antique artificial imitation of an earlier inscription (Newton, Matz). is,
according to my judgment, which coincides with Conze's, decidedly
modern. The letters, scratched on waveringly by an uncertain hand,
are white as sugar, and that too not owing to a modern re-working,
as has been assumed, but ever since their first execution. Repeated
careful examination, also after Matz's second memoir had appeared,
has convinced me that there is nowhere the slightest trace of an earlier
writing to be discovered under the white lines of the letters, while
under the outlines of the figures which are re-traced by such white
lines, the original lines can almost universally be traced. In fact,
the similar confusion of styles which characterises the whole palaeography, the recurrence of ͷ for Λ and the acute-angled Δ, the twisted
stroke in the Χ, &c., throughout confirm Boeckh's conjecture that
this inscription is to be assigned to the same learned forger as is
that of no. 1. The forgery was unquestionably not originated in
Wilton House (the Greek inscriptions by Earl Thomas are in another
style!), but is undoubtedly earlier. Both specimens, nos. 1 and 48,
must accordingly have come to Wilton by the same route. H. 0·39.
L. 0·52. [*C.M.W.*]

   49. Middle piece of the front of a sarcophagus, similar
to, but not identical with, Gori, *Monum. libert. Liviae*, Pl. 6. The
three Graces in the usual arrangement ; the one on the r. holds in her
l. hand a twisted wreath of flowers (ὑπόθυμίς), the identical attribute
in the r. hand of the figure on the l. is restored. On either side a
support (ὑποστάτης) in the shape of a tuba set on the ground, on

which lies a drapery. In the upper part of the field on each side an Eros, both supporting a garland which hangs down behind the Graces. New: of the Graces, the feet, parts of legs and bodies ; of the Eros on the l. only the left foot is antique. H. 0·38. L. 0·35. [*M*]

50. Pine-cone, and foliage in **relief** ; from a larger composition.

51. (Maz. ?) **Bust of an athlete**, with crisp hair, here christened *Dolabella*. Very insignificant. [**B*]

52. **Torso of a boy.** Clarac, v. 878, 2237 B. Creed, Pl. 57. Antique : only the torso, half the advanced l. thigh, a third of the drawn-back r. thigh. The l. arm was lowered, the r. raised. The restorer has given the r. hand an apple or sphere. The curly head seems not to belong to the figure, but this is not certain. H. 0·76. [*]

53. **Statuette of a youthful Satyr.** Clarac, IV. 724, 1671 F. Creed, Pl. 58. The Satyr stands with the l. elbow leant on the stem of a tree, which is overgrown by a vine. He looks up at a bunch of grapes, which he holds up in the r. hand. The slightly bent l. leg only rests on the toes of the foot, as in Michel Angelo's Bacchus and similar figures of his school. The r. arm has been broken off, but is re-set. The whole piece is of the same marble. The Satyr is much polished, the tree and vine very dry. In my opinion the whole figure is modern. H. 0·83. [*]

55. (Maz. ?) **Bust of Vitellius.** Modern. Cf. Inv. Maz., no. 80, " *Une teste de l'Empereur Vitelle, avec son buste armé, un manteau sur l'espaulle gauche et un masque sur la poitrine, le tout de marbre blanc.*"

56. **Statuette of a Roman**, with the inscription *M. Antonius.* Clarac, v. 921, 2345. Creed, Pl. 61. Kennedy, Pl. 9. A man, merely draped in the pallium, which leaves the breast free, with his l. arm akimbo and hidden in the drapery, steps forward somewhat with the l. leg. By the l. foot on the ground there lies a dolphin, under which some water is to be seen. New : the Agrippa-like head and the raised r. arm. Pretty figure, with a free pose and a good flow of folds ; sculpture good and fresh, but not delicate. H. 1·05. [**B*]

57. **Bust of a woman,** inscribed *Porcia.* Modern. [*B*]

58. **Bust of a man,** wrongly named *M. Aurelius.* Modern. [*B*]

59. **Fragment of a relief.** A boy, his head and shoulders hidden in a large mask of Seilenos, walks r., stretching his hand through the opened mouth of the mask and stealing fruit from an altar which is entwined by a wreath. For similar pranks cf. O. Jahn in the *Allgem. Monatsschrift für Literatur,* 1853, pp. 537 ff. [*]

60. **Sarcophagus.** Gori, *Collib. Liviae,* Pl. 10 A. Ghezzi,

Camere sepolcr. de' liberti di Livia Aug., Pl. **8, F.** Piranesi, *Antich. Rom.*, III. Pl. 27, J. In the central field two Corinthian columns support a pediment, the field whereof is adorned with a wreath; on the r. and the l. a palmetto ornament as akroterion, and on each slope of the roof a hippocampus. Below the pediment the doors of the grave, one fold of which is half open. Both folds have on the upper part a gorgoneion, on the lower a lion's head, as symbols to avert evil. On either side a large fluted field, at each end a Corinthian column. On each SIDE a griffin. L. 2·16. H. 0·68. D. 0·59. The sarcophagus comes from the Columbarium discovered on the Via Appia before the Porta San Sebastiano in 1726; cf. nos. 111, 129, 143, 155. [*M*]

61. (Maz.?) **Front of a sarcophagus: adventures of Meleagros.** The representation comprises three intrinsically connected scenes, proceeding from l. to r., intrinsically connected. FIRST SCENE: the fight with the sons of Thestios. On the extreme l. a tree, entwined by a snake (upper and lower corners restored). Next stands Meleagros with drawn sword (r. hand and half the sword new), in the l. the boar's skin, which has slipped on to the ground. Meleagros sets his r. foot on the body of one of his uncles, which is stretched on the ground, whose l. hand has still hold of the skin; a second, bearded Thestiad, with a small cloak and a spear (? upper end restored), draws his sword and presses on Meleagros. In the background a younger companion of Meleagros with chlamys and spear.—SECOND SCENE : Althaea at the altar. Althaea, mother of Meleagros, stands in most violent movement, with fluttering chiton and cloak, throwing the fateful brand into the flame of the altar, while she turns away her face in horror and makes a deprecatory motion with her l. hand. An Erinys, who touches her on the shoulder, stands behind the altar with brandished torch, in girdled chiton, with fluttering hair. Between the two in the background the Moira with the roll of fate in her hand.—THIRD SCENE : death of Meleagros. On the couch, which stands on a high, decorated basis, lies the dead Meleagros at full length, his stomach, hands, and legs covered with a cloth. By him stands, grieving, the aged Oineus, bearded, in cloak and shoes, supported on a knobbed stick; he sets the l. foot on the above-mentioned basis. Leaning against this stands on the l. a large, round shield, ornamented with the gorgoneion in the middle of a design of leaves and with sprays on the border; on the basis further to the r. a helmet, then a sword, then an ewer. Behind the couch are three figures of mourners with the upper part of their bodies visible : the old nurse, with dishevelled hair, both arms thrown back with most excited movement; a younger female, perhaps a sister of the deceased, weeping, raising the l. hand hidden in the drapery toward her face; lastly the paedagogos, who perhaps was originally placing the obolos in the mouth of the dead hero (cf. Zoega, *Bassir.*, Pl. 46). At the head end of the couch stands Atalantè, in short hunting costume, turned away, her head mournfully supported on her r. hand (new : r. forearm): by her a dog looking up at her. On the extreme r. an arched doorway. The sarcophagus is of ordinary work, in excellent preservation. An early drawing, from the Dal Pozzo Collection, is in the possession of Mr Franks in London, another is in the Cod. Coburg., no. 222 Matz. L. 2·15. Inv. Maz., no. 125, "*Un autre bas relief, plus petit* [than no. 163], *représentant la mort de Méléagre et diverses figures.*" [*CMW*]

62. A crouching Seilenos. Clarac, IV. 730 A, 1755 D (bad). The plump Seilenos has seated himself on the ground, with both knees drawn up, and raising with both hands a high, richly ornamented kantharos to his mouth. His longing to drink can be discerned in his bloated face. His drapery consists of anaxyrides, a close-fitting dress which even covers the arms to the wrist, and the legs; of this only a little is visible (the r. knee, lower part of l. leg, and a piece of both arms), as the whole figure is enveloped in a lion's or panther's skin, the jaws of which show their teeth over Seilenos' forehead; below, a thick fillet goes round the forehead. The effect of the whole figure is strange and comic. New : only the l. foot. Coarse Greek marble. Clumsy workmanship. H. 0·39. [*W*]

63. (Maz. 133) **Bust of a beardless Roman,** called "Vibius Volutianus." The mouth projects strongly; beard and moustaches weak. Pupils expressed. New : tip of nose. Certainly antique. Inv. Maz., no. 133, "*Une teste de marbre blanc, sans buste.*" [*B*]

64. (Maz. ?) **Small head of Artemis,** with a fillet passing through the wavy hair, which is brushed off the face; in the middle of the fillet a hole for the crescent. Pupils slightly given in outline. New : nose. The neck was intended for insertion into a statue. On it the modern inscription ΓΡΥΦΙΝΑ. H. 0·29. L. of face 0·14. [*]

65. (Maz. ?) **Bust,** a head with a Bacchic fillet round the forehead, on a mailed bust, all from one piece; christened *Pindar*. Modern. [*B*]

66. (Maz. 13) **Bust of a Roman lady,** of the beginning of the third century A.D., with the head-dress of Julia Mammaea, but

hanging lower on the nape of the neck. The head is prettily inclined a little to its r. Re-worked. New: tip of nose, draped bust
of variegated marble. Inv. Maz., no. 13, "*Une teste de femme,
avec un buste d'alabastre brun.*" [*B]

67. (Maz.?) **Bust of Vespasian**, whom in fact the head somewhat resembles. The slight beard is only rendered by marks of the
chisel. The bust, with the transverse strip of the toga (so-called
laena), is unbroken. The genuineness is very doubtful. [*B]

68. (Maz.?) **Statuette of Dionysos.** Clarac IV. 676, 1563.
Creed, Pl. 39. The youthful god, nude except for the nebris which
hangs slantwise over him, rests on the r. foot, lowering the r., raising
the l. arm. New: the head crowned with ivy, the l. arm with the
bunch of grapes, the r. hand, lower part of r. leg, half the l. leg,
besides half the stem of a tree. Superficial workmanship. Coarse-
grained Parian marble. H. 1·05. We may compare Inv. Maz.,
no. 34, "*Bacchus nud, tenant en sa main droite un vaze appuyé sur un
tronc et de sa main gauche une grappe de raisin, haut de six palmes et
demie.*" [*]

69. (Maz.?) **Bust of Caracalla**, with a sharp turn to its r.
shoulder. Pupils expressed. The mailed bust unbroken. All in
excellent preservation except the nose and the lobe of the r. ear,
which are restored. This bust is of good workmanship and may be
antique, still its genuineness cannot be warranted. [*B]

70. (Maz. 83) **Group of Seilenos with the infant Dionysos.** Clarac, IV. 724, 1680 B. Creed, Pl. 40. This is a poor and
very much spoiled replica of the often repeated and favourite group,
in which only the torso of Seilenos is antique (broken across the
middle) together with the thighs and the shoulders, and on the l.
shoulder the r. hand of the child, which has offered the hint for the
restoration. H. 1·26. The numerous marks of the hammer indicate
the origin from the Mazarin Collection. Inv. Maz., no. 83, "*Saturne
nud, couronné d'espies de blé, tenant entre ses bras un petit enfant appuyé
sur son côté gauche, haut de cinq palmes et demie, ou environ.*" [*]

71. (Maz.?) **Relief of Kleopatra.** Modern. Inv. Maz.,
no. 116, "*Une médaille ronde de bas relief d'une teste de Cléopatre à
demi destachée, avec son buste à demi nud, ayant un serpent sur l'espaule,
le tout de marbre blanc.*"

73. (Maz.?) **Female head** of ideal features, a fillet through
the hair. Small scale. Draped bust of variegated marble. The
whole modern. [*B]

74. (Maz.?) **Egyptian statue.** Al. Gordon, *An Essay towards*

*explaining the hieroglyphical figures on the coffin of the ancient mummy,
belonging to Capt. Will. Lethicullier,* Lond. 1707, Pl. 10 (at that
time already in Wilton House). Creed, Pl. 19. Kneeling statue of
Hefeknecht, a high official of the 26th dynasty (seventh century B. C.),
holding on his knees a portable shrine with a statue of Osiris;
dedicated to the god Phtha. Head and breast are falsely restored
as those of Isis. Basalt. H. 0·89. According to Kennedy, p. 37*,
the statue comes from the Mazarin Collection. [*W*]

76. **Three-sided pedestal,** perhaps of a candelabrum; a hole
on the flat top. *A.* **Seilenos,** girt with an apron, stands facing r., a
lowered torch turned backwards in the r. hand, holding a dish full of
fruit on his l. hand. *B.* **Satyr,** dancing r., with head thrown
back, holds behind him in his r. hand an upright thyrsos, reaching
out a kantharos in his l. hand; the nebris fluttering round his l. arm.
C. **Maenad,** dancing r., the l. arm upraised to the front, the r. arm
lowered behind. Coarse Roman work. H. 0·42. L. 0·33. [*]

78. Modern copy of the bust of the physician **M. Modius
Asiaticus,** in Paris (Visconti, *Iconogr. greque,* 1. Pl. 33). This bust
was obtained by Earl Thomas from the Duke of Argyll. Cf. London,
Stafford House, no. 3. Oxford, no. 238. There is another copy in
the Museum at Bale. [*BC*]

79. (Maz.?) **Bust of a boy,** named, but without warrant,
"Alexander Severus." Head and neck uninjured, the rest modern.
Good head. Coarse-grained Greek marble. H. 0·53. [*B*]

80. (Maz.?) **Bust of a beardless man,** with short curls;
in character about the period of Hadrian. Head and bust to below
the muscles of the breast unbroken, but yet almost certainly modern,
as is the inscription ΑΜΜΟΝΙΟΣ | ΟΑΥΜΙΙΙΑΔ. | ΣΚΘ·. [*B*]

81. (Maz.?) **Head of a boy,** named "Marcellus," uninjured.
Modern. [*B*]

84. (Maz.?) **Bust of a bearded Greek,** with a fillet through
the hair. It is more like Homer than Sophokles, who occurred to
Newton, though it does not quite correspond to a known type. Face
strongly wrinkled. Blindness not expressed. Ears abominable, the

---

* "There are numerous Hieroglyphicks round the Bottom, and behind the
Statue, which at any time may be taken off, by applying to them stiff paper
moistened, and pressed with a Bodkin. One Mr Pulleine, my Lord [Thomas, Earl
of Pembroke] informs us, was the first who practised this Manner at Rome, and
from him the celebrated Antiquary Fabretti learned it. The latter took off a
Port-folio of Hetruscan Inscriptions, which he made a Present of to our Royal
Society." (Kennedy, *l. cit.*) In point of fact, the art of making paper impressions is still older, see Huebner, *Rheinland. Jahrb.,* XLIX. pp. 60 ff.

sculpture generally detestable. New: nose, as well as the draped
bust of variegated marble. [*B]

85. (Maz.?) **Fragment of a Greek sepulchral relief.** On a
couch covered with tapestry lies a male figure (new: head and half of
the l. forearm), the upper part of his body nude, lifting in his r. hand
a cup (partly antique); before the couch a three-legged table with
cakes and fruits. With this fragment of Greek marble, h. 0·44, l. 0·57,
there is joined on the r. side by means of an intervening patch, a
veiled female figure, with a torch in her r. hand, and a dish of fruit on
her l., taken from a sarcophagus (h. 0·27); on the l. a much restored
Athenè with helmet, chiton, and cloak, her shield by her l. leg. Inv.
Maz., no. 123, "*Un bas relief long en travers, haut de deux palmes, ou
environ, où l'on voit un Jupiter assis auprès d'une table ronde chargée de
diverses viandes, tenant une tasse en sa main, et ayant à son costé droit
une Pallas et à gauche une figure qui porte un plat, le tout de marbre
blanc.*" [*CM]

87. Relief: Curtius leaping into the gulph. Kennedy, Pl. 1.
The relief is entirely modern. Kennedy's effusion (see Introd., note
118) is highly amusing; he partly follows Creed, so that the statements
are unquestionably based on Lord Pembroke's views or those of his
authorities. [*]

88. (Maz.?) **Colossal head of "Geta,"** i.e. a replica of the
so-called Annius Verus (Mongez, *Iconogr. rom.*, Pl. 42). Good style,
especially in the hair. New: nose. Neck meant for insertion into
a statue. H. 0·67. L. of face 0·27. [*BC]

89. Mask, of highly exaggerated design, the brows strongly drawn
up, the hair and beard flowing; a fillet in the hair. Much hollowed
out behind; mouth, nostrils and eyeballs perforated, presumably to
let steam or water through. H. 0·49. [*]

90. (Maz. 136) **Head of Dionysos,** bearded and crowned
with ivy; with the inscription *Tmolos.* Modern. Inv. Maz., no.
136, "*Une grande teste d'un Silène couronné de lierre et de raisins,
ayant une grande barbe, sans buste, le tout de marbre blanc.*" [*]

93. (Maz.?) **Bust of "Lucilla,"** similar to the head in Clarac,
vi. 1115 A, 3524 A. Modern. [*BH]

94. (Valletta) **Bust of "Apollonios of Tyana."** Kennedy,
Pl. 14. The hair, which is very deeply undercut, with ridges left
standing in the hollows, has something of the character of a Zeus,
only it is not so erect; it is more like that of a Pluto. The beard is
divided. New: tip of nose. Head and bust belong to each other;
the r. arm, concealed in the cloak, lies before the breast. The work-

M. C.

44

manship, though late and of rather exaggerated style, still is good and full of expression. On the r. arm is the modern inscription AΠΟΛΛΩ-ΝΙΟΣ ΤΥΑΝ. "When the Busto was first sold at Valetta's Sale, a Gentleman gave upwards of 270 *l.* for it. There were then in the South-Sea Time several Antiques sold for above 200 *l.* each...which Thomas Earl of Pembroke afterwards bought" (Kennedy, p. 53. *Ædes Pembroch.*, p. 52). [*B*]

95. Statue of the Ephesian Artemis. Montfaucon, *Ant. Expl.*, 1. 93, 5 (?). Creed, Pl. 45. Antique: only a great part of the body, of white marble. New: head and neck, forearms, feet, all of black marble, as is also the lowest part of the drapery. On the crescent-shaped plate which covers the neck is represented a sea-crab in the middle, on either side a female figure in a chiton, each holding a palm-branch in one hand and a wreath between them with the other; over the l. hand female figure a ram, over the r. hand a scorpion. This representation is surrounded by a thick wreath of *immortelles*, and further by a fine string with pendant charms. On the upper part of each arm the traces of two lions. Below the four rows of breasts the drapery is tightly gathered, and divided into four distinct rows one above another. On the uppermost row winged oxen or griffins (re-worked); the three other rows modern. Then on each side, above, a rosette, below, a bee, again a rosette, and again another bee; above each hip the upper part of the body of winged female figure, the three divisions below this modern. H. 0·88. [*C*]

96. Torso of a Herakles or of an athlete. Clarac, v. 806, 2023 = 870, 2210 D. Creed, Pl. 50. Kennedy, Pl. 5. "Melea-ger." The powerful body rests on the r. leg, with the r. hip much pressed out. Antique: only the torso, the r. thigh, two-thirds of the lowered upper part of the r. arm, half the advanced upper part of the l. arm. H. 0·65. [*H*]

97. Statue of Asklepios. Clarac, IV. 550, 1160. Creed, Pl. 46. Kennedy, Pl. 4. The genuine parts exhibit the usual motive of the god of Pergamon, the exposed breast and the l. arm hidden in the drapery and akimbo. (Newton prefers to recognise an orator.) New: head and neck, half the lowered r. arm, the legs from below the knees downwards. H. 0·71. [*H*]

99. Head of Egyptian sculpture, in granite. New: nose, lips, and chin. Kennedy, p. xxi, observes, "The head of Sesostris is as great a rarity, as is anywhere to be found. Some Italian Gentlemen travelling to the Pyramids in Egypt, discovered it there, and brought it with them."

101. Relief. Kennedy, Pl. 3. Female Satyr, making a child dance on her foot. Rosso antico. Modern copy of a Florentine gem, Müller-Wieseler, II. 45. 563.

103. (Maz.?) **Female head,** named "Octavia," with the head-dress of the younger Agrippina. New: nose and chin, according to Newton also the wreath of ears of wheat. The draped bust of variegated marble is modern. [*B]

104. Front of a child's sarcophagus. In the middle two hovering Cupids hold a blank shield, below which two panthers lie before overturned baskets of fruit. On either corner a Cupid with inverted torch. On each SIDE a griffin with one paw on a goat's head. H. 0·30. L. 0·86. D. 0·36. [M]

105. Lid of a sarcophagus: sea-deities with the arms of Achilleus. Causseus, Mus. Rom., II. p. 114 (sides reversed). At each corner a mask with ruffled hair. From the l. a Triton advances, holding a shield in his hands; on his back sits a Nereid, nude, with cloak waving behind head and back. Before them a second Triton with an anchor, looking round at a Nereid with waving drapery, who is slipping off his back, and who holds a breastplate (?) in her hands. To meet them there advances a bearded Triton, holding out a greave (?) on his r. hand; on his back a Nereid lies at full length, the lower part of her figure draped, holding up on her r. hand a small helmet. On the extreme r. there comes another bearded Triton, a curved object (in Causseus' engraving a dolphin) on his r. arm; on his back a similar Nereid with a sword-belt. Pretty, easy sculpture. H. 0·15. L. 0·93. [M]

106. Recumbent Seilenos. Clarac, IV. 738, 1754 A. Creed, Pl. 34. He leans with the l. arm, which is covered by a cloak, on a female panther, which has been transformed by the restorer into a dog; the r. arm rests on the head. L. leg nude, r. covered by the cloak. The bald, bearded head is not bad. New: part of the pedestal, half the lower part of r. leg, l. hand with cup; besides neck and head of the animal. Much re-worked. H. 0·45. L. 0·80. [*H']

107. (Maz.?) **Head of Apollo.** Kennedy, Pl. 21. The head, which is a little turned up towards its l. shoulder, resembles the Apollo playing on the lyre in the large Saloon of the Capitol. The hair is brushed back and gathered up behind into a great knot. New: tip of nose, bust. H. 0·78. [*B]

109. Sepulchral stele of Dionysios. Sitzungsberichte der Wiener Akad., 1872, LXXI. Pl. 2: pp. 327 ff. (Conze). A high slab with pediment; a rosette in the field of the pediment. Below, a laurel wreath in a shallow hollowed circle, surrounding the words ὁ δῆμος, below this again Διονύσιον Διονυσίου | τοῦ Μητροδώρου (*C. I. Gr.*, 3231): by which inscriptions the conferring of a crown on the deceased by his fellow-citizens is kept in memory on his gravestone. Below, a relief. A youth in chiton and cloak and with sandals holds out his r. hand to a somewhat larger youth (Dionysios), similarly dressed, with a roll in his hand. Behind the latter stands a diminutive attendant (παῖς), in short chiton, his head supported on his r. hand; a similar figure leans against a high stelè in the middle of the scene, the indication of a sepulchre, on the summit of which stands a Siren (cf. Oxford, no. 140; Brocklesby, no. 40) with crossed legs, playing on the lyre. Above in the r. corner a horse's head. Good style, perhaps of the second century B.C. Probably from Smyrna; and therefore perhaps derived from the Arundel Collection. H. 1·13. L. 0·54. H. of relief 0·58. L. of relief 0·46. [*CH*]

110. (Maz. 93) **Bust of "Scipio Asiaticus."** Modern. Inv. Maz., no. 93, "*Une teste avec son buste habillé...de marbre blanc.*" [*B*]

111. **Oval sarcophagus.** Gori, *Monum. libert. Liviae*, Pl. 8. Ghezzi, *Camere sepolcr.*, Pl. 7, C. Piranesi, *Antich. rom.*, III. Pl. 28, D. In the middle a round shield on which are the half length figures of a man with a short beard, in a toga with a transverse strip (the so-called *laena*), and with a roll in his l. hand, and of his wife whose arms are round him. Below, two tragic masks, that to the l. with long curls, that to the r. covered with a head-cloth. On either side twisted flutings. At each end a lion, tearing on the l. an ibex, on the r. a boar. H. 0·75. L. 2·05. Found together with no. 60. [*M*]

112. (Maz.?) **Statue of the sleeping Eros.** Clarac, IV. 678 A, 1567 A. Creed, Pl. 35. On a piece of rock lies the winged boy outstretched in a very pleasing attitude: under him his little cloak, richly draped. In his sleep he lets fall the empty goblet (*kantharos*) from his r. hand, while the r. arm and the head lie on an amphora with a pointed bottom and the opening at the top perforated. The pretty figure was therefore designed to decorate a fountain. Only the feet restored. "Found at Puzzoli," according to Creed. L. 0·58. Cf. Inv. Maz., no. 87, "*Un petit amour nud qui dort sous [sur?] des draperies, long de trois palmes et demie, ou environ, et haut d'une palme et demie.*" [*C*]

113. **Square altar**, without any architectural moulding, adorned on each side with a figure moving r. *A*. **Zeus**, in a long cloak, a short sceptre in the l. arm, holding an eagle on the extended r. hand.

B. **Hermes,** with pointed beard, the short chlamys thrown round the shoulders and lifted with the raised r. hand, the petasos on his head ; on the l. hand traces of the kerykeion (K. O. Müller in Böttiger's *Amalthea,* III. p. 45, recognises Ares in this figure, Newton conjectures Poseidon, Conze Dionysos). *C.* **Hestia.** (?Aphrodite?) in long drapery with chiton and cloak, a knot of hair (*krobylos*) on the nape of the neck, a long sceptre on the l. arm ; the r. arm, quite worn away, probably advanced a little in an upward direction, seems to have held some small object. *D.* **Athene,** grasping her chiton by a corner with the lowered r. hand, with a chlamys like a shawl, aegis, helmet, a large shield on the l. arm ; by her l. foot a snake coils itself up.—The figures are very slender, in stiff hieratic style, coarsely executed. The very low relief is much abraded. H. 0·43. L. 0·27. [*C.M II*]

114. **Head of a rather aged Satyr,** bound with an ivy wreath ; of coarse workmanship but very good character. The tip of the nose is wanting. H. 0·49. [*II*]

115. **Right end of the front of a sarcophagus: sea deities.** On the extreme r. a nude Nereid floats away, leading a sea-horse by the bridle. She is grasped by a Triton who holds a steering paddle on his l. arm, and on the convolutions of his tail, which extend a very long way, he carries another Nereid (Venus according to Newton) whose legs are covered by her cloak and who makes a drapery wave in an arch over her head, looking up to the r. A small Eros with a wreath flies behind her. On the extreme l. lies a third semi-nude Nereid (seen from behind) almost flat on the back of a Triton whom she embraces to kiss him. Imperfect on the l. The Tritons are vandyked about breast and back with indented lines, to show the blending of the human and fishy natures. Below, the modern inscription ΝΗΡΕΙΔΕΣ. [*M II*]

116. (Maz. 48) **Seated female figure,** named *Livia.* Clarac, III. 438 B, 786 E, "Ceres." Creed, Pl. 62. On a massive chair with a cushion on it, the fore-legs being broken off, sits a female figure in girdled chiton, her cloak thrown round the upper part of the lowered l. arm, the stomach and legs, her feet resting on a broad stool. The head, with a cloth over the hair behind, is antique (new : nose), probably however not belonging to the figure. New : neck, three-quarters of the r. arm with the little staff in the hand, the l. forearm with the small orb in the hand, the advanced r. foot. In the absence of the original head and all the attributes the original intention can scarcely be determined ; Newton proposes a Muse. Good

decorative work; the statue is worked in two pieces, which were then put together. Greek marble. H. with pedestal 1·60. Inv. Maz., no. 48, "*Julia assise : habillée, tenante un baston de la main droite et de l'autre une petite roue sans rais, haute de six palmes, ou environ.*" [*II'*]

117. **Seated female figure,** named *Didia Clara.* Clarac, III. 498 A, 1131 E, "*Impératrice en Muse.*" Creed, Pl. 64. On a seat without legs sits a female figure, on whose neck and r. shoulder the smock (*indusium*) is visible under the stola—a rather rare detail. The cloak with rich folds covers the upper part of the l. arm, which is somewhat raised, the stomach, and the legs. The drapery is treated with a lack of repose ; no large masses fall separately, but many comparatively small folds run too much in parallel lines ; only along the legs is the effect better. Probably the figure represented an empress ; the head however (in the style of the third century A.D.) is modern, as also are the nude parts of both arms, the seat, the l. foot, the pedestal. H. 1·32 (without the pedestal). [*BII'*]

118. **Statuette of a female figure,** restored as a Muse. Creed, Pl. 48, "Calliope." She stands on the l. leg, the r. being drawn back. In addition to a girdled chiton she wears a cloak over the l. arm and the legs; the l. forearm was raised, the r. arm lowered. Restored : the head with the stephané, r. arm with flute, l. forearm and a piece of the drapery ; the rest is regarded with suspicion by Newton, but seems to me to be antique. Insignificant sculpture. H. abt. 0·50. [*]

119. (Maz.) **Statuette of Apollo.** Clarac, III. 544, 1144. Creed, Pl. 14. Kennedy, Pl. 10 (former restoration); Clarac, III. 494 B, 954 D (present condition). The god, with his legs in the attitude of the Sauroktonos, leans with a gentle turn of his body over to his own l., somewhere in which direction the arm must always have been supported ; the r. arm is lowered and is close to the body. Slantwise over the breast runs the strap of the quiver. The little figure is placed too high for one to examine it minutely. The following parts seem to be restored : head, r. hand, l. arm from below the elbow, the cithara and the remains of a tripod which serves to support it, the legs from the knees downwards, besides the support covered with a cloak; the rest may be antique. H. 0·53. Inv. Maz., no. 91, "*Apollon nud, appuyé du bras gauche sur son plectre qui est posé sur un foyer triangulaire, à l'entour du quel est entortillé un serpent, la dite figure haute de trois palmes, ou environ.*" [*]

120. "**Cippus,** inscribed D M | PROBVS IM: | CLAVDIAS : : but this inscription is modern ; below, in relief, tripod with the *cortina* of Apollo surmounted by a winged head ; on either side a griffin ; above, an eagle, the wings terminating in two snakes. This front is flanked by two columns, the capitals of which are formed of foliage curiously combined with fish. At the two opposite corners are two pilasters ; between, on each side, is the laurel tree. The cippus is supported by a pedimental cover, on which are two birds, supporting a wreath. The two heads let into the cover are modern." [*Newton*]

121. (Maz.) **Relief**: head of Minerva in porphyry, with a helmet in verde antico. Cf. Kennedy, p. 57, "Alto Relievo of Pyrrhus, the son of Achilles, oval ; the Face is Porphyry ; which the Card. Mazarine so much valued, as to finish his Dress with a Helmet of different coloured marble."

122. (Maz. ?) **Bust of "Cleopatra."** The wavy hair is brushed back and forms behind a bunch of corkscrew-like curls. Restored : nose and all fronr the neck downwards ; the head itself, about which Newton expressed doubts, seems to me to be antique. Bernoulli presumes that it is an ideal head. [*B*]

123. (Maz. ?) **Bust of "Germanicus,"** to whom the head bears only a distant resemblance. A slight beard on the cheeks. The head as well as the bust seems to be modern ; cf. on no. 173. [*B*]

124. (Maz.) **Statue of Eros stringing his bow.** Clarac, IV. 650, 1495. Creed, Pl. 1. 17, 18. Kennedy, Pl. 12. Antique: only the beautiful torso of good, soft work, including the r. shoulder and half the upper part of the r. arm ; it is of Parian marble. By a piece of neck two or three inches broad there has been attached to it a head of different marble, to judge by expression of face and treatment of hair belonging to a girl, very much re-worked ; new: nose and chin. According to Creed and Kennedy, p. 50, "by Cleomenes." H. 1·32. A number of hammer marks on the breast and l. hip prove that it is derived from the Mazarin collection. Cf. Inv. Maz., no. 36, "*Cupidon qui bande son arc, haut de six palmes, ou environ.*" [*CH*]

125. **Greek sepulchral relief.** A beardless man, in chiton and cloak, holds out his r. hand to a seated female figure in chiton and cloak, who rests her r. hand perpendicularly on the chair. Roman imitation of an Attic original, in low relief, of mediocre workmanship and completely re-worked. Below, the inscription...ιιος (– υιος?) Ἀπολ- λώνιος | ......ι Εὐκλέᾳ χαίρειν. Italian marble with black spots. H. 0·57. L. 0·23. [*C*]

127. (Maz. 52) **Bust of "Arsinoë,"** with l. breast exposed.

Modern. Inv. Maz., no. 52, "*Une teste antique d'une femme, avec son buste moitié habillé.... de marbre blanc.*" [*B*]

128. (Maz. ?) **Bust of "Kassandra.**" Kennedy, Pl. 23. The head is artistically encircled by a head-cloth in the fashion of the so-called heads of Sappho (cf. London, Lansdowne House, no. 45). Inserted into the draped bust. The genuineness is doubtful. [*B*]

129. **Sarcophagus.** Gori, *Monum. libert. Liviae*, Pl. 9, B. Ghezzi, *Camere sepolcr.*, Pl. 7, B. Piranesi, *Antich. rom.*, III. Pl. 27, O. In the centre field Meleagros makes an offering from a cup on an altar with burning flame. He is nude except for the chlamys, a spear in his l. hand. The boar's head lies on the ground by the altar. This whole piece is set on its own plinth with architectural mouldings. Then, on the l., Atalantè, in short hunting costume, with quiver on her back, grasps from behind Meleagros' r. shoulder, and gazes at him. The faces of both figures are only blocked out, so as to receive at some time the lineaments of the deceased persons; the grouping of the upper parts of their bodies corresponds, as Conze observes, to that of the married couple on the medallions of numerous sarcophagi. On Meleagros' r. is an attendant with curly hair, undercut with the drill, in a chlamys, only slightly rendered; of the lower part of his figure nothing is visible. On the r. and l. a large field with twisted flutings. At each end, on a separate pedestal, a Dioskuros with the chlamys on his back, and the egg-shaped cap (πίλος) on his head, in one hand a spear, on the other arm a sword.—On the SIDES, angular barbarian's shields and spears crossed, incised in outline. H. 0·64. L. 2·08. D. 0·58. Found together with no. 60. [*CM*]

130. **Statue of a Nymph** (?). Clarac, IV. 594, 1425 A, *Vénus ou Nymphe.* An almost nude female figure, with curls falling far down on the shoulders, rests on the l. leg, the r. leg slightly bent. She leans with r. arm on a square pillar; l. arm akimbo. Over the l. forearm lies a corner of the cloak, which envelopes the lower part of the body at the back and the r. leg in front, and then is gathered in a rather unusual and tasteless fashion between the thighs, forming a kind of knot before the abdomen. The figure is in excellent preservation, the whole, even the pedestal, unbroken. New: only head and neck; the r. hand is missing, and the urn attached to the pillar a little below the same is at all events of doubtful genuineness. This pleasing statue may perhaps represent an Aphrodite. H. 1·19. [*W*]

131. **Statue of Tychè**(?) **seated.** Clarac, III. 438, 786 C, "Ceres." Creed, Pl. 51, "Pomona." A veiled female figure in

girdled chiton and cloak, sits holding in her l. arm a cornucopiae
filled with various fruits; the lowered r. hand may congruously with
this have held the handle of a steering paddle (cf. *e.g. Monum. dell'
Inst.*, VI. Pl. 13). The head belongs to the figure; pupils expressed.
New: part of the hair over the forehead, the l. forearm and the
lower half of the cornucopiae, the r. forearm with a bunch of as it
were ropes in the hand, both legs from the drapery downward, the
piece of rock (restored instead of a chair), and part of the cushion upon
it, the pedestal. Small decorative figure, not bad. H. 0·73. [*]

132. (Maz.) **Statue of a child seated**, restored as Herakles.
Clarac, V. 783, 1957 A. Creed, Pl. 54. On a rock (much re-worked)
sits a child, the modelling of the body soft, in pretty movement, the r.
foot set up somewhat higher than the l. New: head, and both arms,
the r. raised, the l. lowered, each entwined by a snake. Fairly superficial sculpture. H. 0·75. Cf. Inv. Maz., no. 131, "*Un Hercule nud,
assis sur une pierre, tenant dans sa main droite une couleuvre, et de sa
main gauche une autre couleuvre, haut de deux palmes, ou environ.*"
[*]

134. (Maz. 51) **Bust** of "Cato Major," at all events in the
style of a Roman of the last age of the republic; allied to Ince, no.
150, only with the back of the head larger. Probably modern. Inv.
Maz., no. 51, "*Une teste d'un César, avec son buste armé, couvert du
manteau consulaire, et son pied d'estal, le tout de marbre blanc.*" [*B]

135. **Bust of Trajan,** a portrait quite devoid of character, of
poor execution. New: nose and ears. On the pedestal two Victories,
bearing palms and holding a wreath. Genuineness questionable. [*B]

136. "**Cupid**, sleeping on a lion's skin; a small figure, in alto
rilievo." [*Newton*] Creed, pl. 67?

137, 138. **Sarcophagus: Triptolemos.** Montfaucon, *Ant.
expl.*, I. Pl. 45. Gerhard, *Antike Bildwerke*, Pl. 310, 1, 2. Müller-
Wieseler, II. 10, 117. Overbeck, *Atlas zur Kunstmythologie*, Pl. 15,
3 (from a new drawing). From the extensive literature (Overbeck,
Kunstmyth., III. p. 510 note *b*) I give prominence to the remarks
of Newton, Wieseler, Conze (*Arch. Anz.*, 1864, pp. 175, 209),
Förster (*Raub der Persephone*, pp. 264 ff. *Arch. Zeit.*, 1874, p. 102;
1875, pp. 79 ff.), Brunn (*Sitzungsberichte d. Münchn. Akad.*, 1875, I.
pp. 21 ff.), Michaelis (*Arch. Zeit.*, 1874, p. 64), Overbeck, *Kunstmythol.*, III. pp. 571 ff. 665 ff.). **137.** FRONT. On the extreme l. comes
(*a*) Persephonè on a biga, in long chiton, with cloak waving behind
head and back, a fillet in her hair; with both hands she holds the
reins of the two rearing horses, one of which is seized by the bridle

by (*b*) a female figure (Hekatè?), turned l., in short, doubly girt chiton and with flowing cloak behind her head; over her forehead a knot of hair (*korymbos*), on her feet high boots; she carries a whip on her l. arm. Beneath the horses (*c*) Tellus lies on the ground, in chiton and cloak, her head wreathed with vine-leaves and grapes. It is hardly to be doubted that in this scene the return from Hades (ἄνοδος) of Persephonè is represented; its connection with the following scene, the mission of Triptolemos, is however unusual and noteworthy. On the r. of *b* stands (*d*) Dionysos, nude except for the cloak, which however only covers the r. thigh and the l. arm, his hair, which forms a mass on the nape of his neck and falls in long curls on the shoulders, wreathed with vine-leaves. The lowered r. hand rests on a strong vine-stock which divides this entire scene from the preceding, the l. arm rests on the thigh of *c*, towards whom also his gaze is directed. Turned away from him sits (*e*) Demeter, on a piece of rock by which a snake is coiled. She wears chiton and shoes and is completely enveloped in her cloak; on her hair a stephanè; on the l. arm she holds a short sceptre, the lower end of which rests in the hand; her r. hand is extended to *g*. (The object visible under this hand consists of the stalks of the ears of wheat held by *f*.) Close to *e* in the background stands (*f*) a female figure (Hora?) in a doubled chiton, with long hair, carrying ears of wheat in the l. arm. About the middle of the relief stands (*g*) Persephonè, in full face, with the body turned r., but the head turned back and bending towards *e*, to whom she also holds out her r. hand. She is draped with a cloak and the chiton, which slips down off her lowered r. shoulder, and wears shoes: in her l. hand she carries some ears of wheat. Her attitude altogether is like that of a person taking leave. On her r. in the background stands (*h*) a bearded attendant, in the exomis, facing r., with a high basket on his l. shoulder (the whole figure in very low relief). Then comes (*i*) Triptolemos, in full face, stepping up, as it were impatiently, on to a chariot which is on the point of being borne into the air by two large snakes covered with scales which are harnessed under the yoke. With his l. hand Triptolemos holds his chlamys, which makes a deep apron filled with grain, as the sower carries it. He looks back at the two goddesses, and lays his r. hand on Persephonè's l. arm; he evidently wishes to prevail upon her to mount the chariot with him, which is certainly an unusual variation of the myth but still not inappropriate. Between the thumb and forefinger of his r. hand there is to be noticed a small round object, in which Conze would

recognise a single grain (it must then be assumed that the whole
hand is full of grain for sowing): still its shape is not very clear,
and it may very well be nothing more than a little piece of marble
allowed to remain, like a similar piece which is to be seen above the
thumb. Behind the chariot rises an olive-tree with some berries in
the leafy head. On the r. of the snakes stand four figures, all in full
face, all with their heads inclined towards the side of the principal
group. First comes (*k*) a female figure in chiton (slipped down off
the r. shoulder), cloak, shoes, raising the r. hand, so that the open
upturned palm is close in front of the heads of the snakes, and
holding on the l. arm a very long sceptre (broken at the lower end).
Then follows (*l*) a youth in chlamys which covers the body in front
and behind with as it were a pair of wings (cf. Petworth, no. 5); he
lays his hands on the shoulders of the two female figures. Round his
head and over the forehead he wears a fillet. Next comes a female
figure (*m*) draped like *k*, over her forehead a fillet decorated with a
small palmetto-like ornament (consisting of four small leaves). She
holds with both hands a long bundle which can hardly be anything but a bunch of plants; below, over the r. hand, the leaf form
is plain; further up there are fine parallel strokes like stalks, at
the top it is somewhat widened and partly worn away; most probably it is just a bunch of ears of wheat, though peculiarly formed
and without the ears being rendered at the top. On the extreme
r. stands *o*, again corresponding in the drapery to *k*, only that the
l. shoulder is exposed; in the l. hand she carries a sickle, the
lowered r. hand she lays on the head of (*n*) a diminutive nude boy
who stands between *m* and *o* laying hold with both hands of a
tall, narrow sheaf of wheat which stands on the ground. Förster
hazards names for this group, (*k*) Aphroditè, (*l*) Hermes, (*m*, *o*)
two Horae, (*n*) Plutos, but his proposals, at least in the cases of
k and *n*, are not likely to be regarded as certain. The eyes of all the
figures of the front have a narrow opening with a little hole drilled
therein —SIDES. On each a tripod between two griffins.—(**138**) **Lid**.
FRONT. At each corner a youthful mask with long hair and Phrygian
cap. In the long field are the four Seasons represented in the
guise of reclining female figures with attendant boys, excellently
arranged in lines which wave in the forms of garlands, "a beautifully
animated ornament." They are placed from l. to r. in the following
order: *A*. Summer, crowned with ears of wheat (much scoured away),
with the upper part of the body nude, legs, r. arm, back and head
enveloped in a wide cloak, rests on her r. arm and holds in the l. a

large cornucopiae, in this instance, as with those of the other three
female figures, full of apples, grapes, ears of wheat, &c. A winged
boy hovers up to her with a sickle (the handle broken off) on his l.
arm, laying his r. hand on the cornucopiae. *B.* Opposite lies
Autumn on her l. arm, wreathed with vine-leaves, in a chiton, which
leaves the r. breast free, and a cloak, laying her r. hand on the cornucopiae, up to which a winged boy hovers from the l. The Autumn
Hora turns back her head towards *C*, the Hora of Spring, who turns
her face similarly towards Autumn. Spring lies on the r. arm, and is
draped like Autumn, only that the r. breast is still further exposed.
Her single special attribute is the wreath of flowers (scoured away) in
her hair ; her l. hand lies on the cornucopiae, which a winged boy,
standing, supports. On the extreme r. lies *D*, the Hora of Winter,
completely draped, with the back of the head veiled, the r. hand on
a cornucopiae, in which is a pine-cone. A boy without wings approaches her from the l., with a sleeved undergarment and hose
(ἀναξυρίδες), shoes, chiton, and cloak, bringing a hare in his advanced
r. hand. The principal seasons of the year, Summer and Winter, are,
as De Boze (in Montfaucon) has already recognised, placed at the
ends and clearly characterized by their drapery and the attributes of
their attendants; the seasons of transition, Autumn and Spring, which
are draped alike, without any attribute except the distinctive wreath,
occupy the middle. (Conze would recognise in *A* the Spring, in *C*
the Summer, because he overlooked the wreaths and took the sickle
for a bow.) The two boys on the l. hover, those on the r. use their
feet. The essentially similar horns of plenty in the hands of all four
Horae express the collective abundance of blessings bestowed by
the complete year.—SIDES. On each a recumbent torch.—In the
middle of the front is an inscription, the first line of which is on the
lid, the second on the upper border of the sarcophagus (*C. I. Gr.*,
920):

Θ   //// Κ' ΑΥΡΗ'ΛΙΩ' Ε'ΠΑ'ΦΡΟ'ΔΕΙ'ΤΩ'
ϹΥΜ'ΒΙ'Ω'ΑΝ'ΤΩ'ΝΙ'Α'ΒΑ'ΛΕ'ΡΙ'Α'Ε'Θ Η'ΚΕ ❧

(the extraordinary punctuation after almost every syllable is note-
worthy), *i.e.* Θ(εοῖς) κ(αταχθονίοις). Αὐρηλίῳ Ἐπαφροδείτῳ | συμβίῳ
Ἀντωνία Βαλερία ἔθηκε. (The name Αὐρήλιος Ἐπαφρόδειτος recurs in
Hermionè, *C. I. Gr.*, 1224, in Kyzikos, 3665, l. 33, in Lycia, 4303,
h 7, and as ἱερεὺς στολιστὴς Ἴσιδος καὶ Σεράπιδος on an inscription discovered in Attica, edited by Wieseler, *Gött. Nachrichten*, 1874, p. 14.

Förster, *Arch. Zeit.*, 1874, p. 105, note 4, and Wieseler, *Abhandl. d. Gött. Ges. d. Wiss.*, XIX. p. 35, found it possible to regard the last as the personage commemorated on the present sarcophagus, though the character of the writing is different.) The beautiful composition is very well executed, in parts excellently, in such high relief that the figures are in parts completely detached from the field; consequently these small and very well preserved figures produce an effect like that of a carving in ivory. The marble is certainly not Attic, neither Pentelic nor Hymettic, but the dry, opaque, blue-gray grain traversed by blackish streaks suggests (Southern?) Italy, just as also the sculpture thoroughly resembles the sarcophagi made in Rome itself (Matz, *Arch. Zeit*, 1872, p. 15; 1873, p. 30). A replica of the Triptolemos in a somewhat different combination is to be found on the famous (Roman) sarcophagus at Aix la Chapelle, in which the corpse of Charlemagne had been originally buried (Förster, *Raub der Persephone*, p. 177). Of the history of the sarcophagus the following account is given by De Boze (*Mémoires de l'Acad. des Inser.*, IV. p. 648): "*Des voyageurs qui l'avoient découvert dans des ruines près d'Athènes, le transportèrent en France pour en faire présent à M. le Cardinal de Richelieu; mais le Cardinal s'étant trouvé mort à leur arrivée, il demeura comme ignoré entre les mains d'une personne de la maison de Rostaing, d'où il est passé depuis quelques années en celles de M. Foucault Conseiller d'État, et juste estimateur de ces restes précieux.*" Between Richelieu's death (1642) and De Boze's dissertation (read 1716) 74 years had elapsed; for almost the whole of this period the sarcophagus had been lost sight of (*comme ignoré*), so that after so long a period too much faith must not be placed in the trustworthiness of the tradition given above. It would be utterly untenable if Galland, as Böckh (on *C. I. Gr.*, 926) states after an unprinted letter from him, really claimed to have seen the sarcophagus in Athens. For Ant. Galland was not born until four years after Richelieu's death, and was never in Athens before 1673, when he visited that city in the suite of the Marquis of Nointel. I presume however that Galland did not see the sarcophagus in *Athens*, but in *Athies* in France, where Foucault had a house in which he kept a portion of his collections (cf. Montfaucon, I. p. xix.); Galland for several years shared Foucault's house and studies, and got from his collections the material for several works (*Mém. de l'Acad.*, III. pp. 325 ff. *Biogr. Univers.*, art. Galland). Consequently the assertion of the Attic origin of the sarcophagus seems in fact only to rest on a rather weak foundation. It might have arisen owing to the Eleusinian myth and the Greek inscription. If however the sarcophagus should really have been brought to France from Athens, the Italian marble and the Roman work would prove that it must have been sent in early times from Rome to Athens (cf. Cambridge, no. 31). H. 0·65. L. 2·03. D. 0·65. [*CMW]

141. (Maz.?) **Bust of "Poppaea,"** much more likely of the elder Agrippina. At the back the hair is gathered up into—not a plait—but a small knot, and covered with a net. Very much restored ; only the lower half of the face, exclusive of the tip of the nose, which is restored, is certainly genuine. Bust new. [*B]

142. (Maz.?) **Bust of Marcus Aurelius (?),** in his youth, erroneously called "Augustus." Much worn away; probably modern. [*B]

143. **Sarcophagus.** Gori, *Monum. libert. Liviae*, Pl. 9, A. Ghezzi, *Camere sepolcr.*, Pl. 8, D. Piranesi, *Antich. rom.*, III. Pl. 30, B. In the middle a round shield with a male bust in tunica and pallium ; face only blocked out. Below, two crossed horns of plenty. On each side twisted flutings. SIDES. Shields and battle-axes crossed. H. 0·42. L. 1·95. D. 0·50. For the origin cf. on no. 60. [M]

144. (Maz.) **Hermes Kriophóros.** Clarac, IV. 658, 1545 B. Creed, Pl. 22. Müller-Wieseler, II. 29, 324. Overbeck, *Gesch. d. griech. Plastik*, I. p. 194, ed. 2. As Newton proved by comparison of a coin of Tanagra (*Arch. Zeit.*, 1849, Pl. 9, no. 12) the statue is an imitation of the Hermes Kriophóros in Tanagra by Kalamis (Paus. 9, 22, 1); certainly not the original (Overbeck, *Arch. Zeit.*, 1853, p. 46), but a late, very superficial copy, made for decorative purposes. The god stands with his legs close together, quite symmetrically upright, holding in front of his breast with both hands the fore and hind legs of a ram which he is carrying on his back, the neck and head of the animal (restored, remains of a horn antique) over his r. shoulder. The head is in the conventional style of many terminal heads ; two rows of small curls over the forehead, above them a stephanè ; mustaches, beard, and large whiskers very stiff, as are also the two plaits of hair which fall down on to the shoulders ; the pubes also (finished off at the upper part in the shape of a triangle) crisply curled in archaic fashion. The pillar against which the god leans his back is in front and on the sides for the most part covered with a cloak, which forms stiff zigzag folds. The smooth wings on the feet are almost like a crescent. The powerful muscles of the arms, the powerful thighs, the shape of the knee, the flat stomach, bring to mind the characteristic peculiarities of an archaic

original; yet the stomach is too broad, the breast very weak, the forearm clumsy and too short, the shins and ankles clumsy, the drapery superficially treated. The back part is rather flat, not much worked. Seeing that archaic art is wont to render the animal better than the human figure, the superficial representation of the ram, and its smooth, only slightly flocked fleece, is especially striking. The pillar suggests that the figure was turned to account as decoration of a balustrade (cf. Cambridge, no. 4); there is no hole on the top of the pillar, but on each hip of the god are two holes, one close above the other (abt. 0·58 and 0·65 above the pedestal), which suggest that metal rails were here inserted (on the l. side there is another wider hole in the folds of the cloak, 0·70 high); the sides of the pedestal also are so worked that marble lintels were meant to abut upon them. H. 1·26, of the Hermes only 1·12, of the pedestal only 0·12. The marble seems not to be Greek, but Carrara. Grievous marks of the hammer on breast, stomach, and thighs, prove that it is derived from the Mazarin collection, cf. Inv. Maz., no. 60, " *Un Sacerdote antique, nud par devant, portant un mouton sur les espaules couvertes d'un linge, haut de six palmes, ou environ.*" The more ridiculous is the following effusion of Kennedy's : "The Statue of Jupiter Ammon *from Thrace*, not only with Rams Horns, but with a Ram on his Shoulders; it came out of the Temple, said to be built there *by Sesostris*" (p. 31, XVIII). [*CIV*]

145. (Maz. 14) **Statue of Demeter.** Clarac, III. 438, 754 C. Creed, Pl. 65. This pretty figure stands on the l. leg and is, over the chiton, almost completely enveloped in the cloak. The l. arm, in the cloak, is lowered, the r. raised. The latter, which originally grasped a long torch (cf. on no. 158ᵃ), is new, as also the l. hand with the ears of wheat, of which however two stalks are antique, and the veiled head, r. foot and pedestal. Fresh, good work ; back part flatly treated. Greek marble. H. 0·88. Inv. Maz., no. 14, " *Une Cérès qui tient des espies dans ses mains, haute de dix palmes, ou environ.*" The dimensions would rather suggest no. 158ᵃ, but the attribute and the remains of the number 14 on the pedestal seem to point rather to the present statuette, for which indeed an estimate of 1000 livres is very high. [*C*]

146. (Maz. ?) **Statuette of a boy.** Clarac, IV. 650 A, 1481 A. Creed, Pl. 53. *Arch. Zeit.*, 1844, Pl. 16. Antique : the torso with the thighs and a portion of the stem of a tree, also the arms bound fast behind the back (broken, but antique). These parts are of Italian marble. A modern neck connects them with a

child's head in a cucullus, with closed eyes, of coarse-grained Greek
marble (obviously a copy of the *genre* statue of a sleeping boy, cf.
Clarac, v. 882, 2247 D). The torso perhaps belongs to an Eros
enchained by Psyche (cf. Jahn in the *Berichte d. sächs. Ges.*, 1851,
p. 163. Müller-Wieseler, II. 55, 694 f.). H. 0·66. Cf. Inv. Maz.,
no. 96, " *Un Cupidon nud ayant les yeux bandez, lié à un trone
d'arbre par derrière, haut de neuf palmes.*" (The latter statement of
dimensions must be a clerical error, as the statue is only valued at
50 livres). [*CH*]

149 (Maz.?).   Bust called **Aventinus**.   Kennedy, Pl. 13.
In the style of a head of a barbarian, with a lion's skin.   Modern. [ ]

150 (Maz.?).   Bust of " **Marcia Otacilia**."   The hair is plaited
behind into a broad flat band, which is brought over back again
almost to the forehead.   The division between the nostrils goes down
very deep.   Eyebrows and pupils expressed.   Head and neck in
perfect preservation, only the face somewhat worn away.   The bust
ranks as one of the best in the collection.   [*BH*]

151 (Maz.).   Statue of a Satyr.   Clarac, IV. 711, 1693.
Creed, Pl. 4, 5.   Kennedy, Pl. 11.   Replica of the often repeated
Satyr, who twists himself round in violent movement to look
at the little tail on his back, which he grasps with his l. hand (cf.
Conze, *Annali*, 1861, Pl. N, pp. 331 ff.).   As the tail with a few
fingers on it was preserved, the restorer has caught the general
motive correctly, but, as the muscles of the neck prove, he has given
a wrong direction to the head, which is much re-worked, but antique
and belonging to the figure ; it has brutish ears and two little horns
over the forehead.   New : l. arm, three quarters of r. arm with
pedum, the legs from below the knees, the panther and the greater
part of the tree.   The body is in good preservation, and is very well
executed.   Italian marble with black spots.   H. 1·35.   According to
Creed and Kennedy (p. 49) "by Cleomenes," according to the latter
"made at the request of a Roman nobleman" (p. xxx. cf. above on
no. 87).   It is in reality from the Mazarin Collection ; as the marks of
the hammer prove, though I do not find this statue in the Inventory ;
it is described, however, in Sauval's *Hist. des Antiq. de Paris*, II. p.
177, who mentions this and a similar statue in the upper gallery of the
Mazarin Palace as being as much admired as Correggio's marriage of
Saint Catharine and compares it to the horses of Monte Cavallo, the
Laokoon, the Medici Venus &c.   [*CH*]

152.   Greek sepulchral relief, with a flat border.   A beardless
man in chiton and cloak sits on a chair and holds out his r. hand to

a similarly draped young man who stands before him. Below, the remains of an inscription, of which only the middle word, Φιλάργυρε, can be deciphered with certainty (*C. I. Gr.*, 7026). Very low relief, insignificant work of the Roman period. H. 0·29. L. 0·32. [*C*]

155. Oval sarcophagus. Gori, *Monum. libert. Livie*, Pl. 7. Ghezzi, *Camere sepolcr.*, Pl. 8, E. Piranesi, *Antich. rom.*, III. Pl. 28, G. FRONT. In the middle a thyrsos stands upright, upon which is hung on either side a thick garland laden with fruit, the other end of each garland being held up by a Cupid with a chlamys at his back. Within each of the curves formed by the two garlands two large Bacchic heads, facing each other; on the l. Dionysos wreathed with ivy and vine, and Seilenos bearded and bald-headed with a wreath of ivy; on the r. a Satyr with disordered hair and light beard and moustaches wreathed with pine, a pedum beside him, and a Maenad, with a plait wound round her hair, with a wreath of ivy. Beneath each garland lie two animals, on the l. a panther and a bull, turned away from, but looking round at each other, on the r. a goat and a hen, the latter standing up and pecking fruits. The whole is of very rich effect. SIDES. On each a round shield. H. 0·68. L. 2·00. For the origin cf. on no. 60. [*.M*]

157. Bust of Caligula, here named "Metellus"; on a mailed bust. Kennedy, Pl. 16. Modern. [*B*]

158. (Maz.?) **Bust of "Lucanus."** Kennedy, Pl. 22. A rather flimsy head with slight beard. Waagen sees in it "a highly finished work of the time of Adrian;" Newton considers the head suspicious; Bernoulli believes that he recognises the same touch as in no. 78. In my judgment there is no doubt as to its modern origin. [*B*]

158ª. (Maz.) **Statue of Demeter.** Clarac, III. 538 B, 1110 D, "Muse." Creed Pl. 8, "Urania." This figure rather resembles no. 145, but is still more like a statuette of the Palazzo Doria in Rome (Clarac, III. 438 C, 776 A. Overbeck, *Kunstmythol.*, III. p. 465) which is important owing to the preservation of the attributes; on our statue only the veiling of the head is wanting. The head and neck are inserted, but the face is new except half the l. cheek and the l. eye, and the whole head seems not to belong to the statue. New: l. forearm, which should be lower and should hold ears of corn in the hand. The r. forearm which perhaps had always been worked from a separate piece of marble, is broken off; the hand originally grasped the upper end of a long torch. Lastly the lower part of the statue almost from the waist downwards is entirely new, as well as the pedestal with the modern inscription OYPANIA preceded by the representation of a

sphere on a three-sided pedestal. So much the more amusing is
Kennedy's assurance that "Cardinal Mazarine would not suffer any
part to be mended" (p. 103). The genuine antique piece is in fact
excellent. Greek marble. H. 1·80. Cf. on no. 145. [*C]

159. (Maz.?) **Seated female figure.** Clarac, III. 498 A, 990 B,
"Clio." Creed, Pl. 3. On a chair without a cushion sits, sinking in
very deep, a female figure in chiton (confined by a ribbon which
passes from the shoulders under the armpits, cf. Deepdene, no. 7),
abdomen and legs covered by the cloak. The feet are set rather far
from each other on a high stool. The statue has been broken into
three large pieces, first into two by a horizontal fracture through the
waist, then the lower part into two pieces by a vertical fracture between the legs. The head (restored: nose and upper lip) is joined on
by a modern neck; it can hardly belong to the figure, and is perhaps
modern. Certainly modern: both forearms, with the flute in the
r. and the roll in the l. hand, the l. foot, three legs of the chair (the
only antique leg is that in the front by the l. leg of the figure, with a
very favourite profile). Commonplace work. H. 1·05. According to
Creed and Kennedy (p. 9), "Euterpe, by Cleomenes." Inv. Maz., no.
50, "*Uranie assise, tenante une fleur (? flutte) à la main droite et une
cartelle entortillée dans l'autre, haute de cinq palmes, ou environ.*" [*]

161 (Maz. 119). **Bust of a young girl.** A pretty, plump face,
with a snub nose, and a very lively expression about the mouth.
Pupils expressed. The head-dress indicates the third century, the
hair being parted in front and taken up at the back in a band. Very
pretty sculpture, well preserved : bust new. Inv. Maz., no. 119, "*Une
teste d'une petite fille, avec son buste habillé..., de marbre blanc.*" [*B]

162. **Head of Aphroditè**, of doubtful genuineness.

163 (Maz.). **Front of a sarcophagus : death of the children of Niobè.** An early drawing in the Cod. Pigh., no. 163
Jahn (a rough sketch, but still without restorations): two others
from the Dal Pozzo collection in the possession of Mr Franks
in London (cf. Winckelmann, *Monum. Ined.*, on no. 89). The
scene is very picturesquely disposed on a high slab, the various
figures and groups in several instances interlocking. A rocky ground
traverses the whole length, and carries the figures in two tiers one
above the other. LOWER TIER. On the l. stands Amphion, on a
much larger scale than most of the other figures ; he is dressed in
corslet and boots. He is in the act of withdrawing on the l. side,
holding on his r. arm (forearm wanting) a young son (A) who is sinking back ; Amphion looks up to the r. and holds up his extended

l. arm in the same direction, as if to ward off an attack. Beside him
on the ground kneels a bearded paedagogos, in short chiton with a
skin over it, and supports in his arms a boy who is falling forward (*B*),
whose r. hand lies on his shoulder. Outstretched on the ground lies
a daughter (*a*), her r. hand on her breast, draped in chiton and cloak.
A son (*C*), who has slipped off a very small horse, is dragged on the
ground with his legs trailing, as he still grasps the reins in his l. hand:
with the r. he draws the arrow from his body. Over him the aged
nurse (τροφός), in chiton, her cloak girt about her hips, and with the
usual head-cloth, holds a daughter (*b*), who is sinking back, the upper
part of the body nude. Further r. a youth (*D*), whose cloak held in
his r. hand waves over his head, sits on a horse which has fallen to the
ground. At the r. extremity comes Niobè, on a scale corresponding
to her husband, draped in a chiton which leaves the r. breast besides
the arm free, her wide cloak flying in a large arch behind and over
her head (so that it corresponds symmetrically to Amphion's large
shield). She stands nearly as she does in the Florentine group. The
face looks up to the l.; long curls fall on the back of the neck. With
either arm she presses a daughter to her, both draped in the chiton ;
the small one (*c*) comes from the l., the large one (*d*) from the r.—
UPPER TIER. On the extreme l. a youth (*E*) on a galloping horse
tries to escape the destruction, he looks up behind him. Behind his
horse a second bearded attendant or paedagogos, draped with the
chlamys, holds in his arms a grown-up daughter (*e*), who is sinking
forwards; the upper part of her body nude. Close by her a sister (*f*),
draped in a chiton, throws herself on to her knees, supporting her
r. hand on the ground, uplifting in a backward direction her face and
l. arm. In the middle, above the nurse, a youth (*F*) falls backwards
off his horse, which is galloping to the r. Before the horse there is
to be seen the upper part of the body of a sister (*g*) apparently falling
forward, in chiton and cloak (head and both forearms wanting).
Further r. a youth (*G*) falls over forwards on the back of his falling
horse. Above him lies a bearded mountain god ; still higher a few
trees are visible, here and there. All Niobè's sons wear the chlamys.
The glance of most of the figures, full of apprehension, is directed
upwards towards the middle of the scene. On a very similarly
designed sarcophagus in the Lateran Museum (no. 427. *Museo Later.*,
Pl. 3. Stark, *Niobe*, Pl. 19) there are on the lid Apollo on the r.
and Artemis on the l., both represented as shooting an arrow.—The
animated composition, raised in high relief from the rocky ground of
the field, might be traced back to a picture as the original. Execution

moderate. Restorations not numerous, but coarse. Cf. Stark, *Niobe*, p. 189. Heydemann, *Berichte d. sächs. Ges. d. Wiss.*, 1877, pp. 71 f. L. abt. 2·20. H. 0·80—0·90. Inv. Maz., no. 124, " *Un grand bas relief de la fable de Niobé, avec diverses figures à pied et à cheval*." The relief came from Rome, where it stood, according to the Cod. Pigh., about the middle of the fifteenth century *sub Capitolio in pariete privatae domus.* [*CMW*]

164. Female statue, named "Sabina." Clarac, III. 538 B, 1122 C. Creed, Pl. 25. The figure stands quietly on the l. leg, draped in the chiton, over which is a wide cloak which leaves free little more than breast and neck. R. forearm, inside the cloak, bent upwards (half of r. hand new); the whole arm not well detached from the body. L. forearm extended (hand with ears of wheat and wrist new). Details on the folds patched. Head (new: nose) taken from a Venus, and perhaps modern.· Drapery rather heavy. H. abt. 1·85. [*W*]

166 (Maz. 75). **Bust of a Roman emperor**, of the period of Septimius Severus; named "Brutus senior." Bad and much battered, but antique. Inv. Maz., no. 75, " *Une teste d'Empereur, avec son buste armé, ayant un masque sur la poitrine et une draperie sur l'espaule gauche.*" [*B*]

167. Head of a ram, in black basalt, well preserved.

168. (Maz.?) **Bust of "Didia Clara.**" Modern. [*B*]

169. Fragment of a male statue. Clarac, v. 926, 2356 A, "Tiberius." Creed, Pl. 60. "Cæsar's Father when Governor in Ægypt." Merely the middle piece from just above the navel to the knees is antique. Accordingly it was a palliatus, with upper part of body nude, the l. arm akimbo. Coarse-grained Greek marble. Coarse but not bad workmanship. H. 1·06. [*]

170 (Maz. 42). **Statue of an Amazon.** Clarac, v. 810 A, 2031 C. Creed, Pl. 2. On the pedestal the modern inscription AMAZ: I ΒΑΣ:. An Amazon, draped in a short chiton, which leaves r. breast and arm free, has sunk on to the r. knee in violent movement, stretching out the l. leg a long way (this leg broken, but antique). On her feet she wears boots, the pelta on the l. arm; the r. arm was always raised, the head too perhaps always turned in the direction of the l. leg and raised. New: head and neck, r. arm, half of the upper part of the l. arm and the upper third of the pelta; I cannot say positively whether also "one of the hoofs of a horse behind the pelta" belongs, as I conjecture, to this restoration. To judge by dimension and style, the figure certainly does not belong to the votive gifts from Attalos king of Pergamon on the Acropolis of Athens (cf. Brunn, *Annali*, 1870, p. 313). H. with pedestal 0·92, without 0·81; approximate length of body 1·25. According to Creed and Kennedy (p. 10) "by Cleomenes." The breast is quite covered with the marks of the Duke of Mazarin's hammer. Inv. Maz., no. 42, "*Une Amazone ayant un genouil en terre, la mamelle droite et le bras descouverts, l'espée à la main, avec un bouclier, en posture de se deffendre, haute de quatre palmes, ou environ*" (cf. Sauval, *Hist. des antiq. de Paris*, II. p. 176). [*W*]

173. (Maz.?) **Bust of "Alkibiades."** Kennedy, Pl. 25. The bearded head of rigid expression, with hair little curled and falling on the forehead, is akin to a terminal bust in Paris (Clirac, VI. 1070, 2915 B). Bust with paludamentum unbroken. Without doubt modern; in common with the bust no. 123, it has the peculiarity of a piece of drapery bordering the lower edge of the bust. [*B*]

174. **Head of "Anarcharsis,"** bald. Modern. [*B*]

175. (Maz.) **Group of Herakles and a Satyr.** Clarac, V. 790 B, 1987. Creed, Pl. 37. Now called "*Hercules moriens. Pacas.*" On a stone sits a small Satyr with exaggerated features (nose wanting), both legs spread out, and tries with all his might to support the drunken Herakles, whose weighty frame is quite falling over backwards. Both the legs of Herakles are extended in front, with his lowered r. hand he holds the club which rests on the ground, the l. arm is quite enveloped by the huge lion's skin which hangs down from his head to the ground and serves as a material support for the whole group. Herakles' face, with long, weakly beard, is sadly distorted; the head droops towards the r. shoulder, on which a long fillet falls down. Restored: merely the r. arm of Herakles and the greater part of his club; even the detached parts of the fillet on the r. shoulder are unbroken. This circumstance strengthens the suspicions as to the genuineness of the whole group which are suggested as much by the forced design of the whole composition as by the overwrought modelling of the several parts, especially of the faces. The Satyr especially is badly designed, the upper part of the body too long, the l. thigh stunted, the r. foot hopping, the l. hand quite miserable. The whole work very dry. H. 0·93. The marks of the hammer prove that this group is from the Mazarin Collection; however I do not find it in the inventory. [*BW*]

178. **Terminal head of Sokrates.** New: l. eye, nose, r. cheek. Of the type of the two heads in Paris. [*B*]

179. (Maz.?) **Bust of Aelius Verus,** here named "Marcus Aurelius." Modern. [*B*]

The following specimens, which I have only been able to survey cursorily, are not numbered on the originals nor in Newton's Catalogue, in which some of them are not given at all.

LIBRARY.

180. (Maz.?) **Head of a young Pan or a Satyr,** of very delicate forms: according to Bernoulli, those of a young female (*Paniskē*). Ears pointed, over the forehead two little horns of which the stumps are antique. New: nose, half the neck, and the breast. Expression and bending of the head correspond to the heads of the statues by Cerdo in the British Museum (Græco-Roman Sculpt., nos. 188, 190. *Museum Marbles,* i. Pl. 33, 43). L. of face 0·10. [*B*]

181. (Maz.?) **Head of a Roman child,** falsely named "Annius Verus"; good and well preserved. New: nose and part of the back of the head, besides the draped bust in alabaster. [*B*]

SINGLE CUBE ROOM.

182. (Maz.?) **Head of** "**Masinissa,**" with twisted fillet round it. Modern. [*B*]

183. (Maz.?) **Head of** "**Pyrrhus,**" with helmet, of ugly expression. Kennedy, Pl. 18. Modern. [*B*]

184 (Maz. 2). **Bust of Septimius Severus,** good head, patched about the face. Draped bust modern. Inv. Maz., no. 2, "*Une teste antique de Septime Sévère, avec son buste habillé d'albastre couleur de fleur de pesché, posée sur un pied d'estal de marbre Affricain.*" [*B*]

185 (Maz. 107). **Bust of** "**Octavia Maior**"; the hair twisted in plaits into the shape of a basket on the crown, as was usual in the second century A. D. Pupils expressed. New: nose and draped bust. Inv. Maz., no. 107, "*Une teste de femme de marbre blanc, avec son buste habillé d'une draperie d'albastre brun.*" [*]

186 (Maz. 1). **Bust of Tiberius** (not Drusus). New: nose, part of brow and the hair, neck, and bust. Good head. Inv. Maz., no. 1, "*Une teste antique de Tybère, avec son buste* [&c., like no. 184]." [*B**]

187. **Bust of** "**Lucius Verus,**" which can hardly be the right name. Beard cut short, hair curly. Restored: nose, as well as the bust, of four different kinds of marble. The head too has a very modern look. [*]

DOUBLE CUBE ROOM.

188 (Maz. 10). **Bust of "Marcia,"** with high, pointed head-dress. Hair in a plait wound round the head. The countenance thin and worn. New: nose and ear. Inv. Maz., nos. 9 and 10, "*Deux testes antiques de femmes, avec leurs bustes d'albastre oriental, façon de brocard plus obscur;*" cf. no. 189. [*B]

189 (Maz. 9). **Bust of "Drusilla."** A well-preserved girl's head, with plait. New: tip of nose, neck, and bust. Inv. Maz., no. 9, cf. on no. 188. [*B]

190. (Maz.?) **Bust of the consular Horatius.** New: neck, lower part of face up to the nose, and bust. According to Newton the face is that of a Greek youth. Newton regards the genuineness as suspicious, to me it seemed probable. [*]

191 (Maz. 6). **Bust of a youth,** named "Caius Caesar." The face (tip of nose new) is badly polished over with an acid, but is antique; the draped bust is modern. Inv. Maz., nos. 5 and 6, "*Deux testes d'enfans, avec leurs bustes d'albastre oriental trans-parent vené de rouge;*" cf. no. 194. [*B]

192 (Valletta). **Bust of Horatius,** in porphyry. A modern fancy-portrait, multiplied as if authentic by casts, *e.g.* in the Library of Trinity College, Cambridge. Kennedy, pp. 53, 65, testifies to its derivation from the Valletta Collection. The remark of Bernoulli, *Röm. Ikonogr.*, 1. p. 252, refers to this bust, not to no. 190. [*B]

193 (Valletta). **Bust of "Cicero,"** reminding one more of Corbulo. Of dark stone; according to Newton of black marble, according to Bernoulli of basalt, according to Kennedy (pp. 53, 65) of touchstone. The bust, like the last, seems suspicious to Newton and Bernoulli, to me it seemed undoubtedly spurious. [*]

194. (Maz.?) **Bust of a boy,** modestly christened "Lucius." Good. New: nose and draped bust. Probably identical with Inv. Maz., no. 5, cf. on no. 191. [*]

195 (Valletta). **Bust of "Julius Caesar,"** in alabaster, similar to the porphyry bust in Ince, no. 144. Kennedy, Pl. 20. Modern. Cf. Bernoulli, *Röm. Ikonogr.*, 1. p. 163. For its source cf. Kennedy, pp. 53, 64. [*B]

196. (Maz.?) **Bust of an elderly Roman,** named "Marcus Brutus." Kennedy, Pl. 19. Beardless, with underlip somewhat pouting. Of grave expression. A good portrait. New: tip of nose and draped bust. [*]

197. (Maz.?) **Bust of Julia Pia,** antique, but sadly polished.

The tip of the nose and the plait of hair behind restored, as well as the variegated drapery. [*BW]

198. Round marble urn, with two short handles and a lid. On the tablet is the inscription : *D(is) M(anibus) Anniae Trophimeni (Q. Volusius Verus coiugi carissime fecit.* Below a relief : on a couch lies a female figure, the upper part of the body nude, legs and l. arm in her cloak, holding a bird on her r. hand. Before her a small low table, such as is still common in the East, with viands on it. On the wall hangs a mirror and a full bodied basket or jar. At either side of the relief a laurel-tree with a bird pecking at it ; beneath each handle a winged boy with a torch. Sprays of foliage cover the back of the urn and the lid. H. 0·48. Diameter 0·32. [*]

199. Urn, of a sort of pumice stone, with two slightly sketched reliefs, of the so-called mourning bride, whose feet are being washed, and of the old woman offering with two attendant female musicians ; copied from Sante Bartoli, *Admiranda*, Pl. 73, 47. Zoega, *Bassir.*, Pl. 12. Modern. [*W]

200. (Maz.?) **Bust of a youth**, here named " Antinous," designated conjecturally by Newton as a Hermes. The type is to be referred to certain heads in the style of Polykleitos, akin to the so-called *Idolino* in Florence, though faintly rendered. Hair short. New : nose, neck, and bust. A pretty head. Greek marble. L. of face 0·18. [*]

201 (Maz. 4). **Bust of Lucius Verus**, the face much patched, almost half of it modern. Bust new. Inv. Maz., no. 4, "*Une teste de Marc-Aurelle, avec son buste d'albastre oriental vêné de blanc.*" [*B]

202. (Maz.?) **Bust falsely named "Constantinus Magnus."** The hair grows low down on to the nape of the neck. The head, much restored, belongs to an earlier epoch ; the portrait unknown. Bust new. [*B]

203. (Maz.?) **Bust of "Marcellus Consul,"** *i.e.* of an elderly, beardless Roman. New : nose, chin, and draped bust. A good portrait. [*B]

GREAT ANTE-ROOM.

204. (Maz.) **Sleeping Hermaphroditos.** Creed, Pl. 10, "Sleeping Venus ;" according to Kennedy (p. 81) from the Mazarin Collection. Copy of the Borghese statue in the Louvre ; according to Newton probably antique, in my opinion modern. L. 0·51. [*]

205. **Painting**, said to have been brought from the Temple of Juno at Praeneste. Completely smudged over and covered with modern inscriptions; it can hardly be made out whether there are any antique remains underneath this covering, cf. on Brocklesby, no. 36. [*]

206. (Maz.?) **Small head of Otho.** Modern. [*B]

207. **Small head of Vitellius.** Modern. [*B]

LITTLE ANTE-ROOM.

208 (Maz.). **Bust of "Epicurus."** A thoroughly arbitrary nomenclature. Head bearded, bust draped. The little specimen has a Greek look. "Valued by Card. Mazarine" (Kennedy, p. 100), "because there were no others of them known" (p. XII). [*]

209. **Small head of "Achilles,"** i. e. of an Athene of the later type, with very oval face. Rams' heads on the front of the helmet. [C]

This room contains some more small **busts**, apparently of trifling value. [*]

COLONNADE ROOM.

210, 211. **Two bronze busts**, one of which is inscribed *Palemon*. Of doubtful genuineness.

CORNER ROOM.

212. (Maz.?) **Bust of "Pertinax."** Modern.

213. **Small head of Scipio**, named *Solon*. According to Newton modern, according to Bernoulli probably antique. [B]

STAIRCASE.

214. **Bust of "Vibius Varus."** Modern. [*B]

STAIRCASE LEADING TO THE GOTHIC HALL.

215. (Maz.?) **Bust of "Seneca."** Modern. [°]

216. (Maz.?) **Bust of "Heraclitus."** Modern. [*]

217. (Maz. 12) **Bust** perhaps of **Julia Domna** (?). Modern. Inv. Maz., no. 12, "*Une teste moderne d'une femme de marbre blanc, son buste d'albastre véné de plusieurs sortes de couleurs.*" [*]

218 (Maz. 66). **Bust of "Caligula,"** quite wrongly named. It seems to be modern. Inv. Maz., no. 66, "*Une teste de marbre blanc, avec son buste habillé de marbre blanc.*" [*]

219. (Maz.?) **Bust of Antoninus Pius**, here named "Μιλτιάδης." Modern. [*]

220. (Maz.?) **Bust** said to be that of "ΗΡΥΣΙΑΣ." Kennedy, Pl. 24. Short beard; the hair treated like straw, as in Knole, no. 10. Modern. [*]

221. (Maz.?) **Bust of Aphroditè,** with topknot over the forehead; here christened *Semiramis.* Kennedy, Pl. 15. Modern. [*]

222. (Maz.?) **Bust of "Vibius Varus."** Cf. no. 214. Modern. [*]

THE PAVILION.

223. **Group of Herakles and Antæos.** Creed, Pl. 42. Coarse sculpture. Heads and almost the whole of the arms and legs restored. H. abt. 0·77. [*]

224. **Torsos,** antique, and of good sculpture.

225. (Maz.?) **Head of a laughing Satyr.** New: nose. Bad. [*]

226 (Maz. 92). **Bust of Lysimachos (?).** Perhaps modern. Inv. Maz., no. 92, "*Une teste du jeune Empereur Tybère, avec son buste armé, un masque sur la poitrine, le tout de marbre blanc.*" [*]

227 (Maz. 135). **Female head,** after the style of the so-called heads of Sappho. Modern. Inv. Maz., no. 135, "*Une teste couronnée de laurier, de marbre blanc, sans buste.*" [*]

228. (Maz.?) **Head of Apollo,** of slightly pathetic expression, the hair brushed up and fastened together on the top of the head. [*]

229. (Maz.?) **Head of Zeus.** [*]

230. **Statuette of Dionysos.** Clarac, IV. 686, 1625. Creed, Pl. 13. Kennedy, Pl. 17. Antique: only the torso with broad nebris, girt in slanting direction from the l. shoulder, the lowered upper parts of both arms (not the grapes in the r. hand) and the thighs; on the r. thigh a *puntello.* H. abt. 0·50. [*]

WALK LEADING TO HOLBEIN'S PORCH.

231 (Maz.). **"The foster father of Paris."** Creed, Pl. 43. "A youthful figure, in a short goatskin tunic, with short sleeves, round which is a small mantle twisted across his body. In his left hand a shell, in his right a pipe; on his head a Phrygian cap. He wears boots (*socci*), tied with leather thongs at the ankles. Seems antique [entirely?] and curious." [*Newton.*] Inv. Maz., no. 28, "*Mercure en habit de pasteur couvert d'une peau, tenant une flutte en sa main droite, et un limaçon marin dans l'autre, haut de six palmes, ou environ.*"

232. **"A naked male figure,** with two long fillets of flowers hanging down perpendicularly, one on each side, on each flank, as

far as the knee. Restored as Bacchus. Head, both arms, and panther's skin modern." [*Newton.*]

233. Bust of "**Themistocles**." "Drapery modern." [*Newton.*] The three last-mentioned specimens, the description of which I borrow from Newton, I was prevented from looking for.

I cannot identify :

234. (Maz.?) **Statue of Dionysos.** Clarac, IV. 694 C, 1596 B. The god, quite nude, rests on his r. leg and looks at a large bunch of grapes in his l. hand; the r. hand, which likewise holds a bunch of grapes, is supported on the stem of a tree. The head has long curls and a wreath of ivy. About restorations nothing known; I am disposed to believe that either the whole figure is modern, or only the torso antique. H. abt. 1·00. Cf. Inv. Maz., no. 58, "*Un Bacchus nud, couronné de feuilles de vignes, tenant une grappe de raisins dans chaque main, haut de six palmes, ou environ.*"

Besides these there are in Creed engravings of a number of figures, undoubtedly for the most part modern, of which I cannot give the numbers. I just mention them here without any comment. Pl. 11, "Adonis;" 12 "Pandora" (Aphrodite); 15 and 16, "Acis and Galatea;" 20 and 21, "Persian captives;" 23, "Attis, clothed as a woman;" 29, "Flora;" 30, "Apollo with a fine glass;" 31, "Autumnus;" 32, "Bacchus and the young Silenus;" 38, "Shepherd;" 44, "Mercury with wings, caduceus, and a purse;" 47, "Priest sacrificing a hog to Isis;" 49, "Andromeda" (Inv. Maz., no. 106); 59, "Orpheus;" 63, "Manlia Scantilla, bigger than the life, sitting;" 70, "Venus with a vase."

In former days there was at Wilton House a large **collection of Greek and Roman coins**, which is thus spoken of in the *Aedes Pembrochianae*, p. 93: "No cabinet in Europe, in the possession of a subject, is perhaps so richly stored with medals as that of Lord Pembroke. Earl Thomas spared no pains or expense to complete his collection of them." Cf. Goede, *England*, v. p. 136. There appeared a Catalogue of these, *Numismata Pembrokiana*, 1746, which was republished in 1848 for the purpose of the sale which then took place.

WIMBLEDON (Surrey).

I am indebted to Prof. Newton for the following notice :

"Near St Mary's Church in Wimbledon Park estate are a few marbles which were originally in the house called Wimbledon Park, once the property of LORD SPENCER, and now belonging to Mr BEAUMONT. It is supposed that they were brought from abroad by a Lord Spencer who travelled at the beginning of this century. Of these remains the only one of any interest is :

1. **A circular cippus** of white marble, in form like a pedestal or altar, and about 0·66 in diameter, round which seven draped female figures are sculptured in relief. Three of these figures appear to be dancing ; two of them join hands, the third advances from the l., holding out a wreath to the figure nearest to her. These three figures wear mantles and talaric chitons raised so as to shew the ankles. On the r. of this group are a pair of figures who carry between them some object like a bowl or vessel with handles, which one figure holds in the r. and the other in the l. hand. This pair wear talaric chitons and the diploidion. On the l. behind the figure holding out the wreath, is a sixth figure wearing a talaric chiton girt at the waist and a diploidion with a mantle cast over the l. shoulder. There is a seventh figure, but, as the marble was lying on its side, I could not see this. Above the dancing figure is the following inscription :

ΖΩΠΥΡΟΣΖΩΠΥΡΟΥΤΟΝΟΙΚΟΝ
ΕΣΤΙΑΙΚΑΙΤΩΙΔΑΜΩΙ.

The characters seem late [apparently of a good Roman epoch]. The sculpture, which is very much damaged, seems to have been of a good time. The drapery and pose of the dancing figures is slightly hieratic.—Lying by this marble was a fluted drum from a **Doric column** about 0·76 in diameter, in white marble. I was told that the sculptured marble formerly stood on this fluted drum, which has a firm joint at the top, shewing that something has been placed on it. If the other marble stood on the fluted drum, it would seem that we have here an example of a *caelata columna*, but it may have been only an altar.

2. Lying near these marbles was the **fragment of a relief,** exhibiting a reclining male figure, the lower half clothed ; the rudder which he has held in his hand probably indicates an aquatic deity. This fragment, which is much worn, is about 0·90 long.

3. The fragment of the **bust of a draped figure**, the mantle drawn forward over the l. shoulder. A socket shews that the head has been of a separate piece of marble.

4. A large **granite trough** or laver roughly finished.

5. Several **pieces of porphyry**."

WINDSOR CASTLE (Berkshire).

Michaelis, *Arch. Zeit.*, 1874, pp. 66 ff.

The single ancient sculpture in Windsor Castle stands at the end of the long corridor:

1. **Altar on which is a slain ram**, very like the example in the Vatican (*Mon. Matth.*, II. Pl. 69. *Mus. Pio-Clem.*, VII. Pl. 33), which Visconti thought was an unicorn. The animal is so placed on the altar that his head and legs hang down; the collapse of the body in the region of the stomach which this position induces is excellently portrayed. The entrails protrude from the stomach. The tufts of the fleece are only flatly expressed. The altar itself is lower than the one in the Vatican, and the round slab which lies on the latter is missing. New: the head from the eyes downwards, the r. ear, half of each of the four legs, and part of both supports which fasten them to the altar. Good work; at the back traces of earth are still visible. Italian marble. H. 0·59. This altar was purchased from the property left by Queen Charlotte. It was placed first in London at Carlton House. I am informed by G. Scharf that, according to a MS. statement by Mr Jutsham, at one time the inspector of Carlton House, this specimen is probably derived from Herculaneum. [*]

Windsor Castle possesses also a fine collection of ancient and modern **gems**, the most important specimens among which have been edited and described by C. D. E. Fortnum. *Archaeologia*, vol. XLV. A considerable portion of the collection was made by Consul Smith at Venice, and purchased from him by King George III, cf. A. F. Gori, *Dactyliotheca Smithiana*, Ven. 1767, II. Vols. Among the antique stones the following deserve special mention:

2 (no. 180). A fine Oriental cameo of three strata, a fragment of a head of **Zeus Aigiochos**. *Dact. Smith.*, Pl. 1. Fortnum, Pl. 2.

3 (no. 218). A sunk cameo, *intaglio rilievato*, an excellent **portrait** of a beardless elderly **Roman**, the hair clipped very close, not

unlike the portraits of the elder Scipio. Fortnum, Pl. 2. Cf. Bernoulli, *Röm. Ikonogr.*, I. p. 44.

4 (no. 242). A magnificent cameo in Oriental sardonyx of four or five strata; 0·19 high, 0·15 broad : **Emperor Claudius,** crowned with laurel, wearing a corslet and a small aegis, his sword (the handle of which is an eagle's head) by his side and a sceptre or a lance over his r. shoulder ; he is looking to the l. Fortnum, Pl. 1. This is undoubtedly a contemporary portrait; according to C. W. King (*Archæolog. Journ.*, XVIII. p. 312) it would be a portrait of Constantius II. This cameo was already in the possession of Charles I. when he was prince, and was then unfortunately "cracked and broken by the Lady Somerset, when her husband was Lord Chamberlain" (1613—1615).

Lastly, a large number of old **Drawings of Antiques** contained in a series of volumes purchased by King George III., form a great treasure of the R. Library. Woodward's conjectures as to their origin (*Gentl. Mag.*, 1866, p. 29) can be proved to be almost in all cases wrong. For shorter notices of them cf. Conze, *Arch. Anz.*, 1864, p. 240 ; Matz in the *Nachrichten der Göttinger Ges. d. Wiss.*, 1872, p. 65 (from notices by Helbig), and in the *Arch. Zeit.*, 1873, p. 33 ; Michaelis, *Ibid.*, 1874, p. 66 ; Duhn, *Ant. Bildwerke in Rom*, III. pp. 290 ff. As a detailed account of the collection is to be given in another place, a short notice will here suffice. The numbers added in brackets are those of my notice, *l. cit.*

The main portion of these volumes come from the collection of the Commendatore CASSIANO DAL POZZO (*d.* 1657), and were purchased for George III. in 1762 from Cardinal Alessandro Albani's library (cf. Introd. § 50). Among these may be reckoned certainly the following volumes (I.—XVI.) :

I.—IX. (I.—IX.) "*Bassi rilievi antichi.*" Large folio, bound completely in leather, and bearing the arms of George III. An unusually rich collection of bas reliefs, containing also in the last volume statues, busts, etc. Some loose leaves have been bound in with the book which do not come from Dal Pozzo's collection. This division is completed by

IX^a. A number of **loose sheets** marked as having come originally from PIETRO SANTE BARTOLI, but that can hardly be the case with all the leaves. They are nearly all from the Dal Pozzo collection. (For other remains of this collection see under Hamilton Palace. London, Franks.)

X. (XVIII.) "*Bassirilievi antichi.*" The exterior is the same as that of vol. I.—IX., only in a smaller form. 120 sheets with reliefs, chiefly of sarcophagi, all sketched in pen and ink. The origin of this collection is certainly earlier than the time of Dal Pozzo, who must have obtained it as a whole.

XI. XII. (X. XI.) "*Mosaici antichi.*" The exterior is like that of Vol. I.—IX. The inscription of these volumes would have been more correctly "Christian antiquities."

The four following volumes (XIII.—XVI.) have still in its completeness the original exterior of the Dal Pozzo collection : vellum binding and green edges.

XIII. (XII.) "*Disegni di Varie Antichità. Nettuno.*" This contains 220 sheets with illustrations from military, and domestic, and other antiquities, with much that is modern interspersed; further, wall paintings, mosaics, &c.

XIV. (XIII.) " *Disegn[i] d.uer[si].*" Modern architectural designs, nothing antique.

XV. (XIV.) "*Archite[ture] Ciuil[i] Disegnate.*" Several views, designs, details of ancient buildings in Rome and its vicinity ; also some modern architecture.

XVI. (XV.) " *Architectu[re] Ciuil[i] et Mil[itari].*" Plans, bird's-eye views, &c. of modern architecture.

The two following volumes are also bound in vellum, but without the green edges, and certainly do not come from the Dal Pozzo collection :

XVII. (XVIII.) "*Disegni di Antichi Colombar[ii]. Farnese. S. Gio[vanni] Late[rano].* Villa Madama e Teatri di Parma e Roma. R. R. 21." Besides many modern architectural pieces there are also a few columbaria, for example, that of the freedmen of Livia, discovered in 1726 (cf. Wilton, no. 60).

XVIII. (XVII.) "*Antichità Diuerse.*" In somewhat smaller form. Illustrations of antiquities, taken for a great part from printed books.

The following volume was obtained from the MEAD collection by Prince Frederick or by George III. (Introd. § 29):

XIX. (XXII.) " *Pitture Antiche dise[gnate] da Piet[ro] Sanct[e] Bartoli].*" Folio volume bound in leather, with the arms of the Vittoria family and those of George III. The title-page runs thus : " *L'antiche pitture, memorie raccolte dalle ruine di Roma, espresse al' eleganza vetusta, nel museo di D. Vincenzo Vittoria Canonico di Xativa nel regno di Valenza.—L'Architettura è inuentione, e Disegno del Em.ᵐᵒ Sig. Card'. Massimi.—Le Vittorie laterali sono disegnate da Pietro Santi Bartoli.*" 112 leaves with wall paintings, greater part of them the originals of different publications of Bartoli ; of great importance. (Cf. Holkham, no. B.)

The four following volumes (XX.— XXIII.) also come from the two Bartoli, Pietro and Francesco.

XX. "*I disegni originali della colonna Traiana fatti da Pietro Santi Bartoli.*" Leather volume in transverse folio, with George III.'s arms. Very delicate pen and ink sketches, signed here and there with the name Pietro Sante Bartoli.

XXI. (XXI.) "*Terence.*" Leather volume in large transverse folio, with the arms of George III. Coloured copies of the miniatures of the Vatican Terence, perhaps by Francesco Bartoli.

XXII. XXIII. (XIX. XX.) "*Il Vergilio nel Vaticano.*" Leather volume in small transverse folio, with the arms of George III. A double set, first, pen and ink etchings by Pietro Sante Bartoli ; secondly, coloured copies, perhaps by the son, Francesco; the latter are not quite complete. Together making 106 leaves.

The following volumes complete the collection :

XXIV. "*Columna dicta Traiana. A viro excellenti* IULIO CAMPI *Cremonensi non sine magno labore Romae dum vivebat diligentissime delineata.*" Leather volume in transverse folio, with the name of George III. ; in the inside are Consul Smith's arms. Giulio Campi lived 1500—1572. It would be interesting to compare these drawings with those made at about the same epoch by Girolamo Muziano (1530 – 1590), which were engraved by Franc. Villamena and edited by Alf. Ciaccone, Rome, 1576.

XXV. "*Vestigia delle Terme di Tito e loro interne pitture.*" Drawn by FRANC. SMUGGLEWICZ and painted by CARLONI with very gay colours, the original plates of the publication engraved by the latter. The "*Nozze Aldobrandine*" are added as plate 61. Leather volume of very large size, with George III.'s arms.

XXVI. "*Ancient Roman Architecture.*" Leather volume in large folio, with George III.'s arms. 50 sheets with views and ground-plans of Roman ruins, partly restored.

Finally, there is a volume belonging to the original treasures of the royal house :

XXVII. (XXIII.) "*Busts and Statues in* WHITE HALL 'GARDEN.*"

A folio volume, the back of which is vellum; on the first page, "Drawings of statues and Busts that were in the Palace at Whitehall before it was burnt. Preserved by Sʳ John Stanley Bart. who belonged to the Lord Chamberlayne's office at the time the Palace was burnt down." The fire occurred on the 4th Jan., 1698. For particulars about this volume, cf. Introd. §§ 18, 19.

WINTON CASTLE (Scotland).

LADY RUTHVEN, the owner of this Castle, which is not far from Edinburgh, lived for a long time at Athens in the third decade of the present century. She brought hence a number of antiquities (cf. Introd. § 88). I take the following particulars from a letter sent to Prof. Conze by Mr A. S. Murray (for fuller account see *Addenda*):

1. **Greek sepulchral stele**, tall, representing a female figure in a slightly archaic manner, and inscribed Ἀριστομάχη.

2. **Greek sepulchral stele**. Of the Roman period, and inscribed with Roman names.

Lady Ruthven has also a pretty large collection of **vases** obtained from tombs near Athens, which she opened about fifty years ago. Two or three of the vases bear archaic geometric patterns.

WOBURN ABBEY (Bedfordshire).

Outline Engravings and Descriptions of the Woburn Abbey Marbles, 1822, fol. (The letterpress is by Dr Hunt, who was at one time Lord Elgin's chaplain, and at that period Dean of Holkham; the drawings are by Moses and Corbould.) *Catalogue of the Marbles, Bronzes, Terre-cotte, and Casts, in the Sculpture Gallery &c. at Woburn Abbey.* London, 1828 (short notes, printed again with new numbering and some additions, 1867). Waagen, *Treas.*, III. pp. 463, 467 ff. (II. pp. 545, 551 ff.). Conze, *Arch. Anz.*, 1864, p. 211 ff. Matz, *Arch. Zeit.*, 1873, p. 30. Michaelis, *Ibid.*, 1874, pp. 68 ff.—I visited the collection in 1873 and 1877. The numbers in the following catalogue are those of the Catalogue of 1867; in parentheses I have added the numbers of the first edition, published in 1828; the numbers omitted apply to modern specimens.

The idea of adorning Bedford House, the town residence of the DUKES OF BEDFORD, with antique sculptures, originated with FRANCIS,

MARQUIS OF TAVISTOCK (*d.* 1767), the father of Francis the fifth Duke ;
though he only carried out his idea to a very small extent (nos. 171,
210 ; cf. Introd. p. 83). The Gallery in Woburn Abbey, which is
most magnificent, was first erected in 1789 as a conservatory by
DUKE FRANCIS (duke from 1771—1802). It is about 42 metres long
and 7½ wide, and is lighted by eight immense windows, which have a
view over the garden and park. In the centre of the gallery is a
cupola supported by eight antique columns of costly kinds of marble;
opposite the door is a semicircular recess (here stands no. 101).
At either extremity of the gallery stand the Temple of Liberty, with
the busts of the principal Whig leaders (at the entrance, nos. 153,
154), and the Temple of the Graces, with Canova's group of these
goddesses. The room was finished in this way and adapted to the
purposes of a Sculpture Gallery in 1820 by JOHN RUSSELL, SIXTH
DUKE OF BEDFORD (duke from 1802—1839), to whose zeal Woburn
Abbey is also indebted for the main contents of the Gallery ; for his
predecessor had only collected a very few sculptures (nos. 61, 101)
besides purchasing some vases at Lord Cawdor's sale in 1800. In
1815 the new duke visited Italy and returned home with rich booty;
particularly worthy of notice are the six large reliefs from the Villa
Aldobrandini in Frascati (nos. 58, 69, 86, 110, 117, 144) which are an
unusual ornament for an English museum. "Not without difficulty,'
that is, probably, not without payment of handsome douceurs, was
the papal permission obtained for the transport of the treasure to
England. Other valuables were furnished either by excavations made
at the time (for example nos. 104, 147, 204), or by the liberality of
members of princely houses to the head of the Russell family (no.
128), or by the art dealers (nos. 99, 107, 205). After the duke's
return the purchases were continued (nos. 59, 77, 141, 198), among
which must be mentioned as specially valuable the Ephesian sarcophagus with the story of Achilleus (no. 219). Friends and relations
of the family made presents ; Lord George William Russell and Sir
George Hayter presented a collection of small bronzes, Lord Holland
gave a beautiful statue (no. 201). To complete the collection the
duke obtained some very fine modern sculptures by Canova, Thorvaldsen, Chantrey, and Westmacott ; and as these specimens were placed
in the same room with the antiques, a comparison is involuntarily
instituted between ancient and modern art. A picture of the gallery
thus furnished may be seen in Robinson's *Vitruvius Britannicus:
History of Woburn Abbey*, London, 1833, Pl. 4. In 1822 the duke
had ordered engravings to be made of the choicest specimens.

arranged with the help of Dr Hunt (Introd. § 75). They formed a magnificent work, which was only distributed among friends (*Engravings*, &c., see above). The collection has since then been increased by some additions, though not very many (for example nos. 111, 239, 240, 257—259). Cf. Introd. § 86.

32 (33, at the back of the Temple of the Graces). **Bust of** the Empress **Julia.**

33 (34, in the outer wall, near the entrance of the Sculpture Gallery). **Medallion,** in marble, of the Emperor **Vespasian.**

34 (35, *ibid.*). Do. of the Emperor **Hadrian.**

35. Bust of **Homer.**

With regard to these four numbers I cannot say whether they are antique or new.

36—42. Various **architectural fragments** of rosso antico. Found at Hadrian's Villa.

50. Ancient sculptured **altar,** forming the pedestal of the Group of the Graces by Canova.

54 (232). **Bust of Agrippa** (?). Head and upper part of r. arm have been broken off. Over life size. Appears to be modern. [*]

55. **Empress,** seated, restored as a Ceres. She wears chiton and cloak, and her head is not veiled. Head, on which is the stephanè, has been mended in many places. New: neck, r. forearm with ears of wheat in the hand, l. hand. A poor statue, much repaired. H. 1·88. [*]

56 (63). Front of an **ara** or a cippus, with a moulding at the top and bottom, and cut off on both sides. A garland with berries traverses the middle of the relief. Above this garland lies a bearded **Seilenos,** his legs covered with a cloak, stretched out comfortably on an ass, which stands quietly facing r. with its head lowered. Below the garland is the Roman she-wolf with the twin brothers. Elegant high relief. H. 0·56. L. 0·29. [*C]

58 (59). **Fragments of a sarcophagus: Phaedra and Hippolytos.** *Engravings*, Pl. 13. Made up of two pieces, which appear to belong to the same sarcophagus, but which were not originally put together in the same way. LEFT PART (probably a fragment of the front). Phaedra sits in the centre, looking r., in a girdled chiton that has slipped down from her r. shoulder; a cloak conceals her legs and the chair, an apparently separate piece of drapery veils her head and back, and is held by her upraised l. hand (forearm restored). Behind Phaedra to the r., a young

female servant is partly visible, she seems to be arranging the veil on
her mistress' head with her r. hand, and on the other side is an old
nurse in chiton and cap who clasps Phaedra round the waist. Both
Phaedra and the nurse are looking back to the l., where stands a
youth (Hippolytos), seen in full face. He wears a chlamys; the
sword-belt goes across his breast, his r. hand grasps the hilt
of his sword, and before his l. shoulder is a piece of a lance
which by the restorer has been transformed into a slender club (l.
forearm new). Hippolytos turns his face (partly restored) towards
a youth who is standing on the extreme l.; he has a chlamys on his
l. shoulder and over his l. arm; this figure has been sawn through
in the middle. To the r. of Phaedra stands a similar youth, looking l.;
the chlamys hangs from his neck down his back. The lowered r.
forearm with the thin club, the body and parts of the legs are new.
With his l. hand he holds the bridle of a horse, but of the horse only
the head remains.—RIGHT PART (apparently one of the sides).
Five youths, all seen full face, and all nude except for the chlamys.
Counting from the l., on the first the r. arm, both thighs, l. forearm
with the thin club are new. The second holds the shaft of a lance in
his upraised r. hand, and with his l. the bridle of a horse, the head
of which only is visible (slight restorations). On the third figure
(Hippolytos?) the l. hand and all the club are new: the fourth only
appears in the background; the fifth has a new head and r. forearm,
which is raised. I have passed over more insignificant repairs.—The
vastness of the dimensions, the clearness of the composition, and the
grand style of sculpture remind us of the treatment of the same
subject on the sarcophagi at Girgenti (*Arch. Zeit.*, 1847, Pl. 5, 6) and
in St Petersburg (*Mon. dell' Inst.*, VI. 1–3). H. 1·19. L. 2·82
(1·31 + 1·47). Formerly in the Villa Aldobrandini in Frascati.
[*CIII*]

59 (60). **Bust of Marcus Aurelius.** *Engr.* Pl. 25, 2. New:
nose, part of drapery; neck has been mended. Life size. Bought
by Westmacott. [*]

61 (64). **Front of a sarcophagus: Bacchanalian procession.** *Engr.*, Pl. 12. The procession moves from l. to r. In
the very front stands a Maenad in a chiton, beating the tympanon;
a second moves to the r., in a chiton, with the cloak thrown round her
legs; she originally blew a flute; in the background a smaller figure
of a girl, who has a round box on her head and carries a staff in her
l. hand. Then follows the inebriated Seilenos, only very partially
covered by his cloak; he has a cup (? disc?) in his l. hand and a

wreath in his r. ; he is sitting on an ass, supported on either side by a young Satyr ; on the ground lie a huge panther and a wine-skin. Then follows the bearded Pan, skipping with his goat's legs over a cista, under the opened lid of which crawls forth a snake. Next, the chariot of Dionysos, drawn by two panthers : on one panther sits a Cupid with his lyre ; a second Cupid in the chariot is guiding the animals ; the youthful god himself, only partially covered by his cloak, is reclining in the lap of a draped female figure (Ariadne?) ; his l. arm is thrown round her neck, his r. lies on his own head. Partly concealed by the chariot and the panthers, run beside it a Satyr in a chlamys, a figure with a fan (λίκνον, *vannus*) on the head and a thyrsos (?) in the hand, a bearded Seilenos striking cymbals together over his head, a bearded Pan with the pedum. Behind the chariot dances a Satyr with his r. leg much elevated ; he lifts his l. hand to his forehead (ἀποσκοπεύει). H. 0·59. L. 2·09. This marble was brought by Lord Cawdor from Sicily, where it had been used as the front of a cistern to a public fountain ; consequently the whole monument is much injured by the action of the water, though the original excellence of the composition and work is still to be discerned. [*C.M.H*]

62 (65). **Mask.** *Engr.*, Pl. 27, 2. Beardless, of tragic expression, with a Phrygian cap, the peak of which is much bent. New : nose. H. 0·29. [*]

63 (66). **Bust of a child** with curly hair. New : nose and bust. Life size. [*B*]

64 (67). **Bust of a boy.** designated without warrant as Nero. New : tip of nose and bust. Life size. [*B*]

65 (68). **Head of an Egyptian deity.**

66 (57). **Bust of Trajan.** New : nose, ears, part of the back of the head, neck ; the mailed bust with Medusa's head is for the most part antique, but does not belong to the head. Life size. [*B*]

67 (70). **Terminal head,** named "Lycurgus." *Arch. Anz.*, 1864, Pl. A, 2 (Conze). The head is beardless, and its most remarkable feature is the r. eye, which is made so small as to shew that the head was certainly meant to represent some one with one eye. The mouth, too, is crooked and ugly. Neck and bust and nose have been restored ; the other part, which is of coarse grained marble, is superficially treated, the hair in quite an unusual style. The head may after all be antique, but is at least open to grave suspicion. L. of face 0·22. [*C*]

68 (71). **Architectural fragment.** part of the side post of a door (*antepagmentum*), or of a pilaster or something of the

kind. Vine sprays are trained upwards, and among them on a
large basket stand two Cupids, picking fruit. Delicate and elegant.
H. 0·24. L. 0·15. Cf. no. 76. [*]

69 (72). Large relief. *Engr.*, Pl. 11. A winged griffin, with
a head like a lion's, except that it has horns, has sprung from the
r. on to the back of stag, which the violence of the shock has
thrown to the ground, and is driving its fore-claws into the stag's
neck. To the l. a tree bearing fruit (apple tree ?). Above, a cornice
with rich mouldings, to the r. and underneath, a small border.
Certainly not a metope. Hardly restored at all. H. 0·93. L. 1·28.
From the Villa Aldobrandini in Frascati. [*.*M*]

71. Fragment of a sarcophagus, representing Achilleus
at Skyros (cf. no. 117). The fragment comprises only the stomach
and the legs of Achilleus, dressed in a female chiton, hurrying l., his
r. leg coming forth nude from his drapery. Somewhat injured about
the abdomen. Good sculpture. H. 0·66. [*CM*]

74 (80). Fragment of a relief, a woman in short drapery,
either Artemis or an Amazon, hurrying r. Both thighs covered
with the drapery, the r. knee drawn back, and the lower part of
the advanced l. leg to the ankle are preserved. The back of the
fragment is flat and roughly cut; the specimen was evidently intended, like the figures from the frieze of the temple of Polias in
Athens, to be fastened by the back on to a slab. Greek work of
a good period. H. 0·45. [*C*]

75 (86). Terminal head of Poseidon. The face is somewhat raised ; its expression sad and disturbed. The hair is raised up
over the forehead in two divisions and then falls long down. The
beard is more entangled and less dank. A fillet passes through the
hair. The head is in perfect preservation, the terminal bust is new.
Marble with grey stripes. L. of face 0·19. [*]

76 (87). Architectural fragment, with delicate sprays, finely
executed, belonging to no. 68. A groove runs along one side, shewing
that the piece was to have been joined to something; on the other
side is an astragalos. H. 0·26. L. 0.15. [*].

76¹. Architectural fragment, of Greek execution, finely
treated. Portions only of two flowers connected by a spray are
preserved, the one on the l. turned upwards, the one on the r. downwards. Below, a light border; the upper part injured. H. 0·10. [C]

77 (78). Bust of Septimius Severus. *Engr.*, Pl. 24, 2.
The emperor is represented of a rather youthful age. New: nose,
chief part of the beard, the corslet with the paludamentum and the

clasp on which is the inscription *nec spe nec metu.* Life size. Bought from Westmacott. [*B]

78 (83). **Terminal head of Claudius** (??), the hair growing deep down in the back of the neck. New: nose and bust. Below life size. To me the genuineness of the head appeared doubtful. [*B]

79 (84). **Head of a Roman lady,** of the first century, perhaps **Antonia** (Bernoulli). Her wavy hair is concealed by a veil ; her face youthful, but the expression grave. New : nose ; the rest composed of several pieces. [*B]

80 (85). **Bust of Herakles.** *Engr.,* Pl. 27, 1. Small head adorned with a wreath of poplar. New : nose, neck and bust. H. of head 0·27. [*]

81 (82). **Front of a sarcophagus : Kalydonian hunt.** *Engr.,* Pl. 10. The sarcophagus is akin to the one in Broadlands (no. 21) and another one in Richmond (no. 57), and except for a few unimportant repairs, is in excellent preservation. To the l. in front of the arched doorway stands (*a*) the bearded Oeneus in chiton and cloak ; his l. hand holding his cloak, his r. the sceptre. Near him steps forward in the background (*b*) a youthful follower (δορυφόρος) with chlamys and spear, a fillet in his hair, and looking up to the r. (*c*) Artemis advances in the same direction, her cloak broadly girt round her short chiton, holding her spear in both hands ; beside her a dog. The fashion of her hair is maidenly, and she turns her head back to the r., where (*d*) a long-bearded man, looking at Oeneus, is visible in the rear. Then (*e*) the powerful form of Ankaeos starts for the hunt, in a lion's skin, a fillet in his tangled hair and grasping his double axe. Before him (*f, g*) go the Dioskuroi with egg-shaped hats, chlamys and spear ; *g* is seen full face. Further to the r. in the background (*h*) a man with a long beard like *d* moves r. ; in front of him is (*i*) Meleagros, with a fillet in the hair and a chlamys, couching his spear ready for the boar ; beside him is (*k*) Atalantè, draped like Artemis, holding out her bow in her l. hand and drawing an arrow from her quiver with her r. One dog is barking at the boar, a second attacks his r. foreleg, beside it is a marsh plant. The large boar (*l*) advances from his den, which is only indicated by a line, of rock ; near him on the ground lies (*m*) a bearded man, wounded, in chiton, chlamys, sword-belt, and boots ; supporting himself on his l. arm. Over the edge of the den we see the upper part of the body of (*n*) a youth in a chlamys, poising his spear, and (*o*) a second youth, in a chlamys, with two

spears in his l. arm and throwing a stone with his upraised r. hand.
Then comes a tree.   To the r. of the tree, seen from the rear, stands
(*p*) a youth in a chlamys, holding one spear in his l. hand and
brandishing another with his r.   The procession is closed by (*q*) a
bearded man, standing, with his sword at his side, the chlamys on
his back, supporting himself with his l. hand on a spear, placed
perpendicularly.   This spear serves as a frame for the whole scene.
The man lays his r. hand on his wounded thigh and is looking back
at the boar.   The figures are treated in high or low relief according to their position in the foreground or the background.   H. 0·54.
L. 2·12.   Possibly this sarcophagus was once inserted into the wall
along the large stairs leading to S. Maria in Araceli ; at least a description by Pirro Ligorio (Cod. Neapol. xiii. B, 10), who saw such a slab
at that place, appears to be favourable to such a conjecture (cf. on no.
117).   The relief was still at that place in 1736, as is shewn by Casimiro Romano. *Memorie istoriche della chiesa di S. Maria in Araceli*,
p. 28.   (I am indebted to Dr Dessau for these notices from Rome.)
If this conjecture is right, the slab may belong to those purchased
from the Villa Aldobrandini, though there is no record of such an
origin.   [*MII*]

82 (183).   **Cupid sleeping.**

85 (175).   **Bust of Antoninus Pius.**   A poor work, and much
patched (new : nose, pieces on the eyes, and beard).   The corslet, which
has traces of red colouring, is bad, but apparently belongs to the
bust.   Over life size.   [*B*]

86 (89).   **Front of a sarcophagus : Selenè and Endymion.**   *Engr.*, Pl. 9.   An early drawing in the Cod. Coburg, no.
167 M. - Cod. Pigh., no. 170 J.   The central object is the chariot
of Artemis adorned with sprays of vine and drawn by two champing
chargers turning to the l.   A little boy in a chlamys, standing with
his l. foot on the back of one of the horses, holds the bridle in his
l. hand and flourishes the whip with his r.; a winged boy (new :
upper part of his body and torch in his r. hand) seems also to be
occupied in trying to control the horses, and a large winged female
figure (Hora) in a short, girdled chiton standing before the horses is
grasping the bit of the r. horse.   Over her we see a third Cupid with
a torch (head, l. wing and l. arm new).   Selenè (her features intended
probably to be a portrait) is stepping down r. from the chariot, in
girdled chiton, a crescent behind her shoulders, holding her veil,
which waves like an arch over and behind her head, with both hands :
her look is directed to Endymion.   She is guided to him by a winged

youth (Eros?), draped in a chlamys, holding up a long torch with both hands, and looking back at the goddess. A similar form, without wings, appears as the companion of Selenè behind her r. shoulder and above the horse (both forearms and the torch restored). Between the legs of the winged youth sits a dog looking up. On the ground to the r. lies Endymion, in chiton and cloak, supporting himself on his l. arm, in which he holds two staves that have been restored at the top and which were probably spears originally; he lays his r. hand on his head. The features of his face are only blocked out, as they were intended to be replaced later by a portrait of the deceased. The youthful Hypnos, with half-closed eyes, is bending over him; he is clothed in a chlamys and has butterflies' wings, and holds in his l. arm a bunch of poppies; three parts of his advanced r. arm and the cup are new. No doubt he was originally shown dropping juice from his miraculous horn on to the sleeper. In front of Hypnos and quite on the border to the r. stand two boys, each with a torch; of the one the head, r. arm and torch are new, and the other is entirely restored except his feet and the lower half of the torch. Above the latter boy sits another dog. High up in the r. hand corner is a group of two half-nude Naiades standing, one supporting herself against an urn from which water runs, the second embracing the first and holding a reed in her l. hand.—To their l., on the upper border, Selenè (conceived purely as a heavenly body and quite distinct from the goddess in the principal scene) is guiding her chariot, which is drawn to the r. by two cows; she wears a chiton, a flowing cloak and is crowned with the crescent. To the l. of Selenè's veil, between it and the head of the youth without wings, appears the upper part of the body of a small boy; in the old drawing he holds a torch, he is therefore doubtless intended for Phosphoros. He is looking l., where on the other side of the youth just named, the youthful Helios, in a long chiton with sleeves, is guiding his chariot, drawn by four horses, to the r. on the firmament.—The l. end of the sarcophagus is devoted to a scene of shepherd life. The rocky ground is carried up to the top and is entirely covered by a very numerous flock of sheep, among which are a few cows. Quite at the top sits a young mountain god, a branch in his r. arm, the lower part of his body concealed by his cloak; he is listening to a nymph in a chiton who is standing in front of him supporting herself on his knee. A bearded shepherd of much larger proportions sits below beside a tree ; he wears the exomis and boots and a bag slung across his breast; on the ground beside him lies a goblet (?). He stretches out his r. hand to a dog sitting opposite to him; almost the entire arm and the bread in the hand have been restored. Further to the r., under Selene's horses, lies Tellus on the ground, the upper part of her body nude, supporting herself on a basket (?). Her head, the ears of wheat in her r. hand, and the l. with the cornucopiae are all new. Tellus is surrounded by four boys (the Seasons?), of whom one (much restored), standing at her back, holds a plant, two are placed under the belly of the horses, the fourth, at their feet, near the wheel of the chariot, is playing with a sheep.—Some smaller restorations have been passed over in this description.—This very large and high sarcophagus belongs to that class which is remarkable for picturesque composition, and in which an abundance of secondary figures confuses the principal scene; only difference in size between the principal and these accessory figures serves in some degree to keep the main theme clearly in view. H. 1·17. L. 2·39. From the Villa Aldobrandini in Frascati. [*CMW]

89 (231). **Bust,** designated "**Cato.**" Modern copy of a spare head, with a wide mouth and overhanging brow, which reminds us somewhat of Caesar. [*B]

92 (180). **Votive disk.** Cupid reposing on a doe. Perhaps new. [*]

93 (98). **Sculptured tazza.**

94 (177). **Round disk,** in form like a shield. *Engr.*, Pl. 28, 3. Bearded Bacchic head with brutish ears and Ammon's horns, a fillet passed over the forehead and through the curly hair; usually entitled Ammon. Greyish marble. Diameter about 0·30. [*]

95 (99). **Small pilaster,** designed for an angle, delicately sculptured on two adjacent sides. In perfect preservation. The piece may possibly be referred to the Cinquecento period. H. 0·71. Br. each 0·14. [*]

96 (100). **Relief.** A powerful, nude male figure, facing l., kneels on the ground; his l. foot touching the ground, his r. thigh horizontal, the r. foot drawn back so that the toes just touch the ground. The upper part of the body is bent very far forwards, both arms advanced, the r. horizontally, the l. more lowered. New: upper part of the back, part of the r. forearm and both hands with a hatchet, which is held perpendicularly, and which accounts for the title: "A slave working in a mine or quarry." The position however is too insecure for any such employment; in this case the r. foot should be advanced and placed firmly on the ground. It is more likely that the man supported himself by his arms against something, or that he was trying to reach

WOBURN ABBEY 100 (103).

something. Good powerful work, tolerably high relief. H. 0·50.
L. 0·73. (The genuine portion h. 0·34, l. 0·60). [*C]

97 (95). **Bust of Marcus Aurelius**, youthful, without beard.
New: nose, parts of both ears, bust. [*B]

98 (101). **Relief of Harpokrates.** He is represented as a
child, seen in full face, resting on the r. leg. Over the forehead the
remains of a peculiar ornament; hair curly. He lays the fore-finger
of his r. hand on his mouth. In the l. arm he holds a cornucopiae
with grapes and other fruits; his chlamys is flung over his arm. On
his feet he wears sandals with broad thongs. Commonplace work.
H. 0·65. L. 0·39. [*C]

99 (102). **Relief with the Evil Eye.** *Engr.*, Pl. 14. *Archaeologia*, XIX. p. 70, Plate (J. Millingen). *Berichte d. sächs. Ges.*, 1855, Pl.
3, 1; pp. 28 ff. (O. Jahn). In the centre the evil eye (Ital. *malocchio*) is
represented, attacked from all sides, that its evil influence may be overcome. A man in a Phrygian cap, seen from the back, crouches above
the eyebrow; his action is one which undoubtedly indicates con-
tempt. In the upper corner at the r. stands a gladiator (*retiarius*) in
an apron, pointing his trident at the eye, against which below approach
in a circle a lion, a snake, a scorpion, a crane and a raven, all
animals which were usually supposed to have the power of averting evil.
The r. top corner is broken off; comparing this composition with a
golden amulet found in Mayence, in all essentials a replica of it (*Arch.
Zeit.*, 1874, p. 69), we think that in this case too there must once
have been a second gladiator (*murmillo*) attacking the eye with his
sword. On three sides, a simple frame is preserved. Rather coarse
work; greyish marble. It is probable that this relief was let into a
wall or some similar place, that it might serve as a charm against
evil looks and similar magic influences (ἀποτρόπαιον, προβασκάνιον).
H. 0·30. L. 0·255. Bought from J. Millingen. [*W]

100 (103). **Relief of a Greek girl** ("Sappho"). Engraved
by itself, probably in the beginning of our century by Gio. Franc.
Ferrero in Rome. See annexed woodcut. The field is framed
by a simple square listel, and is quite filled by a female figure
stepping l. in a chiton, completely enveloped in her wide cloak.
Her r. forearm lies before her breast, causing her elbow to stand out
rather awkwardly from the lines of the figure; unless the r. hand be
meant, which, however, would involve no less incorrectness of drawing. A kind of cap (*opisthosphendone*) conceals the back of her head.
The countenance is somewhat severe in shape; nose large, chin
high, eye flat and not quite correctly drawn. The treatment of the

surface is very delicate, the folds of the drapery excellently composed and executed. Here and there we observe a slight lack of skilfulness, for example in the back outline of the l. leg; close to that again are very fine details, and the general effect conveys perfect maidenly grace. Attic relief, dating probably about the end of the fifth century; perhaps sepulchral, although the framing is unusual. Light yellowish Pentelic marble of the finest quality. H. 0·79. L. 0·37. The height of the relief above the field only reaches 0·01. [*C]

101 (104). Lante vase. *Engr.,* Pl. 15, 16. Piranesi, *Vasi,* &c., 1. Pl. 42, 43. Moses, *Coll. of Vases,* Pl. 35. On a pedestal 0·80 m. high stands the vessel, somewhat full bodied; it tapers a little towards the top and then terminates in a broad rim; two handles (much mended, but for the chief part antique) unite the rim with the main body of the vase. On either side it is ornamented with four Bacchic masks in very high relief, excellently conceived and well and delicately executed. The heads are as follows. FIRST SIDE. (1) Bearded daemon with snub nose (σῖμος), rough hair sticking up, ears covered; much restored. (2) Seilenos, bald-headed and crowned with ivy; tip of nose and moustaches new. (3) Bearded head, somewhat ideal in form, hair and horns concealed by a handkerchief; nose new. (4) Youthful Pan, with pointed ears, two tolerably long horns and a large tuft of hair between them, long hair; tip of nose and upper lip new. SECOND SIDE. (5) Similar head with short horns, grinning; tip of nose, mouth, chin, r. cheek, restored. (6) Seilenos bald-headed, with a small curl on his forehead, long beard and pointed ears; tip of nose and upper lip new. (7) More noble head with round beard, flat nose and pointed ears, but with earnest expression and more refined character, crowned with pine leaves; tip of nose and parts of l. cheek new. (8) Pan, with horns, a long beard, pointed ears, very snub nose, and with a brutish grin; the horns new except the stumps. Important portions of the upper border have been restored; the pedestal is likewise new. The marble which is not Parian, is of good fine grain with blackish stripes. H. 1·77. Diameter 1·90. This vase, which on account of its size, its tasteful form and ornamentation and its excellent work deserves the fame it enjoys, was found, in fragments, during excavations made in the ruins of Hadrian's Villa. From thence it passed into the collection of the Villa Lante, on Mount Gianicolo. It was afterwards purchased by Volpato, from whom it passed into the possession of Jenkins (*Account of the Statues, &c., at Inee.* p. 7), of whom it was bought by Lord Cawdor, and at his sale

(1800) by John, Duke of Bedford, for £700. A copy, reduced to one half the original size, by B. Lange is to be found in the Louvre (Clarac, II. 145, 124). [*W]

102 (94). **Young Roman**, beardless, wrongly designated "Augustus"; not of the imperial family but probably belonging to the first century A.D. New: nose, upper lip, lobes of the ears, neck and bust. Larger than life. [*B]

104 (106). **Oval sarcophagus.** *Engr.*, Pl. 46, 1. Front fluted. In the centre a barrel. At either end a lion tearing a boar. The lid, in the form of a tiled roof, has in front a slab on which is this inscription : *Eusebie filiae | parentes | contra votum.* On the top along the flat ridge of the roof: *Faustina.* (this word, which is only scratched in, was apparently added later) *deposita xiii Kal. Sep.* Late work. "Found in a sepulchre lately discovered in an excavation made near the Via Appia, at Rome." (*Engravings*). Cf. on no. 204. L. 1·15. H. 0·42. [*M]

105 (107). **Fragment of the lid of a sarcophagus.** Large mask with ruffled hair. From the l. end of the lid. [*]

107 (196). **Bust of Trajan.** *Engr.*, Pl. 26, 1. This representation of the Emperor is so unusually youthful that we are justified in doubting whether it is meant for him. New: nose, patches on the l. eye and l. ear, parts of the neck and drapery. Life size. Bought of Camuccini. [*B]

108 (152). **Bust of Tiberius**, youthful, on a bust of oriental alabaster (antique?). New: tip of nose and neck. Life size. [*B]

109 (110). **Bust of Aelius Verus**, or more likely of some similar person. *Engr.*, Pl. 25, 1. The beard is smooth and short, the curly hair runs forward. No restorations. Life size. [*B]

110 (111). **Front of a sarcophagus : Kalydonian hunt.** *Engr.*, Pl. 3. An early drawing of it is to be found in the Cod. Coburg., no. 218 M. Cod. Pigh., no. 214 J.; another, incomplete and roughly executed, in Windsor (vol. X. fol. 47) with the name of the place where it was then to be found given, "*Ai Porcari*," *i.e.* in the house of Giulio Porcaro near the church of S. Maria sopra Minerva, where Aldroandi saw the sarcophagus in the year 1550 (see L. Mauro, *Antichità di Roma*, 1556, p. 242). The subject is divided into two scenes. LEFT SCENE. Meleagros, wearing only a chlamys, is pressing forward from the l., and lowering his spear at the boar, which crouches on the ground. Atalantè, in boots and a short chiton with a broad girdle, and the quiver on her shoulder, is drawing her bow at the boar. Behind Meleagros may be seen a bearded man in boots, with a short chiton and his chlamys floating in the wind; he wields a broad sword in his upraised r. hand and in his l. he holds a lance. Near Atalantè, but more in the background, is a similar man, raising his r. hand and holding a cloth in his l. as was the custom at boar hunts (ἐφαπτίς, Pollux 4, 116). Above the boar on a champing steed that has a skin for a horse-cloth, gallops a youth in chiton, chlamys and high boots; he is turning round and driving his sword into the boar. By a bad arrangement of the figures this youth occupies the central place as though he, and not Meleagros, were the principal actor. A youth in chiton, chlamys and boots is hurrying up beside the horse; he is raising his r. hand and turning his head back. Three dogs complete the hunting scene, the first standing between Meleagros' legs, the second in front of the boar, barking at him, the third tugging at the l. ear of the boar.—RIGHT SCENE. Atalantè in chiton and boots is standing with her legs crossed; she bears the great boar's head in her hands (her head and the fillet of victory have been restored). In front of her stands a small Eros without wings, in chlamys and shoes, advancing his r. arm towards Atalantè, at whom he is looking, and supporting his torch on the ground with his l. hand. Behind him in the background stands a hunter in chiton, chlamys and boots; his l. hand holds his spear, his r. hand, raised in a warning attitude, is restored. His gaze is directed towards Meleagros, who stands at the extreme r., looking away from the scene in a posture of challenge, with his r. arm akimbo, his l. hand on his lance, his chlamys hanging behind his back, beside him is a dog. It is uncertain whether this end of the sarcophagus is complete. The work has been very much restored, mainly perhaps owing to the remarkably high relief; Eros, for instance, is worked almost in the round like a statue. All the heads are new except Atalantè's in the first scene, and that of the bearded man beside her; also many limbs and attributes; but there can be scarcely any doubt that the restorations are correct. Poor sculpture. From the Villa Aldobrandini, in Frascati, whither it had been brought from the above-named place. H. 0·59. L. 2·25. [*CMW*]

III. **Statue of Minerva**, without head. *Archæologia*, XXXII. Pl. 4, p. 14. The goddess rests on her l. leg. She wears, besides the chiton, a cloak which covers her l. shoulder and the upper part of the arm, her back, hips and thighs, the end falling over her l. forearm, which is advanced in a downward direction. She wears no aegis, but instead of it there is on the breast a large oval

ornament, jagged round the edges and formed like a rosette, which
takes the place of the Medusa's head. Her l. hand rests on a
large round shield (partly broken). This shield stands on a pear-
shaped support, which is on a square pedestal; a snake is coiling
itself upwards on the outside of the shield. Only the upper part
of the r. arm preserved, with a part of the spear which rests
perpendicularly in front of the shoulder. On the hips and the
calf of the leg traces of joints are preserved; the first one was
intended for the r. hand, which is intact, but separated, and which
rests on an owl; in this hand a piece of the shaft of the lance is
visible. Very rough work, of a coarse shelly stone, much corroded.
Found at Sibson. Nearly life size. [*C]

114 (117). **Small male torso,** legs and l. arm in a cloak,
stepping vigorously to the r. The l. foot is lifted high, and near it is a
support like a basket. Head missing; also the r. arm which was
held up, three parts of the l. arm which is slightly lowered, and the
feet. H. 0·33. [*]

115 (118). **Bust of a little child,** a year or two old. Broken,
but entirely antique. H. 0·30. L. of face 0·12. [*]

116 (119). **Torso of an Aphroditè,** nude, resting on her
l. leg; her l. hand covered her lap, her r. arm was lowered. Head is
missing, also the r. arm, half the l. forearm, lower part of the r. leg,
three parts of the l. leg. H. 0·34. [*]

117 (121). **Front of a sarcophagus: Achilleus at Skyros.**
Engr., Pl. 7. Winckelmann, *Mon. Ined.,* before the preface. An early
drawing without restorations in the Cod. Coburg. no. 203 M.; a
rough, arbitrary sketch in Windsor (vol. x. fol. 75) with the name .
of the place where it then was to be found given, "Araceli." This
short notice is explained by the fact that in former times there were
"*ne la scala della chiesa di Araceli attaccate per le mura delle sue
sponde, da otto tauole marmorce con varie, e belle scolture antiche*"
(Aldroandi in L. Mauro, *Antichità di Roma,* 1556, p. 276). A
description of these eight reliefs by Pirro Ligorio is preserved in the
Cod. Neapol., XIII. B, 10, as I am informed by Dr H. Dessau,
to whom I am indebted for a copy of the description of the relief "*di
Achille et di Ulysse,*" which, however, affords no new information.—
A curtain is drawn across two-thirds of the scene on the l., indicating
that there is represented the interior of the females' apartment.
The group of Achilleus and Deidameia forms the centre of the
piece. Achilleus, still in his female dress, from which his powerful
r. leg stands forth nude, is lifting his l. leg very high; either because

his foot rests upon some object which we cannot see, or because he is sitting on the edge of a couch which is shewn in other copies. His head is surrounded by abundant curls. His body is turned somewhat r., but his inspired look is directed to the l. His l. arm is raised and bears a shield; the r. arm and lance have been restored. In front of him on the ground is an enormous helmet with a plume. On the rounded part of the helmet is a relief: an helmeted warrior with his sword drawn is hurrying over a corpse to attack a nude male figure, who kneels defending himself with his shield; in the background is another warrior in chlamys and helmet, and two champing horses; in front on the screen is a ram's head. Deidameia kneels on the ground before Achilleus, in lively movement; she lays her arm entreatingly on Achilleus' knee (l. arm new) and turns her face (head new) towards the disturbers of her peace; her cloak floats at her back. In front of her stands a small Eros with a torch, his arms outspread; only his breast, r. arm, upper part of l. arm, and parts of the wings are antique. A small basket (καλαθίσκος) with wool in it lies at Deidameia's feet; near it stands a second Eros, of whom only the torso, chlamys and r. wing are antique. One of Deidameia's sisters is hurrying above her to the r.; her head, her advanced r. arm and the tip of her cloak in her r. hand are restored; it is certain that she originally did not grasp the curtain, but that her hand was only put out in defence against the interlopers. To the l. of Achilleus are visible four daughters of Lykomedes: one, in a chiton and a chlamys draped like a shawl, and in a position similar to that of Achilleus, is holding a cithara (restored at the top) in her l. arm; another dressed in the same way, is hurrying l. (her forearms and flute have been added by the restorer); of the two other sisters only the heads are visible in the background. To the r., outside the female apartment, stands first Odysseus, much rejoiced at the success of his stratagem. His face is bearded and has curls on either side and he holds it somewhat high; his r. arm, which is advanced, and his l. with the lance have been restored, but probably correctly; he wears an exomis, chlamys, high boots, and a sword at his side. The youthful Diomedes, in helmet, breast-plate, chlamys, and boots, is hurrying up to him from the r., and is on the point of drawing his sword. At his feet lie a sword and a richly ornamented breast-plate adorned with the Medusa's head. Between Odysseus and Diomedes in the background a bearded warrior with a flat cap on his head: on the extreme r. Agyrtes, blowing the trumpet, in helmet and chlamys.—Unimportant restorations have been passed over in my description. Relief much raised ; work not unrefined and in some parts delicate ; the figures in the background flat. H. 0·90. L. 1·89. From the Villa Aldobrandini in Frascati, whither it had been brought from the large staircase of S. Maria in Araceli before the year 1736, as Casimiro Romano (cf. on no. 81) does not mention it. [*CIIIF]

121 (149). **Small female bust,** said to be of the younger Faustina ; her hair arranged in the fashion of the so-called Lucilla at Wilton House (no. 93). New. [°B]

123 (128). **Fragment of the statue of a boy.** Engr., Pl. 28, 1. The torso suggests a brisk movement l., the r. arm (now missing) was raised, the l. (only a stump remains) was lowered ; the graceful childlike head, with the eyes hollowed out, looks fixedly downwards to the r. The legs are missing, the r. was somewhat raised. The figure is graceful and freshly treated, and seems to be the remains of a group, perhaps of morra players, like the charming bronze statuette in the British Museum (Guide to Bronze Room, p. 46, no. 1), or of knucklebone players (cf. Amalthea, 1. Pl. 5) ; or he may be looking down at a dog. Evidently his attention is firmly arrested by something below him ; this idea has led to the fixed look being rendered by hollowing out the eyes. Parian marble. H. 0·42. [*]

125 (181). **Head of a daughter of Niobe.** The head is turned upwards very much to the r. The position of the two eyes is strikingly different : the outer corner of the r. one is lifted, the inner corner of the l. one lowered. A piece of the breast with the drapery belongs to the original work. The nose and lower lip have been restored. This bust may be a portion of a statue, but the suspicion of its modern origin is not altogether to be rejected. [*C]

127 (132). **Small bust of Aphrodite,** of the type of the Venus of Arles, with a fillet in her hair, lowering her head a little to the r. The breast has been re-set. Probably new. L. of face 0·07. [*]

128 (77). **Terminal figure of a Satyr in bronze.** Engr., Pl. 21. Spec., II. Pl. 28. The head has pointed ears, rough hair, small horns, and the goat's warts (φήρεα) on the neck. It is turned up sharply to its owner. The eyes are hollowed out. The body is covered by the drapery, which also partly conceals the terminal shaft ; the l. arm rests on the hip, the r. is raised and pressed closely to the breast ; both are enveloped in the drapery. "The white of

the eyes, the teeth, the budding horns, and the tips of the dewlaps
are of silver; the pupils of the eyes, now open, were once probably
filled with gems or enamel" (*Engravings*). A bronze statue so well
executed is so uncommon that at a first cursory sight one might
suspect its genuineness; but it "was found in an excavation made at
Pompeii, when the Duke of Bedford visited that ancient city, in the
spring of the year 1815, and it was presented to him, on the spot, by
Caroline, then Queen of Naples." Queen Caroline Buonaparte paid
her last visit to Pompeii, the only one in that year, the 11th of April,
1815. In the official inventory of the objects discovered on that
occasion there is no record of our terminal figure, unless it should
be one of "*due idoletti, uno dei quali con sua base cilindrica*" (Fiorelli,
Pompeian. antiquitatum hist., i. 3, p. 274). On the 13th of February
the Princess of Wales, "*con molti signori inglesi*," had paid a visit to
Pompeii, but no special excavation appears to have been made on
that occasion (*Ibid.*, p. 176). H. 0·59. [*CH*]

129 (131). Bust of Ganymedes, rather than Paris. A
graceful, very youthful head, which recurs in many replicas, of very
sentimental conception and inclining downwards to the r. New:
neck, chin, piece of the upper lip, nose, some of the curls, peak of
the cap. Pentelic marble. L. of face 0·15. [*C*]

130 (129). Small female torso, in a chiton with a double
row of folds; preserved as far as the knees. Delicate work. Grey
marble. H. 0·23. [°]

131 (182). Small torso of a female statue in a girdled
chiton, with the upper parts of the arms lowered. Missing: head,
forearms, and lower parts of the legs. H. 0·27. [*]

132. Square cinerarium. In the pediment of the lid are
hammer, anvil and tongs. Below, the inscription: *D(is) M(anibus)
s(acrum). Trebelliae Mel pomene patronae sue bene) merenti) | fece-
runt Trebellia Amplia ta et Trebellius Onesimus | et Trebellius Resti-
tutus.* H. 0·33. L. 0·42. D. 0·28. [*C*]

133 (127). A dove, pluming itself. The figure may be antique.
H. 0·19. L. 0·24. [*]

134 (153). Round sepulchral urn, very small, ornamented
with a race of Cupids. New. [*]

135 (139). Foot of a statue, in terra cotta. Appears to be
new. [*]

136 (140). Fore part of a colossal right foot, furnished
with a sandal and numerous straps which are gathered up in a clasp
shaped like a leaf. Why the foot should have been designated as

belonging to a "statue of the Amazon Smyrna" is not clear.
L. 0·55. L. of the second toe 0·19. [*C]

137 (141). **Left foot** of a small statue. Fragment. [?]

138 (142). **Small male torso**, resting on the r. leg. Remains of a skin, or drapery, appear on the back and across the breast from the l. shoulder to the r. hip. H. 0·24. [*]

139 (143). **Bust of an elderly Roman**, beardless, and with short hair. New: nose, lower lip, ears, neck, and bust. [*B]

141 (147). **Torso of Aphroditè**, of the type of the Medici Venus. *Engr.*, Pl. 22. *Spec.*, II. Pl. 11, 12. Arms and head missing; the r. leg, which is drawn back, is antique as far as the toes, the l. is antique to the ankles only. The legs have been broken in sundry places. There is no trace of a join for the hands. The urn with the drapery is new. The figure is very youthful, the waist being slim, but the breast and stomach are rather full; the legs somewhat long. Good, delicate work, though perhaps not of the first rank. Parian marble, apparently lychnites. H. 1·12. "This torso was lately brought from France" (*Engravings*). [*H]

143 (154). **Bust of an elderly Roman**, beardless, wrongly named "Julius Caesar." The face thin, the eyeballs prominent and with sharply cut lids. New: tip of nose, back of the head and part of the top of the head; the bust with transverse stripe (so-called *laena*) appears to be antique. However, Bernoulli, *Röm. Ikonogr.*, I. p. 177, thinks that the whole bust might be a work of the 18th century. Life size. [*B]

144 (146). **Front of a sarcophagus: triumphal procession of Dionysos and Herakles.** *Engr.*, Pl. 6. An early drawing, without the restorations, in *Cod. Coburg.*, no. 132 M. A copy of Zoega's MS. description of the relief is preserved in the archives of the German Archaeological Institute. The procession consists of a great number of figures all moving r., where at the furthest extremity is a small pillar, entwined with wreaths, on which is a small modern terminal figure. High up in the r. corner sits a small, bearded mountain god (much restored) with a branch in his l. arm; beside him is a pine tree (?). Below, a chariot drawn by a bearded Centaur, playing the lyre, and a female Centaur striking the cymbals. On the chariot stands Herakles, nude except for the lion's skin that hangs over his l. arm. The club is in his l., the large goblet (σκύφος) in his r. hand; across his breast hangs from the shoulder, in the fashion of a sword-belt, a fillet knotted at regular distances. In the background Seilenos is visible, touching his ivy wreath with

his r. hand, and holding a tympanon in his l.; behind Herakles is a
youthful Satyr with a pedum.   Beside Herakles' chariot, in the
foreground, rides on a panther, a boy represented on a smaller scale
(head and pedum restored); he has a wreath in his l. hand; before
him on the ground is a bald-headed, bearded mask and in front of
that, under the Centaurs, a panther crouching and a goat lying
down, and between the two sits a boy with a pedum.—The centre
of the piece is occupied by an elephant.   On his back sit two
captive Indians, in sleeved chitons, cloaks, hose and shoes, and easily
to be recognised by their characteristic long, stiff curls.   Hanging
from the elephant's neck is a long elephant's tooth, and further
back a cup and other booty.   High up in the background is a
Satyr with moustaches, leading a horse and a stag (or a giraffe?); a
small boy is partly visible beside the horse.   An Indian, on a diminutive scale, is passing under the elephant's trunk.   The elephant is
placing his foot on a panther which is lying on the ground, and
the panther in return bites his leg; under the elephant's belly a
young Paniskos, with goat's legs (pedum restored) is leading a
lion.—Behind the lion comes the car of Dionysos, drawn by two
lionesses.   The bridle is held by a big, bearded Pan girt with a
goat's skin.   On the backs of the lionesses sit two diminutive Indians,
dressed in a sort of shirt and with branches in their arms (great
part restored).   Under the lionesses a boy is playing with a goat;
further in front may be seen on the ground a torch alight, an animal's
head, a round wicker basket (cista?) over which a young Pan (head,
legs, syrinx, pedum, new) is sitting and putting one foot on the head
of a goat.   The chariot is ornamented with a garland in relief, and
on it stands Dionysos in a long chiton, nebris and cloak; in his r.
hand he holds the thyrsos and in his l. the restorer has placed the
reins.   Zoega surmises that originally he held a goblet (κάνθαρος) in his
l. hand and that the reins were held by the little Indians.   Dionysos'
curly head is abundantly crowned with vine leaves, and a Nike approaching in front of him places on his head with both her hands a
laurel wreath.   Beside the lionesses a Bacchante blowing a trumpet
is going to the r.; behind her a second bearing a small altar in her
hands (according to Zoega a vessel adorned with masks and filled with
fruits); a third appears in front on the extreme l., carrying a long
staff, which has been restored as a pedum, but which was originally
probably a banner or a tropæon.   All three Bacchantes are crowned
and wear chitons and cloaks.   Finally behind Dionysos appears a
youth, crowned, wearing a nebris and holding thyrsos and pedum.—

Many restorations that are less essential have been passed over in this description. The composition is overcrowded. Commonplace work. H. 1·12. L. 2·43. From the Villa Aldobrandini in Frascati. [*C.MII*]

145 (120). **Bust**, incorrectly named "**Clodius Albinus**," more likely **Hadrian**, though this too is uncertain; the curls are smaller than usual. New: nose, and neck; the bust with the breast-plate is old. Abraded. Life size. [*B*]

147 (1). **Large marble krater** with **Bacchic boys**. *Engr.*, Pl. 4. The whole of the pedestal, parts of the bottom of the vase, which is very full-bodied and adorned with acanthus leaves, the handles and the overhanging border with the vine-wreath are new (the four Seilenos' masks with their pointed ears and ivy wreaths which are at the lower joints of the handles are antique); in the wreath on the border of the vase some of the sprays belong to genuine parts, and so that the general correctness of this ornamentation is established. Lastly, some important portions of the main body of the krater itself and of its reliefs are new. When the krater was first made this main body was put together from a number of sepa-rate pieces; which for the most part are remarkably well preserved. This is the more surprising as the relief is so very high that the figures almost seem to stand out independently. All the antique portions are of coarse-grained Greek marble, and the restorations of Italian marble. The movement of the scene is from l. to r. (*a*) a boy dancing to the r., raising in his l. hand a hare, and in his r., which is extended backwards, a lowered torch (new: r. leg, l. arm and nearly the whole of the hare). (*b*) A boy dancing to the r., with a wine skin on his l. shoulder from which a cloak hangs down, in his r. arm a pedum (new: a piece of the pedum and half the forearm). (*c*) A boy, seen in full face, crowned with vine leaves and with a chlamys fastened round him, is stepping to the r. He places his r. foot upon a cista, below the lid of which emerges a snake; beside him lies a panther on the ground (new: the l. forearm with the goblet, the lowered r. arm with the bunch of grapes). (*d*) A boy dancing to the r. and looking round at *c*; in his l. hand he holds a goblet (*kantharos*), on his r. shoulder he carries a thyrsos (new: r. arm and a piece of the thyrsos). (*e*) A boy seen in full face, draped in the chlamys, holding a flute in his r. hand and a basket with grapes on his r. arm (new: a square piece, comprising almost the whole body from the breast downwards; antique: the head, all the r. arm, l. shoulder and hand and half the basket, important portions

of the cloak which goes round him, half the lower part of the l. leg).
(*f*) A boy treading out grapes in a large vat (new: both arms and
grapes, r. leg). (*g*) A boy approaches from the r. to empty grapes
into the vat (new: some of the grapes on the ground). (*h*) The
eighth boy is entirely new; he is turning to the l. and busying himself
over a basket with grapes; of the whole group only a few of the
grapes beside the basket (new) are antique. Pleasing motives, prettily
carried out. H. 1·40. Diameter 1·03. From Hadrian's Villa, "recently discovered" (*Engravings*). [*]

148 (153). **Front of a sarcophagus: Minerva and the
Muses.** *Engr.*, Pl. 5. An early drawing of this, of the middle of
the 16th century, is to be found in Cod. Coburg., no. 163 M. = Cod.
Pigh., no. 171 J.; a sepia sketch done with the pen, of the 17th
century, and once in the Dal Pozzo Collection, is now in the possession of Mr A. W. Franks, in London. At that time the sarcophagus was in the Villa Giustiniani, where is still to be found a
similar one (Matz-Duhn, *Ant. Bildwerke in Rom*, no. 3271. *Gall.
Giust.*, II. Pl. 90). In the background a curtain is stretched across.
The figures (named here by their usual names) follow each other
from l. to r.; they are all seen in full face, and are placed very
close to each other. (*a*) Erato, in a thin chiton that has slipped
off her r. shoulder and breast, her cloak thrown round her hips; her
l. foot set on a piece of rock; she holds her light lyre in her l. hand,
in her r. she has the plektron (new: head and r. foot). (*b*) Euterpe
in a long-sleeved chiton with a broad girdle, which was the customary
dress in musical and theatrical representations, is holding a long flute
in each hand (new: nose, feathers on the forehead, l. hand and
parts of the flute). (*c*) Melpomenè, draped in the same fashion and
having further a cloak on her back, is supporting the club in her r.
hand on the head of an ox which lies on the ground, and holding up
a tragic mask in her l. (new: parts of the face, the feathers over the
forehead, a piece of the mask). (*d*) Apollo, nude except for the
chlamys which lies on his l. shoulder and falls down his back;
he has long curly hair; the quiver is at his back; in his r.
hand he elevates the plektron and lays his l. on his cithara, which is
richly ornamented and which lies on a globe marked with the constellations; this globe rests in the cauldron (λέβης) of a tripod, round
which a snake is twined; near Apollo's r. leg sits the griffin (new:
nose, three fingers of the r. hand and half of the plektron, the l. hand
and a large piece of the cithara). (*e*) In the background, behind the
cithara, is a Muse, of whom little more than the head is visible. She

has no distinctive attribute, and may possibly be meant to represent Kalliopè (new: lower lip, feather on the forehead). (*f*) Athenè, in a helmet, ornamented with the head of a ram, and plume, chiton and cloak, aegis with the Medusa's head, and a small owl at her feet (new: tip of nose, l. hand with the flute). (*g*) Urania, with the Sirens' feathers on her forehead, in chiton and cloak; she bears in her l. hand the celestial globe adorned with constellations and in her r. the little staff (half of this restored); near her is a bundle of manuscripts. (*h*) Terpsichorè, also adorned with Sirens' feathers, is draped like *c* and with an embroidered girdle; she holds the plektron in her lowered r. hand; her l. rests on the high cithara with twisted horns, which stands on a narrow pillar, partly concealed by Terpsichorè's cloak (new: the l. hand and part of the cithara, parts of the plektron and two fingers of the r. hand). (*i*) Thaleia (?) in chiton and cloak; in her l. hand, which has been restored, she carries a comic mask, also restored, and on it she lays her r. hand (new: the feathers over her forehead). The figures are arranged in couples, placed face to face; thus *a* looks at *b*, &c., except *i*, who looks straight in front. The two Muses that are missing, Kleio and Polyhymnia, were no doubt depicted on the sides, perhaps in the companionship of a historian and a philosopher.— Nearly the whole of the upper border has been restored, except the piece over *g* and *h*, where the remains of a distich have been preserved: ...ον δαπέδον, μνῆμα δὲ τοῦτο πέλε[ι]. Of the lower border the l. corner and the piece going from *c*'s r. foot to the middle of *d*'s feet have been restored. The principal inscription runs the length of the upper surface of this border, and then along the front of it to *d*'s l. foot; of this inscription the following remains are preserved:

— —νμα τό περ μακάρων — — — δύναται
ταῦτα βροτοῖσιν ἅπασιν ἐφημοσύναισιν ἀρίστων |
— — — — δὲ ἐς ἀλλότριον πάμπωσι — — — ν.

At the r. extremity of the front is written: Κ· Εὐχαρίστῳ τῷ ἀπελευθέρῳ μου ἀμίνοτι. The inscriptions are not given, neither in the *C. I. Gr.* nor in Kaibel's *Epigrammata.* H. 1·02. L. 1·81. [*CMW*]

149 (230). **Bust of Vitellius.** New. [*B*]

150 (145). **Bust of Diadumenianus.** *Engr.*, Pl. 26, 2. The head looks sharply to its r. The hair is shaved short. New: the nose and parts of the ears, the l. half of the bust, and the cloak. Pupils expressed. Life size. Graceful work, full of life. From the Palazzo Rondinini in Rome. [*B*]

153 (157). **Bust of the elder Brutus.** New. [*]

154 (158). **Bust of the younger Brutus.** New. [*]

165 (169). **Female bust** of about the Augustan period; the
hair grows low on the forehead; said to be Terentia, Cicero's consort.
Life size. [*B]

166 (185). **Bust of Marcus Aurelius.** New: nose, the
hair on the forehead, the bust. Larger than life. [*B]

169 (172). **Side of a sarcophagus: Nymphs tending
the infant Dionysos.** The scene corresponds to those on the
sarcophagi in the Capitol and in Munich (*Mus. Capitol.*, IV. Pl.
60. Müller-Wieseler II. 34, 402). In the background is a curtain
fastened to two trees. A nymph sits on a rock to the l., her cloak
thrown round her legs. the upper part of her body nude except for
the band under her breast (*strophion*); her hair is concealed by a
cap. The plump infant lies in her lap, supported by her l. hand;
in her r. she holds up a cloth. The second nymph, who has no
drapery except the cloak thrown lightly round her legs, is standing
to the r. and pouring water from a large urn into a wide vessel
with handles that stands on the ground. H. 0·39. L. 0·44. [*CM]

171 (173). **Female statuette** ("Ceres"). *Engr.*, Pl. 20. The
figure rests on the l. leg, the right being drawn back somewhat.
She wears a thin chiton and a cloak which goes from the l. shoulder
down her back, then passes under her r. shoulder across her breast,
falling at last over her l. forearm which is advanced. The attributes of Ceres were only given to the figure by the restorer. New:
head crowned with wheat-ears, neck, r. arm (including the shoulder),
holding a bunch of corn, and l. forearm. Pleasing motive, well-
executed. Parian marble. H. 0·84. "Brought from Italy by the
late Marquis of Tavistock" (*Engravings*). [*]

172 (174). **Female bust.** New: tip of nose and bust. Life
size. [*]

173 (168). **Marble candelabrum.** The lowest division new.
Then comes a triangular pedestal, with a winged youth on each
side; these figures finish off in vine sprays. They represent three
seasons: Autumn crowned with vine leaves, holding a cornucopiae
filled with grapes; Summer crowned with ears of wheat, and also
holding some in both hands; and Spring with flowers in the upraised
r. hand. The reliefs pretty but much touched up. Above this
pedestal we have a round stem formed of three thyrsi involved with
vine sprays; birds fly about in the foliage. Above, leaves of acanthus.
The cup at the top is new. The whole work is graceful. H.
2·16. [*]

174 (179). **Bust of a Roman**, with a short beard and thick hair that falls in disorder over his face. Late work, but good : resembling in style the head in the Braccio Nuovo of the Vatican, no. 63 (" Aelius Caesar "). New : nose and bust. Life size. [*B]

176 (176). **Bust of Pan**. New. [*]

178 (130). **Small terminal bust** of the bearded **Dionysos**, crowned with ivy; appears to be the half of what was originally a double bust. H. 0·16. [*]

179 (114). **Small bust of a Satyr**. New. [*]

180 (135). **Statuette of the Nile**. New. [*]

181 (178). **Bust of Matidia**. *Engr.*, Pl. 28, 2. New : nose and neck ; the bust is antique, and may belong to the head. Below life size. [*]

182 (125). **Small terra cotta**, shaped like a desk. On the slanting surface are three bearded heads, the first with a high bald forehead, the second with rough hair, the third with hair lying flat to his head, and all having the modius on the head. They are meant to represent Poseidon, Zeus, and Pluto, as the special attributes of these deities are to be seen below on the front : viz. a trident, a thunderbolt, and a two-pronged fork (whether the last was an antique attribute of Pluto's is not quite certain). Under the thunderbolt is a kind of table, crowned at the top with a palmetto ornament, and with this inscription in raised letters : *Diis propi.* | *M. Herennii* | *vivatis.* New. Of this specimen there exist many examples, for instance in Paris, Vienna, Würzburg, see *Arch. Anz.*, 1859, p. 115. [C]

183 (179). **Bust of Cicero**. Bernoulli, *Röm. Ikonogr.*, 1. p. 137, supposes it to be a replica of the head in Apsley House, London, no. 1. I think it is new. [*B]

184 (115). **Small bust of Hadrian**. Completely effaced. Nose new. L. of face 0·08. [*]

185 (151). **Small bust of Sabina**, with a stephane indented like a royal crown. New : tip of nose, pieces on the chin and forehead, and the bust. Half life size. [*]

186 (54). **Three square cineraria.** *A*) On the front the inscription : *D(is) M(anibus) Calpurni e Feliciteati* [sic, T made of an E] *Curtilius pate ter* [sic] *filiae pien tissimae f(ecit).* All round is an ivy wreath, below an urn. On the sides ivy, on the lid a wreath.—*B*) Two boys on a pedestal, holding a wreath; below two cocks pecking at a lizard. Inscription tablet empty.—*C*) In front the inscription : *D(is) M(anibus)* | *Valeriae P. f. Valerianae,* | *v(ixit) an(nis) xi*

m(ensibus) viiii d(iebus) xxiiii, | *P. Valerius Cerialis* | *filiae piIssimae.*
All round a garland of fruit, held by two boys with wings. On
the lid is a fruit basket between two birds, at the corners are
masks. [*C*]

189 (184). **Square sculptured capital.** The column terminates in leaves like those of the palm tree; on the top of it in entirely
detached high relief is on each side Dionysos wearing a cloak, the
thyrsos in his l., the kantharos in his r. hand; he is between two
Satyrs, one of whom carries a wine-skin, the other a pedum (in one
instance a twisted trumpet). At each corner a boy with a torch in
the l. hand, and a branch in the r. Sculpture in the style of
sarcophagi. H. 0·25. Diameter of the top plinth 0·21. [*]

190 (136). **Terracotta relief,** with the head of Serapis, seen
in full face, with the modius. Appears to be new. [*]

191. Female bust. Life size. [*]

193. Votive relief of Maridia Polla. *Arch. Anz.,* 1864,
Pl. A, 1 (Conze). The relief is in a frame, and is injured at the
upper l. hand corner; in the centre are two ears, much hollowed
in the inside, and beside each ear is Asklepios' snake twisting itself
up; near to each is a plant like rhubarb, or silphium. Above is the
inscription: [το]ῦ ωτί[ο]ν θεραπεί[ας] Μαριδία Πώλλα | [ἱε]ρῆς
εὔχαρι[σ]τήριον. According to this inscription the relief is a thank-
offering for recovery from some disease of the ear. Very much
scratched. H. 0·28. L. 0·38. [*C*]

198 (56). **Bust of Antoninus Pius.** *Engr.,* Pl. 24, 1. Good
bust. New: nose, lobes of the ears, both shoulders. Larger than
life. Purchased from the collection of Sir Hervey Bruce, Bart. [*B*]

199 (188). **Head of a Satyr.** New: forehead, nose, all the
l. half of the face. Life size. [*]

201 (60). **Statue of Dionysos.** *Engr.,* Pl. 17, 18. The God
is leaning gracefully against the trunk of a tree, over which a nebris
has been thrown; a vine branch with grapes on it winds up the trunk,
and below, a snake is twining itself round the trunk. The head of
the God is somewhat lowered, with the expression of a pleasant
reverie; beside the ivy wreath he has on his head a broad fillet which
partly conceals his forehead; curls fall down on his shoulders. His
l. elbow rests on the trunk of the tree and his hand holds a bunch of
grapes; the r. arm hangs down inactive, but the hand may once have
held something (a goblet?). The body is slender and delicate. The
pedestal, slightly ornamented in front, is antique. The statue has
been much broken, but the essentials are antique; new: the snake's

head, a branch between the trunk of the tree and the bunch of grapes, and perhaps the r. hand. Good work, decidedly surpassing ordinary decorative sculpture. Coarse-grained Parian marble. H. about 1·50. "Brought from Italy by the late Earl of Upper Ossory; presented, in 1822, to the Duke of Bedford by Lord Holland, whose property it had become after the death of his uncle Lord Ossory" (*Engravings*). [*CII*]

202 (61). **Relief**, corresponding to one in the Vatican (*Mus. Pio. Clem.*, IV. Pl. 28). A Seilenos in a small cloak, big and plump, and looking as if he had had far too much wine, is falling forwards, while a Satyr is using all his exertions to support him and prevent his coming quite to the ground. A second Satyr, coming along behind, with a wine-skin on his l. shoulder, is amusing himself by lifting up the back of Seilenos' drapery. The top piece and the l. lower corner of the relief are new. H. 0·41. L. 0·37. [*C*]

204 (191). **Torso of an Eros.** *Engr.*, Pl. 46, 2; 3. He is resting on the r. leg and putting the l. slightly forward. On the l. arm are the remains of a bow; no trace of wings is extant. Both arms lowered. Missing: head, three parts of the r., half the l. arm, more than half of both legs. The youthful body is gracefully executed. Fine, coarse-grained Parian marble. H. 0·56. Found in the sepulchral chamber which contained the sarcophagus no. 104. [*]

205 (194). **Youthful male torso**, said to be of Apollo. *Engr.*, Pl. 23. Missing: head, arms, lower part of r. leg and three parts of the l. leg. Pretty good sculpture. H. 0·79. Found in an excavation made near the Appian Way, in the year 1815, and purchased of J. Millingen. [*]

205a. **Similar torso**, very slender, resting on the r. leg; pose very erect. Missing: three parts of the r. leg, the lower part of the l. leg, both forearms, and the head. Poor sculpture. H. 0·82. [*]

207 (193). **Torso of a youth**, resting on his l. leg, his r. bent; the body is very slender and bends over to the r. Judging from the proportions and the delicacy of the limbs, it may be Dionysos. Missing: head, the lowered arms except the stumps, and the feet. Very well executed; fine Parian marble. H. 0·61. [*]

208 (195). **Female bust.** New: nose and l. cheek. Life size. [*]

209 (197). **Bust of Geta** (?). New: all the lower half of the face, the nose, the r. eyebrow, and parts of the hair. Larger than life. [*B]

210 (90). **Statue of Athenè.** *Engr.*, Pl. 19. The goddess wears a double chiton and has the aegis; she is standing somewhat

stiffly. New: three parts of the lowered r. arm with the shield on which it is supported, the lance in the l. hand, the helmeted head; the l. arm, formed to hold a lance, has been broken twice but appears to be antique. The aegis, treated in a very affected manner, is also antique. The whole figure has been much mended and badly smoothed over; the effect of the work lacks repose. H. 1·46. "Brought from Italy by the late Marquis of Tavistock, and placed in the Great Hall at Bedford House" (*Engravings*). [*CW*]

215 (199). **Head of Ptolemaeos**, son of Juba, according to the opinion of P. E. Visconti, which is apparently correct. *Engr.*, Pl. 27, 3 ("Persius," title quite without foundation). The head looks upwards to the r., and has a broad fillet in the curly hair. By the ears and on the chin are some downy hairs. New : nose. There are other copies in the Vatican, Braccio Nuovo, no. 72 (Visconti, *Opere varie* III. tav. d'agg.), and in the Villa Albani, no. 58. Life size. [*B*]

219 (203). **Sarcophagus : Patroklos, Achilleus, and Hektor.** This large sarcophagus, which has been broken into three pieces, was for a long time let into the wall over a gate of the fortress of Ephesos, so that going from l. to r. at first the greater part of the front (excepting the corner figure at the l.), then the l. side, and finally the l. two-thirds of the back were visible. In this disposition the reliefs have been very superficially copied in Tournefort, *Voyage au Levant*, III. p. 391, and in Choiseul-Gouffier, *Voyage pittoresque de la Grèce*, I. vign., and Pl. 121 ; a copy of the latter engraving is given by Falkener, *Ephesus*, p. 120, and the first and second piece by Inghirami, *Galeria omerica*, Pl. 212, 229. In the year 1819 the reliefs were removed from their position, and at the moving especially the front suffered, all the lower part being broken off, which in the older drawings is represented as perfect. Three small fragments are in Woburn, a larger one (Hektor's corpse) has remained behind at Ephesos, and in 1832 lay there below the gate (cf. Prokesch-Osten, *Denkwürdigkeiten und Erinnerungen*, II. p. 94. Arundell, *Discoveries in Asia Minor*, II. p. 256. Falkener, *Ephesus*, p. 121). The reliefs came to England by way of Smyrna and Malta ; they may have arrived at Woburn between 1822, when the *Engravings* appeared, and 1828, when the first edition of the Catalogue was made ; at any rate we learn from Robinson's *Vitruvius Britannicus*, *Woburn Abbey*, Pl. 4, that in 1833 the sarcophagus already occupied its present position. The annexed plate is copied from a drawing made for the German Archæological Institute.—The

I.

II.

sequence of the scenes appears to be as follows; each front containing two scenes (otherwise Benndorf, *Annali*, 1866, pp. 248, 255). I. RIGHT SIDE (only the r. half preserved). On the extreme r. stands a youth, nude, except for his chlamys and boots, with a lance on his l. arm, holding a horse by the bridle. In front of him stands an armed warrior in helmet, breastplate, chlamys and boots; he holds his sword in his l. arm; his r., like all the rest of him, is lost. Probably the whole scene referred to the arming of Patroklos; if the warrior is not Patroklos himself, it is his comrade, who comes up again just in the same way in the next scene. (Waagen does not mention this scene at all, Conze thinks it is the arming of Achilleus; see however scene III.) II. LEFT SIDE. A youth, nude except for his chlamys, approaches from the l., bearing on his back the corpse of Patroklos, whose head and l. arm hang down over the shoulder of his bearer. A fully armed warrior goes before them to the r.; his sword rests on his l. arm, he holds his r. hand up to his face, which is turned back to gaze at the youth and his burthen; on the ground is a corslet. Beside this man stands a similar warrior, in a similar position; he has, however, no helmet, and his corslet is almost concealed by his chlamys; with his l. hand he grasps a lance near the top; the r. he lifted mournfully to his forehead (the greater part of the arm is now missing). On his r., in a chair with lions' feet and covered with a skin, sits Achilleus, the upper part of his body nude, his legs covered by his cloak. He rests his l. hand on the chair and raises the r., with an expression of the greatest grief, to his curly head. Behind his chair stands a warrior in corslet and chlamys, but without a helmet, who lays his l. hand sympathisingly on Achilleus' shoulder and his r. on his own chin. The whole scene is very lucidly composed, and is full of expression.—III. FRONT, RIGHT HALF. A warrior with abundant curly hair is seen in full face, standing. He already has on his corslet and chlamys, his sword at his side, and high boots; a youth, draped only in a chlamys, stands on his r. hand, holding a helmet with both hands; we see a corslet and a shield on the ground. On the extreme r. a fully-armed warrior, with his sword in his r. arm, is going away; he is looking back at the others and originally raised his l. hand (now broken off), perhaps beckoning them to follow him. Everything here indicates preparation and starting for battle; but quite to the l., near the principal figure, stands a bearded old man, head and body completely enveloped in his ample cloak, and who is shorter by a head than any of the other figures. In his l. hand he

holds a strong, bent staff, he lays his r. imploringly on the arm of
the curly-haired warrior, who however with his hand flat makes the
sign of the refusal, which is so common in representations of Hippolytos. What was the action of the l. arm of the principal actor
is no longer clear, because all the forearm is broken off; Tournefort's
and Choiseul-Gouffier's engravings represent the arm raised as if he
were just about to take the helmet from his companion at his r. The
scene seems intended to portray Achilleus, who in spite of the
warnings of his elderly friend, Phœnix, is preparing to set forth and
avenge Patroklos ; cf. *Arch. Anz.*, 1862, p. 343. (Waagen and
Conze suggest Priam before Achilleus, cf. however scene v.)—IV.
FRONT, LEFT HALF. To the l. stands a fully-armed warrior (his pose
is the exact counterpart of the warrior furthest to the r. in scene III.)
holding the prancing horse of Achilleus' chariot ; a second warrior
like him is behind the horse occupied in a similar way. Carriage-
pole and yoke are distinctly given, but the second horse is left out.
Under the horse are the head and shoulders of a youthful Trojan
who is lying on the ground, in chiton and Phrygian cap ; perhaps one
of the twelve youths who were to be sacrificed to avenge Patroklos.
On the chariot, the wheel of which is preserved as a separate fragment, stands a nude youth, seen from behind, with his sword-belt
across his back ; on his l. is the large shield ; his r. arm is broken
off ; he is looking down on the following scene. This youth is
probably Automedon (Conze thinks it is Achilleus). Nearly in the
centre of the whole front stands Achilleus, who has just descended
from his chariot, in excited movement. He is fully armed, and has
his shield on his l. arm ; his chlamys hangs from his l. forearm down
to the ground. To gratify his thirst for vengeance, and perhaps to
bind it to the chariot, he is tugging at the l. foot of the nude corpse
of Hektor, which lies on the ground. Of Hektor only the raised l.
leg and an individual fragment containing the lowered r. leg below
the knee are preserved ; the body itself, as we have remarked
above, was left at Ephesos. In the older engravings he is represented lying at full length, with his arms over his head ; Tournefort draws him lying on some drapery. In the background,
on either side of Achilleus, we perceive a youthful warrior, in
helmet, corslet, and shield, the one to the r. has also a lance ; both
are looking at Achilleus. A third fragment, a foot fastened to the
ground, which is at Woburn, probably belongs also to this scene.—
V. BACK, RIGHT PART, WHICH IS THE LARGER. On the extreme r.
is preserved the upraised l. arm, with the remains of a breastplate,

and the spear that was held by the hand of Achilleus, sitting ; the
rest of his form, and probably one or two companions in the background, have been quite lost in a large gap, about 0·90 wide, in the
marble. The same accident has affected Priam, who is approaching
in a bent position from the l. and of whom only the back, covered
with a wide cloak, and one foot remain. Behind Priam, suspended
from a strong beam, hang the scales, which were mentioned on
this occasion by Aeschylos in his Φρύγες (Schol. Homer., Il., 22,
351). In the r. hand scale lies a bar, doubtless of gold : a
warrior armed in helmet and coat of mail and with a sword in his r.
arm, keeps watch beside it ; with his l. hand he grasps a spear.
Behind him a bearded Trojan, in chiton and hose and a Phrygian
cap, is bringing a corslet on his shoulder as a contribution to the
ransom money. In the l. hand scale lies Hektor's nude corpse, the
head and legs hanging down. In the background, on the extreme l.,
stands an elderly female figure, made very slim from want of space.
She is veiled and raising her r. hand in grief or entreaty; it can only
be intended for Hekabè, put in by the artist as accompanying Priam,
to enhance the effect.—VI. BACK, LEFT PART, WHICH IS THE
SMALLER. On the extreme l.. in a high chair with a footstool,
sits Andromachè (here again the arrangement is symmetrical ; Andromachè corresponds to Achilleus, who sits at the r. end of the
relief). She is draped in a chiton and a cloak, which also veils the
back of her head. She supports her r. hand (as does the grieving
Achilleus in scene II.) on the chair, and raises her l. sadly to her
forehead. Her look is directed to the little Astyanax, who is being
led away by the bearded Odysseus. The boy is draped as a
Phrygian ; he is looking back at his mother and stretching out his
r. hand to her. Odysseus, too, looks compassionately at Andromachè as he hurriedly goes off to the r.; he is easily recognised by
his egg-shaped hat (πῖλος, pilleus), exomis, boots, and sword in his
l. arm. In the background, above Astyanax, may be seen a youthful
Trojan (female) prisoner, with long hair and a Phrygian cap ; she
wears a chiton and her chin is supported sadly on her l. hand. The
abduction of Astyanax to the camp of the Greeks, where he soon will
meet his death, is the concluding scene in the fate of Hektor and
his family ; thus the avenging of Patroklos is finally consummated.
—The front and the l. side are carefully executed in high relief,
the back and the r. side are more slightly sketched in low relief; the
cornice is ornamented with acanthus leaves in front and on both
sides, on the back it is smooth. We see from this that this sarco-

phagus was not intended, like most of those used in Greece, to stand in the open air (cf. Matz, *Arch. Zeit.*, 1872, p. 11 ff.), but in an underground chamber where the four sides would be exposed to a very different light. It is the same case with the Capitoline and the Cretan Achilleus sarcophagi (*Mus. Capit.*, IV. Pl. 1. Spratt, *Travels in Crete*, I. pp. 279 ff), with the Hippolytos sarcophagi in Girgenti and in S. Petersburg (cf. on no. 58), and other similar sarcophagi, which may be also compared as to the style of the sculpture. Our sarcophagus, though scarcely more carefully, is more frankly executed than most of the others. Parian, or similar marble, of a coarse species. H. 1·90. L. 2·65. D. 1·24. [*CJH*]

220 (201). **Head of a Roman**, beardless, named, without any reason, Domitian. It is more likely to belong to the last century B.C. The mouth protrudes a good deal. New: nose and bust. Life size. [*B*]

222 (204). **Bust of Commodus.** New: nose, chin, lobes of the ears. Less than life size. [*]

223 (210). In the centre of the Gallery are parts of a **mosaic floor** discovered near Rome in 1822; the other pieces of it, as far as they are preserved, are in Rossie Priory, cf. Rossie Priory, no. 136. Unfortunately, I am not in a position to give a description of the Woburn fragments. [*]

257. **Head of a Greek philosopher**, looking up somewhat to his r. The skull is only covered with thin tufts of hair, the mouth is open and the expression full of pain. It reminded me somewhat of the head of Karneades; Bernoulli compares the style to heads of Epikuros and Metrodoros, but without considering it identical with either. New: nose, part of the beard, bust. Larger than life. [*B*]

258. **Female head**, similar to the one in the *Cabinet des médailles* at Paris (*Gaz. Archéol.*, I. Pl. 1). The face is in the shape of a long oval; the hair, parted in the middle, is wavy and combed upwards, giving the idea of greater height; the mouth is open. The head inclines a little to the l.; a slight shade of pathos is observable. New: nose and upper lip, a patch in the l. cheek, both ears, neck; the back of the head is missing. Greek marble, somewhat coarse-grained. H. of the head 0·28. L. of face 0·22. [*]

259. **Head of a youth.** The hair is smooth and comes down low on the nape of the neck; there is a slight down on the cheeks and upper lip. The head reminds us of certain barbarian heads of a finer type, but it seems nevertheless to represent a Roman. Pupils expressed. New: nose. L. of face 0·16. [*]

I have not seen the following specimens which are in the passage leading from the Sculpture Gallery to the Conservatory.

236 (213). Two ancient **terra cottas** of a winged **Victory** sacrificing a bull.

237 (214). Ancient **terra cotta of the boy of Iassos** (Plin., *Nat. Hist.* 9, 27) riding on a dolphin in the sea (?).

239. **Assyrian basrelief,** from Nimrud, about B.C. 880.

240. **The same** from a palace at Nineveh, built by Sardanapallos II. about B.C. 650.

The small **bronzes** and painted **vases,** preserved in the " Museum," appeared to me to be of minor importance. The vases were for the most part purchased by Duke John from the Cawdor collection. Among them are four in the fashion of the Nola vases, having on them scenes from daily life; others from Lower Italy have Bacchic representations; for example one of a Bacchante dancing merrily, for whom a Satyr in a graceful pose blows the flute. [*CII*]

INDEXES.

INDEXES.

I.

COLLECTORS, COLLECTIONS, SOURCES, ETC.

CAPITAL LETTERS distinguish the places of collections in Great Britain.
Italic letters refer to the places where the antiquities have been discovered.
An asterisk (*) marks articles not described in the Catalogue.
§ and n. refer to the paragraphs and notes of the Introduction, p. to the pages of the book.
Numbers immediately following the name of a collection are the numbers of this Catalogue.
St. statues, groups, etc. *H.* heads, busts. *R.* reliefs, vases, etc. *Br.* bronzes.
T. terra cottas. *P.* pictures *V.* painted vases.

Tatham, C. H., n. 443
Tavistock, Marquis of, § 49. 86. Woburn p. 722. no. 171. 210
Temple, Sir William, § 88. 91
Temple, Lord, § 38. *See* Buckingham
Tenos p. 197. *R.* Oxford 93
Thasos p. 196
Thebes (Boeotia) p. 203
Thebes (Egypt) London, Soane 38
Theobald, James, § 22
Thoms § 63
Thorpe § 58. Ince p. 334. no. 9. 22. 27. 34. 118. 161. 243
Thrace *St.* Wilton 144?
Tischbein, Wilh., painter, n. 272. § 64
Tivoli *H.* Holkham 53. Ince 111. *R.* Ince 221. *Mosaic* 411
  Villa d'Este § 47. 58. 59. *St.* Ince 2. 3. 28. 37. 42. 43. 45. 52. 78. Marbury 1. *H.* Ince 123. *R.* Ince 221. 393
Tivoli, neighbourhood:
  Pianella di Cassio § 48
  Villa of Hadrian n. 145. § 48. 86. 87. *St.* Deepdene 8. Ince 2. 3. 34. 37. 42. 43. 52. London, Lansdowne 39. 49. 61. 65. 70. 85. 91. Margam 5. *H.* Knole 6. 12. London, Lansdowne 38. 62. 64. 81. 88. 90. Margam 9–12. *R.* London, Lansdowne 76. 76*a*. Oxford 241. 242. Warwick 1. Woburn 101. 147. *P.* Brocklesby 36. *Mosaic* Holkham 6. 7. 30. *Archit.* Woburn 36–42
  Villa of Varus *St.* Cambridge 36
Topham § 65
Townley, Charles, n. 161. § 46. 52. n. 248. § 56–59. 65. 69. 71. pp. 334. 433. 596 f. *St.* Ince 30. 43. London, Lansdowne 61. *H.* Brocklesby 15
Tradescant § 30
Trentanove, Raim., Rome, *St.* Cambridge 55
TRENTHAM HALL p. 662
Tresham *V.* C. Howard 66
Troy § 6. 12. pp. 186. 187. 196. 197
Trugoni, Florence, *H.* Cambridge 57
Tucker, J. Scott, n. 477
Tuffnell, H., *St.* Cambridge 38
TUNBRIDGE WELLS § 96. pp. 662 f.
Tusculum *H.* London, Crichton
TWICKENHAM n. 174
Tyrwhitt, Thomas, § 65

Ulenbroek, G., Leyden, *R.* Lowther 53
Upper Ossory, Lord, § 69. *St.* Woburn 201
Ursinus, *see* Orsini
Utica § 94

Valletta collection, Naples, § 27. Wilton p. 669. *H.* Wilton no. 46. 94. 192. 193. 195
Vanderborcht *H.* § 16
Vanderdoort, Abr., § 18
Velletri, Villa Ginnetti, *St.* Holkham 34
Venice p. 202. *R.* Cambridge 94
  Grimani-Spago Palace *R.* Richmond 67–69
Vere, Lord, § 59. 71
Vernon, Essex, *R.* Oxford 147
Vernon, Mrs, Twickenham, *St.* Houghton 1. 2
Vernon, Lord, n. 420
Vertue, George, engraver, § 24
Vescovali, art-dealer, Rome, *R.* Cambridge 66
Victoria, H. M. Queen, n. 481. Osborne 2. 3. 5
Villa of Hadrian, *see* Tivoli
Visconti, Ennio Quirino, § 55. 58. 66. 80. 82
Vlochos (Aetolia) *Br.* Cambridge 102
Volpato, engraver and art-dealer, Rome, *St.* Ince 8. 89. *H.* Ince 96. 120. 139. 152. 188. *R.* Ince 380. 404. Woburn 101
Vyner, Lady Mary, *see* Newby

Waller, Edm., § 22
Walmoden, H. L. von, § 53. 55
Walpole, Horatio, § 29. 30. 41. London, Wemyss. *See* Orford. Strawberry Hill
Walpole, Rob., § 67. Cambridge 6. 10
*Walter, Edw., *see* Berry Hill
WALTHAM PLACE § 22

II.

DRAWINGS AND ENGRAVINGS.

Articles of which the Catalogue contains no description are marked by an *.

DRAWINGS.

ENGRAVINGS.

III

SUBJECTS REPRESENTED.

§ and n. refer to the paragraphs and notes of the Introduction; p. to the pages of the book.
Numbers immediately following the name of a collection are the numbers of this Catalogue.
? after a number indicates that the name given to the article is uncertain;
! that it is arbitrary; [ ] refer to articles of indisputably modern origin.
St. statues, groups, etc.   *H.* heads, busts.   *R.* reliefs.   *P.* pictures.
Br. bronzes.   *T.* terra cottas.   *V.* painted vases.
N.B. All the PORTRAITS have been brought together in one article.

Abundantia *St.* C. Howard 3 !

Acanthus bordering busts at bottom Margam 10

Acheloos *R.* Edinburgh, Ant. Mus. 3 ? A. and Herakles *St.* Wilton 5 !

Achilleus *H.* Brocklesby [88]. A. at Skyros *R.* Cambridge 76. Woburn 71. 117. A. wrathful *H.* Margam 14? A. receiving corpse of Patroklos *R.* Woburn 219. Arms carried to A. by Nereids *R.* Wilton 105. A. arming *R.* Woburn 219. A. and Hektor *R.* Cambridge 76. Canterbury [155]. Ince 279. Oxford 111. Woburn 219. A. visited by Priam *R.* Woburn 219. A. and Penthesileia *R.* Cambridge 76. Richmond 58

Achillea statua Lowther 7 ?

Actor sitting on altar *R.* London, Soane 36. A. and Muse *R.* London, Lansdowne [72]

Adonis *St.* n. 174. Lowther 63 ! *H.* Edinburgh, Murray 7 !

Adrastos on mirror Cambridge p. 268

Aeakos in Hades *R.* Ince 306

Aegis on portrait of Claudius *Gem* Windsor 4

Aesculapius *see* Asklepios

Africa *H.* Broadlands 19

Agamemnon and Chryses *R.* Cambridge [66]

Agathodaemon *R.* Edinburgh, Ant. Mus. 3?

Agyrtes at Skyros *R.* Cambridge 76. Oxford 218? Woburn 117

Aias *H.* Petworth 23?

Akroterion of Attic sepulchral stele Cambridge 113. Ince 285. 286

Alabastron entwined with vine *St.* Newby 20

Alkmene on funeral pyre *V.* C. Howard 66

Altars Ince 258? 305. 306. Wilton 113. Wimbledon 1? Woburn 50. 56. *See* Pedestal. A. with slain ram on it Windsor 1.— A. near statue of Demeter Ince 1. A. on sepulchral reliefs Rokeby 1. Wilton

London, Lansdowne 25 ; Mellhuish.
Oxford 109. Richmond 73. Woburn
61 ; wrestling with Eros Cambridge
31. Newby 34. Richmond 73 ;
leading the drunken Herakles Ince
275 ; and sleeping Nymph Ince 275 ;
and three Nymphs Brocklesby 110.
Cambridge 115. P. with human
legs London, Lansdowne 25. Mask
of Pan on sarcophagi Ince 225. 278 ;
on vase Woburn 101.— *Mosaic* C.
Howard 64
Paniska *H.* Wilton 180?
Paniskos in Bacchic company *R.* Woburn 144
Pantheum signum Br. Richmond
25
Panther *Mosaic* Rossie 136 ; on sepulchral monuments *R.* Ince 324. Wilton 104. 105 ; hunted *R.* Ince 252.
307. 393 ; assailed by Centaur *R.*
Ince 267 ; mangling a horse *R.* Lowther 43 ; in Bacchic scenes *R.* Blenheim 3. Cambridge 31. 72. 77.
Ince 229. 305. *Mirror* Liverpool 18.
R. London, Lansdowne 69 ; Soane
28. Newby 34. Richmond 1. 73.
Woburn 61. 144 ; drawing chariot of
Dionysos *R.* Ince 249. Richmond
73. Woburn 61 ; sitting near Diony-
sos *St.* Deepdene 20. C. Howard 8.
R. Wilton 1 ; near Seilenos Wilton
106 ; drawing chariot of Eros *R.*
Lowther 47 ; near Season *R.* Rossie
76 ; forming part of Skylla's body
Oxford 33? ; indicating transforma-
tion of Thetis *Br.* Richmond 37. -
Panther's head at stern of ship *R.*
London, Lansdowne 76 ; on trapezo-
phoros *R.* Rossie 41
Paris. *Statues:* Easton Neston 7?
Hamilton 9? Ince [69. 70]. Lon-
don, Lansdowne 39? Lowther 63?
Marbury 16? Oxford 48 ?—*Heads:*
C. Howard 24? Woburn 129? -
Reliefs: Paris as shepherd, with
apple Ince 263 ; seated Rossie 78? ;
listening to Eros London, Soane 30? ;
and Helena Marbury 36. Richmond

12? ; kneeling on altar *Br.* Liverpool
19
Paris, foster father of, *St.* Wilton 231 !
Parthenon, fragments of, Cambridge 28 !
Chatsworth 5. Deepdene 14 ! Lon-
don, Atkinson ? Marbury p. 515
Pasiteles, youth in the style of, *St.*
Margam 5
Patroklos arming *R.* Woburn 219 ; P.,
corpse of, brought back from battle
R. Woburn 219
Pedestal, round, Oxford 96—104? 237? ;
triangular, with reliefs, of Athené
and Herakles Oxford 242, Bacchic
Broadlands 11. Newby 8. Wilton
76, of Seasons Woburn 173, of Vic-
tories Newby 41. *See* Altar. Cip-
pus.— Pedestals of statues moulded
Holkham 24. Ince 31 ; of unusual
shape Oxford 32
Pegasos *R.* C. Howard 67 ; and
Nymphs *R.* Porta Aurea p. 190
Peirene, nymph of, *R.* Porta Aurea p.190
Peirithoos in Hades *R.* Ince 310 ?
Peleus embracing Thetis *Br.* Richmond
37
Peloponnesian art *H.* Ince 152 ? Ox-
ford 60 ? *R.* Wilton 48 ?
Pelops and Oenomaos *I.* London,
Soane 38
Penthesilea slain by Achilleus *R.* Cam-
bridge 76. Richmond 58
Persephone *H.* Ince 180 ! Rossie 7.
R. London, Soane 19? ; raped by
Pluto Brocklesby 66. Holkham 50.
Ince 281. London, Lansdowne 77 ;
Soane 26 ; standing near Pluto Ince
306 ; returning from Hades Wilton
137 ; taking leave from Demeter
Wilton 137
Perseus and Athené *Mirror* Liverpool
[20]
Phallus as symbol averting evil, near
Eros *St.* Cambridge 5 ; in fan *R.*
Brocklesby 11. Cambridge 71
Phaedra *H.* Wilton 110 ; and Hip-
polytos *R.* Woburn 58
Phoenix warning Achilleus *R.* Woburn
219

recumbent Wilton 106; sleeping C. Howard [10].—*Heads:* Br. § 29. Cambridge 50. 51. C. Howard 28! Ince 92.—*Reliefs:* Seilenos offering Cambridge 71. Wilton 76; lying on ass Woburn 56; in Bacchic company Broadlands 11. Cambridge 31. Ince 243. 288. Newby 34. Woburn 61 (on ass). 144. 202; uncovering a Maenad Oxford 110. Mask of Seilenos Oxford 220. Rossie 69; held by boy Wilton 59, by Satyr Oxford 109; on candelabrum Ince 241; on sarcophagi Ince 228. Wilton 155; on tympanon Newby 34; on vase Warwick 1. Woburn 101. 147

Seiren on sepulchral relief Brocklesby 40. Oxford 140. Wilton 109. Seirens and Odysseus R. Canterbury 45. London, Lansdowne 76. Seiren with fishtail R. Canterbury 45. Seiren's feathers on heads of Muses R. London, Lansdowne 75. Woburn 148

Selene as representative of the moon R. Woburn 86. Head of S. R. Oxford 134. S. and Endymion Porta Aurea p. 189. Cambridge 78? Warwick 2. Woburn 86

Semele in childbed R. Ince 248

Sepulchral amphora, hydria, lekythos *see* Amphora, etc.

Sepulchral column Liverpool 9 (Cyprus); with relief Cambridge 21 (Athens)

SEPULCHRAL RELIEFS.

A. GREEK.

MEN. Brocklesby 13 (Attica). Cambridge 9 (Attica). 28 (Athens)? Ince 260. London, S. Kensington 16 (Smyrna). Lowther 57 (Smyrna?). Oxford 138 (Attica). 154. 206. Richmond 67 (Smyrna). Rokeby 5. Rossie 79. Wilton 109 (Smyrna?) Man and horse Cambridge 27 (Phanagoria). Canterbury 140 (Bosporos). Edinburgh, Murray 2. C. Howard 47. Men on horseback Brocklesby 42 (Attica). 53 (At-

SEPULCHRAL RELIEFS, *continued:* tica). Canterbury 136? 149 (Brussa). Edinburgh, Murray 1. Oxford 208 (Pergamon). 214 (Ephesos). Poet seated London, Lansdowne 2? Boy and bird Oxford 152

WOMEN. Standing Brocklesby 99. Ketteringham 1 (Arles, Greek?). Oxford 90 (Smyrna?). 151. 204 (Smyrna?). Richmond 56 (Sicily). 69 (Smyrna?). 70 (Smyrna?). Rokeby 1. Seated Cambridge 25 (Phanagoria). 26 (Phanagoria). London, Lansdowne 1 (Attica); Soane 21. Lowther 37 (Attica). Marbury 38 (Attica). Oxford 127 (Cyprus). 150. 211. Richmond 68 (Smyrna?). Rokeby 4. Woman and child, standing London, Stafford 5; seated Cambridge 20 (Attica). London, Soane 22. Girl Woburn 100; with doll Winton 1 (Attica); with doves Brocklesby 17 (Paros); with child and dove Richmond 10 (Attica)

FAMILY. Man and wife London, S. Kensington 15 (Asia M.). Lowther 52 (Smyrna). 54 (Smyrna). Oxford 89 (Smyrna?). 205 (Smyrna?). Rokeby 33; and children Rokeby 2; mother and sons Lowther 53 (Smyrna)

Shaking hands Brocklesby 31 (Attica). 34 (Megara). 65 (Attica). 67 (Attica). 111 (Megara). Cambridge 22 (Propontis). 111 (Attica). Liverpool 6 (Ephesos). 8 (Cyprus). Lowther 56 (Smyrna). Marbury 37 (Attica). Oxford 140 (Attica). 141 (Attica). 147 (Smyrna). 148. Wilton 152. Winton 2 (Attica)

Repast Cambridge 18 (Attica). 19. 23. 24 (Patmos). 109. Canterbury 137. 172. 174. Ince 261. Liverpool 7 (Egypt.) London, Soane 20. Lowther 55 (Smyrna). 58 (Smyrna). Oxford 91—95.

IV.

EPIGRAPHICAL INDEX.

Numbers immediately following the name of a collection are the numbers
of this Catalogue.

I. GREEK INSCRIPTIONS.

II. ROMAN INSCRIPTIONS.

III. ETRUSCAN INSCRIPTIONS.

IV. EGYPTIAN INSCRIPTIONS.

CAMBRIDGE: PRINTED BY C. J. CLAY, M.A. & SON, AT THE UNIVERSITY PRESS.

In the Press.

THE ARCHITECTURAL HISTORY
OF THE UNIVERSITY AND COLLEGES
OF CAMBRIDGE,

By the late Professor WILLIS, M.A. With numerous Maps, Plans and Illustrations, continued to the present time and edited by JOHN WILLIS CLARK, M.A., formerly Fellow of Trinity College.

LECTURES ON THE TYPES OF GREEK
COINS.

By PERCY GARDNER, M.A., Disney Professor of Archæology. With Plates. Royal 4to.

ESSAYS ON THE ART OF PHEIDIAS.

By C. WALDSTEIN, M.A. Phil. D., Reader in Classical Archæology in the University of Cambridge. Royal 8vo. With Illustrations.

Now Ready.

THE BACCHAE OF EURIPIDES.

With Introduction, Critical Notes, and Archæological Illustrations, by J. E. SANDYS, M.A., Fellow and Tutor of St John's College, Cambridge, and Public Orator. Crown 8vo. cloth. 10s. 6d.

Cambridge:
AT THE UNIVERSITY PRESS.

London: C. J. CLAY, M.A. & SON.
CAMBRIDGE UNIVERSITY PRESS WAREHOUSE,
17, PATERNOSTER ROW

Lightning Source UK Ltd.
Milton Keynes UK
UKHW010633060820
367798UK00002B/423